McGraw-Hill Ryerson

Calculus
& Advanced Functions

AUTHORS

TECHNOLOGY AND WEB CONSULTANT
Fred Ferneyhough, B.Math., M.Ed.

PEDAGOGICAL CONSULTANT
Cynthia Ballheim, B.Sc., M.A.

ASSESSMENT CONSULTANT
Lynda Ferneyhough, B.Math., M.Ed.

SPECIAL CONTRIBUTIONS
Mary Card, B.A., B.Ed.
Toronto District School Board

Don Curran, B.A., M.A., Ph.D.
Oshawa, Ontario

CHRIS DEARLING
B.Sc., M.Sc.
Burlington, Ontario

SANTO D'AGOSTINO
B.Sc., M.Sc.
Mississauga, Ontario

WAYNE ERDMAN
B.Math., B.Ed.
Toronto District School Board

FRED FERNEYHOUGH
B.Math., M.Ed.
Peel District School Board

LYNDA FERNEYHOUGH
B.Math., M.Ed.
Peel District School Board

MARY-BETH FORTUNE
B.A., B.Ed., B.Sc., M.Ed.
Peel District School Board

O. MICHAEL G. HAMILTON
B.Sc., B.Ed., M.Sc.
Ridley College

GEORGE KNILL
B.Sc., M.S.Ed.
Hamilton, Ontario

CHARLES STEWART
B.Sc., B.Ed.
Toronto District School Board

McGraw-Hill Ryerson

Toronto Montréal Boston Burr Ridge, IL Dubuque, IA Madison, WI New York
San Francisco St. Louis Bangkok Bogotá Caracas Kuala Lumpur Lisbon London
Madrid Mexico City Milan New Delhi Santiago Seoul Singapore Sydney Taipei

McGraw-Hill
Ryerson Limited

A Subsidiary of The McGraw-Hill Companies

McGraw-Hill Ryerson
Calculus & Advanced Functions

Copyright © 2002, McGraw-Hill Ryerson Limited, a Subsidiary of The McGraw-Hill Companies. All rights reserved. No part of this publication may be reproduced or transmitted in any form or by any means, or stored in a data base or retrieval system, without the prior written permission of McGraw-Hill Ryerson Limited, or, in the case of photocopying or other reprographic copying, a licence from CANCOPY (Canadian Copyright Licensing Agency), One Yonge Street, Suite 1900, Toronto, Ontario M5E 1E5.

Any request for photocopying, recording, taping, or information storage and retrieval of any part of this publication shall be directed in writing to CANCOPY.

ISBN 0-07-089276-8/0-07-091709-4

http://www.mcgrawhill.ca

3 4 5 6 7 8 9 0   TRI   0 9 8 7 6 5 4 3

Printed and bound in Canada

Care has been taken to trace ownership of copyright material contained in this text. The publishers will gladly take any information that will enable them to rectify any reference or credit in subsequent printings.

TI-InterActive!™ and CBR™ are trademarks of Texas Instruments.

National Library of Canada Cataloguing in Publication Data

Main entry under title:
  McGraw-Hill Ryerson calculus & advanced functions

Includes index.
ISBN 0-07-089276-8

1. Calculus. 2. Functions. I. Dearling, Chris, date II. Title: Calculus & advanced functions.

QA303.M32 2002   515   C2001-904229-9

PUBLISHER: Diane Wyman
DEVELOPMENTAL EDITORS: Julia Cochrane, Santo D'Agostino, Tom Gamblin
SUPERVISING EDITOR: Cathy Deak
ASSOCIATE EDITOR: Mary Agnes Challoner
JUNIOR EDITORS: Chris Cappadocia, Cheryl Stallabrass
PERMISSIONS EDITOR: Ann Ludbrook
PRODUCTION SUPERVISOR: Yolanda Pigden
PRODUCTION COORDINATOR: Paula Brown
EDITORIAL ASSISTANTS: Joanne Murray, Erin Parton
ASSISTANT PROJECT COORDINATORS: Melissa Nippard, Janie Reeson
INTERIOR DESIGN: Liz Harasymczuk
ELECTRONIC PAGE MAKE-UP: S R Nova Private Limited, Bangalore, India
COVER DESIGN: Sharon Lucas
COVER IMAGE: Ron Watts/First Light

COPIES OF THIS BOOK
MAY BE OBTAINED BY
CONTACTING:

McGraw-Hill Ryerson Ltd.

WEB SITE:
http://www.mcgrawhill.ca

E-MAIL:
orders@mcgrawhill.ca

TOLL-FREE FAX:
1-800-463-5885

TOLL-FREE CALL:
1-800-565-5758

OR BY MAILING YOUR
ORDER TO:
McGraw-Hill Ryerson
Order Department
300 Water Street
Whitby, ON L1N 9B6

Please quote the ISBN and
title when placing your
order.

Student text ISBN:
0-07-089276-8

Student e-book ISBN:
0-07-090755-2

Acknowledgements

Reviewers of *McGraw-Hill Ryerson Calculus & Advanced Functions*

The authors and editors of McGraw-Hill Ryerson Calculus & Advanced Functions wish to thank the reviewers listed below for their thoughtful comments and suggestions. Their input has been invaluable in ensuring that this text meets the needs of students and teachers taking this course.

Paul Alves
Peel District School Board

Mary Card
Toronto District School Board

Eric Forshaw
Greater Essex County District School Board

Jeff Irvine
Peel District School Board

Gwyn Jackson
District School Board of Niagara

Ann Kajander
Lakehead University and Lakehead Public Schools

Dianna Knight
Peel District School Board

Sabina Knight
District School Board of Niagara

Anastasia Liebster
Toronto District School Board

Louis Lim
York Region District School Board

Mike McGowan
Toronto District School Board

Terry Paradellis
Toronto District School Board

Laurissa Werhun
Toronto District School Board

Accuracy Reviewer
Darrell McPhail, B.Sc., M.Sc.
London, Ontario

Contents

Chapter 8 goes beyond the Ontario curriculum in developing the analysis of trigonometric functions.

Preface

Mathematical models play a powerful role in many activities, from business and economics to the social and physical sciences. *McGraw-Hill Ryerson Calculus & Advanced Functions* introduces the key tools of mathematical modelling: the construction, interpretation, and analysis of functions to describe real-world processes. Throughout the book, students explore functions by developing skills of verbal, visual, numerical, and algebraic representation (the rule of four). These skills assist students in developing a thorough understanding of functions and their derivatives.

Text Organization

Chapter 1 introduces further ideas about functions, including the rule of four, and enhances students' use of graphing technology, while Chapter 2 explores the properties of polynomial functions. Chapter 3 introduces the concepts of limit and rate of change. Chapter 4 develops the concepts and skills of differentiation, drawing on the foundations laid in Chapters 1, 2, and 3. Chapter 5 introduces composition of functions, the chain rule, and implicit differentiation. Chapter 6 uses the techniques of differential calculus to build a rich understanding of functions through key features of their graphs. Chapter 7 introduces exponential and logarithmic functions, and applies calculus techniques to their analysis. Chapter 8 goes beyond the Ontario curriculum in developing the analysis of trigonometric functions, which are the fundamental tool in models of periodic processes.

Chapter Features

• **Modelling Math** highlights the power of mathematics to model the real world. Each chapter opens with a description of processes, from airplane cabin pressurization to volcano eruptions, which can be modelled using the techniques of the chapter. The logo shows where these processes are analysed in depth as students work through the chapter.

• **Review of Prerequisite Skills** reinforces the background knowledge students need to be successful with the new learning in the chapter. Purple descriptors refer to topics in **Appendix A: Review of Prerequisite Skills,** which provides an exploration and further practice.

• **Investigate & Inquire** introduces new concepts in an inquiry format, using graphing technology where appropriate. Students then practise the ideas, and develop them further, through worked examples.

• **Key Concepts/Communicate Your Understanding** provides a summary of the key concepts of each section, followed by a short set of questions that allow students to check their grasp of the concepts.

• **Practise** and **Apply, Solve, Communicate** questions, at the end of each section, support and develop skills of understanding, communication, application, and problem solving, through many varied questions and problems.

• **Problem Solving Strategies,** following Chapters 1, 3, 4, and 6, focus on strategies and techniques that can significantly enhance problem-solving skills.

Assessment

• **Achievement Category Descriptors** indicate questions that are particularly well-suited for assessment of thinking/inquiry/problem solving, communication, and application skills.

- **Achievement Check** questions are accessible to all students and provide opportunities for assessing performance in all achievement-chart categories.

- **Investigate & Apply,** after the last section in each chapter, provides a performance task designed to assess, in an inquiry-based investigation, the major concepts of each chapter and performance in all four of the achievement chart categories.

- **Review of Key Concepts, Chapter Test,** and **Cumulative Review** provide frequent opportunities to reinforce learning and simulate real test-taking situations.

Technology

This text makes extensive use of graphing calculators, and worked examples often include an alternative solution using the graphing calculator. However, pencil-and-paper worked examples introduce the concepts so that students will understand the mathematics that the technology uses. This approach also ensures that students who do not have ready access to graphing calculators can follow all of the material in the course.

- **Technology Extensions** provide additional, optional technology instruction using tools such as the TI-92 graphing calculator and TI InterActive!™.

- **Appendix B: Technology** details the functions and keystrokes for the TI-83 or TI-83 Plus graphing calculator, and selected functions for the TI-92 or TI-92 Plus graphing calculator.

The **Student e-book** that accompanies this textbook, in CD-ROM format, contains the complete text, plus a number of enhancements. The Student e-book has interactive Java™ applets demonstrating difficult concepts, data files to support some of the exercises, interactive simulations, additional technology extensions, an instructional tutorial on the use of TI InterActive!™, and an answer section with full graphics. Throughout the printed text, the Student e-book symbol indicates topics with supplementary material on the CD-ROM.

Web Connection

Visit the McGraw-Hill Ryerson web site at **www.mcgrawhill.ca/links/CAF12** for a wealth of links to topics related to the text.

Features to Challenge

- **Challenge Problems** provide enrichment work, at the end of each chapter, that challenges students to deepen their understanding beyond curriculum requirements.

- **Chapter 8: Trigonometric Functions and Their Derivatives** will help students who wish to do extra preparation for math studies at university.

After working with this book, students will have acquired a solid foundation in the basic concepts of calculus and their applicability to the real world, and exciting new modelling tools that can be developed further in a broad range of post-secondary studies.

Chapter 1

Functions and Models

Specific Expectations	Section
Determine, through investigation, using graphing calculators or graphing software, various properties of the graphs of polynomial functions.	1.1, 1.2
Describe intervals and distances, using absolute value notation.	1.1
Determine the key features of a mathematical model of an application drawn from the natural or social sciences, using the techniques of differential calculus.	throughout the book
Compare the key features of a mathematical model with the features of the application it represents.	throughout the book
Predict future behaviour within an application by extrapolating from a mathematical model of a function.	throughout the book
Pose questions related to an application and answer them by analysing mathematical models, using the techniques of differential calculus.	throughout the book
Communicate findings clearly and concisely, using an effective integration of essay and mathematical forms.	throughout the book

One of the main reasons that mathematics is so interesting is that it can be applied to the world around us. First, the simplest features of some realistic situation are described using mathematics. Then, operations are performed on the mathematical description so that predictions about the future are obtained. The predictions are compared with observations to test the validity of the mathematical description. Modifications are made to the description, if necessary, and the whole process is repeated. This process, called mathematical modelling, has produced numerous useful descriptions of our world.

In this chapter, we review functions, which are used extensively as mathematical models, and we explore many mathematical models, which describe such diverse situations as the difficulty of a bicycle ride, the shape of a roller-coaster ride, and the use of fertilizer in a cherry orchard.

Review of Prerequisite Skills

1. Evaluating functions If $f(x) = x^3 + x^2 - 2x + 3$, find
a) $f(0)$ b) $f(1)$ c) $f\left(\dfrac{1}{2}\right)$ d) $f(-1)$
e) $f(0.1)$ f) $f(a)$ g) $f(2x)$ h) $f(-x)$

2. Evaluating functions If $f(x) = 1 - x^2$, find
a) $f(0)$ b) $f(1)$ c) $f(-1)$
d) $f(\sqrt{2})$ e) $f\left(\dfrac{1}{\sqrt{2}}\right)$ f) $f(1-a)$
g) $f(2x)$ h) $f(-x)$

3. Evaluating functions If $f(x) = 1 + \sqrt{x+4}$, find
a) $f(0)$ b) $f(-3)$ c) $f(5)$ d) $f(21)$

4. Evaluating functions If $f(x) = |x - 2|$, find
a) $f(0)$ b) $f(2)$ c) $f(-2)$ d) $f(5)$

5. Interpreting graphs of functions For each graph, evaluate f at the following values of x. Then, state the domain and range of f.
i) $f(2)$ ii) $f(-2)$ iii) $f(0)$ iv) $f(4)$

a)
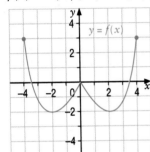

b)

6. Slopes and y-intercepts Find the slope and the y-intercept of each line.
a) $y = 2x - 4$ b) $3x - y + 8 = 0$
c) $x - 2y - 6 = 0$ d) $2(x - 3) - y = 3$

7. Equation of a line given the slope and y-intercept Find an equation of the line with each set of characteristics.

a) slope 1, y-intercept 2
b) slope 5, y-intercept -5
c) slope -2, y-intercept 4

8. Equation of a line given the slope and a point Find an equation of the line with each set of characteristics.
a) slope 3, passing through $(1, 2)$
b) slope -1, passing through $(3, 3)$
c) slope 2, passing through $(-2, 5)$

9. Equation of a line given the x- and y-intercepts Find an equation of the line with each set of characteristics.
a) x-intercept 2, y-intercept 3
b) x-intercept 5, y-intercept -7
c) x-intercept -2, y-intercept 4

10. Equation of a line given two points Find an equation of the line with each set of characteristics.
a) passing through $(1, 2)$ and $(2, -2)$
b) passing through $(5, 3)$ and $(-3, 1)$

11. Equation of a horizontal or vertical line given a point on the line Find an equation of the line with each set of characteristics.
a) passing through $(2, 3)$ and vertical
b) passing through $(-2, -1)$ and horizontal

12. Graphing quadratic functions State the vertex, direction of opening, and vertical stretch for the parabola defined by each equation. Then, graph the parabola.
a) $y = 2(x - 5)^2 + 6$ b) $y = -(x - 1)^2 - 2$
c) $y = \dfrac{1}{2}(x + 4)^2 + 1$ d) $y = -0.4(x + 1)^2 - 9$

13. Completing the square Write each quadratic in the form $y = a(x - p)^2 + q$.
a) $y = x^2 + 6x + 5$ b) $y = 2x^2 + 8x + 3$
c) $y = 3x^2 - 6x - 7$ d) $y = 5x^2 + 9x + 4$

14. Graphs of functions using technology Use a graphing calculator or graphing software to sketch a graph of each function. Then, state the domain and range.
a) $y = \dfrac{1}{x}$ b) $y = \dfrac{5}{x}$
c) $y = -\dfrac{3}{x}$ d) $y = \sqrt{x}$
e) $y = \sqrt{1 - x}$ f) $y = -\sqrt{x + 5}$

15. Transformations Decide whether the transformation of the function f is a vertical stretch, a horizontal stretch, a vertical translation, a horizontal translation, or a vertical reflection.

a) $2f(x)$ b) $-f(x)$
c) $f(x) - 4$ d) $f(3x)$
e) $f(x) + 1$ f) $f(x - 5)$

16. Transformations Describe the transformations applied to the graph of $g(x)$.

a) $\dfrac{1}{2}g(x - 5)$ b) $-3g(x) + 1$

c) $g(2x) - 9$ d) $-\dfrac{1}{3}g(4(x + 1)) - 3$

17. Domain State the domain of each function.

a) $y = \sqrt{9 - 4x}$ b) $f(x) = 5x^2 - 4x + 7$

c) $y = \dfrac{4}{x - 1}$ d) $g(x) = |2x - 9|$

e) $f(x) = \sqrt{2|x| - 8}$ f) $y = \dfrac{1}{\sqrt{x - 1}}$

g) $f(x) = 7x^3 - 2x^2 + 2x + 1$

h) $y = \dfrac{1}{x^2 + 6x + 9}$

18. Transformations The graph of $y = f(x)$ is shown. Match each equation with its graph. Give reasons for your choices.

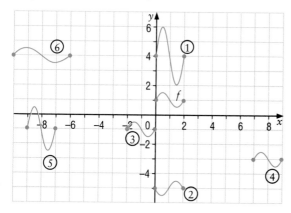

a) $y = f(x - 7) - 4$ b) $y = -f(x) - 4$
c) $y = 4f(x)$ d) $y = 3f(x + 9) - 4$

e) $y = -f(-x)$ f) $y = f\left(\dfrac{1}{2}x + 5\right) + 3$

19. Transformations The graph of $y = f(x)$ is shown. Draw the graph of each of the following functions and state the domain and range.

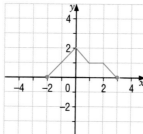

a) $y = f(x + 2)$ b) $y = 2f(x) - 4$
c) $y = -2f(x)$ d) $y = -f(x + 3)$

e) $y = 2f\left(\dfrac{1}{2}x\right)$ f) $y = f\left(\dfrac{1}{2}x + \dfrac{1}{2}\right)$

20. Transformations The graph of $y = f(x)$ is shown. Draw the graph of each of the following functions and state the domain and range.

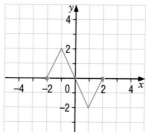

a) $y = f(x - 2)$ b) $y = 2f(x)$

c) $y = -2f(x)$ d) $y = 2f\left(\dfrac{1}{2}x\right)$

e) $y = 2f(-x)$ f) $y = 2f(2x)$

21. Transformations For each function,
i) state the domain
ii) use transformations to sketch the graph

a) $f(x) = (x - 2)^3 + 3$ b) $f(x) = -\dfrac{1}{3}x^3$

c) $f(x) = 2\sqrt{x + 5}$ d) $g(x) = -\sqrt{x - 3} + 1$

e) $h(x) = \dfrac{1}{2}|3x + 6| - 9$

22. Exponential equations Solve each equation for x.

a) $2^x = 64$ b) $5^{x + 2} = 25^x$
c) $4^x = 1024$ d) $3^{2x - 1} = 81^{x + 3}$
e) $2^{2x} - 2^x = 12$

Functions and Their Use in Modelling

Functions are often used to represent a physical situation. For example, an ecologist may want to know the amount of a pollutant in a river at various locations; a sociologist, the average age of people when they marry for the first time; a biologist, the number of bacteria present in a culture.

A function represents how one quantity depends on another. In the first example, the amount of a pollutant in a river may depend on the location along the river. It may be possible to represent the "amount-location" relationship with a function.

The quantities in the other two examples depend on time. The average age of a person at first marriage is greater now than it was in the past, and the number of bacteria in a culture may increase as time passes. It may also be possible to represent these situations with functions.

In this section we review some basic tools for analysing functions, such as symmetry and domain, and various representations of functions that are useful throughout the book. We also review function notation and introduce interval notation. Finally, we discuss the idea of using functions in mathematical modelling, dealing with several specific types of functions, such as power functions and absolute value functions.

Throughout this book, we will represent functions in four ways: verbally (using a description in words), numerically (using a table of values), algebraically (using a formula), and visually (using a graph). We call this four-way description of functions the **rule of four**.

Example 1 Four Ways to Represent a Function

Use the four ways in the rule of four to represent the function that describes converting temperature from degrees Celsius to degrees Fahrenheit.

Solution

1. Verbally
To convert from degrees Celsius to degrees Fahrenheit, multiply degrees Celsius by 1.8, and then add 32.

2. Numerically

Degrees Celsius	Degrees Fahrenheit
−40	−40
−30	−22
−20	−4
−10	14
0	32
10	50
20	68
30	86
40	104

3. Visually

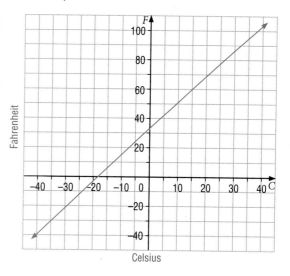

4. Algebraically

The formula that relates the temperature, F, in degrees Fahrenheit, to the temperature, C, in degrees Celsius, is $F = 1.8C + 32$.

Each of the four ways of representing the function of Example 1 describes a rule that takes a given value of C and produces a value of F. As well, each value of C determines exactly one value of F. Thus, F is said to be a **function** of C. Since, in this case, the values of F depend on the values of C, F is referred to as the **dependent variable**. From this point of view, the value of C is specified, and then the corresponding value of F is calculated, so C is called the **independent variable**. Alternatively, C is called the **input variable**, and F is called the **output variable**. On the other hand, if we were converting Fahrenheit temperatures to Celsius temperatures, F would be the independent, or input, variable, and C would be the dependent, or output, variable.

Calculus is particularly useful for analysing functions and making widely applicable statements about them. The formal definition of a function follows.

> A function f is a rule that assigns to each element in a set A, one and only one element in a set B.

In this text, only functions for which A and B are sets of real numbers are considered. The set A is called the **domain** of the function. If x represents a value from A, the symbol $f(x)$ is used for the element of B associated with x, which is referred to as the value of f at x and is read "f at x" or "f of x." The collection of all such values from B, as x varies throughout the domain A, is called the **range** of the function f.

Interval Notation

Certain sets of real numbers form **intervals**. For instance, the collection of all real numbers greater than or equal to −4 and less than 3 is the interval [−4, 3). An algebraic description of this interval is $-4 \le x < 3$. This interval may be viewed graphically on a number line.

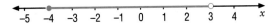

The solid circle at −4 indicates that this endpoint is included in the interval and corresponds to a square bracket in interval notation. The open circle at 3 indicates that this endpoint is not included in the interval and corresponds to a round bracket in interval notation. The solid, dark line means that all the real numbers between −4 and 3 are included in the interval.

The symbol ∞ ("infinity") can be used to represent intervals that are infinite in extent. For example, the set of all real values x such that $x \le 5$ is $(-\infty, 5]$:

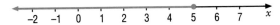

and the set of all real values x such that $x > 2$ is $(2, \infty)$:

The collection of all real numbers may be expressed as the interval $(-\infty, \infty)$.

The graph of an interval on a number line can be a line segment, a ray, or the entire number line. The following table lists the nine possible types of intervals (note that $a < b$).

Notation	Description	Graph	Verbal
			The set of all real numbers …
(a, b)	$a < x < b$		greater than a and less than b
$[a, b]$	$a \le x \le b$		greater than or equal to a and less than or equal to b
$[a, b)$	$a \le x < b$		greater than or equal to a and less than b
$(a, b]$	$a < x \le b$		greater than a and less than or equal to b
(a, ∞)	$x > a$		greater than a
$[a, \infty)$	$x \ge a$		greater than or equal to a
$(-\infty, b)$	$x < b$		less than b
$(-\infty, b]$	$x \le b$		less than or equal to b
$(-\infty, \infty)$	R		The set of all real numbers

Throughout this textbook, we will use interval notation to specify domains and ranges of relations and functions.

In this course, the features of the graphs of various types of functions will be studied. We will start by investigating the simplest polynomial functions, those in the form $y = x^n$. These are known as **power functions**.

Investigate & Inquire: Functions in the Form $y = x^n$

1. a) Graph $y = x^2$, $y = x^4$, and $y = x^6$ in the domain $x \in [-5, 5]$.
If you have access to a graphing calculator or graphing software, use the Window variables
$x \in [-5, 5]$, and determine an appropriate range for y.
b) How do the shapes of the three graphs compare?
c) Describe the symmetry of the graph of each function.
d) What points do all three graphs have in common?

2. Repeat step 1 for $y = -x^2$, $y = -x^4$, and $y = -x^6$.

3. Repeat step 1 for $y = x$, $y = x^3$, and $y = x^5$ in the domain $x \in [-2, 2]$.

4. Repeat step 1 for $y = -x$, $y = -x^3$, and $y = -x^5$ in the domain $x \in [-2, 2]$.

5. Compare and contrast the graphs of the functions in steps 1 to 4.

6. a) Make a conjecture about the shape and symmetry of the graphs of $y = x^n$ for
i) n odd   **ii)** n even
b) Test your conjectures in part a) by graphing $y = x^7$ and $y = x^8$.

Plants, animals, crystals, our bodies, and many other aspects of nature possess
symmetry. Symmetry is also used in the design and manufacture of such items as
automobiles and airplanes. Many designs require mathematical modelling,
which includes the development of functions. Symmetric functions have algebraic
properties that can simplify calculations involving them. The graphs in the investigation
possess symmetry.

In the diagram shown here, the function is a mirror
image of itself with respect to the y-axis. Such a
function is called an **even function**. An even function
satisfies the property $f(-x) = f(x)$ for all x in the
domain of f.

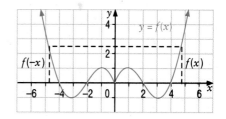

In this diagram, the function is rotationally
symmetric about the origin. That is, if the graph is
rotated 180° about the origin, it does not change.
Such a function is called an **odd function**. An odd
function satisfies the property $f(-x) = -f(x)$ for all x
in the domain of f.

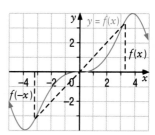

Example 2 Even and Odd Functions

Determine whether each function is even, odd, or neither.

a) $f(x) = x^2$

b) $g(x) = x^3$

c) $h(x) = x^2 - 2x + 1$

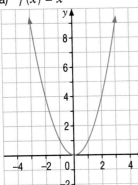

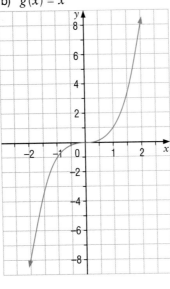

Solution

a) The domain of f is the interval $(-\infty, \infty)$. Let x be any element of the domain. We have

$$f(-x) = (-x)^2$$
$$= (-x)(-x)$$
$$= x^2$$
$$= f(x)$$

Since $f(-x) = f(x)$ for all x in the domain of f, the function is even.

We can also see that the function is even from the diagram. The graph is a reflection of itself in the y-axis.

b) The domain of g is the interval $(-\infty, \infty)$. Let x be any element of the domain. We have

$$g(-x) = (-x)^3$$
$$= (-x)(-x)(-x)$$
$$= -x^3$$
$$= -g(x)$$

Since $g(-x) = -g(x)$ for all x in the domain of g, the function is odd.

We can also see that the function is odd from the diagram. The graph is rotationally symmetric with respect to the origin.

c) The domain of h is the interval $(-\infty, \infty)$. We let x be any element of the domain. We have

$$h(-x) = (-x)^2 - 2(-x) + 1$$
$$= x^2 + 2x + 1$$

Since $h(-x) \neq h(x)$ and $h(-x) \neq -h(x)$, h is neither even nor odd. We use a graphing calculator to graph h to verify the symmetry.

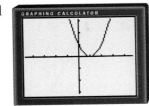

Use Window variables
Xmin = –4.7, Xmax = 4.7,
Ymin = –3.1, Ymax = 3.1
(the friendly window), that is,
$x \in [-4.7, 4.7]$, $y \in [-3.1, 3.1]$.

Another way to look at functions is with an **arrow diagram**. In the diagram, f stands for the function, or rule, and x and $f(x)$ are elements in the domain and range of f, respectively. The diagram shows that the value 2 is in A, the domain of f, and the value $f(2)$ is in B, the range of f.

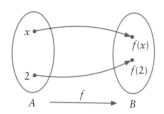

The Role of the Domains of Functions

Recall that we define a function f as a rule that assigns to each element in the domain A one and only one element of the range B. This means that two functions represented algebraically by the same formula may nevertheless be different because they possess different domains.

Example 3 Domains of Functions

Compare the following two functions:
a) the function g that assigns to each positive value x the area of a square with side length equal to x
b) the function whose values are determined by the rule $f(x) = x^2$, with domain $[-2, 2]$

Solution

Since the area of a square with side length x is x^2, the algebraic representation of g is $g(x) = x^2$. The side length of a square is positive, and so the domain of g is $(0, \infty)$. Therefore, the algebraic representations of the functions are as follows.
a) $g(x) = x^2$, with domain $(0, \infty)$
b) $f(x) = x^2$, with domain $[-2, 2]$

Since the functions f and g have different domains, they are different functions. We can also see the difference between the functions by using visual representations of each function:

Graph of g:

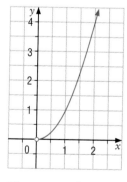

Graph of f:

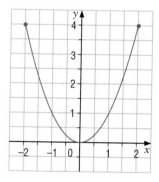

The range of g is $(0, \infty)$.   The range of f is $[0, 4]$.

In Example 3, we translated a verbal representation of a function g into an algebraic representation using a formula, $g(x) = x^2$. It may not always be possible to represent a function using a *single* algebraic formula that is valid throughout its domain. This is true with absolute value functions, which we explore next.

Absolute Value Functions

The **absolute value** of a number x, denoted by $|x|$, may be described in words as the distance between x and 0 on a number line. We require an algebraic representation of this function. Since the distance between x and 0 cannot be negative, $|x| \geq 0$. However, this observation falls short of a formula. Consider the examples on the number line:

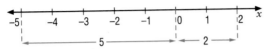

From the diagram we see that $|2| = 2$. From this example, we see that, when $x \geq 0$, $|x| = x$. However, when $x < 0$, the same formula does not hold. For example, $|-5| = -5$ is false.

From the diagram, we see that $|-5| = 5$. When $x < 0$, the correct output is the input multiplied by -1. Thus, $|-5| = (-1)(-5)$, since $(-1)(-5) = 5$. When $x < 0$, $|x| = (-1)x$ or $|x| = -x$. The absolute value of x may be expressed using two functions, $g(x)$ and $h(x)$, as follows:

$g(x) = -x, \ x \in (-\infty, 0)$

$h(x) = x, \ x \in [0, \infty)$

Thus, the algebraic representation for $|x|$ is defined **piecewise**, that is, the formula used depends on the part of the domain it refers to.

The absolute value function is represented algebraically as $|x| = \begin{cases} -x, & x \in (-\infty, 0) \\ x, & x \in [0, \infty) \end{cases}$

Example 4 An Absolute Value Function

Sketch the absolute value function, $f(x) = |x|$.

Solution

From the algebraic representation of the absolute value function, it can be considered a piecewise function, with each piece defined over a separate part of the domain:

$f(x) = \begin{cases} -x, & x \in (-\infty, 0) \\ x, & x \in [0, \infty) \end{cases}$

The graphs of these two pieces in the same coordinate plane, taken as a whole, give the graph of the absolute value function $f(x) = |x|$.

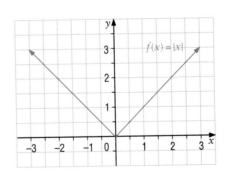

Observe the symmetry of the graph of the absolute value function. Because it is symmetric about the y-axis, $f(x) = |x|$ is an even function.

Example 5 Determining the Symmetry of Absolute Value Functions

Determine whether each function is even, odd, or neither. Use this information to help you graph the function.

a) $f(x) = 2|x| - 1$ b) $g(x) = 2|x - 1|$

Solution

a) $f(-x) = 2|-x| - 1$

From Example 4, we know that the absolute value function is even.

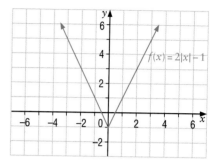

Thus, $|-x| = |x|$.

$f(-x) = 2|x| - 1$

$\qquad = f(x)$

$f(x) = 2|x| - 1$ is an even function, that is, it is symmetric about the y-axis. Therefore, we can plot the function on the interval $[0, \infty)$, and reflect it in the y-axis for the interval $(-\infty, 0)$. On $[0, \infty)$,

$f(x) = 2|x| - 1$

$\qquad = 2x - 1$

Thus, we plot the graph of $y = 2x - 1$ for the interval $[0, \infty)$, and then reflect it in the y-axis for the interval $(-\infty, 0)$.

b) $g(x) = 2|x - 1|$
$\quad g(-x) = 2|-x - 1|$
$\qquad\quad = 2|-(x + 1)|$
Since $|-x| = |x|$, $2|-(x + 1)| = 2|x + 1|$. Thus, $g(-x) = 2|x + 1|$.

Therefore, $g(-x) \neq g(x)$ and $g(-x) \neq -g(x)$. The function is neither even nor odd. The graph of g is a translation of 1 unit left, and a vertical stretch by a factor of 2, of the graph of $y = |x|$. Note that the graph is symmetric about the line $x = 1$.

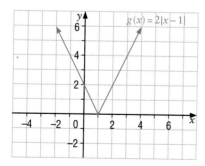

Refer back to the table of interval notation. Note that some intervals can also be written using the absolute value function. For example, the distance from the origin to every number x in the interval $[-2, 2]$ is less than or equal to 2 units, so $x \in [-2, 2]$ can be written as $|x| \le 2$. Similarly, $x \in (-\infty, -3)$ or $x \in (3, \infty)$ can be written as $|x| > 3$, since the distance from the origin to every number in the union of the two intervals is at least 3 units. Study the graph of the absolute value function to verify these statements.

Example 6 Absolute Value Notation for Intervals

Express each interval using absolute value notation.
a) $x \in [2, 10]$ b) $x \in (-\infty, 5]$ or $x \in [8, \infty)$

Solution

a) The midpoint of the interval is

$$\frac{2 + 10}{2} = 6$$

Since $10 - 6 = 4$, each point in the interval is 4 units or less from the number 6. Thus, the interval can be described as

$$|x - 6| \le 4$$

b) The midpoint of the interval $[5, 8]$ is

$$\frac{5 + 8}{2} = 6.5$$

Since $8 - 6.5 = 1.5$, each point in the two intervals is 1.5 units or more from the number 6.5. Thus, the intervals can be described as

$$|x - 6.5| \ge 1.5$$

When mathematics is used to represent relationships in a real-world situation, we say that we have a **mathematical model** of the situation. A useful mathematical model accounts for the known data in a satisfactory way and, more importantly, provides insight into the situation. Ideally, the model will also make predictions that can be tested by further observations. If the observations are consistent with the predictions, confidence in the model may increase. If not, the model may have to be modified or discarded. Even a good model may be refined and improved by taking further factors into consideration. The diagram shows the life cycle of the **mathematical modelling** process.

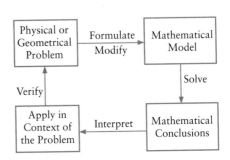

Functions are used extensively in the modelling of physical situations. Consider the speed of a car. At a particular time, a car has a certain speed. A car cannot move with two different speeds at the same time. That is, there is only one output (the speed of the car) for a given input (time). Thus, the speed of the car is a function of time. It could be that the same output occurs at more than one input, or even at all inputs. For example, if the car is not moving, the car maintains the same speed (that is, 0) at all times.

Mathematical models may be expressed in a variety of ways. In situations where two variables, x and y, are related, the mathematical model may be a function, $y = f(x)$. If a model is of the form $y = mx + b$, then the model is referred to as a **linear model**. The visual representation of this model is the graph of a straight line, where m is the slope of the line and b is the y-intercept. The model used to convert degrees Fahrenheit to degrees Celsius, from Example 1, is an example of a linear model.

Frequently, models are used to represent data that have been collected. The graph of the model is often taken to be the curve of best fit for the data. If the data in a scatter plot cannot reasonably be approximated using a straight line, the curve of best fit may be given by another common function, such as the quadratic function in Example 7.

Example 7 Modelling Using Quadratic Regression on a Graphing Calculator

The table shows the percent of drivers in each age group involved in automobile accidents.

a) Find the midpoint of each age range.

b) Make a scatter plot with the interval midpoints on the horizontal axis and the percents on the vertical axis.

c) Describe the slope of the curve over time.

d) Use a quadratic model to determine a curve of best fit.

e) Use the model to predict the accident rate for drivers aged 100.

f) Do you think a quadratic model represents the data well? Explain.

Lower Age	Upper Age	Percent
15	24	6.9
25	34	5.7
35	44	4.8
45	54	4.1
55	64	3.5
65	74	2.8
75	84	2.7

Source: Toronto Star, July 25, 2001 – Ontario Road Safety Annual Report

Solution

a) We add a fourth column to the table for the midpoints of the age ranges.

Lower Age	Upper Age	Percent	Age Midpoint
15	24	6.9	19.5
25	34	5.7	29.5
35	44	4.8	39.5
45	54	4.1	49.5
55	64	3.5	59.5
65	74	2.8	69.5
75	84	2.7	79.5

b) We use the STAT PLOTS menu to plot the data on a graphing calculator with the midpoint of the age range in L1 and the percent in L2.

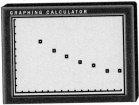

Window variables:
$x \in [0, 80]$, $y \in [0, 10]$

From the scatter plot of the data, we can see that the model is not linear.

c) The curve is fairly steep at the beginning and becomes less steep as age increases.

d) From the scatter plot, a quadratic model seems appropriate. We choose **QuadReg** (quadratic **regression**) from the STAT CALC menu of the graphing calculator.

 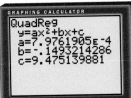 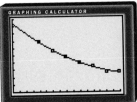

The quadratic function $y = 0.000\,80x^2 - 0.149\,32x + 9.475\,14$ appears to model the data well, because its graph passes through or near all of the data points.

e) We will use the quadratic model we found in part d) to estimate the accident rate for 100-year-old drivers, by pressing ⎡VARS⎤ ▶ 1 1 ⎡(⎤ 100 ⎡)⎤.

The predicted accident rate for 100-year-old drivers is about 2.52%.

f) The model represents the given data well, but does not **extrapolate** well at all. It is unlikely that there are enough 100-year-old drivers around to verify that the result in part e) is valid. And for values of x much greater than 100, we don't expect any drivers, so the model is unrealistic for large values of x.

We have seen curves of best fit that are polynomials. A **linear function** can be regarded as a first-degree polynomial: $P(x) = mx + b$. A **quadratic function** is also called a second-degree polynomial:

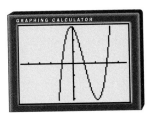

Window variables:
$x \in [-4.7, 4.7]$, $y \in [-3.1, 3.1]$
or use the ZDecimal instruction.

$P(x) = ax^2 + bx + c$. The general form of a **cubic function**, or third-degree polynomial, is $P(x) = ax^3 + bx^2 + cx + d$. For example, the graphing calculator screen shows the cubic function $f(x) = x^3 - 3x^2 - x + 3$.

Another type of function, the **exponential function**, takes the form $y = a^x$, where a is a constant. Exponential functions are often used to model growth and decay situations.

Example 8 An Exponential Model

Luisa, a travelling salesperson, purchased a new car for $24 000. Because she uses the car in her job, she can depreciate its value by 20% of its remaining value each year, for income tax purposes. She intends to keep the car for 8 years.
a) Express the value of the car as a function of its age.
b) Use the model to obtain the value of the car after 5 years.
c) What is the domain of the function in the model?
d) Sketch the graph of the model.
e) Describe the slope of the graph over time.

Solution

a) Because the value of the car decreases by 20% each year, the car is worth $100\% - 20\% = 80\%$ of its remaining value each year. To determine the car's value each year, we multiply the previous year's value by 0.8. The model is exponential and can be represented by the function
$v(t) = 24\,000(0.8)^t$
where $v(t)$ represents the value of the car, in dollars, after t years.

b) $v(5) = 24\,000(0.8)^5$
      $= 7864.32$
The value of the car after 5 years will be $7864.32.

c) The domain is $t \in [0, 8]$ because Luisa will keep her car for 8 years.

d)

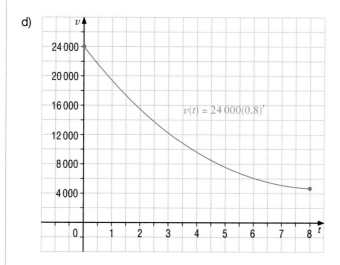

e) The graph is quite steep at the beginning, but becomes less steep as time goes on.

In this section, we discussed linear, quadratic, and exponential models, as well as changing slopes of functions. This course will extend the modelling process to include other types of functions, such as cubic, rational, logarithmic, and trigonometric. Determining the slope of the graph of a function is a very important concept in calculus and is developed in greater detail in Chapter 3.

Key Concepts

- The rule of four states that there are four ways to represent a function: verbally, numerically, algebraically, and visually.
- A function is a rule that assigns to each element in a set A (the domain), one and only one element in a set B (the range).
- The domain of a function, unless otherwise specified, is the collection of all real inputs for which the definition of the function makes sense. The range of a function is the collection of all possible outputs.
- A function f is called even if it is symmetric about the y-axis. An even function satisfies $f(-x) = f(x)$ for every number x in its domain.
- A function f is called odd if it is rotationally symmetric about the origin. An odd function satisfies $f(-x) = -f(x)$ for every number x in its domain.
- A mathematical model is a description of a real-world situation in the language of mathematics.
- A curve of best fit is a function that closely approximates a set of data.

Communicate Your Understanding

1. Describe how you would determine whether a function is even or odd from its visual representation.

2. Give a verbal description of the function $f(x) = |x - 1|$.

3. Describe when to use round brackets and when to use square brackets with interval notation.

4. Describe how intervals can be written using absolute value notation.

5. Explain what a mathematical model is. Describe the characteristics of a good mathematical model.

Practise

A 1. Use interval notation to express the set of real values x described by each inequality. Illustrate each interval on the real number line.

a) $-2 \le x \le 2$ b) $4 \le x \le 13$
c) $-4 < x < -1$ d) $0 < x < 4$
e) $x < 2$ f) $x > -1$
g) $x \le -1$ h) $x \ge 0$

2. Write each interval in question 1 in absolute value notation, if possible.

3. Determine whether each function is even, odd, or neither. Then, graph the function on the interval $|x| \le 4$.

a) $f(x) = 2x^3$ b) $g(x) = x^3 - 4$
c) $h(x) = 1 - x^2$

4. Determine whether each function is even, odd, or neither. Then, graph the function on the domain $[-2, 2]$.

a) $f(x) = \frac{1}{2}x^4$ b) $g(x) = -\frac{1}{2}x^4$
c) $h(x) = x^3 - 6$

5. Determine whether each function is even or odd. Then, graph the function on the domain $(-\infty, \infty)$.

a) $f(x) = -|x|$

b) $g(x) = |x| + 1$

c) $h(x) = |2x^3|$

6. For each function, find

i) $f(2)$ ii) $f(-2)$ iii) $f\left(\dfrac{1}{2}\right)$

iv) $f\left(\dfrac{1}{3}\right)$ v) $f(k)$ vi) $f(1-k)$

a) $f(x) = 1 - x$ b) $f(x) = x^2$

7. Communication For each function, find and simplify

i) $f(3)$ ii) $f(-3)$ iii) $f\left(\dfrac{1}{3}\right)$

iv) $f\left(\dfrac{1}{4}\right)$ v) $f\left(\dfrac{1}{k}\right)$ vi) $\left(\dfrac{k}{1+k}\right)$

a) $f(x) = \dfrac{1}{x^2}$ b) $f(x) = \dfrac{x}{1-x}$

8. Communication The minimum stopping distance, d, in metres, of a particular car on dry asphalt can be modelled using the function $d(s) = 0.006s^2$, where s is the speed, in kilometres per hour, when the brakes are first fully applied. Express the function verbally, numerically, and visually for $s \in [0, 150]$.

9. The data in the table show the population of Ontario from 1990 to 2000.

Year	Population (1000s)
1990	10 299.6
1991	10 472.6
1992	10 570.5
1993	10 690.4
1994	10 827.5
1995	10 964.9
1996	11 100.9
1997	11 249.5
1998	11 384.4
1999	11 513.8
2000	11 669.3

Express the data as a function of time after 1990 verbally, visually (with a scatter plot using the STAT PLOTS menu on a graphing calculator), and algebraically (by finding a curve of best fit using the STAT CALC menu on the graphing calculator).

10. Application i) Determine whether each function is even, odd, or neither.

ii) State the domain of each function in interval notation.

a) $f(x) = x^3 + x$ b) $g(x) = 5 - |x|$

c) $h(x) = 5$ d) $r(x) = x^3 + |x|$

e) $s(x) = \dfrac{1}{x^2}$ f) $t(x) = (x^4)^3$

g) $f(x) = x^3 - 4x^2 + x$ h) $k(x) = \dfrac{x}{(32 - x^5)^2}$

11. A table of data is given.

x	1	2	3	4	5	6	7	8	9	10
y	11	10	9	8	8	7	6	5	5	4

a) Construct a scatter plot of the data and determine an equation of the line of best fit.

b) Using your equation from part a), predict the value of y when $x = 12$.

c) Using your equation from part a), predict the value of x when $y = 0$.

12. a) Construct a scatter plot of the given data using the STAT PLOTS menu on a graphing calculator, and determine the equation of a curve of best fit using the STAT CALC menu on the calculator.

x	2	3	4	5	6	7
y	4.0	7.0	9.0	10.0	11.0	10.9

x	8	9	10	11	12
y	11.0	10.1	8.5	6.7	5.0

b) Using your equation from part a), estimate the value of y when $x = 9.5$.

c) Using your equation from part a), predict the value(s) of x when $y = 0$.

Apply, Solve, Communicate

B **13.** Application Show that the product of two odd functions is an even function.

14. Inquiry/Problem Solving Show that the quotient of two even functions is an even function.

15. Is the product of an odd function and an even function odd or even? Verify your result algebraically.

16. Inquiry/Problem Solving Suppose that the function $y = f(x)$ is odd.
a) Show that $f(0) = 0$, provided that $f(0)$ exists.
b) Give an example of an odd function for which $f(0) \neq 0$.

17. A manufacturer purchases $18\,000$ worth of computer equipment that depreciates linearly so that after 4 years the equipment is worth $9000.
a) Express the value of the equipment as a function of its age.
b) Use the model in part a) to obtain the value of the equipment after 6 years.
c) What is the domain of the function in the model?
d) What does the slope of the linear function in the model represent?
e) Sketch a graph of the model.
f) Describe the slope and how it changes over time.

18. Inquiry/Problem Solving The table gives the population of Prince Edward Island, in thousands, for five consecutive years beginning with 1995.

Year	Population (1000s)
1995	134.8
1996	136.2
1997	136.9
1998	137.0
1999	138.0

a) Make a scatter plot of the data, using the STAT PLOTS menu on a graphing calculator.
b) Find an equation of an approximate line of best fit, using the STAT CALC menu on the graphing calculator.
c) Using the equation of the line of best fit, predict the population of Prince Edward Island in the year 2010.
d) Use the equation of the line of best fit to determine when the population of Prince Edward Island was 0. Is this value reasonable?
e) Use the equation of the line of best fit to predict when the population of Prince Edward Island will be $1\,000\,000$. Do you have confidence in this result? Explain.
f) Does a linear model represent this situation well? Explain.

19. Application The table gives the population of Oshawa, in thousands, for five consecutive years beginning with 1995. Repeat question 18 for the population of Oshawa.

Year	Population (1000s)
1995	272.6
1996	277.1
1997	282.0
1998	287.6
1999	292.9

20. Communication The table gives the average annual pet expenses for individuals with certain incomes.

Income ($)	Pet Expenses ($)
15\,000	104
25\,000	195
35\,000	250
45\,000	350
55\,000	477

a) Make a scatter plot of the data.

b) Find an equation of a curve of best fit.

c) Using the equation of the curve of best fit, estimate the annual pet expenses for a person with a yearly income of $40 000.

d) Using the equation of the curve of best fit, estimate the yearly income for a person with average annual pet expenses of $400.

e) Using the equation of the curve of best fit, predict the annual pet expenses for a professional baseball player, with a yearly income of $7 000 000. Do you have confidence in this prediction? Explain.

f) What does the curve of best fit give as the annual income for a person with no pet expenses? Is it reasonable to use the curve of best fit in this way? Explain.

g) Does your model represent this situation well? Explain.

21. Communication The table below shows the minimum stopping distance on wet asphalt at various speeds.

Speed (km/h)	Stopping Distance (metres)
10	0.9
20	3.2
30	7.3
40	13.0
50	20.1
60	28.6
70	39.1
80	51.3
90	64.8
100	80.0
110	96.5

a) Make a scatter plot of the data.

b) Find an equation of a curve of best fit.

c) Discuss the slope of the curve and how it changes as speed increases.

d) How do the graphs and equations compare to the model for stopping distances on dry asphalt, given in question 8?

22. The value for the first 8 years of an initial investment of $1000 in a particular mutual fund is shown in the table. The values have been rounded to the nearest dollar.

Time (years)	Value
0	$1000
1	$1092
2	$1142
3	$1349
4	$1574
5	$1498
6	$1771
7	$2210
8	$2542

a) Make a scatter plot of the data in the table.

b) Find an equation of an exponential curve of best fit.

c) Discuss the slope of the curve and how it changes.

d) Use your model to predict the value of the investment after 10 years.

23. A constant function is a function that satisfies $f(x) = k$, for some constant k and all numbers x. Which constant functions are even functions? Are there any constant functions that are odd functions?

24. Can the sum of an odd function and an even function be odd? even? Explain.

25. Can a function be both even and odd? Explain.

26. Inquiry/Problem Solving The cost of removing the source of a pollutant leaching into a river is estimated to be

$$C(x) = \frac{25\sqrt{x}}{\sqrt{100 - x}}$$

where C is the cost, in thousands of dollars, and x is the percent of pollutant removed.

a) Suggest a domain for $C(x)$, and explain your choice.

b) Determine the cost of removing the following amounts of pollutant: 25%, 50%, 75%, 99%.

c) What percent of pollutant can be removed for $50 000?

d) According to this model, is it possible to remove all of the pollutant? If so, how much would it cost?

Achievement Check

Knowledge/Understanding

Thinking/Inquiry/Problem Solving

Communication

Application

Liam rides his bike to a soccer field, a trip of about 10 km. He rides at a constant speed until he reaches a steep grade 4 km from home. He slows down as he goes up a 1-km stretch. By the time he reaches the top of the hill, Liam is barely moving, and he stops to rest before coasting down the other side. The hill is less steep on the down side, but Liam coasts down the 2 km fairly quickly. The last 3 km to the field is almost flat.

a) Sketch a graph of Liam's distance from home as a function of time. Describe the behaviour of the graph on each interval.

b) Sketch a graph of Liam's speed as a function of time. Describe the behaviour of the graph on each interval.

c) Copy the sketch from part b), and on the same axes, sketch a graph of Liam's speed on the ride home as a function of time. Describe the behaviour of the graph on each interval.

Technology Extension

Functions on a Computer Algebra System

Computer algebra systems allow us to do complex algebraic manipulations with a few keystrokes. The TI-92 Plus and TI-89 calculators have a computer algebra system built in. There are also software programs that contain computer algebra systems to make mathematical work easier. Some of the more popular programs are TI InterActive!™, Derive™, Maple®, LiveMath, Mathcad®, and Mathematica®.

Using the Define operation, functions can be defined and manipulated. To define a function, press the [F4] function key. The first choice is **Define**. Press [ENTER]. The word Define will appear on the entry line.

Complete the function definition by typing f(x)= and then the expression, as in the screen below, where a cubic function has been defined. After it is defined, a function can be evaluated at any value simply by entering the correct expression in function notation.

In the next screen, the function $f(x)$ has been evaluated for values of x equal to 3, –5, and $\sqrt{6}$. Two different results are shown for $x = \sqrt{6}$. The first is in exact form. For the second, press the green diamond key [♦] before

pressing the [ENTER] key to get the approximate solution.

The TI-92 has several special functions built into the [MATH] menu. In this screen, the absolute value function is selected to be stored in y1, using the abs function.

When the [ENTER] key is pressed, the absolute value function is stored in y1 using correct mathematical notation.

Functions can be graphed on the GRAPH screen by pressing [♦] followed by the letter R. Notice that the word GRAPH appears above the letter in green.

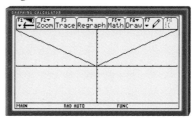

The TI-92 allows you to enter several functions at a time and perform algebraic operations on them. You can also define new functions in terms of old ones using the Define operation.

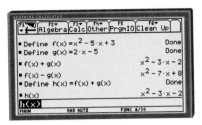

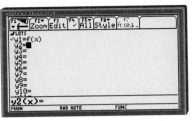

The function has been stored in y1 (above) and graphed (below).

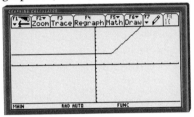

Piecewise functions can also be defined, using the when function. In the next screen, a function has been defined in two parts.

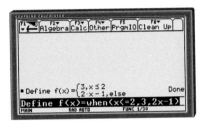

Rather than storing the function in y1, a **Graph** command can be entered in the home screen.

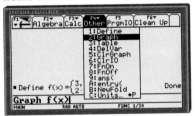

Practise

1. Define the function $f(x) = x^3 - 2x^2 - 5x + 5$. Create a table of values for the function and graph it using your software or calculator. Sketch the graph in your notebook.

2. A piecewise function is made up of a linear part and a quadratic part. For $x \in (-\infty, 2)$, the linear function is $y = 3x - 5$. For $x \in [2, \infty)$, the function is defined by the quadratic $y = x^2 - 3$. Create a table of values for the function and graph it using your software or calculator. Sketch the graph in your notebook.

3. The graph of a function is shown in the screen.

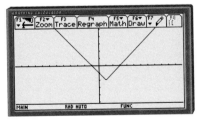

Window variables:
$x \in [-11.9, 11.9]$, $y \in [-5.1, 5.1]$

Use your software or calculator to define it as
a) a piecewise function
b) an absolute value function

Lies My Graphing Calculator Tells Me

Graphing calculators are very powerful tools, but we must be careful to ensure that we understand completely the results they provide. In this section, we will look at some of the ways to avoid misinterpreting what appears on a graphing calculator screen.

Is That a Vertical Asymptote?

Throughout the course we will be looking at rational functions. The screen on the left below shows the graph of the function $f(x) = \dfrac{1}{x-2}$ in the standard viewing window $x \in [-10, 10]$ and $y \in [-10, 10]$. Use the ZStandard instruction, $\boxed{\text{ZOOM}}$ 6, to graph a function in this window. Note that there is a problem in the display when the denominator is zero, that is, when $x = 2$. At first glance, it appears that the calculator has drawn a vertical **asymptote** at $x = 2$, although it is not quite vertical. The graph on the right shows the same function using the window $x \in [-4.7, 4.7]$ and $y \in [-3.1, 3.1]$. Use the ZDecimal instruction, $\boxed{\text{ZOOM}}$ 4, to graph a function in this window, which is sometimes referred to as a "friendly window."

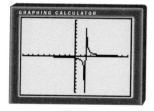 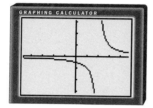

Try this on your own calculator. With the first display on the screen, press the $\boxed{\text{TRACE}}$ key and move the cursor to the right—it moves in increments of 0.212 765 96. This is because the calculator's screen is 94 pixels wide. Since the graphing window goes from −10 to 10 horizontally, each pixel represents a distance of $\dfrac{20}{94}$, which is equal to 0.212 765 96. The calculator is in Connected mode, which means that a segment will be drawn to connect successive points. The last point to the left of $x = 2$ is below the x-axis, while the next point to the right of $x = 2$ is above the x-axis. So, the segment in the first graph is not an asymptote, but a line segment joining two adjacent points. It just happens to be almost vertical.

For the second graph, the window goes from −4.7 to 4.7 for a total distance of 9.4 units. Thus, the horizontal distance for the TRACE step is $\dfrac{9.4}{94} = 0.1$. When the calculator attempts to join points in this window, it finds an error at $x = 2$, so no line segment is drawn, and the graph is displayed correctly. In this window, draw in a vertical asymptote with the Vertical instruction.

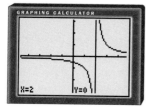

Note that positive integer multiples of the friendly window also make interpreting graphs easier. If we multiply the values in the window by 2, for example, the distance for the TRACE step is 0.2. If we multiply the values by 3, the TRACE step is 0.3, and so on.

Is There a Zero There?

It is possible that the graph of a function on the graphing calculator screen passes so close to the *x*-axis that it is not clear whether there is no **zero**, a double zero, or two zeros. In the first screen below, the function $f(x) = x^3 - 2x^2 - 3x + 6$ is graphed using the ZStandard instruction. To the right of the origin, it is difficult to tell how many zeros there are, if any.

To get a closer look at this area, press ZOOM 1 for the ZBox instruction. Move the cursor to a point above the *x*-axis and to the left of the possible zero. Press ENTER and move to the right and down. As the cursor moves, a box is formed. Move the cursor to a second point below the *x*-axis and to the right of the possible zero. Press ENTER again.

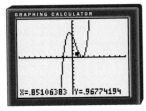

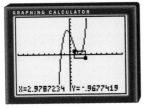

Window variables:
$x \in [-10, 10], y \in [-10, 10]$

The window adjusts to the values determined by the box that we have drawn and the screen shows a close-up of the area framed by that box. The last screen shows that this function has two zeros near *x* = 3. Use the Zero operation to find approximate values for each of them.

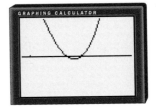

The same situation occurs when two curves pass near each other without intersecting.

What's Wrong With the Domain and Range?

Consider the function $f(x) = \dfrac{1}{\sqrt{4 - x^2}}$. We have already seen that the standard viewing window can be deceptive. Instead, we use the ZDecimal instruction for the first attempt. This produces the graph shown to the right. Using the **TRACE feature**, we could conclude that the domain is $x \in (-2, 2)$. In the same way, we could conclude that the range is $y \in [0.5, 1.6013)$. This is correct for the domain, but incorrect for the range.

However, there are other tools on the calculator for investigating domain and range. In the next set of screens, the TABLE SETUP screen is shown along with the resulting table. The values of *y* in the table are much larger than 1.6013. Using successively smaller increments for the value of △Tbl makes it clear that the range is $y \in [0.5, \infty)$.

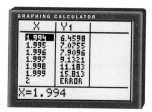

Is That Function Linear?

Look at the graph of the function to the right. Most people would agree that this function appears to be linear. However, it turns out that the Window variables that produced this graph show the function over a very small region. When we Zoom Out on this function, we get the following graphs.

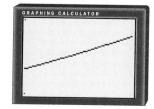

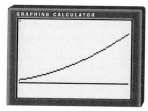
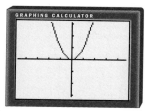

Even from the second graph, we can see that the function is not linear. All three screens display the graph of the quadratic function $y = x^2$ with different Window variables. This demonstrates a feature of all smooth curves called **local linearity**. Any smooth curve will appear to be linear if you focus on a small enough (local) domain, and Zoom In on it enough times.

Why Do I Need to Look at the Graph Twice?

Enter the function $f(x) = \dfrac{x^3 - 2x^2 - 5x - 5}{x^2 - x - 6}$ into the Y= editor of the calculator.

Change the Window variables to $x \in [-9.4, 9.4]$ and $y \in [-9.3, 9.3]$ and graph the function. It should appear as the screen to the right. Notice that the values provided for the Window variables are multiples of the values in a friendly window, so that the almost vertical segments near the asymptotes that are not actually part of the graph are not shown. This window shows a great deal of detail of the function around the origin, but does not show us anything about the function when the values of x and y are very large.

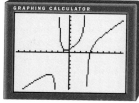

To see the function when the values of x and y are very large, try setting the Window variables to $x \in [-100, 100]$ and $y \in [-100, 100]$ using steps of 10 for each value (i.e., Xscl = Yscl = 10). This view shows that the function appears to be nearly linear far from the origin. We will be looking at more functions like this in Chapter 6.

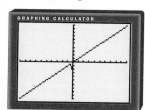

Using multiple viewing windows helps us to understand the nature of the function over its entire domain.

Graphing using any technology can make the work more interesting, but, as we have seen in this section, there are some dangers that must be taken into consideration.

Web Connection

To explore other interesting graphs, go to **www.mcgrawhill.ca/links/CAF12** and follow the links.

Apply, Solve, Communicate

B **1.** Use a graphing calculator or graphing software to graph each function below. Use the Vertical instruction to add in the correct vertical asymptotes. Find the values of all x-intercepts and the y-intercept.

a) $y = \dfrac{1}{(x+3)(x-2)}$

b) $y = \dfrac{1}{x^2 + 2x - 8}$

c) $y = \dfrac{x+1}{6x^2 + 11x - 10}$

d) $y = \dfrac{x^2 - x - 20}{x^2 - x - 30}$

2. Find the x-intercepts, if any, of each function.

a) $y = -2x^2 - 2x - 0.6$

b) $y = 2.5x^2 - 4.7x + 2.1$

c) $y = x^3 + 2x^2 - 5x + 2.3$

d) $y = x^3 - 4.5x^2 + 3.5x - 0.76$

3. Find the point(s) of intersection of each system of equations.

a) $y = x^2 - 2x + 3$ and $y = -x^2 + 2x + 1$

b) $y = 2x + 2$ and $y = x^2 + x + 2.5$

c) $y = x^2 + 8x + 10$ and $y = x^3 - 9x - 12$

d) $y = -x^2 - x - 2$ and $y = x^2 + 5x + 3$

4. Find the domain and range of each function.

a) $y = \dfrac{1}{x-2}$

b) $y = \dfrac{1}{(x+1)^2}$

c) $y = \dfrac{-3}{(x^2 - x - 6)}$

d) $y = \dfrac{5}{\sqrt{9 - x^4}}$

5. Communication **a)** Set angle measure to **Radian** on the Mode settings screen. Graph the functions $y = \sin(96x)$ and $y = \sin(2x)$ together using the Window variables $x \in [-2\pi, 2\pi]$ and $y \in [-1.5, 1.5]$. Use a heavier Graph style for the second function.

b) Explain why the two graphs appear to be identical. Does this have anything to do with the difference in the x-coefficients of the functions?

c) Will this work with any Window variables? Will it work for any other such sine functions whose coefficients of x differ by 94? For which other pairs of sine functions will this work?

6. Use the ZOOM menu on a graphing calculator to find a window that makes a portion of the graph of each function appear linear.

a) $y = x^2 - 2x + 3$

b) $y = x^3 - 9x - 12$

c) $y = \sqrt{9 - x^2}$

d) $y = \dfrac{5}{\sqrt{9 - x^4}}$

7. Application Use as many windows as necessary to show all of the features of the function $y = \dfrac{x^3 - 5x^2 - 3x + 5}{x^2 - 5x + 6}$. Copy the values for each set of Window variables into your notebook.

8. Find Window variables that show the graph of each function properly.

a) $y = \dfrac{1}{x - 1.73}$

b) $y = \dfrac{1}{x - 2.684}$

9. Use a graphing calculator to determine the domain and range of the function

$$y = \dfrac{1}{\sqrt{2.68 - x^2}}.$$

Historical Bite: Function Notation

The function notation $f(x)$ was first used by Leonhard Euler (1707–1783) in 1734.

Investigate & Apply: Designing a Roller Coaster

Knowledge/Understanding

Thinking/Inquiry/Problem Solving

Communication

Application

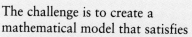

A roller coaster design team is planning a section of a roller coaster. The criteria are as follows:

- a maximum climb or drop of 30 m
- a slope that varies between −1 and 1
- a horizontal length of 120 m

The challenge is to create a mathematical model that satisfies these conditions. Explore possible models and write a report summarizing your conclusions.

Here are some suggestions for your investigation:

The team's initial equation for the path of the roller coaster is

$$y = \frac{x}{2\,000\,000}(x - 30)(x - 50)(x - 90)(x - 100), \quad x \in [0, 100]$$

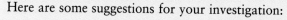

1. Graph the team's initial equation using a graphing calculator or graphing software.

2. Suggest changes to the equation so that the criteria are satisfied. Give reasons for your suggestions.

3. State the new equation and provide a graph of the roller coaster's path. Include the Window variables of your graph.

4. Describe your own criteria for a different section of roller coaster, develop an equation, and draw a suitable graph, including the Window variables.

5. What are some of the constraints that determine the criteria for your roller coaster?

Web Connection

To learn more about the history and design of roller coasters, go to
www.mcgrawhill.ca/ links/CAF12.

1.1 Functions and Their Use in Modelling

Refer to the Key Concepts on page 18.

1. A visual representation of a function *f* is given.

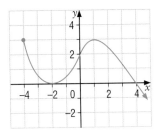

a) Copy and complete the partial numerical representation.

x	y
−2	
−1	
1	
3	

b) State the domain of *f*.

2. For a function with algebraic representation $f(x) = 5 + |x + 3|$,
a) copy and complete the table to give a partial numerical representation

x	y
−6	
−5	
−4	
−3	
−2	
−1	
0	

b) graph the function to give a visual representation
c) give a description in words

3. Write each inequality using interval notation.
a) $x \le 0$ b) $-4 < x$ c) $-5 \le x \le 5$

4. The numerical representations of three functions are given. Classify each function as even, odd, or neither.

x	f(x)	g(x)	h(x)
−4	7	2	−9
−3	−2	−3	2
−2	−3	1	3
−1	−1	−1	−2
0	0	0	10
1	−1	1	−2
2	3	−1	3
3	−2	3	2
4	7	−2	−9

5. Determine whether each function is even, odd, or neither.
a) $f(x) = x^2 + x$ b) $g(x) = |x^2 - 3|$
c) $h(x) = 5x$ d) $r(x) = x^2 - |x|$
e) $s(x) = \dfrac{1}{x^3}$ f) $t(x) = (x^3)^3$

6. Show that the product of two even functions is an even function.

7. A table of data is given.

t	3	4	7	9	12	13	17	20
d	23	22	19	16	14	11	7	4

a) Determine an equation for a line of best fit, using the STAT CALC menu on a graphing calculator.
b) Using the equation of the line of best fit, estimate the value of *d* when *t* = 14.
c) Using the equation of the line of best fit, predict the value of *d* when *t* = 23.

8. A table of data is given. Assuming a quadratic model, find an equation of a curve of best fit, using the STAT CALC menu on a graphing calculator.

x	0	2	3	4	5	6
y	0	0.5	1	2	3	3.5

x	7	8	9.5	10	11
y	5	6.5	8.5	10	12

9. The table gives the total number of passengers, in thousands, of Canadian air-carriers, every two years for the period from 1990 to 1998.

Year	Passengers (1000s)
1990	36 777
1992	32 202
1994	32 868
1996	40 176
1998	45 104

a) Make a scatter plot of the data, using the STAT PLOTS menu on a graphing calculator, and find an equation of a curve of best fit, using the STAT CALC menu.
b) Using the equation of the curve of best fit, estimate the number of Canadian air-carrier passengers in the year 1995. How does your estimate compare to the actual value, 35 999 000?
c) Use the equation of the curve of best fit to predict when the number of Canadian air-carrier passengers will be 50 000 000. Do you have confidence in this result? Explain.

10. The table contains data showing the average fuel economy of a particular car, in litres per 100 km, at various constant speeds, measured at a test track.

Speed (km/h)	Fuel Economy (L/100 km)
10	14.26
20	12.85
30	11.7
40	10.65
50	10.25
60	10.1
70	10.24
80	10.84
90	11.38
100	12.14

Speed (km/h)	Fuel Economy (L/100 km)
110	13.59
120	15.64
130	16.88
140	19.26
150	22.5

a) Make a scatter plot of the data, using the STAT PLOTS menu of a graphing calculator.
b) At what speed does this car have its best fuel economy? What is that fuel economy?
c) Determine a quadratic curve of best fit using the STAT CALC menu, and state its equation.
d) The data are appropriate for a car driven at constant speed for the speeds given. What would the curve look like for a car that is accelerating?
e) This car does not get very good fuel economy. What would the graph look like for a car with better fuel economy? Why?

11. Determine the domain of each function.

a) $f(x) = \dfrac{3}{x+1}$

b) $f(x) = \dfrac{1}{3-x}$

c) $f(x) = \sqrt{x+1}$

d) $f(x) = \dfrac{1}{\sqrt{3-x}}$

e) $f(x) = \sqrt{|x|-1}$

f) $f(x) = \dfrac{1}{\sqrt{x^2+3}}$

g) $f(x) = \dfrac{1}{x^2-2x+1}$

h) $f(x) = \dfrac{1}{x^2+x-6}$

1.2 Lies My Graphing Calculator Tells Me

Refer to page 25.

12. Determine the smallest graphing calculator viewing window that will contain all of the essential features of the graph of each function.

a) $f(x) = \sqrt{4-x^2}$

b) $f(x) = \sqrt{10x-x^2}$

13. Determine appropriate graphing calculator Window variables to exhibit the principal features of each function, and use them to draw the graph.

a) $f(x) = x^2 + 3x$

b) $f(x) = -0.5x^2 + 4$

c) $f(x) = x + \dfrac{1}{x}$

d) $f(x) = x + \sin(x)$

Chapter Test

Achievement Chart

Category	Knowledge/Understanding	Thinking/Inquiry/Problem Solving	Communication	Application
Questions	All	7, 11	5, 11	6, 10, 11

1. For each function, determine

i) $f(1)$ ii) $f(-1)$ iii) $f(2)$ iv) $f\left(\dfrac{1}{2}\right)$

a) $f(x) = x^2$ b) $f(x) = 1 - x^3$

2. Write each inequality using interval notation.
a) $-4 < x < 10$ b) $x \le 5$ c) $0 \le x$

3. Determine whether each graph is even, odd, or neither.

a)
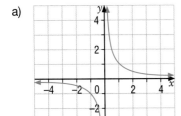

b)
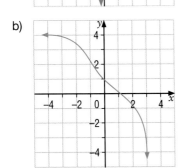

c)
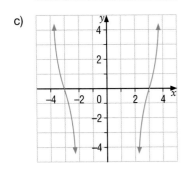

4. The numerical representations of three functions are given. Classify each function as even, odd, or neither.

x	$f(x)$	$g(x)$	$h(x)$
−4	8	2	4
−3	−2	3	2
−2	−3	−1	3
−1	−1	1	2
0	0	5	0
1	−1	1	−2
2	3	−1	−3
3	−2	3	−2
4	−8	2	−4

5. a) Sketch a graph of $y = x^3$.
b) Describe the changing slope of the curve over the interval $[-4, 4]$.
c) Describe the symmetry of the graph.
d) Compare this graph to the graph of $y = x^5$.

6. A table of data is given.

r	1.5	2	3	4.5	6	8	9	9.5
V	4.5	4	5	5.5	6.5	8	9	10

a) Find an equation of a line of best fit, using the STAT CALC menu of a graphing calculator or graphing software.
b) Using the equation of the line of best fit, estimate the value of V when $r = 7$.
c) Using the equation of the line of best fit, predict the value of V when $r = 14$.

7. The period (time for one full swing, back and forth) of a pendulum depends on its length. In a lab during a science class, the period was measured for various lengths of a pendulum, as shown in the table.

Period (s)	0.4	0.6	0.6	0.8	0.9
Length (cm)	5	8	10	15	20

Period (s)	1.1	1.4	1.7	2.0	2.4
Length (cm)	30	50	75	100	150

a) Make a scatter plot of the data, with the period on the x-axis, using the STAT PLOTS menu on a graphing calculator.

b) Decide on an appropriate type of curve to fit the data. Then, determine an equation for the curve of best fit, using the STAT CALC menu.

c) Use your model to determine the period of a pendulum that is 6 cm long.

d) Using your model, how long would a pendulum be if its period is 1 s?

e) Many clocks have adjustable pendulums to help adjust the speed of the clock. Explain how to change the length of a pendulum in order to speed up a clock.

8. Find the domain of each function.

a) $f(x) = \dfrac{1}{x^2 - 1}$

b) $f(x) = \dfrac{1}{\sqrt{x + 3}}$

c) $f(x) = \dfrac{1}{x^2 - 2x - 3}$

d) $f(x) = \dfrac{1}{x^2 + x + 1}$

9. Determine whether each function is even, odd, or neither.

a) $f(x) = x^2 + x^4$

b) $g(x) = |x - 1|$

c) $h(x) = -7x$

d) $r(x) = x^3 + |x|$

e) $s(x) = \dfrac{1 + x^2}{x^2}$

10. Determine appropriate graphing calculator viewing windows to exhibit the principal features of each function and use them to draw the graph.

a) $f(x) = 0.001x^2 + \dfrac{1}{x}$ b) $f(x) = 1000x + \sin x$

Achievement Check

Knowledge/Understanding

Thinking/Inquiry/Problem Solving

Communication

Application

11. A graph of the yield, Y, of a cherry orchard, in bushels, against the amount, a, of fertilizer, in kilograms, used on the orchard is shown.

a) Describe the effect of the amount of fertilizer on the yield of the orchard.

b) What is the vertical intercept? Explain what it means in terms of cherries and fertilizer.

c) What is the horizontal intercept? Explain what it means in terms of cherries and fertilizer.

d) What is the range of the function? What is the domain? Explain any restrictions.

e) How much fertilizer should be used to obtain the highest yield?

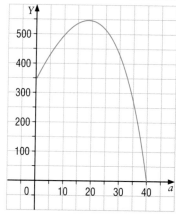

Challenge Problems

1. A baseball player has been officially at bat 322 times and has a batting average of .289. He figures that he will have 53 more times at bat for the rest of the season. What batting average does he have to maintain for the rest of the season in order to end with a season average of .300?

2. Show that a 3 by 3 square chosen from a calendar for any month (providing each square has a date) has the property that the sum of the numbers in the square is nine times the sum of the smallest number and eight.

3. On the Fahrenheit scale, the freezing point of water is 32°F and the boiling point of water is 212°F. On the Celsius scale, the same two points are respectively 0°C and 100°C. For what temperature is the reading of the two scales the same?

4. A reel of plastic tape is wound on a cardboard cylinder of radius 2 cm. When the reel is full, its diameter is 12 cm. What are the distances from the centre of the reel at which the quantity of tape left is

a) $\dfrac{3}{4}$?   b) $\dfrac{1}{2}$?   c) $\dfrac{1}{4}$?

5. A function machine produces results according to the following table:

Input	Output
3 and 5	21
4 and 7	29
0 and 3	9
5 and 0	10
1 and 4	14

What operations are performed on the input numbers to obtain the output numbers?

6. Determine whether $\sqrt{a+x} + \sqrt{a-x}$ is less than, equal to, or greater than $2\sqrt{a}$, where a and x are positive, and $x \le a$.

7. Graph the function $y = |10 - |x||$.

8. Graph the relation $|y| + |x-3| + |x-7| = 15$.

9. Find window settings that show the graph of the function

$$y = \frac{x^3 + 1.11x^2 - 1.4872x - 1.5972}{x^2 + 0.11x - 1.5972} \quad \text{correctly.}$$

Problem Solving Strategy

Principles of Problem Solving

Problem solving is a creative activity that requires not only routines and formulas, but also strategies. Although there are no hard and fast rules for problem solving, we outline some helpful principles, based on the work of George Pólya (1887–1985). We will use some of these principles to solve the following problem.

Frank drove from his house to the lake at an average speed of 50 km/h because of bad weather. On the return trip along the same route, his average speed was 100 km/h. What was his average speed for the whole trip?

**Understand
the Problem**

The first step is to read the problem carefully and make sure that you understand it. Ask yourself the following questions:

1. What information are you given?
2. What are you asked to find?
3. Do you need an exact or an approximate answer?

Find a connection between the given information and the unknown, which will enable you to calculate the unknown.

Average speed is total distance travelled divided by total time elapsed. We know the average speed for both parts of the trip, and that Frank takes the same route to and from the lake. We will let the distance from Frank's house to the lake be d, and the times taken for the trip be t_1 and t_2.

In case you do not see the connection immediately, there are several strategies that can help you, some of which will be discussed in the next three problem solving sections, at the end of Chapters 3, 4, and 6.

**Think
of a Plan**

- *Solve a simpler problem* Try to think of a similar problem that is easier to solve than the original problem.
- *Work backward* Sometimes it is useful to imagine that your problem is solved and work backward, step by step, until you arrive at the given data.
- *Draw a diagram* For many problems it is useful to draw a diagram and label it with the given information.
- *Look for a pattern* Some problems are solved by recognizing a pattern.
- *Introduce something extra* For example, you might draw a new line in a diagram, or introduce a new unknown related to the original unknown.
- *Take cases* You can split a problem into several cases and give a different argument for each.

**Carry Out
the Plan**

For the trip from the house to the lake,

$$50 = \frac{d}{t_1} \qquad \textbf{(1)}$$

For the trip from the lake to the house,

$$100 = \frac{d}{t_2} \qquad \textbf{(2)}$$

$$\text{average speed} = \frac{\text{total distance travelled}}{\text{total time elapsed}}$$

$$= \frac{2d}{t_1 + t_2}$$

From equation (1), $t_1 = \dfrac{d}{50}$, and from equation (2), $t_2 = \dfrac{d}{100}$.

$$\text{average speed} = \frac{2d}{t_1 + t_2}$$

$$= \frac{2d}{\dfrac{d}{50} + \dfrac{d}{100}}$$

$$= \frac{2d}{\left(\dfrac{3d}{100}\right)}$$

$$= \frac{200d}{3d}$$

$$\doteq 66.7$$

His average speed for the entire trip is approximately 66.7 km/h.

Ask yourself the following questions:

1. Does the answer seem reasonable?

2. How could I check that the answer is correct?

Look Back

Suppose that the distance from the house to the lake is 100 km. Then, it takes 2 h to the lake, and 1 h back, for a total time of 3 h. The total distance is 200 km, so the average speed is $\dfrac{200}{3}$, or 66.7 km/h. Note that we cannot determine the correct average speed by adding the two speeds and dividing by 2. Also, the average speed does not depend on the distance from the house to the lake.

Apply, Solve, Communicate

1. Sarah drove from home to school at 90 km/h. She drove from school to home at 70 km/h. What was her average speed, to the nearest tenth, for the round-trip?

2. Three nickels and three dimes are placed in three boxes so that there are two coins in each box. The total number of cents in each box is written on the top of the box. However, the tops of the boxes have been switched so that no box is labelled correctly.

10 cents	15 cents	20 cents

Each box has a slot at the bottom so that, when you shake the box, one coin rolls out. What is the minimum number of coins you must shake out to determine the exact contents of each box?

3. Four people, one of whom was known to have won a lottery, made the following statements when questioned by a reporter.

Sofia: "Paolo won it."
Melissa: "I didn't win it."
Paolo: "Jeff won it."
Jeff: " Paolo lied when he said I won it."

a) If only one of the four statements is true, who won the lottery?

b) If only one of the four statements is false, who won the lottery?

1. A school's debating team consists of four females and four males. The team captain is a female. The team is entered in a regional competition. However, each school is allowed to send only six team members, three males and three females, to the competition. The team captain must be among the members who compete. Other members are equally qualified to compete. How many possible combinations of members could make up the team that competes?

2. You have a 5-L container and a 9-L container and plenty of water. You want exactly 6 L of water in the 9-L container. How can you use the two containers to measure exactly 6 L of water?

3. Four people need to cross a footbridge at night to catch a train, which leaves in more than 15 min but less than 16 min. The bridge can only hold two people at a time. The group has one flashlight, which must be used for each crossing of the bridge. The flashlight must be carried by hand and cannot be thrown back. Because of their different degrees of nervousness, the people take different times to cross the bridge. Juan can cross in 1 min. Sue can cross in 2 min. It takes Alicia 5 min to cross, and it takes Larry 8 min. If they cross in pairs, they cross at the speed of the slower person. How can they all cross and all catch the train?

4. The sum of the numbers of sides of two convex polygons is 11, and the sum of the numbers of their diagonals is 14. Name the two types of polygons.

5. A cube is 20 cm on an edge.
a) How can you cut the cube into six identical pyramids?
b) What are the dimensions of each pyramid?

6. Must each calendar year have at least one Friday the 13th? Explain.

7. A circle is inscribed in an equilateral triangle, and a square is inscribed in the circle.

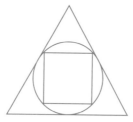

Determine the exact value of the ratio of the area of the triangle to the area of the square.

Chapter 2

Polynomials

Specific Expectations	Section
Determine, through investigation, using graphing calculators or graphing software, various properties of the graphs of polynomial functions.	2.1, 2.6
Compare the nature of change observed in polynomial functions of higher degree with that observed in linear and quadratic functions.	2.1
Solve problems involving the abstract extensions of algorithms.	2.2, 2.3, 2.4, 2.5
Demonstrate an understanding of the remainder and factor theorems.	2.3, 2.4
Factor polynomial expressions of degree greater than two, using the factor theorem.	2.4
Determine, by factoring, the real or complex roots of polynomial equations of degree greater than two.	2.5
Determine the real roots of non-factorable polynomial equations by interpreting the graphs of the corresponding functions, using graphing calculators or graphing software.	2.5
Write the equation of a family of polynomial functions, given the real or complex zeros.	2.5
Sketch the graph of a polynomial function whose equation is given in factored form.	2.6
Solve factorable polynomial inequalities.	2.6
Solve non-factorable polynomial inequalities by graphing the corresponding functions, using graphing calculators or graphing software and identifying intervals above and below the x-axis.	2.6
Describe the nature of change in polynomial functions of degree greater than two, using finite differences in tables of values.	2.7
Determine an equation to represent a given graph of a polynomial function, using methods appropriate to the situation.	2.8

Calculus is a collection of tools for analysing functions. The tools of calculus that we will discuss in later chapters are applied first to polynomials, since they are among the simplest type of function. The same techniques are then extended to more complicated types of functions later in the book.

Polynomials are also among the most widely used functions in practical applications, especially when combined with other types of functions. The paths of baseballs are quadratic functions, and their position-time functions are also quadratic. Higher-degree polynomials are used in modelling in many contexts, from business applications all the way to quantum-mechanical descriptions of atoms. Because of their simplicity, polynomials are frequently used in regression analysis of experimental data.

In this chapter, we study the properties of polynomial functions. Some of the many applications of polynomials that are discussed are their use in modelling motion, such as the motion of a shot put, and their use in modelling the finances of companies, such as the sales, revenue, and profit of a company that manufactures camping trailers.

Review of Prerequisite Skills

1. Simplifying expressions

Expand and simplify.

a) $5(2x + 3) + 4(x - 7)$
b) $2(y - 3) - (y + 4) - 3(3y + 5)$
c) $5(x^2 - x - 2) - 2(x^2 + 3)$
d) $2(w - 3)^2 - (w + 5)(2w - 4)$

2. Dividing a polynomial by a monomial

Simplify each of the following.

a) $\dfrac{6x^2 + 9x}{3x}$

b) $\dfrac{4x^3 - 8x^2 - 12x}{2x}$

c) $\dfrac{8m^2 + 16mn}{4n}$

d) $\dfrac{9x^4 - 6x^3 + 3x^2 - 12x}{3x^2}$

3. Factoring $ax^2 + bx + c$, $a = 1$

Factor.

a) $t^2 + 9t$
b) $w^2 - 196$
c) $x^2 + 8x + 15$
d) $y^2 - 3y - 18$
e) $x^2 + 15x + 56$
f) $w^2 - 38w + 361$
g) $t^2 - 98t - 99$
h) $s^2 + 90s + 89$

4. Factoring $ax^2 + bx + c$, $a \ne 1$

Factor.

a) $2x^2 - 7x + 3$
b) $3y^2 - 11y - 4$
c) $4w^2 + 9w + 2$
d) $10a^2 - a - 3$
e) $6t^2 + 7t + 2$
f) $25x^2 - 9$

5. Simplifying rational expressions

Simplify. State any restrictions on the variables.

a) $\dfrac{x^2 + x - 2}{x - 1}$

b) $\dfrac{x^2 - 9}{x^2 - 6x + 9}$

c) $\dfrac{t^2 - t - 6}{t^2 - 2t - 8}$

d) $\dfrac{a^2 - 9a + 20}{a^2 + a - 30}$

6. Solving quadratic equations by graphing

Solve by graphing. Round solutions to the nearest tenth, if necessary.

a) $2y^2 = y + 3$
b) $4t^2 + 9 = 11t$
c) $2m^2 - 5m = 0$
d) $6w^2 - 4 = 5w$

7. Solving quadratic equations by factoring

Solve by factoring. Check your solutions.

a) $w^2 = 8w$
b) $y^2 + 7y + 10 = 0$
c) $x^2 - x - 21 = 0$
d) $t^2 + 20 = 9t$

8. Solving quadratic equations by factoring

Solve by factoring. Check your solutions.

a) $2x^2 - 5x + 2 = 0$
b) $2y^2 + 7y + 3 = 0$
c) $3w^2 - 2 = w$
d) $6t^2 + 13t = 5$

9. The quadratic formula

Solve using the quadratic formula. Express solutions both in exact form and as approximations to the nearest tenth.

a) $x^2 - x - 5 = 0$
b) $y^2 + 3x + 1 = 0$
c) $2w^2 + w = 4$
d) $0 = 4t^2 + 2t - 1$

10. Complex numbers

Simplify.

a) $\sqrt{-4}$
b) $\sqrt{-100}$
c) $\sqrt{-13}$
d) $\sqrt{-24}$
e) $\sqrt{-27}$
f) $-\sqrt{-32}$
g) i^5
h) $6i \times 5i$
i) $6i^2$
j) $(i\sqrt{3})^2$
k) $(-2i)(3i)$
l) $(3i\sqrt{2})(-2i\sqrt{2})$

11. Complex numbers

Simplify.

a) $5 + \sqrt{-50}$
b) $-3 - \sqrt{-90}$
c) $\dfrac{-12 + \sqrt{-32}}{2}$
d) $\dfrac{14 + \sqrt{-98}}{7}$

12. Operations with complex numbers
Simplify.
a) $(3 + 2i) + (7 - 3i)$
b) $(5 - 4i) - (6i - 4)$
c) $(i - 12) - (8i + 2)$
d) $4(3 - 2i) + 2(5 + 3i)$

13. Operations with complex numbers
Simplify.
a) $\dfrac{2+i}{i}$
b) $\dfrac{5-2i}{3i}$
c) $\dfrac{5}{1-i}$
d) $\dfrac{-5-4i}{1-2i}$

14. The quadratic formula
Find the exact solution using the quadratic formula.
a) $x^2 + 3 = 2x$
b) $y^2 + 9 = 0$
c) $t^2 - t + 3 = 0$
d) $2m^2 + 3m = -3$

15. Evaluating functions
If $f(x) = 7x - 4$, find
a) $f(2)$
b) $f(-7)$
c) $f(0.5)$
d) $f(-1.5)$
e) $f(200)$
f) $f(-150)$

16. Evaluating functions
If $h(x) = \dfrac{2x-1}{2}$, find
a) $h(7)$
b) $h(0)$
c) $h(0.5)$
d) $h(-6)$
e) $h(-1.5)$
f) $h(0.01)$

17. Evaluating functions
If $g(x) = x^2 + 2x - 5$, find
a) $g(0)$
b) $g(3)$
c) $g(-2)$
d) $g(0.6)$
e) $g(-2.5)$
f) $g(100)$

18. Solving first-degree inequalities
Solve. Graph the solution on a number line.
a) $2x - 4 < 5x + 2$
b) $3(x - 7) \geq 5(x + 3)$
c) $2(x - 3) - 4 \leq 3(x - 1) + 2$
d) $-2(x - 5) > -4(2x - 1) + 6$
e) $1.2x - 0.1 < 2.3$
f) $\dfrac{x-1}{2} \geq \dfrac{x-2}{3}$
g) $\dfrac{x-2}{4} - 1 \leq x + \dfrac{1}{5}$
h) $\dfrac{2+3x}{2} > \dfrac{3x-2}{6} - \dfrac{2}{3}$

19. Finite differences
Use finite differences to determine whether each function is linear, quadratic, or neither.

a)

x	y
0	−5
1	−3
2	−1
3	1
4	3

b)

x	y
0	−3
1	−1
2	5
3	15
4	29

c)

x	y
0	4
1	5
2	12
3	31
4	68

d)

x	y
0	19
1	8
2	5
3	10
4	23

e)

x	y
0	−4
2	−14
4	−24
6	−34
8	−44

f)

x	y
−2	−27
−1	−13
0	−11
1	−9
2	5

g)

x	y
−4	33
−2	17
0	9
2	9
4	17

h)

x	y
−3	−5.5
−1	−2.5
1	0.5
3	3.5
5	6.5

Historical Bite: Coordinate Systems

Pierre de Fermat (1601–1665) was probably the first person to use the idea of a coordinate system. However, René Descartes (1596–1650) is generally given the credit for this invention. It is said that Descartes came across the idea while he was in military service. When he was lying on his cot one day, he stared at a fly that was hovering above him. It occurred to him that the fly's position at any moment could be described by its distance from three mutually perpendicular intersecting lines, which we now call axes.

2.1 Investigating Math: Polynomial Functions on a Graphing Calculator

You have previously studied constant, linear, and quadratic functions. Equations for these functions have the form $f(x) = c$, $f(x) = mx + b$, and $f(x) = ax^2 + bx + c$. These functions are special cases of a class of functions called polynomial functions. Other examples of polynomial functions are $f(x) = 2x^2 + 3x - 1$, $f(x) = x^3 + 7$, and $f(x) = 2x^4 - 3x^3 + 14$.

Examples of functions that are not polynomials are $f(x) = \dfrac{1}{x}$, $f(x) = 2^x$, and $f(x) = x^{\frac{2}{3}}$.

A **polynomial function** of degree n, where n is a positive integer, has the form
$$f(x) = a_n x^n + a_{n-1} x^{n-1} + \ldots + a_1 x + a_0$$
where $a_n \neq 0$. The numbers a_n, $a_{n-1}, \ldots, a_1, a_0$ are called the **coefficients** of the polynomial. The number a_0 is the **constant coefficient**. The number a_n, the coefficient of the highest power, is the **leading coefficient**.

In this section, we explore the features of the graphs of polynomial functions.

Quadratic functions are polynomial functions of degree 2. They are also called second-degree functions. Quadratic functions have two zeros, that is, two values of the variable that make the value of the function zero. The corresponding quadratic equations can have two real or two complex **roots**. If the roots are real, they can be distinct or equal.

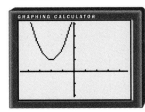
Two complex roots

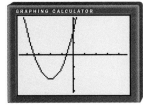
Two distinct real roots

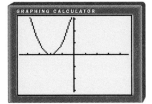
Two equal real roots

When working with functions of degree greater than 2, it is helpful to know that a function of degree n has n zeros. For example, a cubic function, such as $y = x^3 + 3x^2 - 3x - 4$, has three zeros. Cubic functions are also called third-degree functions.

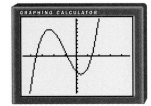

Window variables:
$x \in [-4.7, 4.7]$, $y \in [-9.3, 9.3]$

Cubic Functions

1. Graph each cubic (third-degree) function in the standard viewing window, using the ZStandard instruction. Sketch the graphs in your notebook.

a) $y = x^3 + 2x^2 - 3x - 4$ b) $y = x^3 + 2x^2 - 4x - 8$ c) $y = x^3 - 2x^2 - 2x - 3$

d) $y = x^3 - 3x^2 + 3x - 1$ e) $y = -x^3 - 3x^2 + x + 3$ f) $y = -x^3 + 3x^2 - 5x + 6$

g) $y = -x^3 + x^2 + 5x + 3$ h) $y = -x^3 + 3x^2 - 3x + 1$

2. Using the graphs from step 1, describe the general shape of the graphs of cubic functions.

3. How is the shape of the graph of a cubic function different from the shape of the graph of a quadratic function?

4. The general form of the equation of a cubic function is $y = ax^3 + bx^2 + cx + d$, where $a \neq 0$. Describe how the graphs of cubic functions for which a is positive differ from those for which a is negative.

5. What does the value of d represent on the graph of a cubic function?

6. a) Graph the cubic function $y = x^3 - 2x^2 - 5x + 6$. Find the x-intercepts. Sketch the graph and label the x-intercepts.
b) Do the x-intercepts from part a) satisfy the related cubic equation $x^3 - 2x^2 - 5x + 6 = 0$? Explain.

7. The real roots of a cubic equation are the x-intercepts of the related cubic function. How many real roots does the cubic equation corresponding to each cubic function graphed in step 1 have?

8. State the possible numbers of each of the following types of roots for a cubic equation. Sketch a graph to illustrate each possibility.
a) distinct roots   b) equal real roots   c) complex roots

9. Can a cubic equation have three complex roots? Explain.

10. A cylinder is inscribed in a sphere, as shown. The radius of the sphere is 2 units.
a) Write a formula for the volume, V, of the cylinder in terms of x. What kind of function is V?
b) Argue that negative values of x are reasonable, provided that we think of x as a coordinate and not as a distance. What is the domain of the function in part a)?
c) Determine the roots of the function in part a). Explain the meaning of the roots.

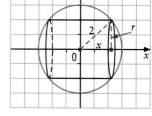

11. Summarize what you have learned about cubic functions and their graphs.

Quartic Functions

A **quartic function**, such as $y = x^4 - 6x^2 - x + 3$, has four zeros. Quartic functions are also called fourth-degree functions.

Window variables:
$x \in [-4.7, 4.7], y \in [-9.3, 9.3]$

1. Graph each quartic function in the standard viewing window. Sketch the graphs.
a) $y = x^4 - 5x^2 + 2x + 2$ b) $y = x^4 + 3x^3 - x - 3$
c) $y = x^4 + 2x^3 + 2x + 6$ d) $y = x^4 - 4x^3 + 6x^2 - 4x + 1$
e) $y = x^4 - 2x^2 + 1$ f) $y = -x^4 + 5x^2 + 4$

g) $y = -x^4 + x^3 + 3x^2 - 2x - 5$ h) $y = -x^4 - 5x^3 - 5x^2 + 5x + 6$
i) $y = -x^4 + 3x^3 + 3x^2 - 7x - 6$ j) $y = -x^4 - 4x^3 - 5x^2 - 4x - 4$

2. Using your graphs from step 1, describe the general shape of the graphs of quartic functions.

3. How is the shape of the graph of a quartic function different from the shape of the graph of a cubic function? a quadratic function?

4. The general form of the equation of a quartic function is $y = ax^4 + bx^3 + cx^2 + dx + e$, where $a \neq 0$. Describe how the graphs of quartic functions for which a is positive differ from those for which a is negative.

5. What does the value of e represent on the graph of a quartic function?

6. a) Graph the quartic function $y = x^4 + x^3 - 7x^2 - x + 6$. Find the x-intercepts. Sketch the graph and label the x-intercepts.
b) Do the x-intercepts from part a) satisfy the related quartic equation $x^4 + x^3 - 7x^2 - x + 6 = 0$? Explain.

7. The real roots of a quartic equation are the x-intercepts of the related quartic function. How many real roots does the quartic equation corresponding to each quartic function graphed in step 1 have?

8. State the possible numbers of each of the following types of roots for a quartic equation. Sketch a graph to illustrate each possibility.
a) distinct real roots   b) equal real roots   c) complex roots

9. An archway for the entrance to the county fair is designed to look somewhat like a rounded letter M. A scale model of the arch passes through the points $(0, 45)$, $(1, 48)$, $(-1, 48)$, $(2, 45)$, and $(-2, 45)$, where all distances are in centimetres. The x-coordinates of the points represent locations across the entrance and the y-coordinates represent heights above the ground.
a) What kind of polynomial should be used to model the arch?
b) Use an appropriate regression to determine the function that models the arch.
c) Determine the roots of the function in part b).
d) Explain what the roots in part c) represent.

10. Summarize what you have learned about quartic functions and their graphs.

Quintic Functions

1. The function $y = x(x^2 - 1)(x^2 - 4)$ is a **quintic** (fifth-degree) **function**. Explain why.

2. What are the zeros of $y = x(x^2 - 1)(x^2 - 4)$? Explain without graphing.

3. Predict the shape of the graph of $y = x(x^2 - 1)(x^2 - 4)$. Then, sketch the graph.

4. a) Graph $y = x(x^2 - 1)(x^2 - 4)$ in the standard viewing window. Sketch the graph and label the x-intercepts.
b) Describe the similarities and differences between your prediction and the actual graph.

5. Graph each function in the standard viewing window. Describe and explain the numbers of distinct real roots, equal roots, and complex roots in each case.
a) $y = x^2(x^2 + 1)(x - 2)$ b) $y = (x - 1)^2(x - 4)^2(3 - x)$
c) $y = (x^2 - x - 2)(x^2 - 1)(x + 1)$ d) $y = (x^2 + x - 2)(x^2 - 1)(x + 1)$

6. Is the graph of a quintic function more like the graph of a quadratic function or more like the graph of a cubic function? Explain.

7. Part of a roller coaster track is being designed. For this part of the track, the coaster will come down a long way, reach a low point, rise up to a high point, go down again to another low point, rise up again to another high point, and then plunge down. In this exercise, you will model this part of the track with a polynomial function.
a) What should the degree of the polynomial be?
b) A coordinate grid is placed on a diagram of the track. The track crosses the x-axis five times, and adjacent crossing points are separated by 2 units. Conjecture a formula for the function that models the track.
c) Is there just one formula that satisfies the conditions in part b)? Explain.
d) Use technology to determine the heights of the high and low points of the track. Are these reasonable values for a realistic roller coaster track? If not, explain how to modify your conjectured formula to make the model reasonable.

8. Summarize what you have learned about quintic functions and their graphs.

Features of Polynomial Graphs

The graph of a polynomial function is continuous, that is, there are no breaks in the graph. You can trace the graph without lifting your pencil.

The graph of the cubic function $y = 2x^3 - 6x - 1$ is shown. The graph has a peak at $(-1, 3)$ and a valley at $(1, -5)$. The point $(-1, 3)$ is called a **local maximum point** of the function. This point does not have the greatest y-coordinate of any point of the function, but no nearby points have as great a y-coordinate. Similarly, the point $(1, -5)$ is called a **local minimum point** of the function. It is the lowest point on the graph among nearby points. Local maximum points and local minimum points are also known as **turning points**.

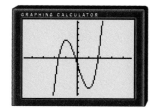

The end behaviour of the graph of a function describes the sign of the values of the function for the left-most and right-most parts of the graph. Polynomial functions can have four types of end behaviour.

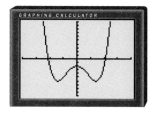

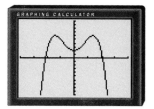

The right-most y-values are positive.
$y \to \infty$ as $x \to \infty$

The left-most y-values are positive.
$y \to \infty$ as $x \to -\infty$

The right-most y-values are negative.
$y \to -\infty$ as $x \to \infty$

The left-most y-values are negative.
$y \to -\infty$ as $x \to -\infty$

$y \to \infty$ means that the values for y get larger and larger, without bound, in the positive direction.

$y \to -\infty$ means that the values for y get larger and larger, without bound, in the negative direction.

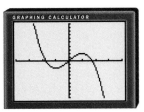

The right-most y-values are positive.
$y \to \infty$ as $x \to \infty$
The left-most y-values are negative.
$y \to -\infty$ as $x \to -\infty$

The right-most y-values are negative.
$y \to -\infty$ as $x \to \infty$
The left-most y-values are positive.
$y \to \infty$ as $x \to -\infty$

1. Graph the following functions in the standard viewing window. Copy and complete the table.

Function	Degree	End Behaviour	Observed Number of Turning Points
a) $y = x + 2$			
b) $y = -3x + 1$			
c) $y = x^2 - 4$			
d) $y = -2x^2 + 3x + 2$			
e) $y = x^3 - 3x$			
f) $y = -x^3 + 2x - 1$			
g) $y = x^4 - 4x^2 + 5$			
h) $y = -x^4 + 4x^2 + x - 2$			
i) $y = x^5 - 2x^4 - 3x^3 + 5x^2 + 4x - 1$			
j) $y = x^5 - 2$			
k) $y = -x^5 + 4x^3 + 2$			

2. For two functions with the same degree, how does the sign of the leading coefficient affect the end behaviour of the graph?

3. A function whose degree is an even number is called an even-degree function.
a) How do the end behaviours of even-degree functions compare?
b) Test your conjecture by graphing functions of even degree higher than 4.

4. A function whose degree is an odd number is called an odd-degree function.
a) How do the end behaviours of odd-degree functions compare?
b) Test your conjecture by graphing functions of odd degree higher than 5.

5. Sketch the graph of a polynomial function that satisfies each of the following sets of conditions.
a) an even-degree function with two local maximum points and one local minimum point
b) an even-degree function with two local minimum points and one local maximum point

c) an odd-degree function with two local maximum points and two local minimum points, and the left-most y-values are negative

d) an odd-degree function with three local maximum points and three local minimum points, and the right-most y-values are negative

e) an even-degree function with four local maximum points and three local minimum points

6. a) What appears to be the maximum possible number of turning points for a linear function? a quadratic function? a cubic function? a quartic function?

b) What appears to be the relationship between the degree of a function and the maximum number of turning points?

c) If the graph of a function has five turning points, what is the minimum possible degree of the function?

7. The graph of $f(x) = x(x - 2)(x + 3)$ is shown. The x-intercepts are 2, 0, and −3. The three x-intercepts divide the x-axis into four intervals.

$(-\infty, -3)$ $(-3, 0)$ $(0, 2)$ $(2, \infty)$

Determine the sign of $f(x)$ in each interval.

Window variables:
$x \in [-4.7, 4.7]$,
$y \in [-9.3, 9.3]$

8. For each of the following functions, sketch the graph and determine the sign of $f(x)$ in the intervals determined by the x-intercepts.

a) $f(x) = (x + 1)(x - 3)$ b) $f(x) = x(x + 2)(x - 4)$

c) $f(x) = -(x - 2)(x + 3)$ d) $f(x) = x(x - 1)(x + 4)$

e) $f(x) = (x + 3)(x - 3)(x + 1)$ f) $f(x) = -(x - 5)(x + 3)(x + 3)$

g) $f(x) = x(x - 3)(x - 5)(x + 4)$ h) $f(x) = -(x + 4)(x + 1)(x - 2)(x - 5)$

9. Summarize what you have learned about the graphs of polynomial functions by listing the key concepts from this section.

2.2 Dividing a Polynomial by a Polynomial

We have previously multiplied polynomials. For example, $(x + 2)(x − 5) = x^2 − 3x − 10$. We have also factored polynomials, which is the reverse process. For example,

$$2x^3 − 2x^2 + 3x − 3 = 2x^2(x − 1) + 3(x − 1)$$
$$= (x − 1)(2x^2 + 3)$$

But polynomials are not always simple to factor. In Sections 2.3 and 2.4, we learn to identify a factor of a polynomial such as $x^3 − 6x^2 + 7x + 6$. In order to find the other factors, we must be able to divide a polynomial by a binomial, such as $x − 1$. In this section, we illustrate this process. In Example 1, division of a polynomial by a binomial is compared to division of a number by a number.

Example 1 Dividing a Polynomial by a Binomial of the Form $x − b$

Divide $x^2 + 5x + 6$ by $x + 3$. State the restriction on the variable.

Solution

Division of a polynomial by a binomial

The first steps are:

$$\begin{array}{r} x \\ x+3\overline{)x^2 + 5x + 6} \\ x^2 + 3x \\ \hline 2x + 6 \end{array}$$

Think $x^2 ÷ x = x$.

Multiply $x(x + 3)$.

Subtract. Bring down the 6.

The final steps are:

$$\begin{array}{r} x + 2 \\ x+3\overline{)x^2 + 5x + 6} \\ x^2 + 3x \\ \hline 2x + 6 \\ 2x + 6 \\ \hline 0 \end{array}$$

Think $2x ÷ x = 2$.

Multiply $2(x + 3)$.

Subtract to get the remainder.

Division of a number by a number

$$\begin{array}{r} 2 \\ 3\overline{)72} \\ 6 \\ \hline 12 \end{array}$$

Think $7 ÷ 3 = 2$ (remainder 1).

Multiply $2(3)$.

Subtract. Bring down the 2.

$$\begin{array}{r} 24 \\ 3\overline{)72} \\ 6 \\ \hline 12 \\ 12 \\ \hline 0 \end{array}$$

Think $12 ÷ 3 = 4$.

Multiply $4(3)$.

Subtract to get the remainder.

Because division by zero is not defined, $x + 3 ≠ 0$, that is, $x ≠ −3$.
So, $(x^2 + 5x + 6) ÷ (x + 3) = x + 2$, where $x ≠ −3$.

The polynomial that is being divided is called the numerator or **dividend,** the polynomial that the numerator is divided by is called the denominator or **divisor,** and the result of the division is called the quotient.

$$\text{denominator}\overline{)\text{numerator}}^{\displaystyle \text{quotient}}$$

Note that just as we write numbers in order of place value, we must write polynomials in order of degree before we divide. Consider Example 2.

Example 2 Dividing a Polynomial by a Binomial of the Form $ax - b$

Divide $-19x^2 + 6x^3 + 18x - 20$ by $2x - 5$. State the restriction on the variable.

Solution

First, rewrite the polynomial with the terms in order of degree, $6x^3 - 19x^2 + 18x - 20$.

$$
\begin{array}{r}
3x^2 - 2x + 4 \\
2x-5\overline{)6x^3 -19x^2 +18x - 20} \\
\underline{6x^3 - 15x^2} \\
-4x^2 + 18x \\
\underline{-4x^2 + 10x} \\
8x - 20 \\
\underline{8x - 20} \\
0
\end{array}
$$

Because division by zero is not defined, $2x - 5 \neq 0$, so $x \neq \dfrac{5}{2}$. Thus,

$(6x^3 - 19x^2 + 18x - 20) \div (2x - 5) = 3x^2 - 2x + 4$, $x \neq \dfrac{5}{2}$.

In Example 2, since $2x - 5$ divides into $6x^3 - 19x^2 + 18x - 20$ evenly (that is, with a remainder of zero), $2x - 5$ is a factor of $6x^3 - 19x^2 + 18x - 20$. Another way of writing the result is $6x^3 - 19x^2 + 18x - 20 = (2x - 5)(3x^2 - 2x + 4)$.

Similarly, in Example 1, $x + 3$ is a factor of $x^2 + 5x + 6$. When the divisor is not a factor of the dividend, the remainder is not zero, as shown in Example 3.

Example 3 Division With a Non-Zero Remainder

a) Divide $-9x - 3 + 6x^3 - 4x^2$ by $2x^2 - 3$.
b) State the restrictions on the variable.

Solution

a) First, rewrite the polynomial as $6x^3 - 4x^2 - 9x - 3$.

$$
\begin{array}{r}
3x - 2 \\
2x^2-3\overline{)6x^3 - 4x^2 - 9x - 3} \\
\underline{6x^3 + 0x^2 - 9x} \qquad \text{Note the use of } 0x^2 \text{ and } 0x \text{ as placeholders.}\\
-4x^2 + 0x - 3 \\
\underline{-4x^2 + 0x + 6} \\
-9
\end{array}
$$

Thus, the remainder is -9. That is, $(-9x - 3 + 6x^3 - 4x^2) \div (2x^2 - 3) = 3x - 2 + \dfrac{-9}{2x^2 - 3}$.

b) Since $2x^2 - 3 \neq 0$,

$2x^2 \neq 3$

$x^2 \neq \dfrac{3}{2}$

$x \neq \pm \dfrac{\sqrt{3}}{2}$

Polynomials can be named, using function notation, as $P(x)$, $Q(x)$, and so on. The result of the division of a polynomial can be represented as

$$\frac{P(x)}{D(x)} = Q(x) + \frac{R(x)}{D(x)}$$

which is equivalent to

$$P(x) = D(x)Q(x) + R(x)$$

Here, $D(x)$ is the divisor, $Q(x)$ is the quotient, and $R(x)$ is the remainder. Written in these forms, the result of Example 3 can be expressed as follows.

$$\frac{P(x)}{D(x)} = Q(x) + \frac{R(x)}{D(x)} \qquad \frac{6x^3 - 4x^2 - 9x - 3}{2x^2 - 3} = 3x - 2 - \frac{9}{2x^2 - 3}$$

$$P(x) = D(x)Q(x) + R(x) \qquad 6x^3 - 4x^2 - 9x - 3 = (2x^2 - 3)(3x - 2) - 9$$

Division of polynomials can help us understand the formula for annuities.

Example 4 Accumulated Value of an Annuity

An annuity is an investment where the same amount of money P is deposited at the end of each month. Interest is applied to the investment at the end of each month starting with the second month. The accumulated amount A of the annuity after n months is

$$A = P\left(\frac{x^n - 1}{x - 1}\right)$$

where $x = 1 + r$, and r is the interest rate per month, expressed as a decimal.

Use long division to verify the formula for A when $n = 3$.

Solution

For $n = 3$, the formula for A is

$$A = P\left(\frac{x^3 - 1}{x - 1}\right)$$

Using long division, we determine the quotient in parentheses.

$$
\begin{array}{r}
x^2 + x + 1 \\
x - 1 \overline{) x^3 + 0x^2 + 0x - 1} \\
\underline{x^3 - x^2} \\
x^2 + 0x \\
\underline{x^2 - x} \\
x - 1 \\
\underline{x - 1} \\
0
\end{array}
$$

Thus,
$$A = P(x^2 + x + 1)$$

There are three deposits altogether, made at the end of the first, second, and third months. The deposit made at the end of the third month earns no interest, so its contribution to the final amount is P. The deposit made at the end of the second month earns interest for one month, so its contribution to the final amount is $P(1 + i)$. Since $x = 1 + i$, $P(1 + i) = Px$. Finally, the deposit made at the end of the first month earns interest for two months, so its contribution to the final amount is $P(1 + i)^2 = Px^2$. Thus, the total accumulated amount is
$$P + Px + Px^2 = P(x^2 + x + 1)$$
which verifies the formula.

Key Concepts

- Polynomials can be divided using long division.
- The result of the division of a polynomial $P(x)$ by the polynomial $D(x)$ can be represented as

$$\frac{P(x)}{D(x)} = Q(x) + \frac{R(x)}{D(x)} \quad \text{or} \quad P(x) = D(x)Q(x) + R(x)$$

Communicate Your Understanding

1. Describe how you would rewrite the expression $(x + 4x^3 - 3) \div (2x - 1)$ before dividing.

2. Explain how to determine the restriction on the variable for the division $(2x^3 - x^2 + 7x - 4) \div (2x + 5)$.

3. Explain the steps for dividing $4x^3 - 2x^2 + 7$ by $2x + 3$ using long division.

Practise

In each of the following, state any restrictions on the variables.

A 1. Divide.
a) $(x^2 + 8x + 15) \div (x + 3)$
b) $(a^2 - 7a + 10) \div (a - 5)$
c) $(y^2 - y - 12) \div (y - 4)$
d) $(t^2 - 4) \div (t + 2)$

2. Divide.
a) $(x^3 + 2x^2 + 3x + 2) \div (x + 1)$
b) $(t^3 + 3t^2 - 5t - 4) \div (t + 4)$
c) $(a^3 - 3a^2 - a + 3) \div (a - 3)$
d) $(4x^2 - 13x + x^3 + 8) \div (x - 1)$
e) $(m^3 - 4 + 3m^2) \div (m + 2)$
f) $(y^3 + 8 - 2y - 4y^2) \div (y - 4)$

3. Divide.
a) $(2x^2 + 11x + 15) \div (2x + 5)$
b) $(3y^2 + 8y - 3) \div (3y - 1)$

c) $(5r^2 - 31r + 6) \div (5r - 1)$
d) $(4t^2 - 3 - 4t) \div (2t + 1)$
e) $(14 + 6r^2 - 25r) \div (3r - 2)$
f) $(21x + 10x^2 + 9) \div (5x + 3)$
g) $(8x^2 + 14x + 15) \div (4x - 3)$

4. Divide.
a) $(x^3 + 2x^2 - x - 2) \div (x^2 - 1)$
b) $(x^3 - 3x^2 + 4x - 12) \div (x^2 + 4)$
c) $(y^3 + 3y + 15 + 5y^2) \div (y^2 + 3)$
d) $(4 - 4a - a^2 + a^3) \div (a^2 - 4)$

5. Divide.
a) $(2x^3 - 2x^2 + 3x - 3) \div (x - 1)$
b) $(3z^3 + 6z^2 + 5z + 10) \div (z + 2)$
c) $(4m^3 + 2m^2 - 6m - 3) \div (2m + 1)$
d) $(6n^3 - 9n^2 - 8n + 12) \div (2n - 3)$
e) $(15d^2 + 4d + 6 + 10d^3) \div (5d^2 + 2)$
f) $(4x + 8x^3 - 6x^2 - 3) \div (2x^2 + 1)$
g) $(3s^2 + 12s^3 - 5 - 20s) \div (3s^2 - 5)$
h) $(8 + 21t^3 - 28t^2 - 6t) \div (7t^2 - 2)$

6. Identify the numerator, denominator, quotient, and remainder.

a) $\dfrac{125}{12} = 10 + \dfrac{5}{12}$

b) $\dfrac{350}{9} = 38 + \dfrac{8}{9}$

c) $\dfrac{a^2 - 5a + 6}{a - 3} = a - 2$

d) $\dfrac{2x^2 + 5x - 2}{2x - 1} = x + 3 + \dfrac{1}{2x - 1}$

e) $\dfrac{t^3 + t^2 + t - 3}{t^2 + 1} = t + 1 + \dfrac{4}{t^2 + 1}$

f) $\dfrac{6x^3 + 3x^2 - x}{3x^2 - 2} = 2x + 1 + \dfrac{3x + 2}{3x^2 - 2}$

7. Identify the dividend, divisor, quotient, and remainder. Can you be sure about the quotient and the divisor? Explain.
a) $255 = (11)(23) + 2$
b) $8y^3 + 6y^2 - 4y - 5 = (4y + 3)(2y^2 - 1) - 2$
c) $(x)(x + 1) + 3 = x^2 + x + 3$

B **8.** Divide. Write each result in the forms
$\dfrac{P(x)}{D(x)} = Q(x) + \dfrac{R(x)}{D(x)}$ and $P(x) = D(x)Q(x) + R(x)$.

a) $(x^2 + 4x + 2) \div (x + 4)$
b) $(x^2 - 3x - 8) \div (x - 3)$
c) $(x^2 - 7x + 10) \div (x - 4)$
d) $(2x^2 + x - 3) \div (x + 2)$
e) $(4x^2 - 7x - 7) \div (x - 2)$
f) $(x^2 - 8) \div (x - 3)$
g) $(5x^2 + 14x + 11) \div (x + 4)$
h) $(6x^2 - 5x - 5) \div (x - 4)$

Apply, Solve, Communicate

9. Communication a) Divide each of the following.

i) $\dfrac{x^3 - 1}{x - 1}$ 　　　 ii) $\dfrac{x^3 - 8}{x - 2}$

iii) $\dfrac{x^3 - 27}{x - 3}$

b) Describe the pattern in the coefficients of the quotients.
c) Predict the coefficients for the quotients of $\dfrac{x^3 - 64}{x - 4}$ and $\dfrac{x^3 - 125}{x - 5}$.
Then, divide to check your prediction.

10. Divide.
a) $(x^5 - 1) \div (x - 1)$ 　　 b) $(x^5 - 32) \div (x - 2)$

11. Divide.
a) $(6x^3 + 4x^2 + 4x + 3) \div (2x^2 + 1)$
b) $(3y^3 - 9y^2 - 3) \div (3y^2 + 1)$
c) $(2t^3 + 4t^2 - 4t - 19) \div (2t^2 - 4)$
d) $(6d^4 - 13d^2 + d + 4) \div (2d^2 - 3)$

12. In Exercise 11, does the value of the remainder depend on the value of the variable? Explain.

13. Find the whole number value of k such that
a) $x + 3$ divides $x^2 - x - k$ evenly
b) $2y - 1$ is a factor of $6y^2 + y - k$
c) the remainder is 3 when $4x^2 + 9x + k$ is divided by $x - 1$
d) the remainder is -5 when $2x^3 + 7x^2 + 5x - k$ is divided by $2x + 1$

14. The area of a triangle is represented by the expression $6x^2 - 5x - 4$.

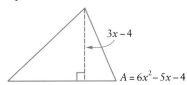

$3x - 4$

$A = 6x^2 - 5x - 4$

If the height is $3x - 4$, what is the base?

15. The area of a trapezoid is represented by the expression $12y^2 - 11y + 2$.

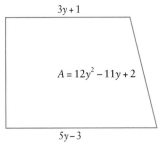

$3y + 1$

$A = 12y^2 - 11y + 2$

$5y - 3$

The bases are $3y + 1$ and $5y - 3$. What is the height?

16. Inquiry/Problem Solving Dividing $5x^2 + 14x - 3$ by $x + 3$ gives a quotient of $5x - 1$. Explain why $\dfrac{5x^2 + 14x - 3}{x + 3}$ is not the same as $5x - 1$.

17. On February 1, Diasetz invests $500 in a guaranteed investment certificate (GIC). At the end of each month, interest is added to the account at the rate of 1% per month, compounded monthly. What is the value of the GIC after
a) 10 months?
b) 25 months?
c) 10 years?

18. Inquiry/Problem Solving After graduating from university, Selena decides to live with her parents and devote her time to unpaid work as a volunteer for a charity. She has saved $10 000 and placed it in a bank account that pays interest of 1% per month, compounded monthly. She withdraws $500 from the account each month to pay for her living expenses.
a) How long will she be able to continue before she exhausts her money and has to obtain paid work? (Hint: A spreadsheet may be helpful.)
b) Construct a scatter plot using the data in part a). Plot time on the horizontal axis and the current value of the GIC on the vertical axis.
c) Draw a smooth curve through the points on the scatter plot of part b). What is the x-intercept? Explain the meaning of the x-intercept.

19. Inquiry/Problem Solving a) Determine each quotient.
i) $\dfrac{x^2 - 1}{x - 1}$
ii) $\dfrac{x^3 - 1}{x - 1}$
iii) $\dfrac{x^4 - 1}{x - 1}$
iv) $\dfrac{x^5 - 1}{x - 1}$
b) Using the results of part a), conjecture a formula for the quotient $\dfrac{x^n - 1}{x - 1}$, where n is a positive integer.
c) Test the conjecture of part b) by judicious choices of specific numbers for x and n. Are you confident that your conjecture is correct? Explain.

20. Application A series of numbers is said to be a **geometric series** if each number is a constant multiple of the one before it in the series. The constant multiple is called the **common ratio** of the series. For example, $3 + 6 + 12 + 24 + 48$ is a geometric series with common ratio 2.
a) Is the series $1 + x + x^2 + x^3 + \cdots + x^k$ geometric? If so, state the common ratio. If not, explain why.
b) Use the results of question 19 to obtain a formula for the sum of the series $1 + x + x^2 + x^3 + \cdots + x^k$.
c) Suppose $1 is invested at the end of each month at an interest rate of i% per month, compounded monthly. If r is the interest rate written as a decimal, determine an expression for the total value of the investment after
i) 1 month
ii) 2 months
iii) 3 months
iv) k months
d) Using the results of parts b) and c), determine the total value of an investment of $1 per month after 10 years, if the interest rate is 1% per month, compounded monthly.
e) Repeat part d) if the monthly investment is $1000.

C **21.** Communication a) When dividing a polynomial by a linear polynomial, can the remainder be a quadratic polynomial? A linear polynomial? Explain.
b) When dividing a polynomial by a quadratic polynomial, can the remainder be a quadratic polynomial? A linear polynomial? Explain.
c) Generalize parts a) and b) by making a general statement about the possible form of the remainders when polynomials are divided by polynomials.

22. Mario manages to save $150 every month. At the end of each month, he deposits this money into a savings account paying 0.2% interest per month, compounded monthly. Every three months, he transfers the balance of his savings account into a GIC that pays 5.2% interest per year, compounded quarterly.
a) How much money does Mario transfer every three months?
b) What is the total value of Mario's GIC after seven years?

The Remainder Theorem

In Section 2.4 we will study the factor theorem, which is used to help determine factors of polynomial expressions. Studying the remainder theorem in this section will help in understanding the factor theorem in the following section.

When a polynomial function is divided by a binomial that is not a factor, there will be a non-zero remainder. In the following investigation, you will explore a possible relationship between such remainders and certain values of the polynomials.

Investigate & Inquire: The Remainder Theorem

1. Copy and complete the table by dividing the polynomial $P(x) = 2x^3 - 2x^2 - 3x + 3$ by the given divisor. Compare your completed table with a classmate's.

Divisor, $x - b$	b	Quotient and Remainder, $\dfrac{P(x)}{x - b}$	$P(b)$
a) $x - 3$			
b) $x - 2$			
c) $x + 2$			
d) $x - 1$			
e) $x + 3$			
f) $x + 1$			

2. Use the results of step 1 to make a conjecture about the relationship between the remainder and the value of $P(b)$.

3. a) Divide the polynomial $x^3 + 2x^2 - 7x - 2$ by each binomial to find the remainder.
i) $x - 1$ ii) $x + 1$ iii) $x - 2$ iv) $x + 3$
b) Use your conjecture from step 2 to find the remainder when $x^3 + 2x^2 - 7x - 2$ is divided by each binomial in part a).
c) Compare your results from parts a) and b).

4. When a divisor is a factor of a polynomial, what is the remainder? Explain.

The division of polynomials by divisors of the form $x - b$, as in the investigation, can be generalized as follows.

If a polynomial $P(x)$, of degree at least 1, is divided by $(x - b)$, the remainder is a constant, R. Furthermore, the value of the constant is equal to the value of the polynomial at $x = b$, which can be shown as follows. From Section 2.2, we have the relation (for constant R)

$P(x) = Q(x)(x - b) + R$

Substituting b for x, we get

$P(b) = (b - b)Q(b) + R$
$\qquad = R$

This relationship between $P(b)$ and R is known as the **remainder theorem**.

> Remainder theorem: When a polynomial $P(x)$ is divided by $x - b$, the remainder is $P(b)$.

Example 1 Determining a Remainder

Determine the remainder when $P(x) = 2x^3 - 4x^2 + 3x - 6$ is divided by $x + 2$.

Solution

Write $x + 2$ as $x - (-2)$. The remainder theorem states that when $P(x) = 2x^3 - 4x^2 + 3x - 6$ is divided by $x - (-2)$, the remainder is $P(-2)$.
$$P(-2) = 2(-2)^3 - 4(-2)^2 + 3(-2) - 6$$
$$= -44$$
The remainder is -44.

Example 2 Determining a Coefficient

When $x^3 - kx^2 + 17x + 6$ is divided by $x - 3$, the remainder is 12. Find the value of k.

Solution

Let $P(x) = x^3 - kx^2 + 17x + 6$
From the remainder theorem, $P(3)$ is the remainder of the division by $x - 3$, so $P(3) = 12$.
$$P(3) = (3)^3 - k(3)^2 + 17(3) + 6$$
$$= -9k + 84$$
$$-9k + 84 = 12$$
$$-9k = -72$$
$$k = 8$$
The value of k is 8.

Example 3 Using a System of Linear Equations

When the polynomial $P(x) = 3x^3 + cx^2 + dx - 7$ is divided by $x - 2$, the remainder is -3. When $P(x)$ is divided by $x + 1$, the remainder is -18. What are the values of c and d?

Solution

Use the given information to write a system of linear equations.
$$P(x) = 3x^3 + cx^2 + dx - 7$$
$$P(2) = 3(2)^3 + c(2)^2 + d(2) - 7$$
$$= 4c + 2d + 17$$
From the remainder theorem, we know that $P(2) = -3$. So,
$$4c + 2d + 17 = -3$$
$$4c + 2d = -20$$
$$2c + d = -10 \qquad (1)$$

$$P(-1) = 3(-1)^3 + c(-1)^2 + d(-1) - 7$$
$$= c - d - 10$$

From the remainder theorem, we know that $P(-1) = -18$. So,

$$c - d - 10 = -18$$
$$c - d = -8 \qquad \textbf{(2)}$$

Solve the system of linear equations.

$$2c + d = -10 \qquad \textbf{(1)}$$
$$c - d = -8 \qquad \textbf{(2)}$$

Add (1) and (2): $3c = -18$
Solve for c: $c = -6$

Substitute -6 for c in (2).

$$c - d = -8$$
$$-6 - d = -8$$
$$d = 2$$

Check in (1).   Check in (2).

L.S. $= 2c + d$ **R.S.** $= -10$ **L.S.** $= c - d$ **R.S.** $= -8$
$= 2(-6) + 2$ $= -6 - 2$
$= -10$ $= -8$
L.S. = R.S.   **L.S. = R.S.**

The value of c is -6, and the value of d is 2.

The remainder theorem can be extended to include divisors in which the coefficient of x is not 1.

If $P(x)$ is divided by $ax - b$ and the division is continued until the quotient is $Q(x)$ and the remainder is a constant, R, then the following division statement is true for all values of x.

$$P(x) = (ax - b)Q(x) + R$$

Substitute $\dfrac{b}{a}$ for x:

$$P\!\left(\frac{b}{a}\right) = \left(\frac{ab}{a} - b\right) Q\!\left(\frac{b}{a}\right) + R$$
$$= R$$

Thus, a more general form of the remainder theorem is as follows.

When a polynomial $P(x)$ is divided by $(ax - b)$, the remainder is $P\!\left(\dfrac{b}{a}\right)$.

Example 4 Dividing by $ax - b$ for $a \ne 1$

Determine the remainder when $2x^3 + 3x^2 - 7x - 3$ is divided by $2x + 5$.

Solution 1
Paper and Pencil Method

Let $P(x) = 2x^3 + 3x^2 - 7x - 3$.

$$P\left(-\frac{5}{2}\right)$$

$$= 2\left(-\frac{5}{2}\right)^3 + 3\left(-\frac{5}{2}\right)^2 - 7\left(-\frac{5}{2}\right) - 3$$

$$= 2\left(-\frac{125}{8}\right) + 3\left(\frac{25}{4}\right) + \frac{35}{2} - 3$$

$$= -\frac{125}{4} + \frac{75}{4} + \frac{70}{4} - \frac{12}{4}$$

$$= 2$$

The remainder is 2.

Solution 2 Graphing Calculator Method

Input the function $y = 2x^3 + 3x^2 - 7x - 3$ in the Y= editor of a graphing calculator.

Press $\boxed{\text{VARS}}$ $\boxed{\blacktriangleright}$ **1 1** to call Y1 to evaluate the function at $x = -\frac{5}{2}$.

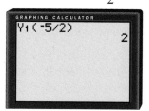

The remainder is 2.

Canadian Catherine Bond-Mills won the bronze medal in the heptathlon at the Commonwealth Games in Victoria, British Columbia, in 1994. In the heptathlon, athletes compete in seven events. One of them is the shot-put.

For a certain "put," the function $h(t) = -5t^2 + 9t + 2$ approximates the height of the shot, in metres, as a function of the time, t, in seconds, since it was released. The formula is only valid until the shot hits the ground.

To find the height at various times, we substitute values of t into the equation for $h(t)$. Doing this can also help us learn more about the equation.

Example 5 Shot-Put Height Formula

Consider the shot-put formula $h(t) = -5t^2 + 9t + 2$.

a) In the division relationship $\dfrac{h(t)}{t-b} = Q(t) + \dfrac{R}{t-b}$, where b is a constant, explain what $Q(t)$ and R mean, both geometrically and physically.

b) What is the remainder when $h(t) = -5t^2 + 9t + 2$ is divided by $t - 2$? What does the remainder represent physically?

Solution

a) Recall that $Q(t)$ represents the quotient and R represents the remainder when $h(t)$ is divided by $t - b$. Recall from the remainder theorem that $R = h(b)$. Thus, R is the y-value on the graph of $h(t)$ at the point where $x = b$. The physical meaning of R, therefore, is the height of the shot after b seconds.

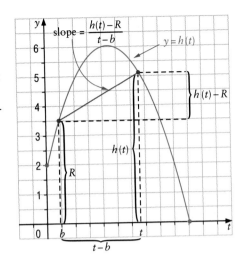

To understand the meaning of $Q(t)$, it is helpful to solve the division relationship

$$\frac{h(t)}{t-b} = Q(t) + \frac{R}{t-b}$$

for $Q(t)$ to obtain

$$Q(t) = \frac{h(t)}{t-b} - \frac{R}{t-b}$$

$$= \frac{h(t) - R}{t-b}$$

Thinking in terms of rise over run, we can see that the previous equation for $Q(t)$ represents the slope of the line segment joining the points (b, R) and $(t, h(t))$. Physically, $Q(t)$ represents the change in height of the shot divided by the time for the time interval that begins b seconds after the shot is launched and ends t seconds after the shot is launched.

b) Using the remainder theorem, the remainder when $h(t)$ is divided by $t - 2$ is $h(2)$.

$$h(2) = -5(2)^2 + 9(2) + 2 = 0$$

The remainder is 0 when $h(t) = -5t^2 + 9t + 2$ is divided by $t - 2$.

Since the remainder represents the height of the shot after 2 s, and this height is 0, we conclude that the shot hits the ground after 2 s.

In Chapters 3 and 4, we will see that the quantity $Q(t)$ from Example 5 can also be interpreted as the average velocity of the shot over the time interval from b to t. In general, such quotients can be interpreted as average rates of change.

Key Concepts

- When a polynomial $P(x)$ is divided by $x - b$, the remainder is $P(b)$.
- When a polynomial $P(x)$ is divided by $ax - b$, the remainder is $P\left(\frac{b}{a}\right)$.
- In the division relationship

$$\frac{P(x)}{x-b} = Q(x) + \frac{R}{x-b}$$

$Q(x)$ and R can be interpreted as quantities on the graph of $y = P(x)$. The quantity R is the height of the graph at $x = b$; that is, $R = P(b)$. The quantity $Q(x)$ is the slope of the line segment joining the points $(b, P(b))$ and $(x, P(x))$.

Communicate Your Understanding

1. Describe how you would determine the remainder when the polynomial $x^3 - 3x^2 + 4x - 7$ is divided by $x - 2$.

2. Describe how you would determine the remainder when the polynomial $2x^3 - 5x + 4$ is divided by $2x - 3$.

3. When a divisor is a factor of a polynomial, what is the remainder? Explain.

Practise

A **1.** For $P(x) = 2x^2 - 3x - 2$, determine the following.

a) $P(1)$ b) $P(0)$

c) $P(2)$ d) $P(-2)$

2. For $g(y) = 2y^3 - 3y^2 + 5$, determine the following.

a) $g(-2)$ b) $g(4)$

c) $g(0)$ d) $g\left(\dfrac{1}{2}\right)$

3. Use the remainder theorem to determine the remainder when each polynomial is divided by $x - 2$.

a) $x^2 - 5x - 3$ b) $2x^2 + x - 10$
c) $x^3 + 2x^2 - 8x + 1$ d) $x^3 - 3x^2 + 5x - 2$
e) $2x^3 + 3x^2 - 9x - 10$ f) $3x^3 - 12x + 2$

4. Use the remainder theorem to determine the remainder when $2x^3 - x^2 - 4x - 4$ is divided by each binomial.

a) $x - 1$ b) $x + 1$
c) $x - 2$ d) $x + 3$

5. Use the remainder theorem to determine the remainder for each division.

a) $(x^2 + 2x + 4) \div (x - 2)$ $P(2) =$
b) $(4n^2 + 7n - 5) \div (n + 3)$
c) $(x^3 + 2x^2 - 3x + 1) \div (x - 1)$
d) $(x^3 + 6x^2 - 3x^2 - x + 8) \div (x + 1)$
e) $(2w^3 + 3w^2 - 5w + 2) \div (w + 3)$
f) $(y^3 - 8) \div (y + 2)$
g) $(x^3 + x^2 + 3) \div (x + 4)$
h) $(1 - x^3) \div (x - 1)$
i) $(m^4 - 2m^3 + m^2 + 12m - 6) \div (m - 2)$
j) $(2 - 3t + t^2 + t^3) \div (t - 4)$
k) $(2y^4 - 3y^2 + 1) \div (y - 3)$

l) $(2 - x + x^2 - x^3 - x^4) \div (x + 2)$
m) $(3x^2 - \sqrt{2}x + 3) \div (x + \sqrt{2})$
n) $(2r^4 - 4r^2 - 9) \div (r - \sqrt{3})$

6. Use the remainder theorem to determine the remainder for each division.

a) $(2x^2 + 5x + 7) \div (2x - 3)$
b) $(6a^2 + 5a - 4) \div (3a + 4)$
c) $(x^3 + 2x^2 - 4x + 1) \div (2x - 1)$
d) $(2y^3 + y^2 - 6y + 3) \div (2y + 1)$
e) $(9m^3 - 6m^2 + 3m + 2) \div (3m - 1)$
f) $(8t^3 + 4t^2 + 17) \div (2t + 3)$

B **7.** For each polynomial, determine the value of k if the remainder is 3.

a) $(kx^2 + 3x + 1) \div (x + 2)$ $- 3$
b) $(x^3 + x^2 + kx - 17) \div (x - 2)$
c) $(x^3 + 4x^2 - x + k) \div (x - 1)$
d) $(x^3 + kx^2 + x + 2) \div (x + 1)$

8. When the polynomial $4x^3 + mx^2 + nx + 11$ is divided by $x + 2$, the remainder is -7. When the polynomial is divided by $x - 1$, the remainder is 14. What are the values of m and n?

9. The polynomial $px^3 - x^2 + qx - 2$ has no remainder when divided by $x - 1$ and a remainder of -18 when divided by $x + 2$. Determine the values of p and q.

10. The polynomial $3x^3 + vx^2 - 5x + w$ has a remainder of -1 when divided by $x + 2$ and a remainder of 109 when divided by $x - 3$. What are the values of v and w?

Apply, Solve, Communicate

11. The divisions $(2x^3 + 4x^2 - kx + 5) \div (x + 3)$ and $(6y^3 - 3y^2 + 2y + 7) \div (2y - 1)$ have the same remainder. Determine the value of k.

12. When $kx^3 - 3x^2 + 5x - 8$ is divided by $x - 2$, the remainder is 22. What is the remainder when $kx^3 - 3x^2 + 5x - 8$ is divided by $x + 1$?

13. The area, $A(h)$, of a triangle is represented by the expression $h^2 + 0.5h$, where h is the height.
a) Determine the remainder when the expression is divided by $2h - 7$.
b) Interpret the remainder.

14. The product of two numbers is represented by the expression $6n^2 - 5n + 8$, where n is a positive integer greater than 4.
a) Determine the remainder when the expression is divided by $2n + 1$.
b) Interpret the remainder.

15. Application The main span of the Tsing Ma Bridge in Hong Kong is the longest span of any suspension bridge in the world. If the origin is placed on the roadway of the main span, below the lowest point on the support cable, the shape of the cable can be modelled by the function $h(d) = 0.0003d^2 + 2$.
where $h(d)$ metres is the height of the cable above the roadway, and d metres is the horizontal distance from the lowest point on the cable.
a) Determine the remainder when $0.0003d^2 + 2$ is divided by $d - 500$.
b) Determine the remainder when $0.0003d^2 + 2$ is divided by $d + 500$.
c) Compare the results from parts a) and b).
d) Use the graph of the function $h(d) = 0.0003d^2 + 2$ to explain your findings.

16. Communication The hammer throw is an Olympic throwing event. The path of the hammer in one throw can be modelled by the function
$h(d) = -0.017d^2 + 1.3d + 2.5$
where $h(d)$ metres is the height of the hammer, and d metres is the horizontal distance of the hammer from the point where it was released.
a) Divide the polynomial $-0.017d^2 + 1.3d + 2.5$ by $d - 50$.
b) Interpret the remainder from part a).
c) Divide the polynomial $-0.017d^2 + 1.3d + 2.5$ by $d - 80$.
d) Does the remainder from part c) have any meaning for the hammer throw? Explain.

17. Communication, Inquiry/Problem Solving A parking officer keeps, a running total of the tickets that she gives during an 8-hour shift. Analysing her results later, she uses regression to approximate the total number of tickets, P, given up to time t by the formula $P(t) = 0.5t^2 + 2t$, where t is measured in hours and $t \in [0, 8]$.
a) Divide $P(t)$ by $t - 2$. State the quotient $Q(t)$ and the remainder R. Explain the meaning of $Q(t)$ and R.
b) Does the formula for $P(t)$ seem realistic? Explain.
c) On another day, the parking officer's formula for the running total of tickets given is $P(t) = -t^2 + 10t$ for $t \in [0, 8]$. Is this formula realistic, or has a mistake been made? Explain.

18. Inquiry/Problem Solving A tree farm operator models the cumulative total number of Christmas trees sold, $C(t)$, during December by the formula $C(t) = 0.1t^2 + 10t + 25$, where $t \in [1, 24]$, $t = 1$ represents December 1, $t = 2$ represents December 2, and so on.
a) Explain the strengths and weaknesses of the formula for $C(t)$. Do you think that it is an exact formula or an approximation? Explain.
b) Divide $C(t)$ by $t - 5$. State the quotient $Q(t)$ and the remainder R. Explain the meaning of $Q(t)$ and R.
c) Do you think that the same formula for $C(t)$ is still valid for $t \geq 25$? Explain.

19. For what values of k does the function $f(x) = x^3 + 6x^2 + kx - 4$ give the same remainder when divided by either $x - 1$ or $x + 2$?

20. When $x^2 + 5x + 7$ is divided by $x + k$, the remainder is 3. Determine k.

21. When the polynomial $bx^2 + cx + d$ is divided by $x - a$, the remainder is zero.
a) What can you conclude from this result?
b) Write an equation that expresses a in terms of b, c, and d.

22. A polynomial, $P(x)$, is divided by $x - b$ to give a quotient, $Q(x)$, and a remainder, R.
a) Predict the quotient and the remainder when $P(x)$ is divided by $b - x$.
b) Use an example with a non-zero remainder to test your prediction.

c) Use the division statements for the division by $x - b$ and the division by $b - x$ to explain your findings.

23. Write a polynomial that satisfies each set of conditions. Check that the polynomial satisfies the conditions, using a different method than the one you used to create the polynomial.
a) a quadratic polynomial that gives a remainder of -4 when it is divided by $x - 3$
b) a cubic polynomial that gives a remainder of 3 when it is divided by $x + 2$
c) a quartic polynomial that gives a remainder of 1 when it is divided by $2x - 1$

24. Divide using long division.
a) $\dfrac{x^4 - 1}{x^2 + 1}$

b) $\dfrac{x^3 + 2x^2 + 5x + 1}{x^2 + 1}$

c) $\dfrac{x^8 - 1}{x^2 - 1}$

d) $\dfrac{2x^3 - 5x^2 + 6x - 7}{x^2 - x}$

25. Application, Inquiry/Problem Solving In light of question 24 and its results, is it possible to extend the remainder theorem to cover cases such as these? If so, conjecture a generalization of the remainder theorem, and test your conjecture. If not, explain why.

Career Connection: *Computer Science*

Like mathematics, a career in computer science is potentially a good "fit" for anyone who enjoys creating and comprehending abstract thought structures. Many computer applications draw heavily on mathematical theory. For example, algorithms are among the most fundamental structures in all computer software, and they are often best expressed in mathematical terms. A computer algebra system is able to replicate many of the processes studied in this chapter, because the software has been developed out of an excellent mathematical understanding of algorithms such as polynomial division to find a quotient and remainder. Software applications from telecommunications networks to video game graphics demand similar skills and aptitudes.

The Factor Theorem

In this section we study the factor theorem, which is helpful in factoring polynomial expressions.

The integer factors of the integer 6 are 1, 2, 3, 6, –1, –2, –3, and –6. The factors all divide 6 evenly, that is, they give a remainder of zero. This concept also applies to polynomials. For example, the quadratic $x^2 - 5x + 6$ can be factored as follows.
$x^2 - 5x + 6 = (x - 2)(x - 3)$
The remainder theorem can be used to find the remainder when $x^2 - 5x + 6$ is divided by each of its factors.

$$P(x) = x^2 - 5x + 6 \qquad\qquad P(x) = x^2 - 5x + 6$$
$$P(2) = 2^2 - 5(2) + 6 \qquad\quad P(3) = 3^2 - 5(3) + 6$$
$$= 0 \qquad\qquad\qquad\qquad = 0$$

Thus, as with integers, dividing a polynomial by one of its factors gives a remainder of zero. Note also that 2 and 3 are factors of the constant term, 6, of the quadratic. In the following investigation, you will test these ideas for other polynomials.

Investigate & Inquire: The Factor Theorem

1. Copy and complete the table for the polynomial $P(x) = x^3 + 2x^2 - 5x - 6$ using the remainder theorem.

Divisor, $x - b$	b	Remainder, $P(b)$	Is $x - b$ a factor of $P(x)$?
a) $x + 1$	−1	0	Yes
b) $x - 2$			
c) $x - 3$			
d) $x + 3$			
e) $x + 4$			
f) $x - 5$			
g) $x + 6$			

2. When a binomial is a factor of a polynomial, is the constant term of the binomial a factor of the constant term of the polynomial? Explain.

3. If the constant term of a binomial is a factor of the constant term of a polynomial, is the binomial always a factor? Explain.

4. a) What are the possible values of b for the binomial factors, $x - b$, of $x^3 + 2x^2 - 13x + 10$?
b) Test the possible values of b to find the three binomial factors of $x^3 + 2x^2 - 13x + 10$.

The **factor theorem**, which is a special case of the remainder theorem, can be stated as follows.

> Factor theorem: A polynomial $P(x)$ has $x - b$ as a factor if and only if $P(b) = 0$.

The factor theorem can be established as follows.
If a polynomial $P(x)$ has $x - b$ as a factor, then
$P(x) = (x - b)Q(x)$
Substitute b for x:
$P(b) = (b - b)Q(b)$
$\quad\quad = 0$

Conversely, if $P(b) = 0$, then, by the remainder theorem, the remainder is zero when $P(x)$ is divided by $x - b$, which means that $x - b$ is a factor of $P(x)$.

The factor theorem can be used to find or verify a factor of a polynomial.

Example 1 Verifying a Factor $x - b$

Show that $x + 2$ is a factor of $x^3 + 5x^2 + 2x - 8$.

Solution 1 Paper and Pencil Method

From the factor theorem, if $P(-2) = 0$, then $x + 2$ is a factor of $P(x) = x^3 + 5x^2 + 2x - 8$.
$P(-2) = (-2)^3 + 5(-2)^2 + 2(-2) - 8$
$\quad\quad\quad = 0$
Since $P(-2) = 0$, $x + 2$ is a factor of $x^3 + 5x^2 + 2x - 8$.

Solution 2 Graphing Calculator Method

From the factor theorem, if $P(-2) = 0$, then $x + 2$ is a factor of $P(x) = x^3 + 5x^2 + 2x - 8$.
Enter the function $y = x^3 + 5x^2 + 2x - 8$ as Y1. Then, find Y1(−2) (press [VARS] [▶] 1 1
[(] [(-)] 2 [)]).

Since Y1(−2) = 0, that is, $P(-2) = 0$, $x + 2$ is a factor of $x^3 + 5x^2 + 2x - 8$.

When attempting to factor a polynomial, it is helpful to know which values of b to try. The **integral zero theorem**, which can be expressed as follows, can help in making a decision.

> Integral zero theorem: If $x = b$ is an integral zero of a polynomial $P(x)$ with integral coefficients, then b is a factor of the constant term of the polynomial.

A zero of a polynomial $P(x)$ is a number b such that $P(b) = 0$. An integral zero is a zero b that is an integer.

For example, the polynomial $P(x) = x^2 - 5x + 6$ is expressed in factored form as $P(x) = (x - 2)(x - 3)$. The zeros of $P(x)$ are therefore 2 and 3, both of which are factors of 6, the constant term of $P(x)$.

If $x = b$ is an integral zero of a polynomial, then $x - b$ is a factor of the polynomial. Therefore, we can use the factors of the constant term of the polynomial to look for possible factors of the polynomial.

Example 2 Factoring Using the Integral Zero Theorem

Factor $x^3 + 3x^2 - 13x - 15$.

Solution 1 Paper and Pencil Method

Find a factor by evaluating $P(x)$ for values of x equal to possible values of b. The possible values of b are the factors of 15. The factors of 15 are ± 1, ± 3, ± 5, and ± 15.

$P(x) = x^3 + 3x^2 - 13x - 15$

Start by testing the simplest possible values of b until a zero is found.

$$P(1) = (1)^3 + 3(1)^2 - 13(1) - 15$$
$$= -24$$

$$P(-1) = (-1)^3 + 3(-1)^2 - 13(-1) - 15$$
$$= 0$$

Since $P(-1) = 0$, $x + 1$ is a factor of $x^3 + 3x^2 - 13x - 15$.

Use division to find another factor.
From the long division, another factor is $x^2 + 2x - 15$.
So, $x^3 + 3x^2 - 13x - 15 = (x + 1)(x^2 + 2x - 15)$.
Factoring $x^2 + 2x - 15$ gives $(x - 3)(x + 5)$.
So, $x^3 + 3x^2 - 13x - 15 = (x + 1)(x - 3)(x + 5)$.

$$
\require{enclose}
\begin{array}{r}
x^2 + 2x - 15 \\[-3pt]
x+1 \enclose{longdiv}{x^3 + 3x^2 - 13x - 15} \\
\underline{x^3 + x^2} \\
2x^2 - 13x \\
\underline{2x^2 + 2x} \\
- 15x - 15 \\
\underline{- 15x - 15} \\
0
\end{array}
$$

Solution 2 Graphing Calculator Method

Alternatively, the factors of the polynomial $x^3 + 3x^2 - 13x - 15$ can be found by graphing the corresponding function $P(x) = x^3 + 3x^2 - 13x - 15$.

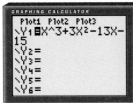
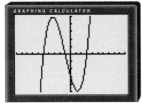

Window variables:
$x \in [-10, 10]$, $y \in [-25, 25]$

The graph has x-intercepts of 3, -1, and -5. These are the real zeros of the function. Using these zeros, the polynomial can be written in factored form as
$P(x) = (x - 3)(x + 1)(x + 5)$

Example 3 Factoring a Polynomial

Factor $x^3 - 1$.

Solution

The factors of 1 are ± 1.

$P(x) = x^3 - 1$

$P(1) = 1^3 - 1$

$\quad = 0$

Therefore, $x - 1$ is a factor. Use long division to find another factor.

From the long division, another factor of $x^3 - 1$ is $x^2 + x + 1$.

The expression $x^2 + x + 1$ cannot be factored.

So, $x^3 - 1 = (x - 1)(x^2 + x + 1)$.

$$
\begin{array}{r}
x^2 + x + 1 \\
x - 1\overline{)\,x^3 + 0x^2 + 0x - 1} \\
\underline{x^3 - x^2} \\
x^2 + 0x \\
\underline{x^2 - x} \\
x - 1 \\
\underline{x - 1} \\
0
\end{array}
$$

The factor theorem can be extended to include polynomials for which the leading coefficient is not 1. If a polynomial $P(x)$ has $ax - b$ as a factor, then

$P(x) = (ax - b)Q(x)$

Substitute $\dfrac{b}{a}$ for x:

$$P\left(\frac{b}{a}\right) = \left[a\left(\frac{b}{a}\right) - b\right]Q\left(\frac{b}{a}\right)$$

$$\quad = 0$$

Conversely, if $P\left(\dfrac{b}{a}\right) = 0$, then, by the remainder theorem, the remainder is 0 when $P(x)$ is divided by $ax - b$, which means that $ax - b$ is a factor of $P(x)$.

Thus, a polynomial $P(x)$ has $ax - b$ as a factor if and only if $P\left(\dfrac{b}{a}\right) = 0$.

Example 4 Verifying a Factor $ax - b$, Where $a \neq 1$

Verify that $2x - 3$ is a factor of $2x^3 - 5x^2 - x + 6$.

Solution 1 Paper and Pencil Method

If $P\left(\dfrac{3}{2}\right) = 0$, then $2x - 3$ is a factor of $P(x) = 2x^3 - 5x^2 - x + 6$.

$$P\left(\frac{3}{2}\right) = 2\left(\frac{3}{2}\right)^3 - 5\left(\frac{3}{2}\right)^2 - \left(\frac{3}{2}\right) + 6$$

$$\quad = \frac{27}{4} - \frac{45}{4} - \frac{6}{4} + \frac{24}{4}$$

$$\quad = 0$$

Since $P\left(\dfrac{3}{2}\right) = 0$, $2x - 3$ is a factor of $2x^3 - 5x^2 - x + 6$.

Solution 2 Graphing Calculator Method

If $P\left(\dfrac{3}{2}\right) = 0$, then $2x - 3$ is a factor of $P(x) = 2x^3 - 5x^2 - x + 6$.

Enter the function $y = 2x^3 - 5x^2 - x + 6$ into the function editor. Then, find $Y1\left(\dfrac{3}{2}\right)$.

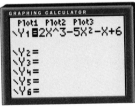
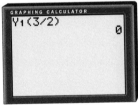

Since $Y1\left(\dfrac{3}{2}\right) = 0$, that is, $P\left(\dfrac{3}{2}\right) = 0$, $2x - 3$ is a factor of $2x^3 - 5x^2 - x + 6$.

When attempting to factor a polynomial, it is helpful to know which values of a and b to try. The **rational zero theorem**, as follows, can help in making a decision.

> Rational zero theorem: If $x = \dfrac{b}{a}$ is a rational zero of a polynomial
>
> $P(x)$ with integral coefficients, then b is a factor of the constant term of the polynomial, and a is a factor of the leading coefficient of the polynomial.

A rational zero is a zero that is a rational number.

If $x = \dfrac{b}{a}$ is a rational zero of a polynomial, then $ax - b$ is a factor of the polynomial.

Therefore, we can use the factors of the constant term of the polynomial and the factors of the leading coefficient of the polynomial to look for factors of the polynomial.

Example 5 Factoring Using the Rational Zero Theorem

Factor $8x^3 - 4x^2 - 2x + 1$ completely.`

Solution

If $8x^3 - 4x^2 - 2x + 1$ has a factor $ax - b$, then b is a factor of the constant term, which is 1, and a is a factor of the leading coefficient, which is 8. The factors of 1 are ± 1. The factors of 8 are ± 1, ± 2, ± 4, and ± 8.

Find a factor by evaluating $P(x)$ for x-values that equal the possible values of $\dfrac{b}{a}$.

The possible values of $\dfrac{b}{a}$ are $\dfrac{1}{1}, \dfrac{1}{-1}, \dfrac{-1}{1}, \dfrac{-1}{-1}, \dfrac{1}{2}, \dfrac{1}{-2}, \dfrac{-1}{2}, \dfrac{-1}{-2}, \dfrac{1}{4}, \dfrac{1}{-4}, \dfrac{-1}{4}, \dfrac{-1}{-4}, \dfrac{1}{8}, \dfrac{1}{-8}, \dfrac{-1}{8}$,

and $\dfrac{-1}{-8}$. Because some of these values are the same, the possible values of $\dfrac{b}{a}$ are ± 1, $\pm \dfrac{1}{2}$,

$\pm \dfrac{1}{4}$, and $\pm \dfrac{1}{8}$. Now, test the values of $\dfrac{b}{a}$ until a zero is found.

$P(x) = 8x^3 - 4x^2 - 2x + 1$

$P(1) = 3$

$P(-1) = -9$

$P\left(\dfrac{1}{2}\right) = 0$

Since $P\left(\dfrac{1}{2}\right) = 0$, $2x - 1$ is a factor of $8x^3 - 4x^2 - 2x + 1$.

Use long division to find another factor.
From the long division, $4x^2 - 1$ is another factor.
Since $4x^2 - 1$ can be factored further, we have

$$
\begin{aligned}
8x^3 - 4x^2 - 2x + 1 &= (2x - 1)(4x^2 - 1) \\
&= (2x - 1)(2x - 1)(2x + 1) \\
&= (2x - 1)^2(2x + 1)
\end{aligned}
$$

$$
\require{enclose}
\begin{array}{r}
4x^2 + 0x - 1 \\[-2pt]
2x - 1 \enclose{longdiv}{8x^3 - 4x^2 - 2x + 1} \\
\underline{8x^3 - 4x^2} \\
0x^2 - 2x \\
\underline{0x^2 - 0x} \\
-2x + 1 \\
\underline{-2x + 1} \\
0
\end{array}
$$

The factoring tools developed in this section are used in Section 2.5 to help solve polynomial equations.

Key Concepts

- A polynomial $P(x)$ has $x - b$ as a factor if and only if $P(b) = 0$.
- A polynomial $P(x)$ has $ax - b$ as a factor if and only if $P\left(\dfrac{b}{a}\right) = 0$.
- If $x = \dfrac{b}{a}$ is a rational zero of a polynomial $P(x)$ with integral coefficients, then b is a factor of the constant term of the polynomial, and a is a factor of the leading coefficient of the polynomial.

Communicate Your Understanding

1. Describe how to verify that $x - 3$ is a factor of $x^3 + 5x^2 - 12x - 36$.
2. Describe how to factor $x^3 - 2x^2 - 5x + 6$.
3. Describe how to factor $2x^3 - 3x^2 - 11x + 6$.

Practise

A **1.** Use the factor theorem to determine whether each polynomial has a factor of $x - 1$.
a) $x^3 - 3x^2 + 4x - 2$ b) $2x^3 - x^2 - 3x - 2$
c) $3x^3 - x - 3$ d) $2x^3 + 4x^2 - 5x - 1$

2. State whether each polynomial has a factor of $x + 2$.
a) $5x^2 + 2x + 4$ b) $x^3 + 2x^2 - 3x - 6$
c) $3x^3 + 2x^2 - 7x + 2$ d) $x^4 - 2x^3 + 3x - 4$

3. Verify that the binomial is a factor of the polynomial.
a) $x^3 + 2x^2 + 2x + 1; x + 1$
b) $x^3 - 3x^2 + 4x - 4; x - 2$
c) $m^3 - 3m^2 + m - 3; m - 3$
d) $x^3 + 7x^2 + 17x + 15; x + 3$
e) $4x^2 - 9x - 9; x - 3$
f) $6x^2 - 11x - 17; x + 1$
g) $2y^3 - 5y^2 + 2y + 1; y - 1$
h) $x^3 - 6x - 4; x + 2$

4. State whether each polynomial has a factor of $2x - 1$. Explain your reasoning.
a) $6x^2 + 5x - 4$ b) $4x^2 + 8x - 7$
c) $2x^3 - x^2 - 6x + 3$ d) $2x^3 + 9x^2 + 3x - 4$
e) $2x^4 - x^3 + 3x - 1$ f) $-4x^3 + 4x^2 + x - 1$

5. Show that the binomial is a factor of the polynomial.
a) $2x^3 + x^2 + 2x + 1; 2x + 1$
b) $2x^3 - 3x^2 - 2x + 3; 2x - 3$
c) $3y^3 + 8y^2 + 3y - 2; 3y - 1$
d) $6n^3 - 7n^2 + 1; 3n + 1$
e) $8x^2 - 2x - 1; 2x - 1$
f) $3x^3 - x^2 - 3x + 1; 3x - 1$

6. Factor completely.
a) $x^3 - 6x^2 + 11x - 6$ b) $x^3 + 8x^2 + 19x + 12$
c) $x^3 - 2x^2 - 9x + 18$ d) $x^3 + 4x^2 + 2x - 3$
e) $z^3 + z^2 - 22z - 40$ f) $x^3 + x^2 - 16x - 16$
g) $x^3 - 2x^2 - 6x - 8$ h) $k^3 + 6k^2 - 7k - 60$
i) $x^3 - 27x + 10$ j) $x^3 + 4x^2 - 15x - 18$

7. Factor.
a) $2x^3 - 9x^2 + 10x - 3$
b) $4y^3 - 7y - 3$
c) $3x^3 - 4x^2 - 17x + 6$
d) $3x^3 - 2x^2 - 12x + 8$
e) $2x^3 + 13x^2 + 23x + 12$

f) $2x^3 - 3x^2 + 3x - 10$
g) $6x^3 - 11x^2 - 26x + 15$
h) $4y^3 + 8y^2 - y - 2$
i) $4x^3 + 3x^2 - 4x - 3$
j) $6w^3 + 16w^2 - 21w + 5$

Apply, Solve, Communicate

B **8.** Application The area, A, in millions of hectares, of forest cut down in a certain part of the world in year t can be modelled by $A(t) = 3t^2 + 2t$, where $t = 0$ represents the year 2000, $t = 1$ represents the year 2001, and so on.
a) Calculate the value of $A(2)$ and explain its meaning.
b) Calculate the value of $A(5) - A(2)$ and explain its meaning.
c) Calculate the value of $\dfrac{A(5) - A(2)}{5 - 2}$ and explain its meaning.
d) Explain the meaning of the quantity $\dfrac{A(t) - A(2)}{t - 2}$.
e) Do you think that $t \in [0, \infty)$ is a reasonable domain for the function $A(t)$? Explain.

9. For each polynomial function $f(x)$, and each value b,
i) factor $f(x) - f(b)$ ii) simplify $\dfrac{f(x) - f(b)}{x - b}$
a) $f(x) = x^2; b = 3$
b) $f(x) = x^2 + 2x - 1; b = 2$
c) $f(x) = 2x^3 + 4x^2 - 5x - 7; b = -1$

10. Consider question 9.
a) Rewrite the division statement $\dfrac{P(x)}{D(x)} = Q(x) + \dfrac{R(x)}{D(x)}$, substituting $f(x)$ for $P(x)$, and substituting $x - b$ for $D(x)$.
b) Since $x - b$ has degree 1, it follows that $R(x)$ is actually a constant in part a). Determine the value of the constant in terms of the function f. (Hint: Begin by multiplying each term by $x - b$.) Rewrite the division statement of part a) by substituting the constant that you have just determined.
c) Solve the division statement from part b) for $Q(x)$.
d) Do you think that $f(x) - f(b)$ can be factored for every polynomial function f? If so,

explain why. If not, provide an example of a polynomial function f for which $f(x) - f(b)$ cannot be factored. (Hint: See part c).)

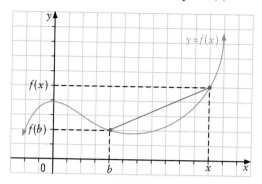

e) Referring to the graph of the function $y = f(x)$, explain the geometric interpretation of the quantity $\dfrac{f(x) - f(b)}{x - b}$.

11. Communication The mass, M, in millions of tonnes, of sulphur dioxide pollutant emitted by a certain factory in the year t can be modelled by $M(t) = 5t^3 + 2t^2 + 10t$, where $t = 0$ represents the year 2000, $t = 1$ represents the year 2001, and so on.
a) Calculate the value of $M(4)$ and explain its meaning.
b) Calculate the value of $M(7) - M(4)$ and explain its meaning.
c) Calculate the value of $\dfrac{M(7) - M(4)}{7 - 4}$ and explain its meaning.
d) Explain the meaning of the quantity $\dfrac{M(t) - M(1)}{t - 1}$.

12. Factor.
a) $x^4 + 4x^3 - 7x^2 - 34x - 24$
b) $x^5 + 3x^4 - 5x^3 - 15x^2 + 4x + 12$
c) $8x^3 + 4x^2 - 2x - 1$
d) $8x^3 - 12x^2 - 2x + 3$

13. The product of four integers is $x^4 + 6x^3 + 11x^2 + 6x$, where x is one of the integers. How are the integers related?

14. The following polynomials each have a factor of $x - 3$. What is the value of k in each case?
a) $4x^4 - 3x^3 - 2x^2 + kx - 9$
b) $kx^3 - 10x^2 + 2x + 3$

15. For the polynomial
$$P(x) = 3x^3 + 7x^2 - 22x - 8,$$
$P(2) = 0$, $P(-4) = 0$, and $P\left(-\dfrac{1}{3}\right) = 0$.
a) Find three factors of the polynomial.
b) Are there any other factors? Explain.

16. The polynomial $6x^3 + mx^2 + nx - 5$ has a factor of $x + 1$. When divided by $x - 1$, the remainder is -4. What are the values of m and n?

17. Show that $(x - a)$ is a factor of the polynomial $x^3 - ax^2 + bx^2 - abx + cx - ac$.

18. Inquiry/Problem Solving a) Factor the polynomials in parts i) to vi).
i) $x^3 - 1$ ii) $x^3 + 1$
iii) $x^3 - 27$ iv) $x^3 + 64$
v) $8x^3 - 1$ vi) $64x^3 + 1$
b) Use the results to decide whether $x + y$ or $x - y$ is a factor of $x^3 + y^3$. State the other factor.
c) Use the results to decide whether $x + y$ or $x - y$ is a factor of $x^3 - y^3$. State the other factor.
d) Use your findings to factor $8x^3 + 125$ and $27x^3 - 64$.
e) Use your findings to factor $x^6 + y^6$.
f) Make and test a conjecture about whether $x + y$ or $x - y$ is a factor of $x^{3n} + y^{3n}$, where n is a positive integer.
g) Make and test a conjecture about whether $x + y$ or $x - y$ is a factor of $x^{3n} - y^{3n}$, where n is a positive integer.

19. Application a) Is $x + 1$ a factor of $x^{100} - 1$? Is $x - 1$? Explain.
b) Is $x + 1$ a factor of $x^{99} + 1$? Is $x - 1$? Explain.
c) Is there an example that contradicts the statement "$x - 1$ is a factor of every polynomial of the form $x^n - 1$, where n is a positive integer"? Explain.
d) Is there an example that contradicts the statement "$x + 1$ is a factor of every polynomial of the form $x^n + 1$, where n is an *odd* positive integer"? Explain.

20. Two spheres have different radii. The radius of the smaller sphere is r. The volume, $V(r)$, of the larger sphere is related to the radius

of the smaller sphere by the equation
$V(r) = \dfrac{4}{3}\pi(r^3 + 9r^2 + 27r + 27)$. What is the radius of the larger sphere? Explain.

21. Communication **a)** Determine whether $x + y$ and $x - y$ are factors of each of the following.
i) $x^4 + y^4$ 　　　　　 ii) $x^4 - y^4$
iii) $x^5 + y^5$ 　　　　　 iv) $x^5 - y^5$
v) $x^6 + y^6$ 　　　　　 vi) $x^6 - y^6$
vii) $x^7 + y^7$ 　　　　　 viii) $x^7 - y^7$
b) Write a rule for deciding whether $x + y$ and $x - y$ are factors of $x^n + y^n$ and $x^n - y^n$.
c) Use your rule to write two factors of $x^8 - y^8$.
d) Use your rule to write a factor of $x^{11} + y^{11}$.

22. In $ax^3 + bx^2 - cx - d$, the values of $a, b, c,$ and d are integers with no common factors. If the zeros of $ax^3 + bx^2 - cx - d$ are integers, what are the possible values of a? Explain.

23. Inquiry/Problem Solving **a)** If $x - 1$ is a factor of $ax^3 + bx^2 + cx + d$, what is the value of $a + b + c + d$? Explain.
b) Use your result to decide whether $x - 1$ is a factor of each of the following polynomials.
i) $3x^3 + 5x^2 - 6x - 2$ 　 ii) $2x^3 - 9x^2 - x - 8$
iii) $-5x^3 + 4x + 1$

C **24.** Verify that $x + y$ is a factor of $x^2(y^2 - 1) - y^2(1 + x^2) + x^2 + y^2$.

25. Factor.
a) $3x^2 - 1 - \dfrac{2}{x^2}$

b) $2x^2 - xy - 3y^2$

c) $x^3 - 6x + \dfrac{11}{x} - \dfrac{6}{x^3}$

d) $15 - 23\dfrac{x}{y} + 9\dfrac{x^2}{y^2} - \dfrac{x^3}{y^3}$

Achievement Check

Knowledge/Understanding

Thinking/Inquiry/Problem Solving

Communication

Application

Let $P(x) = a_3x^3 + a_2x^2 + a_1x + a_0$, where $a_3, a_2, a_1,$ and a_0 are integers.
a) If $P(2) = 0$, one coefficient must be an even integer. Show which coefficient this is and justify your answer.
b) If $P\left(\dfrac{1}{2}\right) = 0$, one coefficient must be an even integer. Show which coefficient this is and justify your answer.
c) If $a_3 = a_0 = 1$, $P(-1) \neq 0$, and $P(1) \neq 0$, is it possible for $P(x)$ to have any rational zeros? Justify your conclusion.

Roots of Polynomial Equations

In this section, we use the procedures developed in the previous sections of this chapter to solve polynomial equations of degree greater than two.

Investigate & Inquire: Roots of Equations and *x*-Intercepts of Functions

To help you understand how to solve polynomial equations, you will explore the relationship between the *x*-intercepts of a function and the roots of the corresponding equation.

1. Draw the graph of $y = x^3 - 2x^2 - 5x + 6$ and label the *x*- and *y*-intercepts.

2. For the cubic function $y = x^3 - 2x^2 - 5x + 6$, the corresponding cubic equation is $x^3 - 2x^2 - 5x + 6 = 0$. How are the *x*-intercepts of the function related to the roots of the equation? Explain.

3. a) Factor the left side of the equation $x^3 - 2x^2 - 5x + 6 = 0$ completely.
b) How can the factors be used to find the solutions of the equation?

4. Solve each equation.
a) $x^3 - x^2 - 4x + 4 = 0$ b) $x^3 - 7x - 6 = 0$ c) $x^3 - 7x^2 + 15x - 9 = 0$

5. A rectangular box has a square base. The height of the box is 2 units more than the length, *x*, of a side of the square base.
a) Write an expression for $V(x)$, the volume of the box.
b) Suppose that the volume of the box is 45 cm³. Graph the function $y = V(x) - 45$.
c) What is the *x*-intercept of the function in part b)? What does the *x*-intercept represent in terms of the box?
d) What are the dimensions of the box?

The solutions of the polynomial equation $(x - 2)(x^2 + 1) = 0$ are the zeros of the polynomial function $f(x) = (x - 2)(x^2 + 1)$.

The real zero, $x = 2$, is the *x*-intercept of the graph of the function $f(x) = (x - 2)(x^2 + 1)$. There are also two complex zeros, $x = \pm i$, which do not correspond to *x*-intercepts of the graph. In general, the *x*-intercepts of the graph of a polynomial function $y = f(x)$ are the real solutions (real roots) of the corresponding polynomial equation $f(x) = 0$.

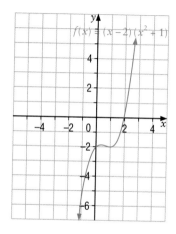

We have used several methods for solving quadratic equations: graphing, factoring, completing the square, and using the quadratic formula. Two of these methods—graphing and factoring—can be used to solve some polynomial equations of degree higher than two. Graphing does not always give exact values of real roots, but if the polynomial is factorable, we can find the exact values of the real and complex roots. In Section 2.4, we factored polynomials using the integral zero theorem and the rational zero theorem.

Example 1 Solving Equations With a Common Factor

Solve the equation $x^3 - 4x = 0$. Check your solution.

Solution 1 Paper and Pencil Method

$$x^3 - 4x = 0$$

We remove the common factor: $x(x^2 - 4) = 0$

Then, we factor the binomial: $x(x - 2)(x + 2) = 0$

Finally, we use the zero product property: $x = 0$ or $x - 2 = 0$ or $x + 2 = 0$

$$x = 2 \qquad\qquad x = -2$$

Now, we check the solution.

For $x = 0$,		For $x = 2$,		For $x = -2$,	
L.S. $= x^3 - 4x$	R.S. $= 0$	L.S. $= x^3 - 4x$	R.S. $= 0$	L.S. $= x^3 - 4x$	R.S. $= 0$
$= (0)^3 - 4(0)$		$= (2)^3 - 4(2)$		$= (-2)^3 - 4(-2)$	
$= 0$		$= 0$		$= 0$	

Solution 2 Graphing Calculator Method

We graph the function $y = x^3 - 4x$ in the friendly window, using the ZDecimal instruction.

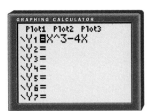 

Window variables:
$x \in [-4.7, 4.7]$,
$y \in [-3.1, 3.1]$

We use the [TRACE] key on the graphing calculator to find the solutions.

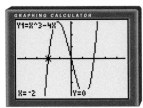 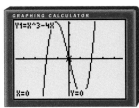 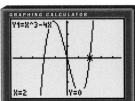

The solutions are $x = -2$, $x = 0$, and $x = 2$.

Example 2 Solving a Polynomial Equation Using the Integral Zero Theorem

A rectangular box for packaging chocolates is to be made from a rectangular piece of cardboard measuring 30 cm by 24 cm. The cardboard is folded according to the figure.

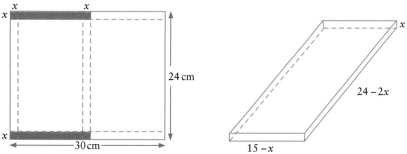

If the box is to have a capacity of 648 cm^3, determine the value of x.

Solution

The capacity, $V(x)$, of the box is the product of its three dimensions.

$$V(x) = x(24 - 2x)\frac{(30 - 2x)}{2}$$
$$= 2x(12 - x)(15 - x)$$
$$= 2x(x - 12)(x - 15)$$

Since the capacity of the box is to be 648 cm^3, we have

$$648 = 2x(x - 12)(x - 15)$$

To solve this equation for x, we begin by expanding the right side.

$$648 = 2x(x - 12)(x - 15)$$
$$\frac{648}{2} = x^3 - 27x^2 + 180x$$
$$0 = x^3 - 27x^2 + 180x - 324$$

Now, we factor the right side of the equation. Let $P(x) = x^3 - 27x^2 + 180x - 324$. First, we test the simplest factors of 324. We test only positive values of x, because x refers to a length.

$$P(1) = 1^3 - 27(1)^2 + 180(1) - 324$$
$$= -170$$
$$P(2) = 2^3 - 27(2)^2 + 180(2) - 324$$
$$= -64$$
$$P(3) = 3^3 - 27(3)^2 + 180(3) - 324$$
$$= 0$$

So, by the factor theorem, $x - 3$ is a factor of $x^3 - 27x^2 + 180x - 324$. We use long division to find another factor.

$$
\begin{array}{r}
x^2 - 24x + 108 \\
x - 3 \overline{\smash{)}\, x^3 - 27x^2 + 180x - 324} \\
\underline{x^3 - 3x^2} \\
-24x^2 + 180x \\
\underline{-24x^2 + 72x} \\
108x - 324 \\
\underline{108x - 324} \\
0
\end{array}
$$

Thus, another factor is $x^2 - 24x + 108$. Therefore,
$$x^3 - 27x^2 + 180x - 324 = (x - 3)(x^2 - 24x + 108)$$
$$= (x - 3)(x - 6)(x - 18)$$
So, $x - 3 = 0$ or $x - 6 = 0$ or $x - 18 = 0$
$$x = 3 \qquad\qquad x = 6 \qquad\qquad x = 18$$
The roots are 3, 6, and 18.

The dimensions of the box are x, $24 - 2x$, and $\dfrac{30 - 2x}{2} = 15 - x$. When $x = 3$, the

dimensions are 3, 18, and 12, and their product is 648, so this is an acceptable solution.
When $x = 6$, the dimensions are 6, 12, and 9, whose product is 648, so this is also an
acceptable solution. When $x = 18$, the dimensions $24 - 2x$ and $15 - x$ are negative, which is
physically impossible. Thus, this solution is rejected. Therefore, there are two acceptable
solutions: $x = 3$ cm and $x = 6$ cm.

Example 3 Solving a Polynomial Equation Using the Rational Zero Theorem

Solve $3x^3 + 8x^2 + 3x - 2 = 0$.

Solution 1 Paper and Pencil Method

The factors of 2 are ± 1 and ± 2. The factors of 3 are ± 1 and ± 3. Thus, for a factor $ax - b$ of

the polynomial $3x^3 + 8x^2 + 3x - 2$, the possible values of $\dfrac{b}{a}$ are ± 1, ± 2, $\pm\dfrac{1}{3}$, and $\pm\dfrac{2}{3}$. Let

$P(x) = 3x^3 + 8x^2 + 3x - 2$. We test the possible values of $P\!\left(\dfrac{b}{a}\right)$ until we obtain a value of 0.

$$P(1) = 3(1)^3 + 8(1)^2 + 3(1) - 2$$
$$= 12$$
$$P(-1) = 3(-1)^3 + 8(-1)^2 + 3(-1) - 2$$
$$= 0$$

Since $P(-1) = 0$, by the factor theorem, $x + 1$ is a factor of $3x^3 + 8x^2 + 3x - 2$. We use long
division to find another factor.

$$
\begin{array}{r}
3x^2 + 5x - 2 \\
x + 1 \overline{) 3x^3 + 8x^2 + 3x - 2} \\
\underline{3x^3 + 3x^2} \\
5x^2 + 3x \\
\underline{5x^2 + 5x} \\
-2x - 2 \\
\underline{-2x - 2} \\
0
\end{array}
$$

Another factor is $3x^2 + 5x - 2$. So,
$$3x^3 + 8x^2 + 3x - 2 = (x + 1)(3x^2 + 5x - 2)$$
$$= (x + 1)(x + 2)(3x - 1)$$
Since
$$(x + 1)(x + 2)(3x - 1) = 0$$
$$x + 1 = 0 \quad \text{or} \quad x + 2 = 0 \quad \text{or} \quad 3x - 1 = 0$$
$$x = -1 \qquad\qquad x = -2 \qquad\qquad x = \dfrac{1}{3}$$

The roots are -1, -2, and $\dfrac{1}{3}$. The roots can be checked by substitution.

Solution 2 Graphing Calculator Method

Graph the function $y = 3x^3 + 8x^2 + 3x - 2$ in the friendly window, using the ZDecimal instruction.

Window variables:
$x \in [-4.7, 4.7]$, $y \in [-3.1, 3.1]$

We can read two of the roots, $x = -2$ and $x = -1$, from the screen. To find the other root, we can use the Zero operation of the graphing calculator.

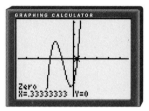

Window variables:
$x \in [-4.7, 4.7]$, $y \in [-3.1, 3.1]$

The third root is $x = \dfrac{1}{3}$.

Example 4 Finding Irrational Roots

Consider the equation $x^3 - 4x^2 + 2x + 3 = 0$.
a) Find the exact roots.
b) Approximate the roots to the nearest hundredth.

Solution

a) We use the integral zero theorem. The factors of 3 are ±1 and ±3.
Let $P(x) = x^3 - 4x^2 + 2x + 3$.
$P(1) = (1)^3 - 4(1)^2 + 2(1) + 3$
$\quad\;\; = 2$
$P(-1) = (-1)^3 - 4(-1)^2 + 2(-1) + 3$
$\quad\quad\; = -4$
$P(3) = (3)^3 - 4(3)^2 + 2(3) + 3$
$\quad\;\; = 0$
So, by the factor theorem, $x - 3$ is a factor.
We find another factor by using long division.

$$
\begin{array}{r}
x^2 - x - 1 \\
x - 3\overline{\smash{)}\,x^3 - 4x^2 + 2x + 3} \\
\underline{x^3 - 3x^2} \\
-x^2 + 2x \\
\underline{-x^2 + 3x} \\
-x + 3 \\
\underline{-x + 3} \\
0
\end{array}
$$

Thus, $x^3 - 4x^2 + 2x + 3 = (x - 3)(x^2 - x - 1)$, and the equation we are required to solve becomes, in factored form, $(x - 3)(x^2 - x - 1) = 0$. The polynomial $x^2 - x - 1$ cannot be factored over the integers. However, we can use the quadratic formula to solve $x^2 - x - 1 = 0$.

$x - 3 = 0$ or $x^2 - x - 1 = 0$

$x = 3$ or $x = \dfrac{-b \pm \sqrt{b^2 - 4ac}}{2a}$

$= \dfrac{1 \pm \sqrt{(-1)^2 - 4(1)(-1)}}{2(1)}$

$= \dfrac{1 \pm \sqrt{5}}{2}$

The exact roots are 3, $\dfrac{1 + \sqrt{5}}{2}$, and $\dfrac{1 - \sqrt{5}}{2}$.

b) We can evaluate the two irrational roots in part a) to the nearest hundredth.
The solutions are 3, –0.62, and 1.62, to the nearest hundredth.
This equation can also be solved using the Zero operation feature of a graphing calculator or graphing software.

Example 5 Roots of Non-Factorable Polynomial Equations

Solve $x^3 + 3x^2 - x - 5 = 0$, to the nearest hundredth, using a graphing calculator.

Solution
We graph the function $f(x) = x^3 + 3x^2 - x - 5$ on the graphing calculator.

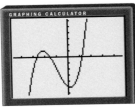

Window variables:
$x \in [-4.7, 4.7]$,
$y \in [-6.2, 6.2]$

To find the approximate values of the x-intercepts, to the nearest hundredth, we use the Zero operation. We must remember to set the number of decimal places from **Float** to **2** in the Mode settings.

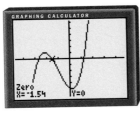
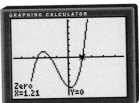

The x-intercepts are –2.68, –1.54, and 1.21, to the nearest hundredth.

Example 6 Real and Complex Roots

Solve $x^3 + 2x^2 - 45 = 0$. Include any complex solutions.

Solution

The factors of 45 are ±1, ±3, ±5, ±9, ±15, and ±45. It seems that ±1, ±15, and ±45 are unlikely candidates for solutions to the equation $P(x) = 0$, since the terms in x would probably be far too small or far too large to combine with −45 to produce 0. So it is reasonable to try the next smallest possibility.

$$P(x) = x^3 + 2x^2 - 45$$
$$P(3) = (3)^3 + 2(3)^2 - 45$$
$$= 27 + 18 - 45$$
$$= 0$$

So, $x - 3$ is a factor of $x^3 + 2x^2 - 45$. Using long division, we find another factor.

$$
\begin{array}{r}
x^2 + 5x + 15 \\
x-3 \overline{)\,x^3 + 2x^2 + 0x - 45} \\
\underline{x^3 - 3x^2} \\
5x^2 + 0x \\
\underline{5x^2 - 15x} \\
15x - 45 \\
\underline{15x - 45} \\
0
\end{array}
$$

Therefore, another factor is $x^2 + 5x + 15$, which cannot be factored further over the real numbers.

$$x^3 + 2x^2 - 45 = (x - 3)(x^2 + 5x + 15)$$
$$(x - 3)(x^2 + 5x + 15) = 0$$
$$x - 3 = 0 \quad \text{or} \quad x^2 + 5x + 15 = 0$$

$$x = 3 \quad \text{or} \qquad x = \frac{-b \pm \sqrt{b^2 - 4ac}}{2a}$$

$$= \frac{-5 \pm \sqrt{25 - 60}}{2}$$

$$= \frac{-5 \pm \sqrt{-35}}{2}$$

$$= \frac{-5 \pm i\sqrt{35}}{2}$$

Web Connection

For a summary of the properties of polynomial functions, go to **www.mcgrawhill.ca/links/CAF12** and follow the links.

The roots are 3, $\dfrac{-5 + i\sqrt{35}}{2}$, and $\dfrac{-5 - i\sqrt{35}}{2}$.

Families of Functions

The functions $f(x) = x + 3$, $f(x) = 2x + 6$, and $f(x) = 3x + 9$ belong to a **family of functions,** since they can all be written in the form $f(x) = k(x + 3)$, for $k \in R$. Each member of this particular family of functions has the same zero.

Example 7 Equations of a Family of Functions

Write the equation of the family of polynomial functions with zeros –2, 3, and 5.

Solution

One polynomial function with zeros –2, 3, and 5 has equation $f(x) = (x + 2)(x – 3)(x – 5)$. The equation of the family of polynomial functions with zeros –2, 3, and 5 is $f(x) = k(x + 2)(x – 3)(x – 5)$, for $k \in R$.

To display some of the curves in this family using a graphing calculator, we input the function as follows. This graphs the family members for $k = \pm2, \pm1$, and ±0.5.

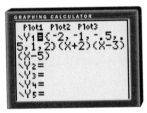
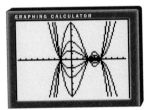

Window variables:
$x \in [-9.4, 9.4]$,
$y \in [-62, 62]$

Notice that all five graphs have the same x-intercepts, but different y-intercepts.

Key Concepts

- To determine the exact roots of a factorable polynomial equation, first use the integral zero theorem or the rational zero theorem, and then, factor.
- To solve non-factorable polynomial equations, use a graphing calculator or graphing software.
- The graphs of the polynomial functions of the form $y = k(x – x_1)(x – x_2)\cdots(x – x_n)$ have the same x-intercepts, but different y-intercepts.

Communicate Your Understanding

1. Describe how you would solve $x^3 – 16x = 0$.
2. Describe how you would solve $x^3 + 3x^2 – 10x – 24 = 0$ using the integral zero theorem.
3. a) The graph of a cubic function intersects the x-axis at only one point. How many real zeros could it have? Explain.
b) The graph of a cubic function intersects the x-axis at only two different points. How many real zeros could it have? Explain.
4. Repeat question 3 for a quartic function.

Practise

A **1.** Solve.
a) $(x + 1)(x - 4)(x + 5) = 0$
b) $(x - 2)(x - 7)(x + 6) = 0$
c) $x(x + 3)(x - 8) = 0$
d) $(x + 6)(x - 3)^2 = 0$

2. Solve by factoring. Check your solutions.
a) $x^3 + x^2 - 6x = 0$
b) $x^3 + 7x^2 + 12x = 0$
c) $y^3 - 9y = 0$
d) $x^3 - 4x^2 + 4x = 0$

3. Solve and check.
a) $x^3 + 3x^2 - x - 3 = 0$
b) $x^3 - 3x^2 - 4x + 12 = 0$
c) $t^3 + 2t^2 - 7t + 4 = 0$
d) $y^3 - 3y^2 - 16y + 48 = 0$
e) $a^3 - 4a^2 + a + 6 = 0$
f) $x^3 - 4x^2 - 3x + 18 = 0$

4. Solve and check.
a) $0 = x^3 - 9x^2 + 15x - 7$
b) $x^3 - 5x^2 = 12x - 36$
c) $k^3 - 19k = 30$
d) $x^3 - 4x^2 - 17x = -60$
e) $0 = w^3 - 5w^2 + 2w + 8$
f) $7x - 5x^2 = 3 - x^3$

5. Solve by factoring. Check your solutions.
a) $2x^3 - 3x^2 - 2x = 0$
b) $3x^3 - 10x^2 + 3x = 0$
c) $9z^3 - 4z = 0$
d) $16x^3 + 8x^2 + x = 0$

6. Solve by factoring.
a) $2x^3 + 9x^2 + 10x + 3 = 0$
b) $3x^3 - 8x^2 + 7x - 2 = 0$
c) $5x^3 - 7x^2 - 8x + 4 = 0$
d) $2d^3 - 3d^2 - 12d - 7 = 0$
e) $2x^3 - 11x^2 + 12x = -9$
f) $9x^3 + 18x^2 = 4x + 8$
g) $6y^3 + 29y - 12 = 23y^2$
h) $x^2(2x - 1) = 2x - 1$

7. For each equation
i) find the exact roots
ii) approximate the roots to the nearest hundredth
a) $x^3 - 8x = 0$
b) $x^3 - 10x + 3 = 0$

c) $x^3 - 6x^2 + 6x + 8 = 0$
d) $0 = x^3 + 3x^2 - 15x - 25$
e) $v^3 + 5v^2 = 18$
f) $x(x + 4)(x + 1) = 4$

8. Find the exact roots.
a) $3x^3 + 9x^2 + 10x + 4 = 0$
b) $5x^3 + 3x = 0$
c) $0 = 2x^3 - 8x^2 + 5x - 20$
d) $3x^3 - 7x^2 + 6x = 2$
e) $2m^3 + 7m^2 + 11m + 10 = 0$
f) $4x^3 = 9x^2 + 7x + 6$

9. Solve using a graphing calculator. Round results to the nearest hundredth, if necessary.
a) $2x^3 + 9x^2 - 7 = 0$
b) $2x^3 + 9x^2 - 16 = 0$
c) $x^3 + x + 2 = 0$
d) $x^3 - 4x^2 + 6 = 0$
e) $x^4 - 3 = 0$
f) $x^3 - 5x^2 + x + 4 = 0$
g) $x^4 + 2x^3 - 3x^2 - 3x + 1 = 0$
h) $2x^3 + 7x^2 - 2x - 5 = 0$

10. Write the equation of the family of polynomial functions given each set of zeros. What is different about the graphs in each family? What is the same?
a) $2, -1, 5$
b) $3, -2, -4$
c) $1, 1 + \sqrt{2}, 1 - \sqrt{2}$
d) $2, -1 + i, -1 - i$

Apply, Solve, Communicate

B **11.** Application A rectangular box is to be constructed from a cardboard sheet of dimensions 60 cm by 60 cm. The box is folded according to the diagram. If the box is to have a capacity of 8000 cm^3, determine the value of x.

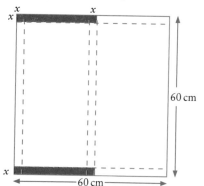

12. Communication, Inquiry/Problem Solving A cone is inscribed in a sphere. The radius of the sphere is 2 units.

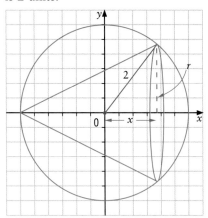

a) Write a formula for the volume, V, of the cone in terms of x.

b) Argue that negative values of x are reasonable, provided that we think of x as a coordinate and not as a distance. What is the domain of the function in part a)?

c) Factor the formula for V in part a). Explain the meaning of the roots.

13. Inquiry/Problem Solving The atrium at the new Municipal Museum of Magnificent Mathematical Monuments is designed in the shape of a cone. The exterior wall of the atrium is to be a portion of a sphere circumscribed around the cone. The radius of the sphere is 10 m.

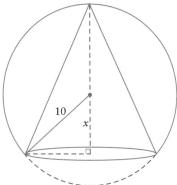

a) Determine a formula for the volume of the cone in terms of x.

b) If the capacity of the atrium is designed to be 1000 m^3, what is the value of x? What are the resulting dimensions of the conical atrium?

c) The Department of Urban Mathematical Buildings overrules the conical design of the atrium and the spherical exterior wall, and decides instead that the atrium must be in the shape of a pyramid with a square base, and with height 2 m more than the side length of the base. If the capacity is still to be 1000 m^3, what should the dimensions of the pyramid be? (Note that the volume of a pyramid is $\frac{1}{3} \times$ area of base $\times$ height.)

14. Application The population in thousands, P, of a city x years from now is modelled by $P(x) = x^3 + x^2 - 2x + 10$, where P is measured in thousands of people. City council decides that, when the population is triple the current value, a bylaw will be passed to limit the number of new homes that can be constructed. When will the bylaw be passed (to the nearest year)?

15. Application The population of a certain type of fish in a region of the Atlantic Ocean x decades from now is modelled by the function $P(x) = -x^3 - 5x^2 - 3x + 12$, where P is measured in millions of fish. The population of the fish is declining due to overfishing and the use of a special net that is dragged along the ocean floor, destroying the breeding grounds of the fish. When the population of the fish has declined to fewer than 1000 fish, the damage is sufficient that the fish in that area are in danger of extinction unless preventive measures are taken. Does the population decline to this level, and if so, when?

16. Find the exact roots of each equation.

a) $8x^3 - 12x^2 + 6x - 1 = 0$

b) $30x^3 + 19x^2 - 1 = 0$

c) $12y^3 - 4y^2 - 27y + 9 = 0$

d) $8a^3 + 27 = 0$

e) $\dfrac{x^3}{2} - \dfrac{x}{3} = 0$ f) $x^3 - \dfrac{13x^2}{4} + x = -3$

g) $1 - \dfrac{1}{x} = \dfrac{1}{x^3} - \dfrac{1}{x^2}$ h) $\dfrac{2}{x-2} - \dfrac{1}{x-1} = x$

17. One root of each equation is -2. Determine k and then find the other roots.

a) $x^3 + kx^2 - 10x - 24 = 0$

b) $3x^3 + 4x^2 + kx - 2 = 0$

18. If $x^3 - 4x^2 + kx = 0$,
a) what values of k result in two equal roots?
b) what are the roots for these values of k?

19. Use a polynomial to find three consecutive integers with a product of -504.

20. Find the exact roots of each equation.
a) $x^4 - 4x^3 + x^2 + 6x = 0$
b) $x^4 + 2x^3 - 7x^2 - 8x + 12 = 0$
c) $t^4 - 2t^3 - 11t^2 + 12t + 36 = 0$
d) $x^4 - 4x^2 + 3 = 0$
e) $x^4 - x^3 - 10x^2 + 10x + 12 = 0$
f) $x^4 - 1 = 0$
g) $2x^4 + 5x^3 + 3x^2 - x - 1 = 0$
h) $4y^4 - 8y^3 - 3y^2 + 5y + 2 = 0$

21. The dimensions of a rectangular solid are shown.

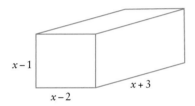

The volume of the solid is 42 cm^3. Find its dimensions using a polynomial method.

22. A toothpaste box has square ends. The length is 12 cm greater than the width. The volume of the box is 135 cm^3. What are the dimensions of the box?

23. A box holds two CD-ROMs and the instruction manual for a multimedia encyclopaedia. The width of the box is 15 cm greater than the height. The length of the box is 20 cm greater than the height. The volume of the box is 2500 cm^3. Find the dimensions of the box by factoring a polynomial.

24. A rectangular prism has dimensions 10 cm by 10 cm by 5 cm. When each dimension is increased by the same amount, the new volume is 1008 cm^3. What are the dimensions of the new prism?

25. The freight station at the Kwai Chung container port in Hong Kong is an enormous building in the shape of a rectangular prism.

The length approximately equals the width. The length is about three times the height. The volume of the building is about 0.009 km^3. Find the approximate dimensions of the building, in metres.

26. Application Selena and Carlos are building a sandbox for their community day care centre. The box is 12 times as wide as it is deep, and 1 m longer than it is wide. It holds 3 m^3 of sand when full. The wood they need costs $2/\text{m}^2$. How much will it cost in total?

27. Solve $x^5 + 3x^4 - 5x^3 - 15x^2 + 4x + 12 = 0$.

28. Write a cubic equation that has a real root of 7 and two imaginary roots.

29. Communication a) Suppose that 5, 2, and -3 are the solutions of a cubic equation. Sketch a graph of the corresponding cubic function. Is there more than one possible graph? Explain.
b) What other information would have to be specified to guarantee that only one graph is possible in part a)?

30. Communication The graph of a polynomial function intersects the x-axis at only three different points. Is it possible to say how many real roots it could have? Explain. If not, what further information would be needed?

31. a) Write a cubic function with x-intercepts of $\sqrt{5}$, $-\sqrt{5}$, and -1, and a y-intercept of -5.
b) Write a cubic function with the same x-intercepts as the function in part a), but with a y-intercept of -10. Explain your reasoning.

32. Inquiry/Problem Solving Decide whether each of the following statements is always true, sometimes true, or never true. Explain your reasoning.
a) A cubic equation has two real roots and one complex root.
b) A cubic equation has three roots.
c) A quartic equation has four complex roots.
d) A cubic equation has one rational root and two irrational roots.
e) A quartic equation has four equal irrational roots.
f) A quadratic equation has two equal complex roots.

33. a) Is it possible for a polynomial to have exactly one complex root? If so, construct an example. If not, explain why.
b) Is it possible for a polynomial to have an odd number of complex roots? If so, construct an example. If not, explain why.
c) What can you conclude about the number of complex roots of a polynomial from parts a) and b)? Explain.

34. a) If a polynomial equation of degree n has exactly one real root, what can you conclude about the value of n? Explain your reasoning.
b) If a polynomial equation of degree n has exactly two real roots, what can you conclude about the value of n? Explain your reasoning.

35. a) All of a polynomial's roots are real except for two, which are complex. Is it possible for the two complex roots to be $x = 1 + i$ and $x = 2 + i$? If so, construct a polynomial with such roots. If not, explain why.
b) All of a polynomial's roots are real except for two, which are complex. One of the complex roots is $x = 1 + i$. Is it possible to determine what the other complex root is? If so, determine the root. If not, explain why.
c) All of a polynomial's roots are real except for four, which are complex. Two of the complex roots are $x = 1 + i$ and $3 + 2i$. Is it possible to determine what the other complex roots are? If so, determine the roots. If not, explain why.

36. Use the results of questions 33, 34, and 35 to explain as much as you can about the properties of the complex roots of a polynomial function.

Historical Bite: Beyond the Quadratic Formula

The familiar formula for finding the roots of a general quadratic equation was first formally devised by the great Arabic mathematician Al-Khwarizmi (c. 780–850 A.D.), from whose name we get the word *algorithm*, in about 830 A.D. However, it was not until 700 years later that methods were found for solving general cubic and quartic equations, amid a bitter controversy over who had found the cubic method first. Much of the credit belongs to Niccolo Tartaglia (1499–1557), who wanted to keep his method a secret (perhaps because he lacked the financial support to get his work published), but in 1539 used it to win a public cubic-solving challenge.

Another Italian mathematician, Girolamo Cardano (1501–1576), heard of Tartaglia's victory and persuaded him to share the secret, promising to keep it between the two of them. However, Cardano then discovered that the essence of the cubic method had already been given by Scipione dal Ferro (1465–1526) in about 1515. Cardano decided to break his word to Tartaglia and publish the cubic method anyway, in his book *Ars Magna* of 1545. While Cardano should surely have given Tartaglia due credit, it is likely that Cardano had a better understanding of the method, particularly where it produced the square roots of negative numbers, which today we understand to be involved in complex roots of polynomial equations. Cardano did give credit to his own student, Lodovico Ferrari (1522–1565), for another highlight of *Ars Magna*, a complete method of solving quartic equations. No single formula gives solutions to any quartic, so Ferrari broke the method down into 20 cases!

Polynomial Functions and Inequalities

At the start of a log flume ride in an amusement park, an electric motor raises the log to the top of a lift hill. Then, the log descends under the influence of gravity. The log speeds up enough to carry it over the rest of the hills.

Investigate & Inquire: Solving a Quadratic Inequality

The purpose of this investigation is to determine over which regions of track the log flume ride is above or below certain heights.

1. As the log descends the lift hill, the function $h(d) = 0.01d^2 - 1.2d + 38$, $d \in [0, 100]$, models its height, $h(d)$, in metres, above the ground as a function of the horizontal distance, d, in metres, the log travels. Graph the function.

2. Find each of the following for $h(d)$.
a) the y-intercept   b) the range   c) the real zeros (if any)

3. Is $h(d)$ continuous?

4. What does each result in steps 2 and 3 mean in terms of the log flume ride?

5. When the log is above 18 m, the passengers can see a beautiful view of the surrounding area. Determine the interval(s) for which $h(d) \geq 18$.

6. As the log nears its lowest point, it passes through water. The surface of the water is about 2.5 m above the ground. On which interval(s) will the riders get wet?

For every polynomial expression, such as $x^3 + 4x^2 - 2x + 3$, we can write a corresponding polynomial function, in this case $f(x) = x^3 + 4x^2 - 2x + 3$. Polynomial functions have one or more values of x for which the value of the function is 0. Such values of x, which may be real or complex, are the zeros of the function and the solutions to the corresponding equation $f(x) = 0$ or $y = 0$. The real zeros of a function are the x-intercepts of its graph.

In this section we study the behaviour of functions over certain intervals. For example, for the function $y = 2x + 1$, we can state that $y > 0$ over the interval $x \in \left(-\dfrac{1}{2}, \infty\right)$.

Window variables:
$x \in [-4.7, 4.7]$,
$y \in [-3.1, 3.1]$
or use the ZDecimal instruction.

Example 1 Interpreting a Graph

For the polynomial function
$f(x) = x^4 - 3x^3 - x^2 + 3x$, determine
a) the domain and range
b) the real zeros
c) the y-intercept
d) the intervals where $f(x)$ is positive

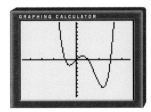

Window variables:
$x \in [-4.7, 4.7]$,
$y \in [-9.3, 9.3]$

e) the approximate coordinates of any local maximums or local minimums
f) any symmetry
g) Suppose that, for the interval $x \in [-2, 3]$, $f(x)$ represents the net worth of the Satori Department Store Corporation, in millions of dollars, at time x, where x is in years. The time $x = 0$ corresponds to now, $x = 1$ cuorresponds to one year from now, $x = -1$ corresponds to one year ago, and so on. Interpret the results of parts d) and e) in terms of the net worth of the company.

Solution

a) The domain is the set of real numbers. The lowest point on the graph has a y-coordinate of about –7. So, the approximate range is the real numbers for which $y \geq -7$.
b) The real zeros are the x-intercepts, –1, 0, 1, and 3.
c) The y-intercept is 0.
d) The intervals where $f(x)$ is positive are the sets of x-values for which the graph is above the x-axis. From the graph, the three intervals where $f(x) > 0$ are $(-\infty, -1)$, $(0, 1)$, and $(3, \infty)$.
e) From the graph, $f(x)$ has a local maximum at about $(0.5, 1)$, and local minimums at about $(-0.5, -1.5)$ and $(2.5, -7)$.
f) The graph has no even or odd symmetry, as we can see from the screen.
g) Between two years ago and one year ago, the company had positive net worth. Then, in the past year, the company was in debt (negative net worth), but this year the net worth will be positive again. However, for the next two years, the net worth will be negative.

The net worth of the company will peak six months from now at $1 million, but two and a half years from now will be the low point, when the company will be $7 million in debt.

Graphing a polynomial function manually is simpler if the function is written in factored form.

Example 2 Graphing a Function in Factored Form

Graph the function $f(x) = (x + 4)(x + 1)(x - 1)$. For $f(x)$, determine
a) the real zeros
b) the domain and range
c) the y-intercept
d) the intervals where $f(x) \leq 0$
e) any symmetry
f) the end behaviour
g) Suppose that, for the interval $x \in [-4, 2]$, $f(x)$ represents the acceleration, in units of g (which is approximately 10 m/s^2), of an experimental acrobatic jet at time x on its training run, where x is measured in minutes. Positive values of x correspond to times after which the jet has passed a tracking station, and negative values of x correspond to times before which the jet has passed the tracking station. If the jet's acceleration exceeds $5\,g$, the pilot will experience particular discomfort. When is the jet's acceleration greater than $5\,g$?

Solution

First, we use the factors to find the real zeros (x-intercepts) of the function, and then plot the corresponding points. Since $f(x) = 0$ when $x = -4$, $x = -1$, or $x = 1$, three points on the graph are $(-4, 0)$, $(-1, 0)$, and $(1, 0)$. We find values of the function that are between or beyond the zeros to find other points on the graph.

x	y
−5	−24
−4	0
−3	8
−2	6
−1	0
0	−4
1	0
2	18

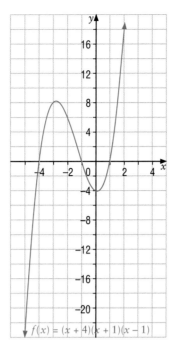

$f(x) = (x + 4)(x + 1)(x - 1)$

To graph the function on a graphing calculator, we can leave its formula in factored form.

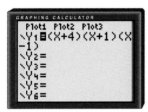
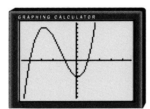

Window variables:
$x \in [-4.7, 4.7]$, $y \in [-9.3, 9.3]$

a) The real zeros are −4, −1, and 1.
b) The domain and range are the set of real numbers.
c) The y-intercept is −4.
d) The condition $f(x) \le 0$ is satisfied when the graph is on or below the x-axis. The intervals for which $f(x) \le 0$ are $(-\infty, -4]$ and $[-1, 1]$.
e) There is no even or odd symmetry, as we can see from the graph.
f) The left-most y-values are negative. The right-most y-values are positive.
g) From the graph, it appears that the acceleration is greater than $5\,g$ approximately in the intervals $x \in [-3.6, -1.8]$ and $x \in [1.4, 2]$. These are the time intervals when the discomfort from the acceleration will be worst.

The real zeros of polynomial functions, or the real roots of polynomial equations, may be distinct or equal. Recall that two equal roots of an equation are sometimes called a double root.

Example 3 Equal Roots

a) Graph the function $f(x) = 2x^3 + 5x^2$.
b) Verify that the equation $f(x) = 0$ has two roots that equal zero.

Solution

a) Graph the function manually or using a graphing calculator.

x	y
−3	−9
−2	4
−1	3
0	0
1	7

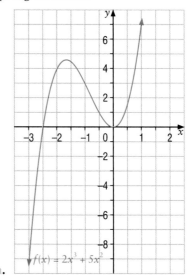

Window variables:
$x \in [-4.7, 4.7]$,
$y \in [-3.1, 3.1]$
or use the
ZDecimal instruction.

b) The graph suggests that the equation $f(x) = 0$ has a double root at $x = 0$.
To verify this, solve the equation $2x^3 + 5x^2 = 0$.

$$2x^3 + 5x^2 = 0$$
$$x(x)(2x + 5) = 0$$
$$x = 0 \text{ or } x = 0 \text{ or } 2x + 5 = 0$$
$$x = -\frac{5}{2}$$

The roots are 0, 0, and $-\dfrac{5}{2}$, so the equation $f(x) = 0$ has two roots that equal 0.

The graph of the function $y = x^2 - 2x - 8$ is shown.

The real zeros of the function are −2 and 4. When $x < -2$, the function is positive. When $-2 < x < 4$, the function is negative. When $x > 4$, the function is positive.

This example verifies that the value of a polynomial function can change sign only at a real zero. This is so because polynomial functions are continuous. For the y-values to change from positive to negative, or from negative to positive, the graph must cross the x-axis. At the crossing point, the y-value is zero.

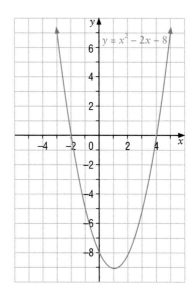

When the real zeros are put in numerical order on the x-axis, they divide the x-axis into intervals. In each interval, the function is either positive for all x-values or negative for all x-values.

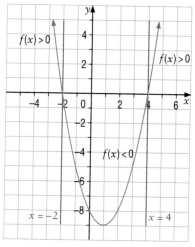

$f(x) < 0$ for $x \in (-2, 4)$,
$f(x) > 0$ for $x \in (-\infty, -2)$ and $x \in (4, \infty)$

Note that not all polynomial functions change sign at a real zero. An example is the function $y = x^2 - 6x + 9$, which has a double root at $x = 3$. In this example, the value of the function is positive both for $x < 3$ and for $x > 3$.

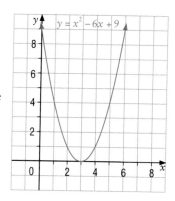

The sign changes of polynomial functions can be used to solve polynomial inequalities. The real zeros of the polynomial determine the **test intervals** of the inequality, in which points on a number line are tested to determine if they satisfy the inequality.

Example 4 Solving a Factorable Quadratic Inequality

Solve $x^2 + x < 6$.

Solution 1 Pencil and Paper Method

$x^2 + x < 6$
$x^2 + x - 6 < 0$
$(x + 3)(x - 2) < 0$

The zeros of the function $f(x) = (x + 3)(x - 2)$ are -3 and 2. The three test intervals are $(-\infty, -3)$, $(-3, 2)$, and $(2, \infty)$.
We choose an x-value in each test interval and determine the sign of $(x + 3)(x - 2)$.

In the test interval $(-\infty, -3)$, use $x = -4$.
$(x + 3)(x - 2) = (-4 + 3)(-4 - 2)$
$\qquad\qquad\qquad = 6$

So, $(x + 3)(x - 2)$ is not less than zero in this interval.

In the test interval $(-3, 2)$, use $x = 0$.

$$(x + 3)(x - 2) = (0 + 3)(0 - 2)$$
$$= -6$$

So, $(x + 3)(x - 2)$ is less than zero in this interval.

In the test interval $(2, \infty)$, use $x = 3$.

$$(x + 3)(x - 2) = (3 + 3)(3 - 2)$$
$$= 6$$

So, $(x + 3)(x - 2)$ is not less than zero in this interval.

The calculations performed above can be summarized using a chart.

	-3		2	
Interval	$(-\infty, -3)$	$(-3, 2)$		$(2, \infty)$
Test value	-4	0		3
$(x + 3)$	$-$	$+$		$+$
$(x - 2)$	$-$	$-$		$+$
Sign of $f(x)$	$+$	$-$		$+$

The two numbers that we have not tested are -3 and 2, which are the zeros of the equation $(x + 3)(x - 2) = 0$, or $x^2 + x = 6$, so they do not satisfy the inequality $x^2 + x < 6$ and they are not included in the solution.

Since $(x + 3)(x - 2) < 0$ in the interval $(-3, 2)$, the solution to the inequality $x^2 + x < 6$ is $x \in (-3, 2)$.

The solution can be graphed on a number line.

Solution 2 Graphing Calculator Method

$x^2 + x < 6$
$x^2 + x - 6 < 0$
We graph the function
$f(x) = x^2 + x - 6$ on a
graphing calculator.

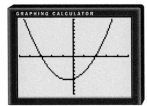

Window variables:
$x \in [-5, 5], y \in [-10, 10]$

Note that $f(x) < 0$ when the graph is below the x-axis. From the graph, we can see that the graph is below the x-axis when $-3 < x < 2$. So, the solution is $x \in (-3, 2)$.

Example 5 Solving a Factorable Cubic Inequality

Solve $x^3 + 3x^2 - x - 3 \geq 0$.

Solution 1 Pencil and Paper Method

We use the integral zero theorem to factor $x^3 + 3x^2 - x - 3$.
$f(x) = x^3 + 3x^2 - x - 3$
$f(1) = (1)^3 + 3(1)^2 - 1 - 3$
$\qquad = 0$
Therefore, $x - 1$ is a factor of $x^3 + 3x^2 - x - 3$.
Use long division to find another factor.

$$
\begin{array}{r}
x^2 + 4x + 3 \\
x - 1 \overline{\smash{)}\, x^3 + 3x^2 - x - 3} \\
\underline{x^3 - x^2} \\
4x^2 - x \\
\underline{4x^2 - 4x} \\
3x - 3 \\
\underline{3x - 3} \\
0
\end{array}
$$

Another factor is $x^2 + 4x + 3$. Factoring $x^2 + 4x + 3$ gives $(x + 3)(x + 1)$. So,
$x^3 + 3x^2 - x - 3 = (x + 3)(x + 1)(x - 1)$.

The zeros of the polynomial $f(x) = (x + 3)(x + 1)(x - 1)$ are -3, -1, and 1.
There are four test intervals: $(-\infty, -3)$, $(-3, -1)$, $(-1, 1)$, and $(1, \infty)$.

Choose an x-value in each test interval and determine the sign of $(x + 3)(x + 1)(x - 1)$. The results can be summarized using a chart. The three numbers that have not been tested are -3, -1, and 1. These numbers are the zeros of the equation $(x + 3)(x + 1)(x - 1) = 0$, or $x^3 + 3x^2 - x - 3 = 0$, so they satisfy the

		-3	-1	1	
Interval		$(-\infty, -3)$	$(-3, -1)$	$(-1, 1)$	$(1, \infty)$
Test value		-4	-2	0	2
$(x + 3)$		$-$	$+$	$+$	$+$
$(x + 1)$		$-$	$-$	$+$	$+$
$(x - 1)$		$-$	$-$	$-$	$+$
Sign of $f(x)$		$-$	$+$	$-$	$+$

inequality $x^3 + 3x^2 - x - 3 \geq 0$ and are included in the solution. Combining these numbers with the results from the table gives the solution $x \in [-3, -1]$ or $x \in [1, \infty)$.

Solution 2 Graphing Calculator Method

Another way of solving polynomial inequalities is by using the **TEST menu** of a graphing calculator. Enter the inequality in the Y= editor of your graphing calculator, using the $\geq$ symbol from the **TEST menu** ([2nd] [MATH]).

Go to Mode settings and set the calculator to Dot mode, and use the ZDecimal instruction to graph the inequality in the friendly window.

When the inequality is true, the graphing calculator plots the point 1. When it is false, the graphing calculator plots the point 0. Thus, from the screen, we can see that $x^3 + 3x^2 - x - 3 \geq 0$ for $x \in (-3, -1)$ or $x \in (1, \infty)$. To determine whether the endpoints are included, press TRACE and then move the cursor to each of the endpoints. If the calculator shows a value for y, then the endpoint is included. If the y-value is blank, then the endpoint is not included.

From the screen, we can see that the endpoint $x = 1$ is included. By tracing, we can also determine that the endpoints -3 and -1 are included. Thus, the solution to the inequality $x^3 + 3x^2 - x - 3 \geq 0$ is $x \in [-3, -1]$ or $x \in [1, \infty)$.

Example 6 Solving a Non-Factorable Inequality Using a Graphing Calculator

Solve $x^3 + 3x^2 - 4x - 4 < 0$, to the nearest hundredth.

Solution
Graph the function $f(x) = x^3 + 3x^2 - 4x - 4$.

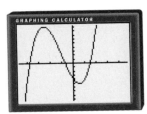

Window variables:
$x \in [-4.7, 4.7], y \in [-9.3, 9.3]$

Find the approximate values of the x-intercepts, to the nearest hundredth, using the Zero operation.

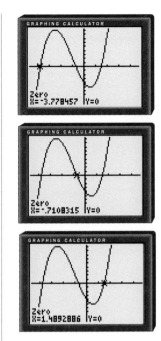

The x-intercepts are -3.78, -0.71, and 1.49, to the nearest hundredth.

$f(x) < 0$ when the graph is below the x-axis.

The graph is below the x-axis when $x < -3.78$ or $-0.71 < x < 1.49$. Thus, the solution to the inequality is approximately $x \in (-\infty, -3.78)$ or $x \in (-0.71, 1.49)$.

Key Concepts

- To graph a function given in factored form, use the factors to find the real zeros, or x-intercepts, of the function. Find several test points between and beyond the x-intercepts. Then, plot the x-intercepts and the test points. Join the points with a smooth curve.
- To solve a factorable polynomial inequality, determine the real zeros of the polynomial. Use the zeros to establish the test intervals, and then, test a convenient value within each test interval.
- To solve a non-factorable polynomial inequality, use a graphing calculator or graphing software to determine the approximate values of the x-intercepts. Then, use the graph to determine the solution.

Communicate Your Understanding

1. Describe how you would graph $f(x) = (x - 4)(x + 1)(x - 2)$, without using a graphing calculator or graphing software.

2. Describe how you would solve $x^2 + x - 2 > 0$.

3. Describe how you would solve a non-factorable polynomial inequality.

Practise

1. Use the graph to determine the domain and range, the approximate coordinates of any local maximums or minimums, and the *y*-intercept of each polynomial function.

a)

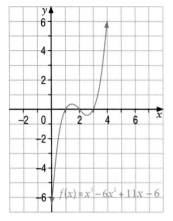

b)

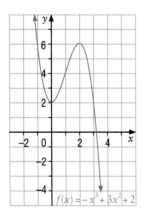

c)

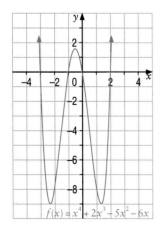

d)

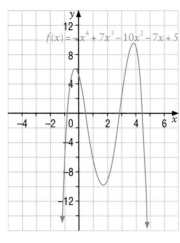

2. Use the graph to identify the real zeros of the polynomial function, and the intervals where $f(x) \geq 0$ and where $f(x) < 0$. Estimate zeros to the nearest tenth, if necessary.

a)

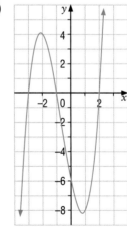

b)

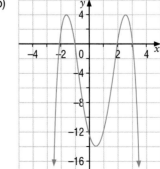

c)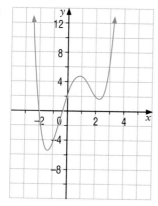

d)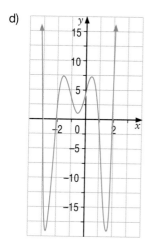

3. Graph each function and determine
i) any real zeros, to the nearest tenth,
if necessary
ii) the domain and range
iii) the y-intercept
iv) the approximate coordinates of any local maximums or local minimums
v) any symmetry
vi) the end behaviour
a) $f(x) = x^2(x^2 - 4)$
b) $y = x^2(x^2 + 4)$
c) $y = x^3 - 3x^2 - 2x$
d) $k(x) = x^3 + 3x + 4$
e) $y = -x^4 + 6$
f) $f(x) = -x^5 + 4x^2$
g) $f(x) = (x - 4)(x + 1)(x + 1)$
h) $f(x) = -(x - 2)(x - 4)(x - 6)$
i) $f(x) = x(x - 3)(x + 2)(x - 1)$
j) $f(x) = -x(x - 1)(x + 3)(x + 3)$

4. Graph each function. Label all the zeros, including the multiple zeros.
a) $f(x) = 3x^3 - 4x^2$
b) $g(x) = x^4 + 2x^3 + x^2$
c) $h(x) = x^3 - 3x^2 + 3x - 1$
d) $k(x) = x^5 - 6x^4 + 12x^3 - 8x^2$

5. Application Solve each inequality using the method of your choice. Graph each solution on a number line.
a) $(x - 3)(x + 2) < 0$
b) $(2x - 1)(2x + 3) \leq 0$
c) $x^2 - 3x \leq 10$
d) $2x^2 - 7x + 3 \geq 0$
e) $x(x - 2)(x - 2) \geq 0$
f) $(2x - 1)(x + 1)(x - 2) \leq 0$
g) $x(x - 2)(x + 1)(x + 5) \geq 0$
h) $x^3 - 2x^2 - x \geq -2$
i) $2x^3 - x^2 > 6x$

6. Write a short paragraph explaining which method you prefer to use when solving inequalities.

7. Solve each non-factorable inequality, to the nearest hundredth.
a) $x^2 - 5 > 0$
b) $2x^2 - x - 2 \geq 0$
c) $2x^2 + 6x + 3 > 0$
d) $x^3 + 4 > 0$
e) $x^3 - 6x^2 + 10x - 4 \leq 0$
f) $3x^3 + 8x^2 - x < 2$
g) $x^4 + 2x^3 - 4x^2 - 6x \leq -3$

Apply, Solve, Communicate

B **8.** Inquiry/Problem Solving Use the graphs of the two functions f and g to identify the approximate intervals where each of the following is true. Estimate to the nearest tenth, if necessary.
a) $f(x) \leq g(x)$

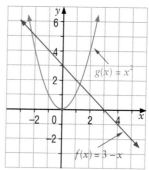

b) $f(x) > g(x)$

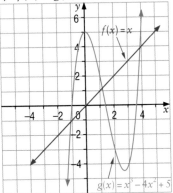

c) $f(x) \geq g(x)$

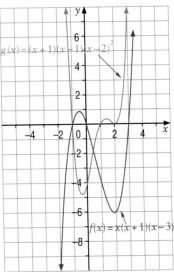

d) $f(x) < g(x)$

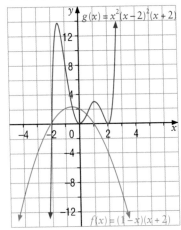

9. Application The cross section of part of a ravine can be approximated by the function $h(x) = x^3 - 6x^2 + 4x + 20$, $x \in [0, 5]$, where $h(x)$, in metres, is the height, and x, in metres, is the width of the ravine.
a) Graph the function using the given domain and a suitable range.
b) Find the vertical distance between the highest and lowest points on this part of the ravine, to the nearest tenth of a metre.

10. a) For a cylinder whose height is twice its radius, write a function to express the volume, V, in terms of the radius, r.
b) Graph the function.
c) Determine the domain and range of the function.

11. Inquiry/Problem Solving A solid is made from 3 cubes, each having a side length of x.

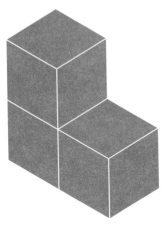

a) Determine a function $A(x)$ that represents the surface area, and a function $V(x)$ that represents the volume of the solid. Graph the functions.
b) For what value of x will the surface area and the volume have the same numerical value?
c) For what values of x will the numerical value of the surface area be greater than the numerical value of the volume? less than the numerical value of the volume?
d) Describe how the graph of $A(x) - V(x)$ can be used to answer parts b) and c).

12. Application The rate of flow of light energy is measured in lumens, represented by the symbol lm. For example, a 100-W incandescent light bulb emits about 1750 lm. The rate, $L(T)$, in lumens, at which a firefly produces light energy is related to the air temperature, T, in degrees Celsius, by the function $L(T) = 10 + 0.3T + 0.4T^2 - 0.01T^3$.

a) What is a realistic domain for the function?

b) Graph the function.

c) Use your graph to find the rate at which a firefly produces light energy at 25°C. Round your answer to the nearest 10 lm.

d) At what temperature, to the nearest degree Celsius, do fireflies produce light energy at the greatest rate?

13. A triangular prism can be used to refract light and separate white light into its component colours.

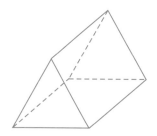

a) Write a polynomial function to represent the volume, $V(x)$, in cubic centimetres, of an equilateral triangular prism with all edges x centimetres long.

b) What is the domain of this function?

c) Graph the function.

d) For a prism with all the edges 5 cm long, what is the volume, to the nearest tenth of a centimetre?

e) Find the edge length, to the nearest tenth of a centimetre, for a prism of volume 20 cm³.

14. Communication a) Solve the inequality $(x + 3)(x + 1)(x - 1) > 0$.

b) A rectangular prism has the dimensions shown. Determine the possible values of x for the rectangular prism.

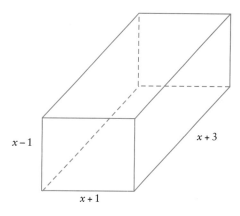

c) Compare the results from parts a) and b), and explain any differences.

15. Write a quadratic inequality with each of the following solutions.

a) $x \in [-1, 2]$

b) $x \in \left(-\infty, -\dfrac{1}{2}\right)$ or $x \in (4, \infty)$

C **16.** Write three quadratic inequalities that have no solution over the real numbers.

17. Find the solutions that satisfy both $x^2 + 4x - 5 > 0$ and $x^2 + 6x - 7 \le 0$.

18. Find the solutions that satisfy both $x^3 + x^2 - 20x \le 0$ and $x^3 + 4x^2 - 11x + 30 < 0$.

19. A cylindrical frame consisting of three circles and four vertical supports is built from 6 m of wire, as shown. The frame is then covered with paper to form a closed cylinder.

a) Determine expressions for the radius r, the surface area S, and the enclosed volume V of the resulting cylinder, in terms of the height h.

b) Determine the restriction on the height if the radius of the cylinder must be at least 10 cm.

A company that manufactures camping trailers estimates that the annual cost, $C(x)$, in dollars, of manufacturing x trailers is given by the function $C(x) = 200\,000 + 100x + 5x^2$. The company's annual revenue, $R(x)$, in dollars, from sales of trailers is given by $R(x) = 8000x - 0.02x^3$.

a) Graph both functions using the domain $x \in [0, 700]$ and the range $y \in [0, 2\,000\,000]$.

b) What is the minimum number of trailers that must be sold for the company to make a profit?

c) What is the maximum number of trailers that the company can sell and still make a profit?

d) Write an equation to represent the profit function, $P(x)$.

e) Graph the profit function. Use the graph to determine the maximum profit the company can make, to the nearest $10\,000, and the number of trailers that must be manufactured to give this profit.

f) How do the graphs show that profits can never be greater than revenues?

g) Can the company make a profit if costs are greater than revenues? if costs are greater than profits? Explain.

Historical Bite: The Quintic Conundrum

With general methods already found for solving quadratic, cubic, and quartic equations, many mathematicians have tried without success to find such a method for quintic equations. The last to do so was the Danish mathematician Niels Abel (1802–1829), who in 1821 wrote a paper presenting what he believed to be a general method for quintic solutions. However, in checking his own work by substituting a numerical example, Abel found a mistake in his theory. Nothing daunted, Abel pursued a different approach to the problem, and in 1824 was able to publish a remarkable conclusion: in the quintic case, no general solution method can exist. His proof of this fact used the theory of permutations of roots, which was an ancestor of modern group theory.

Investigating Math: Finite Differences

The **method of finite differences** can be used to examine the nature of change in polynomial functions, and to determine the equation of a polynomial function given a table of values. The most straightforward way to use finite differences is to have equally-spaced x-values in a table of values. Then the **first differences** are calculated by subtracting consecutive y-values, **second differences** are calculated by subtracting consecutive first differences, and so on. Here is an example.

x	y	Differences 1st	Differences 2nd	Differences 3rd
0	0			
		$1 - 0 = 1$		
1	1		$7 - 1 = 6$	
		$8 - 1 = 7$		$12 - 6 = 6$
2	8		$19 - 7 = 12$	
		$27 - 8 = 19$		$18 - 12 = 6$
3	27		$37 - 19 = 18$	
		$64 - 27 = 37$		$24 - 18 = 6$
4	64		$61 - 37 = 24$	
		$125 - 64 = 61$		
5	125			

Note that the function specified in the table of values is a cubic function, $y = x^3$, and the third differences are constant.

Reviewing Linear Functions, $y = mx + b$

1. Construct a difference table (first differences only) for each linear function.

a) $y = 3x - 2$ b) $y = -x + 3$ c) $y = mx + b$

2. How are the first differences for each function related to the equation of the function?

3. For any linear function, why are the differences between successive y-values the same? What does this value represent?

4. Where does the constant term for each equation occur in the table of values?

5. Describe how you can use a table of values for a linear function and finite differences to write an equation for the function.

6. Use finite differences to write an equation for each function.

a)

x	y
-2	-1
-1	1
0	3
1	5
2	7
3	9

b)

x	y
-2	-14
-1	-9
0	-4
1	1
2	6
3	11

c)

x	y
-2	14
-1	8
0	2
1	-4
2	-10
3	-16

d)

x	y
-2	6
-1	5.5
0	5
1	4.5
2	4
3	3.5

7. Check the results for question 6 using regression on a graphing calculator or graphing software.

Reviewing Quadratic Functions, $y = ax^2 + bx + c$

1. Construct a difference table (first and second differences only) for each quadratic function.

a) $y = x^2 + 1$ b) $y = 2x^2 - 3$ c) $y = 3x^2 - x + 2$

2. What is true about the second differences in each table?

3. a) Make and test a conjecture relating the second difference and the value of a, for the general quadratic function $ax^2 + bx + c$.
b) Construct a difference table for the general quadratic function.
c) Using the results from part b) and the tables you completed in question 1, describe how you can use a table of finite differences to calculate the values of a, b, and c.

4. a) Construct a difference table using the points (-3, 10), (-2, 3), (-1, 0), (0, 1), (1, 6), (2, 15) and (3, 28).
b) Find c.
c) Find a.
d) Find b.
e) Write an equation for the quadratic function.

5. Write an equation for each function using finite differences.

a)

x	y
-2	3
-1	2
0	3
1	6
2	11
3	18

b)

x	y
-2	16
-1	3
0	-2
1	1
2	12
3	31

c)

x	y
-2	-10
-1	-1
0	4
1	5
2	2
3	-5

d)

x	y
-2	-12
-1	-5
0	0
1	3
2	4
3	3

6. Check your results in question 5 using regression on your graphing calculator or graphing software.

Investigating Cubic Functions, $y = ax^3 + bx^2 + cx + d$

1. Construct a difference table for each cubic function. Continue each table until constant differences are reached.

a) $y = x^3 - x^2 + 2x + 1$

b) $y = 2x^3 - 3x + 4$

2. a) For a cubic function, in which column are the differences equal?

b) Make and test a conjecture relating the third differences and the value of a.

3. a) Construct a difference table for the general cubic function, $y = ax^3 + bx^2 + cx + d$.

b) Using your results from part a) and the tables you completed in question 1, describe how you can use a table of finite differences to calculate the values of a, b, c, and d.

4. a) Construct a difference table using the points $(-3, -119)$, $(-2, -48)$, $(-1, -13)$, $(0, -2)$, $(1, -3)$, $(2, -4)$ and $(3, 7)$.

b) Find d.

c) Find a.

d) Find b.

e) Find c.

f) Write an equation for the cubic function.

5. Write an equation for each function.

a)

x	y
-2	11
-1	8
0	3
1	2
2	11
3	36

b)

x	y
-2	-352
-1	-86
0	2
1	8
2	28
3	158

c)

x	y
-2	18
-1	0
0	-4
1	0
2	6
3	8

d)

x	y
-2	6
-1	-10
0	-8
1	-6
2	-22
3	-74

6. Check your results for question 5 using regression on your graphing calculator or graphing software.

Investigating Quartic Functions, $y = ax^4 + bx^3 + cx^2 + dx + e$

1. Construct a difference table for each quartic function.

a) $y = x^4 - 2x^3 - 3x^2 + 1$

b) $y = 2x^4 + x^3 + x^2 - 5$

2. a) For a quartic function, in which column are the differences equal?

b) Make a conjecture about which differences will be equal for a function of degree n.

c) Make and test a conjecture relating the fourth differences and the value of a.

3. a) Construct a difference table for the general quartic function, $y = ax^4 + bx^3 + cx^2 + dx + e$.

b) Using your results from part a) and the tables you completed in question 1, describe how you can use a table of finite differences to calculate the values of a, b, c, d, and e.

4. a) Construct a difference table using the points $(-3, 123)$, $(-2, 29)$, $(-1, 1)$, $(0, -3)$, $(1, -1)$, $(2, 13)$ and $(3, 69)$.
b) Find e. **c)** Find a.
d) Find b. **e)** Find c.
f) Find d. **g)** Write an equation for the quartic function.

5. Write an equation for each function.

a)
x	y
-2	36
-1	7
0	4
1	3
2	4
3	31

b)
x	y
-2	9
-1	-9
0	-7
1	-9
2	9
3	119

c)
x	y
-2	-24
-1	-4
0	-6
1	0
2	20
3	36

6. Check your results for question 5 using regression on a graphing calculator or graphing software.

Writing Equations

1. Write an equation for each function.

a)
x	y
-2	17
-1	11
0	7
1	5
2	5
3	7

b)
x	y
-2	0
-1	-3
0	0
1	-3
2	0
3	45

c)
x	y
-2	-3
-1	0
0	-1
1	0
2	9
3	32

d)
x	y
-2	-21
-1	4
0	7
1	6
2	-5
3	-56

e)
x	y
-2	22
-1	7
0	2
1	7
2	22
3	47

f)
x	y
-2	52
-1	11
0	0
1	7
2	20
3	27

g)
x	y
-2	-21
-1	6
0	7
1	0
2	3
3	34

h)
x	y
-2	-25
-1	-12
0	-5
1	-4
2	-9
3	-20

2. a) Explain what first differences indicate about the graph of a function.
b) Explain what higher differences indicate about the graph of a function.
c) Explain how the degree of a polynomial can be determined from a difference table.
d) Explain how to use finite differences and a table of values to determine the equation of a polynomial function. If the polynomial is of degree n, how many entries are needed in the table of values?

Investigating Math: Determining Equations of Graphs

Given the graph of a polynomial function and the coordinates of points on the graph, we discuss four ways to determine an equation of the graph. The methods are
a) using the zeros of the function and one other point
b) using the regression feature on a graphing calculator or graphing software
c) using finite differences
d) using trial-and-error on a graphing calculator or graphing software
The method chosen may depend on the coordinates of the given points.

Determining an Equation Using the Zeros of the Function

1. a) The graph of a cubic function is shown. The graph has *x*-intercepts −3, −1, and 2, and *y*-intercept −6. What are three factors of the polynomial?
b) Write the equation of the family of cubic functions whose graphs have *x*-intercepts −3, −1, and 2.
c) Use this equation and the *y*-intercept to determine the equation of the function graphed in part a).

2. Can the regression feature on a graphing calculator or graphing software be used to determine an equation of the function? Explain.

Window variables:
$x \in [-4.7, 4.7]$,
$y \in [-9.3, 9.3]$

3. Can finite differences be used to determine an equation of the function? Explain.

4. Write the equations, in expanded form, of the families of functions whose graphs have the same *x*-intercepts as those shown.

a)
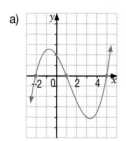

b)
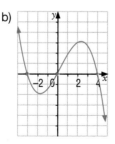

c)
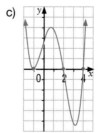

d)
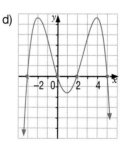

Determining an Equation Using Regression

1. The graph of a cubic function is shown. The points (1, 24), (2, 12), (3, 0), and (6, 24) lie on the graph. Use the regression feature on a graphing calculator or graphing software to determine an equation of the function.

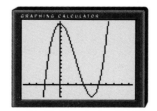

Window variables:
$x \in [-4.7, 9.4]$,
$y \in [-6.2, 31]$

2. Can finite differences be used to determine the equation of the function? Explain.

3. Can the zeros of the function be used to determine an equation? Explain.

4. Use the regression feature on a graphing calculator or graphing software to determine an equation of each function with the given points.
a) a quadratic function with points (–3, 28), (1, 4), (3, 4)
b) a cubic function with points (–4, 1), (–1, 1), (1, 1), (2, 19)
c) a cubic function with points (–3, 36), (0, 3), (1, 4), (3, –12)
d) a quartic function with points (–3, –40), (–2, 0), (0, –4), (2, 0), (3, –40)

Determining an Equation Using Finite Differences

1. The graph of a cubic function is shown. The table gives the coordinates of four points on the graph. Use finite differences to determine an equation of the function.

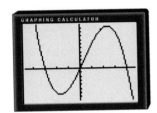

Window variables:
$x \in [-4.7, 4.7]$,
$y \in [-15.5, 21.7]$

x	y
–1	–10
0	0
1	12
2	20
3	18

2. Can the regression feature on a graphing calculator or graphing software be used to determine an equation of the function? Explain.

3. Use finite differences to determine an equation for each function.

a)

x	y
–3	–22
–2	–4
–1	2
0	2
1	2
2	8
3	26

b)

x	y
–3	60
–2	20
–1	0
0	–6
1	–4
2	0
3	0

c)

x	y
–3	–42
–2	0
–1	20
0	0
1	–54
2	–112
3	–120

d)

x	y
–3	–49
–2	0
–1	–25
0	–64
1	–81
2	–64
3	–25

Determining an Equation Using Trial-and-Error on a Graphing Calculator or Graphing Software

1. a) The graph of a cubic function is shown. The table gives the coordinates of seven points on the graph.

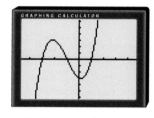

GRAPHING CALCULATOR

Window variables:
$x \in [-4.7, 4.7]$,
$y \in [-6.2, 6.2]$

x	y
−4	−15
−3	0
−2	3
−1	0
0	−3
1	0
2	15

b) Enter the data as two lists on your graphing calculator or graphing software.
c) Make a scatter plot of the data.
d) By entering equations in the function editor and graphing them, use trial-and-error to fit the equation of a cubic function in the form $y = ax^3 + bx^2 + cx + d$, where a, b, c, and d are integers, to the scatter plot.

2. Use trial-and-error with a graphing calculator or graphing software to determine an equation for each function in the form $y = ax^3 + bx^2 + cx + d$, where a, b, c, and d are integers, or in the form $y = ax^4 + bx^3 + cx^2 + dx + e$, where a, b, c, d, and e are integers, for the given points.
a) cubic function   **b)** cubic function   **c)** quartic function   **d)** quartic function

x	y
−2	−6
−1	1
0	2
2	10
3	29

x	y
−2	−8
−1	0
0	0
1	−2
3	12

x	y
−3	12
−1	−3
0	−4
1	−3
2	12
3	77

x	y
−3	25
−2	0
−1	9
0	16
1	9
2	0
4	144

3. Assess the advantages and disadvantages of each method discussed in this section. Are some methods more appropriate than others in certain circumstances? Explain.

Technology Extension

The Graph of a Cubic Function Using TI InterActive!™

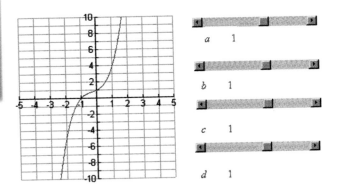

Web Connection

A trial version of TI InterActive!™ is provided by the manufacturer. Go to **www.mcgrawhill.ca/links/CAF12** and follow the instructions there.

Create a graph with $y1(x) := a*x^3 + b*x^2 + c*x + d$. Format the graph with the following window settings: $x\text{Min} = -5$, $x\text{Max} = 5$, $y\text{Min} = -10$, $y\text{Max} = 10$. Use a slider for each of the parameters a, b, c, and d. Give each slider an initial value of 1 and allow each one to vary from -5 to 5, with steps of 1.

1. What is the effect of moving the slider for d?

2. The graph shown has only one x-intercept. Which values will have to be changed in order to produce a graph with two x-intercepts? three x-intercepts?

3. Position the sliders so that the graph has x-intercepts of -3, -1, and 2. Is there an algebraic method that will help with this problem? Is there only one graph with these properties? Explain.

Algebraic Manipulations

Set up a math box to do the following polynomial division question.

$$\frac{6 \cdot x^3 - 19 \cdot x^2 + 18 \cdot x - 20}{2 \cdot x - 5}$$

$$3 \cdot x^2 - 2 \cdot x + 4$$

Consider the polynomial $f(x) = x^3 + x^2 - 4x + 4$. The factors of 4 are ± 1, ± 2, and ± 4, so the possible factors of the polynomial are $(x + 1)$, $(x - 1)$, $(x + 2)$, $(x - 2)$, $(x + 4)$, and $(x - 4)$. Below, we test the factor $(x + 1)$ in two different ways.

First, define the function $f(x)$ in TI InterActive!™.

$$f(x) := x^3 + x^2 - 4 \cdot x - 4 \qquad \text{"Done"}$$

Use the factor theorem.

$$f(-1) \qquad 0$$

Next, divide by $(x + 1)$.

$$\frac{f(x)}{x + 1} \qquad x^2 - 4$$

Thus, $(x + 1)$ is a factor of $f(x)$.

Repeat this procedure for each of the other factors listed and then write $x^3 + x^2 - 4x + 4$ in factored form.

If we are given any two distinct points in the plane, we can find a line (a first-degree function) whose graph passes through those two points.

1. Since two points define a first-degree function, do three points define a second-degree (quadratic) function? Do four points define a third-degree (cubic) function? Explain.

We have discussed several methods for finding the equation of a function given several points on a graph, including finite differences and regression on a graphing calculator. In this investigation, we discuss another method: using an **interpolating polynomial**.

Example

Find a polynomial that passes through the points $(-2, -1)$, $(-1, 7)$, $(2, -5)$, $(3, -1)$.

Solution

Since we are given four points, we will try to find a cubic polynomial that goes through all the points.

We can solve this problem by expressing the unknown polynomial in the form $P(x) = a_0 + a_1(x + 2) + a_2(x + 2)(x + 1) + a_3(x + 2)(x + 1)(x - 2)$. Note the relationship between the factors in the polynomial and the x-values of the first three given points.

$P(-2) = -1$
$a_0 + a_1(0) + a_2(0) + a_3(0) = -1$
$a_0 = -1$

$P(-1) = 7$
$a_0 + a_1(-1 + 2) + a_2(0) + a_3(0) = 7$
$-1 + a_1 = 7$
$a_1 = 8$

$P(2) = -5$
$a_0 + a_1(2 + 2) + a_2(2 + 2)(2 + 1) + a_3(0) = -5$
$-1 + (8)(4) + 12a_2 = -5$
$12a_2 = -36$
$a_2 = -3$

$P(3) = -1$
$a_0 + a_1(3 + 2) + a_2(3 + 2)(3 + 1) + a_3(3 + 2)(3 + 1)(3 - 2) = -1$
$-1 + (8)(5) + (-3)(20) + 20a_3 = -1$
$20a_3 = 20$
$a_3 = 1$

Thus,
$P(x) = -1 + 8(x + 2) - 3(x + 2)(x + 1) + (x + 2)(x + 1)(x - 1)$
$\quad = x^3 - 2x^2 - 5x + 5$

Check that the four given points satisfy the equation. Alternatively, check this equation using a graphing calculator.

In general, the interpolating polynomial for a set of points is given by

$$P(x) = a_0 + a_1(x - x_0) + a_2(x - x_0)(x - x_1) + \cdots + a_n(x - x_0)(x - x_1)(x - x_2) \cdots (x - x_{n-1})$$

2. Explain the reasoning behind the choice of factors in the interpolating polynomial.

3. Find a polynomial equation that passes through $(-1, 3)$, $(0, 1)$, $(1, 1)$, and $(2, 9)$. Verify the equation.

4. Find a polynomial equation that passes through: $(-2, -2)$, $(-1, 1)$, $(0, 6)$, $(1, 1)$, and $(2, -2)$. Verify the equation.

5. Is it possible to use this method to find an equation of a polynomial with roots or x-intercepts at -1, 3, 5, and 7? If so, find such an equation and verify it. If not, explain why.

6. What conditions must exist for it to be possible to use the general form of the interpolating polynomial?

Historical Bite: The Triumph and Tragedy of Evariste Galois

Although Niels Abel had proved that there is no solution of the general quintic equation in 1824, the first mathematician to work out the full theory of polynomial equations and their related permutation groups, of which Abel's result is just one part, was Evariste Galois. Born in 1811, Galois accomplished an extraordinary body of work in a lifetime cut tragically short. Galois was often frustrated by lack of acceptance for his genius and was never the most emotionally stable of young men. After the suicide of his father, who had been falsely accused in a political scandal, Galois fell into depression and despair, and in 1831 died of his wounds after getting into a duel over a young woman. Galois' papers were eventually published in 1846, and the complete body of polynomial mathematics they contain is still known as Galois theory, in his honour.

Review of Key Concepts

2.1 Investigating Math: Polynomial Functions On a Graphing Calculator

Refer to page 42.

1. Graph each of the following functions and
i) determine the type and number of x-intercepts
ii) describe the behaviour near the x-intercepts
iii) determine the type and number of turning points
iv) describe the end behaviours
v) describe any symmetry
a) $f(x) = x(x - 2)(x + 3)$
b) $f(x) = -(x + 1)(x - 1)(x - 3)$
c) $f(x) = x(x + 2)(x - 2)(x + 4)$
d) $f(x) = x^3 + x^2 - 20x$
e) $f(x) = -x^4 + 3x^2 + 4$

2. A cone is circumscribed around a sphere. The radius of the sphere is 5 units.

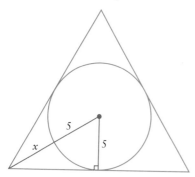

a) Write a formula for the volume, V, of the cone in terms of x. What kind of function is V?
b) Determine the roots of the function in part a). Do the roots have any geometrical meaning? Explain.
c) What is the domain of the function in part a)?

2.2 Dividing a Polynomial by a Polynomial

Refer to the Key Concepts on page 51.
3. Divide. State any restrictions on the variables.
a) $(x^2 + 10x + 16) \div (x + 2)$
b) $(y^3 + y^2 - 2) \div (y - 1)$
c) $(4m^2 - 1 + 4m) \div (2m + 3)$
d) $(x^3 - 3x - 9 + x^2) \div (x + 3)$
e) $(3y^3 - 2y^2 + 12y - 9) \div (y^2 + 2)$

4. The area of a business card can be represented by the expression $28x^2 - 15x + 2$, and the length by the expression $7x - 2$.
a) Write an expression that represents the width.
b) If x represents 13 mm, what are the dimensions of the business card, in millimetres?

5. Divide. State any restrictions on the variable.
a) $(x^3 + 2x^2 - 4x - 3) \div (x + 3)$
b) $(2x^3 - 7x^2 - 7x + 5) \div (2x - 1)$
c) $(15x - 4x^3 - 9x^2 + 3x^4 - 4) \div (3x - 4)$

2.3 The Remainder Theorem

Refer to the Key Concepts on page 58.
6. Use the remainder theorem to determine the remainder for each division.
a) $(x^2 + 5x - 8) \div (x - 2)$
b) $(3m^2 + 7m + 1) \div (m + 3)$
c) $(y^3 - 5y^2 - 3y + 1) \div (y + 1)$
d) $(2x^2 + 5x + 11) \div (2x - 1)$
e) $(8y^3 + 12y^2 - 4y + 5) \div (2y + 3)$

7. For each polynomial, find the value of k if the remainder is -1.
a) $(x^3 - 4x^2 + kx - 2) \div (x - 1)$
b) $(x^3 - 3x^2 - 6x + k) \div (x + 2)$

8. Graziella has recently written a book. Her publisher models the cumulative total number of copies sold, $C(t)$, t days after the book is released, by the formula $C(t) = 0.5t^2 + 20t + 50$, where $t \in [0, 30]$.
a) Explain the strengths and weaknesses of the formula for $C(t)$. Do you think that it is an exact formula or an approximation? Explain.
b) Divide $C(t)$ by $t - 10$. State the quotient $Q(t)$ and the remainder R. Explain the meaning of $Q(t)$ and R.
c) Do you think that the same formula for $C(t)$ is still valid for $t \geq 30$? Explain.
d) A book can be marketed as a bestseller in Canada if 5000 copies are sold. Does Graziella's book become a bestseller in the first month after it is released? If so, when does this occur? If not, when will it become a bestseller if the formula is still valid for $t \geq 30$?

9. Find the integer k such that
a) $x - 2$ divides $3x^3 - 2x^2 + x + k$ evenly
b) the remainder is -15 when $8x^3 + 6x^2 + 2x + k$ is divided by $2x + 3$
c) the remainder is 10 when $4x^2 + kx - 15$ is divided by $x + 5$

2.4 The Factor Theorem

Refer to the Key Concepts on page 67.
10. Show that the binomial is a factor of the polynomial.
a) $x^3 - 2x^2 - 5x + 6$; $x - 1$
b) $y^4 + 4y^3 - 9y^2 - 16y + 20$; $y + 2$
c) $2n^3 - n^2 - 4n + 3$; $2n + 3$
d) $3z^3 + 17z^2 + 18z - 8$; $3z - 1$

11. Factor completely.
a) $x^3 - x^2 - 5x - 3$
b) $x^3 + 5x^2 + 3x - 4$
c) $2x^3 - x^2 - 2x + 1$
d) $3x^3 + 13x^2 - 16$

12. The volume of a rectangular prism is given by $V = 2x^3 - x^2 - 22x - 24$. Determine possible polynomial expressions for the dimensions of the prism.

2.5 Roots of Polynomial Equations

Refer to the Key Concepts on page 78.
13. Solve and check.
a) $y^3 = 9y$
b) $n^3 - 3n - 2 = 0$
c) $3w^2 + 11w = 2w^3 + 6$
d) $3x^3 - 2 = 8x^3 - 7x$

14. Find the exact roots.
a) $x^3 - 3x^2 + x + 1 = 0$
b) $4y^3 - 19y = 6$
c) $x^3 + x^2 + 16x + 16 = 0$
d) $m^3 - m^2 = 2m + 12$

15. A cereal box is a rectangular prism with a volume of 2500 cm^3. The box is 4 times as wide as it is deep, and 5 cm taller than it is wide. What are the dimensions of the box?

16. Recall that the value, A, of an initial investment of P dollars with interest of i per month, compounded monthly, is $A = P(1 + i)^n$.

a) Suppose that P is a constant. What is a reasonable domain for the function $A = P(1 + i)^n$ for ordinary investments?
b) Does the function in part a) have any zeros in the domain you determined in part a)? If so, determine the zeros and explain what they mean. If not, explain why none are expected.
c) Some people think that our environment would be better preserved if interest rates were typically negative. For example, there is currently an incentive to cut down trees, sell the wood, and then invest the money, since the money will grow if interest rates are positive. However, if interest rates were negative, there would be a greater incentive to protect forests, since the money obtained by selling wood would only decline if invested.
   i) Repeat part b) if interest rates are allowed to be negative.
   ii) Write a short essay discussing the implications of negative interest rates and whether you think they would be a good idea.

2.6 Polynomial Functions and Inequalities

Refer to the Key Concepts on page 91.
17. Graph each function and determine
i) the domain and range
ii) the y-intercept
iii) any real zeros
iv) the intervals where $f(x) > 0$ and $f(x) \le 0$
v) any symmetry
vi) the end behaviour
a) $f(x) = x(x + 4)(x - 4)$
b) $f(x) = x(x - 1)(x + 1)(x - 2)$
c) $f(x) = (x - 2)(x + 2)(x + 4)$
d) $f(x) = -(x + 2)(x - 3)(x - 5)$
e) $f(x) = -x(x - 3)(x + 1)(x + 4)$

18. Graph each function and determine
i) the domain and range
ii) the y-intercept
iii) any real zeros, to the nearest tenth, if necessary
iv) the approximate coordinates of any local maximums or local minimums
v) any symmetry
vi) the end behaviour
a) $f(x) = x^2(x^2 - 9)$
b) $f(x) = x^2(x - 5)$
c) $y = -x(x^2 - 4)$
d) $y = (x^2 - 9)(x^2 - 1)$

e) $f(x) = x^4 - 2$ f) $f(x) = -x^3 - 3x^2$
g) $y = -x^3 + 3x^2 - x$ h) $y = x^3 - x^2 - 2x - 3$

19. Solve each inequality.
a) $x(x + 3) > 0$
b) $(x + 4)(x - 1) < 0$
c) $x^2 + 6x \le -9$
d) $(x + 2)(x - 2)(x + 4) \ge 0$
e) $x^3 - 2x^2 - 5x > 6$

20. Solve the following non-factorable inequalities, to the nearest hundredth, using a graphing calculator.
a) $x^2 + x - 4 > 0$ b) $-3x^2 + x \le 7$
c) $x^3 - 3x^2 \ge -1$ d) $x^4 - x^2 < 2$

21. Doctors determine that, for a certain hospitalized patient, the normal range for blood sugar is between 2.5 mmol/L and 25 mmol/L. The blood sugar level, $B(t)$, for this patient can be modelled by the formula $B(t) = 0.2t^4 - 2.6t^3 + 11.3t^2 - 18t + 11$, $t \in [0, 8]$ where t is measured in hours and $B(t)$ is measured in mmol/L. If the blood sugar is outside the normal range, doctors must take action to help the patient. When is the blood sugar outside the normal range?

2.7 Investigating Math: Finite Differences

Refer to page 97.
22. a) Construct a difference table using the points $(-3, 40)$, $(-1, 24)$, $(1, 0)$, $(3, 16)$, $(5, 120)$, $(7, 360)$, and $(9, 784)$.
b) Of what degree is this polynomial function? Explain.
c) Determine the coefficients of the terms.
d) Write an equation for this function.

23. Write an equation for each function.

a)

x	y
-3	29
-2	16
-1	7
0	2
1	1
2	4
3	11

b)

x	y
-3	-9
-2	3
-1	3
0	-3
1	-9
2	-9
3	3

c)

x	y
-3	35
-2	-1
-1	-3
0	0
1	-1
2	14
3	87

d)

x	y
-3	-110
-2	-21
-1	4
0	7
1	6
2	-5
3	-56

e)

x	y
-3	47
-2	22
-1	7
0	2
1	7
2	22
3	47

f)

x	y
-3	135
-2	52
-1	11
0	0
1	7
2	20
3	27

g)

x	y
-3	-92
-2	-21
-1	6
0	7
1	0
2	3
3	34

h)

x	y
-3	-44
-2	-25
-1	-12
0	-5
1	-4
2	-9
3	-20

2.8 Investigating Math: Determining Equations of Graphs

Refer to page 101.
24. Use the given zeros and the y-intercept to determine an equation of each function, in expanded form.

a)

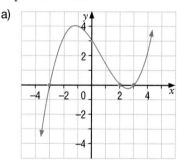

b)

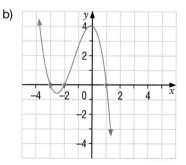

c)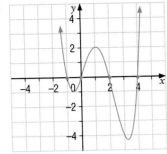

25. Use finite differences to determine an equation for each function.

a)

x	y
−3	−40
−2	−15
−1	−4
0	−1
1	0
2	5
3	20

b)

x	y
−3	138
−2	35
−1	6
0	3
1	2
2	3
3	30

26. A quartic function has x-intercepts of −5, −1, 2, and 4. The point $(3, -8)$ lies on the curve. Determine an equation of the function.

27. Use trial and error on a graphing calculator to determine an equation for each function in the form $y = ax^3 + bx^2 + cx + d$, where a, b, c, and d are integers, or in the form $y = ax^4 + bx^3 + cx^2 + dx + e$, where a, b, c, d, and e are integers, passing through the given points.

a) cubic function

x	y
−1	−27
0	−8
1	−1
2	0
3	1
4	8
5	27

b) quartic function

x	y
−3	83
−2	18
−1	3
0	2
1	3
2	18
3	83

Chapter Test

Achievement Chart

Category	Knowledge/Understanding	Thinking/Inquiry/Problem Solving	Communication	Application
Questions	All	5, 13, 15, 17	17	12, 16, 17

1. Graph each function and
i) determine the domain and range
ii) determine the type and number of x-intercepts
iii) describe the behaviour near the x-intercepts
iv) determine the type and number of turning points
v) describe the end behaviours
vi) describe any symmetry
a) $f(x) = x(x - 2)(x + 3)$
b) $f(x) = -(x + 1)(x - 1)(x - 3)$
c) $f(x) = x(x + 2)(x - 2)(x + 4)$
d) $f(x) = x^3 + x^2 - 20x$
e) $f(x) = -x^4 + 3x^2 + 4$

2. Divide. State the restrictions on the variables.
a) $(x^3 + x^2 - 5x + 2) \div (x - 2)$
b) $(y + 2y^3 - 2y^2) \div (2y^2 + 1)$
c) $(10 + 6x^3 - x^2 - 11x) \div (2x + 3)$

3. The area of the base of a box is given by $3x^2 - 4x - 5$ and its volume is given by $6x^3 - 17x^2 + 2x + 15$. Determine an expression for the height of the box.

4. Use the remainder theorem to determine the remainder for each division.
a) $(p^3 + 4p^2 - 2p + 5) \div (p + 5)$
b) $(4y^3 + y^2 - 12y - 5) \div (4y + 1)$

5. When the polynomial $3x^3 + mx^2 + nx + 2$ is divided by $x - 2$, the remainder is -8. When the polynomial is divided by $x + 3$, the remainder is -88. What are the values of m and n?

6. Show that the binomial is a factor of the polynomial.
a) $x^3 - 5x^2 - x + 5;\ x - 5$
b) $3n^3 + n^2 - 38n + 24;\ 3n - 2$

7. Factor completely.
a) $x^3 + 2x^2 - 21x + 18$
b) $3x^3 - 10x^2 - 9x + 4$

8. Consider the expression $6x^3 - 17x^2 + 7x - 5$. Without factoring, use the rational zero theorem to state the possible factors.

9. Find the exact roots.
a) $y^3 - 3y^2 = 4y - 12$
b) $m^3 - 5m = 5m^2 - 1$
c) $x^3 + 4x^2 + 9x + 10 = 0$
d) $3y^3 - 28y^2 = 8 - 32y$

10. An open box, no more than 5 cm in height, is to be formed by cutting four identical squares from the corners of a sheet of metal 25 cm by 32 cm, and folding up the metal to form sides. The capacity of the box must be 1575 cm^3. What is the side length of the squares removed?

11. Solve each inequality.
a) $x^2 - x - 6 \geq 0$
b) $-x^3 + 13x < 12$

12. Solve the following non-factorable inequalities, to the nearest hundredth, using a graphing calculator.
a) $x^2 - x - 7 \leq 0$
b) $3x^2 - 4x > -3 - x^3$

13. Use the given zeros and the y-intercept to determine an equation of each function, in expanded form.

a)

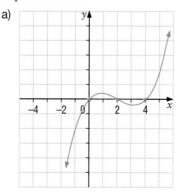

b)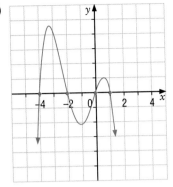

14. Use finite differences to determine an equation for the function.

x	y
-3	-43
-2	-11
-1	3
0	5
1	1
2	-3
3	-1

15. Use trial and error on a graphing calculator or graphing software to determine an equation for the cubic function passing through the following points.

x	y
-4	28
-3	10
-2	3
-1	2
0	1
1	-6
2	-25

16. The cumulative area, $A(t)$, in thousands of hectares, of farmland to be paved over with roads in Progress County after t years is projected to be $4t^3 + 5t^2 + 10$, $t \in [0, 10]$.

a) When will the area of farmland paved over reach 500 000 ha?

b) When will the area of farmland paved over be greater than or equal to 2 000 000 ha?

17. A rectangular storage unit has dimensions 1 m by 2 m by 3 m. If each linear dimension is increased by the same amount, what increase would result in a new storage unit with a volume 10 times the original?

Challenge Problems

1. If $f(x+1) = \dfrac{3f(x) - 1}{2}$ and $f(0) = 5$, find the value of $f(n)$, where n is a positive integer.

2. If $f(x) = 3x^2 - 2ax + b$, where $a \neq b$, $f(a) = b$, and $f(b) = a$, find the value of $a + b$.

3. The length of the diagonal of a rectangle is shorter than half the perimeter by one fifth of the longer side. Find the ratio of the shortest side to the longest side.

4. The height of a point $P(x, y)$ is given by the expression $x^2 + y^2 + 4x - 6y$. Find the lowest point and the height at that point.

5. While riding on a train you can hear the click of the wheels passing over the joins in the rails. If each rail is 10 m long, how many seconds must a passenger count clicks to equal the exact speed of the train in kilometres per hour?

6. a) Show that $4 + i$ and $-4 - i$ are the square roots of $15 + 8i$.
   b) Explain how you would find the square roots algebraically. Then, use the method to determine the square roots of $5 + 3i$.

7. A rectangular container measuring 1 m by 2 m by 4 m is covered with a layer of lead shielding of uniform thickness. Model the volume of the shielding as a function of its thickness. Find the thickness of the shielding, to the nearest centimetre, if the volume of the shielding is 3 m^3.

8. Girolamo Cardano developed a formula for finding the exact zeros of cubic polynomials. The formula is used to determine that one exact zero for $P(x) = x^3 + 6x - 2$ is $x = \sqrt[3]{4} - \sqrt[3]{2}$. Verify this root by finding $P(\sqrt[3]{4} - \sqrt[3]{2})$. Use a graphing calculator to justify this result. Research Cardano's formula and use it to find the exact values of the zeros of $P(x) = x^3 + 9x - 6$.

9. A fuel tank is in the shape of a horizontal right circular cylinder with a hemisphere at each end. If the length of the cylinder is 10 m, and the volume is 2000 m^3, find the common radius of the hemispheres and the cylinder.

10. According to estimates by the Ontario Provincial Police, the stopping distance at various speeds is approximately as follows. (This includes reaction time as well as the time to stop the car.)

Speed (km/h)	Distance (m)
50	22
70	38
90	58
110	82
130	110

If x is the speed, in kilometres per hour, and y is the distance, in metres, find the polynomial $y = f(x)$ of least degree that fits these data.

1. Determine whether each function is even, odd or neither. Then, graph the function on the stated interval.

a) $y = \dfrac{1}{2}(x+1)^3$, $x \in [-4, 4]$

b) $y = 2|x| + 3$, $x \in (-\infty, \infty)$

2. Is the sum of two odd functions odd? Verify your result algebraically.

3. State the domain of each function in interval notation.

a) $f(x) = 2x^5 - 5x^2 + 4$ b) $g(x) = \dfrac{1}{|x-1|}$

c) $h(x) = \sqrt{9 - x^2}$

4. The data in the table show the heights and masses of 10 students.

Height (cm)	Mass (kg)
160	51
172	64
163	54
152	48
176	81
141	46
169	65
171	80
188	95
165	64

a) Draw a scatter plot of the data.
b) Describe the graph.
c) Draw a curve of best fit and define it algebraically.
d) Use your model to estimate the mass of a 195-cm tall student.

5. The number of post-secondary degrees and diplomas granted between 1978 and 1996 are shown in the table.

Year	Number	Year	Number
1978	168 696	1988	202 440
1980	167 923	1990	212 609
1982	173 749	1992	229 265
1984	192 859	1994	246 678
1986	201 599	1996	257 677

Source: Statscan

a) Make a scatter plot of the data in the table.
b) Develop and superimpose a curve of best fit using an exponential model.
c) Discuss the slope of the curve and how it changes.
d) Use your model to predict the number of degrees and diplomas granted in 2006.

6. a) State the domain of $f(x) = 2|x^3| - 1$.
b) Use transformations to sketch a graph of f.

7. Is the graph of $y = |x - 2|^3$ the same as the graph of $y = |(x - 2)^3|$? Explain your reasoning.

8. a) Use a graphing calculator or graphing software to plot the graph of the function
$$y = \dfrac{x+1}{(x-1)(x+5)}.$$
b) Determine the domain and range of the function.
c) Use the **DRAW** menu to add in vertical asymptotes.
d) Find the values of all x- and y-intercepts.

9. On March 1, Tom invested $1000 in a guaranteed investment certificate. At the end of each month, interest was added at a rate of 0.5% per month, compounded monthly. What is the value of the GIC after
a) 6 months?
b) 2 years?

10. Graph each function and
i) determine the y-intercept
ii) determine the type, number, and coordinates of any x-intercepts
iii) determine the type, number, and coordinates of any turning points
iv) describe the behaviour near the x-intercepts
v) describe the end behaviour
vi) describe any symmetry
a) $f(x) = -x(x + 2)(x - 3)$
b) $f(x) = (x + 1)(x - 1)(x - 2)$
c) $f(x) = -x(x + 4)(x - 4)(x + 3)$
d) $f(x) = x^3 - x^2 - 12x$
e) $f(x) = x^4 + 3x^3 + 2x^2$

11. Divide. State any restrictions on the variables.
a) $(m^2 - 5m + 6) \div (m + 6)$
b) $(10y^2 + 17y - 20) \div (5y - 4)$
c) $(x^3 + 3x + 4x^2 + 12) \div (3 + x^2)$

12. Determine the remainder for each division.
a) $(x^3 - 4x^2 + 5x - 2) \div (x - 1)$
b) $(6y^3 + y^2 + 9y + 5) \div (2y + 1)$

13. When $x^4 - 4x^3 + ax^2 + bx + 1$ is divided by $(x - 1)$, the remainder is 7. When it is divided by $(x + 1)$, the remainder is 3. Determine the values of a and b.

14. Factor completely.
a) $x^3 - 8x^2 + 11x + 20$
b) $4x^3 - 11x^2 - 6x + 9$

15. Find the exact roots and check your solution.
a) $x^3 = 25x$
b) $2y^3 - y^2 - 2y + 1$
c) $t^3 + 3t^2 - 10t - 24 = 0$
d) $x^3 - 5x^2 - 22x + 56 = 0$
e) $4y^4 - 13y^3 - 13y^2 + 28y - 6 = 0$
f) $x^3 - 5x^2 - 7x + 51 = 0$

16. Write the equation of the family of functions with zeros -3, 2, and 6.

17. Graph the function $y = x^3 - 2x^2 - 5x + 6$ and determine
a) the domain and the range
b) any real zeros and the y-intercept

c) the approximate coordinates of any local maximums or local minimums
d) the intervals where $f(x) > 0$ and $f(x) < 0$
e) any symmetry
f) the end behaviour

18. Solve each inequality.
a) $x(x - 3) > 0$
b) $x^2 + x - 6 \leq 0$
c) $x^3 + 4x^2 - 11x - 30 \geq 0$

19. Solve each inequality, to the nearest hundredth, using a graphing calculator.
a) $x^2 - x - 7 < 0$
b) $x^3 + 5x^2 - 9x - 25 \leq 0$

20. Use finite differences to determine an equation for each function.

a)

x	y
0	-3
1	-3
2	1
3	9
4	21
5	37

b)

x	y
0	0
1	0
2	24
3	120
4	360
5	840

c)

x	y
0	4
1	0
2	0
3	10
4	36
5	84

Chapter 3

Limits

Specific Expectations	Section
Demonstrate an understanding that the slope of the tangent to a curve at a point is the limiting value of the slopes of a sequence of secants.	3.1
Determine the equation of the tangent to the graph of a polynomial or a rational function.	3.1, 3.2
Demonstrate an understanding that the slope of a secant to a curve represents the average rate of change of the function over an interval, and that the slope of the tangent to a curve at a point represents the instantaneous rate of change of the function at that point.	3.1, 3.4
Demonstrate an understanding that the instantaneous rate of change of a function at a point is the limiting value of a sequence of average rates of change.	3.2, 3.4
Determine the limit of a polynomial or a rational function.	3.3
Demonstrate an understanding that limits can give information about some behaviours of graphs of functions.	3.3
Identify examples of discontinuous functions and the types of discontinuities they illustrate.	3.3
Solve problems of rates of change drawn from a variety of applications (including distance, velocity, and acceleration) involving polynomial or rational functions.	3.4
Pose problems and formulate hypotheses regarding rates of change within applications drawn from the natural and social sciences.	3.4
Calculate and interpret average rates of change from various models of functions drawn from the natural and social sciences.	3.4
Estimate and interpret instantaneous rates of change from various models of functions drawn from the natural and social sciences.	3.4
Explain the difference between average and instantaneous rates of change within applications and in general.	3.4
Make inferences from models of applications and compare the inferences with the original hypotheses regarding rates of change.	3.4

When a linear function is used to model a real-world quantity, the slope of the line has an important interpretation as the rate of change of the quantity, as we will see in this chapter. Linear functions are the simplest types of models, and will apply only to the simplest situations. Most realistic quantities are modelled by more complicated functions, whose graphs are curves, not lines. In these situations, the rate of change of a quantity is also of key importance. How do we calculate rates of change for quantities modelled by non-linear functions? An equivalent question is this: how do we calculate the slope of a curve? These are the most important, fundamental questions of this course. You will learn how to do such calculations in this chapter in order to describe situations such as the following.

If a function models the radius of an oil spill spreading in a circular pattern, then the slope of the curve represents the rate at which the oil is spreading. If a function describes the population of a city as time passes, then the slope of the curve represents the rate of population growth. And finally, if a function represents the position of a moving person as time passes, then the slope of the curve represents the velocity of the person.

1. Slopes and y-intercepts

i) Determine the slope and the y-intercept of each line.

ii) Graph each line.

a) $y = 4x + 2$ b) $y = 2x + 3$
c) $y = x + 5$ d) $y = -2$
e) $y = -0.5x - 1$ f) $y = -x - 4$
g) $y = -2x + 1$ h) $y = -4x - 5$

2. Equation of a line given two points
Determine an equation of the line through each pair of points. Express your answer in slope, y-intercept form.

a) $(-2, -4)$ and $(2, 8)$
b) $(4, 7)$ and $(9, -12)$
c) $(-8, 6)$ and $(-2, -5)$
d) $(-5, -3)$ and $(3, 13)$
e) $(2, 3)$ and $(7, 3)$
f) $(-3, 6)$ and $(9, -18)$

3. Factoring $ax^2 + bx + c$, $a = 1$ Factor.

a) $x^2 + 5x + 6$ b) $x^2 - 7x + 12$
c) $x^2 - 3x - 18$ d) $x^2 + 5x - 14$
e) $x^3 - 9x^2 + 14x$ f) $2x^3 + 4x^2 + 2x$

4. Factoring $ax^2 + bx + c$, $a \neq 1$ Factor.

a) $3x^2 - 10x + 8$ b) $4x^2 + 25x + 6$
c) $15x^2 - x - 2$ d) $-16x^3 + 12x^2 + 18x$
e) $27x^2 + 18x + 3$ f) $4x^3 + 14x^2 - 60x$

5. Factoring $a^2 - b^2$ Factor.

a) $x^2 - 25$ b) $9x^2 - 16$
c) $64 - 36y^2$ d) $y^3 - 49y$

6. Factoring $a^3 - b^3$ or $a^3 + b^3$ Factor.

a) $x^3 - 27$ b) $m^3 + 64$
c) $x^6 - 8$ d) $64y^3 + 216x^3$
e) $8x^3 - 125y^3$ f) $x^6 + 8$
g) $y^4 - 343y$ h) $4x^4 + 4x$
i) $2y^4 - 16y$ j) $27x^5 + 64x^2$
k) $8x^5 - 27x^2$ l) $3x^2y^3 + 81x^2$

7. Factor theorem (Section 2.4) Factor.

a) $x^3 + 5x^2 + 2x - 8$
b) $x^3 - 7x - 6$
c) $2x^3 - 5x^2 - 4x + 3$
d) $x^3 + x^2 - 14x - 24$
e) $x^3 + 2x^2 - 11x - 12$
f) $x^3 + 5x^2 - 2x - 24$
g) $x^4 + 3x^3 - 11x^2 - 3x + 10$

h) $4x^4 + 20x^3 + 29x^2 + 4x - 12$
i) $x^4 - 3x^3 - 7x^2 + 27x - 18$

8. Simplifying rational expressions Simplify. State any restrictions on the variable.

a) $\dfrac{x^2 + 5x + 6}{x + 2}$

b) $\dfrac{x^2 - 8x - 9}{x + 1}$

c) $\dfrac{2x^2 - 9x - 5}{x - 5}$

d) $\dfrac{3x^2 - 5x - 12}{x^2 + 2x - 15}$

e) $\dfrac{2x^2 - 13x - 7}{4x^2 - 1}$

f) $\dfrac{6x^2 + x - 2}{6x^2 - 7x + 2}$

9. Simplifying compound rational expressions Simplify. State any restrictions on the variable.

a) $\dfrac{\dfrac{1}{x+2} - \dfrac{1}{2}}{x}$

b) $\dfrac{\dfrac{2}{x+3} - \dfrac{2}{3}}{x}$

c) $\dfrac{\dfrac{1}{(x+5)^2} - \dfrac{1}{25}}{x}$

10. Rationalizing expressions Rationalize the denominator. State any restriction on the variable.

a) $\dfrac{x}{\sqrt{x+1} - 1}$

b) $\dfrac{9}{\sqrt{x+3} + \sqrt{x}}$

c) $\dfrac{4x}{\sqrt{x+4} - \sqrt{x}}$

d) $\dfrac{x-1}{\sqrt{x+3} - 2}$

e) $\dfrac{x^2}{\sqrt{x^2+4} - 2}$

f) $\dfrac{x}{\sqrt{x+1} - \sqrt{x-1}}$

11. Transformations Given the graph of $f(x) = x^2$, describe how to graph each of the following. Use this information to sketch each new graph.

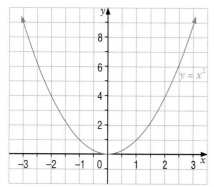

a) $y = f(x) + 2$
b) $y = f(x - 3)$
c) $y = f(x) - 1$
d) $y = f(x + 2)$
e) $y = f(2x)$

12. Evaluating functions Given $f(x) = x^2 + 5x + 6$, find each of the following.
a) $f(2)$
b) $f(h)$
c) $\dfrac{f(3) - f(2)}{3 - 2}$
d) $\dfrac{f(h + 2) - f(2)}{h}$

13. Slopes of lines For each function,
i)   determine the slope of the line that intersects the graph of f at $x = 2$ and $x = 4$

ii)   determine the slope of the line that intersects the graph of f at $x = 2$ and $x = 3$
iii)   determine an expression for the slope of the line that intersects the graph of f at $x = 2$ and $x = 2 + h$
a) $f(x) = x^2$
b) $f(x) = x^2 + 3x - 1$
c) $f(x) = \dfrac{1}{x}$
d) $f(x) = x^3$

14. Finite differences (Section 2.7) Determine an equation for each set of data.

a)

x	y
0	-2
1	1
2	4
3	7
4	10

b)

x	y
0	-4
1	-3
2	0
3	5
4	12
5	21
6	32
7	45

15. Word problems A car moves at a speed of 50 km/h. Determine how long it takes for it to travel 280 km.

16. Word problems Water from a garden hose fills a swimming pool of capacity 50 000 L in 24 h. At what rate, in litres per min, does water flow from the hose?

17. Word problems Fifteen thousand trucks pass through an international border crossing per week. What is the average rate at which trucks cross the border, in trucks per minute?

From Secants to Tangents

In a situation where a quantity is changing, often the most important information is the rate at which the quantity is changing. When a quantity changes at a constant rate, its graph is linear. As we will see, the **slope** of the graph corresponds to the rate of change. When the rate of change of a quantity is not constant, its graph is not linear. To determine the rate of change in such a case requires us to calculate slopes for a curve.

In this section, we will explore the idea of calculating slopes for a curve.

Example 1 Fire Hydrant Pressure Test

The table and graph show how much water passes through a fire hose in a pressure test of a fire hydrant. A line of best fit has been plotted on the graph.

Time (s)	Volume (L)
0	0.0
1	5.2
2	10.3
3	15.6
4	20.7
5	26.0
6	31.2

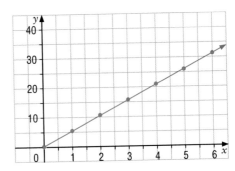

a) Determine the slope of the line of best fit.
b) What are the units of the slope?
c) Explain the meaning of the slope.

Solution

a) The line of best fit passes through the points $(0, 0)$ and $(5, 26)$. The slope of the line is

$$m = \frac{\text{rise}}{\text{run}}$$
$$= \frac{26 - 0}{5 - 0}$$
$$= 5.2$$

b) The units of the slope are litres per second.
c) Every second, approximately 5.2 L of water are pumped from the hydrant.

The slope of a line is the same for every part of the line. However, the same is not true of a curve—some parts of a curve are steeper than others. In the following situation, we will begin to develop a method for determining the slope of a curve.

A serious environmental disaster can result when a supertanker filled with oil develops a leak and millions of litres of oil spread over the surface of the ocean. The area of oil in a particular spill is shown in the table below, assuming that the ocean is calm and the oil spreads in a circular pattern.

Time (s)	Area (m^2)
0	0.0
1	28.1
2	112.9
3	254.7
4	452.2
5	706.7
6	1018.0

Input the data by selecting **1:Edit** on the STAT EDIT menu of a graphing calculator. Then, select **QuadReg** on the STAT CALC menu to find an equation to represent the data, which appear to be quadratic.

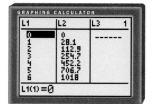  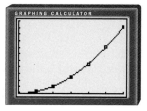

Window variables: $x \in [0, 6]$, $y \in [0, 1100]$

The quadratic regression formula that fits the data is approximately
$y = 28.3x^2 - 0.05x - 0.05$.

Suppose we want to know how fast the oil is spreading after 1 s. As we will see later, this rate corresponds to the slope of the graph at $x = 1$. To estimate this quantity, we determine the slope m_{PQ} of the line joining the points P(1, 28.1) and Q(4, 452.2). A line passing through two points on a curve, such as the line PQ, is called a **secant**.

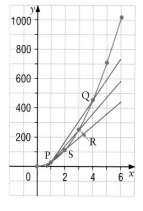

$$m_{PQ} = \frac{\text{rise}}{\text{run}}$$
$$= \frac{y_2 - y_1}{x_2 - x_1}$$
$$= \frac{452.2 - 28.1}{4 - 1}$$
$$\doteq 141.37$$

Thus, the area of the oil slick is increasing at a rate of about 141.37 m^2/s.

As we can see from the graph, the calculation is only an estimate, since it is based on the secant PQ, which approximates the curve near $x = 1$. Now consider the secant PR, where the coordinates of R are (3, 254.7). The secant PR seems to be a better approximation to the curve near $x = 1$, so determining its slope gives a better estimate of how fast the oil is spreading after 1 s.

$$m_{PR} = \frac{rise}{run}$$

$$= \frac{y_2 - y_1}{x_2 - x_1}$$

$$= \frac{254.7 - 28.1}{3 - 1}$$

$$= 113.3$$

The rate 113.3 m²/s is a better estimate of how fast the oil is spreading. Finally, choosing to calculate the slope of the secant PS, where the coordinates of S are (2, 112.9), gives an even better estimate.

$$m_{PS} = \frac{rise}{run}$$

$$= \frac{y_2 - y_1}{x_2 - x_1}$$

$$= \frac{112.9 - 28.1}{2 - 1}$$

$$= 84.8$$

The secant PS resembles the curve more closely than the other two secants near $x = 1$. Thus, 84.8 m²/s is the best estimate (of the three) for how fast the oil is spreading. To calculate better estimates, slopes of secants joining P to points with x-values even closer to $x = 1$ could be chosen.

The same method can be used to estimate the slope of any graph at a point where the graph is smooth. For example, consider estimating the slope of the graph of the function $y = x^2$ at the point P(3, 9). We draw a secant from P to another point Q(x, y) close to P, and find the slope, m_{PQ}, of PQ.

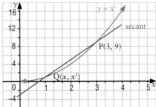

We can then let the point Q approach P more and more closely. The nearer Q approaches P, the better the slope of the secant PQ estimates the slope of the curve at P. An expression for the slope of the secant PQ is

$$m_{PQ} = \frac{y - 9}{x - 3}$$

Since Q lies on the parabola $y = x^2$,

$$m_{PQ} = \frac{x^2 - 9}{x - 3}$$

Notice that we must choose $x \neq 3$, since the denominator cannot be zero. This means that we must choose Q $\neq$ P.

In the following investigation, you will use the above expression for the slope of a secant line PQ, and the idea of letting Q approach P, to estimate the slope of the graph of $y = x^2$ at the point P(3, 9).

Investigate & Inquire: Slope of a Tangent

1. Use a graphing calculator, graphing software, or another method to estimate the slope of the secant m_{PQ} to the parabola $y = x^2$, using P(3, 9) and points Q with the given x-values. In other words, let Q approach P from the left.

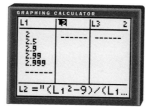

Move the cursor up to L2 to enter the formula "(L₁² – 9)/(L₁ – 3)" in L2.

2. Repeat step 1 for points Q with x-values slightly greater than 3. In other words, let Q approach P from the right.

3. Why does x never equal 3 in the tables?

4. What happens to the secants as the x-values of Q get closer and closer to 3?

5. Examine your results from steps 1 and 2 carefully.
a) What value does m_{PQ} appear to approach in both tables?
b) As the point Q approaches the point P, the secant PQ approaches a line that touches the graph of $y = x^2$ only at P. The line that the secant approaches is called the **tangent** to the graph at P. Make a conjecture about the slope of the tangent at P(3, 9).
c) How confident are you that your conjecture in part b) is correct?
d) Use the Tangent operation of a graphing calculator or graphing software to check your conjecture.

6. Use the slope you found in step 5 to determine an equation for the tangent in slope and y-intercept form.

7. Summarize the steps used in this investigation to determine the slope of a tangent to a curve.

An illustration of the process in the investigation is shown in the figure. As Q approaches P along the parabola, the corresponding secants rotate about P moving closer to the tangent, in blue.

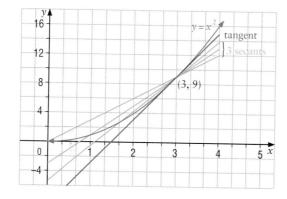

Web Connection

For an animated version of many of these concepts, go to **www.mcgrawhill.ca/links/CAF12**. Which of the listed links are most helpful to your understanding?

Example 2 Slope of the Tangent to a Curve

The point P(1, 5) lies on the curve $y = x^3 + 4x$.
a) If Q is the point $(x, x^3 + 4x)$, find an expression for the slope of the secant PQ that is valid provided $x \neq 1$.
b) Use the expression in part a) to help you conjecture the value of the slope of the tangent to the curve at P.
c) Using the slope from part b), find the equation of the tangent to the curve at P.
d) Sketch the curve, one secant on either side of P, and the tangent. Check your sketch of the curve and tangent using the Tangent operation of a graphing calculator or graphing software.

Solution

a) Since $y = x^3 + 4x$, the slope of a secant PQ is

$$m_{PQ} = \frac{y - 5}{x - 1}$$

$$= \frac{(x^3 + 4x) - 5}{x - 1}$$

The expression for m_{PQ} is valid provided $x \neq 1$.

b) We can use the **TABLE feature** of a graphing calculator or graphing software to calculate values for the slopes of secants. First, we input the formula for the slope in the function editor. Then, we use Ask mode for the independent variable on the TABLE SETUP screen. We input values of x that approach 1 from both the left and the right. In the screens shown, we have chosen enough values that we are fairly confident in the result.

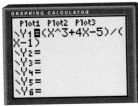
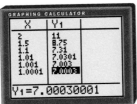

From the values in Y1, the slope of the tangent to the curve at P(1, 5) appears to be 7.

c) We use the point-slope form of the equation of a line to find an equation of the tangent:
$y - 5 = 7(x - 1)$
$y = 7x - 2$

d) The diagram shows the curve, one secant on either side of P, and the tangent at P.

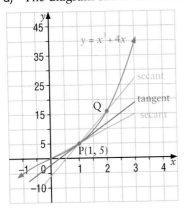

The following screens show how to use the Tangent operation on a graphing calculator to draw a tangent at a given point.

Set the Window variables to the friendly window by pressing ZOOM 4.

So, the slopes of secants provide estimates of the rate of change of a quantity over specific intervals. The slope of the tangent to a curve is the exact rate of change of the quantity at the point of tangency.

Scientific experiments usually produce data from which patterns must be discovered, rather than an explicit equation that can be graphed. In such cases, the previous method for conjecturing a value for the slope of a tangent will not work. The following example shows how to estimate the slope of a tangent to the graph of such data.

Example 3 Estimating Slope From Experimental Data

When a camera flash goes off, it must be recharged before the next flash picture can be taken. The charge is stored in a capacitor. The charge, Q (in microcoulombs, μC), as the flash recharges is shown in the table as a function of time, t (in milliseconds, ms).

t (ms)	Q (μC)
0.00	0.00
20.00	89.45
40.00	141.59
60.00	171.97
80.00	189.67
100.00	200.00

a)   Plot the data on a scatter plot. Then, draw a smooth curve through the points. What does the slope of the graph represent?
b)   Use the graph of the function to estimate the slope of the tangent at $t = 40$.
c)   Use the table to estimate the slope of the tangent at $t = 40$.

Solution

a)   In the figure, we plot the given data and use them to sketch a curve that approximates the graph of the function.

The slope of the tangent represents the rate at which charge flows from the battery to the storage capacitor. The rate of flow is also known as the electric current, and is measured here in milliamperes (mA).

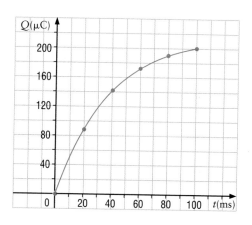

b) We sketch an approximation to the tangent at P(40.00, 141.59), and calculate the slope as shown.

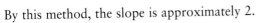

$$m = \frac{\Delta y}{\Delta x}$$
$$= \frac{180 - 100}{60 - 20}$$
$$= 2$$

By this method, the slope is approximately 2.

c) From the given data, find the slopes of the two secants that best approximate the tangent. The points $Q_1(20.00, 89.45)$ and $Q_2(60.00, 171.97)$ are closest to P.

Find the slope of the secant PQ_1:

$$m_{PQ} = \frac{141.59 - 89.45}{40.00 - 20.00}$$
$$= 2.607$$

Find the slope of the secant PQ_2:

$$m_{PQ} = \frac{171.97 - 141.59}{60.00 - 40.00}$$
$$= 1.519$$

Since these secants are the closest ones to the desired tangent, we would expect the slope of the tangent at $t = 40$ to lie somewhere between 1.519 and 2.607. Taking the average of these slopes gives an estimate:

$$\frac{1}{2}(1.519 + 2.607) = 2.063$$

By this method, the slope of the tangent is approximately 2.1. This method provides a slope very close to the one found in part a).

Determining the slope of a tangent using secants that approach the tangent more and more closely is one of the most important ideas in calculus. The numerical method presented in this section is a good starting point, but one can never be sure that the results obtained from tables of values are valid, especially for complicated functions. We need to translate this idea into an algebraic method. This is done in the next section, and leads to the concept of a limit.

Key Concepts

- The slope of the tangent to the graph of a function is the rate of change of the function at the point of tangency.
- The slope of a tangent can be estimated by calculating the slope of a secant that approximates the tangent. By moving the point Q closer and closer to the point P, the secant PQ approximates the tangent at P more and more closely. Use this method if the function is described by an equation.
- The tangent feature of a graphing calculator can be used to find the tangent if the function is described by an equation.

- If the function is expressed in terms of experimental data, and is not described by an equation, there are three methods for estimating the slope of the tangent.
  a) Average the slopes of the two secants that are the best approximations.
  b) Sketch an approximation of the tangent to the graph of the function and calculate the slope.
  c) Input the data into a graphing calculator, find a regression formula, and use either the secant method or the graphing calculator's tangent feature.

Communicate Your Understanding

1. a) Why is it necessary to investigate cases in which Q approaches P gradually rather than choosing a single point Q very close to P? Draw a sketch to support your answer.

b) Why is it necessary to investigate cases in which Q approaches P from *both* sides of P? Draw a sketch to support your answer.

2. a) Explain why the two closest secants on opposite sides of the tangent are used to estimate the slope of the tangent when only experimental data are available.

b) Why do the methods of finding the slopes of tangents in this section result only in estimates?

c) Which of the methods in this section do you consider to be the most accurate? Explain.

d) Which of the methods can be improved upon? Explain.

3. When calculating the slope of a tangent to a curve of experimental data, can you be sure that the slope is reasonable? Would your result be more accurate if more data were available? Explain.

Practise

 1. The point P(2, 2) lies on the curve $y = \frac{1}{4}x^3$.

a) If Q is the point $\left(x, \frac{1}{4}x^3\right)$, use a calculator to find approximate values of the slope of the secant PQ for the following values of x.

i) 3　　ii) 2.5　　iii) 2.1　　iv) 2.01
v) 2.001　vi) 1　　vii) 1.5　viii) 1.9
ix) 1.99　　x) 1.999

b) Explain the choice of x-values in part a).

c) Using the results of part a), guess the value of the slope of the tangent to the curve at P(2, 2).

d) Using the slope from part c), find the equation of the tangent to the curve at P(2, 2).

e) Sketch the curve, one secant on each side of P, and the tangent.

2. Inquiry/Problem Solving For each curve and each point P,

i) Choose five appropriate points Q on either side of P on the curve. Find the slope m_{PQ} for each Q that you chose.

ii) Guess the value of the slope of the tangent to the curve at P.

iii) Find an equation of the tangent to the curve at P.

iv) Sketch the curve, one secant on each side of P, and the tangent.

a) $y = x^2 + 2x$, P(1, 3)
b) $y = x^2 + 2x + 1$, P(1, 4)
c) $y = -x^2 + 4x - 4$, P(1, -1)
d) $y = \frac{1}{x}$, P = (1, 1)
e) $y = \sqrt{x}$, P(4, 2)

Apply, Solve, Communicate

B 3. Communication A tank holding 3000 L of water develops a leak at the bottom resulting in all the water draining out in 50 min. The values in the table show the volume, V, in litres, of water remaining in the tank after t minutes.

t (min)	0	5	10	15
V (L)	3000	2430	1920	1470

t (min)	20	25	30
V (L)	1080	750	480

a) What does the slope of the graph of V versus t represent?

b) Sketch a graph of the function and estimate the slopes of the tangents at P(20, 1080) and R(35, 270) using the method of Example 3b) on page 125.

c) Use one secant on either side of P to estimate the slope of the tangent at P.

d) Estimate the slope of the tangent at R by averaging the slopes of two secants, one on each side of R.

e) Use a graphing calculator or graphing software to find a regression equation for the data. Then, use the Tangent operation to find the slopes of the tangents at P and R. Compare your answers with those in parts b) to d).

f) Use the method of your choice to estimate at what rate the water is flowing from the tank when $t = 10$.

4. Inquiry/Problem Solving A cardiac monitor is used to measure the heart rate of a hospital patient by keeping track of the number of heartbeats after t minutes. The slope of the tangent to the graph of heartbeats versus t represents the heart rate in beats per minute. Because of the patient's condition, the doctor feels the patient is in danger if the heart rate goes beyond the normal range at any time. (The normal range of heart rate for this patient is between 65 and 85 beats/min.)

T (min)	0	2	4	6	8
Heartbeats	0	150	310	466	608

a) Use a graph of the function to estimate the slope of the tangent at each of the following times.
   i) $t = 2$ ii) $t = 4$ iii) $t = 6$

b) Estimate the slope of the tangent at each time in part a) by averaging the slope of two secants.

c) Is there any evidence suggesting that the patient is in danger at any time? From the data collected, can we know for sure if the patient was in danger at any time within the first 8 min?

d) Is there a better way to monitor the situation? Explain.

5. Application According to Boyle's Law, the product of the pressure, P, in atmospheres, and the volume, V, in litres, of a confined gas remains constant as long as the temperature is constant. For a certain gas, $P = \dfrac{10}{V}$. Find the slope of the tangent to the graph of the function at M(5, 2) (meaning $V = 5$) using the following methods.

a) Sketch a graph and use it to estimate the slope of the tangent at M.

b) Estimate the slope of the tangent at M by averaging the slopes of two secants.

c) Estimate the slope of the tangent at M by finding slopes of secants closer and closer to the tangent.

d) Check your results in parts a), b), and c) using a graphing calculator or graphing software to determine which method is most accurate.

6. Application A small town committee estimates that, with the introduction of a large new business in the area, the population, N, of the town will change with respect to time, t, in years, according to the equation $N = 5000\sqrt{1+t}$. Determine the rate at which the population of the town will be increasing with respect to time after 3 years.

7. The heights and masses for some players on the Toronto Raptors basketball team are recorded in the following table.

Height (cm)	Mass (kg)	Height (cm)	Mass (kg)
188	92	206	103
191	89	208	104
196	84	213	116
201	93		

a) Graph the data in the table using a graphing calculator or graphing software.

b) Use regression to find the polynomial equation for the curve that best fits the data.

c) Estimate the slope of the tangent to the curve in part b) at $x = 200$, using any method except the Tangent operation of the graphing calculator or graphing software.

d) Check the result of part c) using a graphing calculator or graphing software.

C **8.** Inquiry/Problem Solving The point P(2, 0) is on the graph of $y = \sin\left(\dfrac{20\pi}{x}\right)$, where angle measure is in radians.

a) Find the slope of the secant PQ where the x-coordinate of Q is

i) 1.5 ii) 1.6 iii) 1.7 iv) 1.8 v) 1.9
vi) 2.5 vii) 2.4 viii) 2.3 ix) 2.2 x) 2.1

b) Are the slopes approaching a value? If so, what is the value?

c) Sketch a graph of $y = \sin\left(\dfrac{20\pi}{x}\right)$ for $x \in (1, 3)$ to explain your result in part b).

d) Why is it a good idea to sketch a graph of a function when estimating slopes of tangents?

e) Estimate the slope of the tangent at (2, 0) using appropriate points Q.

Achievement Check

Knowledge/Understanding

Thinking/Inquiry/Problem Solving

Communication

Application

The table gives the concentration, $C(t)$, in milligrams per cubic centimetre, of a drug in a patient's bloodstream at time t, in minutes.

t	0	0.1	0.2	0.3	0.4	0.5
$C(t)$	0.83	0.88	0.93	0.97	0.99	0.99

t	0.6	0.7	0.8	0.9	1.0
$C(t)$	0.96	0.89	0.78	0.62	0.40

a) Construct a table of estimated values for $R(t)$, the rate of change of $C(t)$ with respect to time, by using the approximate formula $R(t) \doteq \dfrac{C(t + h) - C(t)}{h}$, with $h = 0.1$.

b) Use the table of part a) to graph $C(t)$ and $R(t)$.

c) Describe the graph of $C(t)$. What shape does it seem to have?

d) Estimate the slopes of the tangents to the graph of $C(t)$ at $t = 0.9$ and $t = 1$. How accurate do you think your estimates are? Explain.

e) Explain how the estimates in part d) are related to values of $R(t)$.

f) Extrapolate to estimate a value for $C(1.1)$. When do you think the drug will be completely out of the patient's system? Explain.

3.2 Using Limits to Find Tangents

On March 6, 2001, the 135-tonne Russian space station MIR crashed into the Atlantic Ocean from an orbit 390 km above the surface of Earth. For the safe re-entry of MIR, many factors had to be considered, including the gravitational potential energy of the station. The gravitational potential energy, E, in joules, J, depends on the distance, x, in metres, from the object to the centre of Earth and is given by the equation

$$E = -\frac{5.38 \times 10^{19}}{x}, \text{ where } x \geq 6.38 \times 10^6 \, \text{m}$$

(the radius of Earth). The rate of change of E with respect to x represents the force of gravity on the space station. How the gravitational potential energy changes with respect to the distance from Earth affects the trajectory of the falling space station, and so it must be accounted for. In questions 12 and 13, you will determine how E changes with respect to x by investigating the slopes of the tangents to its graph.

In Section 3.1, we found the slope of the tangent to the parabola $y = x^2$ at the point $(3, 9)$ by computing the slopes of secants that approach the tangent more and more closely. If a curve has equation $y = f(x)$, to find the tangent to the curve at the point $P(a, f(a))$, we first consider a nearby point $Q(x, f(x))$ and compute the slope of the secant PQ.

$$m_{PQ} = \frac{\Delta y}{\Delta x}$$

$$= \frac{f(x) - f(a)}{x - a}$$

In selecting point Q, we must make sure that $x \neq a$, since we need two *different* points on the curve to find the slope of the secant joining them. Otherwise, the formula for the slope m_{PQ} would have 0 in the denominator, which is undefined.

Then, we let Q approach P along the curve by letting x approach a. If m_{PQ} approaches a number m more and more closely as x approaches a, we define the **tangent** to the curve at P to be the line through P with slope m.

This process of calculating a quantity by estimating it, and then making the estimate more and more accurate until it is exact, is known as determining a **limit**. In the notation of limits, the slope of a tangent to the graph of $y = f(x)$ at the point $x = a$ is

$$m = \lim_{x \to a} \frac{f(x) - f(a)}{x - a} \qquad \text{Formula 1}$$

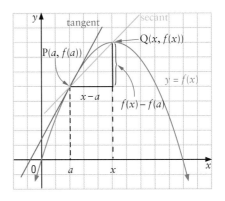

This expression for the slope of a tangent amounts to saying that the tangent is the limiting position of the secants PQ as Q approaches P, as shown in the figure. Only the secants for which Q is on the right side of P are shown in the diagram, but we must examine the slopes of the secants for points Q on both sides of P to be sure that we have the correct slope for the tangent.

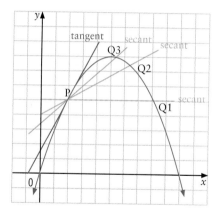

Now we can use limits to find the slopes of tangents to curves. The idea is the same as in the previous section, but, rather than rely on tables of values to work out a limit, we use an algebraic method that provides greater certainty.

Example 1 Determining the Slope of a Tangent to a Curve Using Limits

a) Find the slope of the tangent to the curve $y = x^2 + 2x - 1$ at the point (2, 7).
b) Determine the equation of the tangent in part a).
c) Use a graphing calculator or graphing software to graph the function and the tangent to the graph at (2, 7).

Solution 1 Numerical Method

a) As in the previous section, we construct tables of values to determine the slope of the tangent. The slope of a secant PQ that joins the points P(2, 7) and Q(x, $x^2 + 2x - 1$), where $f(2) = 7$, is

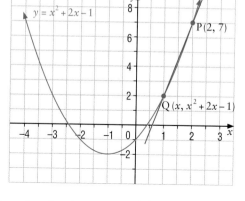

$$m_{PQ} = \frac{f(x) - f(a)}{x - a}$$

$$= \frac{(x^2 + 2x - 1) - (7)}{x - 2}$$

$$= \frac{x^2 + 2x - 8}{x - 2}$$

As the point Q approaches P more and more closely, x approaches 2 more and more closely. The following tables show what happens to the values for the slopes m_{PQ} of the secants PQ as Q approaches P from both the left and the right.

x (x-coordinate of Q)	m_{PQ} (slope of secant PQ)	x (x-coordinate of Q)	m_{PQ} (slope of secant PQ)
3	7	1	5
2.5	6.5	1.5	5.5
2.1	6.1	1.9	5.9
2.01	6.01	1.99	5.99
2.001	6.001	1.999	5.999
2.0001	6.0001	1.9999	5.9999

From the tables, it appears that the slopes of the secants approach 6 as Q approaches P, that is, as x approaches 2. Thus, it appears that the slope of the tangent to the curve at P is 6.

It would be tedious to perform this kind of numerical calculation every time we want to determine the slope of a tangent. A more serious issue is this: for more complicated functions, how could we be sure that the function does not behave in some unusual way for numbers that are beyond what we have included in the tables? An algebraic method, such as the one in Solution 2, shown next, provides us with both precision and certainty.

Solution 2 Algebraic Method

We find the slope of the tangent using Formula 1 (page 130) with $a = 2$ and $f(x) = x^2 + 2x - 1$. That is, we write an expression for the slope of a secant PQ, and then determine the limit as x approaches 2. This is essentially the same process that was used in Solution 1, but here algebra is being used instead of a table of values.

$$m = \lim_{x \to 2} \frac{f(x) - f(2)}{x - 2}$$

$$= \lim_{x \to 2} \frac{(x^2 + 2x - 1) - (7)}{x - 2}$$

$$= \lim_{x \to 2} \frac{x^2 + 2x - 8}{x - 2}$$

$$= \lim_{x \to 2} \frac{(x + 4)(x - 2)}{x - 2}$$

$$= \lim_{x \to 2} (x + 4), \quad x \neq 2$$

Note that the simplified expression $x + 4$ still represents the slope of a secant PQ. This can be verified by using it to reproduce the entries in the tables of Solution 1. But working with this simplified expression means we can achieve the result of the tables by reasoning: as x gets closer and closer to 2, $x + 4$ gets closer and closer to $2 + 4 = 6$. Thus, the slope m of the tangent is

$$m = \lim_{x \to 2} (x + 4)$$

$$= 6$$

The slope of the tangent at $(2, 7)$ is 6.

b) Using point-slope form, we find that an equation of the tangent is

$y - 7 = 6(x - 2)$

which simplifies to

$y = 6x - 5$

c) We graph the function $y = x^2 + 2x - 1$, and use the Tangent operation to draw the tangent at $(2, 7)$.

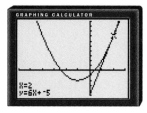

Window variables:

$x \in [-6, 3], y \in [-5, 10]$

An alternative formula for the slope of the tangent to the graph of $y = f(x)$ is obtained by labelling the coordinates of points P and Q as $P(a, f(a))$ and $Q(a + h, f(a + h))$. The diagram illustrates the case where $h > 0$ and Q is to the right of P. If $h < 0$, Q would be to the left of P.

The slope of the secant PQ is

$$m_{PQ} = \frac{f(a+h) - f(a)}{a + h - a}$$

$$= \frac{f(a+h) - f(a)}{h}$$

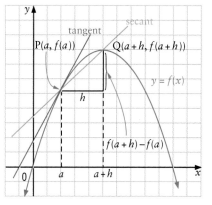

As x approaches a, h approaches 0, and the expression for the slope of the tangent becomes

$$m = \lim_{Q \to P} m_{PQ}$$

$$= \lim_{h \to 0} \frac{f(a+h) - f(a)}{h} \qquad \textbf{Formula 2}$$

Note that, if we substitute $x - a$ for h in Formula 2, the result is Formula 1. Confirm this for yourself. Thus Formula 1 and Formula 2 are equivalent, and which to use is a matter of preference.

Example 2 Determining the Slope of a Tangent Algebraically Using Limits

Use Formula 2 to find the slope of the tangent to $y = x^2 + 3x + 4$ at $x = -2$.

Solution

Use Formula 2 with $a = -2$ and $f(x) = x^2 + 3x + 4$.

$$m = \lim_{h \to 0} \frac{f(a+h) - f(a)}{h}$$

$$= \lim_{h \to 0} \frac{f(-2+h) - f(-2)}{h}$$

$$= \lim_{h \to 0} \frac{(-2+h)^2 + 3(-2+h) + 4 - [(-2)^2 + 3(-2) + 4]}{h}$$

$$= \lim_{h \to 0} \frac{-h + h^2}{h}$$

$$= \lim_{h \to 0} \frac{h(-1 + h)}{h}, \ h \neq 0$$

$$= \lim_{h \to 0} (-1 + h)$$

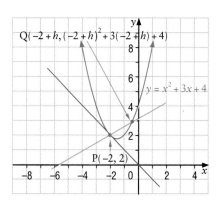

As $h \to 0$, $-1 + h$ approaches $-1 + 0 = -1$. Thus, the slope of the tangent to the curve at the point where $x = -2$ is -1.

Example 3 Determining an Equation of a Tangent to a Curve

a) Find an equation of the tangent to the curve $y = \dfrac{1}{x-1}$ at $(2, 1)$.

b) Graph the curve and the tangent.

Solution

a) First, check that $(2, 1)$ is on the curve $y = \dfrac{1}{x-1}$.

$$y = \frac{1}{x-1}$$
$$= \frac{1}{2-1}$$
$$= 1$$

Thus, the point $(2, 1)$ is on the curve $y = \dfrac{1}{x-1}$.

Second, use Formula 2 with $f(x) = \dfrac{1}{x-1}$ and $a = 2$ to determine the slope of the tangent.

$$m = \lim_{h \to 0} \frac{f(2+h) - f(2)}{h}$$

$$= \lim_{h \to 0} \frac{\dfrac{1}{(2+h)-1} - \dfrac{1}{2-1}}{h}$$

$$= \lim_{h \to 0} \frac{\dfrac{1}{1+h} - 1}{h} \times \frac{1+h}{1+h}$$

$$= \lim_{h \to 0} \frac{1-(1+h)}{h(1+h)}$$

$$= \lim_{h \to 0} \frac{-h}{h(1+h)}$$

$$= \lim_{h \to 0} \frac{-1}{1+h}, \; h \neq 0$$

$$= \frac{-1}{1+0}$$

$$= -1$$

Thus, the slope of the tangent at $(2, 1)$ is -1. The equation of the tangent at $(2, 1)$ is given by

$$y - 1 = -1(x - 2)$$
$$y = -x + 3$$

b) Graph the curve $y = \dfrac{1}{x-1}$ and its tangent using a graphing calculator or graphing software, as in Example 1.

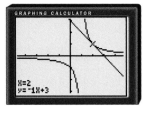

Set the Window variables to $x \in [-4.7, 4.7]$, $y \in [-3.1, 3.1]$ by pressing ZOOM 4.

Example 4 Determining the Slopes of Several Tangents

a) Find the slopes of the tangents to the curve $y = \sqrt{x}$ at the points $(1, 1)$, $(4, 2)$, and $(9, 3)$.
b) Describe how the slopes of the curve change as x increases.

Solution

Since three slopes are required, it will be more efficient to find the slope of the tangent to the curve $y = \sqrt{x}$ at a general point $(a, \sqrt{a})$, and then substitute values for a. We find the slope using Formula 2.

$$m = \lim_{h \to 0} \frac{f(a+h) - f(a)}{h}$$

$$= \lim_{h \to 0} \frac{\sqrt{a+h} - \sqrt{a}}{h}$$

$$= \lim_{h \to 0} \left[\left(\frac{\sqrt{a+h} - \sqrt{a}}{h} \right) \left(\frac{\sqrt{a+h} + \sqrt{a}}{\sqrt{a+h} + \sqrt{a}} \right) \right] \qquad \text{Rationalize the numerator.}$$

$$= \lim_{h \to 0} \frac{(a+h) - a}{h(\sqrt{a+h} + \sqrt{a})} \qquad \qquad \text{Note that the numerator simplifies so}$$
$$\qquad \qquad \qquad \qquad \qquad \qquad \text{that there is a common factor in the}$$
$$= \lim_{h \to 0} \frac{h}{h(\sqrt{a+h} + \sqrt{a})} \qquad \qquad \text{numerator and the denominator.}$$

$$= \lim_{h \to 0} \frac{1}{\sqrt{a+h} + \sqrt{a}}, \quad h \neq 0$$

$$= \frac{1}{\sqrt{a+0} + \sqrt{a}}$$

$$= \frac{1}{2\sqrt{a}}$$

Now we can calculate the slopes for the given points.

For $(1, 1)$, $a = 1$,   For $(4, 2)$, $a = 4$,   For $(9, 3)$, $a = 9$,

$$m = \frac{1}{2\sqrt{1}} \qquad\qquad m = \frac{1}{2\sqrt{4}} \qquad\qquad m = \frac{1}{2\sqrt{9}}$$

$$= \frac{1}{2} \qquad\qquad\qquad = \frac{1}{4} \qquad\qquad\qquad = \frac{1}{6}$$

b) As the x-values in part a) increase, the values of the slopes decrease. In other words, as we move to the right along the graph, the slope of the graph decreases. This can be verified by looking at the graph.

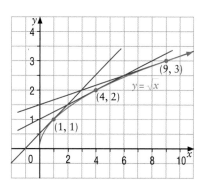

Key Concepts

- To determine the slope of a tangent to a curve at a point P, first determine an expression for the slope of a secant joining P to a point Q on the curve. Then, let Q approach P more and more closely, and the resulting slopes of the secants will approach the slope of the tangent at P more and more closely. The slope of the tangent is the limit of the slopes of the secants.

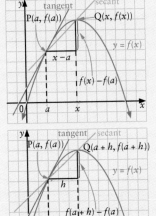

- Expressions for slopes of secants and tangents:

$$m_{PQ} = \frac{f(x) - f(a)}{x - a} \qquad \text{Slope of secant PQ}$$

$$m = \lim_{x \to a} \frac{f(x) - f(a)}{x - a} \qquad \text{Slope of tangent} \qquad \textbf{Formula 1}$$

- Expressions for slopes of secants and tangents:

$$m_{PQ} = \frac{f(a + h) - f(a)}{h} \qquad \text{Slope of secant PQ}$$

$$m = \lim_{h \to 0} \frac{f(a + h) - f(a)}{h} \qquad \text{Slope of tangent} \qquad \textbf{Formula 2}$$

Communicate Your Understanding

1. Consider the limiting process described in this section for determining the slope of a tangent to a curve by working with the slopes of secants.
a) Sketch a diagram that represents the situation. Make sure to include several secants and the tangent. Label the diagram completely.
b) Explain the limiting process represented on your graph in part a).
c) Explain how tables of values can be used to determine the slope of a tangent. Explain how the tables correspond to the graph in part a).
d) Explain how an algebraic procedure can be used to determine the slope of a tangent. Explain how the algebraic procedure corresponds to both the numerical method in part c) and the graph in part a).
2. Two formulas are used to find the slopes of tangents. Explain in your own words, with the aid of a graph, how the expressions are related. Use the following as a guide in your explanation.
a) How is the concept of x approaching a in Formula 1 similar to h approaching 0 in Formula 2?
b) What value does $f(x)$ approach as x approaches a (Formula 1)? What value does $f(a + h)$ approach as h approaches zero (Formula 2)? How are the two cases related?
3. a) Consider functions of the form $y = cx^3$. Which formula would you prefer to use when finding the slope of the tangent at any point on the curve? Explain.
b) Are there any advantages to using the other formula?
4. In the algebraic solution to Example 1, the solution is valid provided that $x \neq 2$, since the expression for the slope of a secant PQ has the expression $x - 2$ in the denominator. Is it valid in the final step of the calculation to substitute $x = 2$ in order to determine the limit? Explain.

Practise

A **1.** A graph is defined by the equation $y = f(x)$.
a) Find an equation for the slope of the secant through the points $P(2, f(2))$ and $Q(x, f(x))$.
b) Find an equation for the slope of the tangent at P.

2. A graph is defined by the equation $y = f(x)$.
a) Find an equation for the slope of the secant through the points $P(2, f(2))$ and $Q(2 + h, f(2 + h))$.
b) Find an equation for the slope of the tangent at P.

3. a) Find the slope of the tangent to the parabola $y = x^2 - 4x + 5$ at the point $(2, 1)$,
i) using Formula 1
ii) using Formula 2
b) Find an equation of the tangent.
c) Graph the parabola and the tangent.
d) Is one formula easier to use than the other in this case? Explain.

4. a) Find the slope of the tangent to the curve $y = x^3$ at the point $(1, 1)$,
i) using Formula 1
ii) using Formula 2
b) Find an equation of the tangent.
c) Graph the curve and the tangent.
d) Is one formula easier to use than the other in this case? Explain.

5. Application Find the slope of the tangent to the curve at the given point.
a) $y = x^2 + 2$ at $(2, 6)$
b) $f(x) = x^2 - 6x + 9$ at $(1, 4)$
c) $g(x) = \sqrt{x - 3}$ at $(7, 2)$
d) $y = \dfrac{1}{x}$ at $\left(2, \dfrac{1}{2}\right)$
e) $h(x) = \dfrac{1}{x - 2}$ at $(3, 1)$
f) $y = \dfrac{1}{x^2}$ at $(1, 1)$
g) $y = \dfrac{x}{1 - x}$ at $(2, -2)$
h) $f(x) = \dfrac{1}{\sqrt{x}}$ at $(1, 1)$

6. Application Find the equation of the tangent to the curve at the given point.
a) $h(x) = x^2 - x + 3$ at $(-1, 5)$
b) $y = 4 - x^2$ at $(-2, 0)$
c) $y = \dfrac{1}{x + 3}$ at $(-4, -1)$
d) $f(x) = \sqrt{3 - x}$ at $(-1, 2)$
e) $y = \dfrac{2x + 1}{x - 1}$ at $(2, 5)$
f) $f(x) = \dfrac{1}{\sqrt{x - 1}}$ at $(2, 1)$

7. a) Find the slopes of the tangents to the parabola $y = x^2 - 8x + 12$ at the points whose x-coordinates are given.
i) 0   ii) 2   iii) 4   iv) 6
b) Graph the parabola and the tangents.

Apply, Solve, Communicate

B **8.** Communication a) Consider the following definition of a tangent: A tangent is a line that touches a curve at only one point over a small interval.
i) Determine an equation of the tangent to the graph of $f(x) = x$ at $x = 2$.
ii) In light of the result of part i), what is your assessment of the definition of the tangent suggested in part a)?
b) Consider the following definition of a tangent: A tangent is a line that touches a curve but does not cross the curve at a point.
i) Determine an equation for the tangent to the graph of $f(x) = x^3$ at $x = 0$.
ii) In light of the result of part i), what is your assessment of the definition of the tangent suggested in part b)?

9. For each of the following curves,
i) find the slope of the tangent at the given point
ii) find the equation of the tangent at the given point
iii) graph the curve and the tangent
a) $y = x^2 - 9$ at $(3, 0)$
b) $g(x) = x^2 + 4x - 1$ at $(-2, -5)$
c) $y = 4 - x^2$ at $(2, 0)$
d) $g(x) = x^3 - 2$ at $(2, 6)$
e) $f(x) = 8 - x^3$ at $(2, 0)$

f) $y = \dfrac{1}{1-x}$ at $(2, -1)$

g) $y = \sqrt{x+2}$ at $(2, 2)$

h) $h(x) = x^4$ at $(1, 1)$

10. Application Find the equation of the tangent to the graph of the given function at the given point.

a) $f(x) = 2x^2 - 3x + 2$, $(1, 1)$

b) $g(x) = x^2 - x^3$, $(0, 0)$

c) $g(x) = \dfrac{x+1}{x-1}$, $(2, 3)$

d) $f(x) = \dfrac{x^2 - 4}{x+4}$, $(0, -1)$

e) $f(x) = \sqrt{x^2 + 9}$, $(4, 5)$

f) $g(x) = \dfrac{1}{\sqrt{x}}$, $\left(4, \dfrac{1}{2}\right)$

11. Communication For each curve,
i)   find the slope of the tangent at the general point whose x-coordinate is a
ii)   find the slopes of the tangents at the points whose x-coordinates are -2, -1, 0, 1, 2
iii)   describe how the slope of the function changes as x increases

a) $y = x^2$

b) $f(x) = x^3$

c) $y = x^2 + 2x - 3$

d) $g(x) = \dfrac{6}{x-3}$

e) $y = \sqrt{x^2 + 1}$

f) $h(x) = \dfrac{1}{x^2 + 1}$

12. Application The gravitational potential energy of the MIR space station, in joules, at a distance of x metres from the centre of Earth, can be described by the equation

$E = -\dfrac{5.38 \times 10^{19}}{x}$. Determine the slope of the tangent to the graph at each value of x.

a) 6.77×10^6 m (radius of MIR's stable orbit, 390 km above Earth's surface)

b) 6.6×10^6 m (220 km above Earth's surface)

c) 6.5×10^6 m (120 km above Earth's surface)

d) 6.38×10^6 m (MIR crashes into the Atlantic Ocean)

13. The slope of the curve in question 12 represents the force on MIR due to gravity. Verify the acceleration due to gravity at Earth's surface by dividing your solution to part d) by MIR's mass, 135 000 kg.

14. Inquiry/Problem Solving A principle used by many investors in the stock market is to buy low and sell high. An investor has just sold all her shares in a stock, which she believes has just reached a peak market value. She then records the price of the stock over the next four days and discovers, using regression, that the market value per share, V, in dollars, is a function of the time, t, in days, and can be expressed by the equation $V = t^3 - 3t^2 + 10$, where $t \in [0, 4]$.

a)   Use a graphing calculator or graphing software to draw the graph of the function.

b)   Did the investor make a wise decision selling the stock at $t = 0$? Explain.

c)   Find the slope of the tangent at $t = 0$ using the calculator or software.

d)   At what time should the investor have reinvested in this stock? Explain. What is the slope of the tangent at this point?

e)   Using one of the formulas, find the slope of the tangent at the value of t you found in part d).

f)   Have you found a new principle for investing or do *both* methods contain an element of risk? Explain.

15. Inquiry/Problem Solving a)   Find the slope of the tangent to the parabola $y = 2x^2 + 3x$ at the point whose x-coordinate is a.

b)   At what point on the parabola is the tangent parallel to the line $y = 14x - 6$?

16. Communication Consider the function $f(x) = (x + 0.001)^{10}$. The object of this question is to find $\lim\limits_{x \to 0} f(x)$.

a)   Determine the values of $f(x)$ for the following values of x, and summarize your results in a table: $x = 10, 1, 0.1, 0.01, 0.001$.

b) Using the table in part a), conjecture a value for $\lim\limits_{x \to 0} f(x)$.

c) Repeat part a) for the following values of x: $x = 0.0001, 0.000\,01, 0.000\,001, 0.000\,000\,1$.

d) Do the results of part c) suggest you revise the conjecture of part b)? Explain.

e) When trying to determine a limit using a table of values, how do you know how far to go in constructing the table? Explain.

f) How confident are you in the conjectures that you made in this question? Explain.

g) Using the results of this question, explain why determining limits using reasoning together with algebraic arguments leads to greater certainty than using tables of values.

17. a) Find the equation of the tangent to $y = x^2 + 6x + 9$ that has a slope of 4.

b) Find equations of the tangents to $y = x^3$ that have a slope of 12.

18. Find the equations of the tangents to the graph of $y = x^3 - x$ at the intersection of the graph with the x-axis. Sketch the graph and the tangents.

19. Find the points of intersection of the parabolas $y = \dfrac{1}{2}x^2$ and $y = 1 - \dfrac{1}{2}x^2$. Show that, at each of these points, the tangents to the two parabolas are perpendicular.

20. Inquiry/Problem Solving The force of gravity, F, in newtons, on a 1000-kg satellite in the gravitational field of Earth can be found by calculating the rate of change of the gravitational potential energy, E, in joules, of the satellite with respect to the distance, x, in metres, of the satellite from the centre of Earth. The gravitational potential energy of the satellite is given by the equation

$$E = -\frac{4 \times 10^{17}}{x}$$

where x must be greater than or equal to the radius of Earth (6.38×10^6 m).

a) Find the force of gravity on a satellite in a circular orbit of two Earth radii above Earth's surface.

b) Where could a satellite be placed in space so that the gravitational force acting on it due to Earth would be zero? Explain.

Historical Bite: The Great Plague and Mathematics

If it were not for the tragedy of the Great Plague, which hit Europe in 1665, Newton may not have been such an important figure in the discovery of calculus. Because of the plague, Cambridge University, where Newton was a student, was forced to close. With a lot of spare time on his hands, Newton began to explore his own ideas more deeply. In the following two years, he discovered calculus, and made many other discoveries in the fields of mathematics and physics.

3.3 The Limit of a Function

As we have seen in the last two sections, the slope of a tangent to a curve can be found using limits. In Section 3.4, we will see that limits also arise in computing velocities and other rates of change. In fact, limits are fundamental to all of calculus. In this section, we give a basic definition of a limit. We also consider limits as they are applied in general, not just for finding the slopes of tangents, and methods for computing them.

To help with the idea of a limit, let us explore the properties of the electric current in the simple direct-current (DC) circuit shown. A battery that supplies a constant voltage of 10 V, a constant resistor, and a variable resistor are connected in parallel as shown. A fuse is used to stop the electric current I, in amperes, from becoming too large. This happens when the resistance R, in ohms, in the variable resistor decreases to values approaching 2 Ω. When the fuse burns out, the current I becomes zero. For values of R greater than 2, the electric current in the circuit is given by the equation

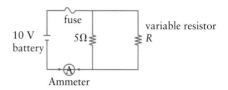

$$I = \frac{2(5 + R)}{R}$$

For values of R less than or equal to 2, the current is zero. Thus,

$$I = \begin{cases} 0, & R \in [0,\ 2] \\ \dfrac{2(5 + R)}{R}, & R \in (2,\ \infty) \end{cases}$$

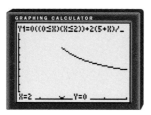

Window variables:
$x \in [0, 5]$, $y \in [0, 10]$

Notice that the function $I(R)$ behaves quite differently over the intervals $R \in [0, 2]$ and $R \in (2, \infty)$. In particular, the behaviour of the function as x approaches 2 from the left side is different from the behaviour as x approaches 2 from the right side. This type of discontinuity will be investigated later in the section.

Defining Limits

We begin investigating limits by examining the behaviour of the rational function

$$f(x) = \frac{x^3 + x^2 - 4x - 4}{x - 2}$$ for values of x near 2. Note that this process is somewhat different

from determining the slope of a tangent to a curve, as was done in the previous two sections. In this case, we are interested only in examining the *values* of the function, not the slopes of any secants or tangents. Also note that the function is not defined for $x = 2$, so we can examine values of the function only for x-values near 2, but not equal to 2.

x	$f(x)$	x	$f(x)$
1.9	11.31	2.1	12.71
1.99	11.9301	2.01	12.0701
1.999	11.993001	2.001	12.007001

We can also determine these values using the **TABLE feature** of a graphing calculator or graphing software, after selecting Ask mode on the TABLE SETUP screen:

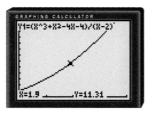

Window variables:
$x \in [0, 4]$, $y \in [0, 24]$

From the table and the graph of $f(x)$, note that when x is close to 2, on either side of 2, $f(x)$ is close to 12. Furthermore, it appears that, as x approaches 2 more and more closely, the values of $f(x)$ approach 12 more and more closely. Verify this by entering values even closer to 2, such as 1.999 999 and 2.000 001, into the graphing calculator. This is expressed as "the limit of $\dfrac{x^3 + x^2 - 4x - 4}{x - 2}$ as x approaches 2 is equal to 12,"

or, in brief,

$$\lim_{x \to 2} \frac{x^3 + x^2 - 4x - 4}{x - 2} = 12$$

> In general, the limit of a function is written $\lim_{x \to a} f(x) = L$, read as "the limit of $f(x)$, as x approaches a, equals L," if the values of $f(x)$ approach L more and more closely as x approaches a more and more closely, from either side of a, but $x \neq a$.

Note the phrase "but $x \neq a$" in the limit definition. This means that, in finding the limit of $f(x)$ as x approaches a, we never consider $x = a$. In fact, $f(x)$ need not even be defined when $x = a$, as in $f(x) = \dfrac{x^3 + x^2 - 4x - 4}{x - 2}$ above. The only thing that matters is how $f(x)$ behaves *near a*. The reason for this is that we want limits to be applicable to the calculation of the slope of a tangent to a curve at a point P, by first determining the slope of a secant PQ and then letting Q approach P. But, as we saw in the previous two sections, the slope of a secant is undefined when Q = P, so we need to exclude Q = P from our reasoning.

The graph of the function $f(x) = \dfrac{x^3 + x^2 - 4x - 4}{x - 2}$ has a hole at $x = 2$ because $f(x)$ is not defined there. This hole is called a **discontinuity**, and the function $f(x)$ is described as being **discontinuous** at $x = 2$. There are three different types of discontinuities: removable, jump, and infinite. The discontinuity in $f(x)$ is called **removable**, because we could remove it by defining $f(x)$ appropriately for the value $x = 2$. We discuss the other two types of discontinuities later in this section.

The figure on the next page shows the graphs of three similar functions that behave differently at $x = a$. In part a), $f(a)$ is defined at a and $f(a) = L$. In part b), $f(a)$ is defined at a and $f(a) \neq L$. In part c), $f(a)$ is not defined at a. But in each case, despite the differences in the values of $f(a)$, we have $\lim_{x \to a} f(x) = L$.

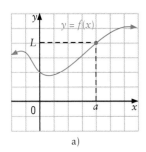

a)

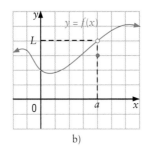

b)

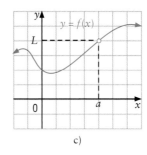

c)

Investigate & Inquire: Discontinuities in Functions

In this investigation, you will explore discontinuities in a specific function and examine the behaviour of the function values near these discontinuities.

1. a) Using a graphing calculator or graphing software, graph $f(x) = \dfrac{x-4}{x^2 - 6x + 8}$.

Use the decimal ("friendly") window by pressing $\boxed{\text{ZOOM}}$ 4.

b) Alternatively, sketch a graph of $f(x)$ for values of x close to 2, on either side of 2. Repeat for values of x close to 4.

c) Describe what happens when $x = 4$ and $x = 2$. Is the function defined at these values of x? How can you tell from the equation of the function?

2. What kind of discontinuity occurs at $x = 4$?

3. Construct tables by finding the values of $f(x) = \dfrac{x-4}{x^2 - 6x + 8}$ for values of x

approaching 4 from both sides, but not equal to 4. Alternatively, use the **TABLE feature** of a graphing calculator or graphing software. Why can x not be equal to 4?

4. a) Find $\displaystyle\lim_{x \to 4} \dfrac{x-4}{x^2 - 6x + 8}$.

b) Suppose $f(x)$ is redefined as $f(x) = \begin{cases} \dfrac{x-4}{x^2 - 6x + 8} & \text{if } x \neq 4 \\ 0.5 & \text{if } x = 4 \end{cases}$

How does this affect the limit calculated in part a)?

5. Factor the function $f(x) = \dfrac{x-4}{x^2 - 6x + 8}$ and simplify it. Call the new factored function $g(x)$. Describe the difference between $f(x)$ and $g(x)$.

6. Construct tables by finding the values of $f(x) = \dfrac{x-4}{x^2 - 6x + 8}$ for values of x

approaching 2 from both sides, but not equal to 2. Alternatively, use the **TABLE feature** of a graphing calculator or graphing software. Why can x not be equal to 2?

7. How does the behaviour of the function at $x = 2$ differ from that at $x = 4$?

In the investigation, the function f has an **infinite discontinuity** at $x = 2$. We have already seen such discontinuities—for example, the function $f(x) = \dfrac{1}{x}$ has an infinite discontinuity at $x = 0$, where the graph also has a vertical asymptote. Discontinuities involving vertical asymptotes will be discussed in detail in Chapter 6.

Another type of discontinuity is often encountered in electric circuits that are turned on and off, in economics problems, and in other situations. Consider the net worth of a company or business that is experiencing financial difficulty. The value of the company is decreasing over time until the net worth is less than zero. Eventually the company declares bankruptcy. At this time, the company's debts are forgiven, its net worth is zero, and so it has a chance to make a new start. If the new business is successful, the net worth of the company could rise rapidly. A function that could be used to model this situation is

$$v(t) = \begin{cases} 2 - 2t & \text{if } t \in [0, 2] \\ (t - 2)^2 & \text{if } t \in (2, \infty) \end{cases}$$

where t is the time, in years, and v is the net worth of the small business, in tens of thousands of dollars. The discontinuity at $t = 2$ is called a **jump discontinuity**, which occurs when there is a break in the graph of the function, as in the DC circuit at the beginning of this section. In effect, the graph of the function "jumps" from one value to another. Some other examples of situations that may be represented by functions with jump discontinuities are the population of Ottawa as a function of time, the cost of a taxi ride as a function of distance, and the cost of mailing a first-class letter as a function of its mass. Such functions can be specified by using different formulas in different parts of their domains.

Remember that a function is a rule. For this particular function, if $t \in [0, 2]$, the value of $v(t)$ is $2 - 2t$. If $t \in (2, \infty)$, the value of $v(t)$ is $(t - 2)^2$. For instance, we compute $v(1)$, $v(2)$, and $v(3)$ as follows.

Since $1 \le 2$,
$v(1) = 2 - 2(1)$
$\quad = 0$

Since $2 \le 2$,
$v(2) = 2 - 2(2)$
$\quad = -2$

Since $3 > 2$,
$v(3) = ((3) - 2)^2$
$\quad = 1$

We can graph piecewise functions using a graphing calculator or graphing software.

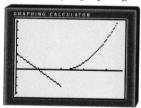

Window variables:
$x \in [0, 4.7]$, $y \in [-3.1, 6.2]$

We now investigate the limiting behaviour of $f(x)$ as x approaches 2 from the left and from the right, that is, for x-values less than and greater than 2.

x	$f(x)$
1.9	−1.8
1.99	−1.98
1.999	−1.998
2.1	0.01
2.01	0.0001
2.001	0.000001

1E−4 means 1.0×10^{-4} or 0.0001.

From the table, we see that $v(t)$ approaches -2 as t approaches 2 from the left, but $v(t)$ approaches 0 as t approaches 2 from the right. The notation used to indicate this is

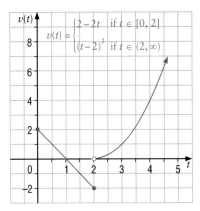

$$\lim_{x \to 2^-} v(t) = -2 \qquad \text{and} \qquad \lim_{x \to 2^+} v(t) = 0$$

Such limits are called **one-sided limits**. Since the function approaches different values from the left and the right, we say that the limit $\lim_{x \to 2} v(t)$ does not exist. For a limit to exist, the one-sided limits must exist and be equal.

In general, a **left-hand limit** is written $\lim_{x \to a^-} f(x)$, which is read as "the limit of $f(x)$ as x approaches a from the left," and a **right-hand limit** is written $\lim_{x \to a^+} f(x)$, which is read as "the limit of $f(x)$ as x approaches a from the right." If the values of $f(x)$ approach L more and more closely as x approaches a more and more closely, with $x < a$, then $\lim_{x \to a^-} f(x) = L$. Similarly, if we consider only $x > a$, if the values of $f(x)$ approach L more and more closely as x approaches a more and more closely, then $\lim_{x \to a^+} f(x) = L$.

As mentioned above, if a function behaves differently to the left and to the right of a number a, then $\lim_{x \to a} f(x)$ does not exist. That is,

If $\lim_{x \to a^-} f(x) \neq \lim_{x \to a^+} f(x)$, then $\lim_{x \to a} f(x)$ does not exist.

If $\lim_{x \to a^-} f(x) = L = \lim_{x \to a^+} f(x)$, then $\lim_{x \to a} f(x) = L$. (This is true even if $f(a) \neq L$.)

Example 1 Limits and Discontinuities

a) The graph of a function f is shown. Use it to find the following limits, if they exist.

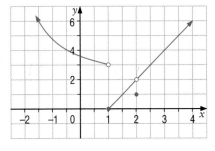

i) $\lim_{x \to 0^-} f(x)$ ii) $\lim_{x \to 0^+} f(x)$ iii) $\lim_{x \to 0} f(x)$

iv) $\lim_{x \to 1^-} f(x)$ v) $\lim_{x \to 1^+} f(x)$ vi) $\lim_{x \to 1} f(x)$

vii) $\lim_{x \to 2^-} f(x)$ viii) $\lim_{x \to 2^+} f(x)$ ix) $\lim_{x \to 2} f(x)$

b) There are two discontinuities on the graph. Identify each as a jump discontinuity, an infinite discontinuity, or a removable discontinuity.

Solution

a) From the graph, the values of $f(x)$ approach 3.5 as x approaches 0 from the left as well as from the right. Therefore,

i) $\lim\limits_{x \to 0^-} f(x) = 3.5$ and ii) $\lim\limits_{x \to 0^+} f(x) = 3.5$

iii) Since the left- and right-hand limits are equal, $\lim\limits_{x \to 0} f(x) = 3.5$.

From the graph, the values of $f(x)$ approach 3 as x approaches 1 from the left, but they approach 0 as x approaches 1 from the right. Therefore,

iv) $\lim\limits_{x \to 1^-} f(x) = 3$ and v) $\lim\limits_{x \to 1^+} f(x) = 0$

vi) Since the left- and right-hand limits are not equal, $\lim\limits_{x \to 1} f(x)$ does not exist.

From the graph,

vii) $\lim\limits_{x \to 2^-} f(x) = 2$ and viii) $\lim\limits_{x \to 2} f(x) = 2$

ix) Since the left- and right-hand limits are equal, $\lim\limits_{x \to 2} f(x) = 2$, despite the fact that $f(2) = 1$.

b) The discontinuity at $x = 1$ is a jump discontinuity, because the function "jumps" from one value to another. The discontinuity at $x = 2$ is a removable discontinuity, since it can be removed by redefining $f(2) = 2$.

Another function with a jump discontinuity is the Heaviside function, named after the electrical engineer Oliver Heaviside (1850–1925). This function describes the electric current in a circuit that is switched on at a specific time, $t = 0$. For $t < 0$, the current is off, which is represented by $H(t) = 0$. For $t \geq 0$, the current is on, which is represented by $H(t) = 1$.

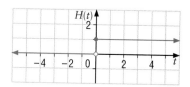

The Heaviside function is defined by

$$H(t) = \begin{cases} 0 & \text{if } t \in (-\infty, 0) \\ 1 & \text{if } t \in [0, \infty) \end{cases}$$

Example 2 Limits of the Heaviside Function

Evaluate the following limits of the Heaviside function, if possible.

a) $\lim\limits_{t \to 0^-} H(t)$ b) $\lim\limits_{t \to 0^+} H(t)$ c) $\lim\limits_{t \to 0} H(t)$

Solution

a) Since $H(t) = 0$ for $t < 0$,

$$\lim_{t \to 0^-} H(t) = \lim_{t \to 0^-} 0$$
$$= 0$$

b) Since $H(t) = 1$ for $t > 0$,

$$\lim_{t \to 0^+} H(t) = \lim_{t \to 0^+} 1$$
$$= 1$$

c) Since $\lim_{t \to 0^-} H(t) \neq \lim_{t \to 0^+} H(t)$, $\lim_{t \to 0} H(t)$ does not exist.

Example 3 Limits of an Absolute Value Function

Show that $\lim_{x \to 0} |x| = 0$.

Solution

Recall that

$$|x| = \begin{cases} x & \text{if } x \in [0, \infty) \\ -x & \text{if } x \in (-\infty, 0) \end{cases}$$

Therefore,

$$\lim_{x \to 0^+} |x| = \lim_{x \to 0^+} x$$
$$= 0$$

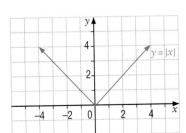

and

$$\lim_{x \to 0^-} |x| = \lim_{x \to 0^-} (-x)$$
$$= 0$$

Since the left- and right-hand limits exist and are equal,

$$\lim_{x \to 0} |x| = 0$$

Example 4 Period and Length of a Pendulum

The period of a pendulum, T, in seconds, is given approximately by the equation $T = 2\sqrt{x}$, where x is the length of the pendulum, in metres.

a) Find $\lim_{x \to 0^+} 2\sqrt{x}$.   b) Explain what the limit in part a) means.

Solution

a) Notice that the function $f(x) = 2\sqrt{x}$ is defined only for $x \geq 0$, so the two-sided limit $\lim_{x \to 0} 2\sqrt{x}$ does not exist. As x approaches 0, $x \geq 0$, $2\sqrt{x}$ approaches 0.

Therefore,

$$\lim_{x \to 0^+} 2\sqrt{x} = 0$$

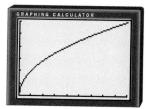

Window variables:
$x \in [0, 9], y \in [0, 6]$

b) As the length of the pendulum gets shorter and shorter, the period also gets shorter and shorter. In other words, the shorter the pendulum, the faster it oscillates.

The result of part b) of Example 4 is true not just for pendulums but for practically all oscillating systems in nature. For instance, earthquakes produce relatively slow (although powerful!) vibrations, but the tiny quartz crystal in a watch vibrates extremely rapidly.

Example 5 Limits of a Function Defined Piecewise

Consider the function
$$f(x) = \begin{cases} x + 3 & \text{if } x \in (-\infty, 0] \\ -x + 2 & \text{if } x \in (0, 2) \\ (x - 2)^2 & \text{if } x \in [2, \infty) \end{cases}$$

Graph the function, and use the graph to determine whether $\lim\limits_{x \to 0} f(x)$ and $\lim\limits_{x \to 2} f(x)$ exist.

Solution

We can graph piecewise functions by including the intervals for each piece in the function definition.

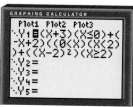
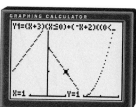

Window variables:
$x \in [-2, 4], y \in [0, 3]$

We first determine the one-sided limits. From the graph, the values of $f(x)$ approach 3 as x approaches 0 from the left, but they approach 2 as x approaches 0 from the right.

Therefore, $\lim\limits_{x \to 0^-} f(x) = 3$ and $\lim\limits_{x \to 0^+} f(x) = 2$.

The left- and right-hand limits are not equal, so $\lim\limits_{x \to 0} f(x)$ does not exist.

However, the values of $f(x)$ approach 0 as x approaches 2 from the left and from the right.

Therefore, $\lim\limits_{x \to 2^-} f(x) = 0$ and $\lim\limits_{x \to 2^+} f(x) = 0$.

The left- and right-hand limits exist and are equal, so $\lim\limits_{x \to 2} f(x) = 0$.

Example 6 Infinite Limits

The magnitude of the repulsive force exerted by an electron at the origin on another electron located at position x on the x-axis is $f(x) = \dfrac{1}{x^2}$, provided the force and distance units are chosen appropriately. Determine $\lim\limits_{x \to 0} f(x)$, if it exists.

Solution

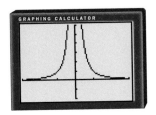

Window variables:
$x \in [-3, 3]$, $y \in [-2, 6]$

First, we graph the function.
From the graph, we can see that the left- and right-hand limits do not exist. For example, as x approaches 0 from the right, the function values get larger and larger, without approaching any specific y-value. The same is true as x approaches 0 from the left. Thus, $\lim\limits_{x \to 0} f(x)$ does not exist.

Example 6 shows the third type of discontinuity, the infinite discontinuity, as also seen in the investigation. If a function does not have a discontinuity at a certain point, it is continuous at that point. A more formal definition follows.

If the limit of a function at a certain value exists, and is equal to the value of the function at that value, then the function is continuous at that value.

> A function f is **continuous at a number** a if $\lim\limits_{x \to a} f(x) = f(a)$.

The definition of continuity implicitly requires three things:
1. $f(a)$ is defined (that is, a is in the domain of f)
2. $\lim\limits_{x \to a} f(x)$ exists $\left(\lim\limits_{x \to a^-} f(x)\text{ and }\lim\limits_{x \to a^+} f(x)\text{ exist and are equal}\right)$
3. $\lim\limits_{x \to a} f(x) = f(a)$

Conversely, if a function f is continuous at a number a, then $\lim\limits_{x \to a} f(x) = f(a)$. If a function has no discontinuities, it is called a **continuous function**. From the definition of a continuous function, if a function $f(x)$ is continuous at $x = a$, to determine $\lim\limits_{x \to a} f(x)$, all we need to do is evaluate $f(a)$.

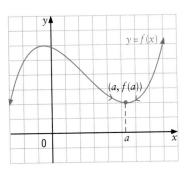

Most physical phenomena, such as the position and velocity of a car, air temperature, and the height of a tree, are continuous. As we saw earlier in this section, a discontinuous function involving electric currents can be written in terms of the Heaviside function, which has a jump discontinuity at $t = 0$ because $\lim\limits_{t \to 0} H(t)$ does not exist.

Using the properties of limits, it can be shown that many familiar functions are continuous. Recall that a polynomial is a function of the form $P(x) = a_n x^n + a_{n-1}x^{n-1} + \cdots + a_1 x + a_0$, where $a_0, a_1, \ldots, a_n$ are constant. A **rational function** is a ratio of polynomials.

a) Every polynomial P is continuous at every number a, that is, $\lim_{x \to a} P(x) = P(a)$.

b) Every rational function $f(x) = \dfrac{P(x)}{Q(x)}$, where P and Q are polynomials, is continuous at

every number a such that $Q(a) \neq 0$, that is, $\lim_{x \to a} \dfrac{P(x)}{Q(x)} = \dfrac{P(a)}{Q(a)}$, provided $Q(a) \neq 0$.

For instance, $f(t) = t^2 + 6t + 5$ is a polynomial, so it is continuous at $t = 3$, and therefore,

$$\lim_{t \to 3}(t^2 + 6t + 5) = f(3)$$
$$= 3^2 + 6(3) + 5$$
$$= 32$$

In this example, as well as others in this section, we are making use of the limit laws.

The Limit Laws

Suppose that the limits $\lim_{x \to a} f(x)$ and $\lim_{x \to a} g(x)$ both exist and c is a constant.

Then, we have the following **limit laws**.

$\lim_{x \to a} c = c$	
$\lim_{x \to a} x = a$	
$\lim_{x \to a} [f(x) + g(x)] = \lim_{x \to a} f(x) + \lim_{x \to a} g(x)$	The limit of a sum is the sum of the limits.
$\lim_{x \to a} [f(x) - g(x)] = \lim_{x \to a} f(x) - \lim_{x \to a} g(x)$	The limit of a difference is the difference of the limits.
$\lim_{x \to a} [cf(x)] = c \lim_{x \to a} f(x)$	The limit of a constant times a function is the constant times the limit of the function.
$\lim_{x \to a} [f(x)g(x)] = \lim_{x \to a} f(x) \lim_{x \to a} g(x)$	The limit of a product is the product of the limits.
$\lim_{x \to a} \dfrac{f(x)}{g(x)} = \dfrac{\lim_{x \to a} f(x)}{\lim_{x \to a} g(x)}$ if $\lim_{x \to a} g(x) \neq 0$.	The limit of a quotient is the quotient of the limits, if the limit of the denominator is not 0.
$\lim_{x \to a} [f(x)]^n = \left[\lim_{x \to a} f(x)\right]^n$ if n is a positive integer.	The limit of a positive integer power is the power of the limit.
$\lim_{x \to a} x^n = a^n$	
$\lim_{x \to a} \sqrt[n]{f(x)} = \sqrt[n]{\lim_{x \to a} f(x)}$ if the root on the right side exists.	The limit of a root is the root of the limit, if the root exists.
$\lim_{x \to a} \sqrt[n]{x} = \sqrt[n]{a}$ if $\sqrt[n]{a}$ exists	

Example 7 Evaluating the Limit of a Function at a Point of Continuity

Evaluate the following limits.

a) $\lim\limits_{x \to 2} \dfrac{x^2 - 3x + 5}{x + 1}$ b) $\lim\limits_{x \to 3} \sqrt{x^2 + 2x + 1}$

Solution

a) Since the function $f(x) = \dfrac{x^2 - 3x + 5}{x + 1}$ is continuous at $x = 2$, the limit is simply $f(2)$.
That is,

$$\lim\limits_{x \to 2} \dfrac{x^2 - 3x + 5}{x + 1} = \dfrac{2^2 - 3(2) + 5}{3}$$
$$= \dfrac{3}{3}$$
$$= 1$$

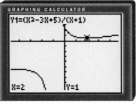

Window variables:
$x \in [-4.7, 4.7], y \in [-18.6, 9.3]$

b) Since $f(x) = \sqrt{x^2 + 2x + 1}$ is continuous at $x = 3$,

$$\lim\limits_{x \to 3} \sqrt{x^2 + 2x + 1} = \sqrt{3^2 + 2(3) + 1}$$
$$= \sqrt{16}$$
$$= 4$$

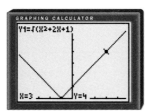

Window variables:
$x \in [-4.7, 4.7], y \in [0, 6.2]$

Example 8 Limit of a Function at a Removable Discontinuity

Evaluate $\lim\limits_{x \to 2} \dfrac{x^2 - 4}{x - 2}$.

Solution

Let $f(x) = \dfrac{x^2 - 4}{x - 2}$.
Graph the function.

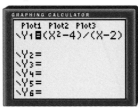   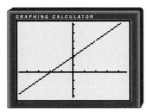

Window variables:
$x \in [-4.7, 4.7], y \in [-3.1, 6.2]$

Note the gap, or hole, in the graph at $x = 2$.

We cannot find the limit by substituting $x = 2$ because $f(2)$ is indeterminate (substituting 2 gives $\dfrac{0}{0}$). Remember that, to determine $\lim\limits_{x \to a} f(x)$, we must consider values of x that are close to a but not equal to a. In this example, $x \neq 2$, so we can factor the numerator as a difference of squares.

$$\lim_{x \to 2} \frac{x^2 - 4}{x - 2} = \lim_{x \to 2} \frac{(x-2)(x+2)}{(x-2)}$$

We are not dividing by 0 since $x \neq 2$.

$$= \lim_{x \to 2} (x + 2)$$

We can substitute because $g(x) = x + 2$ is continuous.

$$= 2 + 2$$
$$= 4$$

Notice in Example 8 that we replaced the given rational function by a continuous function, $g(x) = x + 2$, that is equal to $f(x)$ for $x \neq 2$. Notice also that the graph of $f(x)$ above is identical to the graph of $g(x)$ except at $x = 2$. This is a removable discontinuity.

Key Concepts

- The limit of a function is written as $\lim_{x \to a} f(x) = L$, which is read as "the limit of $f(x)$, as x approaches a, equals L."

- If the values of $f(x)$ approach L more and more closely as x approaches a more and more closely (from either side of a), but $x \neq a$, then $\lim_{x \to a} f(x) = L$.

- The left-hand limit of a function is written as $\lim_{x \to a^-} f(x)$, which is read as "the limit of $f(x)$ as x approaches a from the left."

- If the values of $f(x)$ approach L more and more closely as x approaches a more and more closely, with $x < a$, then $\lim_{x \to a^-} f(x) = L$.

- The right-hand limit of a function is written as $\lim_{x \to a^+} f(x)$, which is read as "the limit of $f(x)$ as x approaches a from the right."

- If the values of $f(x)$ approach L more and more closely as x approaches a more and more closely, with $x > a$, then $\lim_{x \to a^+} f(x) = L$.

- In order for $\lim_{x \to a} f(x)$ to exist, the one-sided limits $\lim_{x \to a^-} f(x)$ and $\lim_{x \to a^+} f(x)$ must both exist and be equal. That is,

  If $\lim_{x \to a^-} f(x) \neq \lim_{x \to a^+} f(x)$, then $\lim_{x \to a} f(x)$ does not exist.

  If $\lim_{x \to a^-} f(x) = L = \lim_{x \to a^+} f(x)$, then $\lim_{x \to a} f(x) = L$.

- To check that a function $f(x)$ is continuous at $x = a$, check that the following three conditions are satisfied:

  a) $f(a)$ is defined (that is, a is in the domain of $f(x)$)
  b) $\lim_{x \to a} f(x)$ exists
  c) $\lim_{x \to a} f(x) = f(a)$

  Also, if $f(x)$ is continuous at $x = a$, then $\lim_{x \to a} f(x) = f(a)$.

- Every polynomial P is continuous at every number, that is, $\lim_{x \to a} P(x) = P(a)$.

- Every rational function $f(x) = \dfrac{P(x)}{Q(x)}$, where P and Q are polynomials, is continuous at every number a for which $Q(a) \neq 0$, that is, $\displaystyle\lim_{x \to a} \dfrac{P(x)}{Q(x)} = \dfrac{P(a)}{Q(a)}$, $Q(a) \neq 0$.

- Discontinuities:

  a) If a function $f(x)$ has a removable discontinuity at $x = a$, then $\displaystyle\lim_{x \to a} f(x) = L$ exists, and the discontinuity can be removed by (re)defining $f(x) = L$ at the single point a.

  b) If a function has a jump discontinuity, the function "jumps" from one value to another.

  c) If a function $f(x)$ has an infinite discontinuity at $x = a$, the absolute values of the function become larger and larger as x approaches a.

Communicate Your Understanding

1. Suppose that $\displaystyle\lim_{x \to 3} f(x) = 7$.

a) How is this equation read?

b) What does the equation mean?

c) Is it possible for the equation to be true if $f(3) = 4$? Explain.

d) Is it possible for the equation to be false if $f(3) = 7$? Explain.

2. Suppose that $\displaystyle\lim_{x \to 2^-} f(x) = 1$ and $\displaystyle\lim_{x \to 2^+} f(x) = 5$.

a) What kind of limit is each equation? What does each equation mean?

b) Does $\displaystyle\lim_{x \to 2} f(x)$ exist? What kind of discontinuity exists at $x = 2$? Explain.

3. a) Can the two-sided limit ever exist at a jump discontinuity? an infinite discontinuity? Explain using diagrams.

b) For which type of discontinuity does the two-sided limit always exist? Explain.

4. Given that

$$\lim_{x \to 2} f(x) = 4 \qquad \lim_{x \to 3} f(x) = 0 \qquad \lim_{x \to 2} g(x) = 0 \qquad \lim_{x \to 3} g(x) = -3$$

explain why each of the following limits does not exist.

a) $\displaystyle\lim_{x \to 2} \dfrac{f(x)}{g(x)}$ b) $\displaystyle\lim_{x \to 2} \dfrac{g(x)}{4 - f(x)}$ c) $\displaystyle\lim_{x \to 3} \left(g(x) - \dfrac{4}{f(x)} \right)$

5. a) Explain in your own words the conditions that must be met for a function $f(x)$ to be continuous at a number a.

b) A student claims, "If the left- and right-hand limits of a function, as x approaches a, are equal, then the function is continuous at a." Discuss the validity of this statement.

c) Draw examples of each of the following discontinuous functions.

i) $f(a)$ is defined, $\displaystyle\lim_{x \to a} f(x)$ exists, $\displaystyle\lim_{x \to a} f(x) \neq f(a)$

ii) $f(a)$ is defined, $\displaystyle\lim_{x \to a} f(x)$ does not exist

6. Explain, using examples, when substitution can be used to solve a limit.

Practise

A **1.** Use the graph of $f(x)$ to state the value of each limit, if it exists. If it does not exist, explain why.

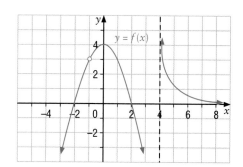

a) $\lim\limits_{x \to -1} f(x)$

b) $\lim\limits_{x \to 0} f(x)$

c) $\lim\limits_{x \to 2} f(x)$

d) $\lim\limits_{x \to 4} f(x)$

e) $\lim\limits_{x \to 6} f(x)$

2. Use the graph of $g(x)$ to state the value of each limit, if it exists. If it does not exist, explain why.

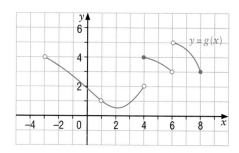

a) $\lim\limits_{x \to -3^+} g(x)$

b) $\lim\limits_{x \to 1^-} g(x)$

c) $\lim\limits_{x \to 1^+} g(x)$

d) $\lim\limits_{x \to 1} g(x)$

e) $\lim\limits_{x \to 2^-} g(x)$

f) $\lim\limits_{x \to 2^+} g(x)$

g) $\lim\limits_{x \to 2} g(x)$

h) $\lim\limits_{x \to 4^-} g(x)$

i) $\lim\limits_{x \to 4^+} g(x)$

j) $\lim\limits_{x \to 4} g(x)$

k) $\lim\limits_{x \to 6^-} g(x)$

l) $\lim\limits_{x \to 6^+} g(x)$

m) $\lim\limits_{x \to 6} g(x)$

n) $\lim\limits_{x \to 8^-} g(x)$

3. Use the graph of $g(x)$ to state the value of each quantity, if it exists. If it does not exist, explain why.

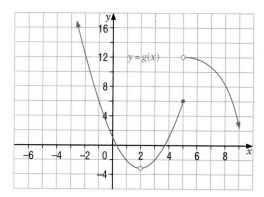

a) $\lim\limits_{x \to -2} g(x)$

b) $\lim\limits_{x \to 0} g(x)$

c) $\lim\limits_{x \to 2^-} g(x)$

d) $g(2)$

e) $\lim\limits_{x \to 2^+} g(x)$

f) $\lim\limits_{x \to 2} g(x)$

g) $\lim\limits_{x \to 5^-} g(x)$

h) $g(5)$

i) $\lim\limits_{x \to 5^+} g(x)$

j) $\lim\limits_{x \to 5} g(x)$

4. Identify each discontinuity in questions 1 to 3 as removable, jump, or infinite.

5. Let
$$f(x) = \begin{cases} -2 & \text{if } x \in (-\infty,\ 1) \\ x - 3 & \text{if } x \in [1,\ \infty) \end{cases}$$

Sketch the graph of $f(x)$. Then, find each limit, if it exists. If the limit does not exist, explain why.

a) $\lim\limits_{x \to 1^-} f(x)$ b) $\lim\limits_{x \to 1^+} f(x)$ c) $\lim\limits_{x \to 1} f(x)$

6. Let
$$g(x) = \begin{cases} x^2 & \text{if } x \in (-\infty,\ 2] \\ -x + 1 & \text{if } x \in (2,\ \infty) \end{cases}$$

Sketch the graph of $g(x)$. Then, find each limit, if it exists. If the limit does not exist, explain why.

a) $\lim\limits_{x \to 2^-} g(x)$ b) $\lim\limits_{x \to 2^+} g(x)$ c) $\lim\limits_{x \to 2} g(x)$

7. Let

$$h(x) = \begin{cases} x+2 & \text{if } x \in (-\infty,\ 0) \\ 0 & \text{if } x = 0 \\ -x-2 & \text{if } x \in (0,\ \infty) \end{cases}$$

Sketch the graph of $h(x)$. Then, find each limit, if it exists. If the limit does not exist, explain why.

a) $\lim\limits_{x \to 0^-} h(x)$ b) $\lim\limits_{x \to 0^+} h(x)$ c) $\lim\limits_{x \to 0} h(x)$

8. Let

$$f(x) = \begin{cases} -x^2 & \text{if } x \in (-\infty,\ -1) \\ 1 & \text{if } x = -1 \\ x & \text{if } x \in (-1,\ \infty) \end{cases}$$

Sketch the graph of $f(x)$. Then, find each limit, if it exists. If the limit does not exist, explain why.

a) $\lim\limits_{x \to -1^-} f(x)$ b) $\lim\limits_{x \to -1^+} f(x)$ c) $\lim\limits_{x \to -1} f(x)$

9. Using a graphing calculator or graphing software, find each limit, if it exists.

a) $\lim\limits_{x \to 0^+} \sqrt[4]{x}$ b) $\lim\limits_{x \to 2} \sqrt[4]{4-2x}$

c) $\lim\limits_{x \to 4^-} |x-4|$ d) $\lim\limits_{x \to 4^+} |x-4|$

e) $\lim\limits_{x \to 4} |x-4|$ f) $\lim\limits_{x \to 0^-} \dfrac{|x|}{x}$

g) $\lim\limits_{x \to 0^+} \dfrac{|x|}{x}$ h) $\lim\limits_{x \to 0} \dfrac{|x|}{x}$

10. Determine the value of each limit.

a) $\lim\limits_{x \to 2} 4$ b) $\lim\limits_{x \to 6} \pi$

c) $\lim\limits_{x \to 5} x$ d) $\lim\limits_{x \to 4} x^2$

e) $\lim\limits_{x \to 2} (3x-4)$ f) $\lim\limits_{x \to -1} (3x^2 - 4x + 10)$

g) $\lim\limits_{x \to 1}(x^3 - x^2 + x - 1)$ h) $\lim\limits_{x \to 0} \dfrac{x-4}{x+2}$

i) $\lim\limits_{x \to 3} \dfrac{x^2 + 8x + 12}{x^2 + 2x}$ j) $\lim\limits_{t \to -2} \sqrt{3t^4 + 4t^2}$

11. Find each limit.

a) $\lim\limits_{x \to 3} \dfrac{x^2 - 9}{x-3}$ b) $\lim\limits_{x \to 2} \dfrac{x-2}{x^2-4}$

c) $\lim\limits_{x \to 4} \dfrac{x^2 - 6x + 8}{x-4}$ d) $\lim\limits_{x \to -2} \dfrac{x+2}{x^2 - 3x - 10}$

e) $\lim\limits_{x \to -3} \dfrac{2x^2 + 7x + 3}{x^2 - 9}$ f) $\lim\limits_{x \to 4} \dfrac{x^2 + 2x - 24}{x^2 - 6x + 8}$

g) $\lim\limits_{x \to 1} \dfrac{5x^2 - 3x - 2}{3x^2 - 7x + 4}$ h) $\lim\limits_{x \to 2} \dfrac{x^3 - 8}{x^2 - 4}$

i) $\lim\limits_{x \to 3} \dfrac{x-3}{x^3 - 27}$ j) $\lim\limits_{x \to -2} \dfrac{x^3 + 8}{x+2}$

k) $\lim\limits_{x \to 4} \dfrac{x-4}{\sqrt{x}-2}$ l) $\lim\limits_{x \to 3} \dfrac{\dfrac{1}{x} - \dfrac{1}{3}}{x-3}$

Apply, Solve, Communicate

B 12. Communication Use the graphs of $f(x)$ and $g(x)$ to evaluate each limit, if it exists. If the limit does not exist, explain why.

a) $\lim\limits_{x \to -2} [f(x) + g(x)]$ b) $\lim\limits_{x \to -2} [f(x)g(x)]$

c) $\lim\limits_{x \to 2} \sqrt{f(x)g(x)}$ d) $\lim\limits_{x \to 0} [f(x) - g(x)]$

e) $\lim\limits_{x \to 0} \dfrac{f(x)}{g(x)}$ f) $\lim\limits_{x \to 0} \dfrac{g(x)}{f(x)}$

g) $\lim\limits_{x \to 4} f(x)$ h) $\lim\limits_{x \to 4} [f(x) + g(x)]$

i) $\lim\limits_{x \to 4^-} \dfrac{f(x)}{g(x)}$ j) $\lim\limits_{x \to 7^-} \dfrac{g(x)}{f(x)}$

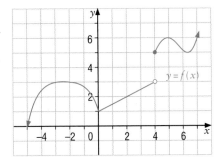

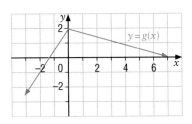

13. Determine where each function is discontinuous.

a) $f(x) = \begin{cases} 3x+1 & \text{if } x \neq 2 \\ 8 & \text{if } x = 2 \end{cases}$

b) $f(x) = \begin{cases} x+2 & \text{if } x \in (-\infty,\ 0] \\ x^2+2 & \text{if } x \in (0,\ 3] \\ 2x+4 & \text{if } x \in (3,\ \infty) \end{cases}$

c) $f(x) = \begin{cases} x & \text{if } x \in (-\infty,\ -1] \\ -x^3 & \text{if } x \in (-1,\ 1) \\ -x & \text{if } x \in [1,\ \infty) \end{cases}$

d) $f(x) = \begin{cases} x^2-1 & \text{if } x \in (-\infty,\ -1) \\ x^2+2x+1 & \text{if } x \in [-1,\ 1] \\ x^2-2x+1 & \text{if } x \in (1,\ \infty) \end{cases}$

14. Inquiry/Problem Solving A paving company decides to simplify its estimates by billing according to the following rules. Any driveway 60 m² or less will be priced at $800. Any driveway larger than 60 m² will be charged an additional $100 for every 10 m² (or part of 10 m²) above 60 m².

a) Draw the graph of the cost, C, in dollars, as a function of the area, A, in square metres.

b) Find each limit, if it exists.

i) $\lim\limits_{A \to 60^-} C(A)$ ii) $\lim\limits_{A \to 60^+} C(A)$

iii) $\lim\limits_{A \to 60} C(A)$ iv) $\lim\limits_{A \to 70^-} C(A)$

v) $\lim\limits_{A \to 70^+} C(A)$ vi) $\lim\limits_{A \to 70} C(A)$

c) Discuss some problems that might occur in terms of customer satisfaction due to this billing procedure.

15. Communication Postal rates for a non-standard (oversized) letter within Canada in the year 2001 are given in the table.

Up To and Including	100 g	200 g	500 g
Mailing Cost	$0.94	$1.55	$2.05

a) Draw the graph of the cost, C, in dollars, of mailing an oversized letter as a function of its mass, m, in grams.

b) Find each limit, if it exists.

i) $\lim\limits_{m \to 100^-} C(m)$ ii) $\lim\limits_{m \to 100^+} C(m)$

iii) $\lim\limits_{m \to 100} C(m)$ iv) $\lim\limits_{m \to 200^-} C(m)$

v) $\lim\limits_{m \to 200^+} C(m)$ vi) $\lim\limits_{m \to 200} C(m)$

c) What are some possible problems with this billing method?

d) Design an improved way of billing that would be fair to both Canada Post and the consumer. Why do you think such a method is not used?

16. Application Calling from Canada to Italy on a discount rate plan costs 40¢ a minute (or part of a minute).

a) Draw a graph of the cost, C, in cents, as a function of the time, t, in minutes.

b) For what values of a is $\lim\limits_{t \to a} C(t)$ not defined? Explain.

17. A taxi company charges $3.00 for the first 0.25 km (or part of a quarter kilometre), and $0.25 for each additional 0.1 km (or part). Draw the graph of the cost, C, in dollars, of a taxi ride, as a function of the distance travelled, x, in kilometres. Where are the discontinuities of this function?

18. Inquiry/Problem Solving A parking lot charges $5 for the first hour (or part of an hour) and $3 for each succeeding hour (or part), up to a daily maximum of $14.

a) Sketch a graph of the cost of parking at this lot as a function of the time parked there.

b) Discuss the discontinuities of this function and their significance to someone who parks in the lot.

C **19.** Application Consider the electric circuit problem posed at the beginning of this section. We defined $I(R)$ with two functions, for $R \in [0, 2]$ and for $R \in (2, \infty)$.

a) Write a single function $I(R)$ that defines the electric current for any resistance $R \geq 0$ of the variable resistor setting. (Hint: Review the Heaviside function.)

b) Draw a graph of $I(R)$.

c) Find the following for $I(R)$.

i) $\lim\limits_{R \to 2^-} I(R)$ ii) $\lim\limits_{R \to 2^+} I(R)$

iii) $I(2)$ iv) $\lim\limits_{R \to 2} I(R)$

20. Consider the function $f(x)$ described by

$$f(x) = \begin{cases} 1 & \text{if } x \text{ is an integer} \\ 0 & \text{if } x \text{ is not an integer} \end{cases}$$

Find each of the following, if it exists.

a) $\lim\limits_{x \to \frac{1}{2}} f(x)$ b) $\lim\limits_{x \to 2} f(x)$

21. Find each limit, if it exists.

a) $\lim\limits_{x \to \sqrt{3}} \dfrac{x^2 - 3}{3 - \sqrt{6 + x^2}}$

b) $\lim\limits_{x \to 8} \dfrac{x - 8}{\sqrt[3]{x} - 2}$

c) $\lim\limits_{x \to 3} \dfrac{\sqrt{7 - x} - 2}{1 - \sqrt{4 - x}}$

22. Find functions $f(x)$ and $g(x)$ such that $\lim\limits_{x \to 0} [f(x) + g(x)]$ exists but $\lim\limits_{x \to 0} f(x)$ and $\lim\limits_{x \to 0} g(x)$ do not exist.

23. Evaluate $\lim\limits_{x \to 1} \dfrac{\sqrt{x} - 1}{\sqrt[3]{x} - 1}$.

24. Let

$$f(x) = \begin{cases} 1 - |x| & \text{if } x \in [-1, \, 1] \\ |x| - 1 & \text{if } x \in [-2, \, -1) \text{ or } x \in (1, \, 2] \\ (x - 3)^2 & \text{if } x \in (2, \, \infty) \\ (x + 3)^2 & \text{if } x \in (-\infty, \, -2) \end{cases}$$

Sketch the graph of $f(x)$ and determine the values of x at which $f(x)$ is discontinuous.

25. For what values of c is the function

$$f(x) = \begin{cases} (cx - 1)^3 & \text{if } x \in (-\infty, \, 2) \\ c^2 x^2 - 1 & \text{if } x \in [2, \, \infty) \end{cases}$$

continuous at every number?

Achievement Check

Knowledge/Understanding

Thinking/Inquiry/Problem Solving

Communication

Application

The **greatest integer function** is defined by $[\![x]\!]$ = the largest integer that is less than or equal to x. For instance, $[\![6]\!] = 6$, $[\![6.83]\!] = 6$, $[\![\pi]\!] = 3$, and $[\![-4.2]\!] = -5$.

a) Sketch the graph of this function.

b) Find $\lim\limits_{x \to 3^-} [\![x]\!]$ and $\lim\limits_{x \to 3^+} [\![x]\!]$.

c) For what values of a does $\lim\limits_{x \to a} [\![x]\!]$ exist?

d) For what values of x is the greatest integer function discontinuous?

e) Sketch the graph of $g(x) = [\![2x + 1]\!]$ Where is it discontinuous?

f) Sketch the graph of $h(x) = x - [\![x]\!]$. Where is it discontinuous?

Technology Extension

Limits on a Graphing Calculator

An important menu on the TI-92 Plus graphing calculator is the Calculus menu. Access this set of operations by pressing F3. In this course, we will use the differentiate, limit, and nDeriv features of the menu.

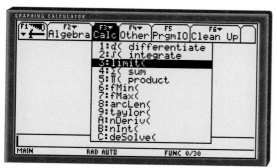

The calculator can determine the limits of functions or expressions. The syntax for the command is shown on the entry line, while the mathematical form of the command and the result are shown in the work area.

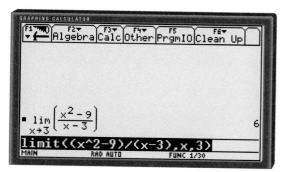

One-sided limits are also easily calculated. In this example, the function is evaluated first without considering an approach from either side. The result "undef" indicates that this limit cannot be evaluated. To find a limit from the right, insert any positive number after the value that x is approaching.
To find a limit from the left, insert any negative number after the value that x is approaching.

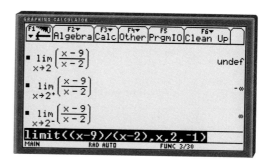

The TI-92 can also be used to illustrate limit laws. This screen demonstrates the limit law for the sum of limits. First, we define two functions, f and g, using the Define operation. Then, we find the individual limits as x approaches 1, and the limit of the sum as x approaches 1.

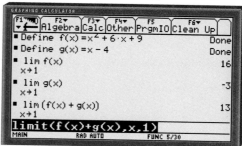

Throughout the course, we will be working with the expression $\lim_{h \to 0} \dfrac{f(x+h) - f(x)}{h}$.

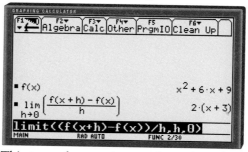

This type of expression can be evaluated on the calculator as shown for the function $f(x) = x^2 + 6x + 9$, which we defined in the previous screen.

Practise

1. Find each limit.

a) $\lim\limits_{x \to 1} \sqrt{x^2 - 2}$ b) $\lim\limits_{x \to 2} |4 - x^2|$

c) $\lim\limits_{x \to 3} \dfrac{x^2 - x - 6}{x - 3}$ d) $\lim\limits_{x \to 0} \dfrac{3x^2 - 2x}{x(x + 1)}$

2. For $g(x) = \begin{cases} x^3 + 1 & \text{if } x \in (-\infty, \, 0] \\ 2x + 3 & \text{if } x \in (0, \, \infty) \end{cases}$,

find each limit.

a) $\lim\limits_{x \to 0^-} g(x)$ b) $\lim\limits_{x \to 0^+} g(x)$

3. For $h(x) = \begin{cases} 3x^2 & \text{if } x \in (-\infty, \, 2) \\ -3x & \text{if } x \in [2, \, \infty) \end{cases}$,

find each limit.

a) $\lim\limits_{x \to 2^-} h(x)$ b) $\lim\limits_{x \to 2^+} h(x)$

4. For $f(x) = \begin{cases} \sqrt{x^2 + 1} & \text{if } x \in (-\infty, \, -1] \\ \sqrt{x + 1} & \text{if } x \in (-1, \, \infty) \end{cases}$,

find each limit.

a) $\lim\limits_{x \to -1^-} f(x)$ b) $\lim\limits_{x \to -1^+} f(x)$

5. Find $\lim\limits_{h \to 0} \dfrac{f(x + h) - f(x)}{h}$ for each function.

a) $f(x) = x$ b) $f(x) = x^2$

c) $f(x) = x^2 + 2x + 1$ d) $f(x) = \dfrac{1}{x}$

e) $f(x) = \dfrac{3}{x^2}$ f) $f(x) = \sqrt{x}$

Career Connection: *Architect*

Architecture is a field where the use of mathematics is growing steadily. Modern architects design highly complex structures that are achievable only through the use of computers and mathematical thinking. The computer software used is based on the principles of calculus—fitting curves by matching tangents, controlling curvature so that it is not too severe, and using parametric equations to develop curved surfaces. Architects often start with a series of points on the building being designed. These are then linked by smooth curves so the tangents, where different curves join, match exactly. The architect must choose which family of curves will best represent the original design concept.

Canadian architect Douglas Cardinal, who designed the Canadian Museum of Civilization in Hull, Québec, was one of the first in the profession to realize the potential of computerization. His distinctive architectural forms appear moulded more by natural forces than by human hand. Rather than using conventional drafting techniques, Cardinal makes use of computer technology to develop his complex curvilinear designs. He uses prestressed and reinforced concrete to create structures with a distinctive style.

Although an architect may start with hand sketches of a design concept, these are quickly translated into computer equations. This allows for basic models to be easily constructed and, more importantly, for subtle changes to be viewed and implemented effortlessly. The architect is guided through the creation process by images on the computer screen as well as the information about the equations, derivatives, and curvature of functions. The use of parametric equations allows the architect to create three-dimensional smooth surfaces. Similar software is used today by designers in their creation of prototypes of airplanes and automobiles as well as consumer goods such as perfume bottles and cutlery.

Rates of Change

Physicists are interested in the rate of change of the position of a moving object with respect to time (velocity). Chemists are interested in the rate of change in the concentration of a reactant with respect to time (rate of reaction). A textile manufacturer is interested in the rate of change of the cost of producing x square metres of fabric per day with respect to x (marginal cost). A biologist is interested in the rate of change of the population of a colony of bacteria with respect to time. Each of these rates of change can be interpreted as the slope of a tangent to an appropriate curve.

A car is driven in one direction on a highway for 2 h and travels 160 km. The average velocity of the car is

$$\text{average velocity} = \frac{\text{change in position}}{\text{time elapsed}}$$
$$= \frac{160}{2}$$
$$= 80$$

The average velocity is 80 km/h. However, the indicator on the speedometer of a car travelling in city traffic does not stay still for very long, that is, the velocity of the car is not constant. It seems that the car has a definite velocity at each moment, but how is this "instantaneous" velocity defined? Before giving a general definition, we will examine the situation of a falling ball in the following investigation.

Investigate & Inquire: Motion of a Falling Object

1. Use a motion detector connected to a graphing calculator or a computer to graph the motion of a ball starting from rest and falling from a height of at least 2 m.

2. Identify the part of the distance-time graph where the ball was actually falling. Then, pick a time $t = a$ in this part of the graph. For better results, pick a time where the graph is relatively smooth.

3. Complete a table like the one that follows using your value of a and smaller and smaller values of h from the graph. To get the final value of h, use the point on the distance-time graph at $t = a + h$ that is closest to $t = a$. For example, using $t = 0.5$ s, find values of t closer and closer to 0.5. The table that follows is partially filled in for $t = 0.5$ s for a ball dropped from a height of 2 m.

$t=a$	$f(a)$	$t=a+h$	$f(a+h)$	$\Delta t=h$	$f(a+h)-f(a)$	$\dfrac{f(a+h)-f(a)}{h}$
0.5	0.775	0.6	0.236	0.1	−0.539	−5.39
0.5	0.775	0.55	0.5178	0.05		
0.5	0.775	0.51	0.7255	0.01		
0.5	0.775	0.501	0.7701	0.001		
0.5	0.775	0.5001	0.7745	0.0001		

4. Note that the last column of the table gives the slope of the secant joining $P(a, f(a))$ to $Q(a + h, f(a + h))$.

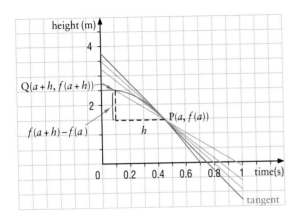

a) What does the slope of the secant PQ represent physically?
b) As h becomes smaller and smaller, what does this slope approach?

5. Compare the average velocities calculated in the table to the velocity at $t = a$ from the velocity-time graph on the graphing calculator or computer. As h decreases, how does the difference between the average velocity and the velocity from the velocity-time graph change?

6. How can the velocity be calculated from a distance-time graph?

7. Choose another point from the graph for $t = a$ and use the same method to estimate the velocity at this time. Compare this velocity to that from the velocity-time graph at the same time.

8. Describe the relationship between the slope of the tangent at $t = a$ and the velocity at that point on the velocity-time graph.

In Example 1 we use the concept of limits to investigate average velocity further.

Example 1 Velocity of a Bungee Jumper

When bungee jumping from a high bridge, the jumper accelerates at a constant rate for a while, until the strong elastic cords slow down the jumper before hitting the water. Find the velocity of a bungee jumper 3.0 s after jumping off the bridge, and before the cords have an effect, if air resistance is ignored.

Solution

To solve this problem, we use the fact, discovered by Galileo, that the distance fallen by any freely falling body is proportional to the square of the time it has been falling, neglecting air resistance. If the distance fallen after t seconds is s, in metres, then Galileo's law is expressed by the equation

$$s(t) = 4.9t^2$$

The difficulty in finding the velocity after 3.0 s is dealing with a single instant of time, $t = 3.0$, so that there is no time interval involved. However, we can approximate the desired quantity by computing the average velocity over the brief time interval of a tenth of a second from $t = 3$ to $t = 3.1$.

$$\text{average velocity} = \frac{\text{change in position}}{\text{time elapsed}}$$
$$= \frac{\Delta s}{\Delta t}$$
$$= \frac{s(3.1) - s(3)}{3.1 - 3}$$
$$= \frac{4.9(3.1^2) - 4.9(3^2)}{0.1}$$
$$= 29.89$$

There is a distinction between speed and velocity. *Average speed* is distance divided by time. *Average velocity* is change in position divided by time. If you take 1 h to walk 7 km, your average speed is 7 km/h. If you end your walk where you started, your change in position is 0, so your average velocity is 0 km/h. We will explore this distinction more deeply in Chapter 4.

The average velocity from 3 s to 3.1 s is 29.89 m/s.

The following table shows the results of similar calculations of the average velocity over successively smaller time periods.

Time Interval (s)	Average Velocity (m/s)
[3, 4]	34.3
[3, 3.1]	29.89
[3, 3.05]	29.645
[3, 3.01]	29.449
[3, 3.001]	29.4049

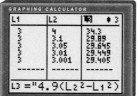

The formula in L3 is $4.9(L2^2 - L1^2)/(L2 - L1)$.

It appears that, as the time period is shortened, the average velocity becomes closer to 29.4 m/s. We compute the average velocity over the general time interval $t \in [3, 3 + h]$:

$$\text{average velocity} = \frac{\Delta s}{\Delta t}$$

$$= \frac{s(t + h) - s(t)}{h}$$

$$= \frac{4.9(3 + h)^2 - 4.9(3)^2}{h}$$

$$= \frac{4.9(6h + h^2)}{h}$$

$$= \frac{4.9h(6 + h)}{h}$$

$$= 4.9(6 + h), \qquad h \neq 0$$

$$= 29.4 + 4.9h$$

As the time interval becomes shorter and shorter, h becomes smaller and smaller, $4.9h$ gets closer and closer to 0, and thus the average velocity becomes closer and closer to 29.4 m/s. The instantaneous velocity, v, when $t = 3$, is defined to be the limiting value of these average velocities as h approaches 0.

$$v = \lim_{h \to 0}(29.4 + 4.9h)$$

$$= 29.4$$

Thus, the instantaneous velocity after 3 s is 29.4 m/s. Note that we do not substitute $h = 0$ in the expression for the average velocity because that would result in the expression $\frac{0}{0}$, which is undefined. Rather, the instantaneous velocity is the *limit* of the average velocities as h approaches 0.

The calculations in Example 1 are very similar to those we used to find tangents. In fact, there is a close connection between the two calculations—if we draw the graph of the position function of the ball, and we consider the points $P(3, 4.9(3)^2)$ and $Q(3 + h, 4.9(3 + h)^2)$ on the graph, then the slope of the secant PQ is

$$m_{PQ} = \frac{4.9(3 + h)^2 - 4.9(3)^2}{h}$$

which is the same as the average velocity over the time interval $t \in [3, 3 + h]$ found in Example 1.

Therefore, the velocity at time t (the limit of these average velocities as h approaches 0) is equal to the slope of the tangent at P (the limit of the slopes of the secants).

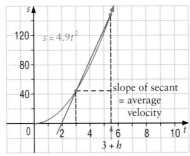

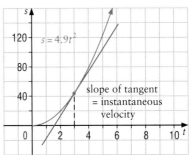

So far we have discussed only situations where an object's direction of motion does not change. Suppose an object can move back and forth along a straight line according to the equation $s = f(t)$, where s is the position of the object at time t. The function $f(t)$ that describes the motion is called the **position function** of the object. In the time interval from $t = a$ to $t = a + h$, the change in position is

$$\Delta s = f(a + h) - f(a)$$

The **average velocity** over this time interval is

$$\frac{\Delta s}{\Delta t} = \frac{f(a + h) - f(a)}{h}$$

which is the same as the slope of the secant PQ, where P is the point for which $t = a$, and Q is the point for which $t = a + h$.

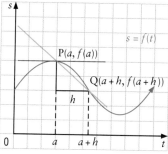

Now suppose we compute the average velocities over shorter and shorter time intervals $[a, a + h]$. In other words, let h approach 0. As in Example 1, we define the **instantaneous velocity**, $v(a)$, at time $t = a$ to be the limit of the average velocities.

Instantaneous Velocity:
$$v(a) = \lim_{\Delta t \to 0} \frac{\Delta s}{\Delta t}$$
$$= \lim_{h \to 0} \frac{f(a + h) - f(a)}{h}, \text{ where } s = f(t) \text{ is the position at time } t$$

This means that velocity at time $t = a$ is equal to the slope of the tangent to the graph of the position function at $t = a$.

Example 2 Instantaneous Velocity

The height, in metres, of a toy rocket launched at an initial upward velocity of 30 m/s, from a height of 1 m, is approximately given by $s = -4.9t^2 + 30t + 1$, where t is measured in seconds.
a) Find the instantaneous velocity of the rocket after 4 s.
b) Sketch a graph of the position function and find the slope of the tangent to the graph at $t = 4$.

Solution

a) Use the formula for instantaneous velocity with $a = 4$.

$$v(4) = \lim_{h \to 0} \frac{s(4 + h) - s(4)}{h}$$
$$= \lim_{h \to 0} \frac{-4.9(4 + h)^2 + 30(4 + h) + 1 - [-4.9(4)^2 + 30(4) + 1]}{h}$$
$$= \lim_{h \to 0} \frac{-9.2h - 4.9h^2}{h}$$
$$= \lim_{h \to 0} \frac{h(-9.2 - 4.9h)}{h}$$
$$= \lim_{h \to 0} (-9.2 - 4.9h), \quad h \neq 0$$
$$= -9.2$$

The velocity after 4 s is −9.2 m/s. The negative sign means the rocket is falling toward the ground.

b) Using a graphing calculator or graphing software, we can graph the function, and we can find the slope using the Tangent operation.

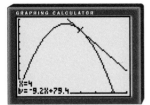

Window variables:
$x \in [0, 7]$, $y \in [0, 50]$

Note that the slope is the same as the velocity we found in part a).

Other Rates of Change

Suppose that y is a function of x, written $y = f(x)$. If x changes from x_1 to x_2, then the change in x is

$$\Delta x = x_2 - x_1$$

and the corresponding change in y is

$$\Delta y = f(x_2) - f(x_1)$$

The quotient

$$\frac{\Delta y}{\Delta x} = \frac{f(x_2) - f(x_1)}{x_2 - x_1}$$

is called the **average rate of change of y with respect to x** over the interval $x \in [x_1, x_2]$. We follow the same procedure as with velocity, that is, we consider the average rate of change over smaller and smaller intervals by letting x_2 approach x_1, which means that Δx approaches 0. The limit of these average rates of change is called the **instantaneous rate of change of y with respect to x** at $x = x_1$ and, as with velocity, can be interpreted as the slope of the tangent to the curve $y = f(x)$ at $P(x_1, f(x_1))$.

$$\text{Instantaneous rate of change} = \lim_{\Delta x \to 0} \frac{\Delta y}{\Delta x}$$
$$= \lim_{x_2 \to x_1} \frac{f(x_2) - f(x_1)}{x_2 - x_1}$$

If a thermometer is taken from indoors to outdoors in the winter, it does not instantly record the accurate outdoor temperature. In Example 3, we examine how long it takes to reach the new temperature in a specific situation.

Example 3 Finding the Rate of Change of Temperature

A thermometer is taken from a room temperature of 20°C to an outdoor temperature of 5°C. Temperature readings (T) are taken every 5.0 min as shown in the table.

t (min)	0.0	5.0	10	15	20	25	30	35	40	45	50
T (°C)	20	15	12	9.8	8.3	7.2	6.5	6.0	5.7	5.5	5.3

a) Find the average rate of change of temperature with respect to time over the following time intervals:

i) $t \in [20, 40]$ ii) $t \in [20, 35]$ iii) $t \in [20, 30]$ iv) $t \in [20, 25]$

b) Sketch the graph of T as a function of t, and use it to estimate the instantaneous rate of change of temperature with respect to time when $t = 20$.

Solution

a) i) Over the interval $t \in [20, 40]$, the temperature changes from $T = 8.3°C$ to $T = 5.7°C$, so

$$\Delta T = T(40) - T(20)$$
$$= 5.7 - 8.3$$
$$= -2.6$$

The change in time is $\Delta t = 40 - 20$ or 20 min.

$$\frac{\Delta T}{\Delta t} = \frac{-2.6}{20}$$
$$= -0.13$$

Therefore, the average rate of change of temperature with respect to time over the interval $t \in [20, 40]$ is $-0.13°C/min$. The negative rate of change indicates that the temperature is decreasing.

ii)
$$\frac{\Delta T}{\Delta t} = \frac{T(35) - T(20)}{35 - 20}$$
$$= \frac{6.0 - 8.3}{15}$$
$$\doteq -0.15$$

The average rate of change of temperature with respect to time over the interval $t \in [20, 35]$ is approximately $-0.15°C/min$.

iii)
$$\frac{\Delta T}{\Delta t} = \frac{T(30) - T(20)}{30 - 20}$$
$$= \frac{6.5 - 8.3}{10}$$
$$= -0.18$$

The average rate of change of temperature with respect to time over the interval $t \in [20, 30]$ is $-0.18°C/min$.

iv)
$$\frac{\Delta T}{\Delta t} = \frac{T(25) - T(20)}{25 - 20}$$
$$= \frac{7.2 - 8.3}{5}$$
$$= -0.22$$

The average rate of change of temperature with respect to time over the interval $t \in [20, 25]$ is $-0.22°C/min$.

b) **Solution 1**   Sketch the Graph

We plot the given data and use them to sketch a smooth curve that approximates the graph of the temperature function.

Then, we sketch the tangent at the point P where $t = 20$. After measuring the side lengths of $\triangle ABC$, we estimate the slope of the tangent to be

$$m = \frac{12 - 7}{5 - 25}$$

$$= -0.25$$

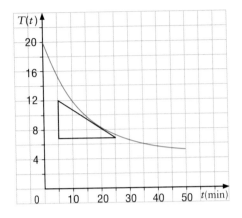

The rate of change of temperature with respect to time after 20 min is about $-0.25°C/min$.

Solution 2   Average the Slopes of Two Secants

We can also estimate the rate of change at $t = 20$ by finding the average of the slopes of two secants, one on either side of P. We use the points $Q_1(15, 9.8)$ and $Q_2(25, 7.2)$.

$$m_{PQ_1} = \frac{9.8 - 8.3}{15 - 20} \qquad m_{PQ_2} = \frac{7.2 - 8.3}{25 - 20}$$

$$= -0.3 \qquad\qquad = -0.22$$

$$\frac{m_{PQ_1} + m_{PQ_2}}{2} = \frac{-0.3 + (-0.22)}{2}$$

$$= -0.26$$

The rate of change of temperature with respect to time after 20 min is approximately $-0.26°C/min$. This result is very close to the result of the first method.

Example 4 Population Growth in a Small Town

The planners in a small town have analysed population growth over the past 100 years and have used regression to model the population with a formula, $P(t) = 0.8t^2 + 100t + 1000$, to describe the growth, where P is the population, and t is time, in years, with $t = 0$ representing the beginning of this year.
a)   What is the population of the town at the beginning of this year?
b)   Find the rate of change of the population after 10 years. What will the population be at that time?
c)   Would the planners be justified in building a new elementary school for 300 students to be ready in 10 years? Explain.

Solution

a)   The population at the beginning of this year is given by $P(0)$.
$P(t) = 0.8t^2 + 100t + 1000$
$P(0) = 0.8(0)^2 + 100(0) + 1000$
$\quad\ = 1000$
The population of the town at the beginning of this year is 1000.

b) When $t = 10$, the rate of change of population, P, with respect to t is given by

$$\lim_{\Delta t \to 0} \frac{\Delta P}{\Delta t} = \lim_{t \to 10} \frac{P(t) - P(10)}{t - 10}$$

$$= \lim_{t \to 10} \frac{0.8t^2 + 100t + 1000 - [0.8(10)^2 + 100(10) + 1000]}{t - 10}$$

$$= \lim_{t \to 10} \frac{0.8(t^2 - 10^2) + 100(t - 10) + 1000 - 1000}{t - 10}$$

$$= \lim_{t \to 10} \frac{0.8(t - 10)(t + 10) + 100(t - 10)}{t - 10}$$

$$= \lim_{t \to 10} (0.8(t + 10) + 100), \qquad t \neq 10$$

$$= \lim_{t \to 10} (0.8t + 108)$$

$$= 0.8(10) + 108$$

$$= 116$$

Ten years from now, we predict the population will be growing at a rate of 116 people per year. The population after 10 years is predicted to be $P(10) = 0.8(10)^2 + 100(10) + 1000$ or 2080.

c) The population may be growing fast enough to justify a new elementary school. Whether children make up a large enough part of the population increase to warrant a new school cannot be determined. It could be that many people are retiring to the community. More information about the ages of people in the community is needed.

As we have seen, finding the slope of a tangent is not just an abstract calculation. It is applicable to many problems in a variety of practical contexts including all areas of science. Any problem involving a rate of change corresponds to finding the slope of a tangent, as we have done in this section.

Key Concepts

- average velocity $= \dfrac{\text{change in position}}{\text{time elapsed}}$

- instantaneous velocity, where s is the position function

$$v(a) = \lim_{h \to 0} \frac{s(a + h) - s(a)}{h}$$

- average rate of change of $y = f(x)$ with respect to x over the interval $x \in [x_1, x_2]$

$$\frac{\Delta y}{\Delta x} = \frac{f(x_2) - f(x_1)}{x_2 - x_1}$$

- instantaneous rate of change of $y = f(x)$ with respect to x

$$\lim_{\Delta x \to 0} \frac{\Delta y}{\Delta x} = \lim_{x_2 \to x_1} \frac{f(x_2) - f(x_1)}{x_2 - x_1}$$

Communicate Your Understanding

1. Explain the difference between average velocity and instantaneous velocity, using at least two specific examples in your explanation.

2. The graph shows the position function, $y = s(t)$, of a car along a straight section of a very busy highway. Use the slopes of the tangents to the graph at the points labelled on the graph to answer the following questions.

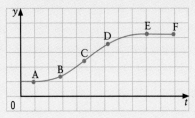

a) What was the velocity of the car at A?
b) At what point was the car moving with the greatest velocity?
c) Was the car speeding up or slowing down at B and D?
d) What was the car's motion from E to F?

3. Under what circumstances are average velocity and average speed the same? Under what circumstances are they different?

Apply, Solve, Communicate

B **1.** The position function of an object is given by the equation $y = 3t^2 - 8$. Write an expression for each of the following.
a) the average velocity of the object from $t = 3$ to $t = 3 + h$
b) the instantaneous velocity at $t = 3$

2. The position function of an object is given by the equation $y = f(t)$. Write an expression for each of the following.
a) the average velocity of the object from $t = a$ to $t = a + h$
b) the instantaneous velocity at $t = a$

3. May and Richard are throwing a Frisbee™ at the beach. When May throws to Richard, the height, in metres, of the Frisbee™ above the sand after t seconds is described by the function $h(t) = -2t^2 + 3t + 1$.
a) Find the average upward velocity of the Frisbee™ for the time period from $t = 1$, lasting

i) 1 s ii) 0.5 s iii) 0.1 s
iv) 0.05 s v) 0.01 s
b) Find the instantaneous upward velocity of the Frisbee™ when $t = 1$.

4. If a firework is shot straight up into the air with an initial upward velocity of 40 m/s, its height, in metres, after t seconds is given by $y = 40t - 4.9t^2$.
a) Find the average velocity for the time period beginning when $t = 2$ and lasting
i) 1 s ii) 0.5 s iii) 0.1 s
iv) 0.05 s v) 0.01 s
b) Find the instantaneous velocity when $t = 2$.

5. The displacement, in metres, of a ball rolling in a straight line on a grassy hill is given approximately by $s = -t^2 + 6t + 5$, where t is measured in seconds.
a) Find the average velocity over the following time periods.
i) $t \in [2, 4]$ ii) $t \in [2, 3]$
iii) $t \in [2, 2.5]$ iv) $t \in [2, 2.1]$

b) Find the instantaneous velocity when $t = 2$.
c) Draw the graph of s as a function of t and draw the secants whose slopes are equal to the average velocities in part a).
d) Draw the tangent whose slope is equal to the instantaneous velocity in part b).

6. Communication The displacement, in metres, of a runner moving in a straight line is given by $s = t^2$, where t is measured in seconds.
a) Find the average velocity over the following time periods.
i) $t \in [3, 5]$ ii) $t \in [3, 4]$
iii) $t \in [3, 3.5]$ iv) $t \in [3, 3.1]$
b) Find the instantaneous velocity when $t = 3$.
c) Draw the graph of s as a function of t and draw the secants whose slopes are equal to the average velocities in part a).
d) Draw the tangent whose slope is equal to the instantaneous velocity in part b).
e) In what kind of race do you think the runner is participating? Explain.
f) What do you think is a realistic domain for the function that models the runner's position? Explain.

7. A race car moves in a straight line, past a stationary observer, with position function $s = 0.4t^2 + 5t$, where t is measured in seconds and s in metres. Find the velocity of the car at time $t = a$. Use this expression to find the velocities after 1 s, 2 s, and 3 s.

8. a) Use the data of Example 3 to find the average rate of change of temperature with respect to time over the following time intervals.
i) $t \in [30, 50]$ ii) $t \in [30, 40]$
iii) $t \in [10, 30]$ iv) $t \in [20, 30]$
b) Use the graph of T to estimate the instantaneous rate of change of T with respect to t when $t = 30$.

9. Application Temperature readings, T, in degrees Celsius, were recorded every 2 h starting at 6:00 a.m. on a spring day in Niagara Falls, Ontario. The time, t, is measured in hours for 24 h. The data were recorded in the table.

t (h)	T (°C)	t (h)	T (°C)
0	3.5	14	10.0
2	5.0	16	8.7
4	7.3	18	6.4
6	9.0	20	4.0
8	10.9	22	1.4
10	12.2	24	1.0
12	11.3		

a) Find the average rate of change of temperature with respect to time over the following time intervals:
i) $t \in [2, 6]$ ii) $t \in [0, 2]$ iii) $t \in [2, 4]$
b) Estimate the instantaneous rate of change of temperature with respect to time at $t = 2$ by graphing the data and then measuring the slope of the tangent.
c) Find the average rate of change of temperature with respect to time over the following time intervals:
i) $t \in [18, 22]$ ii) $t \in [18, 20]$ iii) $t \in [16, 18]$
d) Estimate the instantaneous rate of change of temperature with respect to time at $t = 18$ by measuring the slope of the tangent on your graph from part b).

10. Application The table shows the numbers of outlets of a popular Canadian chain of restaurants from 1978 to 2000.

Year	Number of Outlets	Year	Number of Outlets
1978	100	1995	1100
1984	200	1996	1400
1987	300	1997	1500
1989	400	1999	1800
1991	500	2000	2000
1993	700		

a) Construct a scatter plot of the data in the table.
b) Find the average rate of change in the number of outlets for each time interval.
i) 1984 to 1991   ii) 1991 to 1997
iii) 1989 to 1991   iv) 1991 to 1993

c) Use regression on a graphing calculator or graphing software to find and plot a curve of best fit for the data.

d) Use the Tangent operation of a graphing calculator or graphing software to find the instantaneous rate of change in number of outlets for 1991. Compare your result to the results from part b).

11. Inquiry/Problem Solving The population, P, of the Regional Municipality of Waterloo from 1991 to 2000 is given in the following table.

Year	Population
1991	399 400
1992	406 600
1993	411 500
1994	416 500
1995	420 100
1996	423 800
1997	429 800
1998	436 200
1999	442 300
2000	450 900

a) Find the average rate of growth of the Regional Municipality of Waterloo
i)   from 1994 to 1996
ii) from 1995 to 1996
iii) from 1996 to 1998
iv) from 1996 to 1997

b) Estimate the instantaneous rate of growth in 1996 by graphing the data and then measuring the slope of the tangent.

c) Use regression on a graphing calculator or graphing software to find a cubic function to model the population growth. Then, find the instantaneous rate of growth in 1996 using the Tangent operation.

d) Compare your answers in parts c) and d).

12. Communication a) If $y = \dfrac{4}{x}$, find the average rate of change of y with respect to x over the interval $x \in [2, 3]$. Illustrate by drawing the graph of the function and the secant whose slope is equal to the rate of change.

b) Find the instantaneous rate of change of y with respect to x at $x = 3$. Draw the tangent whose slope is equal to the rate of change.

13. Inquiry/Problem Solving a) A cubic crystal is being grown in a laboratory. Find the average rate of change of volume of the cube with respect to its edge length, x, in millimetres, when x changes from
i)   4 to 5   ii) 4 to 4.1   iii) 4 to 4.01
b) Find the instantaneous rate of change of volume when $x = 4$.

14. If a tank holds 1000 L of water, which takes 1 h to drain from the bottom of the tank, then the volume, V, in litres, remaining in the tank after t minutes is

$$V = 1000\left(1 - \frac{t}{60}\right)^2, \qquad t \in [0, 60]$$

Find the rate at which the water is flowing out of the tank (the instantaneous rate of change of V with respect to t) after 10 min.

15. The profit, in dollars, for producing x units of an instruction manual is $P(x) = 8000 + 20x + 0.10x^2$ for the first 2000 units of the manual.
a) Find the average rate of change of P with respect to x when the production level is changed
i)   from $x = 100$ to $x = 110$
ii) from $x = 100$ to $x = 105$
iii) from $x = 100$ to $x = 101$
b) Find the instantaneous rate of change of P with respect to x when $x = 100$. (This is called the marginal profit and will be explained in Chapter 4.)

C **16.** If a projectile is fired straight upward from the surface of the moon with an initial upward velocity of 40 m/s, its height, in metres, after t seconds is given by $s = 40t - 0.83t^2$.
a) Find the average velocity for the time period beginning when $t = 2$ and lasting
i)   1 s   ii) 0.5 s   iii) 0.1 s
iv) 0.05 s   v)   0.01 s

b) Find the instantaneous velocity when $t = 2$.
c) Find the velocity of the projectile when $t = a$.
d) When will the projectile hit the moon?
e) With what velocity will the projectile hit the moon?
f) The velocity of the projectile at its maximum height is 0 m/s. Find the maximum height of the projectile.

17. The position of a runner is given by $s = 8t - t^2$ for $t \in [0, 10]$, where s is in metres and t is in seconds. Some of the positions are negative because the runner is initially moving to the east and then turns to move to the west.
a) Sketch the position-time graph of the runner.
b) Find the velocity of the runner at $t = a$ and use it to draw a velocity-time graph of the runner.
c) Describe the motion of the runner in a short paragraph. Indicate position, direction of motion, and velocity. Use a diagram to illustrate your description.

18. Application The electric potential energy, E, in joules, between two positively charged spheres of radius 10.0 cm, separated by a distance, x, in metres, measured from the centres of the spheres, is given by the equation $E = \dfrac{90}{x}$.

The electric force of repulsion, F, in newtons, on each sphere is given by the rate of change of the electric potential with respect to x.
a) Find the electric force of repulsion between the two spheres at a distance x_0.
b) Find the electric force of repulsion for each distance:

i) 2.0 m   ii) 10.0 m   iii) 100.0 m
c) Find the electric force of repulsion when the surfaces of the two spheres are 2.0 cm apart.
d) What happens to the electric potential energy and the electric force as the two spheres move very far apart? Explain.

19. Communication Are instantaneous speed and instantaneous velocity identical? If so, explain why. If not, give an example of a motion where they are different, and explain the difference.

Historical Bite: Mathematical Proof in the Time of Newton and Leibniz

Newton and Leibniz, the two men credited with discovering calculus, were not very concerned about formally proving the results for which they are famous. Basically, they said that the fact that their ideas led to so many new discoveries and that the same ideas applied to a number of fields guaranteed their correctness. In the following centuries, Euler, Cauchy, Gauss, and many others encouraged the mathematical community to become much more concerned with formal proofs of mathematical theorems.

Knowledge/Understanding

Thinking/Inquiry/Problem Solving

Communication

Application

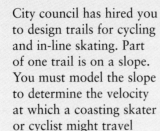

City council has hired you to design trails for cycling and in-line skating. Part of one trail is on a slope. You must model the slope to determine the velocity at which a coasting skater or cyclist might travel down the slope.

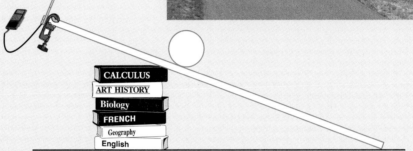

Use a motion detector (CBR), a ball (or cart), and a ramp to model this situation. Graph the motion of the ball as it rolls down the ramp. Compare the position-time graph to the velocity-time graph using the methods investigated in this chapter.

The following suggestions can guide your comparison.

- Using the slopes of secants from the position-time graph, estimate the values of the slopes of the tangents to the curve at five different times. Compare these slopes to the velocities from the velocity-time graph at the same times.
- Using a graphing calculator or graphing software, find the equation that best approximates the position-time graph.
- Use the above best-fit equation and the properties of limits to calculate the slopes of the tangents to the position-time graph at the same times as above.
- Compare these slopes to those estimated previously and to the velocities from the velocity-time graph.
- Which of the two methods yields the most accurate results? Explain the advantages and disadvantages of each method.

Write a report on your findings.

Review of Key Concepts

3.1 From Secants to Tangents

Refer to the Key Concepts on pages 126–127.

1. For each curve and each point P:
i) Choose five appropriate points Q on either side of P on the curve. Find the slope m_{PQ} for each Q you chose.
ii) Estimate the value of the slope of the tangent to the curve at P.
iii) Find the equation of the tangent to the curve at P.
iv) Sketch the curve, one secant on each side of P, and the tangent.
a) $y = x^2 + x$, P(1, 2)
b) $y = x^3 - 2x$, P(2, 4)
c) $y = \sqrt{x+1}$, P(3, 2)

2. A small metal ball with a radius of 5.0 cm is dropped and allowed to fall. The air friction on the ball, F, in newtons, increases with time, t, in seconds, as the ball is falling. Typical values are shown in the tables.

t	F		t	F
0	0		1.0	3.859
0.1	0.478		1.1	4.149
0.2	0.933		1.2	4.425
0.3	1.366		1.3	4.687
0.4	1.778		1.4	4.937
0.5	2.169		1.5	5.174
0.6	2.542		1.6	5.400
0.7	2.896		1.7	5.615
0.8	3.233		1.8	5.820
0.9	3.554		1.9	6.014

a) If P is the point (0.7, 2.896) on the graph of F, find the slope of the secant PQ when Q is the point on the graph with $t = 0.6$; $t = 0.8$.
b) Estimate the slope of the tangent at P by averaging the slopes of the two secants in part a).
c) Estimate the slope of the tangent at (1.5, 5.174) by averaging the slopes of two secants.

d) Use a graph of the function to estimate the slopes of the tangents found in parts b) and c).
e) At what rate is the air friction on the ball changing with respect to time at $t = 1.0$?

3. The amount of active ingredient of a medicine ingested by the body, A, in milligrams, is a function of time, t, in hours, given by

$$A = 10\left(t - \frac{1}{12}t^2\right), \text{ where } t \in [0, 12].$$

a) What does the slope of the function at any point P represent?
b) Estimate the slope of the tangent to A at $P\left(4, \dfrac{80}{3}\right)$ using the method of your choice.

Check your result with a graphing calculator or graphing software.

4. The world record times, in seconds, in the 100-m sprint are shown for women. Graph the data.

Year	Time		Year	Time
1934	11.7		1977	10.88
1937	11.6		1983	10.81
1948	11.5		1983	10.79
1952	11.4		1984	10.76
1955	11.3		1988	10.49
1961	11.2			
1965	11.1			
1972	11.07			
1976	11.04			
1976	11.01			

a) In which years do the times seem to be improving the fastest?
b) Estimate the rate of change of times in 1948 and in 1984. Does what you found verify your answer in part a)? Explain.
c) Find similar data for the men's 100-m sprint. Plot the data and write a short paragraph about the improvement in times over the last 100 years. Use slopes of tangents to describe the improvement.

3.2 Using Limits to Find Tangents

Refer to the Key Concepts on page 136.

5. Find the equation of the tangent to the curve at the given point.
a) $y = x^2 + 1$ at $(2, 5)$
b) $y = x^2 + 4x + 4$ at $(1, 9)$
c) $y = \sqrt{x + 3}$ at $(6, 3)$
d) $y = 1 - x^3$ at $(0, 1)$
e) $y = \dfrac{1}{x - 2}$ at $(3, 1)$
f) $y = \dfrac{1}{\sqrt{x}}$ at $(1, 1)$

6. Find the equation of the tangent to the curve at the given point.
a) $y = 3 - x^2$ at $(-1, 2)$
b) $y = x^2 - 2x + 1$ at $(2, 1)$
c) $y = \sqrt{x^2 + 3}$ at $(1, 2)$
d) $y = \dfrac{1}{x}$ at $\left(4, \dfrac{1}{4}\right)$
e) $y = \dfrac{x + 1}{x + 3}$ at $\left(1, \dfrac{1}{2}\right)$
f) $y = \dfrac{3}{x^2 - 1}$ at $(2, 1)$

7. For each curve,
i)   find the slope of the tangent at the given point
ii) find the equation of the tangent at the given point
iii) graph the curve and the tangent
a) $y = (x - 3)^2$ at $(-1, 16)$
b) $y = x^3$ at $(2, 8)$
c) $y = \sqrt{x - 2}$ at $(11, 3)$
d) $y = \dfrac{1}{x + 1}$ at $\left(-\dfrac{1}{2}, 2\right)$

8. a) Find the slope of the tangent to the parabola $y = x^2 - 3x - 10$ at the general point whose x-coordinate is a.
b) Find the slopes of the tangents to the parabola at the points with x-coordinates $-1, 0, 1, 2, 3$.
c) At which point on the parabola is the slope of the tangent zero?

9. During a hockey game, a forward is skating hard toward the net along the path $y = 2x^2 - 8x + 12$. When the forward reaches the point where $x = 2.5$, she falls and slides along a tangent to her path. The goal line of the net extends along the x-axis between $x = -1$ and $x = 1$, and the goaltender is located somewhere along the goal line.
a) Determine an equation for the tangent that the forward slides along after she falls.
b) Should the goaltender take evasive action to avoid being hit by the sliding forward? Explain.

3.3 The Limit of a Function

Refer to the Key Concepts on pages 151–152.

10. Use the graph of $f(x)$ to state the value of each quantity, if it exists. If it does not exist, explain why.

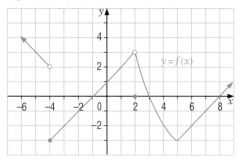

a) $\lim\limits_{x \to -4^-} f(x)$
b) $\lim\limits_{x \to -4^+} f(x)$
c) $f(-4)$
d) $\lim\limits_{x \to -4} f(x)$
e) $\lim\limits_{x \to 2^-} f(x)$
f) $\lim\limits_{x \to 2^+} f(x)$
g) $f(2)$
h) $\lim\limits_{x \to 2} f(x)$
i) $\lim\limits_{x \to 5^+} f(x)$
j) $\lim\limits_{x \to 5^+} f(x)$
k) $f(5)$
l) $\lim\limits_{x \to 5} f(x)$

11. a)   State whether the function $f(x)$, whose graph is shown in question 10, is continuous or discontinuous at the following values of x. Identify each type of discontinuity in the function.
i) -4 ii) 2 iii) 5
b)   Can the discontinuities of a function such as $f(x)$ be used to determine if $\lim\limits_{x \to a} f(x)$ exists? Explain.

12. Use the graph of $g(x)$ to state the value of each quantity, if it exists. If it does not exist, explain why.

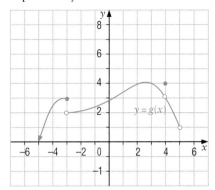

a) $\lim\limits_{x \to -3^-} g(x)$ b) $\lim\limits_{x \to -3^+} g(x)$

c) $g(-3)$ d) $\lim\limits_{x \to -3} g(x)$

e) $\lim\limits_{x \to 2^-} g(x)$ f) $\lim\limits_{x \to 2^+} g(x)$

g) $g(2)$ h) $\lim\limits_{x \to 2} g(x)$

i) $\lim\limits_{x \to 4^-} g(x)$ j) $\lim\limits_{x \to 4^+} g(x)$

k) $g(4)$ l) $\lim\limits_{x \to 4} g(x)$

m) $g(5)$ n) $\lim\limits_{x \to 5^+} g(x)$

13. a) State whether the function $g(x)$, whose graph is shown in question 12, is continuous or discontinuous at the following values of x. Identify each type of discontinuity in the function.
i) -3 ii) 2 iii) 4 iv) 5
b) How does the value of $g(a)$ affect each of the following?
i) $\lim\limits_{x \to a} g(x)$ ii) the continuity of $g(x)$ at a

14. Let
$$g(x) = \begin{cases} x^2 + 2 & \text{if } x \in (-\infty, -1] \\ x + 4 & \text{if } x \in (-1, \infty) \end{cases}$$

Find each limit, if it exists. Then, sketch the graph of $g(x)$.
a) $\lim\limits_{x \to -1^-} g(x)$ b) $\lim\limits_{x \to -1^+} g(x)$ c) $\lim\limits_{x \to -1} g(x)$

15. Let
$$h(x) = \begin{cases} 2x - 1 & \text{if } x \in (-\infty, 1) \\ 2 & \text{if } x = 1 \\ -x + 2 & \text{if } x \in (1, \infty) \end{cases}$$

Find each limit, if it exists. Then, sketch the graph of $h(x)$.
a) $\lim\limits_{x \to 1^-} h(x)$ b) $\lim\limits_{x \to 1^+} h(x)$ c) $\lim\limits_{x \to 1} h(x)$

16. Let
$$f(x) = \begin{cases} x + 3 & \text{if } x \in (-\infty, -2) \\ 1 & \text{if } x = -2 \\ (x+1)^2 & \text{if } x \in (-2, \infty) \end{cases}$$

Find each limit, if it exists. Then, sketch the graph of $f(x)$.
a) $\lim\limits_{x \to -2^-} f(x)$ b) $\lim\limits_{x \to -2^+} f(x)$ c) $\lim\limits_{x \to -2} f(x)$

17. Using a graphing calculator or graphing software, find each limit, if it exists.
a) $\lim\limits_{x \to 2^+} \sqrt{x - 2}$ b) $\lim\limits_{x \to 2^+} \sqrt{x^2 - 4}$

c) $\lim\limits_{x \to 3^-} |-x^2 + 9|$ d) $\lim\limits_{x \to 3^+} |-x^2 + 9|$

e) $\lim\limits_{x \to 3} |-x^2 + 9|$ f) $\lim\limits_{x \to 1^-} \dfrac{|x - 1|}{x - 1}$

g) $\lim\limits_{x \to 1^+} \dfrac{|x - 1|}{x - 1}$ h) $\lim\limits_{x \to 1} \dfrac{|x - 1|}{x - 1}$

18. Evaluate each limit.
a) $\lim\limits_{x \to 2} (4x - 1)$ b) $\lim\limits_{x \to 3} (2x^2 - 4x + 6)$

c) $\lim\limits_{x \to -1} \dfrac{x^2 + 3x - 4}{\sqrt{x + 2}}$ d) $\lim\limits_{x \to 4} \dfrac{x^2 + 9}{\sqrt{x + 3}}$

e) $\lim\limits_{x \to 3} \dfrac{x^2 - 5x + 6}{x^2 + 4x - 21}$ f) $\lim\limits_{x \to 4} \dfrac{x^2 - 2x - 8}{x^2 - 7x + 12}$

g) $\lim\limits_{x \to 4} \dfrac{x - 4}{\sqrt{x^2 - 16}}$ h) $\lim\limits_{h \to 0} \dfrac{\sqrt{3 + h} - \sqrt{3}}{h}$

i) $\lim\limits_{x \to 0} \dfrac{(2 + x)^3 - 8}{x}$

19. Find each limit, if it exists.
a) $\lim\limits_{x \to 5} \dfrac{1}{x - 5}$ b) $\lim\limits_{x \to 0} \dfrac{\dfrac{4}{2 + x} - 2}{x}$

c) $\lim\limits_{x \to 1} \dfrac{x^3 - 1}{x^3 - 2x^2 - 5x + 6}$ d) $\lim\limits_{x \to -3^+} \sqrt{x^3 + 27}$

e) $\lim\limits_{x \to -3^-} \sqrt{x^3 + 27}$ f) $\lim\limits_{x \to -3} \sqrt{x^3 + 27}$

g) $\lim\limits_{x \to 2} \dfrac{3x^2 - 5x - 2}{2x^2 - 9x + 10}$ h) $\lim\limits_{x \to 3} \dfrac{|3 - x|}{3 - x}$

i) $\lim\limits_{x \to -1} \dfrac{x^3 + 1}{x^3 + 3x^2 + 3x + 1}$

Find each limit, if it exists. Then, sketch the graph of $h(x)$.
a) $\lim\limits_{x \to 1^-} h(x)$ b) $\lim\limits_{x \to 1^+} h(x)$ c) $\lim\limits_{x \to 1} h(x)$

3.4 Rates of Change

Refer to the Key Concepts on page 167.

20. If a ball is dropped from the top of a 150-m cliff, then its height after t seconds, and before it hits the ground, is $h = 150 - 4.9t^2$.
a) Find the average velocity of the ball for the following time periods.
i) $t \in [2, 3]$
ii) $t \in [2, 2.1]$
iii) $t \in [2, 2.01]$
b) Find the instantaneous velocity when $t = 2$.

21. The population of a slow-growing bacterial culture can be represented by the function $P(t) = t^2 - 0.7t + 10$, where t is measured in seconds. Find the rate of change of the population after 5 s.

22. The table shows the life expectancy at age 65 for a Canadian from 1921 to 1996. For example, in 1921, a 65-year-old could expect to live for 13.3 more years.

Year	Remaining Years of Life
1921	13.3
1931	13.3
1941	13.4
1951	14.1
1961	14.8
1971	15.7
1981	16.8
1991	18.0
1996	18.4

a) Construct a scatter plot of the data on a graphing calculator or graphing software.
b) Find the average rate of change of life expectancy at age 65 for each time period.
i) 1941 to 1961   ii) 1921 to 1941
iii) 1931 to 1941
c) Use regression to find a curve of best fit for the data.
d) Use the Tangent operation of the graphing calculator or graphing software to estimate the instantaneous rate of change in 1941. Compare your result to your results in part b).

Chapter Test

Achievement Chart

Category	Knowledge/Understanding	Thinking/Inquiry/Problem Solving	Communication	Application
Questions	All	2, 6, 7	6, 7	1, 6, 7

1. The points P(2, 5) and Q(3, 12) lie on the parabola $y = x^2 + 2x - 3$.
a) Find the slope of the secant PQ.
b) Find the slope of the tangent to the parabola at P.
c) Find the equation of the tangent at P.
d) Graph the parabola, the secant, and the tangent.

2. Let
$$f(x) = \begin{cases} 3x - 2 & \text{if } x \in (-\infty, 2] \\ x^2 + 1 & \text{if } x \in (2, \infty) \end{cases}$$

a) Find each limit, if it exists.
i) $\lim_{x \to 2^-} f(x)$ ii) $\lim_{x \to 2^+} f(x)$ iii) $\lim_{x \to 2} f(x)$
b) Sketch the graph of f.
c) Where is f discontinuous? What type of discontinuities does it have?

3. Find each limit, if it exists.
a) $\lim_{x \to 1} \dfrac{x^2 - 1}{x^2 + 3x - 4}$ b) $\lim_{x \to 2} \dfrac{x^3 - 8}{3x^2 - 4x - 4}$

c) $\lim_{x \to 4} \dfrac{\sqrt{x+5}}{x-1}$ d) $\lim_{x \to 0} \dfrac{\sqrt{4-x} - 2}{x}$

e) $\lim_{x \to -3} \dfrac{x^3 + 27}{x^3 - 7x + 6}$ f) $\lim_{x \to 1} \dfrac{\dfrac{1}{\sqrt{x}} - 1}{x - 1}$

4. For each curve, find the slope of the tangent at the given point.
a) $y = 3x^2 + 5x + 2$, (1, 10) 11.38
b) $y = x^3 + 8$, (-2, 0) 12
c) $y = \sqrt{3x + 1}$, (1, 2) .58
d) $y = \dfrac{2x^2 - 5}{x + 2}$, $\left(0, -\dfrac{5}{2}\right)$ 1.39

5. The displacement, in metres, of a particle moving back and forth in a straight line is given by $s = 2t^2 - 11t + 15$, where t is measured in seconds.
a) Find the average velocity over the time interval $t \in [1, 2]$.
b) Find the instantaneous velocity at $t = 1$.

6. A liquid is being poured slowly onto a level surface, making a circular pattern on the surface. Find the rate of change of the area covered on the surface with respect to the radius when the radius is 20 cm. For what situations could scientists use this as a small-scale model?

Achievement Check

Knowledge/Understanding

Thinking/Inquiry/Problem Solving

Communication

Application

7. Karina designs fireworks to explode when they reach their highest point. A firework is fired straight up in the air with an initial upward velocity of 25 m/s. The height, y, in metres, of the firework t seconds after it is launched is $y = 25t - 4.9t^2$.
a) Graph the equation for y using a graphing calculator or graphing software. Record your window variables.
b) Find the instantaneous velocity of the firework at the general time $t = a$.
c) Find the velocity of the firework after 0.5 s and 2 s.
d) At what time will the velocity of the firework be zero? How does this help Karina design the fireworks?
e) For which times does the equation represent the path of the firework? Justify your answer.

Challenge Problems

1. The tangent to the curve $xy = 4$ at a point P in the first quadrant meets the x-axis at A and the y-axis at B. Prove that the area of $\triangle$AOB, where O is the origin, is independent of the position of P.

2. Argue for or against using a continuous function to model each of the following scenarios (it is not necessary to find equations).
a) the cost of filling a car's tank with fuel
b) the amount of fuel when filling a car's tank and then driving
c) the temperature in an oven as it warms, cooks food, and then cools
d) the fines for speeding on a highway
e) the height of a point on a Ferris wheel as it takes on passengers, goes through the ride, and discharges passengers

3. Helga von Koch invented a curve called the Koch Snowflake. The region enclosed in the Koch Snowflake is Koch's Island. To construct the curve, start with an equilateral triangle. Remove the middle third of each side and replace with an equilateral triangle. Continuing the process forever would produce the Koch Snowflake.
a) Calculate the area of the first island. Assume the equilateral triangle has sides of length 1 unit.)
b) Calculate the area of the second island by finding the areas of the three smaller triangles added to the first island.
c) Calculate the area of the third island.
d) Model the area of the nth island.
e) Will there be a limiting value of the area as n gets large? Explain.

4. Evaluate $\lim\limits_{x \to 0} \dfrac{\sqrt[3]{ax+1} - 1}{x}$, where a is a constant.

5. A ski boat travels in a parabolic curve. Let the vertex of the parabola be the origin and let the parabola open upward. The boat is currently at a point 100 m west and 100 m north of the origin, travelling toward the origin. The dock is situated 100 m east and 50 m north of the origin. At what point should the skier release the tow rope to head straight for the dock?

6. At a publicity event, Ayida, a stuntperson, will jump out of a helicopter with a jetpack on her back. The jetpack allows her to achieve a net upward acceleration of 4.4 m/s^2 for a single interval of maximum length 10 s. Ayida wants to time the use of the jetpack so that she lands with zero velocity.
a) If the helicopter is 100 m high, when should Ayida turn on her jetpack? When will she land?
b) If the helicopter is 200 m high, when should Ayida turn on her jetpack? When will she land?
c) What is the maximum height from which Ayida can jump to land with zero velocity?

Solve a Simpler Problem

Capablanca's chess is played on a variation of the standard chessboard, with 80 small squares. If the side length of each small square is 1 unit, then the dimensions of the board are 8 units by 10 units, and the area is 80 square units. The numbers 8 and 10 are factors of 80. Other rectangular boards could be made with the same area, using dimensions 5 by 16, 4 by 20, and so on. Finding the dimensions of all the possible rectangles gives all the factors of 80.

The factors of 360 have a sum of 1170. What is the sum of the reciprocals of the factors?

Understand the Problem

1. What information are you given?
2. What are you asked to find?
3. Do you need an exact or an approximate answer?

Think of a Plan

Start by calculating the sum of the factors, and the sum of the reciprocals of the factors, of small numbers.

Carry Out the Plan

Number	Factors	Sum of Factors	Reciprocals of Factors	Sum of Reciprocals
2	1, 2	3	$1, \dfrac{1}{2}$	$\dfrac{3}{2}$
3	1, 3	4	$1, \dfrac{1}{3}$	$\dfrac{4}{3}$
4	1, 2, 4	7	$1, \dfrac{1}{2}, \dfrac{1}{4}$	$\dfrac{7}{4}$
12	1, 2, 3, 4, 6, 12	28	$1, \dfrac{1}{2}, \dfrac{1}{3}, \dfrac{1}{4}, \dfrac{1}{6}, \dfrac{1}{12}$	$\dfrac{28}{12} = \dfrac{7}{3}$

When finding the sum of the reciprocals of the factors of a number, the common denominator of the reciprocals is the number itself. The numerator of the resulting sum of the fractions is the sum of the divisors. Since the factors of 360 add to 1170, the sum of the reciprocals of the factors of 360 is $\dfrac{1170}{360} = \dfrac{13}{4}$.

Look Back

Does the answer seem reasonable?
How could you check that the answer is correct?

Solve a Simpler Problem

1. Break the problem into smaller parts.
2. Solve the problem.
3. Check that your answer is reasonable.

Apply, Solve, Communicate

1. Find the sum of the reciprocals of the factors of 180.

2. Marisa lives on a farm and is training for a marathon. She takes her dog, on a leash, and jogs at a speed of 10 km/h on a quiet country road. When they are 15 km from home, Marisa turns to go home. She lets her dog off the leash. The dog runs toward home at a speed of 16 km/h. Once he gets there, he turns around and runs back to Marisa. Once he reaches her, he turns and runs back to the house. The dog repeats this until Marisa arrives home. If Marisa maintains her speed of 10 km/h, and the dog keeps running at 16 km/h, how far does the dog run altogether?

3. Find the sum of the first 5000 multiples of 2.

4. What is the value of the following product?
(99 – 9)(99 – 19)(99 – 29)...(99 – 189)
(99 – 199)

5. A total of 3001 digits are used to print the numbers on a roll of cloakroom tickets. The roll starts with number 1. How many tickets are in the roll?

6. Thirty-two posts are placed equal distances apart in a fence that is 400 m long. How far apart are the posts?

7. A welder has 203 metal chains of 100 links each. His task is to combine them into one long chain. How many links must be cut open and then welded shut to complete the task?

8. How many whole numbers less than 1000 do not contain the digit 5?

9. Four hundred regular hexagonal prisms are packed in a pattern with adjacent edges touching as shown.

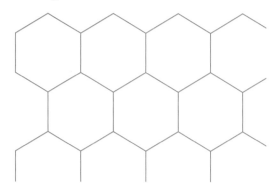

The length of each side of each hexagon is 4 cm. There are twenty prisms in each of twenty rows.
a) What is the perimeter of the shape formed?
b) What is the volume of the smallest box needed to pack the prisms, if each is 15 cm tall?

10. A heavy carton is placed on a conveyor belt. Each of the wheels under the conveyor belt has a circumference of 10 cm.

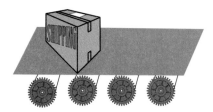

If the wheels all begin turning clockwise at the same speed, how many turns does each wheel have to make to move the carton a distance of 30 cm along the conveyor belt?

Problem Solving: Using the Strategies

1. Imagine that a rope is wrapped around Earth, along the Equator. The rope is removed and cut somewhere, and a 1-m piece of rope is added. This longer rope is then wrapped around Earth at the Equator. Since the rope is longer, there will be a gap between the rope and Earth. How large is the gap, to the nearest tenth of a centimetre?

2. Determine the least number of moves needed to make the white knights and the black knights change places. A knight can move diagonally to the opposite corner of a 3 × 2 rectangle of which it is in the corner. For example, the black knight on square 7 can move either to square 2 or to square 6.

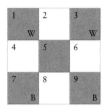

3. The vertices of a cube lie on a sphere of radius 5 cm. Find the volume of the cube, to the nearest tenth of a cubic centimetre.

4. Two concentric circles have centre O. PQ is tangent to the smaller circle at P. The point Q lies on the larger circle. The length of PQ is 4 cm and ∠OPQ = 90°. What is the area of the shaded region?

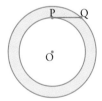

5. When an integer is divided by 15, the remainder is 7. What is the sum of the remainders when the same integer is divided by 3 and by 5?

6. A statistician knocks at a house door. The statistician asks, "How many children do you have?"
The man at the door answers, "Three."
The statistician asks, "What are their ages?"
The man answers, "The product of their ages is 36."

The statistician, unable to determine their ages, asks for another hint.
The man says, "The sum of their ages is the number on the house next door."
The statistician goes next door to determine the number. He returns and asks for another hint.
The man says, "The oldest plays the guitar."
The statistician now knows the ages. What are the ages?

7. The horizontal blue line through the red curve divides the curve into a maximum of 6 parts. Two horizontal lines divide the line into a maximum of 11 parts.

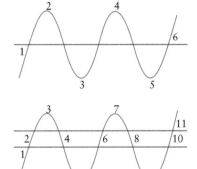

a) How many parts will *n* horizontal lines produce?
b) How many parts will 150 horizontal lines produce?
c) How many horizontal lines are needed to produce 116 parts?

8. Five siblings, Andrew, Barb, Carys, Dianne, and Erik, are all at a cottage on a lake. The following facts are observed one afternoon.

• If Andrew is swimming, so is Barb.
• Either Dianne or Erik, or both of them, are swimming.
• Either Barb or Carys, but not both, are swimming.
• Dianne and Carys are either both swimming or both not swimming.
• If Erik is swimming, then so are Andrew and Dianne.

Who is swimming and who is not?

Chapter 4

Derivatives

Specific Expectations	Section
Demonstrate an understanding that the derivative of a function at a point is the instantaneous rate of change or the slope of the tangent to the graph of the function at that point.	4.1, 4.5, 4.6, 4.7
Determine the derivatives of polynomial and simple rational functions from first principles, using the definitions of the derivative function, $f'(x) = \lim_{h \to 0} \dfrac{f(x+h)-f(x)}{h}$ and $f'(a) = \lim_{x \to a} \dfrac{f(x)-f(a)}{x-a}$.	4.1
Sketch, by hand, the graph of the derivative of a given graph.	4.1
Sketch the graph of a function, given the graph of its derivative function.	4.1
Identify examples of functions that are not differentiable.	4.1
Justify the constant, power, sum-and-difference, product, and quotient rules for determining derivatives.	4.2, 4.3, 4.4
Determine the derivatives of polynomial and rational functions, using the constant, power, sum-and-difference, product, and quotient rules for determining derivatives.	4.2, 4.3, 4.4
Determine second derivatives.	4.5
Sketch the graphs of the first and second derivative functions, given the graph of the original function.	4.5
Identify the nature of the rate of change of a given function, and the rate of change of the rate of change, as they relate to the key features of the graph of that function.	4.5, 4.6
Solve problems of rates of change drawn from a variety of applications (including distance, velocity, and acceleration) involving polynomial or rational functions.	4.6, 4.7
Pose problems and formulate hypotheses regarding rates of change within applications drawn from the natural and social sciences.	4.6, 4.7

MODELLING · MATH

The slope of the tangent to the graph of a function can be interpreted as the rate of change of the quantity modelled by the function, as was discussed in Chapter 3. Because of this interpretation, and the great practical value of rates of change, methods for determining the slope of a tangent to a curve are extremely important.

In this chapter, we build on the methods for determining slopes of tangents to curves that were introduced in Chapter 3. The concept of the derivative of a function is introduced, and rules for determining derivatives are discussed. These rules provide streamlined and powerful means for calculating slopes of tangents, and therefore, rates of change. With the new, powerful techniques of this chapter, we can continue to apply calculus to practical problems, but now much more efficiently. Some of the applications we discuss are the way the velocities of sky-divers change as they fall, the response of human eyes to light, and the growth rate of sunflowers.

1. Limits (Section 3.2) Find each limit.

a) $\lim\limits_{h \to 0}(2h^2 + 5h + 7)$

b) $\lim\limits_{h \to 0} \dfrac{3h + 5}{4h - 5}$

c) $\lim\limits_{h \to 0} \dfrac{2(a + h) - 2a}{h}$

d) $\lim\limits_{h \to 0} \dfrac{2(x + h)^2 - 3(x + h) + 4 - (2x^2 - 3x + 4)}{h}$

e) $\lim\limits_{h \to 0} \dfrac{\sqrt{9 + h} - \sqrt{9}}{h}$

f) $\lim\limits_{h \to 0} \dfrac{\dfrac{1}{2 + h} - \dfrac{1}{2}}{h}$

2. Equation of a line given the slope and a point Find an equation of the line through the given point with slope 4.

a) $(2, 3)$ b) $(-1, 0)$ c) $(-5, -5)$

3. Graphing functions (Section 1.1) Sketch the graph of each function. State the domain.

a) $y = x^2$ b) $y = -2x + 1$

c) $y = \sqrt{x}$ d) $y = |x|$

e) $y = x^3$ f) $y = \dfrac{1}{x}$

4. Graphing functions (Section 1.1)

i) Sketch the graph of each function.

ii) Determine the maximum or minimum point for each function.

a) $y = x^2 + 2x + 1$

b) $y = 3x^2 - x + 2$

c) $y = -2(x - 1)^2 + 1$

5. Graphing functions (Section 1.1)

i) Determine the domain of each function.

ii) Sketch the graph of each function.

a) $y = \dfrac{x - 1}{x}$ b) $y = \sqrt{x + 4}$

c) $y = x^{\frac{3}{2}}$

6. Graphing functions (Section 1.1) The share value y, in dollars, of a stock is modelled by the equation $y = (t - 2)^3 - 3(t - 2) + 3$, where t is time in years, and $t \in [0, 4]$.

a) Sketch the graph of share value versus time.

b) When is the price of the stock increasing?

c) When is the price of the stock decreasing?

d) If you were interested in maximizing profit, when would you buy the stock and when would you sell it?

7. Exponent laws Rewrite using positive exponents.

a) $(2x^3)^{-1}$

b) $\sqrt{x} - 6(\sqrt[3]{x})^{-1}$

c) $a + bx^{-1} - cx^{-2}$

d) $(5x^{-3})^2 - (\sqrt{x})^3$

8. Simplifying expressions Expand and simplify.

a) $x^{-\frac{1}{2}}(2x^2 - 5)^2$

b) $(3x^3 - 5x)(4x + 9)$

c) $(2m^2 - 6m + 3)(5m^2 + 4m - 1)$

d) $3y(y^3 - 8)(y^3 + 8)$

e) $\sqrt{k^2 + 2}\sqrt{k + 6}$

f) $\left(2\sqrt{x} - \dfrac{2}{\sqrt{x}}\right)\left(\sqrt{2x} + \dfrac{1}{2\sqrt{x}}\right)$

9. Slopes of secants (Section 3.1) For each function,

i) determine the slope of the line that intersects the graph of f at $x = 1$ and $x = 4$.

ii) determine the slope of the line that intersects the graph of f at $x = 1$ and $x = 2$.

iii) determine an expression for the slope of the line that intersects the graph of f at $x = 1$ and $x = 1 + h$, where $h \neq 0$.

iv) determine the slope of the line that is tangent to the graph of f at $x = 1$.

a) $f(x) = x(x + 1)$

b) $f(x) = (x + 1)^2$

c) $f(x) = x^3 + x$

10. Slopes of tangents (Section 3.1)

a) Sketch the graph of $f(x) = x^2 - 2x$.

b) Using the graph in part a), sketch the tangents to the curve at $x = -1, 0, 1, 2$, and 3.

c) Using measurements from the sketch in part b) and the definition of slope as rise over run, estimate the slopes of the tangents in part b).

11. Limits of functions (Section 3.3) Consider the absolute value function $f(x) = |x|$.

a) Sketch the graph of f.

b) Determine each limit.

i) $\lim\limits_{x \to 0^+} |x|$ ii) $\lim\limits_{x \to 0^-} |x|$ iii) $\lim\limits_{x \to 0} |x|$

12. Limits of functions (Section 3.3)

a) Sketch the graph of $f(x) = \dfrac{|x|}{x}$.

b) Determine each limit.

i) $\lim\limits_{h \to 0^+} \dfrac{|h|}{h}$ ii) $\lim\limits_{h \to 0^-} \dfrac{|h|}{h}$ iii) $\lim\limits_{h \to 0} \dfrac{|h|}{h}$

13. Limits of functions (Section 3.3) Determine each limit.

a) $\lim\limits_{x \to 0^+} \dfrac{1}{x}$ b) $\lim\limits_{x \to 0^-} \dfrac{1}{x}$ c) $\lim\limits_{x \to 0} \dfrac{1}{x}$

d) $\lim\limits_{x \to 0^+} \sqrt{x}$ e) $\lim\limits_{x \to 0^-} \sqrt{x}$ f) $\lim\limits_{x \to 0} \sqrt{x}$

14. Average velocity (Section 3.4) A particle has position function $s(t) = 2t^2 + 4t + 8$, where s is measured in metres and t in seconds. Determine the average velocity over the first

a) 2 s   b) 10 s

15. Analysing motion (Section 3.4)

a) If a car is travelling at 50 km/h and accelerating, describe what is happening to the speed of the car.

b) If a man is running at 10 km/h and decelerating, describe what is happening to his speed.

c) If a woman is walking at a steady pace, describe her acceleration.

d) If a stone is falling downward, describe what is happening to its height, acceleration, and speed.

16. Analysing motion (Section 3.4) A car travelling at a speed of 50 km/h accelerates so that its speed increases at a rate of 5 km/h every second. How fast is the car moving after 4 s?

17. Rates (Section 3.4) Ravi can spray paint the interior of a warehouse in 3 h. Phyllis can spray paint the same warehouse in 2 h, using a different sprayer.

a) Determine the rate at which each person can work (in m²/min) if the area to be sprayed is 550 m².

b) How long will it take them to spray paint the warehouse if they work together?

18. Finite differences The following table shows the position s, in metres, of an object moving in a straight line, at time t, in seconds.

t	s
1	5
2	20
3	45
4	80
5	125

a) Construct a difference table for the data, including the first and second differences.

b) Divide the first differences by the corresponding time intervals. What are the units for the resulting quantities? Interpret the quantities.

c) Divide the second differences by the corresponding time intervals. What are the units for the resulting quantities? Interpret the quantities.

d) Determine a formula for the position function $s(t)$.

The Derivative

We have developed the concept of finding the slope of the tangent to a curve and have applied it to various problems involving rates of change, such as velocity, marginal cost, and temperature change. This concept has such important and widespread applications that, in this chapter, we will develop a variety of practical techniques for calculating rates of change.

Investigate & Inquire: Exploring Slopes of Tangents With a Graphing Calculator

1. Enter the function $y = x^3 - 2x^2 - 5x + 5$ into the Y= editor on your calculator and graph it in the standard viewing window, using the ZStandard instruction. The Tangent operation allows you to specify an x-coordinate by entering a number. The calculator will draw a tangent to the function at the x-value that you have specified, and display the equation of the tangent at the bottom of the screen. Repeat this for several values of x to complete the table below.

x-coordinate	Value of slope
−2	
−1	
0	
1	−6
2	
3	

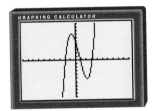 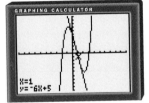

Window variables:
$x \in [-10, 10]$, $y \in [-10, 10]$

2. Use the STAT EDIT menu to enter the values from the table into lists L1 and L2. From these lists, create a scatter plot. What kind of pattern do you see in the points of the scatter plot? Perform an appropriate regression on the data in L1 and L2, using the STAT CALC menu, and record the equation in your notebook. What is the relationship between the original equation and the regression equation?

3. Another way to show this relationship on the calculator is to use the nDeriv function from the **MATH menu**. In the home screen, the nDeriv function will display an approximate value for the slope of a line. Used in the Y= editor, it will plot a set of points, where the y-coordinate of each point is the slope of the function at the corresponding x-coordinate. Use a heavier Graph style for the second function.

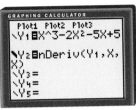

4. Graph the two functions in the standard viewing window, using the ZStandard instruction. What is the relationship between the function and this graph of the nDeriv function? Is it the same as the relationship that you observed in the first activity? In this section, we will look at an algebraic method of determining this relationship.

In Chapter 3, we considered the slope of the tangent to the graph of a function f at a fixed number a to be

$$m = \lim_{h \to 0} \frac{f(a+h) - f(a)}{h}$$

But if we let a vary over the domain of f, we can change our point of view and regard this expression for the slope as a new function.

Given a function $f(x)$, the **derivative** of f with respect to x is the function $f'(x)$ defined by $f'(x) = \lim_{h \to 0} \frac{f(x+h) - f(x)}{h}$ if the limit exists. The value $f'(a) = \lim_{x \to a} \frac{f(x) - f(a)}{x - a}$ gives the slope of the tangent to f at a, as before.

Finding the derivative of a function is also known as **differentiating** the function. Determining a derivative directly from this definition is regarded as the **method of first principles**. Throughout this book, we will develop further methods of finding derivatives.

The domain of this new function f' is the set of all numbers x for which the above limit exists. Since $f(x)$ occurs in the expression for $f'(x)$, the domain of f' will always be a subset of the domain of f.

Example 1 Using the Definition of the Derivative

a) If $f(x) = x^2$, find the derivative of f with respect to x using first principles. State the domain of the function and the domain of the derivative.
b) Find $f'(3)$. Interpret the result.
c) Illustrate by comparing the graphs of f and f'.

Solution

a) The domain of the function $f(x) = x^2$ is R.
In computing the limit that defines $f'(x)$, we must remember that the variable is h, and regard x temporarily as a constant during the calculation of the limit.

$$f'(x) = \lim_{h \to 0} \frac{f(x+h) - f(x)}{h}$$

$$= \lim_{h \to 0} \frac{(x+h)^2 - (x)^2}{h}$$

$$= \lim_{h \to 0} \frac{x^2 + 2xh + h^2 - x^2}{h}$$

$$= \lim_{h \to 0} \frac{2xh + h^2}{h}$$

$$= \lim_{h \to 0} \frac{h(2x + h)}{h}$$

$$= \lim_{h \to 0} (2x + h), \qquad h \neq 0$$

$$= 2x$$

The derivative is the function f' given by $f'(x) = 2x$. The domain of the derivative is R, because the limit exists for any value of x.

b) $f'(3) = 2(3)$
$$= 6$$
The slope of the tangent to the graph of $f(x) = x^2$ at $x = 3$ is 6.

c) Comparing the graphs of $f(x) = x^2$ and $f'(x) = 2x$, we notice that the slopes of the tangents to $f(x) = x^2$ are negative when $x < 0$, and $f'(x) = 2x$ is negative when $x < 0$. When $x = 0$, both $f'(x)$ and the slope of the graph of $f(x)$ are equal to 0. Finally, for $x > 0$, the slopes of the tangents to $f(x)$ are greater than zero and $f'(x) > 0$. Therefore, it seems reasonable that the values of the derivative function $2x$ represent the slopes of tangents to the graph of the original function x^2.

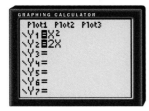
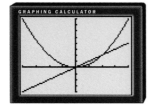

Window variables:
$x \in [-4, 4], y \in [-8, 16]$

Note that $f'(x) = 2x$ is not a tangent to $f(x) = x^2$ at a particular point. It is the derivative function and therefore represents a formula for finding the *slope* of the tangent to $f(x)$ at all points on the graph of $f(x)$.

Example 2 Estimating a Derivative From a Graph

Use the given graph of f to sketch the graph of f'.

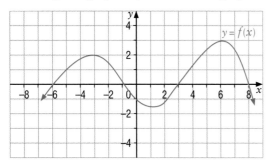

Web Connection
To see animated versions of these concepts, go to
www.mcgrawhill.ca/links/CAF12
and follow the links.

Solution
We can estimate the slopes of the tangents at any values of x by drawing the tangent line at the point $(x, f(x))$ and estimating its slope. This method gives values of f' that we plot directly beneath the graph of f. For example, when $x = 7.5$, we draw the tangent and estimate that the slope is about -2. So $f'(7.5) = -2$. We now plot the point $(7.5, -2)$ on the graph of f' directly beneath the same point on the graph of f.

We get the x-intercepts of f' from the fact that the horizontal tangents have slope 0. Notice that, for $x \in (\infty, -3)$, the tangents have positive slope, and so $f'(x)$ is positive. For $x \in (-3, 1.5)$, the tangents have negative slope, and so $f'(x)$ is negative. For $x \in (1.5, 6)$, the tangents have positive slope, and so $f'(x)$ is positive, and for $x \in (6, \infty)$, the tangents have negative slope, and so $f'(x)$ is negative.

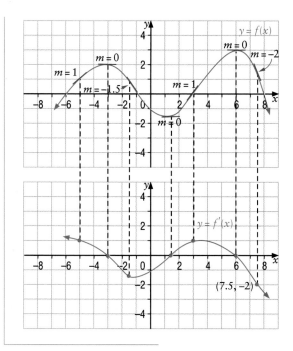

Example 3 Sketching the Graph of a Function From the Graph of the First Derivative

The derivative f' of a function f has the graph shown.

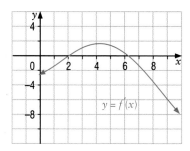

Sketch the graph of f, given that $f(0) = 0$.

Solution

We sketch the curve of f by reversing the procedure of Example 2. As in Example 2, the x-intercepts of f' correspond to the points on the graph of f where the tangent is horizontal. Thus, $f'(2.1) = 0$, so the tangent drawn at the point $(2.1, f(2.1))$ must have slope $m = 0$, therefore being horizontal. Likewise, $f'(6.3) = 0$, so the tangent to the graph of f at $(6.3, f(6.3))$ is horizontal. Between $x = 2.1$ and $x = 6.3$, the values of $f'(x)$ are positive, so the graph of f has tangents with positive slope on the interval $(2.1, 6.3)$, with a maximum tangent slope of $m = 1.6$ at $x = 4.3$. Therefore, the graph of f from $x = 2.1$ to $x = 6.3$ must be a rising curve, almost horizontal near the points $(2.1, f(2.1))$ and $(6.3, f(6.3))$.

Similarly, the values $f'(0) = -2.5$ and $f'(9) = -6$ give tangents to the graph of f with slope $m = -2.5$ at $(0, f(0))$ and $m = -6$ at $(9, f(9))$, respectively. We can complete the sketch of f as follows:

Starting from the given point $(0, 0)$, we draw down at an initial slope of $m = -2.5$, levelling out at $x = 2.1$ to join the upward-curving segment between $x = 2.1$ and $x = 6.3$. For $x > 6.3$, the tangent slopes become negative again, so the graph curves downward to finish at a steep slope of $m = -6$.

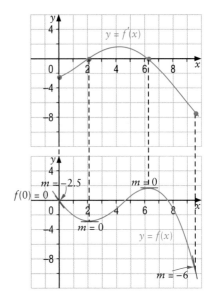

Example 4 Using the Definition of the Derivative

Differentiate the function $f(x) = \dfrac{x+2}{x-1}$ from first principles. State the domain of the function and the domain of the derivative.

Solution

The domain of the function $f(x) = \dfrac{x+2}{x-1}$ is all real values of x except $x = 1$.

$$f'(x) = \lim_{h \to 0} \frac{f(x+h) - f(x)}{h}$$

$$= \lim_{h \to 0} \frac{\dfrac{(x+h)+2}{(x+h)-1} - \dfrac{x+2}{x-1}}{h}$$

$$= \lim_{h \to 0} \frac{\dfrac{(x+h)+2}{(x+h)-1} - \dfrac{x+2}{x-1}}{h} \times \frac{(x+h-1)(x-1)}{(x+h-1)(x-1)}$$

To clear fractions, multiply the numerator and the denominator by the same expression.

$$= \lim_{h \to 0} \frac{(x+h+2)(x-1) - (x+2)(x+h-1)}{h(x+h-1)(x-1)}$$

$$= \lim_{h \to 0} \frac{(x+2)(x-1) + h(x-1) - (x+2)(x-1) - (x+2)h}{h(x+h-1)(x-1)}$$

$$= \lim_{h \to 0} \frac{-3h}{h(x+h-1)(x-1)}$$

$$= \lim_{h \to 0} \frac{-3}{(x+h-1)(x-1)}, \quad h \neq 0$$

$$= \frac{-3}{(x-1)^2}$$

The domain of the derivative $f'(x)$ is all real values of x except $x = 1$. (This is the same as the domain of $f(x)$.)

Other Notations

The German mathematician Gottfried Leibniz introduced another notation for the derivative:

Given $y = f(x)$, the derivative $f'(x)$, in Leibniz notation, is $\dfrac{dy}{dx}$.

In this notation, the results of the previous examples can be expressed as follows.

If $y = x^2$, then $\dfrac{dy}{dx} = 2x$.

If $y = \dfrac{x+2}{x-1}$, then $\dfrac{dy}{dx} = \dfrac{-3}{(x-1)^2}$.

Leibniz used this notation as a reminder of the procedure for finding a derivative:

$$\frac{dy}{dx} = \lim_{\Delta x \to 0} \frac{\Delta y}{\Delta x}$$

For now, the symbol $\dfrac{dy}{dx}$ should not be regarded as a ratio, but rather as a symbol for $f'(x)$. The Leibniz notation has the advantage that both the independent variable x and the dependent variable y are indicated. For instance, if the displacement s of a particle is given as a function of time t, then the velocity, which is the rate of change of s with respect to t, is expressed as

$$v = \frac{ds}{dt}$$

A variation of the Leibniz notation occurs when we think of the process of finding the derivative of a function as an operation, called differentiation, which is performed on f to produce a new function f'. Then, we write

$$\frac{dy}{dx} = \frac{d}{dx} f(x)$$

and think of $\dfrac{d}{dx}$ as a differential operator. Thus, we could write

$$\frac{d}{dx}(x^2) = 2x \quad \text{and} \quad \frac{d}{dx}\left(\frac{x+2}{x-1}\right) = \frac{-3}{(x-1)^2}.$$

Sometimes the symbols D and D_x are also used as notations for the differential operator. These symbols, as well as $\dfrac{d}{dx}$, are called differential operators because they indicate the operation of differentiation, the process of calculating the derivative. Thus, we have the following equivalent notations for the derivative of $y = f(x)$:

$$f'(x),\ y',\ \frac{dy}{dx},\ \frac{d}{dx} f(x),\ Df(x),\ \text{and } D_x y.$$

The notation y' is often used to indicate the derivative of a function when there can be no misunderstanding of what the independent variable is. If we want to indicate the value of a derivative $\dfrac{dy}{dx}$ in Leibniz notation at a specific value $x = a$, we use the notation

$$\frac{dy}{dx}\bigg]_{x=a} \quad \text{or} \quad \frac{dy}{dx}\bigg|_{x=a}$$

which means the same as $f'(a)$.

Web Connection

In their time, there was a controversy over who invented calculus first, Leibniz or Sir Isaac Newton. Go to **www.mcgrawhill.ca/links/CAF12** to learn more.

Differentiable Functions

A function f is said to be **differentiable** at a if $f'(a)$ exists. It is called **differentiable on an interval** if it is differentiable at every number in the interval. In Example 1, we saw that $f(x) = x^2$ is differentiable on R, and in Example 2, we found that $y = \dfrac{x+2}{x-1}$ is differentiable for $x \neq 1$, or on the intervals $x \in (-\infty, 1)$ and $x \in (1, \infty)$.

Example 5 Determining Whether a Function is Differentiable

Show that the function $f(x) = |x|$ is not differentiable at 0.

Solution

We must show that $f'(0)$ does not exist. We investigate this limit:

$$f'(0) = \lim_{h \to 0} \frac{f(0+h) - f(0)}{h}$$
$$= \lim_{h \to 0} \frac{f(h) - 0}{h}$$
$$= \lim_{h \to 0} \frac{|h|}{h}$$

To show that this limit does not exist, we compute the right- and left-hand limits separately. Remember that the right- and left-hand limits must exist, and be equal, for the limit to exist (see Section 3.2).

Since $|h| = h$ if $h \in [0, \infty)$, we have

$$\lim_{h \to 0^+} \frac{|h|}{h} = \lim_{h \to 0^+} \frac{h}{h}$$
$$= \lim_{h \to 0^+} 1$$
$$= 1$$

Since $|h| = -h$ if $h \in (-\infty, 0)$, we have

$$\lim_{h \to 0^-} \frac{|h|}{h} = \lim_{h \to 0^-} \frac{-h}{h}$$
$$= \lim_{h \to 0^-} (-1)$$
$$= -1$$

Since these one-sided limits are different, $f'(0)$ does not exist. Therefore, f is not differentiable at 0.

The geometric significance of Example 5 can be seen from the graph of $f(x) = |x|$ in the screen. The graph does not have a tangent at $(0, 0)$.

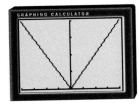

Window variables:
$x \in [-4, 4]$, $y \in [0, 4]$

In general, functions whose graphs have "corners" or **cusps** are not differentiable there. In the figure, $y = f(x)$ is differentiable everywhere except at points B and D.

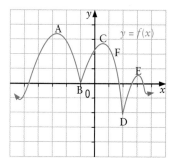

Example 6 Using the Derivative to Determine Rates of Change

The height of a Frisbee™ tossed into the air is given by $H(t) = -\dfrac{1}{2}t^2 + 2t + 2$, where t is measured in seconds and H is measured in metres.

a) Find the rate of change of the height of the Frisbee™ at time t.

b) Find the rate of change of the height of the Frisbee™ after 2 s.

c) Interpret the result of part b).

Solution

a) The rate of change of the height can be found by calculating the derivative $H'(t)$.

$$H'(t) = \lim_{h \to 0} \frac{H(t+h) - H(t)}{h}$$

$$= \lim_{h \to 0} \frac{\left[-\dfrac{1}{2}(t+h)^2 + 2(t+h) + 2 \right] - \left[-\dfrac{1}{2}t^2 + 2t + 2 \right]}{h}$$

$$= \lim_{h \to 0} \frac{-th - \dfrac{1}{2}h^2 + 2h}{h}$$

$$= \lim_{h \to 0} \left(-t - \frac{1}{2}h + 2 \right), \qquad h \neq 0$$

$$= 2 - t$$

b) $H'(2) = 2 - 2$
$\qquad\quad = 0$

After 2 s, the instantaneous rate of change of the height of the Frisbee™ is 0 m/s.

c) This means the Frisbee™ has momentarily stopped rising before it begins to fall to the ground.

Key Concepts

- The derivative of a function f with respect to x is the function f' defined by

$$f'(x) = \lim_{h \to 0} \frac{f(x+h) - f(x)}{h}$$

  if the limit exists.
- The domain of f' is equal to or smaller than the domain of f.
- If $y = f(x)$, some notations for the derivative are

$$f'(x), y', \frac{dy}{dx}, \frac{d}{dx} f(x), Df(x), \text{ and } D_x y.$$

- A function f is said to be differentiable at a if $f'(a)$ exists. A function f is called differentiable on an interval if it is differentiable at every number in the interval.

Communicate Your Understanding

1. a) Explain why f', the derivative of f, is a function.
b) Why is the domain of f' equal to or smaller than the domain of f?
2. Explain an advantage of the Leibniz notation.
3. A function g is not differentiable at a. Describe ways of determining this from
a) the graph of g **b)** the definition of the derivative
4. When sketching a graph of a function $f(x)$, how would you interpret
a) $f'(x) > 0$?   **b)** $f'(x) < 0$?   **c)** $f'(x) = 0$?
5. Explain what is done in each step of the solution to Example 4 (Page 190).

Practise

 1. Sketch each graph for $x \in [-3, 3]$ and estimate the value of each derivative by finding the slopes of the tangents. Use this information to sketch the graph of f'.
a) $y = x^2$ **b)** $y = x^3$
c) $y = x^3 - 3x$
i) $f'(-2)$ **ii)** $f'(-1)$
iii) $f'(0)$ **iv)** $f'(1)$
v) $f'(2)$

2. Communication Each of the graphs a) to d) represents a function. The graphs i) to iv) (page 195) represent the derivatives of these functions. Match the graph of each function with the graph of the derivative. Explain your reasoning.

a)
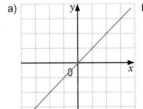

b)
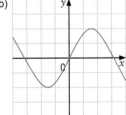

c)
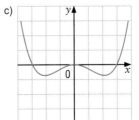

d)
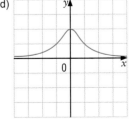

i)

ii)

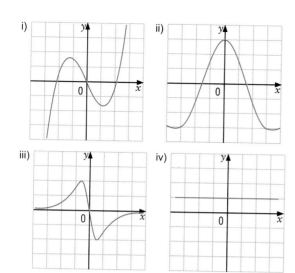

iii)

iv)

3. a) Copy each graph of f, and use it to draw the graph of f' below it.

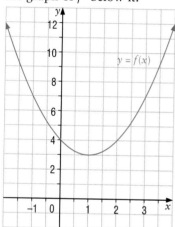

$y = f(x)$

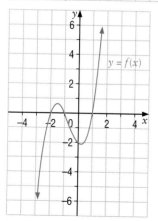

$y = f(x)$

b) Predict the degree of the derivative function, assuming that it is a polynomial. Explain.

4. At which values of x is each function not differentiable? Explain.

a)

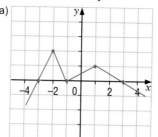

b)

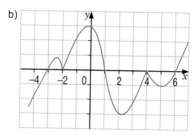

B **5.** Find the derivative of each function from first principles.

a) $f(x) = 2x + 3$ b) $g(x) = x^2 - 4$
c) $h(x) = t^2 + 3t - 1$ d) $N(b) = b^3 - b^2$
e) $y = x^4$ f) $G(x) = 3x^2 - 2x + 1$
g) $T(n) = n - n^3$ h) $f(x) = 4x$
i) $y = 5 - 2x$ j) $y = 2x - x^2$

6. Find the derivative of each function from first principles. Compare the domain of each function and the domain of the derivative.

a) $f(x) = \dfrac{1}{x+2}$ b) $y = \sqrt{x-3}$

c) $f(x) = \sqrt{x} - x$ d) $g(x) = \dfrac{2}{x-4}$

e) $f(x) = \dfrac{x-2}{x+1}$ f) $C(m) = \dfrac{1}{m^2}$

g) $y = x + \dfrac{1}{x}$ h) $P = \dfrac{1}{\sqrt{q-1}}$

7. If $f(x) = \sqrt{x+1}$, find f' and state the domains of f and f'.

8. Each of the following limits represents the derivative of some function f at some number a. State f and a in each case.

a) $\displaystyle\lim_{h \to 0} \dfrac{(1+h)^2 - 1}{h}$ b) $\displaystyle\lim_{h \to 0} \dfrac{(2+h)^2 - 4}{h}$

c) $\displaystyle\lim_{h \to 0} \dfrac{(3+h)^3 - 27}{h}$ d) $\displaystyle\lim_{h \to 0} \dfrac{\sqrt{9+h} - 3}{h}$

Apply, Solve, Communicate

9. Application, Communication The derivative f' of a function f has the graph shown.

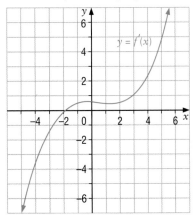

a) Sketch the graph of f, given that $f(0) = 0$.
b) Suppose a function g has the properties that $g'(x) = f'(x)$ for all values of x, and $g(0) = 3$. Sketch the graph of g.

10. Application The height of a ball thrown into the air is modelled by the function $H(t) = -4.9t^2 + 5t + 2$, where t is measured in seconds and H in metres.
a) Find the function, $H'(t)$, that represents the rate of change of the height of the ball.
b) At what time is the rate of change of the height -9 m/s?
c) When is the ball at rest?

11. Inquiry/Problem Solving A cake has been baking in the oven. It is taken out and placed on a counter, where it is allowed to cool to room temperature. The temperature of the cake, T, depends on how long it has been out of the oven.

a) Sketch a possible graph of the temperature, T, as a function of the time, t, that the cake has been out of the oven.
b) Describe how the rate of change of the temperature, T, with respect to t changes as t increases.
c) Sketch a graph of the derivative of T.

12. Application Using a graphing calculator, graph $f(x) = \dfrac{x+2}{x-1}$, and relate the slopes of the tangents to the function to the sign of the derivative over all significant intervals.

13. a) Show that the function $k(x) = |x - 3|$ is not differentiable at $x = 3$.
b) Sketch the graph of k.
c) Find a formula for k' and sketch the graph.

14. a) Sketch the graph of the cube root function $M(n) = \sqrt[3]{n}$.
b) Show that M is not differentiable at 0.

15. a) Show that the function $f(x) = x^{\frac{1}{3}}$ is not differentiable at 0.
b) Sketch the curve $y = x^{\frac{2}{3}}$.

16. Communication a) Sketch the graph of the function $f(x) = x|x|$.
b) State the domain of f'.
c) Use the definition of the derivative to find a formula for f'.
d) Show that f is differentiable for $x = 0$.

17. Inquiry/Problem Solving A function f is defined by the following conditions:
$f(x) = |x|$ if $x \in [-1, 1]$
$f(x + 2) = f(x)$ for all values of x
a) Sketch the graph of f.
b) For what values of x is f not differentiable?

Historical Bite: Newton and the Graphing Calculator

Sir Isaac Newton discovered a general method for estimating solutions to equations of the form $f(x) = 0$. Newton's method, which uses the derivative of $f(x)$, can be applied to any equation, unlike methods such as the quadratic formula, which applies only to quadratic equations. Successive iterations of the method can provide estimates of very high accuracy.
Newton's method is the basis for the algorithms used today by graphing calculators and computer software to estimate numerical solutions to equations.

Basic Differentiation Rules

When a skydiver jumps from an airplane, her velocity increases gradually. If she jumps from high enough, however, eventually her velocity approaches a constant value, called the terminal velocity, which is due to air resistance acting on the skydiver. Once the parachute opens, the skydiver slows down rapidly until a new, much smaller, terminal velocity is reached.

People taking skydiving lessons are first trained how to land safely by jumping from a height of about 3.3 m. From this height a freely falling person hits the ground at the same velocity as a skydiver, who falls at a terminal velocity of about 8 m/s once the parachute is opened. If we ignore air resistance, the distance fallen, in metres, after t seconds is $s = 4.9t^2$. We might like to know the velocity of a jumper at any time during the jump. This is given by the derivative of the position function.

We could use the first principles definition of the derivative to compute the velocity. But if we had to do this every time, it would be very time-consuming. Fortunately, mathematicians have come up with several rules to simplify the process of differentiation. In this section, we begin to study these rules.

Investigate & Inquire: Derivatives of Polynomial Functions

Many functions that model situations in the sciences or social sciences contain power terms such as $4x^3$. We need to develop an efficient way of differentiating powers in order to find rates of change of those functions. In this investigation, you will look more generally at the derivatives of polynomial functions.

1. Using a graphing calculator, enter the functions shown in the screen to the left below. Graph the functions using a suitable window to get the screen to the right.

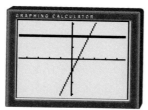

Window variables:
$x \in [-4.7, 4.7]$, $y \in [-3.1, 3.1]$
or use the ZDecimal instruction.

2. The function in Y2 represents the derivative function of Y1. What is the relationship between the original function and the derivative function? Test your hypothesis by entering a different linear function in Y1. Does your hypothesis hold for any linear function?

3. Determine the equation of the derivative function.

4. In the next set of screens, the original function is a quadratic function. What is the relationship between the original function and the derivative function? Test your hypothesis by entering a different quadratic function in Y1. Does your hypothesis hold for any quadratic function?

Window variables:
$x \in [-4.7, 4.7]$, $y \in [-3.1, 3.1]$

5. Determine the equation of the derivative function in step 4 and repeat for the other quadratic equations that you have entered.

6. Repeat this process using cubic functions, and then quartic functions. What is the relationship between the original function and the derivative function? Test your hypothesis by entering different cubic and quartic functions in Y1. Does your hypothesis hold?

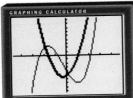

Window variables:
$x \in [-4.7, 4.7]$, $y \in [-9.3, 9.3]$

7. Look back on the equation of each function you explored and the equation of its derivative. Is there a relationship between the equations? Explain.

Power rule: If $f(x) = x^n$, where n is a positive integer, then $f'(x) = nx^{n-1}$ or $\dfrac{d}{dx} x^n = nx^{n-1}$

You will have the opportunity to derive the **power rule** from first principles in question 25 on page 206.

Example 1 Using the Power Rule

Differentiate using the power rule.
a) $f(x) = x^7$
b) $f(x) = x^{20}$
c) $y = t^4$
d) $\dfrac{d}{du}(u^8)$

Solution
a) $f'(x) = 7x^6$
b) $f'(x) = 20x^{19}$
c) $y' = 4t^3$
d) $\dfrac{d}{du}(u^8) = 8u^7$

Note that it is customary to state the derivative in the same notation as the original function.

We have stated the power rule when n is a positive integer, but the rule still applies for any real number n.

Example 2 Using the Power Rule When n Is not a Positive Integer

Use the power rule to find $f'(2)$ for each function, and then check your result using a graphing calculator or graphing software.

a) $f(x) = \dfrac{1}{x^3}$ b) $f(x) = \sqrt{x}$

Solution

a) We use a negative exponent to rewrite the function as

$$f(x) = \dfrac{1}{x^3}$$
$$= x^{-3}$$

Then, the power rule gives

$$f'(x) = (-3)x^{-3-1}$$
$$= (-3)x^{-4}$$
$$= -\dfrac{3}{x^4}$$

so

$$f'(2) = -\dfrac{3}{(2)^4}$$
$$= -\dfrac{3}{16}$$
$$= -0.1875$$

Use the Tangent operation with Window variables:
$x \in [1, 3], y \in [0, 0.2]$.

b) Here we use a fractional exponent.

$$y = \sqrt{x}$$
$$= x^{\frac{1}{2}}$$

$$\dfrac{dy}{dx} = \dfrac{1}{2}\, x^{\frac{1}{2}-1}$$
$$= \dfrac{1}{2}\, x^{-\frac{1}{2}}$$
$$= \dfrac{1}{2\sqrt{x}}$$

At $x = 2$, $\dfrac{dy}{dx} = \dfrac{1}{2\sqrt{2}}$

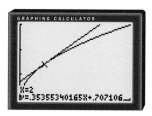

Window variables:
$x \in [0, 9], y \in [0, 3]$

Constant rule: If f is a constant function, $f(x) = c$, then $f'(x) = 0$ or $\dfrac{d}{dx}(c) = 0$.

The screen illustrates the constant rule geometrically. The graph of a constant function $f(x) = 3$ is the horizontal line $y = 3$. The tangent at any point on this line is the line itself. Since the horizontal line has slope 0, the slope of the tangent is zero.

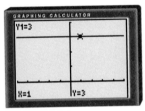

Constant multiple rule: If $g(x) = cf(x)$, then $g'(x) = cf'(x)$ or $\dfrac{d}{dx}[cf(x)] = c\dfrac{d}{dx}f(x)$.

Sum rule: If both f and g are differentiable, then so is $f + g$, and $(f + g)' = f' + g'$ or $\dfrac{d}{dx}(f(x) + g(x)) = \dfrac{d}{dx}f(x) + \dfrac{d}{dx}g(x)$.

Difference rule: If both f and g are differentiable, then so is $f - g$, and $(f - g)' = f' - g'$ or $\dfrac{d}{dx}(f(x) - g(x)) = \dfrac{d}{dx}f(x) - \dfrac{d}{dx}g(x)$.

Example 3 The Constant Rule and the Constant Multiple Rule

For a parachutist in training from a height of 3.3 m, the distance fallen, s, in metres, after t seconds is $s = 4.9t^2$.
a) State the position function.
b) Find the velocity function.
c) Determine the velocity of the parachutist when she hits the ground.
d) Determine the velocity of the parachutist after 1 s.

Solution

a) The position formula, $s = 4.9t^2$, is valid only until the parachutist lands. To find the time to land, let $4.9t^2 = 3.3$. Then,

$t = 0.82$ s

Thus,

$$s(t) = \begin{cases} 4.9t^2, & t \in [0, 0.82] \\ 3.3, & t \in (0.82, \infty) \end{cases}$$

b) The velocity function is

$$v(t) = s'(t) = \begin{cases} 9.8t, & t \in [0, 0.82] \\ 0 & t \in (0.82, \infty) \end{cases}$$

c) $v(0.82) = 9.8(0.82)$
$\qquad\qquad = 8.036$

The velocity of the parachutist when she hits the ground is 8.036 m/s.

d) $v(1) = 0$

The velocity after 1 s is 0 m/s; after the parachutist hits the ground, her speed is 0.

Example 4 Using Derivative Rules

Find the derivative of each function.

a) $y = 3$ b) $f(x) = 8x^{\frac{3}{2}}$ c) $f(x) = 2x^2 - 3x + 4$ d) $g(x) = 5x^3 - \sqrt{x}$

Solution

a) We use the constant rule.

If $y = 3$, then $\dfrac{dy}{dx} = 0$.

b) Using the constant multiple rule, we get

$$f(x) = 8x^{\frac{3}{2}}$$

$$f'(x) = 8\frac{d}{dx}\left(x^{\frac{3}{2}}\right)$$

$$= 8\left(\frac{3}{2}x^{\frac{1}{2}}\right)$$

$$= 12x^{\frac{1}{2}}$$

c) Combining the sum and difference rules with the power rule and the constant multiple rule, we obtain

$$f'(x) = \frac{d}{dx}(2x^2 - 3x + 4)$$

$$= 2\frac{d}{dx}(x^2) - 3\frac{d}{dx}(x) + \frac{d}{dx}(4)$$

$$= 2(2x) - 3(1) + 0$$

$$= 4x - 3$$

d) We use the difference rule, the constant multiple rule, and the power rule:

$$g'(x) = \frac{d}{dx}(5x^3 - \sqrt{x})$$

$$= 5\frac{d}{dx}(x^3) - \frac{d}{dx}\left(x^{\frac{1}{2}}\right)$$

$$= 5(3x^2) - \left(\frac{1}{2}x^{\frac{1}{2}-1}\right)$$

$$= 15x^2 - \frac{1}{2}x^{-\frac{1}{2}}$$

$$= 15x^2 - \frac{1}{2\sqrt{x}}$$

Example 5 Equation of a Tangent

Find the equation of the tangent to the curve $y = \dfrac{1}{x}$ at $x = -2$. Check your result using a graphing calculator or graphing software.

Solution

The curve is the graph of the function $f(x) = x^{-1}$.

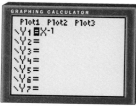
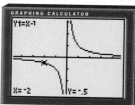

Window variables:
$x \in [-4.7, 4.7], y \in [-3.1, 3.1]$

We know that the slope of the tangent at $x = -2$ is the derivative evaluated at -2, that is, $f'(-2)$.

From the power rule,

$f'(x) = -x^{-2}$

Thus, $f'(-2) = -(-2)^{-2}$

$$= -\frac{1}{4}$$

Also,

$f(-2) = \dfrac{1}{-2}$

$$= -\frac{1}{2}$$

To find the equation of the tangent at $x = -2$, use the point-slope form

$$y - y_1 = m(x - x_1)$$

$$y - \left(-\frac{1}{2}\right) = -\frac{1}{4}(x - (-2))$$

$$y = -\frac{1}{4}x - 1$$

The equation of the tangent line at $x = -2$ is $y = -\dfrac{1}{4}x - 1$.

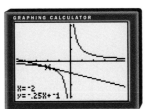

Use the Tangent operation to check this equation.

Example 6 Equations of Tangents

Find the equations of the tangents to the parabola $y = x(x + 2)$ that pass through the point $(1, -6)$. Sketch the curve and the tangents.

Solution

Initially, we expand the brackets so that the equation is written $y = x^2 + 2x$.
(In Section 4.3, we develop a product rule, which will allow us to differentiate without first expanding.)

Let the x-coordinate of the point Q, where the tangent touches the parabola, be a.
Then, the coordinates of the point Q are $(a, a^2 + 2a)$. To determine the values of a, we express the slope of the tangent PQ in two ways. Using the formula for slope, we have

$$m_{PQ} = \frac{y_2 - y_1}{x_2 - x_1}$$

$$= \frac{(a^2 + 2a) - (-6)}{a - 1}$$

Also, we know that the slope of the tangent at Q is $f'(a)$, where $f(x) = x^2 + 2x$. Thus
$f'(x) = 2x + 2$

so the equation $m_{PQ} = f'(a)$ becomes

$$\frac{a^2 + 2a + 6}{a - 1} = 2a + 2$$

Now we solve for a to obtain
$$a^2 + 2a + 6 = (a - 1)(2a + 2)$$
$$a^2 + 2a + 6 = 2a^2 - 2$$
$$a^2 - 2a - 8 = 0$$
$$(a - 4)(a + 2) = 0$$
$$a = 4 \text{ or } -2$$

By substitution,
$$f(4) = (4)^2 + 2(4)$$
$$= 24$$
$$f(-2) = (-2)^2 + 2(-2)$$
$$= 0$$

The points of contact are $(4, 24)$ and $(-2, 0)$. The slopes of the tangents at these points are
$$f'(4) = 2(4) + 2$$
$$= 10$$
and
$$f'(-2) = 2(-2) + 2$$
$$= -2$$

The equations of the tangents at $(4, 24)$ and $(-2, 0)$ are
$$y - 24 = 10(x - 4) \quad \text{and} \quad y - 0 = -2(x - (-2))$$
$$y = 10x - 16 \qquad\qquad y = -2x - 4$$

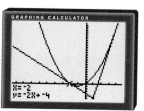

Window variables:
$x \in [-9.4, 4.7]$,
$y \in [-6.2, 24.8]$

Key Concepts

The basic derivative rules:

Rule	Derivative	
	Function Notation	**Leibniz Notation**
Power	If $f(x) = x^n$, then $f'(x) = nx^{n-1}$.	$\dfrac{d}{dx} x^n = nx^{n-1}$
Constant	If f is a constant function, $f(x) = c$, then $f'(x) = 0$.	$\dfrac{d}{dx}(c) = 0$
Constant multiple	If $g(x) = cf(x)$, then $g'(x) = cf'(x)$.	$\dfrac{d}{dx}[cf(x)] = c\,\dfrac{d}{dx}f(x)$
Sum	If both f and g are differentiable, then so is $f + g$, and $(f + g)' = f' + g'$.	$\dfrac{d}{dx}(f(x) + g(x)) = \dfrac{d}{dx}f(x) + \dfrac{d}{dx}g(x)$
Difference	If both f and g are differentiable, then so is $f - g$, and $(f - g)' = f' - g'$.	$\dfrac{d}{dx}(f(x) - g(x)) = \dfrac{d}{dx}f(x) - \dfrac{d}{dx}g(x)$

Communicate Your Understanding

1. Give a geometric explanation for each of the following.
a) The derivative of a constant function is zero.
b) The derivative of a linear function is a constant.

2. Describe how you would find an equation of the tangent to a function of the form $y = cx^n$ at $x = a$.

3. Problems involving tangents come in three forms: finding the tangent equation given a point on the curve; finding the tangent equation, given the slope; or finding the equation of a tangent that passes through a point not on the curve.

a) Describe how to identify which type of problem is being posed.

b) Explain how to solve each type of problem.

4. Describe how to find the derivative of the sum or difference of two differentiable functions.

5. Describe the steps you would use to find the derivative of $y = (ax + b)^2$.

Practise

A **1.** State the derivative of each function.

a) $f(x) = 21$

b) $g(x) = x^5$

c) $h(x) = x^9$

d) $y = x^{14}$

e) $y = 5.31$

f) $M(x) = x$

g) $h(t) = t^{54}$

h) $A(h) = 9^2$

i) $g(x) = x^{-2}$

j) $f(x) = x^{\frac{1}{3}}$

k) $g(x) = x^{-\frac{1}{2}}$

l) $f(x) = x^n$

2. Differentiate.

a) $f(x) = 4x^3$

b) $k(x) = -3x^5$

c) $w(x) = 4x^{\frac{5}{4}}$

d) $s(t) = 9t^{\frac{5}{3}}$

e) $y = \dfrac{1}{x^2}$

f) $f(x) = \dfrac{3}{x^4}$

g) $g(x) = (2x)^3$

h) $N(x) = \left(\dfrac{x}{2}\right)^4$

i) $y = \sqrt[3]{x}$

j) $y = \dfrac{1}{\sqrt{x}}$

k) $y = (x^2)^4$

l) $P(x) = \sqrt{2}x^{\sqrt{2}}$

3. Find the slope of the tangent to the graph of the given function at the point whose x-coordinate is given.

a) $f(x) = 3x^2$, $x = -1$

b) $f(x) = x^3$, $x = 2$

c) $g(x) = x^{-3}$, $x = 1$

d) $g(x) = 8\sqrt[4]{x}$, $x = 1$

e) $y = \dfrac{18}{x}$, $x = 3$

f) $y = \sqrt{x^3}$, $x = 4$

4. Find an equation of the tangent to the curve at the given point.

a) $y = \dfrac{1}{8}x^4$, $(2, 2)$

b) $y = \dfrac{9}{x^2}$, $(3, 1)$

5. Use first principles to verify the power rule for the case $n = -1$, that is, if $f(x) = \dfrac{1}{x}$, then $f'(x) = -\dfrac{1}{x^2}$.

6. Use first principles to verify the power rule for the case $n = \dfrac{1}{2}$, that is, if $f(x) = \sqrt{x}$, then
$$f'(x) = \dfrac{1}{2\sqrt{x}}.$$

7. Differentiate.

a) $f(x) = x^2 + 3x$

b) $f(x) = 4x^2 - 3x$

c) $f(x) = 5x^3 - 6x^2 + 2x$

d) $g(x) = 14x^5 + 23x^3 - 65x$

e) $g(x) = \dfrac{1}{x} - 3x^3$

f) $h(x) = (x + 2)(x - 3)$

g) $h(x) = (x - 1)^2$

h) $f(x) = (2 + x)^3$

i) $f(x) = a + \dfrac{b}{x} + \dfrac{c}{x^2}$

8. Find $f'(x)$ and state the domains of f and f'. In which cases are the domains for f and f' different?

a) $f(x) = x^4 - 3x^2 + 5x + 2$

b) $f(x) = \dfrac{1}{3}x^3 - \sqrt{x}$

c) $f(x) = 4x - 2x^{-5}$

d) $f(x) = (x - 1)^3$

B **9.** Find an equation of the tangent to the curve at the given point.
a) $y = x^3 - 3x^2 + x + 3$ at $(-1, -2)$
b) $y = x^2 - 4\sqrt{x}$ at $(4, 8)$
c) $y = \dfrac{x^4 - 6x^2}{3x}$ at $(3, 3)$
d) $y = -4 + \dfrac{4}{x} - \dfrac{8}{x^2}$ at $(2, -4)$
e) $y = (x^2 - 3)^2$ at $(-2, 1)$
f) $y = (x + 1)^2$ at $(1, 4)$

Apply, Solve, Communicate

10. At what point on the parabola $y = 4x^2$ is the slope of the tangent equal to 24?

11. Find the points on the curve $y = 2 - \dfrac{1}{x}$ where the tangent is perpendicular to the line $y = 1 - 4x$.

12. a) Use a graphing calculator or graphing software to graph $y = x^2$ and two tangents, the first at $x = -2$ and the other at $x = 2$. Where do the two tangents intersect?
b) There are two tangents to $y = x^2$ that pass through the point $(0, -5)$. Find the coordinates of the points where these tangents meet the parabola.

13. Inquiry/Problem Solving The projection for the gain in net worth, in dollars, of a new technology company is given by the equation,
$N(t) = 50000t^{\frac{2}{3}}$, where t is in years.
a) According to this projection, at what rate will the net worth of the company be increasing with respect to time after 7 years?
b) Draw the graph of the function using a graphing calculator or graphing software. If you could invest money in this company only for a short period of time, when would be the best time to invest? Explain.

14. If a ball is thrown upward with a velocity of 30 m/s, its height, h, in metres, after t seconds is given by $h = 1 + 30t - 4.9t^2$. Find the velocity of the ball after 1 s, 3 s, and 5 s.

15. Communication Many materials, such as metals, form an oxide coating (rust) on their

surfaces that increases in thickness, x, in centimetres, over time, t, in years, according to the equation $x = kt^{\frac{1}{2}}$.
a) Find the growth rate, $G = \dfrac{dx}{dt}$, as a function of time.
b) If $k = 0.02$, find the growth rate after 4 years.
c) Using a graphing calculator or graphing software, graph both x and G for $k = 0.02$. What happens to the thickness and the growth rate as t increases?
d) Why is it very important to protect the new metal on cars from rusting (oxidizing) as soon as possible?

16. The position, s, in metres, of an accelerating car on a highway is given by $s = 20 + 5t + 0.5t^2$, where t is measured in seconds. Find the velocity of the car at 4 s, 6 s, and 10 s.

17. Inquiry/Problem Solving A car whose position is given by the equation $d = 25t + t^2$ passes a police car that is travelling at 20 m/s. The police officer turns on the siren and begins to accelerate at 1.5 m/s² to chase the speeding car.
a) At what time is the speeding car moving at 31 m/s?
b) How fast is the police car moving at that time?
c) How far apart are the vehicles at that time?
d) Will the police car catch up to the speeder? Explain.

18. Application At what points does the curve $y = 2x^3 + 3x^2 - 36x + 40$ have a horizontal tangent?

19. Show that the curve $y = 2x^3 + 3x - 4$ has no tangents with slope 2.

20. Inquiry/Problem Solving Find the equations of both lines that pass through the origin and are tangent to the parabola $y = x^2 + 4$.

21. Find the x-coordinates of the points on the curve $xy = 1$ where the tangents from the point $(1, -1)$ intersect the curve.

22. The cost, C, in dollars, for a company to produce x copies of a videotape is given by $C(x) = 100\,000 + 0.1x + 0.01x^2$, $x \in [0, 1000]$
a) Find $C'(x)$ and $C'(101)$.
b) Find the cost of producing the 101st copy of the video using $C(x)$.
c) What does $C'(x)$ represent? Compare $C'(101)$ and your result for part b).

23. Application An oil tanker is leaking oil into the ocean on a calm day when there are few waves. The oil is spreading out in a circular pattern on the surface of the water. The area of the circular oil spill is given by the formula $A = \pi r^2$.
a) Find the area in terms of the diameter.
b) Find the area of the circle when the rate of change of the area with respect to the diameter is 400 square metres per metre.

24. Communication The cost of manufacturing x units of a product is $C(x) = 5(\sqrt[3]{x})$ dollars, ignoring any fixed costs.
a) Find $\dfrac{dC}{dx}$ and explain what it represents.
b) Graph $\dfrac{dC}{dx}$ using a graphing calculator or graphing software. What happens to the graph as x increases? Explain why this might occur when a company produces more units of a product.

[C] **25.** a) Show that, if $f(x)$ is a polynomial function, the quotient $Q(x) = \dfrac{f(x) - f(a)}{x - a}$ is also a polynomial function.
b) Let $f(x) = x^n$, where n is a positive integer. Write a formula for $Q(x)$.
c) Use part b) to derive the power rule from from first principles.

26. Communication The volume of a blood vessel of length h and radius r can be approximated by using the formula for the volume of a cylinder, $V = \pi r^2 h$.
a) Over time the radius of the inside of the blood vessel can decrease due to plaque deposits on the inner wall of the blood vessel. Typically, the length of the blood vessel does not change in these cases. Find $\dfrac{dV}{dr}$ and explain its meaning.

b) In some cases the length of the blood vessel may change, especially in young children who are growing taller. Typically, the radius does not change when the person is growing. Find $\dfrac{dV}{dh}$ and explain what it represents.

27. a) Prove the sum rule using the definition of the derivative.
b) Prove the difference rule.
c) Prove the constant multiple rule.
d) Use realistic examples of rates of change to explain why the rules of parts a) to c) are reasonable.

28. Give a geometric explanation for each of the following.
a) The derivative of $y = cx^n$ is greater than the derivative of $y = x^n$ if $c > 1$ and $x > 0$.
b) The derivative of $y = cx^n$ is less than the derivative of $y = x^n$ if $0 < c < 1$ and $x > 0$.

29. Let
$$f(x) = \begin{cases} 3 - 2x & \text{if } x \in (-\infty, -1) \\ x^2 + 4 & \text{if } x \in [-1, 1] \\ 2x + 3 & \text{if } x \in (1, \infty) \end{cases}$$
a) Sketch the graph of f.
b) Where is f differentiable? Explain.
c) Find an expression for f' and sketch the graph of f'.

30. a) Sketch the graph of $f(x) = |x^2 - 9|$.
b) For what values of x is f not differentiable?
c) Find a formula for f' and sketch the graph.

31. A man is walking on a bus with position function $s(t) = 5t$ with respect to the bus, where s is measured in metres and t, in seconds. The bus has position function $r(t) = 0.02t^2$ with respect to the ground. Find the following with respect to the ground.
a) The velocity of the man if he is walking toward the back of the bus. Explain your reasoning.
b) The velocity of the man if he is walking toward the front of the bus. Explain your reasoning.

The length, L, in millimetres, of a column of liquid inside a thermometer, as a function of temperature, T, in degrees Celsius, is given by the equation

$$L = L_0(1 + T + 0.002T^2)$$

For a certain thermometer, let $L_0 = 30$.

a) What is the length of the column of liquid at the following temperatures?

i) $0°$ ii) $10°$ iii) $20°$ iv) $30°$

b) When designers construct the thermometers, they often assume the relationship is a linear one (ignoring the last term in the equation), and they make the temperature divisions evenly spaced. Where will the manufacturer place the divisions to indicate the temperatures in part a)?

c) Calculate the error for each temperature in part a) if the approximation in part b) is made. What happens to the error as the temperature increases?

d) Find $\dfrac{dL}{dT}$ and sketch its graph. What does $\dfrac{dL}{dT}$ represent?

e) Use your result in part d) to explain the error in the temperature readings.

4.3 The Product Rule

In many cases, the ability to find the derivative of the product of two functions is very useful. A typical example involves the projected number of Internet connections over a year. The function representing the number of connections is the product of the number of subscribers and the average number of connections per subscriber. To be able to find the derivative of this function, we need to develop a rule for differentiating a product of two functions. In the following investigation, you will get a chance to do this.

Investigate & Inquire: The Product Rule

To understand the product rule, consider Emile's collection of sports cards. Let $f(x)$ represent the number of cards that he has in week x, and let $g(x)$ represent the average value of the cards in week x.

1. Express the total value $A(x)$ of his collection in week x in terms of $f(x)$ and $g(x)$.

2. Suppose that the average value of a sports card is increasing at a rate of $g'(x)$. Find an expression for the rate of change of the value of the cards Emile already holds in week x.

3. Suppose that the number of cards Emile owns is also increasing, at a rate of $f'(x)$. Find an expression for the rate of change of the value of Emile's card collection due only to the new cards.

4. Based on your expressions in steps 2 and 3, propose a formula for $A'(x)$, the rate of change of the value of Emile's collection. Justify your conjecture.

5. a) Evaluate your proposed formula for $A'(x)$, if $f(x) = 30x$ and $g(x) = 1 - x + 0.2x^2$.
b) Check your formula by expanding $A(x)$ and differentiating it directly.

6. Make a conclusion about the validity of your conjecture, for general functions $f(x)$ and $g(x)$.

While developing differentiation formulas, the mathematician Leibniz worked with an incorrect formula for the derivative of a product at first before he came up with the correct formula. Here is an algebraic example.

Let $f(x) = x^3$ and $g(x) = x^2$.
Then, $f'(x) = 3x^2$ and $g'(x) = 2x$.
Leibniz's original incorrect formula for the derivative of the product fg was simply to multiply the two derivatives. In this case,
$f'(x)g'(x) = 6x^3$

But $(fg)(x) = f(x)g(x)$
$\qquad\qquad = x^3(x^2)$
$\qquad\qquad = x^5$
so $(fg)'(x) = 5x^4$.

Thus, in general, $(fg)'(x) \neq f'(x)g'(x)$.

The correct formula is called the product rule and was discovered by Leibniz soon after his false start, and was also discovered independently by Newton.

Product rule: If both f and g are differentiable, then so is fg, and

$$(fg)' = gf' + fg' \quad \text{or} \quad \frac{d}{dx}[f(x)g(x)] = g(x)\frac{d}{dx}f(x) + f(x)\frac{d}{dx}g(x)$$

In words, the product rule says that "the derivative of the product of two functions is the second function times the derivative of the first function plus the first function times the derivative of the second function."

Example 1 Verifying the Product Rule

Verify the product rule for $y = (3x^2 + 2)(1 - 2x^2)$.

Solution

Using the product rule, we get

$$\frac{dy}{dx} = (1 - 2x^2)\frac{d}{dx}(3x^2 + 2) + (3x^2 + 2)\frac{d}{dx}(1 - 2x^2)$$

$$= (1 - 2x^2)(6x) + (3x^2 + 2)(-4x)$$

$$= -24x^3 - 2x$$

Notice that we do not actually need the product rule to differentiate the given function. We could have multiplied the factors and differentiated using earlier methods. In fact, this is often easier, as shown.

$$y = (3x^2 + 2)(1 - 2x^2)$$
$$= 3x^2 - 6x^4 + 2 - 4x^2$$
$$= -6x^4 - x^2 + 2$$

Differentiating gives

$$\frac{dy}{dx} = -24x^3 - 2x$$

Both methods result in the same simplified derivative, which verifies the product rule for $y = (3x^2 + 2)(1 - 2x^2)$.

Later, we will come across functions, such as $y = 3x^2 2^x$, that cannot be expanded. In such cases, the product rule must be used. The reasoning you applied in the investigation on page 208 can be visualized using a diagram. Using the diagram, we can develop an algebraic argument that justifies the product rule. Let $A(x)$ be the area of the unshaded rectangle at time x. Suppose that the rectangle is expanding. The increase in the area of the rectangle after a further time h is shown by the shaded part of the diagram. The rate at which the area changes at time x is

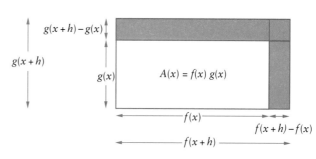

$$A'(x) = \lim_{h \to 0} \frac{A(x + h) - A(x)}{h}$$

Note that the numerator of the quotient is the area of the shaded part of the diagram, which is the area of the vertical strip, $g(x + h)[f(x + h) - f(x)]$, added to the area of the remaining horizontal strip, $f(x)[g(x + h) - g(x)]$. Thus,

$$A'(x) = \lim_{h \to 0} \frac{g(x + h)[f(x + h) - f(x)] + f(x)[g(x + h) - g(x)]}{h}$$

$$= \lim_{h \to 0} \frac{g(x + h)[f(x + h) - f(x)]}{h} + \lim_{h \to 0} \frac{f(x)[g(x + h) - g(x)]}{h}$$

$$= g(x) \lim_{h \to 0} \frac{f(x + h) - f(x)}{h} + f(x) \lim_{h \to 0} \frac{g(x + h) - g(x)}{h}$$

$$= g(x)f'(x) + f(x)g'(x)$$

Example 2 Using the Product Rule

Differentiate $y = \sqrt{x}(2x^2 + 4x - 6)$ and simplify.

Solution

First, we rewrite $\sqrt{x}$ as $x^{\frac{1}{2}}$.

$$\frac{dy}{dx} = (2x^2 + 4x - 6) \frac{d}{dx}(x^{\frac{1}{2}}) + (x^{\frac{1}{2}}) \frac{d}{dx}(2x^2 + 4x - 6)$$

$$= (2x^2 + 4x - 6)\left(\frac{1}{2}x^{-\frac{1}{2}}\right) + (x^{\frac{1}{2}})(4x + 4)$$

$$= 5x^{\frac{3}{2}} + 6x^{\frac{1}{2}} - 3x^{-\frac{1}{2}}$$

Example 3 Using the Product Rule to Find an Equation of a Tangent

Find the equation of the tangent to the graph of the function $y = (5x^2 - 2)(x - 4x^2)$ at the point $(1, -9)$.

Solution

Using the product rule, we obtain

$$\frac{dy}{dx} = (x - 4x^2) \frac{d}{dx}(5x^2 - 2) + (5x^2 - 2) \frac{d}{dx}(x - 4x^2)$$

$$= (x - 4x^2)(10x) + (5x^2 - 2)(1 - 8x)$$

$m = (1 - 4)(10) + (5 - 2)(1 - 8)$
$\quad = -51$

It is not necessary to simplify before substituting $x = 1$, because only the numerical value is required.

The slope of the tangent at $(1, -9)$ is -51.
To find the equation of the tangent, we use the point-slope form of the equation of a line.

$\quad y - y_1 = m(x - x_1)$
$y - (-9) = -51(x - 1)$
$\quad\quad\quad y = -51x + 42$

The equation of the tangent at the point $(1, -9)$ is $y = -51x + 42$.

Example 4 Applying the Product Rule

An Internet service provider has modelled its projected number of business subscribers as $B(t) = 50t + 2500$ and the projected average number of Internet connections per business subscriber as $C(t) = 0.004t^2 + 3.2$, where t is the time, in weeks, over the next year. The projected total number of business Internet connections is then $N(t) = B(t) \times C(t)$.
a) Determine the growth rate of the number of business connections after t weeks.
b) Determine the growth rate of the number of business connections after 12 weeks.

Solution

a) $N(t) = B(t) \times C(t)$
$N(t) = (50t + 2500)(0.004t^2 + 3.2)$

$N'(t) = (0.004t^2 + 3.2)\dfrac{d}{dt}(50t + 2500) + (50t + 2500)\dfrac{d}{dt}(0.004t^2 + 3.2)$

$\qquad = (0.004t^2 + 3.2)(50) + (50t + 2500)(0.008t)$

$\qquad = 0.6t^2 + 20t + 160$

b) $N'(12) = 0.6(12)^2 + 20(12) + 160$
$\qquad\quad = 486.4$
The growth rate after 12 weeks is 486.4 Internet connections per week.

Key Concepts

- Product rule
  If both f and g are differentiable, then so is fg, and $(fg)' = gf' + fg'$
  or

  $$\dfrac{d}{dx}[f(x)g(x)] = g(x)\dfrac{d}{dx}f(x) + f(x)\dfrac{d}{dx}g(x)$$

Communicate Your Understanding

1. Describe how you would find the derivative of the product of two differentiable functions, $H(t)$ and $M(t)$.
2. Explain why the derivative of the product of two functions is not equal to the product of the derivatives of the two functions. (That is, explain why $(fg)' \neq f'g'$.)
3. A student claims that the product rule is not really necessary since any problem where the product rule is applicable can also be solved using other rules. Discuss the validity of this statement.
4. A student determines $f'(1)$ in Example 3 as follows: $f(1) = -9$, and therefore $f'(1) = 0$, since $f(1)$ is equal to a constant value of 9. Assess the validity of this reasoning.

Practise

1. Use the product rule to differentiate each function.

a) $f(x) = x(x^3 - 2x^2)$

b) $h(x) = (3x + 2)x^2$

c) $N(x) = (x^3 - 2x + 1)(x^2 - x)$

d) $g(x) = (x^2 - 3)(4x + 1)$

e) $y = \sqrt{x}(x^4 - x^3)$

f) $f(x) = (x - 1)(3x^2 - 2x + 1)$

g) $h(t) = (6t^{-3} - t^4)(5t + t^{-1})$

h) $p = (m^{-2} + m)(m^3 - m^{-1})$

i) $F(y) = \sqrt{y}\left(3y - 4\sqrt{y} + \dfrac{2}{y}\right)$

j) $G(y) = (y - \sqrt{y})\left(y + \dfrac{1}{\sqrt{y}}\right)$

k) $y = \sqrt[3]{x}(3x - 5x^4)$

l) $c(k) = k^{-2}(k^2 + 3k^3 - k^4)$

m) $y = (x^2 + 1)(x^2 - 1)$

n) $y = \sqrt{x}(x - 5x^3)$

o) $y = (2\sqrt{x} - 5)(x^4 - 7x)$

p) $a(t) = (6\sqrt{t} - 2t^{-2})(t^2 - t^{-1})$

q) $g(u) = (au - bu^3)(bu + au^2)$

r) $A(v) = (v - v^{-1})(\sqrt{v} + v)$

2. Find the slope of the tangent to the given curve at the point whose x-coordinate is given. Is it advantageous to simplify the expression for the derivative before substituting the given x-coordinate? Explain.

a) $y = x(x^3 - 2x)$, $x = 1$

b) $y = (3 - 2x)(x + 1)$, $x = 2$

c) $y = (x^2 - 3x)(4x + 3)$, $x = -1$

d) $y = (1 - 2x + x^2)(3x^4 - 12)$, $x = 1$

e) $y = \dfrac{1}{8}x^3(3x^2 - 8x + 2)$, $x = 2$

f) $y = x^{-4}(3 - 2x^2)$, $x = -1$

g) $y = \sqrt{x}(2x - x^2)$, $x = 4$

h) $y = (2 - 6\sqrt{x})(x^2 + 4\sqrt{x})$, $x = 9$

3. Communication For each of the following, find $f'(2)$ using two methods:

i) Use the product rule.

ii) Expand $f(x)$ first.

iii) Which method is more efficient in each case? Explain.

a) $f(x) = x^2(2x - 3)$

b) $f(x) = (x - 4)(x^3 + 4x)$

c) $f(x) = (x - 3x^2)(2 - 3x + 5x^2)$

d) $f(x) = (\sqrt{x} - x)\left(\sqrt{x} + \dfrac{1}{x}\right)$

4. Find an equation of the tangent to each curve at the given point.

a) $y = (x^3 - 1)(2 - x)$, $(1, 0)$

b) $y = \sqrt{x}(x^2 - 5x + 2)$, $(4, -4)$

c) $y = \left(x - \dfrac{1}{2}x^{-2}\right)(3x + 5x^2)$, $(1, 4)$

d) $y = (2\sqrt{x} - x)(1 + \sqrt{x} - x^2)$, $(1, 1)$

Apply, Solve, Communicate

5. Inquiry/Problem Solving Use the product rule to find the unknown in each case.

a) $f(2) = 4$, $g(2) = 3$, $f'(2) = -1$, $g'(2) = 2$. Find $(fg)'(2)$.

b) $f(3) = -2$, $g(3) = 4$, $f'(3) = 5$, $(fg)'(3) = 30$. Find $g'(3)$.

c) $f(-2) = 5$, $f'(-2) = -3$, $g'(-2) = 6$, $(fg)'(-2) = 15$. Find $g(-2)$.

6. Application If f is a differentiable function, find expressions for the derivatives of the following functions.

a) $g(x) = xf(x)$

b) $g(x) = \sqrt{x}f(x)$

c) $s(t) = t^2f(t)$

d) $A(m) = m^c f(m)$

e) $g(x) = \dfrac{1}{x}f(x)$

f) $N(x) = (x + 2)^2 f(x)$

7. Communication The predicted population of a town t years from now is given by $P(t) = 12(2t^2 + 100)(t + 20)$.

a) What is the current population of the town? What will the population be in 6 years?

b) Find $\dfrac{dP}{dt}$. What does $\dfrac{dP}{dt}$ represent?

c) Use a graphing calculator or graphing software to draw the graphs of P and $\dfrac{dP}{dt}$.

d) The town council wants to build a new school and community centre. Some people think the town is too small for these developments. What do you think? Explain your reasoning.

e) What factors could contribute to such strong growth in a town?

8. Inquiry/Problem Solving In an electric circuit, the current through a resistor, in amperes, is given by $I = 4.85 - 0.01t^2$ and the resistance, in ohms, is given by $R = 15.00 + 0.11t$, where t is the time, in seconds. The voltage, V, in volts, across the resistor is the product of the current and the resistance. Find the rate of change of the voltage

a) after t seconds

b) after 0 s

c) after 3 s

9. Application Given a function $f(x) = (x^2 - 10)(x + 3)$, for which values of x is the tangent to the graph of f horizontal?

10. The wholesale demand function of a calculator is $p(x) = \dfrac{750}{\sqrt{x}} - 5$, where x is the number of calculators sold and p is the wholesale price, in dollars. The revenue function is $R(x) = xp(x)$.

a) Find the rate of change of revenue with respect to number of calculators sold

i) after x calculators are sold

ii) after 1000 calculators are sold

iii) after 10 000 calculators are sold

b) Explain the meaning of the sign of the result in part iii).

C **11.** Inquiry/Problem Solving a) Use the product rule twice to show that if f, g, and h are differentiable, then $(fgh)' = ghf' + fhg' + fgh'$

b) Use part a) to differentiate $y = \sqrt{x}(2x - 1)(x^2 + 3x - 2)$

12. a) Use the product rule with $g = f$ to show that if f is differentiable, then $\dfrac{d}{dx}[f(x)]^2 = 2f(x)f'(x)$.

b) Use part a) to differentiate the following.

i) $y = (x^2 + 3x + 1)^2$

ii) $y = (2 - x^3)^2$

iii) $y = (1 - x)^2(x^3 + x)^2$

13. a) Taking $f = g = h$ in question 11, show that $\dfrac{d}{dx}[f(x)]^3 = 3[f(x)]^2 f'(x)$

b) Use part a) to differentiate each of the following.

i) $y = (x - 1)^3$

ii) $y = (x^2 + 3x - 1)^3$

iii) $y = (\sqrt{x} - x^2)^3$

14. Use the product rule to derive the constant multiple rule.

Career Connection: *Financial Careers*

The modern world increasingly seems to revolve around the economy and its effects on individuals and organizations. Mathematics in general and calculus in particular provide a foundation for almost all useful inquiry in this area. A solid training in mathematics is a prerequisite for many interesting careers.

Financial analysts are interested in the rate of change in the value of equities and other financial instruments. Their challenge is to predict the future value of an instrument with as much accuracy as possible. The tools used range from simple bar and circle graphs to the most sophisticated modelling techniques. For example, one type of tool is a financial derivative, which is a complex instrument whose value depends on the rate of change in value of simpler commodities such as stocks, bonds, or market indices. Since they are based on rates of change, financial derivatives share many properties with the derivative of a function in calculus.

4.4 The Quotient Rule

The pupil in a person's eye becomes smaller in bright light and larger in dim light. Very accurate experiments have been performed to study the reaction of the eye to the brightness of a source of light. The typical reaction is that, when the brightness of the light source is increased, the pupil shrinks (decreasing the area A of the pupil) according to the model

$$A = \frac{40 + 24b^{0.4}}{1 + 4b^{0.4}}$$

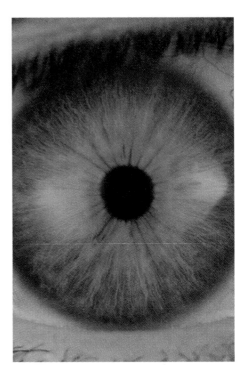

where A is measured in square millimetres and the brightness, b, of the light source is measured in units of brightness. The sensitivity of the eye to a light source is defined as the rate of change of the area of the pupil with respect to the brightness. In other words, to find the sensitivity, we must calculate the derivative of A with respect to b. However, this requires us to calculate the derivative of a quotient of two functions.

Using the product rule, we can develop a formula that allows us to differentiate quotients such as the one above. Consider the functions $f(x)$ and $g(x)$ and their quotient

$$H(x) = \frac{f(x)}{g(x)}$$

This equation can be rewritten as
$$f(x) = H(x)g(x)$$

So, by the product rule,
$$f'(x) = H(x)g'(x) + g(x)H'(x)$$

Solving for $H'(x)$,
$$g(x)H'(x) = f'(x) - H(x)g'(x)$$

$$= f'(x) - \frac{f(x)}{g(x)}g'(x) \qquad \text{Substitute } H(x) = \frac{f(x)}{g(x)}.$$

$$H'(x) = \frac{f'(x) - \dfrac{f(x)}{g(x)}g'(x)}{g(x)}$$

$$= \frac{g(x)f'(x) - f(x)g'(x)}{[g(x)]^2}$$

Quotient rule: If both f and g are differentiable, then so is the quotient $H(x) = \dfrac{f(x)}{g(x)}$. The derivative of the quotient is

$$H'(x) = \frac{g(x)f'(x) - f(x)g'(x)}{[g(x)]^2}$$

which is equivalent to

$$\frac{d}{dx}\left(\frac{f(x)}{g(x)}\right) = \frac{g(x)\dfrac{d}{dx}f(x) - f(x)\dfrac{d}{dx}g(x)}{[g(x)]^2}$$

or

$$\left(\frac{f}{g}\right)' = \frac{gf' - fg'}{g^2}$$

We must be careful to remember the order of the terms in this formula because of the minus sign in the numerator. In words, the quotient rule says that "the derivative of a quotient is the denominator times the derivative of the numerator minus the numerator times the derivative of the denominator, all divided by the square of the denominator".

Example 1 Differentiating a Quotient

Use three methods to differentiate $F(x) = \dfrac{x^4 - 3x^3 + 2x^2}{x^2}$. Verify that all three methods give the same results.

Solution 1 Quotient Rule

Using the quotient rule, we get

$$F'(x) = \frac{x^2 \dfrac{d}{dx}(x^4 - 3x^3 + 2x^2) - (x^4 - 3x^3 + 2x^2)\dfrac{d}{dx}(x^2)}{(x^2)^2}$$

$$= \frac{x^2(4x^3 - 9x^2 + 4x) - (x^4 - 3x^3 + 2x^2)(2x)}{x^4}$$

$$= \frac{2x^5 - 3x^4}{x^4}$$

$$= 2x - 3, \quad x \neq 0$$

Solution 2 Product Rule

Using the product rule, where $f(x) = x^4 - 3x^3 + 2x^2$ and $g(x) = x^{-2}$, we get

$$F' = gf' + fg'$$

$$= x^{-2}\frac{d}{dx}(x^4 - 3x^3 + 2x^2) + (x^4 - 3x^3 + 2x^2)\frac{d}{dx}(x^{-2})$$

$$= x^{-2}(4x^3 - 9x^2 + 4x) + (x^4 - 3x^3 + 2x^2)(-2x^{-3})$$

$$= 2x - 3, \quad x \neq 0$$

Solution 3 Factoring

Factoring first, then differentiating, we get

$$F(x) = \frac{x^4 - 3x^3 + 2x^2}{x^2}$$

$$= \frac{x^2(x^2 - 3x + 2)}{x^2}$$

$$= x^2 - 3x + 2, \quad x \neq 0$$

$$F'(x) = 2x - 3, \quad x \neq 0$$

All three methods give the same result.

Example 2 Using the Quotient Rule

Differentiate $H(x) = \dfrac{x^2 - 2x + 4}{x^2 - 1}$.

Solution

By the quotient rule, we have

$$H'(x) = \frac{(x^2 - 1)\dfrac{d}{dx}(x^2 - 2x + 4) - (x^2 - 2x + 4)\dfrac{d}{dx}(x^2 - 1)}{(x^2 - 1)^2}$$

$$= \frac{(x^2 - 1)(2x - 2) - 2x(x^2 - 2x + 4)}{(x^2 - 1)^2}$$

$$= \frac{2x^3 - 2x^2 - 2x + 2 - 2x^3 + 4x^2 - 8x}{(x^2 - 1)^2}$$

$$= \frac{2(x^2 - 5x + 1)}{(x^2 - 1)^2}$$

After using the quotient rule, it is usually worthwhile, but not always necessary, to simplify the resulting expression.

Example 3 Using the Quotient Rule

Find $\dfrac{dy}{dx}$ if $y = \dfrac{\sqrt{x}}{x^2 + 1}$.

Solution

$$\frac{dy}{dx} = \frac{(x^2 + 1)\dfrac{d}{dx}x^{\frac{1}{2}} - x^{\frac{1}{2}}\dfrac{d}{dx}(x^2 + 1)}{(x^2 + 1)^2}$$

$$= \frac{(x^2 + 1)\left(\dfrac{1}{2}x^{-\frac{1}{2}}\right) - x^{\frac{1}{2}}(2x)}{(x^2 + 1)^2}$$

Multiply the numerator and denominator by $2x^{\frac{1}{2}}$ to eliminate the fractional and negative exponents.

$$= \frac{(x^2 + 1) - 2x(2x)}{2x^{\frac{1}{2}}(x^2 + 1)^2}$$

$$= \frac{1 - 3x^2}{2\sqrt{x}(x^2 + 1)^2}$$

Example 4 Sensitivity of the Eye

Recall that the reaction of the eye to a light source of brightness b is modelled by the equation

$$A = \frac{40 + 24b^{0.4}}{1 + 4b^{0.4}},$$

where A is the area, in square millimetres, of the pupil. The sensitivity, S, is defined as the derivative of A with respect to b.

a) Find the sensitivity.
b) Use a graphing calculator or graphing software to graph both A and S.
c) Comment on the significance of the values of A and S for small and large values of b $(b > 0)$.

Solution

a) $S = A'(b)$

$$= \frac{(1 + 4b^{0.4}) \dfrac{d}{db}(40 + 24b^{0.4}) - (40 + 24b^{0.4}) \dfrac{d}{db}(1 + 4b^{0.4})}{(1 + 4b^{0.4})^2}$$

$$= \frac{(1 + 4b^{0.4})(9.6b^{-0.6}) - (40 + 24b^{0.4})(1.6b^{-0.6})}{(1 + 4b^{0.4})^2}$$

$$= \frac{9.6b^{-0.6} + 38.4b^{-0.2} - 64b^{-0.6} - 38.4b^{-0.2}}{(1 + 4b^{0.4})^2}$$

$$= \frac{-54.4b^{-0.6}}{(1 + 4b^{0.4})^2}$$

$$= \frac{-54.4}{b^{0.6}(1 + 4b^{0.4})^2}$$

The fact that the derivative is negative means that, as the brightness increases, the area of the pupil decreases.

b)

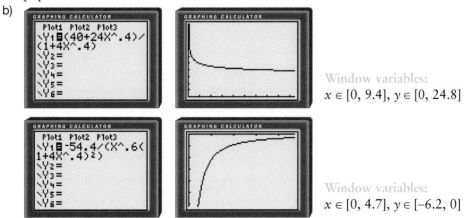

Window variables:
$x \in [0, 9.4]$, $y \in [0, 24.8]$

Window variables:
$x \in [0, 4.7]$, $y \in [-6.2, 0]$

c) When b approaches 0, A approaches 40. This means that at low brightness, the area of the pupil approaches 40 mm². When b is large, A approaches 6. So, at high brightness, the pupil shrinks, approaching a minimum area of 6 mm².

When b is small, S is negative and has a large absolute value. This means that, at low brightness, small increases in brightness produce large decreases in the area of a pupil. You can test this by sitting in a dark room for a while, and then turning on the lights and watching how the area of the pupil changes. (You could look in a mirror, or look at someone else's eyes.) When b is large, S approaches 0. This means that, at high brightness, increases in brightness produce only very small decreases in the area of the pupil.

Key Concepts

- Quotient rule: If both f and g are differentiable, then so is the quotient
  $H(x) = \dfrac{f(x)}{g(x)}$. The derivative of the quotient is

  $H'(x) = \dfrac{g(x)f'(x) - f(x)g'(x)}{[g(x)]^2}$

  which is equivalent to

  $\dfrac{d}{dx}\left(\dfrac{f(x)}{g(x)}\right) = \dfrac{g(x)\dfrac{d}{dx}f(x) - f(x)\dfrac{d}{dx}g(x)}{[g(x)]^2}$

  or

  $\left(\dfrac{f}{g}\right)' = \dfrac{gf' - fg'}{g^2}$

Communicate Your Understanding

1. Describe how you would find the derivative of the quotient of two differentiable functions.

2. Is the derivative of the quotient of two functions equal to the quotient of the derivatives of the two functions? If so, provide a convincing argument to explain why. If not, give a counterexample (an example of two functions for which the statement is not true).

Practise

 1. Differentiate. Evaluate the derivative at $x = 2$. Compare the domain of f with the domain of the derivative.

a) $f(x) = \dfrac{x-1}{x}$

b) $N(x) = \dfrac{x^2}{2x+1}$

c) $H(x) = \dfrac{2-3x}{x^2-1}$

d) $g(x) = \dfrac{2x}{x^2+3x-2}$

e) $M(x) = \dfrac{x^2+2}{3-2x}$

f) $A(x) = \dfrac{x^3-1}{x^2+2x+1}$

g) $y = \dfrac{\sqrt{x}}{x-1}$

h) $y = \dfrac{\sqrt{x}+1}{\sqrt{x}-x^2}$

i) $y = \dfrac{x^2-3x+2}{x^2+4x+1}$

j) $f(x) = \dfrac{1}{x^2+4x+4}$

k) $g(x) = \dfrac{ax+b}{cx+d}$

l) $h(x) = \dfrac{1+\dfrac{1}{x}}{x+1}$

m) $w(x) = \dfrac{2+x}{1-2x}$

n) $f(x) = \dfrac{x}{x^2-1}$

o) $p(x) = \dfrac{\sqrt{x}}{x^2+1}$

p) $v(x) = \dfrac{1-\dfrac{1}{x}}{1+\dfrac{1}{x}}$

q) $y = \dfrac{x^4}{x^2-9}$

r) $f(x) = \dfrac{x^2-3x}{x^4-16}$

B **2.** Find an equation of the tangent to the curve at the given point. Which functions are easier to differentiate using the quotient rule? Why?

a) $y = \dfrac{2x}{x-1}$, $(2, 4)$

b) $y = \dfrac{2+x}{2-3x}$, $(1, -3)$

c) $y = \dfrac{1}{x^2-1}$, $\left(2, \dfrac{1}{3}\right)$

d) $y = \dfrac{x^2-1}{x}$, $(1, 0)$

e) $y = \dfrac{x^3+5}{x^2+2x+3}$, $(1, 1)$

f) $y = \dfrac{\sqrt{x}+3}{\sqrt{x}}$, $(9, 2)$

Apply, Solve, Communicate

3. Communication a) Show that there are no tangents to the curve $y = \dfrac{2x+1}{4x+3}$ with negative slope. What can be concluded about the graph? What does it mean if a graph has only tangents with negative slope?

b) Show that there are no tangents to the curve $y = \dfrac{x^2}{x^2-x}$ with positive slope. What can be

concluded about the graph? What does it mean if a graph has only tangents with positive slope?

4. Communication At which points on the curve $y = \dfrac{x^2}{2x+1}$ is the tangent horizontal? What can be concluded about the graph at those points? What does it mean if a graph has only horizontal tangents?

5. Find the points on the curve $y = \dfrac{x}{x+1}$ where the tangent is parallel to $x - y = 2$.

6. If f is a differentiable function, find expressions for the derivatives of the following functions.

a) $y = \dfrac{1}{f(x)}$

b) $y = \dfrac{f(x)}{x}$

c) $y = \dfrac{x}{f(x)}$

7. Inquiry/Problem Solving The average productivity, $A(n)$, of the work force of a company depends on the total value $p(n)$, in dollars, of the product produced, and the number of workers, n, employed by the company according to the equation

$$A(n) = \dfrac{p(n)}{n}$$

a) Find $A'(n)$. Does productivity get better or worse if the number of workers increases but the total value produced stays the same? Explain.

b) A company hires more workers at a time when $A'(n) > 0$. Why would the company do this?

c) What might the company do if $A'(n) < 0$? Explain.

d) Show that $A'(n) > 0$ if $p'(n) > A(n)$.

e) Under what conditions will the company neither hire nor fire any workers?

f) An automobile parts manufacturer models the average productivity on one of its assembly lines as $A(n) = \dfrac{300n - 0.12n^2}{n}$. Discuss where this function fits into the analysis of parts a) to e).

8. Application A person driving a boat turns off the engine and allows the boat to coast into the dock. The distance, x, in metres, from the boat to the dock as a function of time t, in seconds, is $x(t) = \dfrac{6(8-t)}{4+t}$ for $0 \le t \le 8$.

a) When does the boat hit the dock?

b) Find $\dfrac{dx}{dt}$. What does $\dfrac{dx}{dt}$ represent?

c) At what velocity does the boat strike the dock?

d) What was the velocity of the boat when the engine was turned off?

e) Do you think the boat was damaged when it hit the dock? Explain.

9. Communication Tests on a new pair of sunglass lenses shows that when people wear the sunglasses, the reaction, A, of their eyes to a light source of brightness b can be modelled by the equation

$A = \dfrac{32 + 19.6b^{0.4}}{1 + 3.8b^{0.4}}$.

Recall that the sensitivity S is defined as the derivative of A with respect to b.

a) Find the sensitivity.

b) Using a graphing calculator, graph both S and A.

c) Compare your results to Example 4 (page 217). What effect does wearing sunglasses have on the reaction and sensitivity of the eye?

10. During a chemical reaction, the mass, in grams, of a compound being formed is modelled by the function $M(t) = \dfrac{5.8t}{t + 1.9}$, where t is the time after the start of the reaction, in seconds. What is the rate of change of the mass after 5 s?

11. Inquiry/Problem Solving Use three methods to differentiate $y = \dfrac{(3x^2 + 1)(x + 1)}{x^2 + 2x + 1}$. Verify that all three methods give the same results.

12. In Section 4.2, we developed the power rule for positive integer exponents. Use the quotient rule to deduce the power rule for the case of negative integer exponents, that is, show that $\dfrac{d}{dx}(x^{-n}) = -nx^{-n-1}$ when n is a positive integer.

13. Application The power, in watts, produced by a certain generator is given by $P = \dfrac{144R}{(R + 0.6)^2}$, where R is the resistance, in ohms.

a) For which value(s) of R will the rate of change of the power be 0?

b) What is the significance of the values you found in part a)?

Achievement Check

Knowledge/Understanding

Thinking/Inquiry/Problem Solving

Communication

Application

Given the values in the table, find $h(x)$ and $h'(x)$ for the following.

a) $h(x) = 2g(x)$, $x = 0$

b) $h(x) = \dfrac{f(x)}{g(x)}$, $x = 0$

c) $h(x) = f(x) \times g(x)$, $x = 0$

d) $h(x) = f(x) - g(x)$, $x = 1$

e) $h(x) = \dfrac{1}{f(x)}$, $x = 1$

f) $h(x) = f^2(x) + g^2(x)$, $x = 1$

x	$f(x)$	$f'(x)$	$g(x)$	$g'(x)$
0	6	−5	−1	1
1	1	−1	−3	−4

Derivatives of Derivatives

Consider a hybrid sunflower plant with height, h, in metres, modelled by the equation

$h = \dfrac{3t^2}{4+t^2}$, where t is the time, in months,

after the seed is planted. The growth rate, g, of a plant is defined by the rate of change of height with respect to time. Therefore, the growth rate is equal to the first derivative of h, $g(t) = h'(t)$. However, $g(t)$ is a function, so we can also differentiate it to find the rate of change of the growth rate, which produces a function $k(t)$. The function $k(t)$ is called the **second derivative** of $h(t)$, since, starting with $h(t)$, we have to differentiate twice to arrive at $k(t)$. We will discuss what is meant by the rate of change of the growth rate in Example 4 (page 222).

Given a function $y = f(x)$, with derivative $\dfrac{dy}{dx} = f'(x)$, the second derivative of the function f is the derivative of the function f', and is written $f''(x)$.

Alternatively, $f''(x) = \dfrac{d}{dx}\left(\dfrac{dy}{dx}\right)$, and we abbreviate this as $\dfrac{d^2y}{dx^2}$.

If we use D-notation, the symbol D^2 (or D_x^2) indicates that the operation of differentiation is performed twice (with respect to x). Thus, we have the following equivalent notations for the second derivative of a function $y = f(x)$:

y'', $f''(x)$, $\dfrac{d^2y}{dx^2}$, $D^2f(x)$, and $D_x^2 f(x)$.

Example 1 Determining a Second Derivative

Find $\dfrac{d^2y}{dx^2}$ if $y = x^5$.

Solution

$\dfrac{dy}{dx} = 5x^4$

$\dfrac{d^2y}{dx^2} = \dfrac{d}{dx}\left(\dfrac{dy}{dx}\right)$

$\qquad = \dfrac{d}{dx}(5x^4)$

$\qquad = 20x^3$

Example 2 Determining a Second Derivative

Find the second derivative of $f(x) = 4\sqrt{x} - 3x^2$.

Solution

$$f(x) = 4\sqrt{x} - 3x^2$$

$$= 4x^{\frac{1}{2}} - 3x^2$$

$$f'(x) = 4\left(\frac{1}{2}x^{-\frac{1}{2}}\right) - 6x$$

$$= 2x^{-\frac{1}{2}} - 6x$$

$$f''(x) = 2\left(-\frac{1}{2}x^{-\frac{3}{2}}\right) - 6$$

$$= -x^{-\frac{3}{2}} - 6$$

Example 3 Determining the Value of a Second Derivative

Find $f''(2)$ if $f(x) = x^4 - 2x^2 + 5$.

Solution

$$f'(x) = 4x^3 - 4x$$

$$f''(x) = 12x^2 - 4$$

$$f''(2) = 12(2)^2 - 4$$

$$= 44$$

The value of the derivative (also called the **first derivative**) at a point can be interpreted as the slope of the tangent at that point. So, the second derivative can be interpreted as the rate of change of the slope of the tangent. This interpretation will be pursued in Chapter 6, where we use derivatives to sketch accurate graphs of functions. Other interpretations of a second derivative are explored in Example 4.

Example 4 Interpreting a Second Derivative

Recall from the beginning of this section that the height, h, in metres, of a certain sunflower plant is modelled by $h = \dfrac{3t^2}{4+t^2}$, where t is the time, in months, after the seed is planted.

a) Find $g(t) = h'(t)$, the growth rate of the sunflower.
b) Find $g'(t) = h''(t)$. What does the second derivative represent physically?
c) How is $g'(t) = h''(t)$ related to $g(t) = h'(t)$ geometrically?
d) Explain why $g'(t)$ is a useful function for plant breeders.

Solution

a) Since $h = \dfrac{3t^2}{4+t^2}$,

then

$$g(t) = h'(t)$$

$$= \frac{(4+t^2)6t - 3t^2(2t)}{(4+t^2)^2}$$

$$= \frac{24t}{(4+t^2)^2}$$

b) To differentiate $g(t)$ using the quotient rule, let $u(t) = 24t$ and $v(t) = 4 + t^2$, so that

$$g(t) = \frac{u(t)}{(v(t))^2}$$

Differentiating,

$$g'(t) = \frac{(v(t))^2\, u'(t) - u(t)\dfrac{d}{dt}\left[(v(t))^2\right]}{(v(t))^4}$$

$$= \frac{(v(t))^2\, u'(t) - u(t)\,[v(t)v'(t) + v(t)v'(t)]}{(v(t))^4}$$

$$= \frac{(v(t))^2\, u'(t) - u(t)2v(t)v'(t)}{(v(t))^4}$$

$$= \frac{(4+t^2)^2(24) - (24t)2(4+t^2)2t}{(4+t^2)^4}$$

$$= \frac{24(4+t^2)[(4+t^2) - 4t^2]}{(4+t^2)^4}$$

$$= \frac{24(4 - 3t^2)}{(4+t^2)^3}$$

The second derivative of h represents the rate of change of the growth rate with respect to time.

c) The y-values of $g'(t) = h''(t)$ represent the slopes of the tangents to the graph of $g(t) = h'(t)$. Also, the second derivative of h represents the rate of change of the slopes of the tangents to the graph of h.

d) Using a graphing calculator to graph $g(t)$ and $g'(t)$ can help us see how the two functions are related.

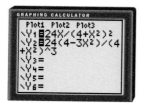

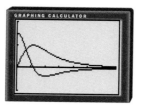

Window variables:
$x \in [0, 7], y \in [-1, 2]$

Notice that, when the growth rate is increasing, the second derivative is positive; at the maximum value of the growth rate, the second derivative is zero; and when the growth rate is decreasing, the second derivative is negative. Therefore, $g'(t) = h''(t)$ provides some very important information about how the sunflower will grow. These observations could very well promote further research into the factors that affect growth rate.

Example 5 Sketching First and Second Derivatives From a Graph

Use the given graph of f to sketch the graphs of f' and f''.

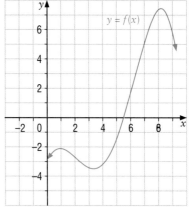

Solution

We can extend a technique from Section 4.1, Example 2 (page 188) to produce estimated or sketched graphs of the first and second derivatives of a function f, given the graph of f. The slope of the tangent at the point $(x, f(x))$ gives an estimate of the value of $f'(x)$. In particular, the points where the tangent is horizontal give the x-intercepts of f'. Using these and other points, we develop a sketch of f'. We can then repeat the procedure with f' in place of f, to develop a sketch of f''.

For the function f graphed above, estimates of the tangent slopes at $x = 0, 1, 2.5, 3.4, 5.5, 8.2,$ and 9 are shown. These estimates are then plotted directly beneath, as the values of $f'(x)$ at the same x-values. The sketch of f' is completed as a smooth line connecting these points. Thus, on the interval $(1, 3.4)$, the tangents to the graph of f have negative slopes, so f' is negative on this interval. Similarly, f' is positive on the intervals $(0, 1)$ and $(3.4, 8.2)$, and negative on the interval $(8.2, 9)$.

Looking at the graph of f', the tangents appear to be negative for $x < 2.1$, positive for $2.1 < x < 6.3$, and negative again for $x > 6.3$. Using this information and estimated slope values, we can sketch the graph of f'' in the same way that we sketched f'.

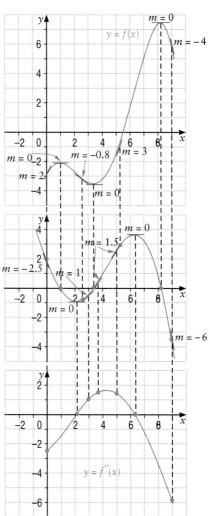

Practise

A **1.** Find the first and second derivatives of each function.

a) $f(x) = x^3 - 2x$

b) $f(x) = \dfrac{1}{4}x^4 + 2x^3 - 5x^2 + x - 4$

c) $g(x) = \dfrac{1}{x}$

d) $m(t) = \dfrac{1}{t+2} - 5t$

e) $y = (x^2 + 1)(x - 2)$

f) $y = \dfrac{x}{x-2}$

g) $w = (2u - u^2)(3 + 2u)$

h) $h(x) = \dfrac{x^2 - 1}{2x - x^2}$

i) $v(u) = \dfrac{6}{\sqrt{u}}$

j) $M(x) = x^3 + \dfrac{1}{x^2}$

2. Find $f''(2)$ for each function.

a) $f(x) = x^4 - 2x^3 + x^2$

b) $f(x) = \dfrac{1}{x-1}$

c) $f(x) = \sqrt{x}(x+2)$

d) $f(x) = \dfrac{x^2 - 3}{4x}$

3. Find the slope of the tangent and the rate of change of the slope of the tangent to each function at $x = 3$.

a) $f(x) = x^4$

b) $g(x) = 2 - 4x + x^2 - x^3$

c) $y = \dfrac{1}{x+1}$

d) $y = -\dfrac{2}{\sqrt{x}}$

e) $g(x) = (x - 1)(2x + 3)$

f) $f(x) = \dfrac{1}{x^3}$

4. For each graph below, sketch the corresponding graphs of f' and f''.

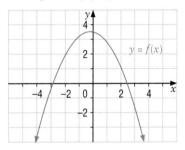

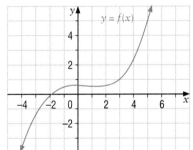

Apply, Solve, Communicate

B **5.** Application Find a quadratic function f such that $f(3) = 33$, $f'(3) = 22$, and $f''(3) = 8$.

6. When the temperature is warm and there are pollutants in a lake, an algal bloom may occur. This means that while most of the other living organisms in the lake are dying, the amount of algae in the lake is drastically increasing. For a certain lake, the amount of living algae in the lake, A, in kilograms, as a function of time, t, in days, is given by the equation

$$A(t) = \frac{1}{2}t^2 + 5$$

for the next two weeks.
a) Find the growth rate, $A'(t)$, and also find $A''(t)$.
b) What does $A''(t)$ represent? What does $A'(t)$ indicate about the amount of algae in the lake over the next two weeks?
c) Sketch the graphs of $A(t)$, $A'(t)$, and $A''(t)$.
d) After two weeks, the environment can no longer support the large amount of algae and it begins to die. Complete possible graphs of $A(t)$, $A'(t)$, and $A''(t)$ for an additional week given that all the algae will die by the end of that week.

7. Communication It takes 2 g of chemical A and 1 g of chemical B to produce 3 g of the product chemical C. Twenty grams of A is mixed with water to form a solution. Eight grams of B is mixed with water to form another solution. The two solutions are gradually mixed together and the chemical reaction forms C according to the equation

$$C(t) = 24 - \frac{24}{6t+1}$$

where $C(t)$ is in grams and t is time, in seconds.
a) Find the rate at which chemical C is formed. Also, determine $C''(t)$.
b) What can be learned about the rate of production by examining $C''(t)$?
c) Sketch the graphs of $C(t)$, $C'(t)$, and $C''(t)$.
d) Sketch two separate graphs of $A(t)$ and $B(t)$, the amounts of each reactant as a function of time.
e) Describe the first two derivatives of each of the reactants, and sketch their graphs on the same axes used in part d). Explain your reasoning.

8. Inquiry/Problem Solving The height, h, in metres, of a tomato plant after it is planted is modelled by the equation

$$h(t) = \frac{t^3}{8+t^3}$$

where t is time, in months.
a) Find an equation for the growth rate.

b) Find $h''(t)$. What does it represent?
c) Use $h''(t)$ to find the time when the maximum growth rate occurs. What is the maximum growth rate? (Hint: Describe $h'(t)$ when $h''(t) > 0$ and when $h''(t) < 0$. What happens when $h''(t) = 0$?)
d) The average daytime temperature for each of the first seven months is listed in the table.

Month	1	2	3	4	5	6	7
Temperature (°C)	15	25	26	22	20	17	14

How are the growth rate and h'' related to average daytime temperature? What other factors might affect these quantities?

9. Application Derivatives higher than the second can also be defined. For example, the third derivative is the derivative of the second derivative: $f''' = (f'')'$. Other equivalent notations are y''', $\dfrac{d^3y}{dx^3}$, $D^3f(x)$, and $D_x^3 f(x)$.
a) Find the first six derivatives of $y = x^4 - x^3 + 5x^2 + 2x - 3$.
b) What is the value of $y^{(n)}$, the nth derivative, for $n \geq 5$? Explain.

10. Find the first six derivatives of the function $f(x) = x^5 + x^4 + x^3 + x^2 + x + 1$.

11. If $g(x) = \dfrac{1}{2x-4}$, find $g'''(3)$.

12. Inquiry/Problem Solving Suppose that $f(x) = g(x)h(x)$.
a) Express f'' in terms of g, g', g'', h, h', and h''.
b) Find a similar expression for f'''.

13. a) If $f(x) = |x^2 - 1|$, find f' and f'' and state their domains.
b) Sketch the graphs of f, f', and f''.
c) Compare the domains of f, f', and f''.

14. a) If $f(x) = x^n$, find $f''(x)$ and $f'''(x)$.
b) Find a formula for $f^{(n)}(x)$.

15. Communication a) When taking higher-order derivatives of a polynomial function, how many can you take before the derivative starts repeating?
b) What is the value of the derivative when this occurs?

Velocity and Acceleration

To understand the world around us, we must understand as much about motion as possible. The study of motion is fundamental to the principles of physics, and it is applied to a wide range of topics, such as automotive engineering (crash tests, racing, performance tests), satellite and rocket launches, and improvement of athletic performance (kinesiology).

We have already defined and computed velocities in Section 3.4. Now we can compute them more easily with the aid of the differentiation formulas developed in this chapter.

Suppose an object moves along a straight line. (Think of a ball being thrown vertically upward or a car being driven along a road or a stone being dropped from a cliff.) Suppose the position function of the object is $s(t)$. Another way to say this is that $s(t)$ is the displacement (directed distance) of the object from the origin at time t. Recall that the instantaneous velocity of the object at time t is defined as the limit of the average velocities over shorter and shorter time intervals.

$$v = \lim_{h \to 0} \frac{s(t+h) - s(t)}{h}$$

The **velocity function** is the derivative of the position function, $v = s'(t) = \dfrac{ds}{dt}$.

Example 1 TV Advertisement for a New Football Helmet

To dramatically advertise the effectiveness of a new football helmet, a melon is taped inside it and the helmet is dropped from a tower 78.4 m high. The height of the helmet, h, in metres, after t seconds is given by $h = 78.4 - 4.9t^2$, until it hits the ground.
a) Find the velocity of the helmet after 1 s and 2 s.
b) When will the helmet hit the ground?
c) The manufacturer's demonstration will be effective if the melon is undamaged after impact. The melon will remain intact if the impact speed is less than 30 m/s. Is the demonstration effective?

Solution

a) The position function is $h = 78.4 - 4.9t^2$, so the velocity at time t is

$$\frac{dh}{dt} = -9.8t$$

The velocity after 1 s is given by

$$\frac{dh}{dt}\bigg]_{t=1} = -9.8(1)$$

$$= -9.8$$

The velocity after 1 s is -9.8 m/s.
The velocity after 2 s is given by

$$\frac{dh}{dt}\bigg]_{t=2} = -9.8(2)$$

$$= -19.6 \text{ m/s}$$

The velocity after 2 s is -19.6 m/s.

The negative signs for the velocities indicate that the helmet is moving in the negative direction (down).

b) The helmet will hit the ground when the height is 0.
$h = 78.4 - 4.9t^2$
$\quad = 0$
$t^2 = 78.4/4.9$
$\quad = 16$
Since $t > 0$, $t = 4$. So, the helmet hits the ground after 4 s.

c) Substitute $t = 4$ into the velocity function.
$v(4) = h'(4)$
$\quad\quad = -9.8(4)$
$\quad\quad = -39.2$
Since the speed (that is, the absolute value of the velocity) of 39.2 m/s is greater than 30 m/s, the melon is damaged on impact. Thus, the demonstration fails.

Example 2 Analysis of a Cheetah's Motion

The position function of a cheetah moving across level ground in a straight line chasing after prey is given by the equation
$s(t) = t^3 - 15t^2 + 63t$
where t is measured in seconds and s in metres.

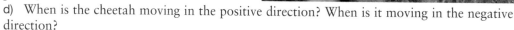

a) What is the cheetah's velocity after 1 s? 4 s? 8 s?
b) When is the cheetah momentarily stopped?
c) What are the positions of the cheetah in part b)?
d) When is the cheetah moving in the positive direction? When is it moving in the negative direction?
e) Find the position of the cheetah after 10 s.
f) Find the total distance travelled by the cheetah during the first 10 s.
g) Compare the results of parts e) and f).

Solution

a) The velocity after t seconds is
$v = s'(t)$
$\quad = 3t^2 - 30t + 63$
After 1 s,
$s'(1) = 3(1)^2 - 30(1) + 63$
$\quad\quad = 36$
The velocity after 1 s is 36 m/s.
After 4 s,
$s'(4) = 3(4)^2 - 30(4) + 63$
$\quad\quad = -9$
The velocity after 4 s is −9 m/s.

After 8 s,
$$s'(8) = 3(8)^2 - 30(8) + 63$$
$$= 15$$
The velocity after 8 s is 15 m/s.

b) The cheetah stops momentarily when $v(t) = 0$.
$$3t^2 - 30t + 63 = 0$$
$$t^2 - 10t + 21 = 0$$
$$(t - 3)(t - 7) = 0$$
$$t = 3 \text{ or } t = 7$$
Thus, the cheetah is momentarily stopped after 3 s and 7 s.

c) At $t = 3$,
$$s(3) = (3)^3 - 15(3)^2 + 63(3)$$
$$= 81$$
At $t = 7$,
$$s(7) = (7)^3 - 15(7)^2 + 63(7)$$
$$= 49$$
The cheetah momentarily stops when it is 81 m and 49 m from its starting position.

d) The cheetah moves in the positive direction when $v(t) > 0$, that is,
$$t^2 - 10t + 21 = (t - 3)(t - 7) > 0$$

This inequality is satisfied when both factors are positive, that is, $t \in (7, \infty)$, or when both factors are negative, that is, $t \in [0, 3)$. Thus, the cheetah moves in the positive direction in the time intervals $t \in [0, 3)$ and $t \in (7, \infty)$. It moves in the negative direction when $t \in (3, 7)$. We can demonstrate this using a number line with the factors listed underneath. The +, 0, and − symbols show where the quantities are positive, zero, and negative.

The graph of the displacement, $s(t) = t^3 - 15t^2 + 63t$, is shown below.

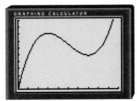

Window variables:
$x \in [0, 10], y \in [0, 10]$

e) At $t = 10$ s,
$$s(10) = (10)^3 - 15(10)^2 + 63(10)$$
$$= 130$$
The cheetah is 130 m from where it started after 10 s.

f) The path of the cheetah is modelled in the figure. (Remember that the cheetah goes back and forth along a straight line)

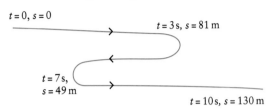

$t = 0, s = 0$

$t = 3\,s, s = 81\,m$

$t = 7\,s,$
$s = 49\,m$

$t = 10\,s, s = 130\,m$

To find the total distance travelled, first determine the change in position over each interval for which the cheetah does not change direction. The total distance travelled is the sum of these quantities. From part d), the cheetah changes direction at $t = 3$ and $t = 7$.

The distance travelled in the time interval $[0, 3]$ is
$|s(3) - s(0)| = |81 - 0|$
$\qquad\qquad\quad = 81$

The distance travelled in the time interval $[3, 7]$ is
$|s(7) - s(3)| = |49 - 81|$
$\qquad\qquad\quad = 32$

The distance travelled in the time interval $[7, 10]$ is
$|s(10) - s(7)| = |130 - 49|$
$\qquad\qquad\qquad = 81$

The total distance travelled by the cheetah is $(81 + 32 + 81)$ m or 194 m.

g) The difference between the total distance travelled by the cheetah and its final position is $(194 - 130)$ m or 64 m.
The cheetah's displacement from its starting point is 64 m less than its total distance run.

Acceleration

The **acceleration** of an object is the rate of change of its velocity with respect to time. Therefore, the **acceleration function** $a(t)$ at time t is the derivative of the velocity function:

$$a(t) = v'(t) = \frac{dv}{dt}$$

Since the velocity is the derivative of the position function $s(t)$, it follows that:

> The acceleration is the second derivative of the position function. Thus,
>
> $$a(t) = v'(t) = s''(t)$$
>
> or
>
> $$a = \frac{dv}{dt} = \frac{d^2s}{dt^2}$$

If s is measured in metres and t in seconds, the units for acceleration are metres per second squared, or m/s^2.

Investigate & Inquire: Motion With Variable Acceleration

1. Use a motion detector (CBR) connected to a graphing calculator to record the motion of a lab cart acted on by a non-constant force, such as a stretched spring or a long chain hanging over the edge of a table.

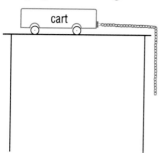

The mass of the chain hanging over the edge causes both cart and chain to accelerate. The mass hanging over the edge is not constant.

2. Compare the slopes of the tangents to the velocity-time (*v-t*) graph to the acceleration from the acceleration-time (*a-t*) graph at the same time. Record your observations in a table similar to the one shown below.

Time (s)	Slope of *v-t* graph	Acceleration from *a-t* graph

3. How is the slope of the *v-t* graph related to the acceleration?

4. Given the velocity of an object as a function of time, how would you find the acceleration?

5. What is the geometrical interpretation of acceleration?

Example 3 Motion With Non-Constant Acceleration

The position function of a person on a bicycle pedalling down a steep hill with steadily increasing effort in pedalling is $s(t) = \dfrac{1}{6} t^3 + \dfrac{1}{2} t^2 + t$, where *s* is measured in metres and *t* in seconds, $t \in [0, 4]$.
a) Find the velocity and acceleration as functions of time.
b) Find the acceleration at 2 s.

Solution

a) The velocity is
$$v = \frac{ds}{dt}$$
$$= \frac{1}{6} (3t^2) + \frac{1}{2} (2t) + 1$$
$$= \frac{1}{2} t^2 + t + 1$$

and the acceleration is

$$a = \frac{dv}{dt}$$

$$= t + 1$$

b) We substitute $t = 2$ in the acceleration equation.

$a = 2 + 1$

$= 3$

After 2 s, the acceleration is 3 m/s².

Example 4 Analysis of a Position-Time Graph

The graph shows the position function of a bicycle. Determine the sign of the velocity and acceleration in each interval, and relate them to the slope of the graph and whether the slope is increasing or decreasing (that is, how the graph bends).

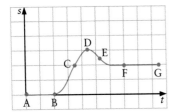

Solution

Interval	Description of graph	Velocity	Acceleration
A to B	Slope = 0, horizonal segment	0	0
B to C	Positive slope, slope increasing	positive	positive
C to D	Positive slope, slope decreasing	positive	negative
D	Slope = 0, momentarily horizontal	0	negative
D to E	Negative slope, slope decreasing	negative	negative
E to F	Negative slope, slope increasing	negative	positive
F to G	Slope = 0, horizontal segment	0	0

Note that the table in Example 4 reflects our understanding that the velocity of the bicycle is the slope of the position-time graph. Furthermore, the acceleration is the rate of change of velocity, which corresponds to the rate of change of the slope of the position-time graph.

Example 5 Motion Along a Vertical Line

In a circus stunt, a person is projected straight up into the air, and then falls straight back down into a safety net. The position function is $s(t) = 30t - 5t^2$ for the upward part of the motion and $s(t) = -4.8(t - 3)^2 + 45$ for the downward part of the motion, where s is in metres and t is in seconds.

a) Determine the acceleration for the upward part of the motion.

b) Determine the acceleration for the downward part of the motion.

c) Compare the results of parts a) and b) and explain the difference.

Solution

a) $s(t) = 30t - 5t^2$

$\dfrac{ds}{dt} = 30 - 10t$

$a = \dfrac{d^2s}{dt^2}$

$\quad = -10$

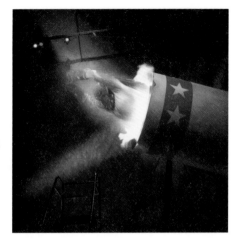

The acceleration for the upward part of the motion is 10 m/s^2, directed downward.

b) $s(t) = -4.8(t - 3)^2 + 45$

$\dfrac{ds}{dt} = -9.6(t - 3)$

$a = \dfrac{d^2s}{dt^2}$

$\quad = -9.6$

The acceleration for the downward part of the motion is 9.6 m/s^2, directed downward.

c) The acceleration due to gravity near Earth's surface is about -9.8 m/s^2. When the person is moving upward, gravity acts to slow the person. Since air resistance opposes the motion, it also acts to slow the person down. The effect of gravity and air resistance together produce the acceleration of 10 m/s^2.

When the person is moving downward, gravity acts to make the person go faster. In this case, air resistance still opposes the motion, which means it acts to slow the person down. Thus, air resistance opposes gravity, so that the absolute value of the total acceleration is a little less than what gravity by itself would produce—only 9.6 m/s^2 instead of 9.8 m/s^2.

Negative acceleration,

$a = \dfrac{dv}{dt} < 0$

indicates that velocity is decreasing (as at point A in the figure). This follows from the fact that the acceleration is the slope of the tangent to the graph of the velocity function.

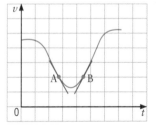

Likewise, positive acceleration,

$a = \dfrac{dv}{dt} > 0$

means that velocity is increasing (as at B).

This can be a little confusing, since there is a distinction between velocity and speed. Velocity has both magnitude and direction, whereas speed is simply the magnitude of the velocity, with no direction indicated. If the velocity is negative and the acceleration is negative, then the velocity is decreasing but the speed is increasing (because speed is the absolute value of the velocity). A summary of the effect of acceleration on speed (how fast the object is moving without regard for the direction) is as follows:

If $a(t)v(t) > 0$, then the object is speeding up at time t.
If $a(t)v(t) < 0$, then the object is slowing down at time t.

In words, we can say that, if the acceleration and the velocity have the same sign at a particular time (they are in the same direction), then the object is speeding up at that time. This occurs because the object is being pushed in the direction of motion. If the acceleration and the velocity have opposite signs at a particular time (they are in opposite directions), then the object is slowing down at that time, since the object is being pushed in a direction opposite to its motion.

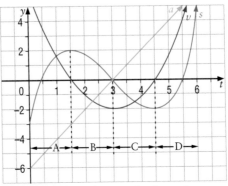

A: slows down   C: slows down
B: speeds up   D: speeds up

We can use similar reasoning to determine if an object is moving away from the origin or toward the origin. The origin is defined as the position equal to 0. If an object has a positive position and positive velocity, it is moving away from the origin. Similarly, if an object has a negative position and a negative velocity, it is moving away from the origin. In both cases, the product of the position and the velocity is positive.

$s < 0, v < 0, sv > 0$
Object is moving away from origin.

$s > 0, v > 0, sv > 0$
Object is moving away from origin.

If an object has a positive position and negative velocity, it is moving toward the origin. Similarly, if an object has a negative position and a positive velocity, it is moving toward the origin. In both cases, the product of the position and the velocity is negative, indicating that the object is moving toward the origin.

$s < 0, v > 0, sv < 0$
Object is moving toward the origin.

$s > 0, v < 0, sv < 0$
Object is moving toward the origin.

To summarize:

> If $s(t)v(t) > 0$, then the object is moving away from the origin at time t.
> If $s(t)v(t) < 0$, then the object is moving toward the origin at time t.

Example 6 Speeding Up or Slowing Down?

In a science-fiction movie, a computer-generated robot appears to be moving about the scene. The actors and the robot are not on the set at the same time. The robot is added to the shot later. For the movie to look realistic, the actors must be given exact instructions about the robot's motion so they can respond at exactly the right time. The position of the robot is defined by the function $s(t) = t^3 - 12t^2 + 36t$, where t is measured in seconds, $t \in [0, 10]$, and s in metres.

a) Find the velocity and the acceleration at time t.

b) Find the velocity and the acceleration after 3 s and 5 s. Is the robot speeding up or slowing down at these times?

c) Graph the position, velocity, and acceleration functions for the first 10 s.

d) When is the robot speeding up? When is it slowing down?

Solution

a) $s(t) = t^3 - 12t^2 + 36t$

$v(t) = \dfrac{ds}{dt}$

$\qquad = 3t^2 - 24t + 36$

$a(t) = \dfrac{dv}{dt}$

$\qquad = 6t - 24$

b) At $t = 3$,

$v = 3(3)^2 - 24(3) + 36$

$\quad = -9$

and

$a = 6(3) - 24$

$\quad = -6$

After 3 s, the velocity is -9 m/s and the acceleration is -6 m/s^2.
Since $a(3)v(3) = 54 > 0$, the robot is speeding up at this time.

At $t = 5$,

$v = 3(5)^2 - 24(5) + 36$

$\quad = -9$

and

$a = 6(5) - 24$

$\quad = 6$

After 5 s, the velocity is -9 m/s and the acceleration is 6 m/s^2.
Since $a(5)v(5) = -54 < 0$, the robot is slowing down at this time.

c) The three graphs are shown below on the same set of axes.

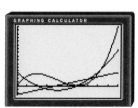

Window variables:
$x \in [0, 10], y \in [-25, 160]$

d) Factoring the velocity function gives

$v = 3t^2 - 24t + 36$

$\quad = 3(t - 2)(t - 6)$

and so the velocity is positive for $t \in [0, 2)$ and $t \in (6, 10]$ and negative for $t \in (2, 6)$
(see the graph).

For the acceleration function, we have

$a = 6t - 24$

$\quad = 6(t - 4)$

and so the acceleration is negative for $t \in [0, 4)$ and positive for $t \in (4, 10]$
(see the graph).

We can summarize this information in the following number line diagrams.

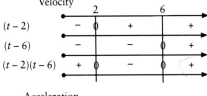

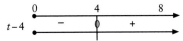

The table and the graph below show when the robot is slowing down and when it is speeding up.

Slowing Down		Speeding Up	
$v > 0, a < 0$	$v < 0, a > 0$	$v < 0, a < 0$	$v > 0, a > 0$
$t \in [0, 2)$	$t \in (4, 6)$	$t \in (2, 4)$	$t \in (6, 10]$

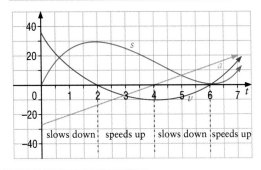

Key Concepts

- If a particle has position function $s(t)$, then its velocity function is

$$v(t) = \frac{ds}{dt} = s'(t)$$

  and its acceleration function is

$$a(t) = \frac{dv}{dt} = \frac{d^2s}{dt^2} = v'(t) = s''(t)$$

- If $a(t)v(t) > 0$, then the object is speeding up.
- If $a(t)v(t) < 0$, then the object is slowing down.
- If $s(t)v(t) > 0$, then the object is moving away from the origin.
- If $s(t)v(t) < 0$, then the object is moving toward the origin.

Communicate Your Understanding

1. Explain how to find the velocity and acceleration of a particle given its position function.

2. Given the position function of a particle, explain how to determine when
a) the velocity is zero
b) the acceleration is zero

3. a) Under what conditions on the acceleration is the velocity of a particle increasing? Under what conditions is the velocity of a particle decreasing?
b) Under what conditions on the acceleration is a particle speeding up? Under what conditions is a particle slowing down?
c) Why are the results of parts a) and b) different?

4. Discuss the validity of each statement. Provide examples to illustrate your answer.
a) "If the acceleration is positive, the object is speeding up. If the acceleration is negative, the object is slowing down."
b) "If the velocity is positive, the object is moving away from the origin. If the velocity is negative, the object is moving toward the origin."

Apply, Solve, Communicate

B **1.** Communication The graph shows the position function of a car.

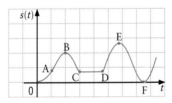

a) What is the initial velocity of the car?
b) Is the car going faster at A or at B?
c) Is the car slowing down or speeding up at A, B, and C?
d) What happens between C and D?
e) What happens at F?

2. The graph of a velocity function is shown.

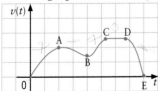

State whether the acceleration is positive, zero, or negative
a) from 0 to A
b) from A to B
c) from B to C
d) from C to D
e) from D to E

3. The graph of a position function is shown.

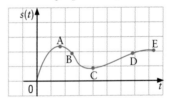

a) For the part of the graph from 0 to A, use slopes of tangents to decide whether the velocity is increasing or decreasing. Is the acceleration positive or negative?
b) State whether the acceleration is positive, zero, or negative
i) from A to B
ii) from B to C
iii) from C to D
iv) from D to E

4. Communication On the graph are shown the position function, velocity function, and acceleration function of an object. Identify each curve and explain your reasoning.

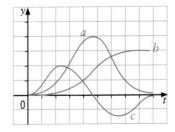

5. The figure shows the graphs of the position function, the velocity function, and the acceleration function of a car that is undergoing a test to determine its performance level. Determine when the car is speeding up and when it is slowing down.

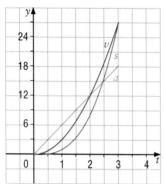

6. Each position function gives s, in metres, as a function of t, in seconds. Find the velocity and acceleration as functions of time.
a) $s = 9 + 4t$
b) $s = 3t^2 + 2t - 5$
c) $s = t^3 - 4t^2 + 5t - 7$
d) $s = \dfrac{t^3}{t+1}$
e) $s = (t - 2\sqrt{t})(2t^2 - t + \sqrt{t})$
f) $s = \dfrac{6t}{1 + \sqrt{t}}$

7. Each position function gives s, in metres, as a function of t, in seconds. Find the velocity and acceleration for any t and for $t = 4$ s.
a) $s = 6 + 3t$ b) $s = 4t^2 - 7t + 14$
c) $s = t^3 - 6t^2 + 12t$ d) $s = \dfrac{3t}{1+t}$
e) $s = \sqrt{t}(t^2 - 2t)$ f) $s = \dfrac{2 + 3t^2}{t + 4}$

8. If a stone is thrown downward with a speed of 10 m/s, from a cliff that is 90 m high, its height, h, in metres, after t seconds is $h = 90 - 10t - 4.9t^2$. Find the velocity after 1 s and after 2 s.

9. Inquiry/Problem Solving If a ball is thrown directly upward with an initial velocity of 29.4 m/s, then the height, h, in metres, after t seconds, is given by $h = 29.4t - 4.9t^2$.

a) Find the velocity of the ball after 1 s, 2 s, 4 s, and 5 s.
b) When does the ball reach its maximum height?
c) What is its maximum height?
d) When does it hit the ground?
e) With what velocity does it hit the ground?

10. The position of a motorcycle moving down a straight highway is $s = \dfrac{1}{2}t^2 + 15t$, where t is measured in seconds and s, in metres.
a) When does the motorcycle reach
i) 15 m/s? ii) 25 m/s?
b) What is the acceleration of the motorcycle?

11. The position of a person on a skateboard is given by $s = t^2 - 8t + 12$, where s is measured in metres and t, in seconds.
a) Find the velocity after 2 s and 6 s.
b) When is the person at rest?
c) When is the person moving in the positive direction?
d) Draw a diagram to illustrate the motion of the person.

12. Inquiry/Problem Solving A new motion detector is used to graph the position of a sports car. If the motion detector is not calibrated properly, it might give unrealistic graphs and data. The position of the car is described by the function $s = 2t^3 - 21t^2 + 60t$, $t \in [0, 6]$, where s is measured in metres and t, in seconds. It is known that the largest possible acceleration of the car is 12 m/s². Investigate if the detector is working properly.
a) i) What is the initial velocity of the car?
ii) When is the car at rest?
iii) When is the car moving in the forward direction?
b) Draw a diagram to illustrate the motion of the car.
c) Find the total distance travelled by the car in the first 6 s.
d) Find the maximum acceleration of the car.
e) List all the evidence that you can to show the company that the equation of motion is not realistic for a sports car.

13. Application If a weighted and coiled rescue rope is thrown upward with a velocity of 2 m/s from the top of a 23 m cliff, then the height, in metres, of the rope above the base of the cliff, after t seconds, is $s = 23 + 2t - 4.9t^2$.

a) When does the rope reach its maximum height?

b) Use the quadratic formula to find how long it takes for the rope to reach the ground.

c) Find the approximate velocity with which the rope strikes the ground.

14. A position function is given by $s = s_0 + v_0 t + \frac{1}{2}gt^2$, where s_0, v_0, and g are constants. Find

a) the initial position

b) the initial velocity

c) the acceleration

15. Application A stunt car driver is practising for a movie. The position function of the car is $s = \frac{1}{3}t^3 - 25t$, $t \geq 0$, where s is measured in metres and t, in seconds. Find the acceleration at the instant the velocity is zero.

16. An unoccupied test rocket meant for orbit is fired straight up from a launch pad. Something goes wrong and the rocket comes back down. The height of the rocket above the ground is modelled by $h = 5t^2 - \frac{1}{6}t^3$, $t \geq 0$, where h is measured in metres and t, in seconds.

a) When is the acceleration positive and when is it negative?

b) When is the velocity zero?

c) Find the maximum height of the rocket.

d) At what velocity does the rocket hit the ground?

e) When is the rocket speeding up? When is the rocket slowing down?

17. The position of a cougar chasing its prey is given by the function $s = t^3 - 6t^2 + 9t$, where t is measured in seconds and s, in metres.

a) Find the velocity and acceleration at time t.

b) When is the cougar moving toward the origin? When is it moving away?

c) When is the cougar speeding up? When is it slowing down?

d) Graph the position, velocity, and acceleration for the first 4 s.

C **18.** The shaft of a well is 15 m deep. A stone is dropped into the well and a splash occurs after 1.6 s. How far down the well is the surface of the water?

19. Application A hawk is flying at 20 km/h horizontally and drops its prey from a height of 30 m.

a) State equations representing the horizontal displacement, velocity, and acceleration of the falling prey.

b) If the prey falls at an acceleration due to gravity of -9.8 m/s^2, state equations representing the vertical displacement, velocity, and acceleration.

c) When is the vertical speed greater than the horizontal speed?

d) Develop an equation representing the overall velocity of the prey.

e) What is the equation representing the overall acceleration of the prey?

f) What is the acceleration of the prey after 2 s?

Extension: Antiderivatives

Scientific descriptions of the natural world usually begin by relating the rates of natural changes to their causes. For example, Newton's second law of motion can be written as $a = \dfrac{F}{m}$, where a is the acceleration of an object, m is the mass of the object, and F is the total force acting on the object. Since acceleration is the derivative of velocity, Newton's second law can be written as

$$\frac{dv}{dt} = \frac{F}{m}$$

Forces can cause objects to move. However, Newton's second law specifies, not the velocity of a moving object, but the rate of change of velocity. To determine the velocity of the moving object, we need to reverse the process of differentiation, so that we can obtain the velocity function from its derivative.

Investigate & Inquire: Reversing the Process of Differentiation

1. a) Given the following position functions, determine functions representing the velocity and the acceleration.

i) $s(t) = 5t^2 + 12t + 3$ ii) $s(t) = 5t^2 + 12t - 6$ iii) $s(t) = 5t^2 + 12t + 6$

b) What is the initial displacement for each function?
c) What is the initial velocity for each function?
d) What is the acceleration for each function?
e) Describe the similarities and differences between the different cases.

2. Using a graphing calculator and a motion detector (CBR), set the time to 15 s and set the display to VEL (for velocity). Begin walking at a steady pace, without accelerating (If you do not have access to a CBR, go on to step 5.)
a) What is your acceleration?
b) Describe your velocity.
c) What should the velocity-time graph look like? Check the graph in your graphing calculator.
d) Predict the shape of your position-time graph.
e) Describe the possible y-intercepts of the position graph.

3. Using a graphing calculator and a motion detector (CBR), set the time to 15 s and the display to ACCEL (for acceleration). Begin walking with constant acceleration.
a) What should the acceleration-time graph look like? Check the graph in your graphing calculator.
b) Predict the shape of your velocity-time graph.
c) Predict the shape of your position-time graph.
d) Describe the possible y-intercepts of the position graph.

4. Consider the results of steps 1, 2, and 3. If you are given a constant acceleration of a units, what is the form of the equation that represents the velocity? What is the form of the equation that represents the position?

5. An object is moving with a constant acceleration of 2 m/s^2.
a) State a general equation representing the velocity.
b) If the initial velocity is 8 m/s, state the equation representing the velocity.

c) If the initial velocity is 8 m/s, state a general equation representing the position.

d) If the initial velocity is 8 m/s and the initial position is 5 m, state the equation representing the position.

6. There are situations where a moving object has an acceleration that is not constant. Given a function representing the acceleration, explain how to find equations representing the velocity and position.

Example 1 Non-Constant Acceleration

An object's acceleration function is $a(t) = 2t$, where t is measured in seconds and a is measured in metres per second squared. Determine the object's position after 10 s if it starts at a position of 0 m and has an initial velocity of 20 m/s.

Solution

$a(t) = 2t$

So,

$$\frac{dv}{dt} = 2t$$

Now, we have to conjecture a function (actually a family of functions) whose derivative is $2t$. Based on the investigation, a good conjecture is

$v(t) = t^2 + C_1$

where C_1 is a constant. You can verify this by differentiating $v(t)$ to see that the result is indeed $a(t)$.

When $t = 0$, $v = 20$. Substituting, we obtain

$20 = (0)^2 + C_1$

$C_1 = 20$

Since $v(t) = \dfrac{ds}{dt}$, it follows that

$$\frac{ds}{dt} = t^2 + 20$$

Once again, we must conjecture a family of functions whose derivative is $t^2 + 20$. The result is

$s(t) = \dfrac{1}{3}t^3 + 20t + C_2$

When $t = 0$, we have $s(t) = 0$, so

$0 = \dfrac{1}{3}(0)^3 + 20(0) + C_2$

$C_2 = 0$

Thus,

$s(t) = \dfrac{1}{3}t^3 + 20t$

To find $s(10)$, we substitute.

$s(10) = \dfrac{1}{3}(10)^3 + 20(10)$

$ = \dfrac{1600}{3}$

The particle's position is approximately 533 m after 10 s.

The process of going from an acceleration function to a velocity function to a position function can be extended to general functions and is called **antidifferentiation**. Given a function $f'(x)$, the **antiderivatives** are the family of functions $f(x) + C$, where C is a constant. In other words, the family of functions $f(x) + C$ all have the same derivative.

When finding the derivative of a power, we multiply the coefficient by the exponent and reduce the exponent by 1. When finding an antiderivative, we reverse this process. Thus, the antiderivative of a power, ax^n, is $\dfrac{a}{n+1}x^{n+1} + C$, that is, we increase the exponent by 1, and then divide the coefficient by the new exponent. Notice that this formula is not valid when $n = -1$, since it would involve dividing by 0. The antiderivative of $f(x) = \dfrac{1}{x}$ is a special function, which will be introduced in Chapter 7.

Example 2 Determining an Antiderivative

Find the general antiderivative of $f'(x) = 3x^2 - 8x + 5$.

Solution

$f'(x) = 3x^2 - 8x + 5$

$f(x) = \dfrac{3}{3}x^{2+1} - \dfrac{8}{2}x^{1+1} + \dfrac{5}{1}x^{0+1} + C$

$\quad = x^3 - 4x^2 + 5x + C$

This family of functions represents the family of curves with tangents that have slopes specified by $f(x) = 3x^2 - 8x + 5$.

Practise

1. Find the velocity function for the given acceleration and initial velocity.
a) $a(t) = 5$ m/s², $v(0) = 10$ m/s
b) $a(t) = -9.8$ m/s², $v(0) = 2.3$ m/s
c) $a(t) = 5t$, $v(0) = 3$ km/h

2. Find the displacement function for the given velocity and initial displacement.

a) $v(t) = 6t$, $s(0) = 5$ m
b) $v(t) = 2t + 1$, $s(0) = 25$ m
c) $v(t) = 3t^2 - 8t$, $s(0) = 10$ km

3. Find the general antiderivative of each function.
a) $f(x) = 2x + 3$
b) $g(x) = 3x^2 - 4$
c) $h(x) = 12x^3 - 6x^2 + 4x$

d) $f(x) = \dfrac{x^4}{5} - \dfrac{x^3}{3}$

e) $C(x) = \dfrac{1}{x^2}$

f) $P(x) = \sqrt{x}$

g) $f(x) = \sqrt[3]{x}$

h) $g(x) = 4\sqrt{x} + \dfrac{1}{2x^3}$

i) $f(x) = \dfrac{1}{x^5} + \dfrac{1}{x^4}$

4. Find the curve $y = F(x)$ that passes through the given point and satisfies $\dfrac{dy}{dx} = 4x - 5$.

a) $y = 0$ when $x = 0$
b) $y = -2$ when $x = 0$
c) $y = 3$ when $x = 1$
d) $y = 0$ when $x = 4$

5. Find the function F if the point $(1, 3)$ is on the graph of $y = F(x)$.

a) $F'(x) = 2x - 1$

b) $F'(x) = 3x^2 - 8x$

c) $F'(x) = \dfrac{12}{x^3}$

d) $F'(x) = \dfrac{1}{x^2} + 3x^4$

e) $F'(x) = 3\sqrt{x}$

f) $F'(x) = 3x^2 - 4x + 2$

B **6.** The slope of the tangent to the graph of a function at each point is given. Find an equation of such a function whose graph passes through the origin.

a) $\dfrac{dy}{dx} = x^3$

b) $\dfrac{dy}{dx} = 3x^4 - 2$

c) $\dfrac{dy}{dx} = x - 4x^2$

7. The line $x + y = 0$ is tangent to the graph of $y = F(x)$. Find $F(x)$ if

a) $F'(x) = x$

b) $F'(x) = x^3$

c) $F'(x) = -x^5$

d) $F'(x) = -1$

Apply, Solve, Communicate

8. Inquiry/Problem Solving A runner slows down and then reverses her direction to go back to where she started with velocity function $v(t) = 6t - 3t^2$, where v is measured in metres per second.

a) How far does she move in the first second?

b) How far does she move in the first two seconds?

c) She is back where she started when $t = 3$. How far did she travel to get there?

9. Application A canister is dropped from a helicopter hovering 500 m above the ground. Unfortunately, the canister's parachute does not open. The canister has been designed to withstand an impact speed of 100 m/s. Will it burst? (Use $a = -9.8$ m/s^2.)

10. Application A stone is thrown down, with a speed of 10 m/s, from the edge of a cliff 74.1 m high. How long does it take the stone to hit the ground at the foot of the cliff?

11. Inquiry/Problem Solving A stunt person for a movie is launched up into the air at 10 m/s from the top of a building 38.4 m high, and lands safely in an airbag below. If an onlooker takes 2 pictures every second, how many are taken during the stunt?

12. A test pilot is demonstrating a new jet moving at 120 m/s when she begins to accelerate according to $a = t$. Determine

a) the acceleration after 12 s

b) the velocity after 12 s

c) the distance travelled in the 12 s after the pilot started accelerating

13. a) Inquiry/Problem Solving A cyclist has found that, by a proper choice of gears, he can increase his speed at a constant acceleration. One day he sets out and, increasing his speed steadily, achieves his cruising speed of 12 m/s after 48 s. How far did he travel in that 48 s?

b) Communication Sketch the cyclist's acceleration, velocity, and position with respect to time.

14. Since raindrops grow steadily as they fall, their surface area increases, and, therefore, the air resistance to their downward motion increases. A raindrop has an initial downward speed of 10 m/s and its downward acceleration is given by

$$a(t) = \begin{cases} 9 - 0.9t, & 0 \le t \le 10 \\ 0, & t > 10 \end{cases}$$

a) What is the velocity of the raindrop after 1 s?

b) How far does the raindrop fall in the first 10 s?

c) If the raindrop is initially 600 m above the ground, how long does it take to reach the ground?

C **15.** The lines $x + y = 0$ and $x + y = \dfrac{4}{3}$ are tangent to the graph of $y = F(x)$, where F is an antiderivative of $-x^2$. Find F.

16. A cliff is h_0 metres high. A stone is tossed from the cliff with an upward velocity of v_0 metres per second. How long does it take the stone to reach the ground?

Extension: Antiderivatives MHR **243**

Technology Extension

Using TI InterActive!™ for Derivatives

Begin each of the following derivative expressions by creating a **Math Box**. On the palette, click on the **Math Menu**, the **Calculus** sub-menu and the **Derivative option**.

The software can find any of the derivatives that we have done and convert them to simplest form.

Power rule:

$$\frac{d}{dx}\left(4 \cdot x^3\right) \qquad 12 \cdot x^2$$

Product rule:

$$\frac{d}{dx}\left((2 \cdot x + 5)^3 \cdot (5 \cdot x - 7)^4\right)$$

$$2 \cdot (2 \cdot x + 5)^2 \cdot (5 \cdot x - 7)^3 \cdot (35 \cdot x + 29)$$

Quotient rule:

$$\frac{d}{dx}\frac{(5 \cdot x - 3)^2}{(4 \cdot x + 2)^3} \qquad \frac{-(5 \cdot x - 14) \cdot (5 \cdot x - 3)}{4 \cdot (2 \cdot x + 1)^4}$$

The software can also perform the types of antiderivatives that we have covered.

Power rule:

$$\int \left(3 \cdot x^2 - 4 \cdot x + 5\right) \, dx \qquad x^3 - 2 \cdot x^2 + 5 \cdot x$$

The symbol used for antidifferentiation here is called an **integral sign**. TI InterActive!™ finds only the antiderivative that has a constant equal to zero.

Practise

1. Differentiate.
   a) $y = x^{-5}$
   b) $y = 3x^4$
   c) $f(x) = (2x^2 - 1)(x^4 + 3x + 12)$
   d) $g(x) = \sqrt{x}(x^2 - 1)$
   e) $y = \dfrac{x^2 + 2}{x^2 - 5}$
   f) $f(x) = \dfrac{\sqrt{x} - 2}{3 - x^2}$

2. Determine $f(x)$ if $f(0) = 0$.
   a) $f'(x) = x^2$
   b) $f'(x) = 3x + 1$
   c) $f'(x) = \dfrac{2x}{(1 - x^2)^2}$
   d) $f'(x) = \sqrt{x} + \dfrac{1}{\sqrt{x}}$

Web Connection

A trial version of TI InterActive!™ is provided by the manufacturer. Go to **www.mcgrawhill.ca/links/CAF12** and follow the instructions there.

Historical Bites: The Fields Medal

Canadian John Charles Fields (1863–1932) is best remembered for conceiving and funding an international medal for mathematical distinction. Adopted at the International Congress of Mathematicians at Zurich in 1932, the first medals were awarded at the Oslo Congress of 1936. The Fields Medal is now recognized as the top prize for mathematicians in the world.

Fields Medals are awarded to two to four mathematicians younger than 40 every four years at the International Congress of Mathematicians. These conditions were set out in Fields' will, and the awards recognize both completed work and the potential for future achievement.

Rates of Change in the Social Sciences

Rates of change can be readily applied to business, economics, and other social sciences. For example, the rate of change of the cost to produce a product, and the rate of change of both revenue and profit, allow companies to determine the best prices at which to sell their products. Population growth rates allow demographers and urban planners to study and plan future growth. Yield rates from plantings help farmers reduce the cost of seed. In this section, we use derivatives to investigate rates of change in the social sciences.

In business, the cost to produce x units of a commodity or service is called the **cost function**. The cost function is often represented by a polynomial such as $C(x) = a + bx + cx^2 + dx^3 + \ldots$, where a represents the fixed cost, and the x terms represent variable costs associated with producing x units.

Economists call the instantaneous rate of change of cost, with respect to the number of items produced, the **marginal cost**. Thus, the marginal cost is the derivative of the cost function,

$$\text{marginal cost} = \frac{dC}{dx}$$
the derivative

Example 1 Marginal Cost

A rubber manufacturer produces rubber tires for many kinds of bicycles. The owner of the company uses regression to estimate that the cost, in dollars, of producing a certain tire for their top-selling mountain bicycle is $C(x) = 4930 + 8.4x - 0.0006x^2$, $x \in [0, 2000]$.
a) Find the marginal cost at a production level of 500 tires.
b) Find the actual cost of producing the 501st tire.

Solution

a) The marginal cost function is represented by $C'(x)$.
$C(x) = 4930 + 8.4x - 0.0006x^2$.
$C'(x) = 8.4 - 0.0012x$
When $x = 500$,
$C'(500) = 8.4 - 0.0012(500)$
$\qquad = 7.8$
The marginal cost when $x = 500$ is $7.80/tire.
b) For the 501st tire,
$C(501) - C(500) = [4930 + 8.4(501) - 0.0006(501)^2] - [4930 + 8.4(500) - 0.0006(500)^2]$
$\qquad\qquad = 8987.7994 - 8980$
$\qquad\qquad = 7.7994$
The actual cost of producing the 501st tire is $7.7994.

Notice the similarity between the marginal cost of the 500th tire and the cost of producing the 501st tire. For n very large, the marginal cost of producing n units is approximately equal to the cost of producing one more unit, the $(n + 1)$st unit.

Not only do businesses need to analyse costs, they must also account for revenue and profits. The price per unit, $p(x)$, that the marketplace is willing to pay for a given product or service at a production level of x units is known as the **demand function** (also called the **price function**). With this function, x often depends on the price, p. However, economists always define p in terms of x and, when graphing, place p on the vertical axis. These functions are often modelled using a scatter plot and regression analysis.

If x units are sold and the price per unit is $p(x)$, then the total revenue is $R(x) = xp(x)$, which is known as the **revenue function**.

The derivative of the revenue function, $R'(x)$, is called the **marginal revenue function** and is the rate of change of revenue with respect to the number of units sold.

In general, if x units of a product are sold, the total profit is obtained by subtracting the cost from the revenue. $P(x)$ is defined to be the **profit function** at x units, and thus $P(x) = R(x) - C(x)$.

The **marginal profit function** is then $P'(x)$, the derivative of the profit function.

The **supply function**, $p(x)$, is the price per unit at which a company is willing to sell its product or service at a production level of x units. As with the demand function, x often depends on the price, p, but economists always define p in terms of x. The **marginal supply function** is the derivative, $p'(x)$.

Example 2 Economic Analysis

Glacé Fabrice, a popular ice-cream parlour, has performed a market survey that shows that the yearly demand for milkshakes is modelled by $p(x) = \dfrac{500\,000 - x}{100\,000}$, where p is the price in dollars and x is the number of milkshakes produced per year.
a) Graph the demand function.
b) Use the graph to determine the quantity of milkshakes demanded corresponding to the following prices: $0.00, $1.00, $2.00, $3.00, $4.00, $5.00
c) Find the marginal revenue at a production level of 200 000 milkshakes per year. Explain its significance.
d) Glacé Fabrice estimates that the cost, in dollars, of making x milkshakes per year is $C(x) = 220\,000 + 0.63x$. Calculate the profit and the marginal profit when 300 000 milkshakes are sold per year. Explain the meaning of the marginal profit.

Solution

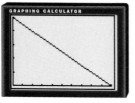

Window variables:
$x \in [0,\ 500\,000]$, $y \in [0,\ 5]$

b) The negative slope of the graph indicates that the lower the price of the milkshake, the greater the quantity demanded. This trend is shown in the table.

p	0	$1.00	$2.00	$3.00	$4.00	$5.00
x	500 000	400 000	300 000	200 000	100 000	0

c) The revenue function is

$R(x) = xp(x)$

$$= x\left(\frac{500\,000 - x}{100\,000}\right)$$

$$= \frac{1}{100\,000}(500\,000x - x^2)$$

The marginal revenue function is the derivative of $R(x)$.

$$R'(x) = \frac{1}{100\,000}(500\,000 - 2x)$$

When $x = 200\,000$,

$$R'(200\,000) = \frac{1}{100\,000}[500\,000 - 2(200\,000)]$$

$$= 1$$

The marginal revenue is $1.00/milkshake when $x = 200\,000$.

The marginal revenue of $1.00 is the rate at which revenue is increasing with respect to an increase in sales. It represents the approximate additional income to the company per additional item sold. Thus, when the production level is 200 000 milkshakes per year, an additional milkshake produced will result in an increase in revenue of $1.00.

d) The profit function is

$P(x) = R(x) - C(x)$

$$= \frac{1}{100\,000}(500\,000x - x^2) - (220\,000 + 0.63x)$$

$$= 5x - \frac{x^2}{100\,000} - 220\,000 - 0.63x$$

$$= -\frac{x^2}{100\,000} + 4.37x - 220\,000$$

At $x = 300\,000$,

$$P(300\,000) = -\frac{300\,000^2}{100\,000} + 4.37(300\,000) - 220\,000$$

$$= 191\,000$$

The marginal profit function is the derivative of $P(x)$, which is

$$P'(x) = -\frac{x}{50\,000} + 4.37$$

At $x = 300\,000$,

$$P'(300\,000) = -\frac{300\,000}{50\,000} + 4.37$$

$$= -1.63$$

At a production level of 300 000 milkshakes, the profit is $191 000 and the marginal profit is -$1.63/milkshake.

The negative marginal profit shows that, when 300 000 milkshakes have been sold, an additional milkshake sold will decrease profit by $1.63. This is because the cost of producing each extra milkshake is now more than the revenue from that milkshake, perhaps due to such factors as higher equipment, maintenance, and labour costs.

Example 3 Analysis of Population Data

The predicted population of a small town is modelled using the formula
$P(t) = 950 + 20t - 100t^{-1}$, where t is measured in years.
a) What is the rate of change in the population after 5 years?
b) What is the rate of change of the population after 30 years?
c) Graph both $P(t)$ and $P'(t)$.
d) Analyse the changes in population using the results of parts a), b), and c).

Solution

a) To determine the rate of change, find the derivative of $P(t)$.
$P(t) = 950 + 20t - 100t^{-1}$
$P'(t) = 20 + 100t^{-2}$
$P'(5) = 20 + 100(5)^{-2}$
$\quad\quad = 24$
The predicted population increase is 24 people/year after 5 years.
b) $P'(30) = 20 + 100(30)^{-2}$
$\quad\quad\quad\ \doteq 20.1$
The predicted population increase is about 20 people/year after 30 years.

c)

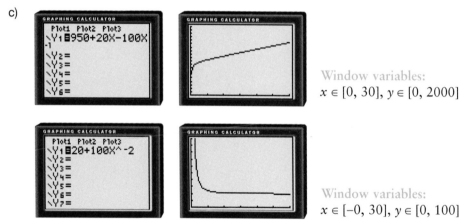

Window variables:
$x \in [0, 30]$, $y \in [0, 2000]$

Window variables:
$x \in [-0, 30]$, $y \in [0, 100]$

d) The graph of P increases, and the rate of increase approaches a constant as time passes. The rate of change of the population is always positive, even though it decreases as time passes. Therefore, the population increases over time, but at a slower rate as time passes. In the long run, there is a nearly steady increase of about 20 people per year.

Key Concepts

- The price per unit, $p(x)$, that the marketplace is willing to pay for a given product or service at a production level of x units is known as the demand function (also called the price function).

- The supply function, $p(x)$, is the price per unit at which a company is willing to sell its product or service at a production level of x units.
- If x units are sold and the price per unit is $p(x)$, then the revenue function is $R(x) = xp(x)$.
- $P(x)$ is defined to be the profit function, $P(x) = R(x) - C(x)$, where $C(x)$ is the cost function.
- Economists use the term marginal to represent instantaneous rates of change. For example, the marginal cost function is $C'(x)$; the marginal profit function is $P'(x)$; the marginal supply function is $p'(x)$.

Communicate Your Understanding

1. Define each of the following pairs of functions. Explain the relationship between each pair of functions from a manufacturer's point of view.
a) $C(x)$ and $C'(x)$
b) $R(x)$ and $R'(x)$
c) $P(x)$ and $P'(x)$

2. Describe how a city government could use information on population growth rates.

3. Explain the significance of
a) a positive marginal profit
b) a negative marginal profit

Apply, Solve, Communicate

B 1. A company estimates that the cost, in dollars, of manufacturing x garden sheds is given by $C(x) = 2500x - 1.05x^2$, $x \in [0, 1000]$.
a) Find the marginal cost function.
b) Explain what the marginal cost function represents.
c) Find the marginal cost at a production level of 300 units. Explain what this means to the manufacturer.
d) Find the cost of producing the 301st unit.
e) Compare and comment on the results from parts c) and d).

2. The cost, in dollars, for the production of x units of a 52-inch TV is given by $C(x) = 13\,800 + 950x - 0.003x^2$, $x \in [0, 1000]$.
a) Find the marginal cost function.
b) Find the marginal cost at a production level of 5500 TVs.
c) Find the cost of producing the 5501st TV.

d) Compare and comment on the results of parts b) and c).

3. Communication Korchnoi's Classic Cars company determined that the revenue earned from selling n units of a certain type of car is $R(n) = 5000n - 0.08n^2$.
a) Find the marginal revenue function.
b) Explain what the marginal revenue function represents to the owner, Korchnoi.
c) Find the marginal revenue when 850 units are sold. Explain what this means to the manufacturer.
d) Compare this to the actual increase when the 851st unit is sold.

4. David's Culinary Supply company estimates that the cost of manufacturing x measuring cups is $C(x) = 11x + 2x^2$, and the revenue function is $R(x) = 19x + 4x^2$.
a) Find the profit function.
b) Find the marginal profit function.

c) Find the marginal profit when 700 measuring cups are sold.

d) Compare this to the actual increase when the 701st measuring cup is sold.

5. Hassan's Hamburgers has determined that the yearly demand for their hamburgers is given by $p(x) = \dfrac{600\,000 - x}{200\,000}$, where p is in dollars, and the cost of making x hamburgers is $C(x) = 110\,000 + 0.95x$.

a) Use graphing technology to graph the demand function.

b) Use the graph to copy and complete the table to illustrate the demand for Hassan's product at each price.

p	x
0	
$0.50	
$1.00	
$1.50	
$2.00	
$2.50	
$3.00	

c) Find the revenue function.
d) Find the marginal revenue function.
e) Find the marginal revenue when $x = 200\,000$.
f) Find the profit function.
g) Find the marginal profit function.
h) Find the marginal profit when $x = 300\,000$.

6. Communication The number of births in Saskatchewan each year from 1972 to 2000 can be modelled using the equation $N(y) = 0.2y^4 - 11.5y^3 + 195.85y^2 - 964.325y + 16\,434.625$, where y is the number of years after 1972.

a) Determine the function representing the rate of change of the number of births in Saskatchewan.

b) What was $N'(y)$ in 1995?

c) Compare $N'(y)$ in 1995 to the actual change in births based on the model.

7. Inquiry/Problem Solving The quantity of coffee beans, in kilograms, consumed in a certain salesperson's region during month x of the year is modelled by the equation $Q(x) = -0.1749x^5$ + $5.2682x^4 - 53.3763x^3 + 203.679x^2 - 233.2x + 600$.

a) Determine the rate of change function for the quantity of coffee consumed.

b) Use graphing technology to graph both $Q(x)$ and $Q'(x)$.

c) Compare the quantities of coffee consumed in the months of January and October.

d) Compare the rates of change of the quantity of coffee consumed in the months of January and October.

e) Analyse the fluctuations in coffee sales with respect to quantity and rate of change.

8. Eva manufactures and sells flower pots. She has determined that the monthly demand for her product is given by $p(x) = \dfrac{60\,000 - x}{10\,000}$, where p is in dollars, and the cost of making x flower pots is $C(x) = 8000 + 1.2x$.

a) Use graphing technology to graph the demand function.

b) Use the graph to copy and complete the table illustrating the demand for Eva's product at each price.

p	x
0	
$1.00	
$2.00	
$3.50	
$4.00	
$5.50	
$6.00	

c) Find the revenue function.
d) Find the marginal revenue function.
e) Find the marginal revenue for 5000 flower pots.
f) Find the profit function.
g) Find the marginal profit function.
h) Find the marginal profit function for 20 000 flower pots.

9. The Let's Play Games Co. estimates that its production costs, in dollars, for x games are $C(x) = 5000x - 2.8x^2$, $x \in [0, 500]$, and the demand function for this product is $p(x) = 80 - 0.018x$.

a) Find the marginal cost function.
b) Find the marginal revenue function.
c) Find the marginal profit function.
d) Find the marginal profit at a production level of 75 games.

10. Inquiry/Problem Solving Sudbury Carpet Mills estimates that its production costs, in dollars, for x rolls of carpeting, are given by $C(x) = 5000 + 2200x + 0.06x^3, x \in [0, 300]$, and the demand function for this product is given by $p(x) = 10\,000 - 0.05x^2$.
a) Find the marginal cost function.
b) Find the marginal revenue function.
c) Find the marginal profit function.
d) Find the marginal profit at a production level of 130 rolls of carpet.
e) At what production level would the marginal cost and marginal revenue be the same?

11. The supply function for a certain high-end stereo component is $p(x) = 1000 + 2\sqrt{x}$, where p is in dollars and x is the number of units sold. What is the rate of change in price at a production level of 500 units?

12. The number of bacteria in a culture after t hours can be approximated using the function $N(t) = 120\,000 + 1000t^3$.
a) What is the rate of change of the number of bacteria after
i) 1 h?   ii) 8 h?   iii) 24 h?
b) Describe what is happening to the growth rate.

13. The annual quantity of black and white inkjet cartridges demanded by the marketplace can be modelled using the equation $Q(I) = -I^2 - 100I + 2505, I \in [0, 70]$, where I is the annual income, in thousands of dollars, of a given household. What is the rate of change of the number of cartridges demanded at an income level of $60\,000?

14. Application The Consumer Price Index (CPI) represents the price of a representative "basket" of food. A model for this index between 1984 and 2000 is given by the equation $C(t) = 0.000\,052t^5 - 0.0005t^4 - 0.0153t^3 + 0.05t^2 + 4.404t + 69.5$, where t is measured

in years since 1984 and $C(t)$ is measured in 1992 dollars.
a) Determine the function representing the rate of change of the CPI in year t.
b) What was the rate of change of the CPI in 1984? 1999?
c) Compare the rates of change in part b) with the actual changes based on the model.

15. Application The number of people who use public transit more than once a week to get to the downtown area of a certain city is modelled using the equation $N = 21\,000 + 420d - 5d^2$, where d is the distance, in kilometres, of their residence from downtown, and $d \in [0, 20]$.
a) Determine the function representing the rate of change of transit ridership.
b) Compare the rates of change of ridership for people who live 2 km and 20 km from downtown.

16. The projected commercial output, in millions of dollars, for the city of Torville has been modelled by the function $C(t) = 97.42\sqrt{t} + 295.01$. The projected commercial output, in millions of dollars, for the city of Thunderton has been modelled by the function $C(t) = 102.58t + 403.75$, where t is the time in years and $t \in [0, 5]$. After how many years will the two cities' marginal outputs be the same? What is the marginal output at that time?

17. The yield, Y, in kilograms, of wheat from 1 ha of farmland when x kilograms of a particular brand of seed is planted, is modelled using the formula $Y(x) = -0.08x^2 + 35x + 3575$, $x \in [40, 180]$. What is the marginal yield with respect to the mass of seed used, when 75 kg of seed is planted?

C **18.** The population of a bee colony is modelled by the equation $P(t) = 100\sqrt{t} + \dfrac{200}{t+1}$, where t is measured in days after the colonization of the beehive, and $t \in [0, 300]$.
a) Determine the growth rate of the bee population after
i) 1 day
ii) 10 days
iii) 60 days

b) Explain the change in the growth rate of the population over time.

19. The demand function for a commodity is given as $p(x) = ax^2 + bx + c$. The cost function is given as $C(x) = dx^3 + ex^2 + fx + g$. Determine functions representing the profit and marginal profit.

20. A pizza chain estimates its marginal cost per pizza to be given by the function

$C'(x) = 0.000\,25 - \dfrac{10}{x^2}$, where x is the number of pizzas made in a day. Determine a family of equations that could represent the cost per pizza.

Historical Bite: Female Pioneers in Calculus

In the early development of calculus, women's names are rare, because they were generally not allowed to go on to higher education. However, several women played a large part, in some cases by deception. Sophie Germain (1776–1831) was not allowed to attend the École Polytechnique in Paris in 1794 because she was a woman. To get around this, male friends obtained lecture notes for her, and she submitted assignments and questions under the false name Monsieur Le Blanc. One hundred years later, Sonja Kovalevsky (1850–1891) was not allowed to study at a foreign university unless she was married. She and her sister found a man willing to marry her so she could go to university. Both Germain and Kovalevsky went on to make important discoveries in calculus.

Investigate & Apply: Zooming in on Tangents

We know that the graph of a tangent lies close to the graph of the function near the point of tangency. Suppose that we choose a function $y = f(x)$, two specific x-values, $x = a$ and $x = b$ and a tangent drawn to the function at $(a, f(a))$.

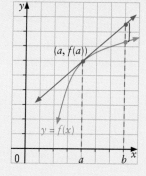

We could conjecture that the greater the distance between a and b, the greater the vertical distance at $x = b$ between the graph of the function and the graph of the tangent.

Investigate this conjecture for the function $f(x) = \dfrac{1}{x}$.

The following suggestions may aid your inquiry:

- Let $a = 1$ and $b = 2$. That is, find the value of $f(2)$. Find the equation of the tangent to the curve at $x = 1$, and use it to approximate the value of f at $x = 2$.
- Find the equation of the tangent to the curve at $x = 100$, and use it to approximate the value of f at $x = 2$.
- Which tangent lies closer to the curve at $x = 2$? Explain.
- Does your result support the original conjecture? Explain.
- If the conjecture is valid in this case, do you think it is valid in general? Is it valid under certain conditions? Explain.
- If the conjecture is not valid in this case, are there conditions for which the conjecture is valid? Explain.

Write a summary of your results.

4.1 The Derivative

Refer to the Key Concepts on page 194.

1. Each limit represents the derivative of a function f at a number a. State f and a in each case.

a) $\displaystyle \lim_{h \to 0} \frac{(3+h)^2 - 9}{h}$

b) $\displaystyle \lim_{h \to 0} \frac{[(1+h)^3 + 4] - 5}{h}$

c) $\displaystyle \lim_{h \to 0} \frac{\sqrt{4+h} - 2}{h}$

d) $\displaystyle \lim_{x \to 1} \frac{x^2 - 1}{x - 1}$

e) $\displaystyle \lim_{x \to 4} \frac{\sqrt{x} - 2}{x - 4}$

f) $\displaystyle \lim_{x \to -3} \frac{(x^3 + 20) + 7}{x + 3}$

2. Determine $f'(4)$ for each function from first principles.

a) $f(x) = x^2 + 5$ b) $f(x) = 2x^2 + 3x$

c) $f(x) = \sqrt{x} + x$

3. If $f(x) = x^2 + x$, find $f'(a)$ using first principles, and use it to find the slopes of the tangents to the parabola $y = x^2 + x$ at the points $(-2, 2)$, $(-1, 0)$, $(0, 0)$, $(1, 2)$, and $(2, 6)$. Illustrate by sketching the curve and the tangents.

4. Find $f'(-2)$ for each function using first principles.

a) $f(x) = 4x^2 - 3$

b) $f(x) = x^2 - 8x + 16$

c) $f(x) = \sqrt{x + 3}$

d) $f(x) = x^3 + 2$

e) $f(x) = \dfrac{1}{x^3}$

f) $f(x) = \dfrac{1}{\sqrt{x + 4}}$

5. The position of a train moving along a straight part of a track is given by

$$s(t) = \frac{1}{4}t^2 + 10t,$$ where t is measured in seconds and s, in metres. Find $s'(t)$ using first principles, and use it to find the velocity of the train after 2 s, 4 s, and 6 s.

6. Use the graph of f to sketch the graph of f'.

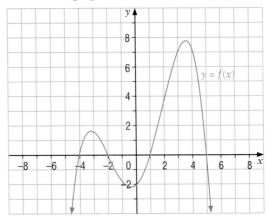

4.2 Basic Differentiation Rules

Refer to the Key Concepts on page 203.

7. Differentiate each function.

a) $y = x^9$ b) $y = 12x^{\frac{4}{3}}$

c) $y = -\dfrac{3}{x^4}$ d) $f(x) = \dfrac{8}{3}\sqrt[4]{x^3}$

e) $f(x) = -\dfrac{1}{10}x^{-5}$ f) $f(x) = 3x^{n+1}$

8. Differentiate each function.

a) $f(x) = x^2 + 4x$

b) $f(x) = 5x^3 - 2x^4$

c) $f(x) = x^5 - 7x^4 + 3x^3$

d) $g(x) = \dfrac{1}{2}x^4 - \dfrac{1}{x}$

e) $g(x) = (2x - 3)^2$

f) $g(x) = \dfrac{1}{9}x^{-3} - \dfrac{1}{6}x^{-2}$

g) $y = \dfrac{1}{3}\sqrt{x} - \dfrac{2}{\sqrt{x}}$

h) $y = 6\sqrt[4]{x} - 3\sqrt[3]{x} + \dfrac{10}{\sqrt[5]{x}}$

i) $y = (x^2 - 2x)^3$

9. Find an equation of the tangent to the curve at the given point.

a) $y = \dfrac{x^3}{3} - 2x^2$, $(3, -9)$

b) $y = x^2 - 2x + 5$, $(-1, 8)$

c) $y = \sqrt{x} + \dfrac{4}{\sqrt{x}}$, $(4, 4)$

d) $y = 2ax^2 + ax$, $(2, 10a)$

10. The value of a stock, V, in dollars, is modelled by the equation $V(t) = 2\sqrt{t} + 1$, where t is measured in months.
a) Find $V'(t)$ and explain what it represents.
b) Would you recommend this stock to investors as a long-term investment?
c) If you had to invest in this stock as a short-term investment (buy and sell a short time later), when would you invest? Explain.

11. If a ball is dropped from the top of a cliff 200 m high, then its height, h, in metres, after t seconds is given by $h = 200 - 4.9t^2$. Find the velocity of the ball after 1 s, 2 s, and 5 s.

12. Find the point on the parabola $y = 3x^2 - 7x + 4$ where the tangent is parallel to the line $5x + y = 3$.

13. Find the equations of both lines that pass through the point $(2, -3)$ and are tangent to the parabola $y = x^2 + x$.

4.3 The Product Rule

Refer to the Key Concepts on page 211.
14. Differentiate each function.
a) $f(x) = (x + 1)(x^2 + 2x)$
b) $g(x) = \sqrt{x}(3x^2 - 8x^3)$
c) $s(t) = t^{-2}(3t + 2t^{-2})$
d) $m = (k^2 - 4k)(3k - 4k^2 + k^3)$
e) $y = (6\sqrt{x} - 4)(3 + 2\sqrt{x})$
f) $y = (ax + b)(ax^2 - bx)$

15. Find the equation of the tangent to the curve at the given point.
a) $y = (x + 3)(x^2 - 1)$, $(1, 0)$
b) $y = (x^2 + x)(x^3 + 5)$, $(-2, -6)$
c) $y = \sqrt{x}\left(x + \dfrac{9}{x}\right)$, $(9, 30)$
d) $y = \dfrac{1}{x^2}(4 + 3x)$, $(4, 1)$

16. Suppose $f(5) = 2$, $f'(5) = 4$, $g(5) = -3$, and $g'(5) = 3$. Determine each derivative when $x = 5$.
a) $(fg)'(x)$
b) $\dfrac{d}{dx}(x^2 g(x))$
c) $\dfrac{d}{dx}(x^2 f(x)g(x))$

17. If g is a differentiable function, find expressions for f' in terms of g and g'.
a) $f(x) = (x^2 + 2)g(x)$ b) $f(x) = x^{-3}g(x)$
c) $f(x) = ax^2 g(x)$

4.4 The Quotient Rule

Refer to the Key Concepts on page 218.
18. Differentiate each function.
a) $f(x) = \dfrac{2x}{x^2 + 1}$ b) $g(x) = \dfrac{x^3}{x - 2}$
c) $h(x) = \dfrac{2x + 1}{\sqrt{x}}$ d) $C(x) = \dfrac{x - 2}{1 - x}$
e) $N(t) = \dfrac{t - t^2}{2 - t}$ f) $f(x) = \dfrac{\sqrt{x} + 3}{\sqrt{x}}$

19. Find the equation of the tangent to the curve at the given point.
a) $y = \dfrac{2}{1 - x}$, $(2, -2)$
b) $y = \dfrac{x}{2 - x^2}$, $(2, -1)$
c) $y = \dfrac{x^2 + 4}{2x}$, $(2, 2)$

20. If g is a differentiable function, find expressions for f' in terms of g and g'.
a) $f(x) = \dfrac{g(x)}{\sqrt{x}}$ b) $f(x) = \dfrac{g(x)}{x}$
c) $f(x) = \dfrac{xg(x)}{x + 1}$

21. Through government funding, a town develops its parks and some new tourist attractions. Many new short-term jobs are created. The population, P, in hundreds, of the town, is given by the equation
$$P(t) = \dfrac{500t^2}{(1 + t^3)} + 100$$
where t is in years.
a) Find $P'(t)$. What does it represent?
b) At what time is $P'(t) = 0$? What does this indicate?
c) Graph $P(t)$ and $P'(t)$ using a graphing calculator. Describe how the population of the town changes with time and explain how it is related to $P'(t)$.
d) What might be the cause in the fluctuations in the graph of $P(t)$ and $P'(t)$?

4.5 Derivatives of Derivatives

Refer to the Key Concepts on page 225.

22. Find $\dfrac{d^2y}{dx^2}$.

a) $y = x^2 - 3x + 2$

b) $y = 4x^3 - 2\sqrt{x}$

c) $y = \sqrt{x}(x^2 + 1)$

d) $y = (x - 2)(x^2 + 3x)$

e) $y = \dfrac{x - 1}{x + 1}$

f) $y = \dfrac{x^2}{x + 2}$

23. Find the slope of the tangent to the curve $f'(x)$ at $x = 2$ given the function $f(x) = x^3 - 2x^2 + 3x$.

24. In a science experiment, a student suspends a weighted string in a saturated solution. Over time, the substance dissolved in the water will collect on the string, forming crystals according to the equation $s(t) = \dfrac{Mt}{C + t}$, where s is the mass, in grams, of dissolved substance collecting on the string, t is the time, in weeks, and M and C are positive constants.

a) Show that after a very long time the mass that collects on the string approaches M but does not exceed M.

b) Find the initial growth rate of the mass of dissolved substance on the string.

c) Find $s''(t)$. What does it represent? What does it indicate about the growth rate?

d) How long will it take to reach half the largest possible mass? Find $s''(t)$ at that time.

4.6 Velocity and Acceleration

Refer to the Key Concepts on page 236.

25. The position function of a particle is given by $s = 2t^3 + 4t^2 - t$, where s is measured in metres and t in seconds.

a) Find the velocity and acceleration as a function of t.

b) Find the velocity and acceleration after 4 s.

26. The motion of a particle is described by the position function $s = t^3 - 12t^2 + 45t + 3$, $t \geq 0$, where t is measured in seconds and s, in metres.

a) When is the particle at rest?

b) When is the velocity positive and when is it negative?

c) When is the acceleration positive and when is it negative?

d) Find the velocity when the acceleration is zero.

e) Draw a diagram to illustrate the motion of the particle.

f) Find the total distance travelled in the first 8 s.

27. If a colony is ever established on the moon, the inhabitants must become accustomed to a different (lower) acceleration due to gravity. If a tool is sent accidentally upward on the moon with a velocity of 6.5 m/s, its height, s, in metres after t seconds is given by $s = 6.5t - 0.83t^2$.

a) Find the velocity of the tool after 1 s.

b) Find the acceleration of the tool after 1 s.

c) When will the tool hit the moon?

d) With what velocity will it hit the moon?

e) How do the results of parts c) and d) compare for the same event on Earth. (The tool is sent straight up at 6.5 m/s with $s = 6.5t - 4.9t^2$.)

4.7 Rates of Change in the Social Sciences

Refer to the Key Concepts on pages 248–249.

28. A company determines that the cost, in dollars, of producing x items is given by $C(x) = 15x + 0.07x^2$.

a) Find the marginal cost function.

b) Find the marginal cost at a production level of 250 items.

c) Find the cost of producing the 251st item.

d) Compare and comment on the results in parts b) and c).

29. The population of a town after t years is modelled by the function $n = 1200 - 170t + 18t^2$.

a) Find the growth rate after

i) 4 years

ii) 5 years

iii) 10 years

b) Describe the change in growth over the first 10 years.

30. A company that produces sunscreen estimates that the cost of manufacturing x bottles of the product is given by $C(x) = 480 - 0.32x + 0.0005x^2$, and the revenue is given by $R(x) = 0.78x + 0.0003x^2$.
a) Find the profit function.
b) Find the marginal profit function.
c) Find the profit and marginal profit when
i)   300 bottles of sunscreen are sold
ii) 500 bottles of sunscreen are sold
iii) 700 bottles of sunscreen are sold

31. Recycling boxes are produced at a company that estimates that its production costs, in dollars, for x items, are given by $C(x) = 61\,000 + 8x + 0.009x^2$, and the demand function for this product is $p = 90 - 0.03x$.
a) Find the marginal cost function.
b) Find the marginal revenue function.
c) Find the marginal profit function.
d) Find the marginal profit at a production level of 200 items.

32. The number of people using a toll highway depends on their distance travelled on the highway and is modelled by the function $N(d) = 58.6\sqrt{d}$, where d is measured in kilometres.
a) Determine the function representing the rate of change of highway usage.
b) What is the rate of change of the number of users at a driving distance of
i)   50 km?   ii) 100 km?

Extension: Antiderivatives

Refer to page 240.
33. Find the antiderivative of f.
a) $f(x) = 3x^2$
b) $f(x) = 5x^4 + 8x^3$
c) $f(x) = 12x^2 - 6x^3 + \dfrac{1}{3}x^4$

34. Find the antiderivative of f on the interval $(0, \infty)$.

a) $f(x) = \dfrac{1}{2x^2}$ b) $f(x) = \dfrac{4}{\sqrt{x}}$

c) $f(x) = 6x^{-3} - 12x^{-4} + 5x^{-2}$

35. Find the function F given that the point $(-1, 4)$ is on the graph of $y = F(x)$ and that $F'(x) = 2x^2 - 3x$.

36. A raindrop has an initial downward speed of 13 m/s and its acceleration a downward is given by

$$a = \begin{cases} 8.4 - 0.7t, & 0 \le t \le 12 \\ 0, & t > 12 \end{cases}$$

a) How far does the raindrop fall in the first 12 s?
b) What is the velocity of the raindrop after 12 s?
c) If the raindrop is initially 1 km above the ground, how long does it take to fall?

37. In most of the motion problems we have considered so far, we have ignored air resistance. Air resistance acts on moving objects in the direction opposite to their motion. For an object moving upward, air resistance and gravity both act downward. For an object moving downward, gravity acts downward but air resistance acts upward. Thus, the acceleration for an object moving upward has a greater magnitude than the acceleration for an object moving downward. A simple model for the motion of an object thrown straight up with an initial speed of 40 m/s is

$$a = \begin{cases} -10 \text{ as the object is moving up} \\ -9.6 \text{ as the object is moving down} \end{cases}$$

a) Find the time required for the object to reach its maximum height.
b) Find the maximum height of the object.
c) Find a continuous velocity function for the motion of the object.
d) At what velocity will the object strike the ground?
e) Find a continuous position function for the motion of the object.

Chapter Test

Achievement Chart

Category	Knowledge/Understanding	Thinking/Inquiry/Problem Solving	Communication	Application
Questions	All	10, 12, 13, 14	12, 13, 14	9, 11, 14

1. i) State the first principles definition of the derivative $f'(x)$.

ii) Use your definition in part a) to find the derivative of each function.

a) $f(x) = x^2 - 3x + 2$ b) $f(x) = \dfrac{1}{x+2}$

2. Use the derivative rules to find the derivative of each function.

a) $f(x) = x^3 - 2x^2 - 4x^{-1}$

b) $g(x) = \sqrt[4]{x^3}$

c) $s(t) = (2t + 1)(t^2 - 3t)$

d) $h(x) = \sqrt{x}(2x^4 - \sqrt{x})$

e) $f(x) = \dfrac{x^2}{x-4}$

f) $A(x) = \dfrac{3-x}{x^2+2}$

3. Determine an equation for the tangent to each curve at the indicated point.

a) $y = (x^3 - 3)(5 - 2x)$ at $(2, 5)$

b) $y = \dfrac{4x+3}{x^2+x}$ at $\left(-3, -\dfrac{3}{2}\right)$

c) $y = \dfrac{x^3 - 5x - 7}{x}$ at $x = -2$

4. Find $\dfrac{d^2y}{dx^2}$ at $x = 2$.

a) $y = 6x^3 - 5x^2 + 8x - 1$

b) $y = \sqrt{x}(x^2 - 2)$

c) $y = \dfrac{1}{(x-3)^2}$

5. a) Find the point on the parabola $y = x^2 - 4x + 3$ where the tangent is parallel to the line $3x + y = 2$.

b) Determine an equation of the tangent at that point.

6. Two functions f and g are such that $f(4) = 3$, $f'(4) = -2$, $g(4) = 7$, and $g'(4) = 5$. Determine each value.

a) $(fg)'(4)$

b) $\left(\dfrac{f}{g}\right)'(4)$

c) $(g^2)'(4)$

d) $\left(\dfrac{1}{f}\right)'(4)$

7. The power P, in watts, delivered to a small light bulb is $P = I^2R$, where I is the current, in amperes, flowing through the bulb, and R is its resistance, in ohms. The current is given by $I = 5 - 0.01t$, and the resistance is given by $R = 10 + 0.08t$, where t is time measured in seconds. Determine the rate of change of power

a) after t seconds

b) after $10\,\text{s}$

8. The position function of a particle is given by $s = t^3 - 6t^2 + 9t + 1$, $t \geq 0$, where t is measured in seconds and s, in metres.

a) Find the velocity after 4 s.

b) Find the acceleration after 4 s.

c) When is the particle at rest?

d) When is the particle moving in the positive direction?

e) Find the velocity when the acceleration is 0.

f) Find the total distance travelled in the first 4 s.

9. The population of a bacteria colony after t hours is given by $n = 750 + 120t + 13t^2 + 2t^3$.

a) Find the growth rate after

i) 10 min

ii) 3 h

iii) 8 h

b) Describe the changing growth rate and how it is affecting the bacteria population.

10. A toothbrush manufacturer has determined that the monthly demand function for x toothbrushes is $p(x) = \dfrac{40\,000 - x}{10\,000}$, where p is in dollars, and the cost of making them is given by $C(x) = 2500 + 0.04x$.

a) Graph the demand function.
b) Use the graph to copy and complete the table.

p	x
0	
$1.00	
$2.00	
$3.50	
$4.00	

What happens to the price as demand increases? decreases?
c) Find the revenue function.
d) Find the marginal revenue function.
e) Find the marginal revenue when $x = 10\,000$.
f) Find the profit function.
g) Find the marginal profit function.
h) Find the marginal profit when $x = 30\,000$.

11. The linear density of a rod is the derivative of the mass with respect to length. The mass, in kilograms, of a wire, x metres in length, is given by the equation $M = 0.4\sqrt{x}$. Find the linear density of such a wire 3 m in length.

12. The terminal speed of a falling body occurs during free fall when the air resistance force on a falling body increases enough so that it equals the gravitational force, and so the acceleration of the body is zero. Terminal speed depends on the shape and size of the falling body. For a skydiver with arms and legs fully extended, terminal speed is about 56 m/s.

A skydiver jumps from an airplane flying at a height of 500 m. Assuming no air resistance, a model for the skydiver's height, in metres, after t seconds, is given by the equation $h = -4.9t^2 + 500$.

a) Using the model appropriate for no air resistance, how long will it take to reach a speed of 56 m/s?
b) At what height will this occur?
c) Determine a velocity function for the falling skydiver.
d) Draw a sketch of the velocity-time graph if air resistance is not modelled.
e) How would the sketch in part d) be different if air resistance were modelled? How would the results of parts a) and b) change if air resistance were modelled? Explain.

13. Why is a person not able to throw a ball from the ground to the height of the CN tower (550 m)? Support your reasons using mathematical calculations.

Achievement Check

Knowledge/Understanding

Thinking/Inquiry/Problem Solving

Communication

Application

14. A pebble is tossed upward at 25 m/s from the edge of a bridge 46 m above a river. How many seconds elapse between toss and splash? How high does the pebble reach? Explain your answers.

Challenge Problems

1. An equation of the tangent to the parabola $y = cx^2 + d$ at $x = 1$ is $y = 2x + 3$. Find the constants c and d.

2. Sketch the graph of $y = x^2$ and show the two tangents to this graph that pass through the point $(0, -4)$. Find the equations of both tangents.

3. Suppose that the tangent at a point P on the curve $y = x^3$ intersects the curve again at a point Q. Show that the slope of the tangent at Q is four times the slope of the tangent at P.

4. Use the principle of mathematical induction and the product rule to prove the power rule,
$\dfrac{d}{dx} x^n = nx^{n-1}$, when n is a positive integer.

5. The tangent to the graph of $y = \sqrt{x}$ at the point $P(16, 4)$ intersects the x-axis at Q. Prove that the y-axis bisects PQ.

6. Determine the coordinates of all points on the curve $y = 5x^2 - 4x^3$ where the tangent passes through $(0, 0)$.

7. The tangent to the curve $y = x^4 - 8x^3 - 2x^2 + 24x - 14$ at $P\left(\dfrac{1}{2}, -\dfrac{55}{16}\right)$ meets the curve again at points A and B. Determine the quadratic equation whose roots are the x-coordinates of A and B.

8. If $f(x + y) = 2f(x)f(y)$ for all x and y, $f(x) = \dfrac{1}{2} + xg(x)$, and $\lim\limits_{x \to 0} g(x) = 1$, use the definition of a derivative to prove that $f'(x) = 2f(x)$.

9. A commercial 37-cup coffee urn (1 cup = 0.24 litre) delivers coffee through a spout. If the spout is left open, then the volume of coffee remaining in the urn after t minutes is
$Q(t) = 0.09\sqrt{8 + t^2}\,(t - 7)^2$

a) What volume of coffee is in the urn 7 min after opening the spout?
b) Find the average rate of delivery during the first 7 min.
c) What is the rate of delivery at the second minute?

10. A **normal** to a curve at a point is a line that is perpendicular to the curve's tangent at that point. The normal intersects the tangent at the point of tangency. Consider three points A, B, and C on the curve $y = x^2$ for which the normals to the curve at A, B, and C all intersect at a common point. Show that the sum of the x-coordinates of A, B, and C is 0.

11. A flexible tubing system has supports that must be perpendicular to the tubes. If a section of the tube follows the curve $y = \dfrac{4}{x^2 + 1}$, along which lines must the supports be directed if they are located at $x = -1$, $x = 1$, and $x = 0$?

Work Backward

Reverse engineering is the process of analysing a product, such as a cellular phone or a computer program, by taking the product apart and working backward to see how it was designed. Reverse engineering is also an indispensable part of software maintenance and cannot be performed without a complete understanding of the system. The ability to work backward is an important problem-solving skill required in many professions.

Consider this problem in population modelling. In 2000, the population of Terrace was twice the population of Smithville. From 1995 to 2000, the population of Terrace increased by 11.8%, and the population of Smithville decreased by 4.9%. From 1985 to 1995 the population of Terrace increased by 4.8%, and the population of Smithville decreased by 8.6%. Find the ratio of the population of Terrace to the population of Smithville in 1985, to the nearest hundredth.

Understand the Problem

1. What information are you given?
2. What are you asked to find?
3. Do you need an exact or an approximate answer?

Think of a Plan

For each town, start in 2000 and work backward to find the 1985 population in terms of the 2000 population. Begin with Smithville, and repeat the process with Terrace.

Carry Out the Plan

Let p represent the population of Smithville in 2000, and let x represent the population of Smithville in 1995. Since the population decreased by 4.9% from 1995 to 2000,

$p = (100 - 4.9)\%$ of x

$\quad = 0.951x$

$x = \dfrac{p}{0.951}$

The population of Smithville in 1995 was $\dfrac{p}{0.951}$.

Let y represent the population of Smithville in 1985. Since the population decreased by 8.6% from 1985 to 1995,

$x = 0.914y$

$y = \dfrac{x}{0.914}$

$\quad = \dfrac{p}{(0.951)(0.914)}$

$\quad \doteq 1.15p$

Now consider Terrace. The population of Terrace in 2000 was $2p$. Since the population increased by 11.8% from 1995 to 2000, the population of Terrace in 1995 was $\dfrac{2p}{1.118}$. Since the population of Terrace increased by 4.8% from 1985 to 1995, the population of Terrace in 1985 was $\dfrac{2p}{(1.118)(1.048)} \doteq 1.71p$.

The ratio of the population of Terrace to the population of Smithville in 1985 was $1.71p : 1.15p$, or $1.49 : 1$, to the nearest hundredth.

Look Back

Does the answer seem reasonable? How could you check that the answer is correct?

Work Backward
1. Start with the information (results or current data) you are given.
2. Work backward to get the information you need.
3. Check that your answer is reasonable.

Apply, Solve, Communicate

1. Every Friday evening three friends get together and play cards. One evening they agree that whenever one of them loses a game, that person must pay so as to double the money of each of the others. After three games, each friend has lost once and is left with $24. How much did each friend have to start with?

2. Mario decides to give away his collection of comic books. He gives half of the books plus one extra to his sister Ella. Then, he gives half of the remainder plus one extra to his cousin Stephan. Then, he gives half of the comic books that are left plus one extra to a neighbour. Finally, he gives the remaining 74 to a charity shop. How many comic books did Mario have in his collection?

3. The arithmetic mean of a set of 100 numbers is 38. Two numbers of the set, 45 and 55, are discarded. What is the arithmetic mean of the remaining set of numbers?

4. In 1996, the population of Freeport was a perfect square. In 1998, the population had increased by 100 and was 1 more than a perfect square. By 2000, the population had increased by a further 100 and was again a perfect square. What was the population of Freeport in 1996?

5. If the sum of two numbers is 4 and the product of the numbers is –60, find the sum of the squares of the reciprocals of the numbers.

Problem Solving: Using the Strategies

1. In a very long and narrow school hallway, there are 1000 lockers in a row. The lockers are numbered from 1 to 1000. All the locker doors are open. A student walks down the hall and closes every second locker door, starting with locker number 2. Then, a second student walks down the hall and changes the state of every third locker, that is, the student closes the door if it is open, and opens the door if it is closed. A third student then changes the state of every fourth locker. This process continues until the 999th student changes the state of the 1000th locker. Will locker number 757 be open or closed?

2. Apollonius of Perga, an ancient Greek mathematician, studied various shapes, including the circle and the parabola. One of the circle problems that Apollonius posed was as follows: Given three fixed non-overlapping circles, draw another circle that touches them all. There are eight solutions to this problem. In the two solutions shown, the red circle touches the three fixed non-overlapping blue circles. The word "touches" is interpreted to mean that the two circles intersect in exactly one point.

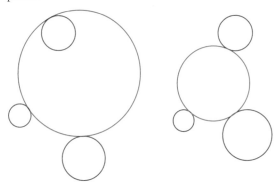

Draw the other six solutions.

3. Find the last digit in the number 3^{142}.

4. You have a 9-L bottle and a 4-L bottle, and an unlimited supply of water. Describe how to get all the possible whole numbers of litres of water between 1 L and 13 L.

5. Each letter represents a different digit in the addition.

    HALF
  + HALF
  ───────
   WHOLE

Find the possible values of each digit.

6. a) Copy and complete the magic square.

17	24	1		15
		7	14	
4		13		22
	12	19	21	3
11	18		2	

b) If columns two and four are interchanged, will the square still be a magic square? Explain your reasoning.
c) In your completed magic square, find pairs of numbers that add to 26. Describe the relationship between the positions of the pairs of numbers that add to 26.

7. Out of 100 applicants for a job, 10 had never taken a university course in history or geography, 70 had taken at least one university course in history, and 82 had taken at least one university course in geography. How many of the applicants had taken at least one university course in history and at least one university course in geography?

8. Convert FLOUR to BREAD by changing one letter at a time to make a new word each time. The best solution has the fewest steps.

Chapter 5

The Chain Rule and Its Applications

Specific Expectations	Section
Identify composition as an operation in which two functions are applied in succession.	5.1
Demonstrate an understanding that the composition of two functions exists only when the range of the first function overlaps the domain of the second.	5.1
Determine the composition of two functions expressed in function notation.	5.1
Decompose a given composite function into its constituent parts.	5.1
Describe the effect of the composition of inverse functions.	5.1
Justify the chain rule for determining derivatives.	5.2
Determine the derivatives of polynomial and rational functions, using the chain rule for determining derivatives.	5.2
Determine derivatives, using implicit differentiation in simple cases.	5.3
Determine the equation of the tangent to the graph of a polynomial, a rational function, or a conic.	5.3
Solve related-rates problems involving polynomial and rational functions.	5.4

As we have seen in Chapter 3, in most change situations it is the *rate of change* that is most important. In practical applications, there are often many related quantities that all change together. In such cases, the rates of change of the various quantities are also related. For example, the rate at which a car moves (its speed) is related to the rate at which the tires (and axles) turn, which is related to the rate at which the drive shaft turns, which is related to the rate at which the pistons move up and down (their speed), which is related to the rate at which the crank shaft turns, and so on. Similarly, the rate at which lava approaches nearby towns can be estimated by observing the rate at which lava is pouring out of a volcano, since the two rates of change are related. And finally, if the sun were to increase in volume, then it would also increase in radius, which would, in turn, increase the temperature on Earth. Once again, all of these rates of change are related.

In order to calculate the relation between rates of change, the chain rule is an essential tool. In order to use the chain rule, we must understand composition of functions, with which we begin the chapter.

1. Functions and relations Define the term relation. Give two examples of relations, one in the form of an equation, and one in the form of a graph.

2. Functions and relations Define the term function. Give two examples of relationships that are functions, one in the form of an equation, and one in the form of a graph.

3. Functions and relations Mohammed says that all functions are relations but not all relations are functions. Claire says that all relations are functions but not all functions are relations. Decide who is correct and explain why.

4. Functions and relations For each equation,
i) state the domain and range
ii) graph the relation
iii) state whether the relation is a function and explain why

a) $y = -10x - 3$ b) $6x + 2y - 14 = 0$

c) $y = 4x^2 + 8$ d) $y = \frac{1}{2}(x+3)^2 - 5$

e) $x^2 + y^2 = 64$ f) $x^2 + y^2 - 6x + 4y - 3 = 0$

g) $y = \frac{1}{x}$ h) $y = \sqrt{x-3}$

5. Evaluating functions Given $f(x) = 3x - 4$, $g(x) = x^2$, and $h(x) = \sqrt{6x+6}$, find
a) $f(3)$
b) $4h(5)$
c) $5g(-7)$

6. Evaluating functions For $f(x) = \sqrt{3x-5}$, determine
a) $f(a)$ b) $f(x+1)$ c) $f(x^2-1)$

7. Equation of a line given the slope and a point Find an equation of the line that
a) has slope -5 and goes through the point $(10, -2)$
b) has slope $-\frac{3}{7}$ and goes through the point $\left(1, \frac{5}{2}\right)$

c) has y-intercept 4 and slope $-\frac{1}{2}$

8. Equation of a line given two points Find an equation of the line passing through each pair of points.
a) $(8, 1)$ and $(6, 7)$

b) $\left(3, \frac{1}{2}\right)$ and $\left(\frac{7}{3}, -1\right)$

c) $(2, -5)$ and $(-7, -10)$
d) $(7.6, -3.1)$ and $(2.5, -8.2)$

9. Distance between two points Determine the distance between the points in each pair.
a) $(1, -2)$ and $(3, 5)$
b) $(2, 0)$ and $(7, 0)$
c) $(1.5, -3.1)$ and $(-7.2, 5.3)$

d) $\left(\frac{2}{5}, -2\right)$ and $\left(\frac{4}{5}, -3\right)$

10. Pythagorean theorem Calculate x for each of the following:

a)
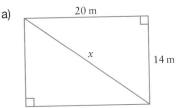

b)
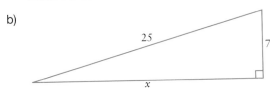

c)
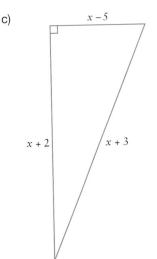

11. Similar triangles Calculate x for each of the following:

a)
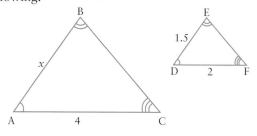

b)
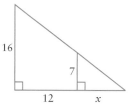

c)
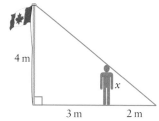

12. Similar triangles Two neighbouring buildings, one 40 m tall and the other 32 m tall, cast shadows proportional to their height. If the taller building's shadow is 12 m long, how long is the shorter building's shadow at the same time?

13. Derivatives (Chapter 4) Find the derivative of each function.

a) $y = x^7$

b) $y = 15x^{-\frac{2}{3}}$

c) $y = x^2 + 8x$

d) $y = x^4 + 6x^3 - 12x$

e) $y = (x + 2)(x^2 - 3x)$

f) $y = x^3(9x + 4x^{-2})$

g) $y = (x^2 + 7x)(2x - 5x^2 + x^3)$

h) $y = \dfrac{x^4}{x + 3}$

i) $y = \dfrac{x + 1}{5 - x}$

j) $y = \dfrac{\sqrt{x} - 6}{\sqrt{x}}$

14. Functions and relations State the domain and range of each relation, sketch a graph of the relation, and then determine if it is a function.

a) $y = \dfrac{1}{x}$ b) $x^2 + y^2 = 25$

c) $x^3 + y^3 = 125$ d) $y = \sqrt{9 - x^2}$

15. Inverses Find the inverse of each function.

a) $f(x) = 3x + 2$ b) $f(x) = x^2 + 5$

c) $f(x) = x^3$ d) $f(x) = \sqrt{3x - 7}$

e) $f(x) = \dfrac{1}{x}$ f) $f(x) = \dfrac{2x + 3}{5x - 2}$

16. Inverses In question 15, which inverses are functions? Explain.

Historical Bite: Communication Among Mathematicians

During the development of calculus, in the period 1750 to 1830, the ways of sharing ideas among mathematicians were limited. Communication between individuals was restricted to the mail or face-to-face meetings. A popular way of sharing new material among many mathematicians was through journals published by academic societies. Some mathematicians, such as J.L. Cauchy (1789–1857), submitted so much material so quickly that, due to the expense, journals began to limit the new submissions from any particular author. This inspired Cauchy to start his own journal, which became profitable enough to support itself. Today, on the Internet, mathematicians can share new ideas with many people quickly and cheaply.

5.1 Composite Functions

In Chapter 4, we learned how to differentiate four types of combinations of functions—sums, differences, products, and quotients. One type of combination was not discussed—composite functions. Once we have learned how to differentiate composite functions, we will have a complete set of tools for differentiation. In this section, we will learn what composite functions are. In the next section, we will learn how to differentiate them.

Composite functions emerge in practical applications when a change in one quantity produces a change in another quantity, which, in turn, produces a change in a third quantity. Thus, a chain of dependency exists. For example, an oil tanker runs aground and leaks oil into the sea. The spilled oil spreads in a roughly circular pattern. As time passes, the radius of the circular oil slick increases, and that leads to an increase in the area of the oil slick.

In the following investigation, you will examine the composition of two functions that might model a chain of dependency of the staff requirements in the delivery department of a newspaper.

Investigate & Inquire: Composition of Functions

1. Assume that, for every 50 subscribers to a newspaper, one delivery person is required. Two extra delivery persons are needed to fill in for absent workers. Let the number of subscribers be x, and the number of delivery persons be p. Determine a function $p = f(x)$ to model the number of delivery persons in terms of x.

2. Assume that each supervisor is responsible for 10 delivery persons. If the number of supervisors is s, determine a function $s = g(p)$ to model approximately the number of supervisors in terms of p.

3. a) Construct a table of values using the two functions you determined in steps 1 and 2. Use several values of x and determine the corresponding values of p and s.
b) Using your completed table, describe how to determine the number of supervisors when given the number of subscribers.

4. a) Use substitution to write s in terms of x, and explain what this means.
b) Add a fourth column to your table from step 3. Complete the column by determining the corresponding values of s using the function you determined in part a). Are the numbers in the last two columns of the table related? Explain.

5. Which do you think is the more efficient way to find the number of supervisors required for a given number of subscribers? Explain.
a) finding p in terms of x, and then s in terms of p
b) finding s in terms of x

6. Use the function in the last column of the table to determine how many supervisors are needed if the number of subscriptions increases to 8900.

7. Explain the chain of dependency linking s and x. What other factors might affect the number of supervisors required?

The function determined in step 4 of the investigation is a composite function. The function s depends on the function p, which depends on x. In general, we have the following definition.

> Given two functions f and g, the **composite function** $f \circ g$, also called the composition of f and g, is defined by $(f \circ g)(x) = f(g(x))$.

The written form $f(g(x))$ is read as "f of g at x." Given $f \circ g$ and a number x, we first apply the function g to x, and then apply the function f to the result. In other words, $f(g(x))$ can be understood as "f following g." This order is important, as illustrated in Example 4.

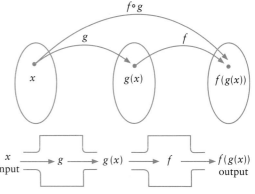

Another way to describe the process of combining functions is to think of each function as a machine with an input and an output.

For the function f, if x is the input, the output is $f(x)$. Similarly, for the function g, if x is the input, the output is $g(x)$. For the composition $f \circ g$, the function machines are placed one after the other. Thus, if x is the input to the first function, g, the output is $g(x)$. Then, $g(x)$ becomes the input to the second function, f, so that the final output is $f(g(x))$.

The notations $(f \circ g)(x)$ and $f(g(x))$ are equivalent.

Example 1 Composition of Functions

If $f(x) = x + 2$ and $g(x) = x^2$, find the following.
a) $(f \circ g)(3)$ b) $g(f(-8))$ c) $(f \circ f)(4)$ d) $g(f(3x + 4))$

Solution 1 Paper and Pencil Method

a) $(f \circ g)(3) = f(g(3))$
$\qquad\qquad\quad = f(3^2)$
$\qquad\qquad\quad = f(9)$
$\qquad\qquad\quad = 9 + 2$
$\qquad\qquad\quad = 11$

We determine $g(3)$ by substituting 3 for x in the function g.

b) $g(f(-8)) = g(-8 + 2)$
$\qquad\quad = g(-6)$
$\qquad\quad = (-6)^2$
$\qquad\quad = 36$

We determine $f(-8)$ by substituting -8 for x in the function f.

c) $(f \circ f)(4) = f(f(4))$
$\qquad\qquad = f(4 + 2)$
$\qquad\qquad = f(6)$
$\qquad\qquad = 6 + 2$
$\qquad\qquad = 8$

d) $g(f(3x + 4)) = g(3x + 4 + 2)$
$\qquad\qquad\quad = g(3x + 6)$
$\qquad\qquad\quad = (3x + 6)^2$

Solution 2 Graphing Calculator Method

Input $f(x) = x + 2$ as Y1 and $g(x) = x^2$ as Y2 in the Y= editor.

a) Evaluate Y1(Y2(3)) by pressing [VARS] [▶] 1 1 [(] [VARS] [▶] 1 2 [(] 3 [)] [)].

b) Evaluate Y2(Y1(−8)) by pressing [VARS] [▶] 1 2 [(] [VARS] [▶] 1 1 [(] [(-)] 8 [)] [)].

c) Evaluate Y1(Y1(4)) by pressing [VARS] [▶] 1 1 [(] [VARS] [▶] 1 1 [(] 4 [)] [)].

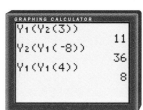

d) Unless it has a computer algebra feature, a graphing calculator cannot evaluate a composite function if the argument contains a variable. So, we cannot evaluate $g(f(3x + 4))$ using a typical graphing calculator.

Example 2 Domain and Range of Functions in a Composition

State the domain and range of f and g. Use the graphs of f and g to evaluate each expression, if it exists. If it does not exist, explain why.

a) $g(f(-1))$ 　　　　b) $(f \circ g)(0)$

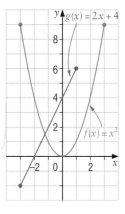

Solution

The domain of f is $x \in [-3, 3]$. The range of f is $y \in [0, 9]$.
The domain of g is $x \in [-3, 1]$. The range of g is $y \in [-2, 6]$.

a) From the graph, $f(-1) = 1$. Thus,
$g(f(-1)) = g(1)$
Again, from the graph, $g(1) = 6$.
Thus, $g(f(-1)) = 6$.

b) From the graph, $g(0) = 4$. Thus,

$(f \circ g)(0) = f(g(0))$
$\qquad\qquad = f(4)$

But 4 is not in the domain of f. So, $(f \circ g)(0)$ does not exist.

Example 3 Domain of a Composition of Functions

a) If $f(x) = \dfrac{1}{x}$ and $g(x) = x^2 - 4$, find $f(g(2))$.

b) What is the domain of $f \circ g$?

Solution

a) $f(g(2)) = f(2^2 - 4)$
$\qquad\quad = f(0)$
$\qquad\quad = \dfrac{1}{0}$

which is undefined. Thus, $f(g(2))$ does not exist.

b) Since $f(g(2))$ does not exist, the domain of $f \circ g$ does not include $x = 2$. Are there other values of x for which $f(g(x))$ is undefined? Since $f(x) = \dfrac{1}{x}$ is undefined for $x = 0$, $f(g(x))$ is undefined for $g(x) = 0$.

$g(x) = 0$
$x^2 - 4 = 0$
$x^2 = 4$
$x = \pm 2$

Therefore, the domain of $f \circ g$ includes all real numbers except 2 and -2. Thus, $x \in (-\infty, -2)$ or $x \in (-2, 2)$ or $x \in (2, \infty)$.

Example 4 Is Composition of Functions Commutative?

a) If $f(x) = 4x - 3$ and $g(x) = \sqrt{x}$, determine

i) $(f \circ g)(x)$ ii) $(g \circ f)(x)$

b) Compare your results from part a).

Solution

a) i) $(f \circ g)(x) = f(g(x))$ 　　　　ii) $(g \circ f)(x) = g(f(x))$
$\qquad\qquad\qquad = f(\sqrt{x})$ 　　　　　　　　　$= g(4x - 3)$
$\qquad\qquad\qquad = 4\sqrt{x} - 3$ 　　　　　　　　$= \sqrt{4x - 3}$

b) The results of part a) show that, in this case, $(f \circ g)(x) \neq (g \circ f)(x)$.

The result in Example 4 is true in general—the order in which functions are applied in a composition is important. In other words, the composition of functions is not commutative. An example of this is putting on your socks and shoes. If you put your socks on first, and then your shoes, the result is different than if you try to put your shoes on first, and then your socks. On the other hand, if you put your gloves on first, then your hat, the result is the same as if you reversed the order. Similarly, there are certain functions for which the order of composition does not matter, as shown in Example 5.

Example 5 Composition of a Function and Its Inverse

If $f(x) = x - 4$ and $g(x) = 3x + 1$, determine
a) $f^{-1}(x)$ b) $(f \circ f^{-1})(x)$ and $(f^{-1} \circ f)(x)$ c) $g^{-1}(x)$ d) $(g \circ g^{-1})(x)$ and $(g^{-1} \circ g)(x)$

Solution

a) $f(x) = x - 4$ or $y = x - 4$

To find $f^{-1}(x)$, we interchange x and y to obtain
$x = y - 4$
and then solve for y to obtain
$y = x + 4$
So, $f^{-1}(x) = x + 4$.

b) $\begin{aligned}(f \circ f^{-1})(x) &= f(f^{-1}(x)) \\ &= f(x + 4) \\ &= x + 4 - 4 \\ &= x\end{aligned}$ $\begin{aligned}(f^{-1} \circ f)(x) &= f^{-1}(f(x)) \\ &= f^{-1}(x - 4) \\ &= x - 4 + 4 \\ &= x\end{aligned}$

c) $g(x) = 3x + 1$, or $y = 3x + 1$

To find $g^{-1}(x)$, we interchange x and y, and then solve for y.
$x = 3y + 1$
$y = \dfrac{x - 1}{3}$

So, $g^{-1}(x) = \dfrac{x - 1}{3}$.

d) $\begin{aligned}(g \circ g^{-1})(x) &= g(g^{-1}(x)) \\ &= g\left(\dfrac{x - 1}{3}\right) \\ &= 3\left(\dfrac{x - 1}{3}\right) + 1 \\ &= x - 1 + 1 \\ &= x\end{aligned}$ $\begin{aligned}(g^{-1} \circ g)(x) &= g^{-1}(g(x)) \\ &= g^{-1}(3x + 1) \\ &= \dfrac{3x + 1 - 1}{3} \\ &= \dfrac{3x}{3} \\ &= x\end{aligned}$

The results in parts b) and d) of Example 5 show that the composition of the function f and its **inverse** f^{-1}, and of the function g and its inverse g^{-1}, results in x, no matter in which order the composition is done. This is true in general, and is also a method of determining whether two functions are inverses of each other.

For any function f, $(f \circ f^{-1})(x) = (f^{-1} \circ f)(x) = x$.

Examine the diagram to see why this is true. Consider $(f^{-1} \circ f)(x)$. First, the function f takes an element x in its domain A and maps it to an element $f(x)$ in its range B. Then, the function f^{-1} maps $f(x)$ back to x. The reverse happens with $(f \circ f^{-1})(x)$. The function f^{-1} takes an element x in its domain B and maps it to an element $f^{-1}(x)$ in its range A. Then, the function f maps $f^{-1}(x)$ back to x.

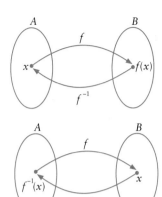

When we begin differentiating composite functions in Section 5.2, we will need to know how to "decompose" a composite function. This is illustrated in Example 6.

Example 6 "Decomposing" a Composition of Functions

Given $F(x) = \sqrt[3]{x + 5}$, find functions f and g such that $F = f \circ g$.

Solution

One way of composing F is to take x and add 5, and then take the third root of this result. We start with the inner function, $g(x)$, and let $g(x) = x + 5$.

Then, we define the outer function, $f(x)$, as $f(x) = \sqrt[3]{x}$.

To check, we compose the function $F(x)$ using our functions $g(x)$ and $f(x)$.

$$(f \circ g)(x) = f(g(x))$$
$$= f(x + 5)$$
$$= \sqrt[3]{x + 5}$$
$$= F(x)$$

Two other functions f and g that solve the problem in Example 6 are $f(x) = x^{\frac{3}{2}}$ and $g(x) = (x + 5)^2$. The solution in the example is simpler, and therefore preferable, but there is an infinite number of solutions to any problem such as this.

Key Concepts

- Given functions f and g, the composite function $f \circ g$ is formed by taking the inside function, g, and substituting it into the formula for the outside function, f.
- The composite function $(f \circ g)(x) = f(g(x))$ is only possible when the range of the inside function, $g(x)$, overlaps with the domain of the outside function, $f(x)$. That is, there must be at least one element in the range of g that is also in the domain of f.
- To determine the domain of $f \circ g$, start with the domain of g and eliminate all values x from the domain of g for which $g(x)$ is not in the domain of f. That is, determine all values of $g(x)$ such that $f(g(x))$ is not defined.
- For a function, f, and its inverse, f^{-1}, $(f \circ f^{-1})(x) = (f^{-1} \circ f)(x) = x$.

Practise

A 1. Use the table to evaluate each expression, if possible. If it is not possible, explain why.

x	0	1	2	3	4	5	6
$f(x)$	0	2	4	6	8	10	12
$g(x)$	7	6	5	4	3	2	1

a) $g(f(2))$　　b) $(f \circ g)(4)$　　c) $f(g(3))$
d) $(g \circ f)(6)$　　e) $(g \circ f)(1)$　　f) $f(g(0))$

2. a) State the domain and range of f and g.

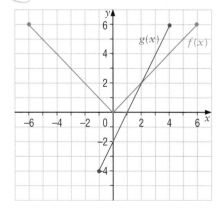

b) Use the graphs of f and g to evaluate each expression, or explain why the expression is undefined or cannot be evaluated.

i) $(f \circ g)(1)$　　ii) $g(f(1))$　　iii) $f(g(0))$
iv) $g(f(0))$　　v) $(g \circ f)(-2)$　　vi) $(g \circ f)(5)$

3. If $f(x) = x^2 + 1$ and $g(x) = x - 3$, find each of the following.

a) $f(12)$　　b) $g(9)$
c) $f(8r - 6)$　　d) $f(g(x))$
e) $g(g(x))$　　f) $(f \circ g)(-2)$
g) $(g \circ f)(x^2)$　　h) $f(f(0))$
i) $g(f(3x - 2))$

4. If $f(x) = \dfrac{1}{x}$ and $g(x) = 2x - 5$, find each of the following, if it exists.

a) $g(-10)$　　b) $f\left(\dfrac{2}{3}\right)$

c) $f\left(g\left(\dfrac{5}{7}\right)\right)$　　d) $(f \circ g)(4)$

e) $(g \circ f)(2x + 6)$　　f) $g(g(0))$

g) $f(f(x))$　　h) $f(g(x))$

i) $g(f(x))$　　j) $f\left(g\left(\dfrac{5}{2}\right)\right)$

5. Find expressions for $f \circ g$ and $g \circ f$ for each pair of functions and state their domain.

a) $f(x) = \dfrac{1}{x}$, $g(x) = 4x + 3$

b) $f(x) = 2x - 3$, $g(x) = x + 6$

c) $f(x) = \sqrt{x}$, $g(x) = x - 5$

d) $f(x) = \sqrt{x + 8}$, $g(x) = 4x + 1$
e) $f(x) = x^2$, $g(x) = x + 2$
f) $f(x) = x^3$, $g(x) = 2x + 5$
g) $f(x) = x^3 - x$, $g(x) = x^2$
h) $f(x) = \sqrt{x^2 + 49}$, $g(x) = x^4$

6. Given $f(x) = x - 8$ and $g(x) = \sqrt{x}$, find each of the following functions and state their domains.
a) $(f \circ f^{-1})(x)$
b) $(f^{-1} \circ f)(x)$
c) $(g \circ g^{-1})(x)$
d) $(g^{-1} \circ g)(x)$

Apply, Solve, Communicate

B **7.** Given $f(x) = \sqrt{x}$ and $g(x) = x + 4$, find
a) $f(g(x))$
b) the domain of $f(g(x))$
c) the range of $f(g(x))$
d) $g(f(x))$
e) the domain of $g(f(x))$
f) the range of $g(f(x))$

8. Inquiry/Problem Solving The function $C(F) = \dfrac{5}{9}(F - 32)$ relates Celsius temperatures, C, and Fahrenheit temperatures, F. The function $K(C) = C + 273.15$ relates Celsius temperatures, C, and Kelvin temperatures, K.
a) Use composition of functions to write a function to relate Fahrenheit temperatures to Kelvin temperatures.
b) What temperature is 25°F in Kelvins?

9. An oil tanker in trouble at sea is discharging oil at a constant rate. The circular oil slick is expanding on the water such that its area is increasing at a rate of 500 m²/min.
a) Express the area, A, in square metres, of the oil slick as a function of time, t, in minutes.
b) Express the radius, r, in metres, of the oil slick as a function of its area, A.
c) Determine a formula for $r \circ A$ and explain what it represents.
d) What is the radius of the oil slick 1 h after the spill begins?

10. A certain honeydew melon is approximately spherical and grows so that its volume increases at a rate of 50 cm³/day (on average).

a) Express the radius of the melon as a function of time, t, in days.
b) Determine the radius of the melon eight weeks after it begins growing.

11. Communication In a newspaper delivery department, the number of subscribers is x, the number of delivery personnel is approximately $p = f(x) = \dfrac{x}{45} + 1$, and the number of supervisors is approximately $s = g(p) = \dfrac{p}{12}$.
a) Using the investigation at the beginning of this section as a guide, explain how the formulas for p and s were determined.
b) Express the number of supervisors needed as a function of x, the number of subscribers.
c) Approximately how many supervisors are needed if there are 5000 subscribers?

12. Application A furniture salesperson earns 5% commission on her sales, plus a flat rate of $200 per week. Let s represent her average sales per day and a represent her sales in a 5-day week.
a) Determine an equation for her sales per week.
b) Determine an equation for her gross wages, w, in dollars, per week, in terms of a.
c) Substitute the equation from part a) to determine her gross wages per week in terms of s, her average sales per day.
d) Determine her gross wages in a week in which she sold an average of $2500 in furniture per day.
e) If she works on the weekend, she earns 7% commission. Determine her extra wages on a weekend in which she sold $3000 on Saturday and $1500 on Sunday.

13. A supernova explosion creates a spherical shock wave that travels outward at a speed of approximately 3000 km/s.
a) Express the radius, r, in kilometres, of the supernova as a function of time, t, in seconds, if the radius of the supernova before it explodes is 1 000 000 km.
b) If V is the volume of the supernova as a function of the radius, find $V \circ r$ and explain what it represents.
c) What is the volume of the supernova 15 s after it explodes?

14. A forest fire spreads in a roughly circular pattern, with the radius of the burned area increasing at a rate of about 600 m per day. Two weeks later, an intense rain storm extinguishes the fire. What area of forest has been burned in this time period?

15. Inquiry/Problem Solving A scenic bicycle path is parallel to a canal. The canal and path are 15 m apart. A cyclist travelling at 15 km/h passes a lock on the canal at 1:00 p.m.

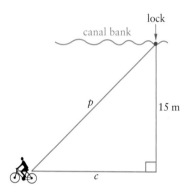

a) Express the distance, p, in metres, between the lock and the cyclist as a function f of c, the distance the cyclist has travelled since 1:00 p.m.

b) Express c as a function g of the time, t, in seconds, since 1:00 p.m.

c) Find $f \circ g$. What does this function represent?

d) How far from the lock will the cyclist be 10 s after 1:00 p.m.?

16. Application For each function $F(x)$, find functions f and g such that $F = f \circ g$.

a) $F(x) = 32x^2 + 3$

b) $F(x) = \sqrt{6x^2 + 7}$

c) $F(x) = \sqrt{\dfrac{1}{x}}$

d) $F(x) = (3x^2 - 5x^3)^{-5}$

C **17.** If $f(x) = 4x - 3$ and $h(x) = 4x^2 - 21$, find a function g such that $f \circ g = h$.

18. If $g(x) = 8x + 6$ and $h(x) = \dfrac{1}{8x + 9}$, find a function f such that $f \circ g = h$.

Achievement Check

Knowledge/Understanding

Thinking/Inquiry/Problem Solving

Communication

Application

An airplane is flying at a speed of 350 km/h at an altitude of 1 km and passes directly over a radar station at time $t = 0$.

a) Express the horizontal distance, d, in kilometres, that the plane has flown as a function of the time, t, in hours.

b) Express the distance, s, in kilometres, between the plane and the radar station as a function of the distance, d.

c) Use composition to express s as a function of time and explain what this new function means.

The Chain Rule

The foundation piles for a building are made of concrete. For each pile, the concrete is poured in the shape of a cylinder with a radius of 0.9 m. If the concrete is poured at a rate of 2 m^3/min, at what rate is the height of each pile increasing? We will return to this problem in Example 5.

In the construction example, the volume depends on time, and the height depends on the volume, so the height can be thought of as the composite function $(h \circ V)(t)$. In this section, we study how to differentiate composite functions using the chain rule. The chain rule completes our set of rules for differentiating all possible combinations of functions.

In the following investigation, you will get a chance to conjecture a formula for differentiating composite functions.

Investigate & Inquire: Derivatives of Composite Functions

1. Consider the function $f(x) = (x^3 + 4)^2$.
a) Expand the formula for $f(x)$ so that it is in the form of a polynomial.
b) Determine $f'(x)$ using your result from part a).
c) Factor the expression you obtained in part b) fully.

2. Repeat step 1 for the function $f(x) = (x^3 + 4)^3$.

3. Repeat step 1 for the function $f(x) = (x^2 - 5x)^3$.

4. Conjecture a formula for the derivative of a function of the form given in steps 1, 2, and 3. Test your formula on the functions in steps 1 to 3.

5. Test your conjecture in step 4 using the function $f(x) = (x^4 - 2x^3)^2$ and other suitable functions.

In the investigation, you made use of the **chain rule** to differentiate several composite functions.

> Chain rule: If f and g are differentiable, and $F = f \circ g$ is the composite function defined by $F(x) = f(g(x))$, then F is differentiable, and F' is given by the product $F'(x) = f'(g(x))g'(x)$.
> In Leibniz notation, if $y = f(u)$ and $u = g(x)$ are differentiable functions, then
> $$\frac{dy}{dx} = \frac{dy}{du}\frac{du}{dx}.$$

The chain rule gives us an efficient way to differentiate composite functions. In using the chain rule, we work from the outside to the inside. We differentiate the outer function, f, evaluated at the inner function, $g(x)$, and then multiply by the derivative of the inner function, evaluated at x.

$$\frac{d}{dx} f(g(x)) = f'(g(x)) \, g'(x)$$

outer function inner function

derivative of outer function evaluated at inner function

derivative of inner function

To understand the chain rule as expressed in Leibniz notation, suppose that y is the salary Beth earns for selling cars, u is the number of cars she sells, and x is time. Then $\frac{dy}{du}$ represents the salary Beth earns per car sold ($/car), $\frac{du}{dx}$ is the rate at which Beth sells cars (cars/month), and their product, $\frac{dy}{dx}$, is the rate at which Beth earns her salary ($/month).

Notice how the units are related: $\dfrac{\$}{\text{month}} = \dfrac{\$}{\text{car}} \times \dfrac{\text{cars}}{\text{month}}$

You can work through a sketch proof of the chain rule in question 14 on page 283.

Example 1 Using the Chain Rule

Find the derivative of $F(x) = (x^2 + 1)^2$.

Solution

We use the chain rule with $F(x) = (f \circ g)(x)$, where $g(x) = x^2 + 1$ and $f(x) = x^2$. Thus,
$$\begin{aligned} F'(x) &= f'(g(x))g'(x) \\ &= 2(x^2 + 1)(2x) \\ &= 4x(x^2 + 1) \end{aligned}$$

As in the investigation, we can check the result of Example 1 by first expanding $y = (x^2 + 1)^2$, and then differentiating each term.
$$\begin{aligned} y &= (x^2 + 1)^2 \\ &= x^4 + 2x^2 + 1 \\ \frac{dy}{dx} &= 4x^3 + 4x \\ &= 4x(x^2 + 1) \end{aligned}$$

This confirms the result obtained with the chain rule.

So, the chain rule allows us to determine the derivative of a composite function without having to simplify first, and differentiate the terms separately. Expansion is sometimes a more efficient method. However, when expansion is not possible, the chain rule is the *only* possible method. Such is the case in Example 2.

Example 2 Using the Chain Rule

Use the chain rule $\dfrac{dF}{dx} = \dfrac{dF}{du}\dfrac{du}{dx}$ to find $F'(x)$ if $F(x) = \sqrt{x^2 + 5x}$.

Solution

Since expansion is not possible, the chain rule is the only method of differentiation. First, rewrite $F(x)$ as a power. Then, differentiate.

$F(x) = (x^2 + 5x)^{\frac{1}{2}}$

Let $u = x^2 + 5x$.

$F(x) = u^{\frac{1}{2}}$

$$\frac{dF}{dx} = \frac{dF}{du}\frac{du}{dx}$$

Substitute $u = x^2 + 5x$ in $\dfrac{du}{dx}$:
$$= \frac{d}{du}u^{\frac{1}{2}}\frac{d}{dx}(x^2 + 5x)$$

$$= \frac{1}{2}u^{-\frac{1}{2}}(2x + 5)$$

Substitute $u = x^2 + 5x$ in $u^{-\frac{1}{2}}$:
$$= \frac{1}{2}(x^2 + 5x)^{-\frac{1}{2}}(2x + 5)$$

$$= \frac{2x + 5}{2\sqrt{x^2 + 5x}}$$

Example 3 Combining the Chain Rule With the Product and Quotient Rules

Use the chain rule to determine the slope of the tangent to the graph of each function at $x = 0$.

a) $y = (x^2 + 5)^3(4x - 3)$ b) $y = \dfrac{x^3 + 2}{(x^2 + 3x - 1)^3}$

Solution

a) To find the derivative of y, use the product rule and the chain rule.

$y = (x^2 + 5)^3(4x - 3)$

$\dfrac{dy}{dx} = (x^2 + 5)^3 \dfrac{d}{dx}(4x - 3) + (4x - 3)\dfrac{d}{dx}(x^2 + 5)^3$

$\quad = (x^2 + 5)^3(4) + (4x - 3)[3(x^2 + 5)^2 \dfrac{d}{dx}(x^2 + 5)]$

$\quad = 4(x^2 + 5)^3 + (4x - 3)[3(x^2 + 5)^2(2x)]$

Now, we substitute $x = 0$ to determine the slope, m, of the tangent:

$m = 4(0^2 + 5)^3 + (4(0) - 3)[3(0^2 + 5)^2(2(0))]$

$\quad = 4(125) + (-3)(0)$

$\quad = 500$

The slope of the tangent at $x = 0$ is 500.

b) To find the derivative of y, we use the quotient rule and the chain rule.

$$y = \frac{x^3 + 2}{(x^2 + 3x - 1)^3}$$

$$\frac{dy}{dx} = \frac{(x^2 + 3x - 1)^3 \frac{d}{dx}(x^3 + 2) - (x^3 + 2)\frac{d}{dx}(x^2 + 3x - 1)^3}{(x^2 + 3x - 1)^6}$$

$$= \frac{(x^2 + 3x - 1)^3(3x^2) - (x^3 + 2)\left[3(x^2 + 3x - 1)^2 \frac{d}{dx}(x^2 + 3x - 1)\right]}{(x^2 + 3x - 1)^6}$$

$$= \frac{(x^2 + 3x - 1)^3(3x^2) - (x^3 + 2)[3(x^2 + 3x - 1)^2(2x + 3)]}{(x^2 + 3x - 1)^6}$$

Now, we substitute $x = 0$ to determine the slope, m, of the tangent:

$$m = \frac{(-1)^3(0) - (2)[3(-1)^2(3)]}{(-1)^6}$$

$$= -18$$

The slope of the tangent at $x = 0$ is -18.

Web Connection

For more chain rule examples, go to
www.mcgrawhill.ca/links/CAF12.

Example 4 Applying the Chain Rule to Graphs of Functions

Using the graphs of the functions f and g, and the formula $F(x) = f(g(x))$, estimate each derivative. If the derivative does not exist, explain why.

a) $g'(-2)$ b) $F'(-2)$

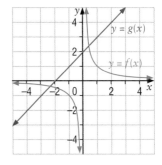

Solution

a) The graph of g is a straight line with slope 1. Thus, the derivative of g is 1 for all values of x. Therefore, $g'(-2) = 1$.

b) First, use the chain rule.
$F'(-2) = f'(g(-2))g'(-2)$

From the graph, $g(-2) = 0$. Substitute this and $g'(-2) = 1$ into the above equation.
$F'(-2) = f'(0)(1)$
$= f'(0)$
Again, from the graph, since $f(0)$ is not defined, $f'(0)$ is not defined, so $F'(-2)$ is not defined.

Example 5 Applying the Chain Rule to a Rate Problem

The foundation posts of a building are made of concrete and each is poured in the shape of a cylinder with a radius of 0.9 m. If the concrete is poured at a rate of 2 m³/min, at what rate is the height of a post increasing?

Solution

The volume of a cylinder is $V = \pi r^2 h$. Solving this relation for h results in $h = \dfrac{V}{\pi r^2}$.

Since $r = 0.9$, we have

$$h = \frac{V}{0.81\pi}$$

Using the chain rule, we have

$$\frac{dh}{dt} = \frac{dh}{dV}\frac{dV}{dt}$$

$$= \left[\frac{d}{dV}\left(\frac{V}{0.81\pi}\right)\right](2)$$

$$= \frac{2}{0.81\pi}$$

$$\doteq 0.786$$

The volume is increasing at 2 m^3/min, so $\dfrac{dV}{dt} = 2.$

The height of a post increases at a rate of approximately 0.786 m/min.

Key Concepts

- The chain rule can be used to differentiate composite functions. It completes the set of basic differentiation formulas for combinations of functions.
- If f and g are both differentiable and $F(x) = f(g(x))$, then the derivative of F is given by the product $F'(x) = f'(g(x))g'(x)$. That is, differentiate the outer function, f, at the inner function, $g(x)$, and then multiply by the derivative of the inner function, g.
- In Leibniz notation, if $y = f(u)$ and $u = g(x)$ are both differentiable functions, then $\dfrac{dy}{dx} = \dfrac{dy}{du}\dfrac{du}{dx}$.

Communicate Your Understanding

1. If $h(x) = f(g(x))$, explain how to find $h'(x)$.

2. a) Expand the polynomial $F(x) = (x^2 + 2)^2$, and then find its derivative. Factor the result.

b) Find the derivative of $F(x) = (x^2 + 2)^2$ using the chain rule.

c) Compare and explain your results for parts a) and b).

3. Zack works as an Internet salesperson. He earns commission at a rate of $6.00 per sale. Yesterday he averaged three sales per hour.

a) Write equations for Zack's commission per sale and his sales per hour.

b) What would a composition of the two equations in part a) represent? Write an equation for this composition.

c) What would you have to do to find Zack's rate of change of commission earnings with respect to time?

Practise

A **1.** Copy and complete the table.

$F(x) = f(g(x))$	$f(x)$	$g(x)$	$g'(x)$	$f'(g(x))$	$F'(x) = f'(g(x))g'(x)$
$(x^7 + 3)^5$	x^5	x^7+3	$7x^6$	$5(x^7+3)^4 \cdot (x^6)$	$5(x^7+3)^4 \cdot (7x^6)$
$(x^3 - 2x^2)^{-4}$					
$(x^4 + 5)^{\frac{1}{2}}$	$x^{\frac{1}{2}}$	x^4+5	$4x^3$	$\frac{1}{2}(x^4+5)^{-\frac{1}{2}}$	$\frac{1}{2}(x^4+5)^{-\frac{1}{2}}(4x^3)$
$\dfrac{1}{x^2 + 2x}$					
$\sqrt{2x - 1}$					
$(x^2 + 5x - 8)^4$					

2. Differentiate.
a) $f(x) = (x^4 - 5)^2$
b) $f(x) = (x^2 - 7x + 4)^2$
c) $f(x) = \sqrt{x^3 - 9}$
d) $f(x) = \sqrt[4]{2x + 1}$
e) $f(x) = \dfrac{1}{(x^2 + 6x - 3)^5}$
f) $f(x) = \dfrac{1}{3x^2 + 8}$

3. Find $\dfrac{dy}{dx}$ for each of the following.
a) $y = \sqrt{2x + 7}$ b) $y = (x^2 + 6)^3$
c) $y = \sqrt[3]{3x - 1}$ d) $y = (2x - 2)^2$
e) $y = \sqrt{x^2 + 6}$ f) $y = \dfrac{1}{x^2 + 3x - 8}$

4. Communication Use the graphs of the functions f and g, and $F(x) = f(g(x))$, to estimate each derivative. If the derivative does not exist, explain why.

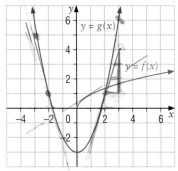

a) $g'(-2)$ b) $f'(0)$
c) $F'(2)$ d) $F'(0)$

Apply, Solve, Communicate

B **5.** Communication Water is flowing into a holding tank at a rate of 15 L/min. Each litre of water added raises the water level by 0.2 cm.
a) Write the given rates of change as derivatives.
b) Use the chain rule to determine how fast the water level is rising.

6. Pollutants from a smoke stack accumulate on the surrounding land in a roughly circular pattern. The radius of this circle is increasing at a rate of 2 m/s. What is the rate of change of the area of the polluted region when the radius is
a) 8 km?   b) 4 km?   c) 0.1 km?

7. Determine the derivative of each function.
a) $G(x) = \left(\dfrac{x - 9}{x + 4}\right)^3$ b) $h(x) = (3 + 2\sqrt{x})^2$
c) $F(x) = \sqrt{4x^2 + x}$ d) $f(x) = (2x + 1)(4x - 1)^5$
e) $H(x) = (x^2 - 4)^3(3 - 5x)$

8. Inquiry/Problem Solving Air is escaping a spherical balloon. When the radius of the balloon is 30 cm, it is decreasing at a rate of 5 cm/min. At this moment, what is the rate of change of the volume of the balloon with respect to time?

9. A certain insect pest has infested a cornfield. The pests are spreading through the field in a roughly circular pattern at a rate of 3 m/day when the radius of the infested area is 70 m. How fast is the area of the infested region increasing at that moment?

10. Application Grain is pouring out of a silo at a constant rate of 4 m³/min. As it falls, the grain forms a conical pile that has a radius twice its height. How fast is the radius increasing when the radius is 7 m?

11. Inquiry/Problem Solving If $F(x) = f(g(x))$, where $g(2) = 6$, $g'(2) = 4$, and $f'(6) = 108$, find $F'(2)$.

C **12.** Determine the derivative of each function.

a) $y = \sqrt[3]{x^2 - 4}$

b) $g(x) = \dfrac{1}{(x^3 + 1)^5}$

c) $h(x) = \left(\dfrac{x^2 + 1}{x + 1}\right)^8$

d) $F(x) = \dfrac{x}{\sqrt{3x + 2}}$

e) $G(x) = (3x - 2)^3 (2x^2 + 5)^4$

f) $y = \left(\dfrac{2x - 1}{x^2 + 1}\right)^3$

g) $f(x) = \sqrt[4]{\dfrac{x^3 - 1}{x^3 + 1}}$

h) $H(x) = \dfrac{\sqrt{x - 2}}{\sqrt[3]{x + 2}}$

i) $g(x) = \dfrac{1}{\sqrt{x^2 - 3}}$

13. Application Find an expression for the derivative with respect to x for each function.

a) $y = h(g(f(x)))$

b) $y = [g(h(x))]^2$

c) $y = g([h(3x - 2)]^2)$

d) $y = g\left(f\left(\dfrac{1}{\sqrt{x + 1}}\right)\right)$

e) $y = f\left(\dfrac{1}{x + g(x)}\right)$

14. Let f and g be differentiable functions over the real numbers. Complete a sketch proof of the chain rule as follows.
a) If $g(x) = c$ is a constant function, prove that the chain rule holds for $F = f \circ g$. State any rules of differentiation from Chapter 4 that you use.
b) Suppose g is not a constant function, and suppose that, if x is very close to a but $x \neq a$,

$g(x) \neq g(a)$. Write the limit $\lim\limits_{x \to a} \dfrac{f(g(x)) - f(g(a))}{x - a}$

as the product of two limits, both rational functions.
c) Use a limit law to evaluate these two limits separately. Express the result in terms of F', f', g, and g'.

Historical Bite: The Abel Prize

Beginning in 2002, there will be another annual prize to celebrate the highest level of excellence in mathematics. This award, known as the Abel Prize, was established by the government of Norway to commemorate the 200th anniversary of the birth of Niels Henrik Abel (1802–1829). Mathematics has never before had an international prize of the same stature as the Nobel Prize, because Alfred Nobel did not think mathematics was a practical science from which humanity could benefit.

Technology Extension

Composite Functions

On the TI-92, we can define composite functions, as shown in the screen to the left, using the Define operation. Then, we can use the calculator to differentiate these functions.

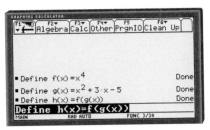

Each function can be differentiated with respect to x as shown, using the differentiate function. Note how the derivative of the composite function relates to the derivatives of its two parts.

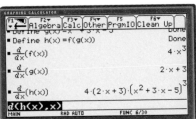

Another way to define a composite function is to use the "such that" symbol | found above the letter **K**. In this case, the volume of a cone is defined as a function of variables r and h, where r is also a function of h.

The second line shows how the calculator would express the function simply as a function of h. The derivative is then calculated using the power rule.

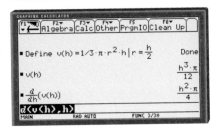

Practise

1. Express each of the following as a composition of two functions, $h(x) = f(g(x))$. Check your work by defining different parts of the functions as $f(x)$ and $g(x)$ in the computer algebra system of your software or calculator.
a) $h(x) = (x^2 - 5x + 6)^3$ b) $h(x) = \sqrt{x^2 - 4}$

2. For each part of question 1, find
a) $f(g(x))$ b) $g(f(x))$ c) $f(g(-2))$ d) $g(f(-2))$
e) $f'(x)$ f) $g'(x)$ g) $h'(x)$

3. In the gravel pits south of Caledon Village, gravel is poured off a conveyor belt onto an empty, flat spot on the ground at the rate of 0.4 m³/s. After a little while, the pile on the ground forms an inverted cone 1 m high with a base radius of 1.5 m. As more gravel is added to the pile, the ratio of the height to the base radius remains the same.
a) Find an expression for the radius in terms of the height.
b) Find an expression for the volume of the pile of gravel in terms of the height.
c) How high will the pile be after 1 h?
d) How long will it take the pile to reach a height of 10 m?

Implicit Differentiation

To this point, we have differentiated only equations where one variable could be explicitly defined in terms of another variable. For example, we have differentiated equations such as $y = (x + 2)^2$, or in general terms, $y = f(x)$. In the form $y = (x + 2)^2$, where y is isolated on one side of the equals sign, y is an **explicitly defined function** of x. In this section, we will see how to differentiate relations for which y is not defined explicitly as a function of x. Consider the problem of finding the slope of a tangent to the circle $x^2 + y^2 = 100$.

Example 1 Slope of a Tangent to a Circle

Find the slope of the tangent to the circle $x^2 + y^2 = 100$ at the point $(6, 8)$.

Solution

We begin by solving the equation $x^2 + y^2 = 100$ for y explicitly in terms of x. Note that the resulting expression has two parts. We can solve for y to get $y = \sqrt{100 - x^2}$, which represents the upper half of the circle, and $y = -\sqrt{100 - x^2}$, which represents the lower half of the circle.

Solution 1 Paper and Pencil Method

Since the point $(6, 8)$ is on the upper half of the circle, we find $\dfrac{dy}{dx}$ for $y = \sqrt{100 - x^2}$, and then substitute $x = 6$ to find the slope of the tangent to the circle at $(6, 8)$.

Using the chain rule, the result is

$$\frac{dy}{dx} = \frac{d}{dx}\sqrt{100 - x^2}$$

$$= \frac{d}{dx}(100 - x^2)^{\frac{1}{2}}$$

$$= \frac{1}{2}(100 - x^2)^{-\frac{1}{2}}\frac{d}{dx}(100 - x^2)$$

$$= \frac{1}{2\sqrt{100 - x^2}}(-2x)$$

$$= -\frac{x}{\sqrt{100 - x^2}}$$

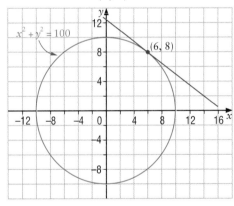

This formula for $\dfrac{dy}{dx}$ represents the slope of the tangent to the upper half of the circle at a point (x, y). Now, substitute $x = 6$ to obtain the slope of the tangent at the point $(6, 8)$.

$$\frac{dy}{dx} = -\frac{x}{\sqrt{100 - x^2}}$$

$$\frac{dy}{dx}\bigg|_{x=6} = -\frac{6}{\sqrt{100 - 6^2}}$$

$$= -\frac{6}{\sqrt{64}} = -\frac{3}{4}$$

Thus, the slope of the tangent to the circle $x^2 + y^2 = 100$ at the point $(6, 8)$ is $-\dfrac{3}{4}$.

Solution 2 Graphing Calculator Method

Since the point (6, 8) is on the upper half of the circle, we graph $y = \sqrt{100 - x^2}$, and then use the Tangent operation on the graphing calculator to find the slope of the tangent to the circle at (6, 8).

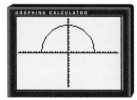  

Window variables:
$x \in [-18.8, 18.8]$,
$y \in [-12.4, 12.4]$

The Tangent operation tells us that the slope of the tangent at the point (6, 8) is −0.75.

You can round to two decimal places by changing **Float** to 2 in the Mode settings.

In Example 1, we could solve the equation for y. But there are many cases in which we cannot solve an equation for one of the variables. Consider how we can differentiate $x^2 + y^2 = 100$ without first solving for y. We do not need to define y explicitly in terms of x, which is what solving for y does. We can differentiate each side of the equation with respect to x, using the chain rule, and then solve the resulting equation for $\dfrac{dy}{dx}$. When we do not solve for y, then y is said to be an **implicitly defined function** of x. This technique is called **implicit differentiation**. Implicit differentiation is an application of the chain rule.

Using implicit differentiation, we have
$x^2 + y^2 = 100$

$\dfrac{d}{dx}(x^2 + y^2) = \dfrac{d}{dx}(100)$

$\dfrac{d}{dx}(x^2) + \dfrac{d}{dx}(y^2) = 0$

$\dfrac{d}{dx}(x^2) + \dfrac{d}{dy}(y^2)\dfrac{dy}{dx} = 0$

$2x + 2y\dfrac{dy}{dx} = 0$

We must use the chain rule to differentiate y^2 with respect to x, because y is a function of x.

$y\dfrac{dy}{dx} = -x$

$\dfrac{dy}{dx} = -\dfrac{x}{y}$

Thus, the slope of the tangent to the circle at a point (x, y) is $-\dfrac{x}{y}$. At the point (6, 8), we have $x = 6$ and $y = 8$. Substituting these values into the slope formula results in

$\dfrac{dy}{dx} = -\dfrac{x}{y}$

$= -\dfrac{6}{8}$

$= -\dfrac{3}{4}$

We obtain the same result using both methods. However, the first method is cumbersome. Before differentiating, we had to manipulate the equation to isolate y, so it was defined *explicitly* in terms of x. The second method, implicit differentiation, allows us to differentiate immediately, which is often more efficient.

In this case, we had a choice of methods, but sometimes implicit differentiation is the *only* method. For example, implicit differentiation is the only possible method for differentiating $x^3 + x^2y + 4y^7 = 6$, since the equation cannot be solved for y explicitly in terms of x (try it!).

Example 2 Differentiating Implicitly to Find an Equation of a Tangent to a Curve

Determine an equation of the tangent to the curve $x^3 + y^3 = 9$ at the point $(2, 1)$.

Solution

Using implicit differentiation, we have

$$\frac{d}{dx}(x^3 + y^3) = \frac{d}{dx}(9)$$

$$3x^2 + 3y^2\frac{dy}{dx} = 0$$

$$\frac{dy}{dx} = -\frac{x^2}{y^2}$$

The slope of the tangent at the point $(2, 1)$ is

$$\frac{dy}{dx} = -\frac{x^2}{y^2}$$

$$= -\frac{2^2}{1^2}$$

$$= -4$$

Window variables: $x \in [-4.7, 4.7]$, $y \in [-3.1, 3.1]$ or use the ZDecimal instruction.

The equation of the tangent at the point $(2, 1)$ is
$$y - 1 = -4(x - 2)$$
$$y = -4x + 9$$

In Example 2, we could have solved explicitly for y in terms of x, and then differentiated to determine the slope of the tangent. Try this and decide which method you prefer.

Example 3 Finding Slopes of Tangents

A satellite orbits Earth in an elliptical path described by the equation $2x^2 + y^2 = 36$. Find the slopes of the tangents to the ellipse $2x^2 + y^2 = 36$ at the points $(-4, 2)$ and $(-4, -2)$. Illustrate the results with a diagram.

Solution

We must determine $\dfrac{dy}{dx}$. To do this, we could first

solve the given equation explicitly for y in terms of x. However, this would result in two differentiation problems, since $(-4, 2)$ is on the upper half of the ellipse,

requiring the use of the equation $y = \sqrt{36 - 2x^2}$, and $(-4, -2)$ is on the lower half of the ellipse, requiring the

use of the equation $y = -\sqrt{36 - 2x^2}$.

By using implicit differentiation, we can deal with the relation as a whole, and not have to separate it into two parts.

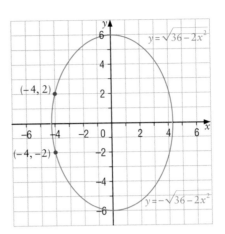

Using the method of implicit differentiation to

find $\dfrac{dy}{dx}$, we have

$$\frac{d}{dx}(2x^2 + y^2) = \frac{d}{dx}(36)$$

$$4x + 2y\frac{dy}{dx} = 0$$

$$\frac{dy}{dx} = -\frac{2x}{y}$$

At the point $(-4, 2)$,   At the point $(-4, -2)$,

$$\frac{dy}{dx} = -\frac{2x}{y} \qquad\qquad \frac{dy}{dx} = -\frac{2x}{y}$$

$$= -\frac{2(-4)}{2} \qquad\qquad = -\frac{2(-4)}{-2}$$

$$= 4 \qquad\qquad\qquad = -4$$

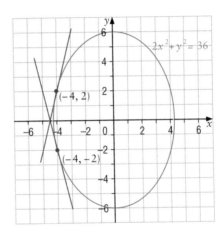

Example 4 Finding a Derivative Using Implicit Differentiation

Find $\dfrac{dy}{dx}$ if $x^3 + x^2y + 4y^3 = 6$.

Solution

Using implicit differentiation, we get

$$\frac{d}{dx}(x^3 + x^2y + 4y^3) = \frac{d}{dx}(6)$$

We use the product rule and the chain rule for the second term, and the chain rule for the third term.

$$3x^2 + x^2\frac{dy}{dx} + y\frac{d}{dx}(x^2) + 12y^2\frac{dy}{dx} = 0$$

$$3x^2 + x^2\frac{dy}{dx} + 2xy + 12y^2\frac{dy}{dx} = 0$$

Now, solving for $\dfrac{dy}{dx}$, we have

$$(x^2 + 12y^2)\dfrac{dy}{dx} = -(3x^2 + 2xy)$$

$$\dfrac{dy}{dx} = -\dfrac{3x^2 + 2xy}{x^2 + 12y^2}$$

Key Concepts

- Implicit differentiation allows us to find $\dfrac{dy}{dx}$ for an equation without first having to solve the original equation for y in terms of x. This is the *only* method that can be used to differentiate an equation that cannot be solved for y explicitly in terms of x.

Communicate Your Understanding

1. Describe two methods that can be used to find $\dfrac{dy}{dx}$ for $x^2 + y^2 = 49$ without using technology.

2. Explain why implicit differentiation is the only method, without using technology, to find $\dfrac{dy}{dx}$ for $x^3 + y^6 = 6xy$.

3. Describe the relationship between the chain rule and the method of implicit differentiation.

Practise

A 1. Communication a) Find the slope of the tangent to $3x^2 - y^2 = 23$ at the point $(4, 5)$ as follows:
i)   first solve for y explicitly as a function of x, then differentiate with respect to x
ii) use implicit differentiation to differentiate with respect to x
b) Compare the two methods of differentiating in part a). Which method do you prefer? Explain why.

2. Determine $\dfrac{dy}{dx}$.

a) $x^2 + y^2 = 25$ b) $x^3 + x^2y + 4y^2 = 6$
c) $x^3 + y^3 = 17$ d) $4x^2 - y^2 = 36$
e) $y^3 + y = 3x$ f) $xy = 9$
g) $y^5 + x^2y^3 = 1 + x^4y$ h) $\sqrt{x} + \sqrt{y} = 9$

3. Determine an equation of the tangent to the curve at the given point.
a) $x^2 + 9y^2 = 37$, $(1, 2)$ b) $xy = 36$, $(9, 4)$
c) $x^2y^2 + xy = 30$, $(-3, 2)$ d) $y^4 + x^2y^3 = 5$, $(2, 1)$

Apply, Solve, Communicate

B 4. i) Find the slope of the tangent to each curve at the given point.
ii) Find an equation of the tangent to each curve at the given point.
iii) Use graphing technology to illustrate your solution with a graph of the curve and the tangent at the given point.
a) $(x - 3)^2 + (y + 1)^2 = 16$, $(3, -5)$
b) $y^2 - 2xy = 11$, $(5, -1)$
c) $x^2 + y^2 - 4x + 6y = 87$, $(12, -3)$
d) $x^2 - xy + y^3 = 3$, $(-1, 1)$

5. Application a) Find an equation of the tangent to the circle $x^2 + y^2 - 6x + 2y = 15$ at the point $(6, 3)$.
b) Sketch the circle and the tangent. Verify your result using technology.

6. Application a) Given a circle $x^2 + y^2 + 4x - 12y = 60$ with centre C, show that the tangent at point P(4, –2) is perpendicular to the radius, CP.

b) Show that any tangent, at point P, to a circle with centre C is perpendicular to the radius CP.

7. Inquiry/Problem Solving The satellite in Example 3 has been boosted into a higher orbit around Earth, described by the equation $4x^2 + y^2 = 100$. The satellite's radio antenna has a broken aiming mechanism, so the antenna always points forward in the direction the satellite is moving. If an astronaut on the moon, located at $(-5, 20)$, wishes to receive signals from the satellite, where in its orbit does the satellite have to be?

8. Communication The pressure, P, volume, V, and temperature, T, of the gas in a combustion chamber satisfy the equation $PV = kT$, where k is a constant. When the piston compresses the gas, all three of the variables P, V, and T change.

a) Differentiate the equation $PV = kT$ implicitly with respect to V to obtain an equation relating the rates of change of P and T.

b) Is the sign of k positive or negative? Explain.

c) For the air in a car tire or a squash ball, the equation $PV = kT$ is still valid, but V is nearly constant and k has a different value. Differentiate the equation $PV = kT$ implicitly with respect to temperature under these conditions. Should the sign of k be positive or negative so that the rate of change of pressure with respect to temperature is as you expect? Explain.

C **9.** The curve with equation $2(x^2 + y^2)^2 = 25(x^2 - y^2)$ is called a lemniscate and is shown in the figure.

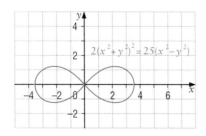

a) Find $\dfrac{dy}{dx}$.

b) Find an equation of the tangent to the lemniscate at the point $(-3, 1)$.

c) Find the points on the lemniscate where the tangent is horizontal.

10. The curve with equation $x^{\frac{2}{3}} + y^{\frac{2}{3}} = 1$ is called an astroid and is shown in the figure.

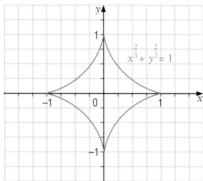

a) Find $\dfrac{dy}{dx}$.

b) Find an equation of the tangent to the astroid at the point $\left(\dfrac{1}{8}, \dfrac{3\sqrt{3}}{8} \right)$.

c) Find the points on the astroid where the tangent has slope 1.

11. Find all points on the curve $x^2 y^2 + xy = 2$ where the slope of the tangent is -1.

12. Inquiry/Problem Solving Two curves are orthogonal if they meet at right angles. In other words, their tangents must be perpendicular at the point of intersection. Families of curves are orthogonal trajectories of each other if every curve in one family is **orthogonal** to every curve in the other family. Show that the two families of curves, $x^2 - y^2 = A$ and $xy = B$, are **orthogonal trajectories** of each other.

13. Suppose that a race car moves on a track described by the curve $y^2 = x^2 - x^4$. The direction of the car when it is at the origin is specified by the slope of the tangent at the origin. Assuming that the car moves in a figure-8 path, determine the slope of the tangent to the curve at the origin.

Related Rates

Whenever quantities are related, their rates of change are also related. For example, the rate of increase in the number of violent storms is thought to be related to the rate of increase of the atmosphere's average temperature ("global warming"). The rate of increase of the atmosphere's average temperature is related to the rate of change of the concentration of "greenhouse gases" in the atmosphere, which, in turn, is related to several other rates: the rate of increase of the number of cars, the rate at which forests are being destroyed, the rate at which fossil fuels are burned to produce electricity, and so on. The chains of dependency described here might remind you of the chain rule, and indeed the chain rule is essential for solving related-rates problems.

Investigate & Inquire: Motion of a Simplified Piston

Consider a piston moving within a combustion chamber of a car's engine. The up-and-down motion of the piston is caused by a circular motion of the crankshaft.

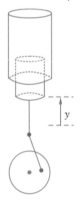

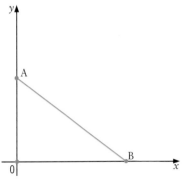

In question 6 of Section 8.5 you will analyse how the up-and-down motion of the piston is related to the circular motion of the crankshaft. As an aid to understanding that situation, we begin with a simpler one. Imagine a straight rod moving so that one end, A, is always touching a vertical wall, and the other end, B, is always touching the horizontal floor. How is the velocity of A related to the velocity of B?

1. Do you think the velocities of points A and B are related? If so, conjecture what the relation is.

2. Do you think that the relationship you conjectured in step 1 depends on the length of the rod? If so, pick some length for the rod (say 10) and stay with it for the rest of the investigation.

3. Let y represent the position of A and let x represent the position of B. Start with the rod placed so that $x = 0$ and $y = 10$. Then, move the rod so that y changes by 1 unit; that is, now $y = 9$. Determine the value of x and the amount by which x has changed.

4. Do the results of step 3 lead you to modify the conjecture you made in step 1?

5. Move A to several different positions and calculate the resulting positions of B. Record all the results in a table and construct a scatterplot.

6. Use the results of step 5 to make a revised conjecture about how the velocities of A and B are related.

In related rates problems, we first determine an equation that relates the two quantities. Then, using the given rate of change of one quantity, we can determine the rate of change of the other quantity with the help of the chain rule. Consider the following example.

Example 1 Speed of a Bicycle Related to the Rate at Which Its Tires Turn

A bicycle has tires with radius 35 cm. If the bicycle moves forward at a speed of 6 m/s, at what rate do the tires turn?

Solution

As in the investigation, it is easiest to solve this problem by finding a relation between the distance, x, travelled by the bicycle, and the number, N, of rotations of its tires. The rate of change of the distance with respect to time (the speed) is the derivative $\dfrac{dx}{dt}$, and

the rate of change of the number of rotations with respect to time is $\dfrac{dN}{dt}$.

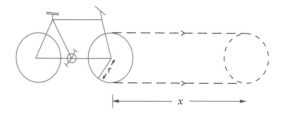

Notice that when a tire turns once, the distance travelled by the bicycle is $2\pi r$, where r is the radius of the tire. If the tire turns twice, the bicycle travels twice as far, if the tire turns three times, the bicycle travels three times as far, and so on. Thus, $x = 2\pi rN$. Since the radius of the tire is 35 cm, which is 0.35 m, $x = 0.7\pi N$.

The equation $x = 0.7\pi N$ is valid as long as the bicycle tire rolls without slipping. In other words, it represents a function with a certain domain. Thus, we can differentiate the equation implicitly with respect to time to obtain

$$\frac{dx}{dt} = 0.7\pi \frac{dN}{dt}$$

Since the speed is 6 m/s, we have

$$\frac{dx}{dt} = 0.7\pi\frac{dN}{dt}$$

Thus,

$$\frac{dN}{dt} = \frac{6}{0.7\pi}$$
$$\doteq 2.73$$

The tires turn at a rate of about 2.73 revolutions per second.

When solving related rates problems, it is helpful to apply the following problem solving process.

1. Read the problem carefully so that you understand what you are asked to determine.

2. Identify the key pieces of information in the question. Draw a diagram to organize the information.

3. Assign variables to the relevant quantities.

4. Determine the relationship between the quantities and write an equation that relates them.

5. Express the given information and the required rate in terms of derivatives.

6. Differentiate both sides of the equation found in step 4 with respect to time.

7. Substitute the given information into the resulting equation and solve for the unknown rate. Remember to substitute the given information into the equation after differentiating, not before.

Example 2 Expansion of the Sun

It is thought that the sun is expanding rapidly enough that, in a few billion years, it will be too hot on Earth for life to exist. Assume that the sun's surface area is increasing at a rate of 5000 km²/year. Determine the rate of increase of the sun's radius when it reaches a radius of 1 000 000 km. The current radius of the sun is about 700 000 km.

Solution

We start by identifying two things, the given information and the unknown. Given that the rate of increase in surface area of the sun is 5000 km²/year, we want to determine the rate of increase of the sun's radius when the radius is 1 000 000 km.

Now we identify the variables and relate them in an equation. Let S represent the surface area of the sun, in square kilometres, let r represent its radius, in kilometres, and let t represent time, in years. The quantities S and r are related by the equation $S = 4\pi r^2$.

In this problem, the surface area and the radius are both functions of time, t. The rate of change of the surface area with respect to time is the derivative $\frac{dS}{dt}$, and the rate of change of the radius with respect to time is $\frac{dr}{dt}$.

Using the chain rule to differentiate each side of the equation $S = 4\pi r^2$ with respect to t, we have

$$\frac{dS}{dt} = \frac{dS}{dr}\frac{dr}{dt}$$

$$= \frac{d}{dr}(4\pi r^2)\frac{dr}{dt}$$

$$= 8\pi r\frac{dr}{dt}$$

Substituting the known information, $\frac{dS}{dt} = 5000$ and $r = 1\,000\,000$, into the equation allows us to solve for the unknown:

$$\frac{dS}{dt} = 8\pi r\frac{dr}{dt}$$

$$5000 = 8\pi(1\,000\,000)\frac{dr}{dt}$$

$$\frac{dr}{dt} = \frac{5}{8000\pi}$$

$$\doteq 0.000\,199$$

Web Connection

To learn more about changes in the size of the sun and other aspects of astrophysics, go to **www.mcgrawhill.ca/links/CAF12**.

So, when the radius of the sun is $1\,000\,000$ km, the radius is increasing at a rate of approximately 19.9 cm/year.

Example 3 Simplified Crankshaft

As a simplified crankshaft (a more realistic crankshaft will be analysed in question 6 of Section 8.5), imagine a 5-m rod sliding in a track that has a right-angled bend in it. The upper part of the track is vertical and the lower part is horizontal. When the bottom of the rod is 3 m from the bend in the track, it is slipping away from the bend at a rate of 20 cm/s. How fast is the top of the rod moving down the vertical part of the track when the bottom of the rod is 3 m from the bend?

Solution

First, we draw a diagram of the information in the problem. Let y metres be the distance from the top of the rod to the bend, and let x metres be the distance from the bottom of the rod to the bend.

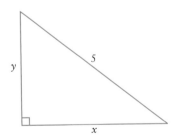

The relationship between x and y is given by the Pythagorean theorem:
$$x^2 + y^2 = 5^2$$
$$x^2 + y^2 = 25$$

We are given the rate of change of x with respect to time: $\frac{dx}{dt}$ is 20 cm/s, which is equivalent

to 0.2 m/s. We need to find $\frac{dy}{dt}$, the rate of change of y with respect to time when $x = 3$ m.

Using the chain rule to differentiate each side with respect to t, we have

$$\frac{d}{dt}(x^2 + y^2) = \frac{d}{dt}(25)$$

$$2x\frac{dx}{dt} + 2y\frac{dy}{dt} = 0$$

$$x\frac{dx}{dt} + y\frac{dy}{dt} = 0$$

Using the Pythagorean theorem, we can solve for y since we know that $x = 3$ at the time we are considering.

$$x^2 + y^2 = 25$$
$$3^2 + y^2 = 25$$
$$y^2 = 16$$
$$y = \pm 4$$

The way we have set up the diagram, y is positive, so $y = 4$. Substituting $\frac{dx}{dt} = 0.2$, $y = 4$, and $x = 3$ gives us

$$(3)(0.2) + (4)\frac{dy}{dt} = 0$$

$$4\frac{dy}{dt} = -0.6$$

$$\frac{dy}{dt} = -0.15$$

Notice that $\frac{dy}{dt}$ is negative, which means that the distance from the top of the rod to the bend is *decreasing*. The rod is sliding *down* at a rate of 0.15 m/s or 15 cm/s.

Example 4 Automobile Crash Test

In an automobile crash test, two cars are approaching an intersection. Car A travels west at a speed of 45 km/h, and car B travels south at a speed of 60 km/h. The force of the impact is proportional to the rate of change of the distance between the two cars. Determine this rate when car A is 0.6 km from the intersection point and car B is 0.8 km from the intersection point.

Solution

First, we draw a diagram of the information in the problem. At time t, in hours, let x be the position of car A, let y be the position of car B, and let z be the distance between the cars. The positions and distances are measured in kilometres.

The distance z is related to the positions x and y by the Pythagorean theorem.

$$x^2 + y^2 = z^2$$

We are required to find $\frac{dz}{dt}$, the rate at which the distance

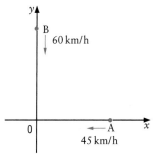

between the two cars is changing. We use the chain rule to differentiate each side of the previous equation implicitly with respect to t.

$$\frac{d}{dt}(x^2 + y^2) = \frac{d}{dt}(z^2)$$

$$2x\frac{dx}{dt} + 2y\frac{dy}{dt} = 2z\frac{dz}{dt}$$

$$x\frac{dx}{dt} + y\frac{dy}{dt} = z\frac{dz}{dt}$$

We are given that $x = 0.6$ and $y = 0.8$ at the time we are considering, so we can find z at this time using the Pythagorean theorem.

$$x^2 + y^2 = z^2$$
$$0.6^2 + 0.8^2 = z^2$$
$$z^2 = 1$$
$$z = \pm 1$$

Since distances are positive, $z = 1$.

Since the cars are both moving toward the origin in the diagram, $\dfrac{dx}{dt} = -45$ and $\dfrac{dy}{dt} = -60$. The derivatives are negative because the x-value and y-value are decreasing.

Now we substitute all the known information into the equation for $\dfrac{dz}{dt}$:

$$x\frac{dx}{dt} + y\frac{dy}{dt} = z\frac{dz}{dt}$$

$$(0.6)(-45) + (0.8)(-60) = (1)\frac{dz}{dt}$$

$$\frac{dz}{dt} = -75$$

Notice that the negative value for $\dfrac{dz}{dt}$ means that the distance between the two cars is decreasing. The distance between the two cars is decreasing at a rate of 75 km/h.

Example 5 Volcanic Eruption

A volcano erupts, pouring lava over its slopes. Assume that the lava stays on the slopes and that the shape of the expanding volcano is a cone whose height is twice as large as the radius of the base. When the volcano is 70 m high, its height is observed to be increasing at a rate of 0.2 m/s. At what rate is lava pouring out of the volcano at this time?

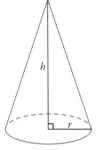

Solution

First, we draw a diagram.

Let V be the volume of the volcano, r, the radius of the base, and h, the height at time t, in seconds. The volume is measured in cubic metres, and the radius and height are in metres. Since the volcano is in the shape of a cone, the quantities V, h, and r are related by the equation $V = \dfrac{1}{3}\pi r^2 h$.

Since we are assuming that all the lava stays in the shape of a cone, the rate at which the volume of the cone is increasing, $\dfrac{dV}{dt}$, is also the rate at which lava is flowing out of the volcano. We are given $\dfrac{dh}{dt} = 0.2$ m/s when $h = 70$ m. We are asked to find $\dfrac{dV}{dt}$ at this time.

In order to differentiate $V = \dfrac{1}{3}\pi r^2 h$, we need to write V as a function of h alone. The given relation between h and r is $h = 2r$, so $r = \dfrac{h}{2}$. We substitute $r = \dfrac{h}{2}$ into $V = \dfrac{1}{3}\pi r^2 h$ to eliminate r.

$$V = \dfrac{1}{3}\pi r^2 h$$

$$= \dfrac{1}{3}\pi \left(\dfrac{h}{2} \right)^2 h$$

$$= \dfrac{\pi}{12} h^3$$

Using the chain rule to differentiate both sides of the equation with respect to t, we have

$$\dfrac{dV}{dt} = \dfrac{dV}{dh}\dfrac{dh}{dt}$$

$$= \dfrac{d}{dh}\left(\dfrac{\pi}{12} h^3 \right)\dfrac{dh}{dt}$$

$$= \dfrac{\pi}{4} h^2 \dfrac{dh}{dt}$$

Web Connection

To learn more about volcanic eruptions, go to **www.mcgrawhill.ca/links/CAF12**. What is the most likely location for the next volcanic eruption?

Substituting $\dfrac{dh}{dt} = 0.2$ and $h = 70$ into the equation,

$$\dfrac{dV}{dt} = \dfrac{\pi}{4} h^2 \dfrac{dh}{dt}$$

$$= \dfrac{\pi}{4} (70)^2 (0.2)$$

$$\doteq 770$$

Therefore, lava is pouring out of the volcano at a rate of about $770 \text{ m}^3/\text{s}$.

Key Concepts

- To solve related rates problems, the following steps may be helpful.
  a)   Read the problem carefully so that you understand what you are asked to determine.
  b)   Identify the key pieces of information in the question. Draw a diagram, if needed, to organize the information.
  c)   Assign variables to the relevant quantities.
  d)   Determine the relationship between the quantities and write an equation that relates them.
  e)   Express the given information and the required rate in terms of derivatives.

f) Differentiate both sides of the equation found in step d) with respect to time.

g) Substitute the given information into the resulting equation and solve for the unknown rate. Remember to substitute the given information into the equation after differentiating, not before.

Communicate Your Understanding

1. Describe two examples of a rate that is decreasing and two examples of a rate that is increasing.

2. If V is the volume of a sphere with radius r, and the volume of the sphere decreases as time passes, express $\dfrac{dV}{dt}$ in terms of $\dfrac{dr}{dt}$. Describe this relationship in words.

3. In Example 5, a student reasons as follows: "$V = \dfrac{\pi}{12}h^3$. So, when $h = 70$, $V = \dfrac{\pi}{12}(70)^3 \doteq 90\,000$. Thus, $\dfrac{dV}{dt} = 0$." Explain why the reasoning is incorrect.

4. Explain why numerical information from a related rates problem must be substituted into an equation only after the equation has been differentiated implicitly.

Practise

A **1.** If $y = x^2 + 4x$ and $\dfrac{dx}{dt} = 10$, find $\dfrac{dy}{dt}$ when $x = 5$.

2. Given $V = \dfrac{4}{3}\pi r^3$, find $\dfrac{dr}{dt}$

a) if $\dfrac{dV}{dt} = 5$ when $r = 8$

b) if $\dfrac{dV}{dt} = -20$ when the diameter is 10

3. Given $V = \pi r^2 h$ and $r = h$, find $\dfrac{dh}{dt}$ if $\dfrac{dV}{dt} = -5$ when $r = 2$.

Apply, Solve, Communicate

B **4.** How fast is the area of a square increasing when the side is 6 m in length and growing at a rate of 2 m/min?

5. Inquiry/Problem Solving In a baseball pitching machine, two rotating wheels with radius 60 cm project the ball toward the batter. For the ball's speed to be 60 km/h, at what rate should the wheels turn, in revolutions per second? (Hint: Review Example 1 on page 292.)

6. A piece of lumber at a construction site is resting against the frame of a house on a cement floor. The lumber is 4 m long. If the bottom of the lumber slides away from the wall at a rate of 0.25 m/s, how fast is the top of the lumber sliding down the wall, when the bottom of the lumber is 2 m from the wall?

7. Application Refer to Example 2 on page 293.
a) When will the sun's radius be 10% larger than it is today?
b) At what rate is the volume of the sun increasing when its radius is 1 000 000 km?
c) What is the sun's density today? Density is mass divided by volume, and the sun's mass is about 2×10^{30} kg.
d) At what rate is the density of the sun changing when its radius is 1 000 000 km? Assume that the sun's mass is constant.

8. Inquiry/Problem Solving A water tank has the shape of an inverted circular cone with base radius 3 m and height 10 m.
a) If water is leaking out of the tank at a rate of 1 m³/min, at what rate is the water level decreasing when the water is 2 m deep?
b) If the empty tank is being filled with water at a rate of 1.5 m³/min, find the rate at which the water level is rising when the water is 7 m deep.

9. Kruno and Zarko leave Coffee World at the same time and head for their respective homes. Kruno rollerblades east at 20 m/min and Zarko bicycles north at 26 m/min. At what rate is the distance between Kruno and Zarko increasing 2 min later?

10. David pours pancake batter into a frying pan. The circular pattern of the expanding batter flows outward at a rate of 3 cm/s. Find the rate at which the area within the circle is increasing after 4 s.

11. Communication Refer to Example 4. Determine the rate of change of the distance between the two cars when their positions are as follows:
a) Car A: $x = 0.45$ km; Car B: $y = 0.6$ km
b) Car A: $x = 0.3$ km; Car B: $y = 0.4$ km
c) Car A: $x = 0.15$ km; Car B: $y = 0.2$ km
d) Compare the results of parts a), b), and c). Explain why the results are related in the way they are.
e) Does your explanation in part d) suggest an alternative way to solve Example 4? Explain.
f) Write formulas for x and y as functions of time t. Use the formulas and your ideas in part e) to obtain an alternative solution to Example 4.

12. Application A cubic crystal is being grown as a science experiment.
a) If the sides of the crystal are increasing in size at a rate of 0.01 mm/s, how fast is the volume of the crystal increasing when its sides are 2.3 mm long?

b) If the value of the crystal is $4/mm^3$, how fast is the value of the crystal increasing when its sides are 2.7 mm long?

C **13.** An outdoor sensor light is at the top of a 3-m gate. Faye is 1.5 m tall, and walks away from the gate in a straight path with a speed of 0.5 m/s. How fast is the tip of her shadow moving when she is 10 m from the gate?

14. A spotlight on the ground shines on a wall 14 m away. If a dog, 0.5 m tall, runs from the spotlight toward the building at a speed of 1 m/s, how fast is the height of the animal's shadow on the building decreasing when the dog is 5 m from the building?

15. Communication Lava erupts from a volcano at a constant rate of $20\,000\ m^3/s$. The volcano maintains the shape of a cone with height 50% greater than the radius of the base. However, not all of the lava stays on the slopes of the volcano. Some of the lava flows on the flat ground beyond the slopes to make a circular pattern. The height of the volcano is increasing at a rate of 0.01 m/s when the height is 700 m.
a) At what rate is lava flowing beyond the slopes of the volcano when the height of the volcano is 700 m?
b) If the thickness of the circular pattern of lava beyond the volcano is 20 cm, how fast is the lava flow approaching nearby villages when the height of the volcano is 700 m and the radius of the circular lava pattern is 500 m?

Achievement Check

Knowledge/Understanding

Thinking/Inquiry/Problem Solving

Communication

Application

The town of Redville is 1 km east of the regional airport control tower. A road passes through Redville, on which cars can travel north or south. A plane is flying north directly above the road. When the plane passes over Redville, its altitude is 2 km and increasing at a rate of 20 m/s, and its speed is 300 km/h. Determine the rate at which the distance from the plane to the control tower is increasing when the plane is directly over Redville.

Investigate & Apply: Interpreting Rates of Change

One factor that determines a car's fuel efficiency is how fast it is being driven. Let $g(v)$ be the gas consumption, in litres per kilometre, of a car going at a speed of v kilometres per hour. Tests on a particular car show that $g(80) = 0.08$ and $g'(80) = 0.0005$.

1. **a)** Let $d(v)$ be the distance the same car goes on 1 L of gas at speed v. What is the relationship between $g(v)$ and $d(v)$? Find $d(80)$ and $d'(80)$.
b) Let $c(v)$ be the gas consumption in litres per hour. What is the relationship between $c(v)$ and $g(v)$? Find $c(80)$ and $c'(80)$.
c) Explain the meaning of the values of these functions and their derivatives to a driver who has never taken calculus.

2. Choose at least three vehicles that interest you. Refer to the Internet or other sources to obtain $g(80)$ and $g'(80)$ for each vehicle. Write a report comparing the fuel efficiency of your chosen vehicles.

Career Connection: *Climatologist*

Climatologists are scientists interested in solving the problem of forecasting our climate and weather. This problem is challenging because there are so many variables that are not easily measured.

In recent years, significant progress has been made with mathematical models and computer simulations. Satellites and ground stations provide data about current climate and weather conditions. For a mathematical model to be reasonably accurate, all of the components of climate—land, oceans, sea ice, atmosphere, and biosphere—must be represented as numerical data.

The general circulation model is one such model, developed from polynomial expansions that fit collected data. The model is run on supercomputers, approximating climate and giving clues to the past and future behaviour of climate change. One use of the model is to perform experiments to measure the rates of change of climate variables in response to human influences on the environment. Scientists can refine the model by comparing its results with actual future and past data measurements.

To obtain accurate data relating to Earth's climate of the past, climatologists travel to places such as Greenland and Antarctica to collect cores of ice from glaciers. These ice cores provide an excellent record of the chemical and physical properties of the atmosphere of the past, such as temperature, atmospheric chemistry, vegetation, volcanic activity, and environmental alterations created by the presence of humans.

Review of Key Concepts

5.1 Composite Functions

Refer to the Key Concepts on page 273.

1. Given $f(x) = \dfrac{x+4}{x}$ and $g(x) = 2x + 3$, determine

a) $f(2)$
b) $(g \circ f)(2)$
c) $g(-4)$
d) $(f \circ g)(-4)$
e) $(f \circ g)(x)$
f) $(g \circ f)(x)$
g) $(f \circ f)(x)$
h) $(g \circ g)(-11)$

2. Given $f(x) = \dfrac{x-2}{x+3}$ and $g(x) = 2x + 5$, why is it not possible to calculate $f(g(-4))$? Explain fully, making reference to the domain and range of f and g.

3. Find functions f and g such that $F = f \circ g$ if $F(x) = \sqrt[3]{x + 12}$.

4. $H(x) = (f \circ g)(x)$ and $g(x) = 3x + 2$. Find $f(x)$ if $H(x) = \dfrac{1}{3x + 2}$.

5. A spherical hailstone grows in a cloud. The hailstone maintains a spherical shape while its radius increases at a rate of 0.2 mm/min.
a) Express the radius, r, in millimetres, of the hailstone, as a function of the time, t, in minutes.
b) Express the volume, V, in cubic millimetres, of the hailstone, in terms of r.
c) Determine $(V \circ r)(t)$ and explain what it means.
d) What is the volume of the hailstone 1 h after it begins to form?

6. a) If $f(x) = x^2 + 5$, for $x \in [0, \infty)$, and $g(x) = -3x + 1$, calculate each of the following:
i) $(f \circ f^{-1})(x)$
ii) $(f^{-1} \circ f)(x)$
iii) $(g \circ g^{-1})(x)$
iv) $(g^{-1} \circ g)(x)$
b) What do you notice about your results in part a)? Summarize your results in a general statement about the composition of functions and their inverses.
c) Provide a convincing argument that your statement in part b) is true for all functions whose inverses are also functions.

5.2 The Chain Rule

Refer to the Key Concepts on page 281.

7. Consider the function $y = (x^2 - 5x)^3$.

a) Expand the polynomial, and then find $\dfrac{dy}{dx}$.

b) Use the chain rule to find $\dfrac{dy}{dx}$.

c) Compare your solutions in a) and b). Explain any advantages or disadvantages in using the chain rule to find the derivative of $y = (x^2 - 5x)^3$.

8. Determine $\dfrac{dy}{dx}$.

a) $y = (2x + 8)^2$
b) $y = \sqrt{x^2 + 7x}$

c) $y = \dfrac{1}{(x^4 + 5x)^3}$
d) $y = \sqrt[3]{2x^8 - 2}$

e) $y = (6x^2 + 4x)^{\frac{1}{4}}$

9. Differentiate.

a) $y = (x^4 - 2x^3)^2$
b) $y = \sqrt{x^2 + 8x - 6}$
c) $y = (x^3 + 9x)^5$
d) $y = (x^2 + x - 10)^3$
e) $y = \sqrt[5]{x^2 + 12}$
f) $y = \dfrac{1}{x^3 - 4x}$

g) $y = \dfrac{1}{\sqrt{5x - 2}}$
h) $y = (x^3 + 6x)^{\frac{1}{3}}$

10. Andrew is an ecologist investigating a pond. He notices that an algal bloom is growing in the pond. The outside edge of the growth is roughly circular, and Andrew estimates that when the radius of the bloom is 40 m, it is growing at a rate of 3 mm/min.
a) At what rate is the area covered by the algae increasing at this time?
b) Assuming that the area covered by the algae increases at the constant rate determined in part a), at what rate is the radius increasing 5 h later?

5.3 Implicit Differentiation

Refer to the Key Concepts on page 289.

11. a) Find $\dfrac{dy}{dx}$ for the relation $9x^2 + y^2 = 36$ using each method.
i) Solve for y explicitly as a function of x. Then, differentiate with respect to x.
ii) Use implicit differentiation to differentiate with respect to x.

b) For what type of relations is implicit differentiation the only possible way to find $\dfrac{dy}{dx}$, without using technology?

12. Find a formula for the slope of the tangent at any point (x, y) on each curve.

a) $x^2 + y^2 = 25$

b) $x^3 y^2 + 4x^2 y = 12$

c) $x^2 y^3 + 2xy = 20$

d) $2y^3 + x^2 y^2 = 29$

e) $(x - 2)^2 + (y + 7)^3 = 64$

f) $x^2 + y^3 x - 6x + 8y = 9$

13. i) Find the slope of the tangent to each curve at the given point.

ii) Find an equation of the tangent to each curve at the given point.

iii) Check your results by illustrating your solution with a sketch of each curve and the tangent.

a) $(x + 1)^2 + (y + 4)^2 = 13$, $(2, -2)$

b) $y^3 + 2xy = 20$, $(3, 2)$

c) $x^3 y - y^3 = 60$, $(1, -4)$

d) $x^2 y^3 + xy + 30 = 0$, $(-6, -1)$

5.4 Related Rates

Refer to the Key Concepts on page 297–298.

14. Given $V = \dfrac{1}{3}\pi r^2 h$ and $r = h$, find $\dfrac{dr}{dt}$ if $\dfrac{dV}{dt} = 4$ when $r = h = 6$.

15. A spotlight on the ground shines on the outside wall of a parking garage 12 m away. If a 2-m tall man walks toward the garage at a speed of 0.75 m/s, how fast is the height of the man's shadow on the garage wall decreasing when he is 4 m from the building?

16. Cassandra and Marissa leave at the same time from their homes and head toward the park for their weekly soccer game. Cassandra rides her scooter west at 32 m/min, and Marissa skateboards south at 26 m/min. As the teammates approach the park, at what rate is the distance between them changing when Cassandra is 1.8 km from the park and Marissa is 1.2 km from the park?

17. After a fun morning in the snow, Emily props her 1.5 m aluminum sled up against the house and goes in for lunch. When the bottom of the sled is 1.0 m from the wall, it is slipping farther away from the wall at 15 cm/s. How fast is the top of the sled moving down the wall?

18. In a medical procedure called balloon angioplasty, a long tube with a balloon on the end is inserted into a patient's artery that has narrowed because of plaque deposits. The balloon is then expanded for a short time to make the passageway for the blood wider. For a particular patient, the doctor conducting the procedure decides that the best results will be achieved if the balloon's radius increases at a rate of 0.15 mm/s. Determine the rate at which air should be pumped into the balloon when its radius is 1 mm,

a) assuming that the balloon is spherical

b) assuming that the balloon is cylindrical with length 1 cm

19. Boyle's law states that when a sample of gas is compressed at a constant temperature, the pressure, P, and volume, V, satisfy the equation $PV = C$, where C is a constant. At a certain instant, the volume is 450 cm^3, the pressure is 150 kPa, and the pressure is increasing at a rate of 15 kPa/min. At what rate is the volume decreasing at this instant?

Chapter Test

Achievement Chart

Category	Knowledge/Understanding	Thinking/Inquiry/Problem Solving	Communication	Application
Questions	All	8, 10, 11	2, 4, 5, 11	3, 7, 9, 11

1. Given $f(x) = x^2 - 3$ and $g(x) = -6x + 5$, find
a) $f(3)$
b) $f(g(-2))$
c) $(f \circ g)(x)$
d) $g(f(x + 2))$
e) $(g \circ f)(x)$
f) $(g \circ g)(-3)$

2. Does $(f \circ g)(x)$ give the same result as $(g \circ f)(x)$? Explain with examples.

3. $H(x) = (f \circ g)(x)$ and $f(x) = \sqrt{x}$.
If $H(x) = \sqrt{7x - 2}$, find $g(x)$.

4. Consider the functions $f(x) = \dfrac{1}{x}$ and $g(x) = 2x - 3$.
a) Determine $(f \circ g)(x)$.
b) Determine $(g \circ f)(x)$.
c) Is it possible to calculate $(f \circ g)(1.5)$? Explain.
d) Determine the domain and range of f and g.
e) Determine the domain and range of $f \circ g$ and $g \circ f$.

5. Consider the function $f(x) = 3x - 7$.
a) Determine $f^{-1}(x)$.
b) Determine $(f^{-1} \circ f)(x)$.
c) Is it possible to solve part b) without doing any calculations? Explain.

6. Differentiate.
a) $y = (x^2 + 2x^4)^3$
b) $y = \dfrac{1}{x^2 + x - 3}$
c) $y = \sqrt{x^4 + 3x}$
d) $y = \dfrac{1}{\sqrt{x^3 + 6x}}$
e) $y = (x^3 + 2x^2 - 5)^{\frac{1}{4}}$
f) $y = (x^5 + 6x^3 - x)^4$
g) $y = \dfrac{x^2 + 2}{x^2 - 2}$
h) $y = \dfrac{\sqrt{x^3 - 2}}{\sqrt{x^2 - 1}}$

7. A spherical weather balloon is losing air at a rate of 3 m³/min when its radius is 12 m. At this moment, what is the rate of change of the balloon's radius with respect to time?

8. Find an equation of the tangent to each curve at the given point.
a) $(x + 2)^2 + (y - 3)^2 = 2$, $(-1, 2)$
b) $2x^2y^3 + 3xy + 5 = 0$, $(1, -1)$
c) $x^3 + y^3 = 2xy$, $(1, 1)$
d) $xy^3 + 4y = 16$, $(-3, -2)$

9. A comet passing near the sun "evaporates," and the evaporated material forms the tail of the comet. Assume that the comet always maintains a spherical shape and that its surface area is decreasing at 250 m²/min. Find the rate at which the radius decreases when the radius is 5 km.

10. A water tank at a filtration plant is built in the shape of a circular cone with height 4 m and diameter 5 m at the top. Water is being pumped into the tank at a rate of 1.2 m³/min. Find the rate at which the water level is rising when the water is 3 m deep.

Achievement Check

Knowledge/Understanding

Thinking/Inquiry/Problem Solving

Communication

Application

11. Faye, Nene, and Kalpesh leave school from the same front entrance at the same time. Faye walks north at a speed of 1.0 m/s and Nene jogs west at a speed of 2.5 m/s. Kalpesh walks east at 1.5 m/s for a distance of 12 m and then turns south at the same speed. After 2 min, at what rate is the distance between the friends in each pair changing?

a) Faye and Nene   b) Nene and Kalpesh   c) Faye and Kalpesh

Challenge Problems

1. If $f(x) = 4x - 3$ and $h(x) = 4x^2 - 21$, find a function $g(x)$ such that $f(g(x)) = h(x)$.

2. If $g(x) = 8x + 6$ and $h(x) = \dfrac{1}{8x + 9}$, find a function $f(x)$ such that $(f \circ g)(x) = h(x)$.

3. a) If $F(x) = (f \circ g)(x)$, $f(2) = 8$, $f'(2) = 12$, $f'(1) = 3$, $g(1) = 2$, and $g'(1) = 4$, find $F'(1)$.
   b) If $H(x) = (g \circ f)(x)$, what additional information would you need to be able to determine $H'(1)$?

4. a) Two curves are orthogonal if they meet at right angles. Show that $2x^2 + y^2 = 3$ and $x = y^2$ are orthogonal.
   b) $f(x) = \dfrac{x - 4}{x}$ and $g(x) = \dfrac{x + 2}{x^2 - 4x}$ intersect at $(2, -1)$. Are they orthogonal at that point? Are the curves orthogonal at their other point(s) of intersection?

5. The altitude of a triangle is increasing at a rate of 1 cm/min while the area of the triangle is increasing at a rate of 2 cm²/min. At what rate is the base of the triangle changing when the altitude is 10 cm and the area is 100 cm²?

6. Assume that a blood vessel, such as a vein or an artery, has the shape of a cylindrical tube with radius R and length L. Because of the friction at the walls of the tube, the velocity, v, of blood flowing through the blood vessel is greatest along the central axis of the tube and decreases as the distance r from the axis increases until v becomes 0 at the wall. The relationship between v and r is given by the law of laminar flow, discovered by the French physician Poiseuille in 1840. This law states that
$$v = \frac{P}{4\eta L}(R^2 - r^2)$$
where η is the viscosity of the blood and P is the pressure difference between the ends of the tube. If P and L are constant, then v is a function of r. In a typical human artery, the values are $\eta = 0.004$, $R = 0.008$ cm, $L = 2$ cm, and $P = 400$ Pa·s. Find the velocity gradient (the rate of change of v with respect to r) when $r = 0.003$ cm.

7. Find one point on the curve $y = \dfrac{1}{x^2 + 1}$ such that the tangent at that point passes through the point $(6, -2)$. Is there another such point?

8. If $g(x) = 2x - 3$ and $(f \circ g)(x) = 4x^2 - 12x + 6$, find the value of $f(2)$.

9. Find all points on the curve $y^2 = x^2 - x^4$ at which the slope of the tangent is equal to $\dfrac{1}{\sqrt{3}}$.

1. For the curve $y = 2x - 3x^2$ and the point P(2, –8) on the curve:

a) Choose five appropriate points Q on either side of P on the curve. Find the slope m_{PQ} for each Q you choose.

b) Estimate the value of the slope of the tangent to the curve at P.

c) Find an equation of the tangent to the curve at P.

d) Sketch the curve, one secant on each side of P, and the tangent.

2. One end of a long metal rod is placed in boiling water and the temperature of the other end is measured at equal time intervals. The data are recorded in the table.

Time (s)	Temperature (°C)
0	20
5	59
10	75
15	82
20	86
25	89
30	90

a) Estimate the slope of the tangent at $t = 10$ s and $t = 20$ s by averaging the slopes of two secants.

b) Graph the function and use it to estimate the slopes of the tangents at $t = 10$ s and $t = 20$ s.

c) At approximately what rate is the temperature changing with respect to time at $t = 10$ s and $t = 20$ s?

d) Compare your answers in part c). Will the temperature at the top of the rod eventually reach 100°C? Explain.

3. Find the derivative of each function from first principles.

a) $g(x) = x^2 - 3$ b) $y = \sqrt{x - 1}$

c) $m(w) = \dfrac{1}{w^2}$

4. The limit $\lim\limits_{h \to 0} \dfrac{(2 + h)^3 - 8}{h}$ represents the derivative of a function f at some number a. State the values of f and a.

5. If $f(x) = x^2 + 5$ and $g(x) = x - 3$, find

a) $(f \circ g)(4)$ b) $g(f(-7))$
c) $(f \circ f)(-1)$ d) $f(g(2x - 8))$
e) $g^{-1}(12)$ f) $(g \circ g^{-1})(n)$

6. If $f(x) = \dfrac{1}{x}$ and $g(x) = 4x + 1$,

a) determine $(f \circ g)(x)$

b) state the domain and range of $(f \circ g)(x)$

c) determine $(g \circ f)(x)$

d) state the domain and range of $(g \circ f)(x)$

7. Given $H(x) = \sqrt[4]{x + 6}$, find functions f and g such that $H = f \circ g$.

8. For each curve,

i) find the slope of the tangent at the given point

ii) find the equation of the tangent at the given point

iii) graph the curve and the tangent

a) $y = x^2$ at (–2, 4)

b) $y = (x - 1)^2 - 3$ at (3, 1)

c) $y = \sqrt{x}$ at (9, 3)

d) $y = \dfrac{2}{x + 1}$ at (1, 1)

9. Use the graph of $f(x)$ to state the value of each quantity, if it exists. If it does not exist, explain why.

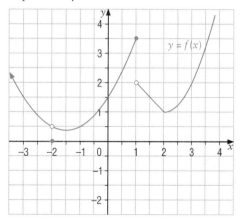

a) $\lim\limits_{x \to -2^-} f(x)$ b) $\lim\limits_{x \to -2^+} f(x)$

c) $\lim\limits_{x \to -2} f(x)$ d) $f(-2)$

e) $\lim\limits_{x \to 1^-} f(x)$ f) $f(1)$

g) $\lim\limits_{x \to 1^+} f(x)$ h) $\lim\limits_{x \to 1} f(x)$

i) $\lim_{x \to 2^-} f(x)$ j) $\lim_{x \to 2^+} f(x)$

k) $\lim_{x \to 2} f(x)$ l) $f(2)$

10. Differentiate.

a) $g(x) = 7x^5 + 3x^3 - 5x + 4$

b) $y = 3x^{-5} + \sqrt{x}$

c) $s(t) = \sqrt{t} - \sqrt[4]{t}$

d) $h(x) = (x - 6)^2$

11. An orange is approximately spherical. Suppose it grows so that its volume increases at an average rate of 4 cm^3/day.
a) Express the radius of the orange as a function of time, t, in days.
b) Determine the radius of the orange six weeks after it begins growing.

12. Differentiate.

a) $f(x) = (x^2 + 3)^2$

b) $g(x) = \sqrt[3]{7x - 4}$

c) $h(x) = \dfrac{1}{4x^2 + 3x - 2}$

d) $f(x) = \sqrt{2x^2 + x}$

13. Find an equation of the tangent to the graph of $y = (x^2 + 1)^3(5x)$ at $x = 0$.

14. Evaluate each limit, if it exists

a) $\lim_{x \to 2}(3x - 4)$ b) $\lim_{x \to 3} \dfrac{x - 3}{x^2 - x - 6}$

c) $\lim_{x \to -2} \dfrac{3x^2 + 2}{x + 2}$ d) $\lim_{x \to 1} \dfrac{x^2 - 1}{\sqrt{x - 1}}$

e) $\lim_{x \to 2} \dfrac{x - 2}{|x - 2|}$ f) $\lim_{x \to 3} \dfrac{x^2 - 5x + 6}{x^2 - 9}$

g) $\lim_{x \to 0} \dfrac{(x - 3)^2 - 9}{x}$ h) $\lim_{x \to 4} \dfrac{1}{x - 4}$

15. Find an equation of the tangent to each function at the given value of x.

a) $g(x) = (2x - x^2)(1 - 13x + 4x^2)$, $x = 1$

b) $f(x) = (2x - \sqrt{x})\left(\dfrac{1}{\sqrt{x}} + 2x\right)$, $x = 4$

c) $y = \dfrac{\sqrt{x} + 1}{\sqrt{x} - x^2}$, $x = 4$

d) $y = \dfrac{x^2 - 3x + 2}{x^2 + 4x + 1}$, $x = 0$

16. Find $f''(3)$ for each function.

a) $f(x) = x^3 - 5x^2 + 4x$

b) $f(x) = \dfrac{1}{3 - x}$

c) $f(x) = (2x + 1)(\sqrt{x} + 2)$

d) $f(x) = \dfrac{3x^2 - 1}{x^2 - 1}$

17. Find $\dfrac{dy}{dx}$ for each of the following.

a) $x^2 + y^2 = 36$ b) $x^3 + x^2y + 5y^2 = 10$

c) $xy = 12$ d) $y^3 + 3xy = 7$

18. Determine an equation of the tangent to each curve at the given point.

a) $x^3 + y^3 = 9$, $(1, 2)$

b) $(x + 2)^2 + (y - 3)^2 = 29$, $(3, 5)$

19. A baseball hit straight up into the air from an initial height of 1 m has a height, h, in metres, after t seconds of $h = 1 + 40t - 4.9t^2$.
a) Find the average velocity of the ball over the first 2 s.
b) Determine the instantaneous velocity of the ball after 3 s.
c) Estimate the minimum height of the roof of an indoor baseball stadium to ensure the ball will not hit the roof.

20. After studying market trends and past production levels, the manager of a manufacturing company modelled the projected annual production value, in millions of dollars, for its products by the function $V(t) = 15.2\sqrt{t} + 1.43t$, where t is in years, and $t \in [0, 10]$.
a) Determine an equation representing the rate of change of the company's production value.
b) What is the rate of change of the production value after 4 years? 10 years?
c) With the aid of a graphing calculator or graphing software, sketch a graph of $V(t)$ and $V'(t)$.

21. The population of frogs in a provincial park was measured over several years. The data were used to determine a model to predict the future population, as follows:
$P(t) = 50(t^2 - 2t + 20)(0.5t + 1)$, where t is measured in years.

a) What is the current frog population? What will the population be in 5 years?

b) Find $\dfrac{dP}{dt}$. What does $\dfrac{dP}{dt}$ represent?

c) Use a graphing calculator or graphing software to draw the graphs of P and $\dfrac{dP}{dt}$.

22. The surface of a particular metal oxidizes such that its thickness, in centimetres, after t years is given by $y = 0.015t^{\frac{1}{2}}$.

a) Find $\dfrac{dy}{dt}$ and $\dfrac{d^2y}{dt^2}$ after 4 years.

b) What do the values in part b) represent?

23. The position of a particle is given by s, in metres, as a function of t, in seconds. Find the velocity and acceleration as functions of time.

a) $s = 5t^2 + 3t - 1$ 　　 b) $s = \dfrac{\sqrt{t}+6}{1-t}$

24. For each function in question 23, determine when the particle is speeding up and when it is slowing down.

25. The position function of a car is given by $s = 2t^3 - 2t + 3$, $t \geq 0$, where s is measured in metres and t in seconds. Find the position and velocity at the instant the acceleration is 0.

26. After studying the market and past performance, a manufacturer estimates that its production cost, in dollars, for x camera lenses is given by $C(x) = 200\sqrt{x} + 12\,000$, and the demand function for this product is given by $p(x) = 10\,000 - 0.015x$, $x \in [0, 10\,000]$.
a) Find the marginal cost function.
b) Find the marginal revenue function.
c) Find the marginal profit function.

d) Find the marginal profit at a production level of 400 lenses.

27. Three resistors with resistances R_1, R_2, and R_3 are connected in parallel in an electric circuit. The total resistance, R, in ohms (Ω), is given by

$$\dfrac{1}{R} = \dfrac{1}{R_1} + \dfrac{1}{R_2} + \dfrac{1}{R_3}$$

R, R_2, and R_3 are increasing at rates of 0.1 Ω/s, 0.5 Ω/s, and 0.7 Ω/s, respectively. Determine the rate at which R_1 is changing when $R = 20\,\Omega$, $R_2 = 70\,\Omega$, and $R_3 = 60\,\Omega$.

28. According to Charles's law, if the pressure of a sample of gas remains constant while it is being compressed, the temperature, T, in degrees Celsius, and the volume, V, in cubic centimetres, satisfy the equation $\dfrac{V}{T} = C$, where C is a constant. At a certain time the volume is 400 cm^3 and the temperature is 20°C. If, at the same time, the temperature is increasing at a rate of 0.5°C/min, determine the rate of change of the volume.

29. A police car is travelling west toward the intersection with a north/south road. A car is travelling south on the intersecting road. The police radar detects that the other car is speeding. At the time of the reading,
- the police car is 2 km east of the intersection travelling at 80 km/h
- the other car is 1.5 km south of the intersection, travelling south
- the speed limit on the north/south road is 90 km/h
- the distance between the two cars is decreasing at 1 km/h

Is the other car speeding? If so, by how much?

Chapter 6

Extreme Values: Curve Sketching and Optimization Problems

Specific Expectations	Section
Describe the key features of a given graph of a function, including intervals of increase and decrease, critical points, points of inflection, and intervals of concavity.	6.1, 6.2, 6.3, 6.6
Determine, from the equation of a polynomial or a rational function, the key features of the graph of the function, using the techniques of differential calculus, and sketch the graph by hand.	6.1, 6.2, 6.3, 6.6
Identify the nature of the rate of change of a given function, and the rate of change of the rate of change, as they relate to the key features of the graph of that function.	6.2, 6.3, 6.7, 6.8
Determine, from the equation of a rational function, the intercepts and the positions of the vertical and the horizontal or oblique asymptotes to the graph of the function.	6.4, 6.5, 6.6
Solve optimization problems involving polynomial and rational functions.	6.7, 6.8

Practical applications of calculus are often concerned with optimization. It is not merely the solution to a problem that is required, but the best solution. We want, not merely to clean up the oil spill, but to clean it up in the best possible way, in the minimum time, with the minimum damage to the environment, and with most efficient use of resources.

In studies of nature, we are often interested in extremes. When we study the tides, we want to know which are the highest in the world, where are the tidal ranges the smallest, and for any particular location, when are the tides highest and lowest. Physicists, who study the fundamental particles of matter in giant particle accelerators, need to understand how the forces between particles increase or decrease as the distance between the particles changes.

All of these applications of calculus involve finding maximum and minimum values of functions, which are known as extreme values. Graphs provide a powerful way of visualizing the overall behaviour of a function, including the extreme values. In this chapter, we develop methods for determining the graph of a function, and methods for solving optimization problems. As you will see, similar tools are involved in both.

Review of Prerequisite Skills

1. Solving radical equations Solve and check.

a) $\sqrt{x} = 5$

b) $\sqrt{x} - 2 = 0$

c) $\sqrt{2x + 1} = 3$

d) $\sqrt{4 - 3x} - 2 = 0$

e) $2\sqrt{x - 1} - 2 = 8$

f) $-3\sqrt{x + 2} + 4 = 1$

g) $\sqrt{x + 1} = \sqrt{x + 7}$

h) $\sqrt{x - 1} - 3\sqrt{x - 3} = 0$

i) $\sqrt{x - 5} = 9 - \sqrt{x + 4}$

j) $\sqrt{x + 6} - \sqrt{x + 13} = -1$

k) $3 = \sqrt{x + 3} + \sqrt{x}$

l) $\sqrt{3x + 1} = \sqrt{x - 1} + 2$

2. Using technology to solve equations
(Section 2.5) Solve for x using technology.

a) $x^3 + 6x^2 + 9x + 2 = 0$

b) $x^4 - 4x^3 - 8x^2 - 1 = 0$

c) $x^3 - x^2 = x - 1$

d) $x^4 - x^2 = -16$

e) $2x^3 - 3x^2 = 36x + 62$

f) $x^5 - 2x^4 - 3x^3 = 1 - 4x - 5x^2$

g) $0.1x^3 - 3.2x = 5.1$

h) $-0.32x^3 + 2.45x^2 - 3.11 = 0$

i) $0.001x^3 - 3x^2 + 12 = 0$

j) $0.01x^5 - 3.02x^3 = 22.31$

3. Function notation Evaluate the following.

a) If $f(x) = 3x^3 + 2$, find $f(2)$.

b) If $f(x) = 3x + 5$, find $f(-1)$.

c) If $A(x) = x(4 + 2x)$, find $A(5)$.

d) If $P(x) = x^2 + \sqrt{x}$, find $P(1)$.

4. Function notation Graph the points on
$y = f(x)$ defined by

a) $f(3) = -1$

b) $f(-1) = 2$

c) $f(0) = 5$

d) $f(1) = 1$

5. Function notation Answer true or false, and
justify your response.

a) If $f(x) = 3x - 2$, then $f(-3) < f(-2)$.

b) If $g(x) = x^2 - 3$, then $g(1) > g(2)$.

c) If $f(x) = \sqrt{2x + 1}$, then $f(0) > f(1)$

d) If $f(x) = \dfrac{1}{x}$, then $f(1) \le f(2)$.

6. Interval notation (Section 1.1) Translate into
interval notation.

a) $2 \le x \le 5$

b) $-3 < x < 11$

c) $0 \le x \le 2$

d) $-4 < x \le 4$

7. Interval notation (Section 1.1) Rewrite the
interval notation as an inequality.

a) $x \in (2.01, 2.99)$

b) $x \in (2, 22]$

c) $x \in [0, 1]$

d) $x \in (-\pi, \pi)$

8. Polynomial inequalities (Section 2.6) Solve
for x.

a) $3(1 + x) \le 2$

b) $2x \ge 2(x - 1)$

c) $(3x + 1)(2x - 1) < 0$

d) $x^2 + 3x - 4 < 0$

9. Word problems A rectangular picture, 20 cm
by 30 cm, is to be framed with a mat such that
the width of the mat is equal on all sides of the
picture and the area of the mat is equal to the
area of the picture. Find the width of the mat.

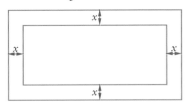

10. Word problems A paper tray is made from a
sheet of metal that is 30 cm wide and 50 cm
long. The ends are folded up a height of h
centimetres to contain the paper. If the capacity
of the tray is 6000 cm^3, determine the height of
the tray.

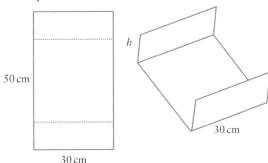

11. Domain State any restrictions on the domain
of the variable x for each function.

a) $f(x) = x^3 + 2x^2 - 3x + 4$

b) $y = \dfrac{1}{x - 3}$

c) $t(x) = \dfrac{1}{4 + x}$

d) $y = \dfrac{x}{(x-2)(x+3)}$ e) $y = \dfrac{x}{x^2 - 5x - 24}$

f) $h(x) = \dfrac{x-2}{x^2 - 5x}$ g) $f(x) = \sqrt{x}$

h) $y = \sqrt{x^2 - 16}$

12. Intercepts (Chapter 2) Find the intercepts of each curve.
a) $y = x^2 - 1$
b) $y = x^2 - 2x - 8$
c) $g(x) = x^2 + 7x + 12$
d) $s(t) = t^2 + t + 5$
e) $V(r) = 2r^2 + 7r + 6$
f) $y = x^3 + 5x^2$
g) $y = x^3 + 6x^2 + 11x + 6$
h) $f(x) = 2x^2 - 3x + 7$

13. Intercepts (Chapter 2) Find the intercepts of the curve $y = 12x - 4x^3$ and use them, together with the methods of Chapter 2, to sketch the curve.

14. Symmetry (Section 1.1) State whether each function is even, odd, or neither.

a)
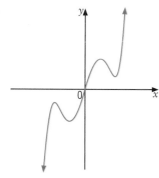

b)
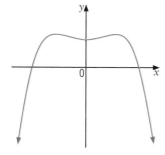

c)
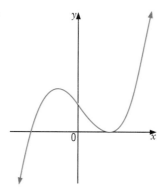

d)
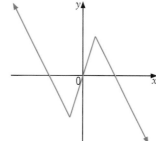

15. Symmetry (Section 1.1) Determine whether each function is even, odd, or neither.
a) $f(x) = x^6$ b) $y = x^5$
c) $f(x) = x + x^4$ d) $f(x) = \dfrac{2}{x^4 + 12}$
e) $y = \dfrac{x}{1 + x}$ f) $g(x) = x^5 + \dfrac{2}{x}$
g) $s(t) = \dfrac{t^2}{t^4 + 2t^2 - t}$ h) $y = |x^3|$

16. Division of polynomials (Section 2.2) Find the quotient and the remainder for each division.
a) $\dfrac{3x^2 + 4x - 3}{x}$ b) $\dfrac{3x^2 + 4x - 3}{x - 1}$
c) $\dfrac{x^2 - 4}{x + 3}$ d) $\dfrac{x^3 + 2x^2 - 15x}{x^2 - 5x - 14}$

6.1 Increasing and Decreasing Functions

One of the most practical applications of calculus is to determine the best, or optimal, solution to a problem. This often involves determining the largest value or the smallest value of a function over a certain interval. For example, a beverage company

- designs containers to minimize the cost of producing them
- chooses industrial machinery and processes to minimize production time and cost
- selects routes and schedules to minimize transportation time and cost
- uses marketing strategies to maximize sales
- makes business decisions to maximize profits

We examine such examples in detail in this chapter. To help us understand how to determine the maximum and minimum values of functions in the following sections, we first explore how to determine where functions increase and where they decrease.

Imagine that the graph of a function represents a hill, and you are riding a mountain bike on the hill from left to right. If you are riding uphill, the function is increasing. If you are riding downhill, the function is decreasing.

A function is increasing if, as we move from left to right along its graph, the y-coordinates increase in value. A function is decreasing if, as we move from left to right along its graph, the y-coordinates decrease in value. This definition can be stated formally as follows:

> A function f is **increasing** on an interval (a, b) if $f(x_2) > f(x_1)$ whenever $x_2 > x_1$ in the interval (a, b).
>
> A function f is **decreasing** on an interval (a, b) if $f(x_2) < f(x_1)$ whenever $x_2 > x_1$ in the interval (a, b).

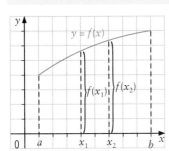

Increasing on (a, b)

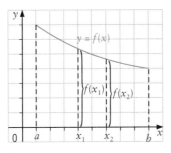

Decreasing on (a, b)

The function in the figure is increasing from F to G, that is, for $x \in (-1.2, 0)$. It is also increasing from H to K, for $x \in (2, 3.4)$. It is decreasing from G to H, for $x \in (0, 2)$.

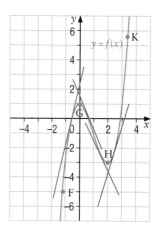

The definitions of increasing and decreasing functions express precisely what is meant by those terms. However, using these definitions is not a practical way to determine where a function is increasing or decreasing, since we would have to check every pair of points.

In the figure to the right, notice that, where the function is increasing, the tangents to the curve all seem to have positive slopes, and where the function is decreasing, the tangents all seem to have negative slopes. This suggests that perhaps the derivative of a function can be used to determine where it is increasing and where it is decreasing. You will explore this in the following investigation.

Investigate & Inquire: Increasing or Decreasing and the Derivative

1. Sketch the graph of $f(x) = x^3 - 12x$ over the interval $x \in [-5, 5]$. If you use a graphing calculator, select the Window variables for the y-axis appropriately.

2. Determine a formula for the derivative $f'(x)$.

3. Using the same axes or window as in step 1, graph f'.

4. Use the graph of f to estimate the intervals on which f increases and the intervals on which f decreases.

5. Use the graph of f' to make a statement about the values of f' on the intervals that you found in step 4.

6. Repeat steps 1 to 5 for three other functions of your choice.

7. Do you think there is any connection between the values of the derivative of each function in steps 1 and 6, and whether the function increases or decreases? If so, clearly describe the connection. Explain why you think the connection is valid. Do you think the connection applies to all functions? Explain.

The ideas considered in step 7 of the investigation lead to the following test:

Test for intervals of increase/decrease: Suppose that f is differentiable on the interval (a, b).
If $f'(x) > 0$ for all $x \in (a, b)$, then f is increasing on (a, b).
If $f'(x) < 0$ for all $x \in (a, b)$, then f is decreasing on (a, b).

Example 1 Intervals of Increase and Decrease

Without graphing the function, find the intervals on which the function $f(x) = -x^3 + 192x$ is increasing and the intervals on which it is decreasing.

Solution

First we find the derivative of $f(x)$.
$f'(x) = -3x^2 + 192$
To find the intervals of increase and decrease, we need to determine the intervals for which $f'(x) > 0$ and the intervals for which $f'(x) < 0$. We begin by determining the values of x for which $f'(x) = 0$.
$-3x^2 + 192 = 0$
$-3(x^2 - 64) = 0$
$-3(x - 8)(x + 8) = 0$
$x - 8 = 0$ or $x + 8 = 0$
$x = 8$ or $x = -8$

The numbers $x = 8$ and $x = -8$ are boundary points that separate the domain into three intervals: $(-\infty, -8)$, $(-8, 8)$, and $(8, \infty)$. Since the derivative is continuous, it does not change sign within any of these intervals.

If the derivative did change sign in the interval, it would have to cross the x-axis first. Therefore, it would have another zero. Since there are no other zeros in the interval, there can be no change of sign.

Thus, determining the sign of the derivative at a single test value within an interval indicates the sign of the derivative throughout that interval. An interval chart can be used to organize the information.

$f'(x) = -3(x - 8)(x + 8)$

	$(-\infty, -8)$	-8	$(-8, 8)$	8	$(8, \infty)$
Intervals	$(-\infty, -8)$		$(-8, 8)$		$(8, \infty)$
Test values	-10		0		10
Signs of $f'(x)$	$-$	0	$+$	0	$-$
Nature of graph	decreasing		increasing		decreasing

Thus, f is decreasing for $x \in (-\infty, -8)$ and for $x \in (8, \infty)$, and increasing for $x \in (-8, 8)$. The graph of $f(x)$ illustrates our findings.

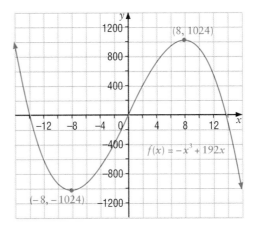

Example 2 Rate of Growth of a Cell Culture

A cell culture experiencing changing environmental conditions has a rate of growth modelled by the function $r(t) = 32t^2 - t^4$, $t \in (0, 6)$, with $r(t)$ measured in cells per hour.
a) When is the rate of growth of the cell culture increasing?
b) Does the rate of growth ever decrease? Explain.

Solution

a) We begin by finding the derivative of $r(t)$. Differentiating, $r'(t) = 64t - 4t^3$.
To find the intervals of increase, we first solve $r'(t) = 0$.
$$64t - 4t^3 = 0$$
$$4t(16 - t^2) = 0$$
$$t(4 - t)(4 + t) = 0$$
$$t = 0, 4, \text{ or } -4$$

The numbers -4, 0, and 4 separate the domain into four intervals: $(-\infty, -4)$, $(-4, 0)$, $(0, 4)$, and $(4, \infty)$.
As in Example 1, we need

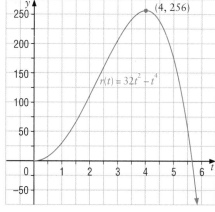

$r'(t) = t(4 - t)(4 + t)$

	-4		0		4	
Intervals	$(-\infty, -4)$	$(-4, 0)$		$(0, 4)$		$(4, \infty)$
Test values	-10	-1		1		10
Signs of $r'(t)$	$+$	$-$		$+$		$-$
Nature of graph	increasing	decreasing		increasing		decreasing

only test a single value in each interval to determine the sign of the derivative throughout the interval.

Since the domain is restricted to $t \in (0, 6)$, the cell growth rate is increasing for $t \in (0, 4)$. This is illustrated by the graph of $r(t)$.

b) The cell growth rate decreases for $t \in (4, 6)$. If the cells are in a controlled environment, it may be that the nutrients necessary for growth are rapidly depleted after 4 h. The cells may also have a limited lifespan of 2 or 3 hours.

It was noted in Example 1 that a continuous function can change sign only if it crosses the x-axis at a zero. It is possible for a discontinuous function to change sign at a point of discontinuity, where it does not have a zero.

For example, the function $y = \dfrac{1}{x}$ changes sign at its

discontinuity at $x = 0$; it is positive to the right of the discontinuity and negative to the left of the discontinuity. Therefore, in an analysis of the signs of a function, we should make note of the function's zeros and its points of discontinuity, as shown in Example 3.

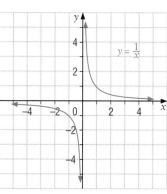

Example 3 Containing an Oil Spill

Oil spills in the ocean are contained by various sizes of rectangular booms. The formula $b = \dfrac{200\,000}{w} + 3w$ relates the total length of boom required for a particular rectangular design of area 100 000 m² and width w metres. For which intervals of the width, w, is the length of the boom decreasing?

Solution

$$b = \frac{200\,000}{w} + 3w$$

$$b' = -\frac{200\,000}{w^2} + 3$$

Boundaries for the increasing and decreasing intervals are found when $b' = 0$. For a rational function, points where b' is undefined also define boundaries for these intervals.
If $b' = 0$,

$$w^2 = \frac{200\,000}{3}$$

$$w \doteq \pm 258$$

If $w = 0$, b' is undefined.
Note that in this example, the function $b(w)$ is not defined when $w = 0$ and the domain is only meaningful when $w > 0$. Therefore, the only intervals that need to be considered are (0, 258) and (258, ∞).

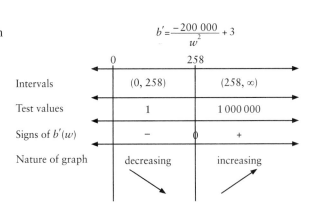

The length of the boom is decreasing as the width changes from 0 to 258 m. The graph supports this conclusion.

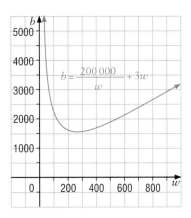

Key Concepts

- A function f is increasing on an interval (a, b) if $f(x_2) > f(x_1)$ whenever $x_2 > x_1$ in the interval (a, b).
- A function f is decreasing on an interval (a, b) if $f(x_2) < f(x_1)$ whenever $x_2 > x_1$ in the interval (a, b).
- Suppose that f is differentiable on the interval (a, b).
  If $f'(x) > 0$ for all $x \in (a, b)$, then f is increasing on (a, b).
  If $f'(x) < 0$ for all $x \in (a, b)$, then f is decreasing on (a, b).

Communicate Your Understanding

1. Is it possible for a function to have neither intervals of increase nor intervals of decrease? If so, give an example. If not, explain why.

2. Can an increasing function ever have an undefined slope? Explain.

3. If a function describes the height of a projectile fired from the ground, what intervals of increase and decrease would you expect to find?

4. a) In the examples, why were the given test values chosen instead of some other test values?

b) Would different test values give the same results? Explain.

Practise

A 1. Given each derivative $f'(x)$, which intervals need to be tested to determine where the function $f(x)$ is increasing or decreasing?
a) $f'(x) = 2 - x$
b) $f'(x) = -3(3 + x)$
c) $f'(x) = (x + 3)(x - 3)$
d) $f'(x) = -3x - 3$
e) $f'(x) = x(x + 2)(x + 3)$
f) $f'(x) = -x^2(x - 1)(x - 2)$
g) $f'(x) = 3x^2 + 12x + 9$
h) $f'(x) = 4x^3 - 12x^2 - 16x$
i) $f'(x) = \dfrac{x + 2}{x}$
j) $f'(x) = \dfrac{(x + 1)(x - 2)}{x^2}$

B 2. Without graphing, determine the intervals of increase and decrease for each function.
a) $y = 4x + x^2$
b) $y = (x + 1)^2$
c) $y = (x^2 - 1)^2$
d) $y = x^3 - 3x + 1$
e) $y = 16 - x^3$
f) $y = x^2 - 10x + 2$
g) $y = x^5 - 3125x + 25$
h) $y = 48x - x^3 - 10$

i) $y = x^6 + 192x + 1$
j) $y = 3 - 3x^2 + x^3$
k) $y = \dfrac{1}{x^2 + 1}$
l) $y = \dfrac{6}{x} + 5x$
m) $y = \dfrac{3x^2 - 2}{x}$
n) $y = \dfrac{1 - x^2}{x}$

Apply, Solve, Communicate

3. Application Temperature fluctuations can often be modelled by functions. Suppose the temperature at a certain location t hours after noon on a certain day is T degrees Celsius, where $T = \dfrac{1}{3}t^3 - 3t^2 + 8t + 10$ for $t \in [0, 5]$. During which time intervals is the temperature falling?

4. Inquiry/Problem Solving **a)** Show that the function $f(x) = x^3$ is always increasing even though $f'(x)$ is not positive at every point. Give an example of another function with the same property.

b) Do the functions in part a) contradict the test for intervals of increase/decrease? Explain.

5. Communication The absorption of an initial dose, D_0, of a medication into the bloodstream can be modelled by the function $D(t) = \dfrac{D_0}{1+t^2}$, where D is the amount of medication present t hours after ingestion.
a) Find the intervals when the amount of medication is decreasing.
b) Is the amount of medication ever increasing? Explain.
c) According to the model, does the medication ever completely leave the bloodstream?
d) Does the function accurately model the situation for all time? Explain.

6. Inquiry/Problem Solving The height, h, in metres, t seconds after a stone is hurled upward from the roof of a building 10 m high, is given by $h = -4.9t^2 + 8t + 10$.
a) During which interval is the stone rising?
b) When will the stone hit the ground?
c) For how many seconds is the stone falling?

7. Application Given $f(x) = x^2 - 3x + 2$ and $g(x) = x + 1$, determine the intervals of increase and decrease of $h(x)$, where
a) $h(x) = f(x) + g(x)$ b) $h(x) = g(f(x))$

c) $h(x) = f(x)g(x)$ d) $h(x) = \dfrac{f(x)}{g(x)}$

8. Application A manufacturing company finds that the profit for a production level of x motors per hour is $p = 400\sqrt{12x - x^2} - 100$, $x \in (0, 12]$. For what range of production level is the profit
a) increasing?   b) decreasing?

9. Application, Communication The altitude, in metres, after t seconds, of an airplane at an airshow is given by the equation $h = 4t^3 - 50t^2 + 2000$, $t \in [0, 15]$.
a) Determine the intervals in which the airplane is descending and ascending.
b) Describe the motion of the plane.

10. Application An electrical generator produces power, in watts, according to the formula $P = \dfrac{120R}{(R+0.5)^2}$, where R is the resistance, in ohms, of the circuit. During which intervals is the power
a) increasing?   b) decreasing?

11. Determine the range of values of k such that $f(x) = kx^3 - 3x + 3$ is decreasing on the interval $(0, 3)$.

12. Find an example of a function that has a positive derivative throughout its domain, and yet the function is not always increasing. Explain why your example does not contradict the test for intervals of increase/decrease.

13. Suppose that f decreases for $x \in (m, n)$ and increases for $x \in (n, p)$. Under what conditions can you conclude that f decreases for $x \in (m, n]$ and increases for $x \in [n, p)$?

14. a) Determine the intervals of increase and decrease for the function
$$f(x) = (1+x)^{\frac{5}{2}} - \frac{5}{2}x - 1$$
b) Prove that $(1+x)^{\frac{5}{2}} > 1 + \frac{5}{2}x$ for $x \in (0, \infty)$.

Maximum and Minimum Values

Some of the most practical applications of calculus involve the determination of optimal solutions to problems. This involves determining extreme values, that is, maximum or minimum values of a function. Manufacturers want to maximize profits, contractors want to minimize costs, and physicians would like to select the minimum dosage of a drug that will cure a disease.

We need to develop a variety of tools for solving optimization problems, depending on whether we are given a verbal description, data, a graph, or an equation.

Investigate & Inquire: Optimal Shape for a Can

What is the most economical shape for a beverage can of fixed volume? Suppose the required volume for a cylindrical can is 355 cm^3. We need to find the height, h, and radius, r, in centimetres, that minimize the amount of metal used to make the can.

Consider the possible dimensions.

1. Let $r = 1$ cm. What is the value of h, given $V = 355$ cm^3 and $r = 1$ cm? Sketch the can.

2. What is the surface area of the can? Label the sketch with this information.

3. Repeat steps 1 and 2 for $r = 2$ cm, 3 cm, 4 cm, 5 cm, and 6 cm.

4. Which radius in steps 1 to 3 results in the minimum surface area for the can?

5. How can you refine the search for the radius that minimizes the surface area?

6. Do you have the best possible value for the radius? How confident are you that your answer is optimal?

Volume of a cylinder = $\pi r^2 h$

Surface area of a cylinder = $2\pi r^2 + 2\pi rh$

7. What assumptions have been made regarding the construction of the can? What other factors might be necessary to consider when designing a can?

8. Describe, and suggest reasons for, any patterns that you found in your search for the optimum radius.

In Example 2 of Section 6.7, we will use calculus techniques to obtain the solution to the problem of designing the most economical can. As a first step, we develop some tools related to functions and their graphs.

Consider the graph of the function f in the following figure. Note that the domain of f is $x \in [0, 8]$.

Suppose the graph of f represents two hills with a valley between them. The point $(6, 5)$ on the second hill is higher than any nearby point (say for $x \in [5.9, 6.1]$). Thus, we call 5 a **local maximum value** of the function f. Similarly, 7 is a local maximum value of f, since the point $(2, 7)$ is higher than nearby points on the first hill. However, since 7 is greater than any other value of f in its domain, 7 is also called the **absolute maximum value** of f.

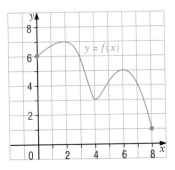

Similarly, the value 3 is called a **local minimum value** of f, since the point $(4, 3)$ is lower than nearby points in the valley. Consider the point $(8, 1)$. Since 1 is less than any other value of f in its domain, 1 is called the **absolute minimum value** of f.

These concepts are summarized in the following formal definitions.

A function f has a local maximum (or relative maximum) value $f(c)$ at $x = c$ if $f(c) > f(x)$ when x is close to c (on both sides of c).
A function f has an absolute maximum (or global maximum) value $f(c)$ at $x = c$ if $f(c) > f(x)$ for all x in the domain of f.
A function f has a local minimum (or relative minimum) value $f(c)$ at $x = c$ if $f(c) < f(x)$ when x is close to c (on both sides of c).
A function f has an absolute minimum (or global minimum) value $f(c)$ at $x = c$ if $f(c) < f(x)$ for all x in the domain of f.

Look again at the point $(8, 1)$ in the graph of f above. According to the definition of local minimum, we must consider values of f on both sides of $x = 8$. Since the graph is only defined to the left of $x = 8$, $(8, 1)$ cannot be a local minimum. Thus, on a closed interval, neither local minimum values nor local maximum values can occur at the endpoints. However, absolute minimum and maximum values *can* occur at the endpoints.

Local maximum and local minimum values of a function are often called local extreme values, or **local extrema** (sometimes called **turning points**). Similarly, absolute maximum and absolute minimum values of a function are often called absolute extreme values, or **absolute extrema**. Also, absolute maximum and minimum values are often called simply maximum and minimum values.

Extrema is the plural of extremum.

Example 1 Determining Local Extrema From Graphs

Determine the local and absolute extrema for each function.

a) $y = f(x)$ for $x \in [0, 12]$

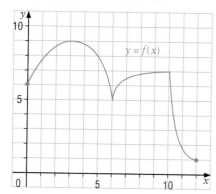

b) $y = |x^2 - 4|$ for $x \in [-3, 4]$

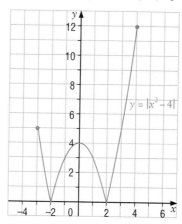

Solution

a) Reading from the graph, there are local maximum values of $f(3) = 9$ and $f(10) = 7$. The absolute maximum value is 9.

The local minimum value is $f(6) = 5$. We can see from the graph that the absolute minimum value occurs at the rightmost endpoint, where $x = 12$. Thus, the absolute minimum value is 1.

b) The local maximum value is $f(0) = 4$. We can see from the graph that the absolute maximum value occurs at the rightmost endpoint. The function value at this endpoint is $f(4) = |(4)^2 - 4| = 12$. Thus, the absolute maximum value is 12.

The local minimum values are $f(-2) = 0$ and $f(2) = 0$. Thus, the absolute minimum value is 0.

Critical Points and Local Extrema

How can we determine the maximum and minimum values of a function without graphing? You will investigate this problem next.

Investigate & Inquire: Determining Local Extrema

In Section 6.1, you learned how to determine when a function is increasing and when it is decreasing. In this investigation, you will explore how to use this information to determine the local maximum and local minimum values of a function.

1. Determine the intervals of increase and decrease for each function.
a) $f(x) = x^2 + 4x + 3$ b) $f(x) = x^3 - 3x^2 + 7$
c) $f(x) = -x^4 + 2x^2$ d) $f(x) = -x^3 + 6x$

2. For each function in step 1, determine the value of f' at the endpoints of the intervals you determined. What do you notice?

3. Graph each function in step 1 and use the graph to determine the local maximum and local minimum values.

4. Explain how to use the intervals of increase and decrease in step 1 and your results from step 2 to determine the local maximum and minimum values without graphing.

5. Note that the functions in step 1 are all differentiable. Conjecture a test for finding the local maximum and local minimum values of a differentiable function using intervals of increase and decrease and the values of the derivative of the function at the endpoints of the intervals.

Notice that, in this investigation, the value of f' at the endpoints of the intervals of increase and decrease for each function is 0. For other functions, it could happen that the graph has a cusp (sharp corner) between intervals of increase and decrease. For example, consider the function $f(x) = |x|$. We know that f is not differentiable at $x = 0$, that is, $f'(0)$ does not exist. But if we look at the graph, we can see that the function $f(x) = |x|$ decreases for $x < 0$ and increases for $x > 0$.

 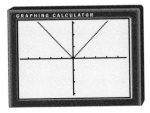

Window variables:
$x \in [-4.7, 4.7]$, $y \in [-3.1, 3.1]$
or use the ZDecimal instruction.

We call an x-value for which the derivative is equal to 0 or does not exist a **critical number**.

> A number c in the domain of f is a critical number of f if either $f'(c) = 0$ or $f'(c)$ does not exist.
> The point $(c, f(c))$ is called a **critical point**.

It appears from the preceding discussion that local maximum and local minimum values occur at critical points of functions. This is true in general, and is called **Fermat's theorem**.

> Fermat's theorem: If f has a local maximum value or local minimum value at $x = c$, then either $f'(c) = 0$ or $f'(c)$ does not exist.

Be careful: just because $f'(c) = 0$ or $f'(c)$ does not exist is no guarantee that f has a local maximum or minimum value at $x = c$. For instance, consider the graphs of $f(x) = x^3$ and $g(x) = x^{\frac{1}{3}}$.

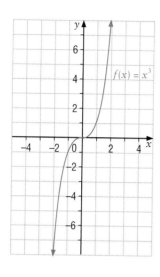

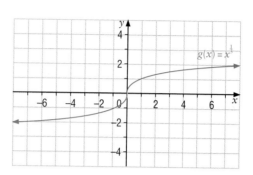

Notice that f has a horizontal tangent at the origin (that is, $f'(0) = 0$), and g has a vertical tangent at the origin (that is, $g'(0)$ does not exist). Yet neither f nor g has a local maximum or local minimum value at $x = 0$. What Fermat's theorem says is that if f has a local maximum or a local minimum value at $x = c$, then $f'(c)$ is either 0 or does not exist; but the converse is not necessarily true, as the two previous graphs show.

If we are looking for local maximum or local minimum values, Fermat's theorem tells us where to look: at the critical numbers. Once we have determined the critical numbers, how do we decide whether the function value at a critical number is a local maximum, a local minimum, or neither? To visualize this, think about the following graphs as representing hills and valleys.

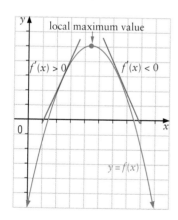

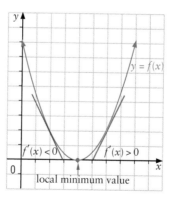

In the graph on the left, as you walk from left to right, first you walk uphill, then you reach the peak, and then you walk downhill. That is, the function is increasing, then the local maximum is reached, and then the function is decreasing.

In the graph on the right, it is the other way around: first the function is decreasing, then the local minimum is reached, and then the function is increasing.

Since f is increasing when $f'(x) > 0$ and f is decreasing when $f'(x) < 0$, we obtain the **first derivative test**.

> The first derivative test: Let c be a critical number of a continuous function f.
> If $f'(x)$ changes from positive to negative at c, then f has a local maximum at c.
> If $f'(x)$ changes from negative to positive at c, then f has a local minimum at c.
> If $f'(x)$ does not change sign at c, then f has neither a local maximum nor a local minimum at c.

Example 2 Determining Local Extrema

Determine the local maximum and local minimum values of the function $f(x) = x^3 - 3x + 2$.

Solution

Since f is differentiable, the critical numbers are the x-values for which $f'(x) = 0$.
$$f'(x) = 3x^2 - 3$$
Setting the derivative equal to 0 and solving for x, we obtain
$$3x^2 - 3 = 0$$
$$x^2 - 1 = 0$$
$$x = 1 \text{ or } -1$$
Thus, the critical numbers are $x = 1$ and $x = -1$. We test $f'(x)$ at x-values on the left and right of the critical numbers using an interval chart.

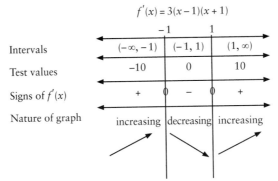

By the first derivative test, f has a local maximum at $x = -1$. Its value is $f(-1) = 4$. The first derivative test also indicates that f has a local minimum at $x = 1$. Its value is $f(1) = 0$. The graph of f illustrates our findings.

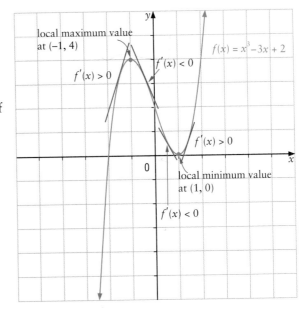

Consider the function $f(x) = x$ with domain $x \in [-1, 2]$.
Notice that the absolute maximum value 2 occurs at the
right endpoint of the domain, and the absolute minimum
value -1 occurs at the left endpoint of the domain.
Now consider the function $g(x) = x^2 + 1$ with domain
$x \in [-1, 2]$. For this function, the absolute minimum value
of 1 occurs at the critical number $x = 0$, and the absolute
maximum value of 5 occurs at the right endpoint of the
domain. Therefore, if we are looking for the absolute
extrema of a function for which the domain is a closed
interval, we should test the values of the function at
the critical numbers and at the endpoints of the
interval.

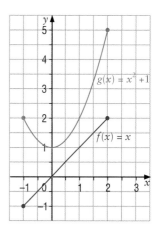

Example 3 Determining Absolute Extrema

Find the absolute maximum and absolute minimum values of the function
$f(x) = 2x^4 - 4x^2 + 4$ for $x \in [-2, 0.5]$.

Solution

Using Fermat's theorem, we first determine the critical numbers of f. Since f is
differentiable for all values of x in its domain, we need only determine the x-values
for which $f'(x) = 0$.
$f'(x) = 8x^3 - 8x$
If $f'(x) = 0$, then
$$8x^3 - 8x = 0$$
$$8x(x + 1)(x - 1) = 0$$
$8x = 0 \quad$ or $\quad x + 1 = 0 \quad$ or $\quad x - 1 = 0$
$\ x = 0 \qquad\qquad x = -1 \qquad\quad x = 1$
The value $x = 1$ is not in the domain $[-2, 0.5]$ so we do not consider it.
The values of f at the other two critical numbers are
$f(0) = 2(0)^4 - 4(0)^2 + 4 \quad$ and $\quad f(-1) = 2(-1)^4 - 4(-1)^2 + 4$
$\quad\ = 4 \qquad\qquad\qquad\qquad\qquad\quad = 2$
The values of f at the endpoints of the interval are
$f(-2) = 2(-2)^4 - 4(-2)^2 + 4 \quad$ and $\quad f(0.5) = 2(0.5)^4 - 4(0.5)^2 + 4$
$\quad\ = 20 \qquad\qquad\qquad\qquad\qquad\quad = 3.125$

Considering the values 4, 2, 20,
and 3.125, the absolute maximum
is 20, which occurs at $x = -2$ (an
endpoint), and the absolute minimum
is 2, which occurs at $x = -1$. Note
that 2 is also a local minimum
value. The graph illustrates our
conclusions.

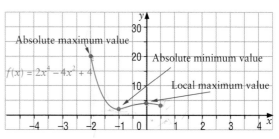

Example 4 Acidity Caused by Eating Candy

The pH in a person's mouth t minutes after eating candy can be modelled by the equation $P = -0.000\,20t^3 + 0.014t^2 - 0.24t + 6.22$ for $t \in [0, 30]$. Determine the time when the pH is lowest (most acidic) after eating candy.

> **pH is a measure of acidity: the lower the number, the stronger the acid.**

Solution

The derivative is
$P' = -0.000\,60t^2 + 0.028t - 0.24$.
To determine the critical numbers, we set the derivative equal to 0 and solve for t:
$-0.000\,60t^2 + 0.028t - 0.24 = 0$

$$t = \frac{-0.028 \pm \sqrt{0.028^2 - 4(-0.000\,60)(-0.24)}}{2(-0.000\,60)}$$

$\doteq 11.31$ or 35.35

We do not consider $t = 35.35$ because it is outside the interval $[0, 30]$. Thus, the only critical number is $t = 11.31$.

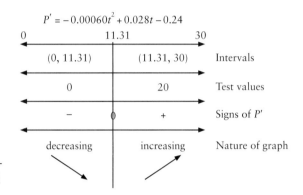

We use an interval chart to organize the information. From the chart, and the first derivative test, the pH has a local minimum at $t = 11.31$ and its value is $P(11.31) = 5.01$. The pH values at the endpoints of the interval are
$P(0) = 6.22$
$P(30) = 6.22$
Since both values are greater than 5.01, the absolute minimum pH of 5.01 occurs after 11.31 min. A sketch of the pH function illustrates our calculations.

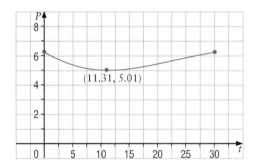

Key Concepts

- A critical number of a function is an x-value for which the derivative of the function is 0 or does not exist.
- Local maximum and minimum values occur at critical numbers, but not all critical numbers give rise to local maximum or minimum values.
- Fermat's theorem: If f has a local maximum value or local minimum value at $x = c$, then either $f'(c) = 0$ or $f'(c)$ does not exist.
- To find the absolute maximum and absolute minimum values of a continuous function with domain $x \in [a, b]$,
  a) Identify the critical numbers and endpoints of the interval.
  b) Find the values of f at the critical numbers of f in $[a, b]$.

c) Find the values of f at the endpoints of the interval.
d) The greatest of the values from steps b) and c) is the absolute maximum value and the least of these values is the absolute minimum value.
• Use the first derivative test to determine whether a function has a local maximum value, a local minimum value, or neither, at a critical number.
Let c be a critical number of a function f.
If $f'(x)$ changes from positive to negative at c, then f has a local maximum at c.
If $f'(x)$ changes from negative to positive at c, then f has a local minimum at c.
If $f'(x)$ does not change sign at c, then f has neither a local maximum nor a local minimum at c.

Communicate Your Understanding

1. Explain the difference between an absolute maximum and a local maximum.
2. Is it possible for a function f to have a critical number at which f has neither a local maximum value nor a local minimum value? If it is possible, sketch a graph of a function that satisfies this condition; if it is not possible, explain why.
3. Name the two types of critical numbers and how they differ.
4. If a function is differentiable on an interval, and the interval contains no critical points, why does the slope of the graph at one test point in the interval reveal the increasing/decreasing nature of the function over the entire interval?

Practise

A **1.** Find the absolute maximum and absolute minimum values of each function.

a)

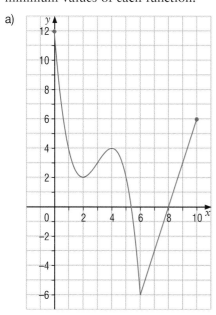

b)

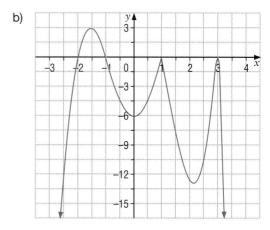

B **2.** Without graphing, find the absolute maximum and minimum values of each function.
a) $f(x) = 3x + 2$ for $x \in [-1, 1]$
b) $f(x) = 4 - 2x$ for $x \in [0, 3]$
c) $f(x) = 9 - x^2$ for $x \in [-2, 1]$
d) $f(x) = x^2 + 2x - 2$ for $x \in [-4, 4]$
e) $f(x) = x^3 - 27x + 1$ for $x \in [0, 4]$
f) $f(x) = 2x^2 - x^4$ for $x \in [0, 4]$
g) $f(x) = 3 + 2(x + 1)^2$ for $x \in [-3, 2]$

h) $f(x) = x^3 - 12x + 2$ for $x \in [1, 4]$
i) $f(x) = x^4 - 2x^2 + 7$ for $x \in [-3, 1]$
j) $f(x) = x^5 - 15x^3 + 1$ for $x \in [-1, 4]$
k) $f(x) = |x^2 - 1| + 1$ for $x \in [-2, 2]$
l) $f(x) = |12x - x^3| + 1$ for $x \in [-1, 3]$

3. Determine the critical numbers of each function and apply the first derivative test to determine whether the critical numbers correspond to local maximum or local minimum values. Determine the local maximum or local minimum values.

a) $y = x - x^2$
b) $y = (x - 2)^2$
c) $y = (x^2 - 2)^2$
d) $y = 2x^3 - 6x + 1$
e) $y = x - \sqrt{x}$
f) $y = 3x^2 - 8x + 4$
g) $y = 3x^{\frac{1}{3}}$
h) $y = 2x^4 - 16x^2 + 12$
i) $y = x^5 - 5x^3$
j) $y = |x + 2|^3$
k) $y = x^{\frac{2}{3}}(x - 1)^2$
l) $y = x^2 \left(1 - \dfrac{4}{x}\right)$

4. Application Determine the local extrema, and sketch each function.

a) $y = x^2 - 4x + 7$
b) $y = -2x^2 - 4x + 3$
c) $y = x^3 - 3x$
d) $y = x^4 - 2x^2$
e) $y = x^2 - x^5$
f) $y = 2x^3 - 15x^2 + 36x - 18$
g) $y = x^2 - \sqrt{x}$
h) $y = 6\sqrt{x} - x$

Apply, Solve, Communicate

5. The volume of a shed in the shape of a rectangular prism with height x metres is given by $V = 120x - 46x^2 + 4x^3$ for $x \in [0, 4]$. Determine the height of the shed that has absolute maximum volume.

6. The height, $h(t)$, in metres above the ground, of a flare as a function of time, t, in seconds after the flare is fired, is given by the function $h(t) = -4.9t^2 + 44t + 2$ for $t \geq 0$.
a) Determine the height of the flare when it is fired.
b) Determine the maximum height of the flare.
c) When does the flare hit the ground, to the nearest second?

7. Application Weather forecasts in the winter refer to wind-chill factor. Wind chill is the additional cooling that occurs when skin is exposed to wind. One of the equations used to model wind chill is $W = -0.17v^3 + 18.4v^2 - 584v - 239$ for $v \in [0, 45]$, where v is the wind speed in metres per second. The units for W are megajoules per square metre per hour. Determine the speed of the wind that gives a minimum wind-chill factor.

Web Connection

To learn more about modelling wind chill, go to **www.mcgrawhill.ca/links/CAF12** and follow the link.

8. Application The speed of air escaping through your trachea when you cough is a function of the force due to chest contraction and the size of the trachea. It can be modelled by the equation $S = F(1 + 0.9r^2 - r^3)$, where F is the constant force of your chest contraction, r is the radius of your trachea, in centimetres, and S is the speed of the airflow, in centimetres per second.
a) Determine the maximum speed of airflow that can be attained.
b) Sketch the graph of S versus r (use $F = 1$).

9. Inquiry/Problem Solving Three students, Lawrie, Gavin, and Rebekah, were asked to analyse the function $f(x) = \dfrac{1}{4}x^4 - 2x^2 + 1$.

Lawrie said, "There is a critical point at $x = 0$, and I have tested neighbouring points on either side. I tested $x = -3$ and $x = 3$ and found a negative slope to the left and a positive slope to the right, hence there is a local minimum at $x = 0$." Gavin countered, "But I have found, using the first derivative test, that the adjacent critical point at $x = 2$ is also a local minimum. How can that be? Adjacent critical points cannot both be minimum values."
a) Rebekah sorted it out for them. What was her argument?
b) Explain any errors in Lawrie's and Gavin's explanations.

10. A marine biologist in Burncoat Head, Nova Scotia, collected the following tidal data at hourly intervals from 4:00 until 19:00.

Time	Tide Height	Time	Tide Height
4	3.0	12	11.8
5	1.4	13	11.1
6	0.8	14	9.2
7	1.5	15	6.5
8	3.4	16	3.9
9	6.2	17	1.8
10	8.9	18	0.8
11	11.0	19	0.9

a) Use regression to determine a quartic function to model the data.

b) Find the times, between 4:00 a.m. and 7:00 p.m., when the height of the tide is increasing, and when it is decreasing. At what time is the height of the tide neither increasing nor decreasing?

c) When, during the day, is the height of the tide a maximum? a minimum?

11. Application The predicted population, in millions, of a small country has been modelled using the equation $P = \dfrac{x^2}{400} - \dfrac{x}{10} + 5$, where x is the number of years after 2001, and $x \in [0, 30]$.

a) Determine the intervals of increase and decrease in population.

b) Determine when the population reaches a minimum. What is the minimum population?

c) Sketch a graph of the population over the 30 year period.

C **12.** Find the absolute maximum and absolute minimum values of the function defined by

$$f(x) = \begin{cases} -x - 3 & \text{for } x \in [-4, -2] \\ x^2 + 3x + 1 & \text{for } x \in (-2, 2) \\ 13 - x & \text{for } x \in [2, 4] \end{cases}$$

13. Determine the absolute maximum and absolute minimum values of the function $g(x) = |x^2 - 9|$ on the interval $x \in [-5, 5]$.

14. Determine the absolute maximum of $y = x(r^2 + x^2)^{-\frac{3}{2}}$ for $x \in [0, r]$, where r is a constant.

15. Inquiry/Problem Solving a) If a function is *not* restricted to a closed interval, can it have an absolute maximum or an absolute minimum? If yes, give an example of each. If no, explain why.

b) Must a differentiable function on a closed interval have an absolute maximum? If no, give an example. If yes, explain why.

16. Communication a) If a differentiable function $f(x)$ has $f'(1) = 3$ and $f'(2) = -3$, will it have a local maximum? Explain.

b) Would your conclusion in part a) be the same if f were not differentiable for all values of x? Explain.

Historical Bite: Fermat's Long-Unproven Theorem

Fermat's theorem (page 322) is not the same as the famous Fermat's last theorem, although the same mathematician, Pierre de Fermat (1601–1665), was responsible for both results. Fermat's last theorem states that the equation $x^n + y^n = z^n$ has integer solutions x, y, and z only for $n = 1$ or 2, solutions in the case $n = 2$ being Pythagorean triples. Fermat wrote down no proof of this theorem, simply stating in his notes that "I have discovered a beautiful proof of this result, which unfortunately this margin is too small to contain." Today, mathematicians believe that Fermat was mistaken in believing he had a proof, because theory developed much later revealed complications that he would not have known about. It was not until 1993 that Andrew Wiles (1953–) made headlines with a complete—and highly complex—proof of Fermat's last theorem.

6.3 Concavity and the Second Derivative Test

Imagine driving along a curved road from R to T as shown. As the car moves from R to S, the road curves to the left, and you feel the seat of the car exert an additional force on you to the left. This force tends to decrease as you approach S, and reaches zero at S. The road then curves to the right and the additional force from the seat points to the right. In this section, we explore curves that behave in this fashion, and points such as S.

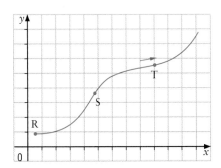

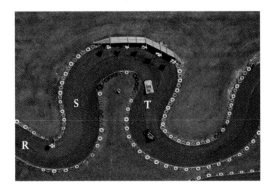

If we think of the road as the graph of a function, then the curve from R to S is described as concave upward (curving so as to enclose the space above it). From S to T the curve is concave downward, and from T on it is concave upward. To distinguish between these two types of curves, examine the graphs of the functions f and g below. Each graph connects point A to point B, but the two graphs bend in different ways. If we draw tangents to the curves at various points, the graph of f lies above its tangents and is called concave upward, while the graph of g lies below its tangents and is called concave downward.

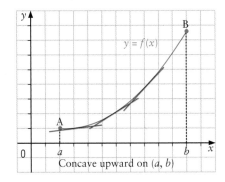
Concave upward on (a, b)

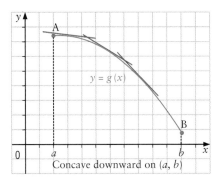
Concave downward on (a, b)

> The graph of f is said to be **concave upward** on an interval (a, b) if it lies above all of its tangents on (a, b).
> The graph of f is said to be **concave downward** on (a, b) if it lies below all of its tangents on (a, b).

For instance, the function shown below is concave upward on the intervals $(-\infty, 1)$, $(3, 5)$, and $(5, 6.5)$, and concave downward on $(1, 3)$ and $(6.5, \infty)$.

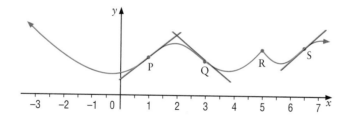

A point P on a curve is said to be a **point of inflection** if the curve changes from concave upward to concave downward or from concave downward to concave upward (that is, it changes concavity) at P. For instance, the graph just considered has three points of inflection, namely, P, Q, and S. Point R is a cusp but is not a point of inflection, since the concavity does not change at R. Also, notice that if a curve has a tangent at a point of inflection, as at points P, Q, and S in the figure, the tangent crosses the curve there. In the following investigation, you will explore the connection between concavity and tangents.

Investigate & Inquire: Concavity and Inflection Points

1. Graph each function. Estimate the intervals on which the function is concave upward, the intervals on which it is concave downward, and the point(s) of inflection.
a) $f(x) = x^3 - 3x^2$
b) $f(x) = 2x^3 - 4x^2 + 5x + 3$
c) $f(x) = 3x^4 - 5x^3 - 6x$
d) $f(x) = -x^5 - 5x^3$

2. Calculate $f'(x)$ and $f''(x)$ for each function in step 1. Graph the function and its derivatives on the same set of axes.

3. For each graph in step 2, determine the sign of $f''(x)$ on each interval on which the graph is concave upward. Repeat this for each interval on which the graph is concave downward.

4. Make a conjecture about the sign of $f''(x)$ when the graph is concave upward. Repeat when the graph is concave downward.

5. Draw a vertical line through the point of inflection of each graph of f in step 2. Let the x-coordinate of the point of inflection be a.

6. How does the first derivative behave near an inflection point $(a, f(a))$? Conjecture a test for inflection points using only the first derivative. Test your conjecture.

7. How does the second derivative behave near an inflection point $(a, f(a))$? Conjecture a test for inflection points using only the second derivative. Test your conjecture.

8. What is the value of the second derivative at each inflection point you found?

Note from the investigation that the sign of the second derivative affects the direction of concavity. If the second derivative is positive, the graph is concave upward. If the second derivative is negative, the graph is concave downward. This can be understood by thinking of the second derivative as the rate of change of the slope of a graph. Thus, if $f''(x) > 0$, the slope of the graph of f is increasing at x. Examine the following graph of a function that is concave upward on (a, b).

We can see that the slopes of the tangents to the function are increasing as x increases. The slopes on the left are negative, increasing through negative values up to 0, and then increasing through positive values. A similar argument can be made for a function that is concave downward on an interval.

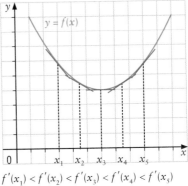

Test for concavity: If $f''(x) > 0$ for all $x \in (a, b)$, then the graph of f is concave upward on (a, b). If $f''(x) < 0$ for all $x \in (a, b)$, then the graph of f is concave downward on (a, b).

It follows from the test for concavity and the definition of a point of inflection, that there is a point of inflection at any point where the second derivative changes sign. Note that the second derivative must be zero or not exist at a point of inflection. This compares closely with Fermat's theorem (page 322), which relates critical numbers to the *first* derivative. As with Fermat's theorem, the condition "$f'' = 0$ or does not exist" does not guarantee that a point of inflection exists, as Example 1 shows.

Example 1 A Function With Zero Second Derivative but no Point of Inflection

Show that the function $f(x) = x^4$ satisfies $f''(0) = 0$ but has no point of inflection.

Solution

Since $f(x) = x^4$, we have $f'(x) = 4x^3$ and $f''(x) = 12x^2$, so $f''(0) = 0$. But $12x^2 > 0$ for both $x < 0$ and $x > 0$, so the concavity does not change and there is no point of inflection.

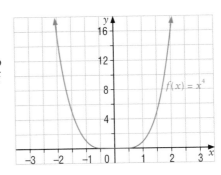

Example 2 Concavity and Points of Inflection for a Cubic Function

a) Determine where the curve $f(x) = x^3 - 3x^2 + 5x + 2$ is concave upward and where it is concave downward.

b) Find the points of inflection.

c) Use this information to sketch the curve. Draw the tangent at the point of inflection.

Solution

a) If $f(x) = x^3 - 3x^2 + 5x + 2$
then $f'(x) = 3x^2 - 6x + 5$
and $f''(x) = 6x - 6$
$\qquad\qquad = 6(x - 1)$

We use an interval chart to determine when $f''(x)$ is negative and when it is positive.

The curve is concave downward (since $f''(x) < 0$) for $x \in (-\infty, 1)$ and concave upward (since $f''(x) > 0$) for $x \in (1, \infty)$.

b) The curve changes from concave downward to concave upward when $x = 1$, so the point $(1, 5)$ is a point of inflection.

		$f''(x) = 6(x-1)$	
		1	
Intervals		$(-\infty, 1)$	$(1, \infty)$
Test values		0	100
Signs of $f''(x)$		$-$	$+$
Nature of graph		concave downward	concave upward

c) Next, we determine the critical numbers of $f(x)$. Since f is continuous, we need only consider x-values for which $f'(x) = 0$.
$3x^2 - 6x + 5 = 0$

$$x = \frac{-(-6) \pm \sqrt{(-6)^2 - 4(3)(5)}}{2(3)}$$

$$= \frac{6 \pm \sqrt{-24}}{6}$$

Since there is no real value of x for which $f'(x) = 0$, the function has no critical points. Hence, the function is either always increasing or always decreasing. We test a particular point to determine which. Since $f'(0) = 5 > 0$, the function is always increasing. This information, together with parts a) and b) and the y-intercept, $f(0) = 2$, allows us to sketch the curve. We also need to determine the equation of the tangent at the point of inflection. The slope of the tangent is

$m = f'(1)$

$\quad = 3(1)^2 - 6(1) + 5$

$\quad = 2$

The equation of the tangent is
$y - y_1 = m(x - x_1)$
$y - 5 = 2(x - 1)$
$\qquad y = 2x + 3$

Note that the information regarding concavity is very helpful in sketching the curve.

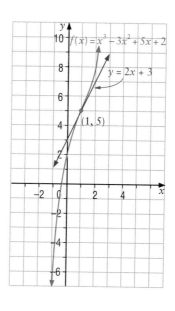

Example 3 Concavity and Points of Inflection for a Rational Function

Discuss the curve $y = \dfrac{1}{x^2+1}$ with respect to concavity and points of inflection.

Solution

Let $f(x) = \dfrac{1}{x^2+1}$.

Then

$f'(x) = -(x^2+1)^{-2}(2x)$

$ = \dfrac{-2x}{(x^2+1)^2}$

$f''(x) = \dfrac{(x^2+1)^2(-2) - (-2x)2(x^2+1)(2x)}{(x^2+1)^4}$

$ = \dfrac{2(3x^2-1)}{(x^2+1)^3}$

We determine when f'' is negative and when it is positive in order to determine the concavity. To do this, we first determine when $f''(x) = 0$.

$\dfrac{2(3x^2-1)}{(x^2+1)^3} = 0$

We can multiply both sides of the equation by the denominator, which is always positive.

$2(3x^2-1) = 0$

$3x^2 = 1$

$x = \pm\dfrac{1}{\sqrt{3}}$

We consider the intervals

$\left(-\infty, -\dfrac{1}{\sqrt{3}}\right)$, $\left(-\dfrac{1}{\sqrt{3}}, \dfrac{1}{\sqrt{3}}\right)$, and $\left(\dfrac{1}{\sqrt{3}}, \infty\right)$.

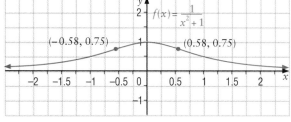

$f''(x) = \dfrac{2(3x^2-1)}{(x^2+1)^3}$

	$\left(-\infty, -\dfrac{1}{\sqrt{3}}\right)$	$\left(-\dfrac{1}{\sqrt{3}}, \dfrac{1}{\sqrt{3}}\right)$	$\left(\dfrac{1}{\sqrt{3}}, \infty\right)$
Intervals			
Test values	-100	0	100
Signs of $f''(x)$	$+$	$-$	$+$
Nature of graph	concave upward	concave downward	concave upward

The curve is concave upward for $x \in \left(-\infty, -\dfrac{1}{\sqrt{3}}\right)$ and $x \in \left(\dfrac{1}{\sqrt{3}}, \infty\right)$, and concave

downward for $x \in \left(-\dfrac{1}{\sqrt{3}}, \dfrac{1}{\sqrt{3}}\right)$. The points of inflection are $\left(-\dfrac{1}{\sqrt{3}}, \dfrac{3}{4}\right)$ and $\left(\dfrac{1}{\sqrt{3}}, \dfrac{3}{4}\right)$.

The graph verifies these calculations.

The Second Derivative Test

The following investigation explores the possibility of using the second derivative of a function to determine if a local extremum is a local maximum or a local minimum.

Investigate & Inquire: Distinguishing Local Maxima from Local Minima

1. Examine the graphs of the functions f, f', and f'' from step 2 in the investigation on page 331. Draw vertical lines through the local minimum and maximum points of each graph of f.

2. How do the derivatives f' and f'' behave at these local extrema?

3. Can the second derivative be used to distinguish local maximum points from local minimum points? If so, conjecture a general rule.

4. Test your rule on two additional functions.

Note, from the investigation, that the second derivative can be used to determine whether a local extremum is a maximum or a minimum value of a function f. We assume that $f''(x)$ exists and is continuous throughout the domain of f.

The figure below shows the graph of a function f with $f'(c) = 0$ and $f''(c) > 0$. Since $f''(c) > 0$, the graph of f is concave upward near c, and therefore lies above its tangents at $(c, f(c))$. But since $f'(c) = 0$, this tangent is horizontal. Therefore, f has a local minimum at c.

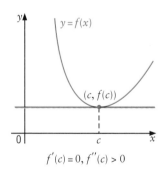

$f'(c) = 0, f''(c) > 0$

Similarly, as shown in the figure on the right, if $f'(c) = 0$ and $f''(c) < 0$, then the graph of f is concave downward near c, and therefore lies below its horizontal tangent at $(c, f(c))$. Thus, f has a local maximum at c.

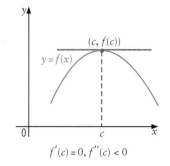

$f'(c) = 0, f''(c) < 0$

> **Second derivative test:**
> If $f'(c) = 0$ and $f''(c) > 0$, then f has a local minimum at c.
> If $f'(c) = 0$ and $f''(c) < 0$, then f has a local maximum at c.

Example 4 Local Maximum and Minimum Values, Concavity, and Points of Inflection

Find the local maximum and minimum values of the function $y = \dfrac{1}{4} x^4 - 2x^3$. Use these, together with concavity and points of inflection, to sketch the curve.

Solution

Let $f(x) = \dfrac{1}{4} x^4 - 2x^3$.

Then
$f'(x) = x^3 - 6x^2$
$\quad = x^2(x - 6)$
$f''(x) = 3x^2 - 12x$
$\quad = 3x(x - 4)$

To find the critical numbers, we set $f'(x) = 0$ and obtain $x = 0$ and $x = 6$. Then, to use the second derivative test, we evaluate f'' at these numbers:
$f''(0) = 0$ and $f''(6) = 36$

Since $f'(6) = 0$ and $f''(6) > 0$, $f(6) = -108$ is a local minimum. Since $f''(0) = 0$, the second derivative test gives no information about the critical number 0. But, since the first derivative does not change sign at $x = 0$ (it is negative on both sides of $x = 0$), the first derivative test tells us that f has no maximum or minimum at $x = 0$. Since $f''(x) = 3x(x - 4)$, $f''(x) = 0$ at $x = 0$ and at $x = 4$. We determine the concavity using an interval chart as shown above to the right.

Thus, f is concave upward on $(-\infty, 0)$ and $(4, \infty)$ and concave downward on $(0, 4)$. The points of inflection are $(0, 0)$ and $(4, -64)$. Now, we graph the function using this information.

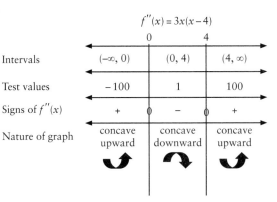

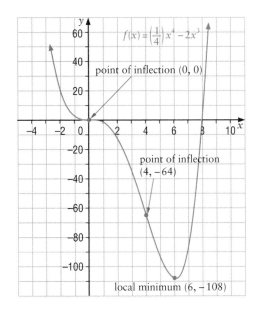

Example 4 shows that the second derivative test gives no information when $f''(c) = 0$. It also fails when $f''(c)$ does not exist. In such cases, we must use the first derivative test.

Key Concepts

- The graph of f is called concave upward on an interval (a, b) if it lies above all of its tangents on (a, b). It is called concave downward on (a, b) if it lies below all of its tangents on (a, b).

- A point P on a curve is called a point of inflection if the curve changes concavity at P.

- Test for concavity
  If $f''(x) > 0$ for all x on (a, b), then the graph of f is concave upward on (a, b).
  If $f''(x) < 0$ for all x on (a, b), then the graph of f is concave downward on (a, b).

- At a point of inflection, $f'' = 0$ or f'' does not exist. However, this condition on f'' may also be true at other points. Therefore, inflection points cannot be located simply by setting $f''(x) = 0$.

- A point of inflection for f occurs when the sign of f'' changes at that point.

- Second derivative test
  If $f'(c) = 0$ and $f''(c) > 0$, then f has a local minimum at c.
  If $f'(c) = 0$ and $f''(c) < 0$, then f has a local maximum at c.

- The second derivative test does not apply when $f''(c) = 0$ and when $f''(c)$ does not exist.

Communicate Your Understanding

1. Referring only to the characteristics of a graph, describe the terms
a) concave upward   b) concave downward

2. Draw two different curves, each with a point of inflection, so that one of the curves is differentiable at its point of inflection and the other is not. Mark each point of inflection and explain why it is a point of inflection.

3. Explain each statement.
a) If f is concave upward on an interval, then the slopes of the tangents are increasing from left to right on that interval.
b) If f is concave downward on an interval, then the slopes of the tangents are decreasing from left to right on that interval.

4. Chris claims that, to find inflection points, all you have to do is find where the second derivative is 0 or undefined. Discuss the validity of this statement.

5. If $f'(c) = 0$ and $f''(c) \neq 0$, what can you conclude about the point on the graph of f where $x = c$?

6. Does the second derivative test apply to the function $f(x) = x^{\frac{2}{3}}$ at $x = 0$? If yes, apply it. If no, explain how to determine whether f has a maximum value, a minimum value, or neither at $x = 0$.

Practise

A **1. a)** State the intervals on which f is concave upward and the intervals on which it is concave downward.
b) State the coordinates of the points of inflection.

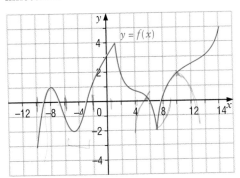

2. The figure is a sketch of f'' for a function f. State the intervals on which the graph of f is concave upward and the intervals on which it is concave downward. Determine the x-coordinates of any inflection points of the graph of f.

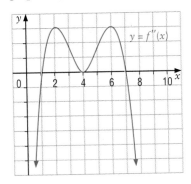

3. The graph of the first derivative f' of a function f is shown.
a) On which intervals is f increasing? decreasing?
b) On which intervals is f concave upward? concave downward?
c) State the x-coordinates of any local maximum or minimum points of the graph of f.

d) State the x-coordinates of any points of inflection of f. Explain why each is a point of inflection.

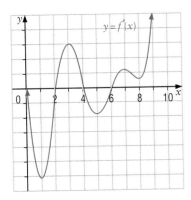

4. The following are graphs of the first and second derivatives of a function $y = f(x)$. For each graph,
i) identify all the critical numbers of f and explain if they relate to a maximum, a minimum, or you cannot decide, using only the second derivative test
ii) for the numbers for which the second derivative test fails, use the first derivative test to decide the nature of the related point

a)

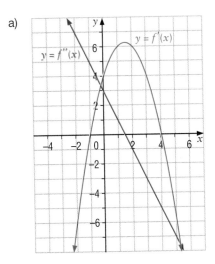

b)

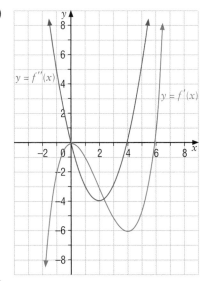

c)

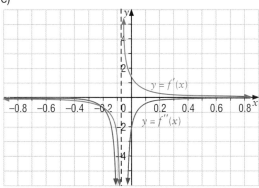

5. Find the intervals on which each curve is concave upward and the intervals on which it is concave downward. State any points of inflection.

a) $f(x) = 2x^2 - 3x + 5$

b) $y = 6 + 5x - 3x^2$

c) $g(x) = 2x^3 - 3x^2 - 12x + 6$

d) $y = x^3 + 2x^2 - 4x + 3$

e) $f(x) = 16 - 3x + 3.5x^2 + 2x^3$

f) $y = 3x^4 - 4x^3 - 6x^2 + 2$

g) $h(x) = 3 + 6x - x^6$

h) $y = 3x^5 - 5x^3 + 2$ i) $f(x) = \dfrac{x-1}{3-x}$

j) $g(x) = \dfrac{1}{x^2 + 1}$ k) $y = \dfrac{1 - x^2}{x}$

6. Use the second derivative test to find the local maximum and minimum values of each function, wherever possible.

a) $y = 5 + 8x - x^2$

b) $f(x) = 2x^3 - 24x + 10$

c) $g(x) = 4 + 12x^2 - x^3$

d) $f(x) = x^3 - 9x^2 + 24x$

e) $y = x^4 + 4x^3 + 4$

f) $f(x) = 5 + 5x - x^5$

g) $h(x) = (x^4 - 8x^2)^2$

h) $y = x^2 - \dfrac{2}{x}$

7. Find the local maximum and minimum values of each function.

a) $g(x) = x^4 - 6x^2 + 10$ b) $y = \dfrac{x}{(x-1)^2}$

c) $h(x) = \dfrac{x^2}{2x+3}$ d) $y = \dfrac{9}{x} - x^2$

8. Use the first and second derivative tests to determine the maximum points, minimum points, and points of inflection for each function. Graph each function.

a) $f(x) = x^2 - 4x + 6$ b) $f(x) = x^3 - 6x^2$

c) $y = x^3 + x^2 + 6x$ d) $f(x) = x^4 + 8x^3 + 50$

e) $y = x^6 - 2x^3$ f) $h(x) = x^{\frac{2}{3}}$

g) $y = \dfrac{1}{x+1}$ h) $y = \dfrac{x}{4+x^2}$

Apply, Solve, Communicate

B 9. a) Determine where f is positive, where it is negative, and where it is zero. Repeat for f' and f''.

b) Is there an interval where $f < 0$, $f' > 0$, and $f'' < 0$? If so, state the interval.

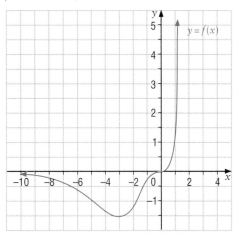

10. A manufacturer keeps accurate records of the cost, $C(x)$, of producing x items in its factory. The graph shows the cost function.

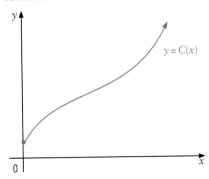

a) Explain why $C(0) > 0$.
b) Explain the significance of the point of inflection.
c) Use the graph of C to sketch the graph of the marginal cost function, $C'(x)$.

11. Application A typical predator-prey relationship for foxes and rabbits is shown in the graph.

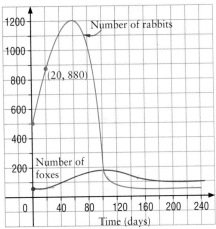

a) Estimate the intervals on which the graph of the prey population is concave upward; concave downward.
b) Estimate the coordinates of the points of inflection of the prey graph.
c) Describe the predator-prey relationship in terms of maximum and minimum values, intervals of increase and decrease, and concavity.

12. Communication A software company estimates that it will sell N units of a new product after spending x dollars on TV ads during football games. The relationship can be modelled by $N(x) = -x^2 + 200x + 12$, $x \in [0, 150]$, where x is measured in thousands of dollars.
a) Find the minimum and maximum number of sales.
b) Does more advertising always lead to more sales? Explain.

13. Inquiry/Problem Solving Water is poured into a cone-shaped vase, as shown, at a constant rate.
a) Sketch a rough graph of $H(t)$, the height of the water in the vase as a function of time.
b) Sketch rough graphs of $H'(t)$ and $H''(t)$.
c) Explain the shape of all three graphs in terms of the shape of the vase. Explain the concavity in the graph of $H(t)$.

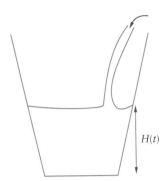

14. For the function $f(x) = x^{\frac{1}{3}}(x+2)^{\frac{2}{3}}$, determine
a) the intervals of increase and decrease
b) the local maximum and minimum values
c) the intervals of concavity
d) the points of inflection

15. Inquiry/Problem Solving If possible, sketch the graph of a continuous function with domain R satisfying each set of characteristics. If it is not possible, explain why not.
a) The first and second derivatives are always positive.
b) The function is always positive and the first and second derivatives are always negative.

c) The first derivative is always positive and the second derivative is always negative.

d) The first derivative is always negative and the second derivative is always positive.

e) The first derivative is always positive and the second derivative alternates between positive and negative.

f) The function is always negative and the first and second derivatives are always negative.

16. Application Use a graphing calculator or graphing software. Give results to three decimal places.

i) Draw the graph of f.

ii) Find all extrema for f.

iii) Find all points of inflection for f.

a) $f(x) = 6x^5 + 5x^4 + 80x^3 + 90x^2 + 200x$

b) $f(x) = \dfrac{x^3(x+1)^2}{(x-2)^2(x-4)^2}$

C **17.** Is it possible to use the graph of the second derivative of a function to determine all the x-coordinates of the maximum and minimum points without any knowledge of the first derivative? Explain.

18. For what values of the constants c and d is $(4, 3)$ a point of inflection of the cubic curve $y = x^3 + cx^2 + x + d$?

19. Graph several members of the family of polynomials defined by $f(x) = cx^4 - 2x^2 + 1$.

a) For which values of c do the curves have maximum points?

b) Prove that the minimum and maximum points of each of these curves lie on the parabola defined by $y = 1 - x^2$.

20. Sketch the graph of a continuous function that satisfies all these conditions.

- $f(0) = f(3) = 2$, $f(-1) = f(1) = 0$
- $f'(-1) = f'(1) = 0$
- $f'(x) < 0$ for $x \in (-\infty, -1)$ and for $x \in (0, 1)$
- $f'(x) > 0$ for $x \in (-1, 0)$ and for $x \in (1, \infty)$
- $f''(x) > 0$ for $x < 3$ ($x \neq 0$), $f''(x) < 0$ for $x \in (3, \infty)$
- $\lim\limits_{x \to \infty} f(x) = 4$, $\lim\limits_{x \to -\infty} f(x) = \infty$

21. Sketch the graph of a continuous function that satisfies all of the following conditions.

- $f'(x) > 0$ for $x \in (0, 1)$, $f'(x) < 0$ for $x \in (1, \infty)$
- $f''(x) < 0$ for $x \in (0, 2)$, $f''(x) > 0$ for $x \in (2, \infty)$
- $\lim\limits_{x \to \infty} f(x) = 0$
- f is an odd function

22. Communication The function $f(x) = x^2(x - 1)(2x - 1)^2$ was graphed with technology.

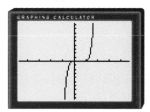

a) Use calculus techniques to determine any local extrema and points of inflection for this curve.

b) Do the window settings chosen show all the relevant features of the graph? Explain.

c) If your answer in part b) was no, give appropriate window settings for graphing this function using technology.

Vertical Asymptotes

Rational functions are used to model many situations involving economics and medicine. Many phenomena in nature, such as the intensity of light as it travels through space, the force of gravity, and electrostatic force, follow an inverse square law, that is, a function of the form $f(x) = \dfrac{k}{x^2}$.

Investigate & Inquire: Force Between Two Charged Particles

Consider two electrically charged particles, A and B. A is fixed in its position at the origin and B is free to move along the x-axis. The magnitude of the electrostatic force F between these two particles is inversely proportional to the square of the distance between them. This force, measured in newtons, is given by $F(x) = \dfrac{1}{10x^2}$, where x is the position of B, in metres. What happens to the magnitude of the electrostatic force as B comes close to A on either side of A? In the following steps, you will examine the force $F(x) = \dfrac{1}{10x^2}$ for x close to 0.

1. Construct a table of values for F for values of x close to 0, on both sides of 0. You can do this by hand, or using a spreadsheet, a graphing calculator, or graphing software.

2. What happens to the electrostatic force, F, as the distance between the two small particles decreases from 2 m to almost 0 m for positive values of x? for negative values of x?

3. Graph F for the interval $x \in [-2, 2]$.
a) What happens to $F(x)$ as x approaches 0 from the left and from the right?
b) Does $\lim\limits_{x \to 0} F(x)$ exist? Is F continuous at $x = 0$? Explain your reasoning.
c) What is the magnitude of the electrostatic force when $x = 0$?

4. If you were to draw the line $x = 0$ (the y-axis), would the graph of F intersect this line? Does drawing this line show anything else about the graph of F?

From the investigation, note that the closer we take x to 0, the larger $\dfrac{1}{10x^2}$ becomes. In fact, it appears that, by taking x close enough to 0, we can make $F(x)$ as large as we like. Since the values of $F(x)$ do not approach a particular number as x approaches 0, we say that $\lim\limits_{x \to 0} \dfrac{1}{10x^2}$ does not exist (as a numerical value) and write $\lim\limits_{x \to 0} \dfrac{1}{10x^2} = \infty$. We say that the line $x = 0$ is a vertical asymptote of the graph of $F(x) = \dfrac{1}{10x^2}$.

Notice in the investigation that F is not defined at $x = 0$, and so F is not continuous at $x = 0$. This type of discontinuity is called an infinite discontinuity. (Refer to Chapter 3.)

In general, if $f(x)$ is defined on either side of the number a, we write $\lim\limits_{x \to a} f(x) = \infty$ if the values of $f(x)$ can be made arbitrarily large (as large as we like) by taking x sufficiently close to a, *but not equal to* a. This type of limit is called an **infinite limit**.

The expression $\lim\limits_{x \to a} f(x) = \infty$ is usually read as "the limit of $f(x)$ as x approaches a is infinity" or "$f(x)$ increases without bound as x approaches a." This does not mean that ∞ is a number or that the limit exists. It simply expresses the particular way in which the limit does not exist, because the magnitude of $g(x)$ grows arbitrarily large as x approaches a.

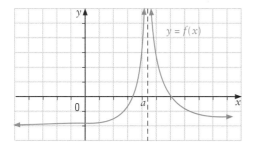
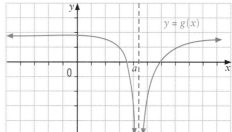

These figures illustrate two kinds of infinite limits, $\lim\limits_{x \to a} f(x) = +\infty$ and $\lim\limits_{x \to a} g(x) = -\infty$.

The latter means that the values of g decrease without bound as x approaches a or that the limit of $g(x)$ as x approaches a is negative infinity. Once again, the limit does not exist, because the magnitude of $g(x)$ grows arbitrarily large as x approaches a.

One-sided infinite limits can also be defined, as shown in the figures below. The notation for each limit is shown with its diagram. In each case shown in the figures, the limit does not exist.

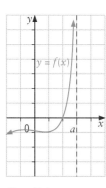
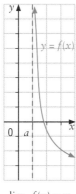
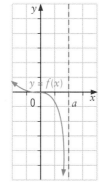
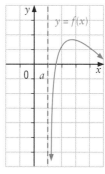

$\lim\limits_{x \to a^-} f(x) = \infty$ $\lim\limits_{x \to a^+} f(x) = \infty$ $\lim\limits_{x \to a^-} f(x) = -\infty$ $\lim\limits_{x \to a^+} f(x) = -\infty$

Remember that $x \to a^-$ means that x approaches a from the left, and $x \to a^+$ means x approaches a from the right.

> The line $x = a$ is called a **vertical asymptote** of the curve $y = f(x)$ if at least one of the following is true:
>
> $$\lim_{x \to a} f(x) = \infty \qquad \lim_{x \to a^-} f(x) = \infty \qquad \lim_{x \to a^+} f(x) = \infty$$
>
> $$\lim_{x \to a} f(x) = -\infty \qquad \lim_{x \to a^-} f(x) = -\infty \qquad \lim_{x \to a^+} f(x) = -\infty$$

Example 1 Fundamental Limits

Evaluate $\lim_{x \to 0^+} \dfrac{1}{x}$ and $\lim_{x \to 0^-} \dfrac{1}{x}$, and state whether they exist.

Solution

Consider the graph of $y = \dfrac{1}{x}$.

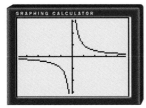 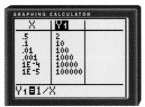 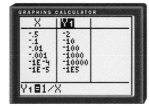

Window variables:
$x \in [-4.7, 4.7]$,
$y \in [-3.1, 3.1]$
or use the
ZDecimal
instruction.

We determine values of y for x-values close to 0, on either side of 0, selecting Ask mode on the TABLE SETUP screen of a graphing calculator. As x approaches 0 from the right, $\dfrac{1}{x}$ becomes increasingly large. Therefore, $\lim_{x \to 0^+} \dfrac{1}{x} = \infty$. If x is close to 0, but negative, then $\dfrac{1}{x}$ is a negative number with an arbitrarily large magnitude. Thus, $\lim_{x \to 0^-} \dfrac{1}{x} = -\infty$.

Therefore, $\lim_{x \to 0^+} \dfrac{1}{x}$ and $\lim_{x \to 0^-} \dfrac{1}{x}$ do not exist.

These limits can also be seen from the graph of $y = \dfrac{1}{x}$. The line $x = 0$ (the y-axis) is a vertical asymptote.

Example 2 An Infinite Limit

Find $\lim_{x \to 5} \left[4 - \dfrac{3}{(x - 5)^2} \right]$.

Solution

We select Ask mode on a graphing calculator to create a table of values to get an idea of the limit. We look at values of x close to 5, on either side of 5.

Let $y = 4 - \dfrac{3}{(x - 5)^2}$.

We can conjecture from the table that $\lim_{x \to 5} \left[4 - \dfrac{3}{(x - 5)^2} \right] = -\infty$.

Consider only the term $\dfrac{3}{(x-5)^2}$. If x is very close to 5, on either side of 5, then $(x-5)^2$ is very small, but positive. This means that $\dfrac{3}{(x-5)^2}$ is very large and positive. Therefore, $4 - \dfrac{3}{(x-5)^2}$ is arbitrarily large in magnitude, but negative.

Therefore, our conjecture that the limit does not exist is correct:

$$\lim_{x \to 5}\left[4 - \frac{3}{(x-5)^2}\right] = -\infty.$$

To find the vertical asymptotes of a rational function, we first determine whether the numerator and the denominator have any common factors. If they do, we simplify the function, noting any restrictions. We then find the values of x where the denominator is zero, and compute the limits of the function from the right and the left at those values of x.

Example 3 Determining Vertical Asymptotes

Find the vertical asymptotes of each function and sketch its graph near the asymptotes.

a) $f(x) = \dfrac{x+1}{x^2 + 3x + 2}$ b) $g(x) = \dfrac{x}{x^2 + 2x - 15}$

Solution

a) First, we factor the denominator.

$$f(x) = \frac{x+1}{x^2 + 3x + 2}$$

$$= \frac{(x+1)}{(x+1)(x+2)}$$

The numerator and the denominator have a common factor of $(x+1)$. Thus, we simplify the function as follows:

$$f(x) = \frac{1}{x+2}, \qquad x \neq -1$$

Now, we can determine the limit as x approaches -1 from both sides.

$$\lim_{x \to -1} f(x) = \lim_{x \to -1} \frac{1}{x+2}, \qquad x \neq -1$$

$$= \frac{1}{-1+2}$$

$$= 1$$

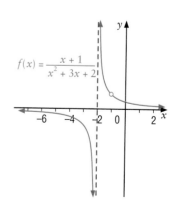

$$f(x) = \frac{x+1}{x^2 + 3x + 2}$$

Thus, f has a removable discontinuity at $x = -1$, and therefore $x = -1$ is not an asymptote. However, $x = -2$ is an asymptote. For $x < -2$, $f(x) < 0$, and for $x > 2$, $f(x) > 0$.

Thus, $\lim\limits_{x \to -2^-} f(x) = -\infty$ and $\lim\limits_{x \to -2^+} f(x) = \infty$. Now we can sketch the part of the graph that lies near the asymptotes. Note the gap in the graph at $x = -1$. This is the removable discontinuity.

b) First, we factor the denominator:

$$g(x) = \frac{x}{x^2 + 2x - 15}$$

$$= \frac{x}{(x + 5)(x - 3)}$$

Since the denominator is 0 when $x = -5$ or 3, and the numerator and denominator have no common factors, the lines $x = -5$ and $x = 3$ are vertical asymptotes. To help with the graph, we also consider when the numerator is zero (at $x = 0$), since the graph might change sign. We use an interval chart to determine the behaviour of the graph on either side of the asymptotes and near $x = 0$.

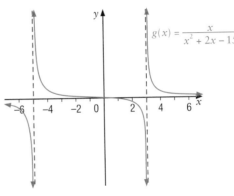

$$g(x) = \frac{x}{(x + 5)(x - 3)}$$

	-5		0		3	
Intervals	$(-\infty, -5)$		$(-5, 0)$		$(0, 3)$	$(3, \infty)$
Test values	-10		-1		1	10
Signs of $g(x)$	$-$	U	$+$	0	$-$ U	$+$

Thus, the y-values of the function approach negative infinity as x approaches -5 from the left and as x approaches 3 from the left. The y-values of the function approach positive infinity as x approaches -5 from the right and as x approaches 3 from the right. Thus, we have $\lim\limits_{x \to -5^-} g(x) = -\infty$, $\lim\limits_{x \to 3^-} g(x) = -\infty$, $\lim\limits_{x \to -5^+} g(x) = \infty$, and $\lim\limits_{x \to 3^+} g(x) = \infty$.

Also, the y-values change from positive to negative at $x = 0$. Now we can sketch the parts of the graph that lie near the asymptotes and near $x = 0$.

$$g(x) = \frac{x}{x^2 + 2x - 15}$$

We will be able to complete such graphs with the methods discussed in the following sections.

Key Concepts

- In general, if $f(x)$ is defined on both sides of the number a, we write $\lim\limits_{x \to a} f(x) = \infty$ if the values of $f(x)$ can be made arbitrarily large (as large as we like) by taking x sufficiently close to a.
- We write $\lim\limits_{x \to a} f(x) = -\infty$ if the values of f are negative and their magnitudes increase without bound as x approaches a.

- To indicate one-sided limits involving vertical asymptotes, we write

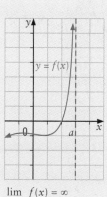 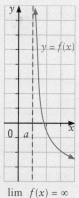  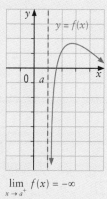

$$\lim_{x \to a^-} f(x) = \infty \qquad \lim_{x \to a^+} f(x) = \infty \qquad \lim_{x \to a^-} f(x) = -\infty \qquad \lim_{x \to a^+} f(x) = -\infty$$

to indicate the behaviour of the function on either side of the asymptote.

Communicate Your Understanding

1. Explain what is meant by a vertical asymptote.
2. What is the meaning of an infinite discontinuity? Use a graph in your explanation.
3. a) Explain how you would find the vertical asymptotes of each function.

i) $f(x) = \dfrac{2x}{x^2 - 3x - 4}$ \qquad ii) $g(x) = \dfrac{2x + 1}{2x^2 - 5x - 3}$

b) Explain how you would sketch the graph of the function near each asymptote.

4. How can you determine the behaviour of the graph of a function near its vertical asymptotes?

5. Explain each expression in your own words.

a) $\lim_{x \to 2} f(x) = \infty$ \qquad b) $\lim_{x \to 1^-} f(x) = -\infty$

6. Write a brief paragraph to assess the following reasoning. "Suppose that $\lim_{x \to 1^+} f(x) = -\infty$ and $\lim_{x \to 1^-} f(x) = -\infty$. Since the left- and right-hand limits are equal, $\lim_{x \to 1} f(x)$ exists and $\lim_{x \to 1} f(x) = -\infty$."

Practise

 1. The graph of f is given.

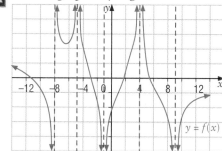

a) State the equations of the vertical asymptotes.

b) State the following.

i) $\lim_{x \to -5^-} f(x)$ \qquad ii) $\lim_{x \to -5^+} f(x)$

iii) $\lim_{x \to -1^-} f(x)$ \qquad iv) $\lim_{x \to -1^+} f(x)$

v) $\lim_{x \to 4^-} f(x)$ \qquad vi) $\lim_{x \to 4^+} f(x)$

vii) $\lim_{x \to 9^-} f(x)$ \qquad viii) $\lim_{x \to 9^+} f(x)$

c) Find the following limits, if possible. If it is not possible, explain why.

i) $\lim\limits_{x \to -5} f(x)$ ii) $\lim\limits_{x \to -1} f(x)$

iii) $\lim\limits_{x \to 4} f(x)$ iv) $\lim\limits_{x \to 9} f(x)$

2. Give an equation for a function having
a) vertical asymptote $x = -3$
b) vertical asymptotes $x = -2$ and $x = 3$
c) vertical asymptotes $x = 5$ and $x = -5$, and $f(x) > 0$ for all other values of x

B **3.** Find each limit.

a) $\lim\limits_{x \to 5} \dfrac{1}{(x-5)^2}$ b) $\lim\limits_{x \to -6} \dfrac{-3}{(x+6)^2}$

c) $\lim\limits_{x \to -4} \dfrac{x}{(x+4)^2}$ d) $\lim\limits_{x \to 7} \dfrac{5-x}{(x-7)^2}$

e) $\lim\limits_{x \to 2} \dfrac{x^2+4}{(x-2)^2}$ f) $\lim\limits_{x \to -1} \dfrac{-5-x^2}{(x+1)^2}$

4. Find each limit, if possible. If it is not possible, explain why.

a) $\lim\limits_{x \to 2^-} \dfrac{1}{x-2}$ b) $\lim\limits_{x \to 2^+} \dfrac{1}{x-2}$

c) $\lim\limits_{x \to -3^-} \dfrac{-2}{x+3}$ d) $\lim\limits_{x \to -3^+} \dfrac{-2}{x+3}$

e) $\lim\limits_{x \to 4^-} \dfrac{x-6}{x-4}$ f) $\lim\limits_{x \to 4^+} \dfrac{x-6}{x-4}$

g) $\lim\limits_{x \to 2} \dfrac{x}{x-2}$ h) $\lim\limits_{x \to -2} \dfrac{x}{x+2}$

i) $\lim\limits_{x \to -2} \dfrac{x-2}{x+2}$

5. Find the vertical asymptotes of each function and sketch the graph near the asymptotes.

a) $f(x) = \dfrac{4}{x-2}$ b) $y = \dfrac{4}{x+2}$

c) $k(x) = \dfrac{5}{(x-3)^2}$ d) $g(x) = \dfrac{x^2+4x}{(x+4)^2}$

e) $y = \dfrac{1}{1-x^2}$ f) $y = \dfrac{x}{1-x^2}$

g) $h(x) = \dfrac{4x^4+8x}{x^2+6x+8}$ h) $y = \dfrac{1}{x^2(x+2)}$

i) $y = \dfrac{x+3}{x^4-9x^2}$ j) $q(x) = \dfrac{3}{x^3-4x}$

6. Communication Sketch a graph satisfying each set of conditions.
a) $f(0) = 1$, $f(1) = 2$,
$\lim\limits_{x \to 2^-} f(x) = \infty$, $\lim\limits_{x \to -1^+} f(x) = -\infty$

b) $f(0) = 0$, $f(4) = 6$, $\lim\limits_{x \to 2} f(x) = \infty$
c) $g(0) = 0$, $\lim\limits_{x \to -2^-} g(x) = -\infty$, $\lim\limits_{x \to -2^+} g(x) = \infty$

Apply, Solve, Communicate

7. Application A consultant has issued an environmental report on the cost of cleaning up a property that was previously the site of a chemical factory. Costs can increase dramatically depending on the percent of pollutants that needs to be removed. Her report gives the cost, C, in dollars, of removing $p\%$ of the pollutants from the site as

$$C(p) = \dfrac{50\,000}{100-p}.$$

a) What is the cost of removal for half of the pollutants? 90% of the pollutants?
b) Determine $\lim\limits_{p \to 100^-} C(p)$.
c) Would it be affordable to remove all of the pollutants? Explain.
d) In light of your response to part c), is the model realistic for p in the entire domain [0, 100]?

8. Application Determine $\lim\limits_{x \to 1^+} \dfrac{1}{x^3-1}$ and
$\lim\limits_{x \to 1^-} \dfrac{1}{x^3-1}$
a) by evaluating $f(x) = \dfrac{1}{x^3-1}$ for values of x that approach 1 from the left and from the right
b) by using a graphing calculator or graphing software

9. Communication According to Newton's law of gravitation, the force of gravity between any two masses (m_1 and m_2) is given by the equation $F = \dfrac{Gm_1m_2}{d^2}$, where G is a positive constant, and d is the distance between the centres of the masses as shown.

a) Find $\lim\limits_{d \to 0} \dfrac{Gm_1m_2}{d^2}$.

b) Explain why the limit found in part a) is not reasonable for normal objects of non-zero size.

c) Black holes are postulated to be very massive objects of very small size. Explain why the limit found in a) would apply in this case, if we assume Newton's equation holds for such extreme conditions.

10. How small must x be so that

$$\frac{1}{x^4} > 100\,000\,000?$$

11. Find $\lim\limits_{x \to 0^+} \left(\dfrac{5}{x} - \dfrac{2}{x^3} \right)$.

12. Inquiry/Problem Solving According to Einstein's special theory of relativity, the mass, m, of a particle with velocity v relative to an observer is

$$m = \frac{m_0}{\sqrt{1 - \dfrac{v^2}{c^2}}}$$

where m_0 is the mass of the particle when it is at rest and $c = 3.0 \times 10^8$ m/s, the speed of light.

a) What happens to the mass as $v \to c^-$?

b) It is thought that a particle that is travelling with a speed less than the speed of light can approach the speed of light but not reach or surpass it. Explain why this is so according to the relativistic equation for mass.

C **13.** Inquiry/Problem Solving Let $f(x) = \dfrac{p(x)}{(x-a)^n}$, where n is a positive integer and $p(x)$ is a polynomial function. Assume that $x - a$ is not a factor of $p(x)$.

a) Under what conditions is $\lim\limits_{x \to a^-} f(x) = +\infty$ and under what conditions is $\lim\limits_{x \to a^-} f(x) = -\infty$?

b) Repeat part a) for $\lim\limits_{x \to a^+} f(x)$.

14. For any real number a, $a - a = 0$.

a) What is the meaning of the symbol $\infty - \infty$? Does it have a numerical value?

b) Use the two functions $f(x) = \dfrac{x^2}{(x-3)^2}$ and $g(x) = \dfrac{6x-9}{(x-3)^2}$, and the properties of limits to show that the symbol ∞ does not represent a real number.

Historical Bite: Who Invented Limits?

The roots of calculus can be traced to the calculations of areas and volumes by early Greek scholars such as Archimedes (287–212 B.C.) and Eudoxus (408–355 B.C.). They used the "method of exhaustion" as a precursor of our modern notion of limit. Although the limit idea was implicit in their work, they never actually formulated the concept. Sir Isaac Newton (1642–1727) was the first to recognize the importance of limits that "approach nearer than by any difference." It was left to the French mathematician Augustin Cauchy (1789–1857), many years later, to make these ideas more precise.

6.5 Horizontal and Oblique Asymptotes

In Section 6.4, you investigated the behaviour of the inverse square law for the electrostatic force between two charges, A and B, as B approached the fixed charge A. Now you will investigate the force as B moves farther and farther away from A, on either side of A.

Investigate & Inquire: Force Between Two Charged Particles

1. Consider two charged particles, A, fixed at the origin, and B, with position x on the x-axis. Construct a table of values for the force $F(x) = \dfrac{1}{10x^2}$ between A and B for positive and negative values of x with large absolute value. You can do this by hand, or using a graphing calculator, graphing software, or a spreadsheet.

2. What happens to the value of the force as charge B moves farther and farther away from charge A to the right? to the left?

3. Use a graphing calculator to graph F for large positive values of x.

4. Repeat step 3 for negative values of x with large absolute values.

5. Do you think the limit of the force exists as x approaches infinity? Explain your reasoning.

6. Repeat step 5 for the limit as x approaches negative infinity.

7. Repeat steps 1 to 6 for the function $g(x) = \dfrac{2x^2 + 1}{x^2 + 3}$.

8. Make a conjecture about what conditions must be true for the limit of a general function $h(x)$, as x approaches positive or negative infinity, to exist.

For the function $F(x) = \dfrac{1}{10x^2}$, note that, as $x \to \infty$ and $x \to -\infty$, the values of $F(x)$ get closer and closer to 0. On a graph of $y = F(x)$, the points approach the x-axis. We can make the points get as close to the x-axis as we like by taking positive or negative values for x with arbitrarily large absolute values. Similarly, the values of $g(x)$ get closer and closer to 2 as $x \to \infty$ and $x \to -\infty$. On the graph, the points approach the line $y = 2$. When the points approach a horizontal line in this way, the line is called a horizontal asymptote.

> A number L is a **limit at infinity** for a function f if the values of $f(x)$ can be made as close to L as we like by taking positive or negative values of x with sufficiently large absolute values. We write this relationship either as $\lim\limits_{x \to \infty} f(x) = L$ or $\lim\limits_{x \to -\infty} f(x) = L$, whichever is appropriate.

Again, the symbol ∞ is not a number. The expression $\lim\limits_{x \to \infty} f(x) = L$ is read as "the limit of $f(x)$ as x approaches infinity is L" or "the limit of $f(x)$ as x increases without bound is L." The expression $\lim\limits_{x \to -\infty} f(x) = L$ is read as "the limit of $f(x)$ as x approaches negative infinity is L" or "the limit of $f(x)$ as x decreases without bound is L."

The line $y = L$ is called a **horizontal asymptote** of the curve $y = f(x)$ if either $\lim\limits_{x \to \infty} f(x) = L$ or $\lim\limits_{x \to -\infty} f(x) = L$, or both.

For instance, note that in the investigation, the line $y = 0$ is a horizontal asymptote of the function $F(x) = \dfrac{1}{10x^2}$ and the line $y = 2$ is a horizontal asymptote of the function $g(x) = \dfrac{2x^2 + 1}{x^2 + 3}$.

The diagrams show several of the many ways for a curve to approach a horizontal asymptote.

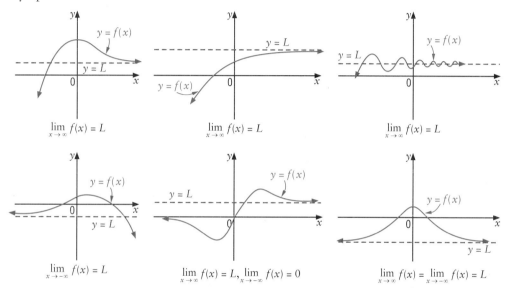

Note that it is possible for the graph of a function to cross a horizontal asymptote, as can be seen in some of the figures. The line $y = L$ is a horizontal asymptote if the function approaches arbitrarily closely to L as x approaches either positive or negative infinity (or both). The graph of the function could cross the asymptote once or many times without affecting this condition. Note that the second-last function has two horizontal asymptotes.

Example 1 Basic Limits at Infinity

Find $\lim\limits_{x \to \infty} \dfrac{1}{x}$ and $\lim\limits_{x \to -\infty} \dfrac{1}{x}$. Find the horizontal asymptote of $\dfrac{1}{x}$.

Solution

When x is large, $\dfrac{1}{x}$ is small. We can demonstrate this by calculating the reciprocal of successively larger numbers.

$$\frac{1}{100} = 0.01 \qquad \frac{1}{10\,000} = 0.0001 \qquad \frac{1}{1\,000\,000} = 0.000\,001$$

In fact, by taking large enough values of x, we can make $\dfrac{1}{x}$ as close to 0 as we like.

Therefore, $\lim\limits_{x \to \infty} \dfrac{1}{x} = 0$.

If we choose negative values for x with large absolute values, $\dfrac{1}{x}$ is a negative number with small absolute value. Again, $\dfrac{1}{x}$ can be made as close to 0 as we like by choosing negative values for x with sufficiently large absolute values. Therefore, $\lim\limits_{x \to -\infty} \dfrac{1}{x} = 0$.

Thus, the line $y = 0$ (the x-axis) is a horizontal asymptote of the curve $y = \dfrac{1}{x}$.

Using a similar argument leads to the following important rules for calculating limits.

If r is a positive integer, then $\lim\limits_{x \to \infty} \dfrac{1}{x^r} = 0$ and $\lim\limits_{x \to -\infty} \dfrac{1}{x^r} = 0$.

Example 2 Long-Term Behaviour of Average Cost

A photocopying store charges a flat rate of \$2 plus \$0.05/copy.
a) Write a function $f(x)$ to represent the average cost per copy.
b) Determine $\lim\limits_{x \to \infty} f(x)$.
c) What is the significance of this limit for the customer?

Solution

a) The cost of x copies is $2 + 0.05x$.

The average cost per copy is $f(x) = \dfrac{2 + 0.05x}{x}$.

b) $\lim\limits_{x \to \infty} \dfrac{2 + 0.05x}{x} = \lim\limits_{x \to \infty} \left(\dfrac{2}{x} + \dfrac{0.05x}{x} \right)$

$= \lim\limits_{x \to \infty} \dfrac{2}{x} + \lim\limits_{x \to \infty} 0.05$

$= 2 \lim\limits_{x \to \infty} \dfrac{1}{x} + 0.05$

$= 2(0) + 0.05$

$= 0.05$

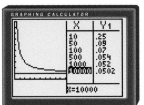

c) The more copies the customer makes, the closer the average rate per copy comes to \$0.05. The flat rate of \$2 becomes less and less significant as more copies are made.

Window variables:
$x \in [0, 100]$, $y \in [0, 0.5]$

In the following example, we compute a more complicated limit.

Example 3 Limit of a Rational Function

Evaluate $\lim\limits_{x \to \infty} \dfrac{10x^2 - 2x - 1}{5x^2 - 3x + 1}$.

Solution

Keep in mind that the symbol ∞ is not a number. We cannot substitute this symbol into the expression and evaluate it. However, we can evaluate limits of the form $\lim\limits_{x \to \infty} \dfrac{1}{x^r}$. Therefore, to evaluate the limit at infinity of a rational function, we first divide both the numerator and the denominator by the highest power of x that occurs in the denominator, so that all limits will be in this form. (We can assume that we are not dividing by zero because we are interested only in values of x that have large absolute values.) In this case, the highest power of x is x^2, so we proceed as follows.

$$\lim_{x \to \infty} \frac{10x^2 - 2x - 1}{5x^2 - 3x + 1} = \lim_{x \to \infty} \left[\frac{10x^2 - 2x - 1}{5x^2 - 3x + 1} \times \frac{\frac{1}{x^2}}{\frac{1}{x^2}} \right]$$

$$= \lim_{x \to \infty} \frac{10 - \dfrac{2}{x} - \dfrac{1}{x^2}}{5 - \dfrac{3}{x} + \dfrac{1}{x^2}}$$

$$= \frac{10 - 0 - 0}{5 - 0 + 0}$$

$$= 2$$

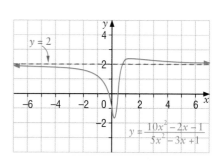

The graph of $y = \dfrac{10x^2 - 2x - 1}{5x^2 - 3x + 1}$ and its horizontal asymptote $y = 2$ are shown in the figure.

Note that the graph crosses the horizontal asymptote at a small value of x.

Infinite Limits at Infinity

Some rational functions approach horizontal asymptotes at infinity, but others do not. The following investigation will explore the behaviour of rational functions further.

Investigate & Inquire: Limits at Infinity of Rational Functions

1. For each function,

i)   draw a graph of the function

ii) construct tables of values for y for negative and positive x-values with large absolute value

iii) determine $\lim\limits_{x \to \infty} f(x)$ and $\lim\limits_{x \to -\infty} f(x)$

a) $\quad y = \dfrac{x^2 + 1}{x^3 + 1}$
b) $\quad y = \dfrac{2x - 5}{x^2 - 1}$
c) $\quad y = \dfrac{10x^4 + 50}{x^5}$
d) $\quad y = \dfrac{3x^2 + 2x + 4}{x^4 + x^2 - 1}$

2. Compare the degree of the numerator to the degree of the denominator for each function in step 1. What general conclusions can you draw from your results?

3. Repeat steps 1 and 2 for the following functions.

a) $y = \dfrac{x^2 + 2}{x^2 + 1}$ b) $y = \dfrac{2x^2 + 1}{3x^2 + 4}$ c) $y = \dfrac{-3x^3 - 1}{x^3 + 1}$ d) $y = \dfrac{x^4 - 20}{2x^4 + 5}$

4. Repeat steps 1 and 2 for the following functions.

a) $y = \dfrac{x^2 + 1}{x + 1}$ b) $y = \dfrac{2x^2 + 3x + 7}{3x - 2}$ c) $y = \dfrac{1 - 2x + x^2}{x + 2}$ d) $y = \dfrac{5x^4 - 3}{3x^2 + 1}$

When evaluating limits at infinity for rational functions, it is often helpful to use a shortcut to determine if the limit is 0 or a particular non-zero number such as 2, or if there is no horizontal asymptote at all. To do this, we compare the degree of the numerator to the degree of the denominator, as in the preceding investigation.

For example, note that in step 1 of the investigation, the degree of the numerator is less than the degree of the denominator for each function. For this type of function, the limits at

infinity are zero. For example, $\lim\limits_{x \to \infty} \dfrac{x^2 + 1}{x^3 + 1} = 0$ and $\lim\limits_{x \to -\infty} \dfrac{x^2 + 1}{x^3 + 1} = 0$.

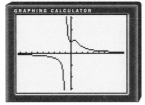

Window variables:
$x \in [-9.4, 9.4]$, $y \in [-3.1, 3.1]$

This makes sense because the absolute value of the denominator will increase at a far greater rate than that of the numerator for values of x with arbitrarily large absolute values, and so the limit is 0.

Then, note that in step 3 of the investigation, the degree of the numerator is equal to the degree of the denominator for each function. In each case, the limit at infinity is equal to the leading coefficient of the numerator divided by the leading coefficient of the

denominator. For example, in part b), $\lim\limits_{x \to \infty} \dfrac{2x^2 + 1}{3x^2 + 4} = \dfrac{2}{3}$.

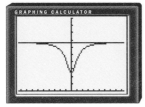

Note how quickly the graph approaches the asymptote in this example.

Window variables:
$x \in [-9.4, 9.4]$, $y \in [0, 1]$

The terms that determine the degrees of the numerator and denominator, $2x^2$ and $3x^2$, will dominate the behaviour of the function as the absolute value of x becomes arbitrarily large; all other terms will be small in comparison.

Note that in step 4 of the investigation, the degree of the numerator is greater than the degree of the denominator. There is no horizontal asymptote in this case. The numerator grows faster than the denominator and so the absolute value of the function increases

without bound. For example, in part d), $y = \dfrac{5x^4 - 4}{3x^2 + 1}$ has no horizontal asymptote.

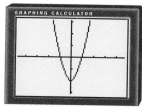

Window variables:
$x \in [-4.7, 4.7]$, $y \in [-3.1, 3.1]$
or use the ZDecimal instruction.

This is because the numerator will be dominated by $5x^4$ as the absolute value of x gets arbitrarily large, and the denominator will behave like $3x^2$, whose value increases much more slowly than $5x^4$. We write $\lim\limits_{x \to \infty} \dfrac{5x^4 - 4}{3x^2 + 2} = \infty$ and $\lim\limits_{x \to -\infty} \dfrac{5x^4 - 4}{3x^2 + 2} = \infty$ to express this.

Infinite limits at infinity: The notation $\lim\limits_{x \to \infty} f(x) = \infty$ means that the values of $f(x)$ increase without bound as x increases without bound.

There are similar meanings for the following expressions.
$$\lim\limits_{x \to \infty} f(x) = -\infty \qquad \lim\limits_{x \to -\infty} f(x) = \infty \qquad \lim\limits_{x \to -\infty} f(x) = -\infty$$

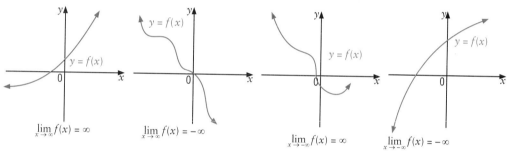

All non-constant polynomial functions behave in this manner. For example, we can see from the graphs of $y = x^2$ and $y = x^3$ that

$$\lim\limits_{x \to \infty} x^2 = \infty \qquad \lim\limits_{x \to -\infty} x^2 = \infty \qquad \lim\limits_{x \to \infty} x^3 = \infty \qquad \lim\limits_{x \to -\infty} x^3 = -\infty$$

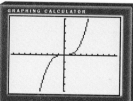

Window variables:
$x \in [-4.7, 4.7]$, $y \in [0, 20]$

Window variables:
$x \in [-9.4, 9.4]$, $y \in [-75, 75]$

In the previous examples, we studied vertical and horizontal asymptotes. However, there are many curves that approach asymptotes that are not horizontal or vertical as the absolute value of x becomes large. In step 4, part a) of the investigation, note that $\lim\limits_{x \to \infty} \dfrac{x^2 + 1}{x + 1} = \infty$

and $\lim\limits_{x \to -\infty} \dfrac{x^2 + 1}{x + 1} = -\infty$. It also appeared that the graph was straightening out as the absolute value of x became very large. In fact, it appeared that the curve was getting closer and closer to the line $y = x$. Such a line is called a linear oblique (or slant) asymptote.

 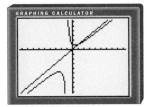

Window variables:
$x \in [-9.4, 9.4]$, $y \in [-9.3, 6.2]$

> The line $y = mx + b$ is a **linear oblique asymptote** for a curve $y = f(x)$ if the vertical distance between the curve and the line approaches 0 as the absolute value of x gets large for either positive or negative values of x.
>
> We write this as $\lim\limits_{x \to \infty} [f(x) - (mx + b)] = 0$ or $\lim\limits_{x \to -\infty} [f(x) - (mx + b)] = 0$

For rational functions, linear oblique asymptotes occur when the degree of the numerator is exactly one more than the degree of the denominator. The equation of the linear oblique asymptote can be found by dividing the numerator by the denominator, as in Example 4.

Example 4 Determining Linear Oblique Asymptotes

Find an equation of the linear oblique asymptote for each curve.

a) $y = \dfrac{2x^3 - x^2 + 3}{x^2}$ b) $y = \dfrac{2x^2 - 7x - 2}{2 - x}$

Solution

a) Note that the degree of the numerator is 1 more than the degree of the denominator. We can divide to obtain

$$y = \dfrac{2x^3 - x^2 + 3}{x^2}$$
$$= 2x - 1 + \dfrac{3}{x^2}$$

If the absolute value of x is very large, the value of $\dfrac{3}{x^2}$ approaches 0 and becomes insignificant in comparison to the other two terms. Thus, the curve approaches the line $y = 2x - 1$. This oblique asymptote (in blue) can be seen on the graph. Note that we would also expect to find a vertical asymptote at $x = 0$.

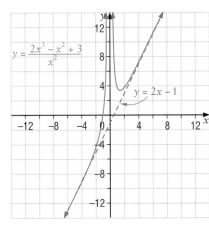

b) We begin with long division.

$$-x+2 \overline{\smash{\big)}\, 2x^2 - 7x - 2} \qquad \underset{-2x+3}{}$$

$$\underline{2x^2 - 4x}$$
$$-3x - 2$$
$$\underline{-3x + 6}$$
$$-8$$

Thus,

$$y = \frac{2x^2 - 7x - 2}{2 - x}$$

$$= -2x + 3 - \frac{8}{2 - x}$$

As in part a), we conclude that the oblique asymptote is
$y = -2x + 3$. The graph shows the curve and the oblique
asymptote added in blue. Again, we would expect to see a
vertical asymptote at $x = 2$, resulting from setting the
denominator equal to 0.

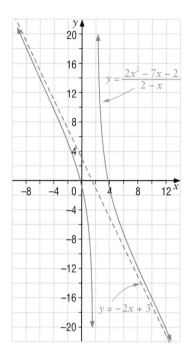

Example 5 Determining the Asymptotes to a Curve

Find all asymptotes to the curve $y = \dfrac{x^2 - x - 2}{x - 1}$, and use this information to sketch the curve.

Solution

First, we ensure that the numerator and the denominator have no common factors.

$$y = \frac{x^2 - x - 2}{x - 1}$$

$$= \frac{(x + 1)(x - 2)}{x - 1}$$

Since there are no common factors, we set the denominator equal to 0 to obtain the vertical
asymptote $x = 1$.

The degree of the numerator is 1 more than the degree of the denominator, so the graph of
the function has a linear oblique asymptote.
Long division gives

$$x-1 \overline{\smash{\big)}\, x^2 - x - 2} \qquad \underset{x}{}$$

$$\underline{x^2 - x}$$
$$-2$$

Thus,

$$y = \frac{x^2 - x - 2}{x - 1}$$

$$= x - \frac{2}{x - 1}$$

Therefore, the equation of the linear oblique asymptote is $y = x$.

To help us sketch the curve, we find the intercepts. The y-intercept is $f(0) = 2$.
The x-intercepts occur when the numerator equals 0.
$$x^2 - x - 2 = 0$$
$$(x - 2)(x + 1) = 0$$
$$x = 2 \text{ or } x = -1$$
Using the above information, we sketch the curve, with the asymptotes shown as dotted lines.

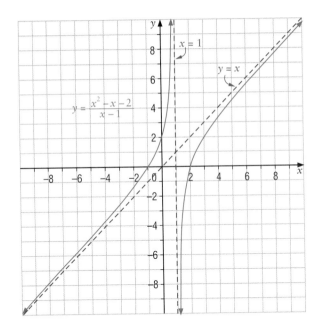

Key Concepts

- Limits at infinity
  a) The line $y = L$ is called a horizontal asymptote of the curve $y = f(x)$ if $\lim_{x \to \infty} f(x) = L$, $\lim_{x \to -\infty} f(x) = L$, or both.

  b) If r is a positive integer, then $\lim_{x \to \infty} \dfrac{1}{x^r} = 0$ and $\lim_{x \to -\infty} \dfrac{1}{x^r} = 0$.

  c) Infinite limits at infinity can be expressed as
  $$\lim_{x \to \infty} f(x) = \infty \qquad \lim_{x \to \infty} f(x) = -\infty \qquad \lim_{x \to -\infty} f(x) = \infty \qquad \lim_{x \to -\infty} f(x) = -\infty$$

- The line $y = mx + b$ is a linear oblique asymptote for the curve $y = f(x)$ if the vertical distance between the curve and the line approaches 0 as the absolute value of x gets large.

- A summary of the possible end behaviour of a rational function:
  a) if degree of numerator < degree of denominator, the graph has a horizontal asymptote $y = 0$
  b) if degree of numerator = degree of denominator, the graph has a horizontal asymptote other than $y = 0$
  c) if degree of numerator = degree of denominator + 1, the graph has a linear oblique asymptote
  d) if the degree of the numerator exceeds the degree of the denominator by more than 1, the graph will have neither a horizontal asymptote nor a linear oblique asymptote

Communicate Your Understanding

1. a) What does $\lim\limits_{x \to \infty} f(x) = L$ mean?

b) Explain the difference between $\lim\limits_{x \to \infty} f(x) = L$ and $\lim\limits_{x \to -\infty} f(x) = L$.

2. How can you convince someone who has not studied limits at infinity that $\lim\limits_{x \to \infty} \dfrac{1}{x^r} = 0$ if r is a positive integer?

3. If $f(x)$ is a rational function, state the steps necessary to evaluate $\lim\limits_{x \to \infty} f(x)$.

4. a) Under what conditions does a rational function have a linear oblique asymptote?
b) Explain how to find the linear oblique asymptote of a rational function that satisfies the conditions in part a).

5. Linear oblique asymptotes to a rational function occur when the degree of the denominator is 1 less than the degree of the numerator. Explain why this is so.

6. If a rational function has a linear oblique asymptote, can it also have a horizontal asymptote? Explain.

Practise

A **1.** For each of the following, state the equations of the horizontal and vertical asymptotes, if they exist. If they do not exist, explain why.

a)

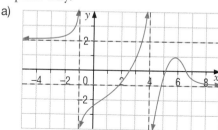

b)

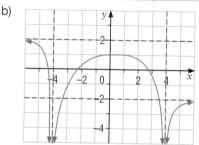

2. Determine whether each curve has a linear oblique asymptote. If it does, state its equation.

a) $f(x) = 2x^2 + 3 + \dfrac{1}{x}$

b) $y = 3 - x - \dfrac{1}{x}$

c) $h(x) = 3x - 2 + \dfrac{2}{x} + \dfrac{3}{x^2}$

d) $g(x) = 5 - \dfrac{3}{x}$

e) $g(x) = \dfrac{x^2 - 2x + 3}{x}$

f) $y = \dfrac{x^2 + 1}{x^3 + 2x^2 + 3x - 4}$

B **3.** Find each limit.

a) $\lim\limits_{x \to \infty} \dfrac{3}{x}$

b) $\lim\limits_{x \to -\infty} \dfrac{12}{x}$

c) $\lim\limits_{x \to \infty} \dfrac{4x}{x^6}$

d) $\lim\limits_{x \to -\infty} \dfrac{6}{x^3}$

e) $\lim\limits_{x \to -\infty} \dfrac{-5}{x^5}$

f) $\lim\limits_{x \to \infty} \dfrac{3x + 2}{x - 1}$

g) $\lim\limits_{x \to -\infty} \dfrac{3x + 2}{x - 1}$

h) $\lim\limits_{x \to \infty} \dfrac{4 - x^3}{3 + 2x^3}$

i) $\lim\limits_{x \to \infty} \dfrac{x + 7}{x^2 - 7x + 5}$

4. Find each limit.

a) $\lim\limits_{x \to -\infty} \dfrac{x^2 + 5x - 9}{x^2 - 4x + 7}$

b) $\lim\limits_{x \to \infty} \dfrac{x^2 - 2x + 7}{x^2 + 8x + 1}$

c) $\lim\limits_{x \to \infty} \dfrac{x^2 - 1}{(x + 2)(2x - 5)}$

d) $\lim\limits_{x \to -\infty} \dfrac{5x^3 - 12x^2 + 11}{x^3 + 4x^2 + 6}$

e) $\lim\limits_{x \to \infty} \dfrac{6x^2 - 5x + 2}{3x^3 + 3x^2 - 4}$

f) $\lim\limits_{x \to -\infty} \dfrac{x^4 - x + 5}{x^5 - 3x + 6}$

Apply, Solve, Communicate

5. Find the equation of the horizontal asymptote of each curve.

a) $f(x) = \dfrac{2x-3}{5-x}$

b) $g(x) = \dfrac{x}{x^2-4}$

c) $y = \dfrac{3-8x}{2x+5}$

d) $y = \dfrac{x^2+1}{x^2-1}$

e) $h(x) = 1 - \dfrac{x}{x^2-9}$

f) $y = \dfrac{6x^2+4x+1}{5-3x^2}$

6. Find an equation of the oblique asymptote of each curve.

a) $y = \dfrac{3x^2-4x+5}{x}$

b) $h(x) = \dfrac{x^3-4}{x^2}$

c) $y = \dfrac{2x^2+4x+1}{x+1}$

d) $y = \dfrac{6x^2}{3x-2}$

e) $f(x) = \dfrac{x^3+5x^2+3x+10}{x^2+2}$

f) $g(x) = \dfrac{2x-x^2-x^4}{x^3-2}$

7. Find all horizontal and vertical asymptotes. Use them, together with the intercepts, to sketch the graph.

a) $g(x) = \dfrac{3}{x-1}$

b) $y = \dfrac{3x}{x+2}$

c) $y = \dfrac{x-1}{x+1}$

d) $v(r) = \dfrac{6r+7}{2r-7}$

e) $y = \dfrac{3x+4}{1-x}$

f) $g(t) = \dfrac{9t-6}{1-3t}$

8. Find the linear oblique asymptote of each curve and use it to help you sketch the graph. Use a graphing calculator or graphing software to check your result.

a) $y = 2x+3+\dfrac{3}{x+1}$

b) $g(x) = -2x+\dfrac{2}{x+2}$

c) $y = \dfrac{x^2+4}{x}$

d) $y = \dfrac{x^2-4}{x-4}$

e) $s(t) = \dfrac{t^2-3t-10}{1-t}$

f) $y = \dfrac{x^2+5x+4}{x-1}$

9. Application A piece of machinery depreciates in value, V, in dollars, over time, t, in months. The value is given by

$$V(t) = 5000 - \dfrac{2000t^2}{(t+2)^2}$$

a) Find the value of the machinery after
   i) 1 month   ii) 6 months
   iii) 1 year   iv) 10 years

b) Would you expect to find a local maximum or minimum value in the interval $[0, \infty)$? Explain.

c) Find $\lim\limits_{t \to \infty} V(t)$.

d) Will the machinery ever have a value of 0?

e) In light of your result in part d), does $V(t)$ model the value of the machinery for all time?

10. Inquiry/Problem Solving A telecommunications company's sales for the last 20 years can be modelled by the function $S(n) = \dfrac{20n^2+2n+4}{17n+4}$, where $S(n)$ represents annual sales, in millions of dollars, and n represents the number of years since the company's founding.

a) Find $\lim\limits_{n \to \infty} S(n)$. Interpret this result.

b) If the long-term average rate of inflation is 3.3%, what is the true rate of growth of the company?

11. Application A company that installs carpet charges $600 for any area less than or equal to 40 m^2 and an additional $20/m^2 for any area over 40 m^2.

a) Find a piecewise function $y = c(x)$ to represent the average cost, per square metre, to install x square metres of carpet.

b) Find $\lim\limits_{x \to \infty} c(x)$. Explain what this limit means.

c) Graph $y = c(x)$ for values of $x > 0$.

d) Would you call this company to carpet a very small area? Explain.

12. Application A new employee at a computer store suggests to the manager that they are not giving good enough incentives for customers who place large orders. Their current pricing is a flat rate of $100 for delivery (no matter how many computers are ordered) and $1200 per computer. The employee suggests a new billing formula, $C(x) = \dfrac{100+1200x-2x^2}{x}$, where $C(x)$ represents the average cost per computer for x computers.

a) Write a formula for $A(x)$, the average cost per computer, using the company's current pricing.

b) Graph $A(x)$ and $C(x)$ on the same set of axes for the domain $x \in [0, 100]$. Which pricing formula is better for the customer who orders a large number of computers? Explain.

c) Find $\lim\limits_{x \to \infty} A(x)$ and explain its meaning.

d) Find $\lim\limits_{x \to \infty} C(x)$. Is this limit meaningful? Explain.

e) In light of your response to part d), should the computer company use a different formula for orders of more than 100 computers? Explain.

C **13.** Find the horizontal asymptotes of $y = \dfrac{2x}{|x| + 1}$.

14. Find each limit.

a) $\lim\limits_{x \to \infty} \dfrac{\sqrt{4x^2 + 5}}{2x - 1}$ b) $\lim\limits_{x \to \infty} (\sqrt{x^2 + 3x + 5} - x)$

15. Application Two curves are said to be asymptotic if the vertical distance between the two approaches zero in some limit. For a rational function, if the degree of the numerator exceeds the degree of the denominator by more than 1, then the graph of the function is asymptotic to a polynomial of degree more than 1.

a) Let $f(x) = \dfrac{x^3 + 1}{x}$. Show that $\lim\limits_{x \to \infty} [f(x) - x^2] = 0$. To which curve is the graph of f asymptotic?

b) Sketch the graph of f. On the same axes, graph the polynomial function to which f is asymptotic.

c) The polynomial to which a rational function is asymptotic can be determined in the same way as linear oblique asymptotes, by dividing the numerator by the denominator and then taking an appropriate limit. Determine the polynomial function to which each rational function is asymptotic. Then, sketch the rational function and the asymptotic curve.

i) $g(x) = \dfrac{5x^4 + 1}{x^2 + 1}$ ii) $h(x) = \dfrac{3x^3 - 2x^2 + 1}{x + 1}$

d) Show that for a rational function, if the degree of the numerator exceeds the degree of the denominator by k, then the function is asymptotic to a polynomial of degree k. State any restrictions on the value of k.

16. Find $\lim\limits_{x \to \infty} \left(1 - \dfrac{3}{x}\right)^x$ using

a) a graphing calculator or graphing software to obtain a result correct to two decimal places

b) any method to obtain an answer correct to four decimal places

Historical Bite: Mathematics Before Algebra

In the middle ages, algebraic notation was not yet invented. As an example, Luca Pacioli (1445–1557) wrote in 1494 on how to solve a quadratic equation:

"If a thing and its square equal a number, you must square half of the thing and add it to the number. Then subtract half of the thing from the root of the total. You will have left the root plus the square."

It is amazing that any problems were solved when all of the techniques had to be recorded like this.

Curve Sketching

As modelling becomes more sophisticated in our technologically advanced society, more and more complicated functions are being used. Graphing technology is usually able to provide a good picture of the features of a graph. However, there are many occasions when a graph so produced is deceptive. For example, the function $f(x) = 4x^5 + 45x^4$ appears as shown when it is graphed in the standard window $x \in [-10, 10]$, $y \in [-10, 10]$.

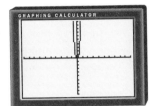

This function actually has a local maximum point in addition to the evident local minimum at $(0, 0)$. Our knowledge of calculus will lead us to this additional information. The analytic tools that we have developed so far in this chapter complement the tools that technology provides.

Depending on the situation, it may be better to use one or the other of technology and analytic tools exclusively, or else a combination of the two, to determine the important features of a function.

To begin, we focus on the analytic tools. Our general strategy for sketching curves is to
- frame the curve (domain restrictions, asymptotes, general shape)
- find important points (intercepts, extrema, points of inflection)
- add details (symmetry, intervals of increase/decrease, concavity)
- sketch the curve

Our goal will be to use as few tools as necessary to develop a sketch showing the important features of the function. The order and completeness of steps taken may vary with the nature of the function and the tools used.

Example 1 Using Analytic Tools to Sketch a Graph

Sketch the curve $y = x^3 - 6x^2 + 9x$.

Solution

Although technology can readily produce this graph, we use the initial examples to illustrate the tools of calculus.
- Frame the curve

This is a cubic polynomial whose domain is $x \in (-\infty, \infty)$.
The general shape of this curve is one of two possibilities as shown.
A polynomial has no asymptotes, but it is still useful to note that

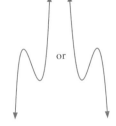

$$\lim_{x \to \infty}(x^3 - 6x^2 + 9x) = \infty \text{ and } \lim_{x \to -\infty}(x^3 - 6x^2 + 9x) = -\infty. \text{ This}$$

eliminates the second possibility for the shape of the curve.

- Find important points

The y-intercept is 0. (Let $x = 0$.)
The x-intercepts occur when $y = 0$.
$$x^3 - 6x^2 + 9x = 0$$
$$x(x^2 - 6x + 9) = 0$$
$$x(x - 3)^2 = 0$$

The x-intercepts are 0 and 3. Note that, since the factor $(x - 3)$ is squared, there is a double root at $x = 3$, and the y-values do not change sign at this point. Combining all we know so far, we get the approximate sketch at right.

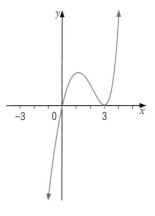

Next, we determine the coordinates of the local maximum and local minimum.

$y' = 3x^2 - 12x + 9$
$\quad = 3(x^2 - 4x + 3)$
$\quad = 3(x - 1)(x - 3)$
$y'' = 6x - 12$
$\quad = 6(x - 2)$

To determine the critical numbers, set $y' = 0$. The critical numbers are $x = 1$ and $x = 3$. Just by looking at the sketches we made, we can tell that a local minimum occurs at $(3, 0)$ and a local maximum occurs at $(1, 4)$. We could use the second derivative test to verify this.

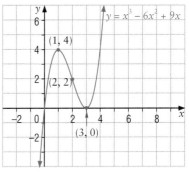

To determine the point of inflection, note that y'' changes sign at $x = 2$. Thus, $(2, 2)$ is a point of inflection.

- Sketch the curve

The graph shows the completed sketch.

The graph shows the completed sketch.

Example 2 Using Analytic Tools to Sketch a Graph

Sketch the graph of the function $f(x) = \dfrac{x^2}{1 - x^2}$ using analytic tools.

Solution

- Frame the curve

In factored form, the function is written as $f(x) = \dfrac{x^2}{(1 - x)(1 + x)}$.

Since the numerator and the denominator have no common factors, we set the denominator equal to zero to find the vertical asymptotes.

$(1 - x)(1 + x) = 0$
$x = 1 \quad \text{or} \quad x = -1$

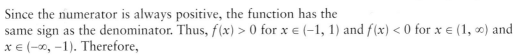

Since the numerator is always positive, the function has the same sign as the denominator. Thus, $f(x) > 0$ for $x \in (-1, 1)$ and $f(x) < 0$ for $x \in (1, \infty)$ and $x \in (-\infty, -1)$. Therefore,

$$\lim_{x \to -1^-} \frac{x^2}{1 - x^2} = -\infty \qquad \lim_{x \to -1^+} \frac{x^2}{1 - x^2} = \infty \qquad \lim_{x \to 1^-} \frac{x^2}{1 - x^2} = \infty \qquad \lim_{x \to 1^+} \frac{x^2}{1 - x^2} = -\infty$$

Since the degree of the numerator is equal to the degree of the denominator, there is a horizontal asymptote other than $y = 0$. We find the horizontal asymptote by dividing each term by x^2.

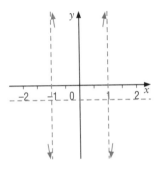

$$\lim_{x \to \pm\infty} \frac{x^2}{1-x^2} = \lim_{x \to \pm\infty} \frac{1}{\frac{1}{x^2} - 1}$$

$$= \frac{1}{0-1}$$

$$= -1$$

The horizontal asymptote is $y = -1$.

- Find important points

The y-intercept is $f(0) = 0$. The origin is also the only x-intercept.

There is almost enough information to sketch the curve. We need to check for the presence of extrema and points of inflection. We need the first and second derivatives.

$$f'(x) = \frac{(1-x^2)(2x) - x^2(-2x)}{(1-x^2)^2}$$

$$= \frac{2x}{(1-x^2)^2}$$

$$f''(x) = \frac{(1-x^2)^2(2) - (2x)2(1-x^2)(-2x)}{(1-x^2)^4}$$

$$= \frac{2 + 6x^2}{(1-x^2)^3}$$

The critical numbers are 0 (when $2x = 0$) and ± 1 (when f' is undefined). We already know how f behaves at the asymptotes $x = \pm 1$. To determine whether the function has a maximum or a minimum value at $x = 0$, note that $f''(0) = 2 > 0$, so the point $(0, 0)$ is a local minimum.

To determine points of inflection, we need to find where $f''(x)$ changes sign. If we examine the expression for $f''(x)$, we see that the only places it can change sign are at $x = 1$ and $x = -1$. Since the function is not defined at these points, there are no points of inflection.

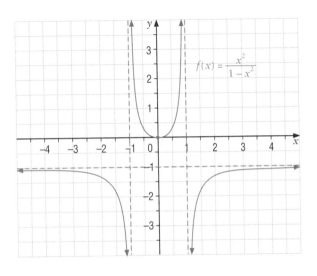

- Add details

Since $f(-x) = f(x)$, this is an even function. Thus, it is symmetric about the y-axis. It is not necessary to determine intervals of increase/decrease or concavity when the other information we have collected is considered.

- Sketch the curve

Example 3 Using Analysis and Technology to Sketch a Graph

Analyse the function $f(x) = \dfrac{x^3 + 1}{x^2 + 3x}$ and sketch its curve.

Solution

It may appear that this function can be easily analysed using calculus techniques. However, we shall see that the details are sufficiently complex that technology is a good tool here.

• Frame the curve

This is a rational function, so we set the denominator equal to zero to find the asymptotes.

$x^2 + 3x = 0$

$x(x + 3) = 0$

Therefore, $x = 0$ and $x = -3$ are vertical asymptotes.

Since the degree of the numerator is one more than the degree of the denominator, we expect to find a linear oblique asymptote. Use long division to rewrite the function.

$$
\begin{array}{r}
x - 3 \\
x^2 + 3x \overline{\smash{\big)}\, x^3 + 0x^2 + 0x + 1} \\
\underline{x^3 + 3x^2} \\
-3x^2 + 0x + 1 \\
\underline{-3x^2 - 9x} \\
9x + 1
\end{array}
$$

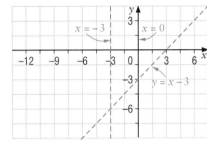

Thus, $f(x) = x - 3 + \dfrac{9x + 1}{x^2 + 3x}$.

In the second term, the absolute value of the denominator grows much more quickly than the numerator as x approaches positive or negative infinity. Thus, the linear oblique asymptote is $y = x - 3$.

• Add details

We check the behaviour of the curve near the asymptotes using Ask mode on the TABLE SETUP screen.

  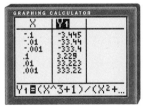

$$\lim_{x \to -3^-} \frac{x^3 + 1}{x^2 + 3x} = -\infty \quad \lim_{x \to -3^+} \frac{x^3 + 1}{x^2 + 3x} = \infty \quad \lim_{x \to 0^-} \frac{x^3 + 1}{x^2 + 3x} = -\infty \quad \lim_{x \to 0^+} \frac{x^3 + 1}{x^2 + 3x} = +\infty$$

To determine where the graph of f is in relation to its linear oblique asymptote, test a large positive value and a large negative value.

$$f(100) = \frac{100^3 + 1}{100^2 + 3(100)} \qquad f(-100) = \frac{(-100)^3 + 1}{(-100)^2 + 3(-100)}$$

$$\doteq 97.1 \qquad\qquad\qquad \doteq -103.1$$

At $x = 100$, $y = x - 3$ is equal to 97. Thus, the function is above the asymptote. At $x = -100$, $y = x - 3$ is equal to -103. Thus, the function is below the asymptote.

- Find important points

There is no y-intercept since $x = 0$ is not in the domain of the function.
To find the x-intercepts, determine when $f(x) = 0$.

$$\frac{x^3 + 1}{x^2 + 3x} = 0$$

$$x^3 + 1 = 0$$

Use the factor theorem. One factor is $x + 1$.

Find the other factor using long division.

$$
\begin{array}{r}
x^2 - x + 1 \\
x + 1 \overline{)\, x^3 + 0x^2 + 0x + 1} \\
\underline{x^3 + x^2} \\
-x^2 + 0x \\
\underline{-x^2 - x} \\
x + 1 \\
\underline{x + 1} \\
0
\end{array}
$$

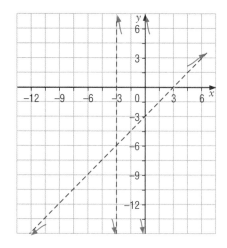

Web Connection

For more technological approaches to graph sketching, go to **www.mcgrawhill.ca/links/CAF12** and follow the link.

Since $x^2 - x + 1$ is not factorable over the real numbers, the only x-intercept is $x = -1$.

To determine the critical numbers, find the first derivative.

$$f'(x) = \frac{(x^2 + 3x)3x^2 - (x^3 + 1)(2x + 3)}{(x^2 + 3x)^2}$$

$$= \frac{3x^4 + 9x^3 - (2x^4 + 3x^3 + 2x + 3)}{x^2(x + 3)^2}$$

$$= \frac{x^4 + 6x^3 - 2x - 3}{x^2(x + 3)^2}$$

After some algebra, $f''(x)$ turns out as follows.

$$f''(x) = \frac{6(3x^3 + x^2 + 3x + 3)}{x^3(x + 3)^3}$$

To find the critical numbers, we set $f'(x) = 0$.
Thus, $x^4 + 6x^3 - 2x - 3 = 0$.
The critical numbers can be found with the aid of technology.

 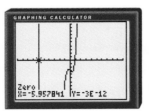 

Window variables: $x \in [-10, 10]$, $y \in [-10, 10]$ or use the ZStandard instruction.

The critical numbers are approximately $x = -5.958$ and $x = 0.885$.

From our sketches so far, we can see that a local maximum occurs at the first critical number, and a local minimum occurs at the second critical number. The function values at these points are approximately -11.944 and 0.492, respectively. Thus, the local maximum occurs at approximately $(-5.958, -11.944)$, and the local minimum occurs at approximately $(0.885, 0.492)$.

We can again use technology to determine when the second derivative changes sign. The second derivative changes sign at the asymptotes, but these cannot be points of inflection because the function is not defined there. To determine where else the second derivative changes sign, set $f''(x) = 0$.

$$\frac{6(3x^3 + x^2 + 3x + 3)}{x^3(x + 3)^3} = 0$$

$$3x^3 + x^2 + 3x + 3 = 0$$

Use the Zero operation to find the zeros.

Window variables: $x \in [-10, 10]$, $y \in [-10, 10]$

There is one point of inflection. Its x-value is approximately -0.757. The coordinates of the point of inflection are approximately $(-0.757, -0.333)$.

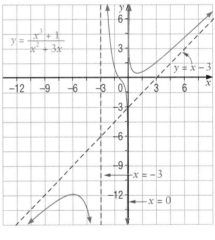

$$y = \frac{x^3 + 1}{x^2 + 3x}$$

$y = x - 3$

$x = -3$

$x = 0$

• Sketch the curve

It appears that this function would have been better handled by technology alone. If we use the ZDecimal instruction to graph it in the friendly window, $x \in [-4.7, 4.7]$, $y \in [-3.1, 3.1]$, most relevant details appear. However, we would still have to calculate the coordinates for the point of inflection and the local extrema.

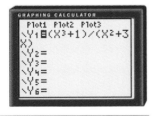 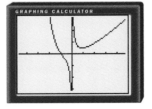

Example 4 Using Technology and Analysis to Sketch a Graph

Graph the function $f(x) = \dfrac{x^2(x+2)^3}{(x-2)^2(x-4)^4}$.

Solution

We begin with the graphing calculator in the standard window, $x \in [-10, 10]$, $y \in [-10, 10]$.

 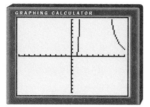

This is a good start but it appears that we will have to zoom out to get the overall picture and also zoom in to get detail about critical points.

To guide our zooming, we examine the formula for f. We expect vertical asymptotes at $x = 2$ and $x = 4$, because that is where the denominator is equal to 0. From the graph, we

can see that $\displaystyle\lim_{x \to 2^-} \dfrac{x^2(x+2)^3}{(x-2)^2(x-4)^4} = \infty$ and $\displaystyle\lim_{x \to 4^+} \dfrac{x^2(x+2)^3}{(x-2)^2(x-4)^4} = \infty$. But what happens

between $x = 2$ and $x = 4$? Use the [TRACE] key to find a couple of y-values in this region.

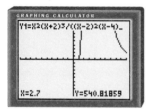 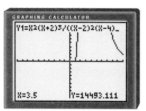

Clearly, the values of f are very large in this region. We look at the graph in a region with very large y-values.

The almost vertical line is a result of the graphing calculator trying to connect points across the asymptote $x = 2$, so we ignore it. It appears that there is a local minimum in this area. We can also determine the behaviour of the function near the asymptotes in this region:

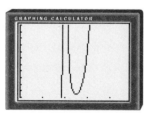

Window variables:
$x \in [0, 4.7]$, $y \in [400, 1500]$

$$\lim_{x \to 2^+} \dfrac{x^2(x+2)^3}{(x-2)^2(x-4)^4} = \infty \text{ and } \lim_{x \to 4^-} \dfrac{x^2(x+2)^3}{(x-2)^2(x-4)^4} = \infty$$

Since the degree of the denominator is greater than the degree of the numerator, the x-axis is a horizontal asymptote.

Examining the numerator, we see that 0 and –2 are *x*-intercepts. Since the first factor is squared, we know that the function does not change sign at this point. The graph does cross the *x*-axis at –2 since the second factor, $(x + 2)$, is cubed. This suggests that our curve should look roughly as shown (not to scale).

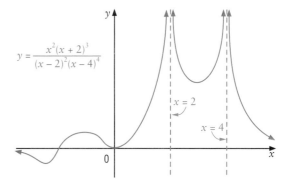

$$y = \frac{x^2(x + 2)^3}{(x - 2)^2(x - 4)^4}$$

Zooming by trial and error using the Zoom In and Zoom Out instructions produces the following screens that show the important details.

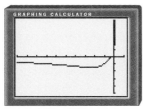

$x \in [-100, 10]$,
$y \in [-0.05, 0.05]$

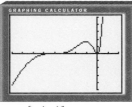

$x \in [-4, 1]$,
$y \in [-0.001, 0.001]$

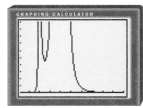

$x \in [0.2, 10]$,
$y \in [-10, 1000]$

If we need more precise information about the maximum or minimum points, or points of inflection, graphing technology can provide approximations. The calculation of f' and f'' by hand would be a tedious task; a computer algebra system would make it easy.

The only way to show all of this information in one image is to draw a sketch by hand, such as our rough sketch above, but with significant details added.

Key Concepts

- Curve sketching can be performed with analytic calculus tools, with technology, or with a combination of both. Tools should be selected carefully, but every step should be justifiable with the tools of calculus.
- The tools of technology and calculus complement each other when sketching curves and investigating important aspects of functions.
- A graph can be sketched analytically using the following steps:
  a) frame the curve
  b) find important points
  c) add details
  d) sketch the curve
- Technology can help you graph functions that are too complicated to graph using calculus alone.
- Calculus can help you spot important features of a graph that are not initially seen using graphing technology.

Communicate Your Understanding

1. If you have a graphing calculator, explain why you still need calculus to graph functions.

2. Answer each question and explain your reasoning.

a) The domain of a function is $(-\infty, \infty)$. Can the function have a vertical asymptote? What about a horizontal or oblique asymptote?

b) A function has a vertical asymptote. Can the domain of the function be $(-\infty, \infty)$?

c) A function is even. Can the function have only one local maximum or minimum value? What if the function is odd?

d) If $f'(a) = 0$, and $f(a)$ is a local maximum or a minimum value, can it also be a point of inflection?

e) If $f'(a)$ is not defined, and $f(a)$ is a local maximum or a minimum value, can it also be a point of inflection?

f) Can a function have a maximum, a minimum, or a point of inflection at $x = a$, if a is not in the domain of f?

3. The sketch of a graph is given. Discuss the significance of the parts of the graph indicated.

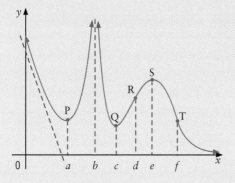

a) points P, Q, R, S, T

b) intervals $(-\infty, a)$, (a, b), (b, c), (c, d), (d, e), (e, f), (f, ∞)

Practise

A **1.** Match the graphs opposite with the functions below, using your knowledge of limits and asymptotes.

a) $f(x) = \dfrac{1}{x-2}$

b) $g(x) = \dfrac{x}{x-2}$

c) $y = \dfrac{1}{x^2-4}$

d) $f(x) = \dfrac{1}{(x-2)^2}$

e) $y = \dfrac{1}{2-x}$

f) $q(x) = \dfrac{x^2}{x-2}$

g) $f(x) = \dfrac{x}{x^2-4}$

h) $y = \dfrac{x}{(x-2)^2}$

i) $g(x) = \dfrac{x^2}{2-x}$

j) $k(x) = \dfrac{x^2}{x^2-4}$

k) $y = -\dfrac{1}{(2-x)^2}$

l) $f(x) = \dfrac{x^3}{x^2-4}$

i)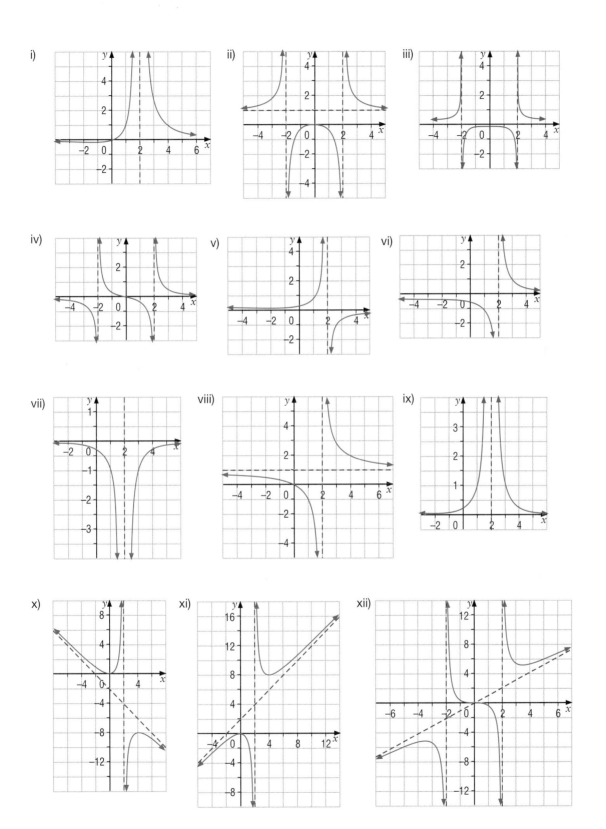

ii)

iii)

iv)

v)

vi)

vii)

viii)

ix)

x)

xi)

xii)

2. Jessica was sketching the graph of a function but did not have time to finish it. She lost some of her notes, including the formula for the function, but still has the information below. Use the information to sketch the graph.

The domain of the function is the set of all real numbers except $x = 1$ and $x = -1$.

$$\lim_{x \to 1^+} f(x) = -\infty$$

$$\lim_{x \to 1^-} f(x) = \infty$$

$$\lim_{x \to -1^-} f(x) = -\infty$$

$$\lim_{x \to -1^+} f(x) = \infty$$

$$\lim_{x \to \infty} f(x) = 0, \ f(x) < 0 \text{ as } x \to \infty$$

$$\lim_{x \to -\infty} f(x) = 0, \ f(x) < 0 \text{ as } x \to -\infty$$

The y-intercept is 2. There are no x-intercepts.

Apply, Solve, Communicate

B 3. Sketch each function. Find the exact coordinates of all maximum and minimum points, and points of inflection.
a) $y = x^3 + x$
b) $y = 2x^3 + 15x^2 - 36x$
c) $g(x) = (x^2 - 4)^3$
d) $f(x) = 3x^5 - 5x^3$
e) $y = 3x^4 - 4x^3 - 12x^2 + 2$
f) $h(x) = 2 - 15x + 9x^2 - x^3$

4. Inquiry/Problem Solving Sketch each function without using technology. Following the format of the examples, show enough steps to justify your sketch.

a) $y = \dfrac{x - 2}{x + 2}$
b) $f(t) = \dfrac{24}{12 + t^2}$

c) $y = \dfrac{x^2 - 1}{x^2 + 1}$
d) $y = \dfrac{x}{x^2 - 4}$

e) $y = \dfrac{3x}{x^2 + 1}$
f) $g(x) = \dfrac{2x^2}{x^2 - 1}$

g) $y = \dfrac{4x}{(x - 1)^2}$
h) $h(x) = \dfrac{3}{x - x^3}$

i) $y = \dfrac{x^2 - 1}{x^3}$

5. Sketch each curve using technology and analytic calculus methods where appropriate. For each curve, determine the equations of the asymptotes and the exact coordinates of any local extrema.

a) $f(x) = x - \dfrac{1}{x}$
b) $f(x) = 1 + 2x + \dfrac{x}{x - 1}$

c) $y = 1 + 2x + \dfrac{x}{x^2 - 1}$
d) $y = \dfrac{x^2 + 4}{x}$

e) $y = \dfrac{x^2 - 2x - 3}{x}$
f) $h(t) = \dfrac{t^3}{t^2 - 1}$

g) $y = \dfrac{-2(x - 1)^3}{x^2}$
h) $f(x) = \dfrac{x^2}{x + 2}$

6. Application In order to fit properly into an architectural design, a pipe needs to be manufactured with the equation $y = \dfrac{2}{x^2 + 1}$, for $x \in [-4, 4]$, defining its shape. All measurements are in centimetres. Sketch a graph of the pipe's shape.

7. Application A cylindrical drum is to be made to have a capacity of 40 L. The resulting formula for the height is $h = \dfrac{40\,000}{\pi r^2}$, and for the surface area of the sheet metal is $S = 2\pi r^2 + \dfrac{80\,000}{r}$, where r is the radius in centimetres.
a) Sketch a graph of the relation between height and radius.
b) Sketch a graph of the relation between surface area and radius.

8. Communication According to Coulomb's law, the force between two charged particles is directly proportional to the product of the charges and inversely proportional to the square of the distance between them. The figure shows three charges, one positive charge placed at the origin, another equal positive charge placed at $x = 4$, and a negative charge that can move along the x-axis. The positions of the positive charges are constant. From Coulomb's law, the magnitude of the force on the negative charge is given by the equation $F(x) = \dfrac{1}{(x - 4)^2} - \dfrac{1}{x^2}$.

MODELLING MATH

(provided the units are chosen appropriately), where x is the position of the negative charge, and $0 < x < 4$.

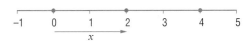

a) Sketch the graph of the force function.
b) Where is the force undefined? Explain, physically, why this is so.
c) Where is the force 0? Explain in the context of physics.

9. Sketch each function.

a) $f(x) = \begin{cases} \dfrac{x-3}{x-1}, & x \le 0 \\ \dfrac{1}{x^2}, & x > 0 \end{cases}$

b) $f(x) = \begin{cases} \dfrac{1}{x}, & x < 0 \\ -2, & x \ge 0 \end{cases}$

10. Application i) Use technology to obtain the graph of each function.
ii) From the graph, give a rough estimate of the intervals of concavity and the location of any points of inflection.
iii) Use the graph of g'' to give better estimates for these values.
a) $g(x) = 4x^5 - 40x^3 + 30x^2$
b) $g(x) = -3x^5 + 25x^3 - 15x^2 + 110x$

11. Application i) Use technology to graph each function.
ii) From the graph, estimate the local maximum and minimum values.
iii) Find the exact values of the extrema in part a).
a) $h(x) = \dfrac{x^4}{(x-3)^2}$

b) $h(x) = 4 - 3x + \dfrac{6x-9}{x^2+3x}$

12. Communication Sketch a graph by hand for each function, using intercepts and asymptotes, but not derivatives. Make your sketch as accurate as possible.

a) $y = \dfrac{(x+5)(x-4)^2}{x^4(x-2)}$

b) $h(x) = \dfrac{5x(x-2)^4}{(x-3)^3(x+1)^2}$

c) $y = \dfrac{x^4(x-3)}{(x-2)^2(x+4)^3}$

d) $f(x) = \dfrac{x^3(x-3)^2}{(x-2)(x+1)^3}$

13. Inquiry/Problem Solving Consider the family of curves defined by $y = \dfrac{(x-1)^2(x^2+2x+k)}{x^3}$.
a) Using technology, sketch the curve for five different values of k. Do the graphs have any similar features? Describe them.
b) Show that $y = x$ is a linear oblique asymptote for every value of k.
c) For what values of k do the curves intersect the asymptote?
d) Which values of k lead to two x-intercepts?

C **14.** Consider the function f, where f and f' are both differentiable, $f'(x) > 0$ for all x, $f''(x) < 0$ for $x < 0$, and $f''(x) > 0$ for $x > 0$.
Let $g(x) = f(x^2)$.
a) For which values of x does g have a critical number?
b) Discuss the concavity of g.

15. Find a cubic function $f(x) = ax^3 + bx^2 + cx + d$ that has a local maximum at $(-3, 3)$ and a local minimum at $(2, 0)$.

16. a) Show that a cubic function has exactly one point of inflection.
b) If the graph has x-intercepts p, q, and r, show that the x-coordinate of the point of inflection is $\dfrac{p+q+r}{3}$.

17. a) For which values of p does the quartic polynomial function $Q(x) = x^4 + px^3 + x^2$ have each number of points of inflection?
i) exactly two   ii) exactly one
iii) zero
b) Illustrate your results in part a) by sketching Q for several values of p.

18. Consider the general cubic function, $f(x) = ax^3 + bx^2 + cx + d$, where $a \neq 0$.

a) Show that $f''(x) = 0$ when $x = -\dfrac{b}{3a}$.

b) Show that the graph of f has an inflection point, and determine its coordinates.

c) Determine a translation of the graph of f that brings its inflection point to the origin. One way to do this is to introduce new coordinates X and Y, and to determine equations that relate the new coordinates to the old ones, such that, when expressed in the new coordinates, the cubic curve has its inflection point at the origin.

d) The cubic curve in part c), which has its inflection point at the origin, defines a new function, $Y = F(X)$. Determine a formula for F.

e) Determine the symmetry properties of the function of part d).

f) Using the results of parts a) to e), make a general conclusion about the symmetry properties of all cubic functions.

19. Consider question 18. Pose and solve a related problem for quadratic functions, which culminates in a general conclusion about the symmetry properties of all quadratic functions.

20. a) Is it possible to generalize the analysis of questions 18 and 19 to general quartic functions? Before tackling this general problem, begin by graphing a number of specific quartic functions. Do they all share the same symmetry properties? If so what is the property? If not, what other conclusions can you make?

b) If it is possible to state a general symmetry property of all quartic functions, make such a conjecture and adapt the ideas of questions 18 and 19 to prove the conjecture.

c) If it is not possible to make a general statement about the symmetry properties of all quartic functions, is it possible to make a statement about a large class of quartic functions? If so, determine the largest class of quartic functions that shares a nice symmetry property. If not, explain why.

d) If possible, extend your analysis to polynomials of higher degree.

Achievement Check

Knowledge/Understanding

Thinking/Inquiry/Problem Solving

Communication

Application

a) Sketch a graph of a continuous function that satisfies all of the following conditions.

- $f'(x) > 0$ for $x \in (0, 1)$
- $f'(x) < 0$ for $x \in (1, \infty)$
- $f''(x) < 0$ for $x \in (0, 2)$
- $f''(x) > 0$ for $x \in (2, \infty)$
- $\lim\limits_{x \to +\infty} f(x) = 0$
- f is an odd function

b) Is your sketch the only solution? Explain.

c) If there is more than one solution, what are some of the necessary features? If your solution is the only one, which features cannot occur in any other function?

Introducing Optimization Problems

Packaging products in order to minimize the amount of materials used is a primary concern in operating a business. Furthermore, reducing packaging is an environmental concern for society as a whole. The problem of optimal packaging can be simplified to finding the optimal dimensions for geometric figures when given certain constraints. In this section, we will put our knowledge of finding maximum and minimum values of functions to practical use.

Investigate & Inquire: Optimal Dimensions of a Cereal Box

Consider a cereal box in the shape of a rectangular prism. Assume the box must have a capacity of 5000 cm^3, and the thickness of the box must be between 5 cm and 10 cm to allow for a comfortable grasp by most people. Use a graphing calculator to determine the dimensions of the box that require the minimum amount of materials for various fixed thicknesses. Ignore any overlap in order to join the faces of the box.

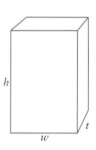

There are a number of ways to proceed. One strategy is as follows.

1. Write an equation for the surface area, A, in square centimetres, of the cereal box, and another equation for the capacity, V, in cubic centimetres, enclosed by the box. Given that $V = 5000$, solve the equation for V for one of the dimensions (not t) in terms of the other two. Then substitute this expression into the formula for A. The result should be an expression for A in terms of two variables, t and either w or h, depending on which you chose to solve for.   **$V = hwt$ and $A = 2hw + 2ht + 2wt$**

2. Now choose a value, for example $t = 5$, for the thickness of the box. Substitute this value into the formula for A obtained in step 1.

3. Enter the formula obtained in step 2 into the function editor of a graphing calculator or graphing software. Using the TABLE SETUP screen or the TRACE key, estimate the minimum value of the surface area.

4. Repeat steps 2 and 3 for several other values of t. Record your results for the minimum area in a table. Do you notice any patterns?

5. Which value of t appears to lead to the overall minimum surface area? What does the minimum surface area appear to be?

6. What are the approximate dimensions of the box that result in a minimum surface area and are also consistent with the stated restrictions?

7. Describe, and suggest reasons for, the patterns you observed in the minimum surface area as you changed the value of t.

You may have noticed a pattern in the results of your investigation: it seems that the greater the thickness of the box (at least for thicknesses between 5 cm and 10 cm), the smaller the minimum surface area of the box. This suggests that the minimum surface area of the box, consistent with the restrictions, occurs for a thickness of 10 cm. Using this fact, the dimensions of the optimal box can be found using methods developed in this chapter. This is done in Example 1.

Example 1 Optimal Dimensions of a Cereal Box

A cereal box in the shape of a rectangular prism is required to have a capacity of 5000 cm^3, and the thickness of the box must be 10 cm to allow for a comfortable grasp by most people. What dimensions of the box require the minimum amount of materials? Ignore any overlap needed to join the faces of the box.

Solution

A good strategy is to sketch the situation, identifying constant given data, and introducing appropriate variables. Also, we record any relationships among constants and variables as equations.

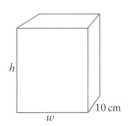

Variables: height h, width w, surface area A
Constants: thickness = 10 cm, capacity = 5000 cm^3

First, we write an equation for the quantity to be optimized, the surface area A.

A = area of front and back + area of top and bottom + area of left and right sides
$= 2(hw) + 2(w \times 10) + 2(h \times 10)$
$= 2hw + 20w + 20h$

To differentiate A, we must first express the equation for A in terms of one variable by relating h and w using given information. Since the capacity is 5000,
$5000 = h \times w \times 10$
$$w = \frac{500}{h}$$

Substituting this expression for w into the equation for A results in

$$A = 2h\left(\frac{500}{h}\right) + 20\left(\frac{500}{h}\right) + 20h$$

$$= 20\left(50 + \frac{500}{h} + h\right)$$

To minimize the function A, we find the critical numbers of A.

$$A' = 20\left(-\frac{500}{h^2} + 1\right)$$

Set the derivative equal to zero to obtain
$h^2 = 500$

$$h = \pm 10\sqrt{5}$$

Since h is the height of a real object, $h > 0$, we reject the negative result. Thus, $h = 10\sqrt{5}$.

To determine whether this value of h gives a maximum or a minimum value of A, we use the second derivative test.

$$A'' = \frac{20\,000}{h^3}$$

Since $A'' > 0$ for $h > 0$, $h = 10\sqrt{5}$ gives a minimum value of A.

To find the corresponding width of the box, substitute the value of h into the equation for w in terms of h, to obtain

$$w = \frac{500}{h}$$

$$= \frac{500}{10\sqrt{5}}$$

$$= 10\sqrt{5}$$

$10\sqrt{5} \doteq 22.4$, so the minimum surface area of the cereal box is obtained for dimensions 10 cm, 22.4 cm, and 22.4 cm. The graph of the function A verifies that a width of $w = 10\sqrt{5}$ gives a minimum, not a maximum.

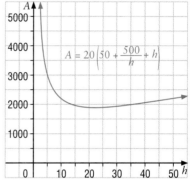

Example 2 Optimal Radius of a Can

Determine the most economical shape for a can of capacity 355 cm^3.

Solution

The capacity, V, in cubic centimetres, of a cylindrical can is given by $V = \pi r^2 h$, where the radius, r, and the height, h, are measured in centimetres. The surface area, S, in square centimetres, is given by $S = 2\pi rh + 2\pi r^2$. We want to find the minimum value of the surface area. Since the capacity is 355 cm^3, we will express the height in terms of the radius, and substitute this back into the formula for the surface area.

$$V = \pi r^2 h$$
$$355 = \pi r^2 h$$
$$h = \frac{355}{\pi r^2}$$

$$S = 2\pi rh + 2\pi r^2$$

$$= 2\pi r\left(\frac{355}{\pi r^2}\right) + 2\pi r^2$$

$$= \frac{710}{r} + 2\pi r^2$$

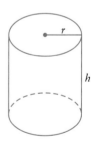

To find the critical points of $S(r)$, we determine when $S'(r) = 0$.

$$S'(r) = -\frac{710}{r^2} + 4\pi r$$

$$-\frac{710}{r^2} + 4\pi r = 0$$

$$2\pi r^3 = 355$$

$$r \doteq 3.84$$

Determine the value of $S'(r)$ on either side of the critical number 3.84. Test $r = 3$ and $r = 4$.

$$S'(3) = -\frac{710}{3^2} + 4\pi(3)$$

$$\doteq -41.2$$

$$S'(4) = -\frac{710}{4^2} + 4\pi(4)$$

$$\doteq 5.89$$

So, $S(r)$ is decreasing to the left of the critical number 3.84, and increasing to the right. Thus, $S(r)$ is a minimum at $r \doteq 3.84$. Determine the height at this radius.

$$h = \frac{355}{\pi r^2}$$

$$= \frac{355}{\pi(3.84)^2}$$

$$\doteq 7.66$$

Thus, the most economical cylindrical can has a radius of approximately 3.84 cm and a height of approximately 7.66 cm. Note that the height is approximately twice the radius. If we had not rounded the values, this relationship would be exact.

Example 3 Oil Spill Containment

The oil spill that is generally regarded as having caused the most serious ecological damage in the world occurred when the oil tanker Exxon Valdez ran aground in 1989. Over 40 000 000 L of crude oil contaminated the sea near Alaska. To contain oil spills, rectangular booms that have a cross-link to provide stability are used. The cross-link joins the long sides and is parallel to the short sides.

a) What is the minimum total length of boom required to enclose an oil spill covering 100 000 m² of water?
b) Is the result of part a) different if the oil boom can only be constructed from 10-m sections?

Solution

Identify the variables and constants in the problem and sketch a diagram.

Variables: width of structure w, length of structure x, total boom length L

Constants: surface area $A = 100\,000$ m²

Relationships: $A = xw$, $L = 2x + 3w$

The equation to be optimized for the total boom length L is $L = 2x + 3w$.

We can express L in terms of one variable by first relating x and w using the given information that $A = 100\,000$.

$$xw = 100\,000$$

$$x = \frac{100\,000}{w}$$

We substitute this expression for x into the equation for L.

$$L = 2\left(\frac{100\,000}{w}\right) + 3w$$

$$= \frac{200\,000}{w} + 3w$$

Then, we determine the critical numbers.

$$L' = -\frac{200\,000}{w^2} + 3$$

$$0 = -\frac{200\,000}{w^2} + 3$$

$$w^2 = \frac{200\,000}{3}$$

$$w = \pm\sqrt{\frac{200\,000}{3}}$$

But $w > 0$, so

$$w = \sqrt{\frac{200\,000}{3}}$$

$$\doteq 258.20$$

We use the second derivative test to determine whether this value of w gives a maximum or a minimum.

$$L'' = \frac{400\,000}{w^3}$$

Since $L'' > 0$ for $w > 0$, this value of w gives a minimum value of L.

To determine the corresponding length of the structure, we substitute the value for w into the expression for x.

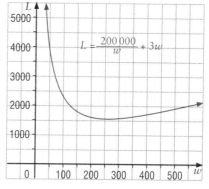

$$x = \frac{100\,000}{w}$$

$$\doteq 387.30$$

The minimum total boom length is $L = 2x + 3w$ or 1549.20 m.

The graph of L versus w verifies this result.

b) For 10-m sections, the function modelling the length of the boom has domain $\{10, 20, 30, \ldots\}$. Thus, the function consists of discrete points only. However, the new value of w that produces the minimum length will occur near the w-value found in part a). Thus, we examine $w = 250$ and $w = 260$.

$L(250) = 1550$ and $L(260) \doteq 1549.2$

Since the boom is constructed from 10-m sections, L must be a multiple of 10. Thus, we reject the second value of w. So, the minimum length of boom is 1550 m, for which the width is 250 m and the length is 400 m.

Example 4 Optimal Dimensions for a Silo

Canada and the United States are the world's leading producers of corn, with an approximate combined annual production of 300 million tonnes. Corn silos are usually in the shape of a cylinder surmounted by a hemisphere. If the average yield on a given farm requires that the silo contain 1000 m³ of corn, what dimensions of the silo would use the minimum amount of materials?

Solution

Variables: radius of silo, r, in metres, height of silo, h, in metres
Constants: capacity of silo, $V = 1000$ m³

Relationships: A = area of base + area of sides + area of hemispherical top, V = capacity of cylinder + capacity of hemisphere

We want to optimize (minimize) the surface area, A.

$$A = \pi r^2 + 2\pi rh + \frac{4\pi r^2}{2} \qquad \text{(surface area of a sphere} = 4\pi r^2\text{)}$$
$$= 3\pi r^2 + 2\pi rh$$

We can relate r and h using the given information that $V = 1000$.
     V = capacity of cylinder + capacity of hemisphere

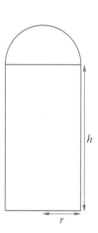

$$1000 = \pi r^2 h + \frac{1}{2}\left(\frac{4}{3}\pi r^3\right) \qquad \left(\text{capacity of a sphere} = \frac{4}{3}\pi r^3\right)$$
$$3000 = 3\pi r^2 h + 2\pi r^3$$
$$h = \frac{3000 - 2\pi r^3}{3\pi r^2}$$

Substituting this expression for h in the equation for A, we have

$$A = 3\pi r^2 + 2\pi r\left(\frac{3000 - 2\pi r^3}{3\pi r^2}\right)$$
$$= 3\pi r^2 + \frac{2000}{r} - \frac{4}{3}\pi r^2$$
$$= \frac{5}{3}\pi r^2 + \frac{2000}{r}$$

Differentiating, we obtain

$$A' = \frac{10}{3}\pi r - \frac{2000}{r^2}$$

Setting A' equal to zero and solving for r to find the critical numbers, we get

$$\frac{10}{3}\pi r - \frac{2000}{r^2} = 0$$
$$10\pi r^3 - 6000 = 0$$
$$r = \sqrt[3]{\frac{600}{\pi}}$$
$$\doteq 5.7588$$

Thus, the critical number is $r \doteq 5.7588$. We determine the second derivative to decide whether this value of r gives a maximum or a minimum.

$$A'' = \frac{10}{3}\pi + \frac{4000}{r^3}$$

Since $A'' > 0$ for $r > 0$, this value of r gives a minimum value of A.

To determine the corresponding height, note that, since $r^3 = \frac{600}{\pi}$, $2\pi r^3 = 1200$. Thus,

$$h = \frac{3000 - 2\pi r^3}{3\pi r^2}$$

$$= \frac{3000 - 1200}{3\pi r^2}$$

$$= \frac{1800}{3\pi r^2}$$

$$= \frac{600/\pi}{r^2}$$

$$= \frac{r^3}{r^2}$$

$$= r$$

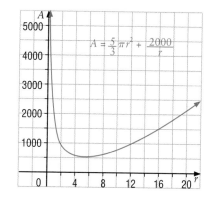

Thus, the height of the cylinder and the radius of the hemispherical top are equal for minimum surface area.

The optimal dimensions of the silo have both the radius and the height equal to approximately 5.7588 m.

Key Concepts

Procedure for solving optimization problems
- Identify the variables and the constants in the problem and sketch a well-labelled diagram.
- Express relationships among variables and constants as equations.
- Construct an equation for the quantity, say Q, to be optimized.
- Express the equation for Q in terms of one variable only, by using the equations relating variables and constants.
- Find the critical numbers and test them.
- Determine the required minimum or maximum value.
- Check that the result satisfies any restrictions on the variables.

Communicate Your Understanding

1. The steps required to maximize a quantity are identical to the steps required to minimize a quantity. Explain why.

2. What is meant by the phrase "express the quantity to be optimized in terms of one variable"? If a quantity Q is originally expressed in three variables, how many equations relating given information are required to express it in terms of one variable?

3. Explain the difference between a constant and a variable dimension of a geometric figure.

4. Compare Example 1 (page 376) and its solution to actual cereal boxes. Do you think that actual cereal boxes have dimensions that minimize their surface areas? If not, what other factors do you think the manufacturers consider besides minimizing packaging costs?

5. In Example 2 (page 377), the most economical shape for a can is one for which the height is equal to twice the radius of the base. Few cans in the retail world have this shape. Suggest some reasons why this is the case.

Practise

B **1.** Suppose that $R = m + n$ and $mn = 1000$. Find the value of m that minimizes R, for $R > 0$.

2. If $K = pq$ and $p - q = 1500$, find the value of p that makes K a minimum.

3. If $W = g^2h$ and $g^2 + 4gh = 2700$, find the value of h that maximizes W, if $g > 0$ and $h > 0$.

Apply, Solve, Communicate

4. A rectangular backyard playpen for a child is to be enclosed with 16 m of flexible fencing. What dimensions of the rectangle will provide the maximum area for the child to play?

5. A rectangular corral is to be enclosed along the side of a horse barn with the barn serving as one side of the corral. What dimensions of the corral, using 40 m of fencing, will enclose the maximum area for the horses?

6. A rectangular garden plot requires an area of 32 m² for the variety of vegetables that are to be planted. What dimensions of the plot will use the least amount of fencing to enclose the garden?

7. Communication A county fair has a holding area for the prize sheep that are entered in a contest.

a) The holding area is made up of 12 identical pens arranged in a three by four grid. If 100 m of fencing is available, what dimensions of each pen will maximize the total holding area?

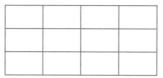

b) If the pens were arranged in a two by six grid, what dimensions would maximize the holding area?

c) Which arrangement would you recommend, the three by four grid or the two by six grid? Explain your reasoning.

8. Communication A child's play tunnel is to be made from a 4-m wide sheet of cardboard. The sheet will be folded as shown.

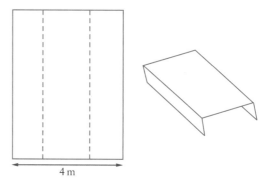

4 m

a) Where should the fold be made in order to maximize the cross-sectional area of the tunnel?

b) Will the resulting tunnel be high and wide enough for a child to crawl through? Should the dimensions determined in part a) be modified? Explain.

9. A typical automotive battery has six cells, divided by walls as shown in the top-view diagram below.

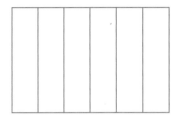

a) What dimensions will give the smallest total wall length including the outside perimeter if the top of each cell must have an area of 65 cm^2?

b) A popular battery has dimensions 22.5 cm by 17.5 cm, with each cell having a width of 3.75 cm. Has the battery designer used the minimum wall length as a design consideration?

10. Application An eccentric architect is experimenting with window design. To ensure adequate illumination, the area of the windows needs to be 12 m^2. What dimensions will minimize the amount of outside trim required to frame the window if the window is

a) a rectangle?

b) an isosceles triangle?

c) a rectangle surmounted by a semicircle?

d) a rectangle surmounted by an equilateral triangle?

11. A soda cracker package (in the shape of a rectangular prism) is to be constructed with a square base. The total capacity of the package must be 1000 cm^3.

a) What dimensions provide the minimum surface area?

b) Compare the dimensions found in part a) with those of an actual soda cracker package. What factors do you think influenced the designers of the package?

12. An open metal box for removing ashes from a fireplace is to be constructed from a rectangular piece of sheet metal that is 1 m by 1.5 m. Squares are to be cut from each corner of the sheet metal, the sides folded upward to form the box, and then the seams welded. What is the maximum capacity of a box that is constructed in this way?

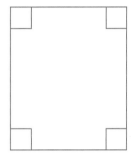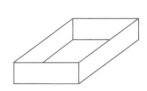

13. A closed display case for student artwork, in the shape of a rectangular prism, is to be constructed from a 2 m by 3 m sheet of acrylic. The net used for the construction is shown.

waste	waste	back	waste
top	left side	base	right side
waste	waste	front	waste

2 m

3 m

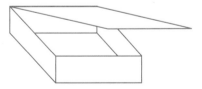

What dimensions of the case provide the maximum capacity?

14. Inquiry/Problem Solving The Canada Postal Guide lists the following requirements for parcels to be sent within Canada.

• No dimension can be more than 2 m.

- The length plus the girth (distance around) of the parcel may not exceed 3 m.
- The mass may not exceed 30 kg.
What size rectangular box with square ends will allow you the largest capacity?

15. A juice manufacturer is studying the most economical shape to use for a beverage container. Each unit will contain 355 cm^3 of juice. The manufacturer is considering a cylinder versus a rectangular prism with a comfortable hand-held depth of 4 cm. Which method of packaging, the can or the juice box, will use the minimum amount of materials?

16. A chocolate manufacturer uses an equilateral triangular prism package. If the volume of chocolate to be contained in the package is 400 cm^3, what dimensions of the package will use the minimum amount of materials?

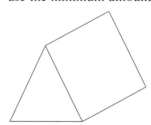

17. A cylindrical kite frame is to be constructed from a 4-m length of light bendable rod. The frame will be made up of two circles joined by four straight rods of equal length. In order to maximize lift, the kite frame must be constructed to maximize the volume of the cylinder. Into what lengths should the pieces be cut in order to optimize the kite's flight?

18. A cylindrical glass vase is to be made in order to hold large bouquets of flowers. If the capacity of the vase is to be 1000 cm^3, what dimensions for the vase would use the minimum amount of glass? Would these dimensions be practical?

19. Application A 3 m-long feed trough, in the shape of an isosceles triangular prism, is to be made with steel ends and two boards 30 cm wide. How wide should the top of the trough be to maximize the capacity of the trough?

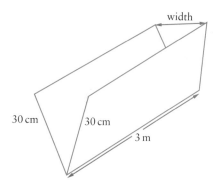

20. Inquiry/Problem Solving A heritage home features a semicircular window of radius 1 m. A local artisan is commissioned to accent the window with a rectangular pane of stained glass. The stained glass will be attached to the inside of the window frame. What dimensions of the rectangular pane will provide the greatest possible area for the stained glass accent?

21. Application A landscape architect is creating a rectangular rose garden to be located in a local park. The rose garden is to have an area of 60 m^2 and be surrounded by a lawn. The surrounding lawn is to be 10 m wide on the north and south sides of the garden and 3 m wide on the east and west sides. Find the dimensions of the rose garden if the total area of the garden and lawn together is to be a minimum.

22. The rate of blood flow through an artery of radius r is a function of the blood pressure, resistance pressure, density of the blood, and stress factors. The flow rate, F, can be expressed as $F = -kr^4 + cr^3$, where k and c are constants determined by the various factors.
a) Determine the maximum flow rate when the constants have values $k = 8$ and $c = 12$.
b) Determine the maximum flow rate in terms of k and c.

23. A plane follows a straight path described by the linear equation $y = 2x + 3$ (all distances in kilometres) for $x \in [-2, 1]$. If the flight tower is at the origin $(0, 0)$, at what point is the plane closest to the tower?

24. A cell culture under stressful conditions has a rate of growth of $G = 48t - t^2$, for $t \in [0, 48]$ where t is measured in hours. What is the maximum rate of growth and when is it reached?

25. The "gait" of an animal is a measure of how jerky or smooth the animal's motion appears while it is running. Gait, g, can be shown to be related to the power, P, necessary for the animal to run at a given speed. For an animal 1 m long, running at a velocity of 10 m/s, the power is given by

$$P = 0.1g + \frac{1000}{1 + g}$$

Determine the gait that minimizes the required power for the animal to run.

26. A variation of a triathlon competition has a contestant swimming from a point, A, on one shore of a lake, to a point C on the opposite parallel shore, then running to the finish, B, further along the lakeshore. The lake is 4 km wide and the finish line is 10 km down the lake. If a contestant can swim at 2 km/h and run at 10 km/h, determine the point C that will minimize the total time for the race.

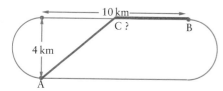

27. The flight of a gliding bird depends upon the lift provided by the bird's outstretched wings and by the drag caused by air resistance. Drag, D, can be expressed as a function of the gliding speed, v, in metres per second:

$$D = 30v^2 + \frac{150^2}{25v^2}$$

What speed minimizes the drag?

28. Inquiry/Problem Solving Holly and Geordie are attending an outdoor music festival where two bands are playing on stages that are 100 m apart. One band is three times as loud as the other. The two friends are interested in finding the quietest location along the line joining the stages. If the intensity of sound is directly proportional to the volume of the band and inversely proportional to the square of the distance from the source, find the best location.

29. The parabolic arch of a bridge over a one-way road can be described by the equation $y = -x^2 + 6$, where x and y are measured in metres. A transport truck is 3 m wide and 3.5 m high. What is the maximum clearance (from the closest part of the bridge) of the truck's top corners if it passes under the bridge?

30. Imagine that an exploration vessel from Earth is visiting another solar system in the year 3002. The people on the vessel decide that the best place to park their vehicle is at the point on the line between two planets where the net gravitational force acting on the vessel is minimized. The magnitude of the force, F, acting on the vessel from either of the planets is

$$F(x) = G \frac{Mm}{x^2}$$

where G is a constant, M is the mass of the planet, m is the mass of the vessel, and x is the distance between the planet and the vessel. If the mass of one planet is twice the mass of the other planet, where should the vessel be located to minimize the net gravitational force on it?

31. Application The reaction of the body to a dose of medicine can be represented by the function $P = M^2 \left(k - \frac{M}{3} \right)$, where M is the amount of medicine absorbed into the blood-stream, in millilitres, P is the blood pressure, in millimetres of mercury, and k is a constant depending on the particular medicine. The sensitivity of the body to a particular medicine is measured by the derivative $\frac{dP}{dM}$. Find the amount of medicine to which the body is most sensitive.

32. Inquiry/Problem Solving Two identical sodium vapour light standards A and B are located 20 m apart in a parking lot. A light sensor is to be placed at a point P on a line l that is parallel to the line joining the light standards and at a distance of k metres from it. Intensity of light from a single source is proportional to the strength of the source and inversely proportional to the square of the distance from the source. Find the location of P so that the intensity of light is minimized using the following procedure.

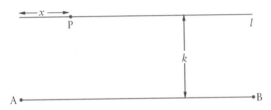

a) Find a function $I(x)$ for the intensity of light at point P. Focus on the domain $x \in [0, 20]$.
b) If $k = 5$, show that the minimum value for $I(x)$ occurs at the midpoint of l.
c) If $k = 20$, show that $I(x)$ is not minimized at the midpoint of l.
d) Find the value of k, between 5 and 20, where the minimum illumination point abruptly changes location.
e) Describe the changes in the behaviour of $I(x)$ as k changes from 1 to 20. Emphasize the location and type of the extrema.
f) Use the results of part e) to help you explain physically the phenomenon in part d).

C **33.** Consider a room that has a floor with dimensions 4 m by 5 m, and walls that are 3 m high. A spider is on one of the shorter walls, 1 m from the floor, and 2 m from either of the adjacent walls. It wants to get to a point on the opposite wall 1 m from the ceiling and 0.2 m from an adjacent wall. What is the minimum distance that the spider must walk?

34. Find the point on the parabolic arc $y = x^2$, with domain $x \in \left[0, \dfrac{1}{\sqrt{k}}\right]$, that is closest to the point (0, 1). Then, find the point on the arc that is most distant from the point (0, 1).

35. a) Find the dimensions of the largest cylinder that can be inscribed in a sphere of radius k.
b) Find the dimensions of the largest cylinder that can be inscribed in a cone of height k and base radius k.

36. A cone-shaped paper drinking cup is made by removing a sector from a disk of radius r, and then joining the two straight edges. Find the maximum capacity of such a cup.

37. a) Determine the conditions on the function $y = Q(x)$ for which the functions $y = Q(x)$ and $y = Q^2(x)$ have the same type of extremum at each of their common critical numbers. (That is, they are either both local maximum or both local minimum values, or neither of them is a local maximum or local minimum.)
b) Determine the conditions on the functions P and Q for which the functions $y = Q(x)$ and $y = P(Q(x))$ have the same critical numbers.
c) Assume that the functions P and Q satisfy the conditions of part b). Determine the conditions on the functions P and Q for which the functions $y = Q(x)$ and $y = P(Q(x))$ have the same type of extremum at each of their common critical numbers. (Hint: First explore some specific functions, such as $P(x) = x^2$, $P(x) = \dfrac{1}{x}$, and so on.)

38. The path of a football in an attempted field goal is given by the function $y = -0.008\,x^2 + 0.41x$, where y, in metres, is the height above the ground and x, in metres, is the horizontal distance from the point at which the ball is kicked. The centre of the horizontal bar of the goal is 40 m away, 3 m above the ground.
a) Does the football clear the horizontal bar of the goal posts?
b) Determine the smallest distance between the ball and the bar. (Hint: The result of question 37 may help.)

39. Communication In question 38, another way to determine the point on the path that is closest to the goal post bar is to determine when the tangent at the point is perpendicular to the line joining the bar with the point.

a) Explain, using diagrams, why this approach results in the minimum distance.

b) Use this approach to verify the result of question 38.

Achievement Check

Knowledge/Understanding

Inquiry/Problem Solving

Communication

Application

A container for wooden matches consists of an open-topped box (to contain the matches) that slides into an outer box, open at both ends. The length of the boxes is fixed at 10 cm to match the length of the matches. The outer box is designed so that one side completely overlaps for gluing.

a) If the outer box is made from a sheet of cardboard that is 16 cm by 10 cm, what dimensions for the *outer box* will maximize the capacity?

b) What size should the sheet of cardboard be, to make the inner box in this case?

c) Repeat the problem, for matches of the same size, if the volume is fixed at 100 cm^3 and you want to minimize the amount of material to make both boxes.

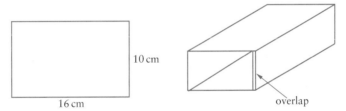

10 cm

16 cm

overlap

Career Connection: *Operations Research*

Operations research, sometimes called management science, is a professional area related to business and finance that relies heavily on the techniques of mathematics. Mathematical modelling on computers is a primary tool used to forecast the implications of various choices in the search for the optimum alternative. There is a very human dimension to this mathematical problem solving, as the models constructed must function effectively in the real world as well as being theoretically correct. Operations researchers solve problems such as how to price the seats on an airline flight, what is the most efficient method for routing a long distance telephone call, or how a clothing manufacturer should lay out a pattern to minimize wasted fabric.

Optimization Problems in Business and Economics

Common business practice is concerned with minimizing costs and maximizing profits. Many companies have teams of analysts, performing what is called operations research, whose job it is to determine optimum production levels and sales targets.

In Chapter 4, we introduced business applications as rate problems. Here, we will apply our tools for determining maximum and minimum values to business-related problems. We use the techniques illustrated in the previous section.

Example 1 Determining the Optimum Selling Price

Market research has shown that for every drop in price of a product there is usually an increase in sales. Similarly, an increase in price usually leads to a decrease in sales. A large retailer selling mountain bicycles has found that, for every \$20 reduction in price on the Rockhopper model, 2 more bicycles are sold per month. The Rockhopper usually sells for \$900 and at that price the store sells 50 bicycles per month.
a) Determine the optimum selling price in order to maximize revenue. How many bicycles are sold at that price?
b) Describe the shape of the graph relating price vs. number of bicycles sold.
c) Describe the shape of the graph relating revenue vs. number of bicycles sold.

Solution

a) The problem requires us to maximize revenue, R, in dollars.
Variables: price, p; number sold, x; revenue, R

The revenue function is
R = number sold × price
$\quad = xp$

To express R in one variable, we relate x and p. The relationship is linear. We determine two points on the line, and then find the slope and the equation.

x	p	(x, p)	
50	900	$(50, 900)$	(given)
52	880	$(52, 880)$	(after one \$20 reduction in price)

$$m = \frac{\Delta p}{\Delta x}$$
$$= \frac{900 - 880}{50 - 52}$$
$$= -10$$

The linear equation that relates p and x is
$(p - p_0) = m(x - x_0)$
$p - 900 = -10(x - 50)$
$\quad\quad p = -10x + 1400$

Substituting this expression for p into the equation for R we obtain

$$R = x(-10x + 1400)$$
$$= -10x^2 + 1400x$$

The derivative of the revenue function is

$$R' = -20x + 1400$$

As usual, we set the derivative equal to zero to obtain the critical number.

$$-20x + 1400 = 0$$
$$x = 70$$

We need the second derivative to determine whether $x = 70$ gives a maximum or a minimum value of R.

$$R'' = -20$$

Since R'' is always negative, $x = 70$ gives a maximum value of R. The maximum revenue occurs when the number of bicycles sold is 70 per month. The price at this level is $p(70) = \$700$.

b)   The graph relating price and number of bicycles sold is a straight line with negative slope ($p(x) = -10x + 1400$).

c)   The graph relating revenue and number of bicycles sold is a parabola opening downward ($R(x) = -10x^2 + 1400x$).

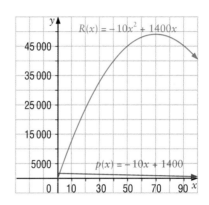

Brief review of terminology:
If x is the number of units of a commodity (its production level), then
- $C(x)$ is the cost function, which is the total cost to produce x units.
- $p(x)$ is the demand function (also called the price function), or the price per unit that a product can be sold for, at a production level of x units.
- $R(x)$ is the revenue function, which is the total revenue obtained by selling x units.
- $P(x)$ is the profit function, which is the total profit earned by selling x units.

The marginal cost function is the derivative, that is, the instantaneous rate of change, of the cost function. The marginal demand, marginal revenue, and marginal profit functions are similarly defined.

In practice, the cost and demand functions are only established after extensive market research and analysis. The revenue and profit functions are as follows.

revenue: $R(x) = xp(x)$ (number of units × price per unit)
profit: $P(x) = R(x) - C(x)$ (total revenue – total cost)

Example 2 Maximizing Revenue and Profit

The beverage industry in Canada produces over \$10 billion worth of product annually. Based on a 10-year study of production costs, a winery in the Niagara region has determined that the cost of producing x bottles of wine is

$C(x) = 12\,000 + 4x + 0.0002x^2$

Market research shows that the demand for the wine is given by the price function

$p(x) = 12 - 0.0001x$

a) Determine the production level that maximizes the revenue.
b) Determine the production level that maximizes the profit.
c) Show graphically the relationship between cost, revenue, and maximum profit.

Solution

a) Optimize the revenue function.

$$\begin{aligned} R(x) &= xp(x) \\ &= x(12 - 0.0001x) \\ &= 12x - 0.0001x^2 \end{aligned}$$

The derivative of the revenue function (the marginal revenue) is

$R'(x) = 12 - 0.0002x$

Setting the marginal revenue equal to zero and solving for x to obtain the critical number, we get

$$\begin{aligned} 12 - 0.0002x &= 0 \\ 0.0002x &= 12 \\ x &= 60\,000 \end{aligned}$$

We determine the second derivative to decide whether $x = 60\,000$ corresponds to a minimum or a maximum value of R.

$R''(x) = -0.0002$

Since R'' is always negative, $x = 60\,000$ corresponds to a maximum value of R.
A production level of 60 000 bottles maximizes the revenue.

b) Optimize the profit function.

$$\begin{aligned} P(x) &= R(x) - C(x) \\ &= x(12 - 0.0001x) - [12\,000 + 4x + 0.0002x^2] \\ &= -12\,000 + 8x - 0.0003x^2 \end{aligned}$$

The derivative of the profit function (the marginal profit) is

$P'(x) = 8 - 0.0006x$

Setting the marginal profit function equal to zero and solving for x, we get

$$\begin{aligned} 8 - 0.0006x &= 0 \\ x &\doteq 13\,333 \end{aligned}$$

We determine the second derivative to decide whether $x = 13\,333$ corresponds to a minimum or a maximum value of P.

$P''(x) = -0.0006$

Since P'' is always negative, $x = 13\,333$ corresponds to a maximum value of P.
Thus, a production level of about 13 300 bottles maximizes profits.

c) Graphs of the cost function, revenue function, and profit function are shown. The shaded region indicates when profit is positive. The vertical dotted line shows the relationship between the maximum point on the profit curve and the vertical difference between the revenue and cost functions. Note also that the marginal cost equals the marginal revenue when the profit is a maximum; that is, the slopes of the graphs of $R(x)$ and $C(x)$ are equal when the difference $R(x) - C(x)$ is greatest.

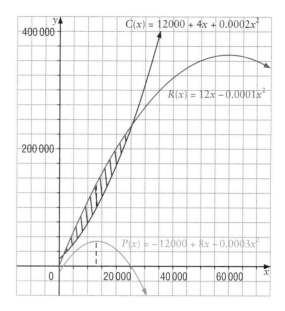

For all the examples in this section, the number of units, x, is an integer. However, we are assuming that this leads to continuous (and differentiable) functions for cost, revenue, and profit. This is acceptable since regression techniques lead to continuous curves that fit the discrete points well. This closeness of fit determines how good the mathematical model of the situation is, and its value in making inferences. When calculus techniques suggest an optimal production level that is not an integer, we choose the closest convenient integer. (Sometimes we round to recognize that items are packaged in units such as hundreds.)

Key Concepts

- $C(x)$, the cost function, is the total cost to produce x units.
- $p(x)$, the demand function (also called the price function), is the price per unit that a company can sell its product for, at a production level of x units.
- $R(x)$, the revenue function, is the total revenue obtained by selling x units.
  revenue: $R(x) = x\, p(x)$ (number of units × price per unit)
- $P(x)$, the profit function, is the total profit earned selling x units.
  profit: $P(x) = R(x) - C(x)$ (total revenue − total cost)

Communicate Your Understanding

1. Explain the difference between the revenue function and the profit function.

2. Explain why the production level that maximizes revenue does not necessarily maximize profit.

3. There is always an initial startup cost for any manufacturing process. What term of the cost function represents this expense?

4. Is it reasonable to assume that the price function is linear? Explain.

5. Will the revenue function always be quadratic? Explain.

6. Will a cost function always be an increasing function for $x > 0$? Explain.

7. How is marginal revenue related to the graph of the revenue function?

Practise

B **1.** For the given cost and demand functions, find the production level that will maximize profit.

a) $C(x) = 10 + 4x$, $p(x) = 50 - 0.5x$
b) $C(x) = 500 + 5x + 0.01x^2$, $p(x) = 10$
c) $C(x) = 500 + 5x + 0.01x^2$,
$p(x) = 10 - 0.002x$
d) $C(x) = 1000 + 20x + x^2 + 0.0001x^3$,
$p(x) = 50 - 0.01x$
e) $C(x) = 1 + 4x - 3x^2 + x^3$, $p(x) = 9 - 2x$

Apply, Solve, Communicate

2. Communication The graph shows the cost and revenue functions for a local music retailer.

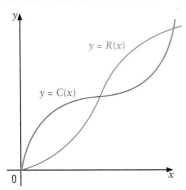

a) Identify on the graph the x-value that corresponds to the maximum profit.
b) Sketch a graph of the profit function, P.
c) Sketch a graph of the marginal profit function, P'.
d) What is the meaning of $P'(x) > 0$?

3. Application A car manufacturing company analysed painting costs and tabulated the following results:

Number of Cars, x	Cost of Painting, $C(x)$ ($)
100	120 000
500	200 000
1000	390 000
2000	750 000
5000	2 000 000

a) Using quadratic regression to fit a function to the data, determine a function, $C(x)$, for the cost of painting x cars.
b) What is the total cost of painting 3000 cars?
c) The price function for painting x cars is $p(x) = 1000 - 0.01x$. Find the revenue earned painting 3000 cars.
d) Find the production level that maximizes revenue.
e) Find the production level that maximizes profit.

4. A textile manufacturer uses regression to determine that the cost of producing x metres of woven fabric is $C(x) = 100 + 8x - 0.1x^2 + 0.001x^3$. It forecasts that it can sell the fabric for $p(x) = 16 - 0.03x$ dollars per metre. Determine the production level that will give maximum profit.

5. Inquiry/Problem Solving A large electronic retailer has been selling digital cameras for $850 each. At this price the store sells 120 per month. From past experience, for every $10 discount in price, the number of sales increases by 5 each month, and for every $10 increase in price, the number of sales decreases by 5 each month.
a) Find the price function.
b) At what price should the cameras be sold in order to maximize revenue?

c) What is the percent reduction in price that the retailer is offering the consumer at the price in part b)?

6. A professional basketball team plays in a stadium that holds 23 000 spectators. With ticket prices at $60, the average attendance had been 18 000. When ticket prices were lowered to $55, the average attendance rose to 20 000. Based on this pattern, how should ticket prices be set to maximize revenue?

7. Application The Eco-venture charter company offers local environmental excursions. The fare is $45 per person if 18 to 30 passengers sign up for the trip. The company does not offer the trip if fewer than 18 people sign up. If more than 30 people sign up, the fare for every passenger is reduced by $1 for each passenger in excess of 30. The bus can hold only 48 passengers. Determine the number of passengers that generates the greatest revenue for the charter company.

8. An ice cream vendor has found that the cost of supplying x cones is $C(x) = 25 + 0.12x + 0.007x^2$ and also that the demand for the cones increases when the price drops. Approximately 500 cones will sell per day if they are priced at $1.20, but for every price drop of 10¢, the number sold per day increases by 20. Similarly, for every price increase of 10¢, the number sold per day decreases by 20.
a) Determine the price of the cones that maximizes revenue.
b) Determine the price of the cones that maximizes profit.

9. Inquiry/Problem Solving Glynn is considering buying a truck and becoming a professional driver. The truck manufacturer indicates that he can expect his running costs when driving at v kilometres per hour to be approximated by the function $c(v) = 0.85 + 0.0004v^{\frac{3}{2}}$, where the cost, c, is in dollars per kilometre. Glynn plans to pay himself $15/h while he is driving. Find the speed that will minimize his costs for a 1500-km trip.

10. The manager of a 240-room ski resort has found that, on average, 150 rooms are booked when the price is $175 per night and 160 rooms are booked when the price is $160 per night. What price should the manager set for the rooms to maximize revenue?

11. The yield of a crop, in tonnes, is dependent upon the time, t, in days, between planting and harvesting, according to the following formula.

$$Y(t) = \begin{cases} 80t - t^2 - 1500 & \text{if} \quad t \in [30, 50] \\ 0 & \text{if} \quad t \in [0, 30) \\ & \text{or} \quad t \in (50, \infty) \end{cases}$$

On which day is the maximum yield reached, and what is the maximum yield?

12. Application Two buildings in a school complex need to be connected with fibre optic cable. Building A is 70 m from a roadway and building B is 200 m down the road. There are two choices in laying the cable. If laid underground, the cost is $1000/m, and if laid above ground, the cost is $500/m. The cable must be laid underground across the playing fields. The cable will be laid from A underground to a point C on the road, and then above ground to B.

a) Where should C be chosen to minimize the total cost of laying the cable?

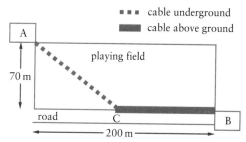

b) What other costs might need to be considered?

13. Application An analyst has predicted that the growth rate, as a percent, for a specific mutual fund can be modelled by the equation $r = 0.5x^{\frac{3}{2}} - 6x^{\frac{2}{3}} + 10.1$, where x is the number of months and $x \in [0, 24]$. Determine the best and worst times to invest in this mutual fund.

14. Inquiry/Problem Solving A steering wheel manufacturer finds that, by manufacturing x steering wheels per day, there are fixed costs of $5000, and $1.50 in labour and materials costs per steering wheel. An agreement with the materials supplier to pay for part of the transportation costs leaves the company with a cost of $\dfrac{\$50\,000}{x}$. The maximum capacity of the factory is 500 steering wheels. Determine the number of steering wheels that should be produced daily in order to minimize costs.

15. Inquiry/Problem Solving A 5000 m² rectangular area of a field is to be enclosed by a fence, with a moveable inner fence built across the narrow part of the field, as shown.

The perimeter fence costs $10/m and the inner fence costs $4/m. Determine the dimensions of the field to minimize the cost.

16. The demand function for a certain artist's print is modelled by the equation $p(x) = \sqrt{8000 - x^2}$, where p is the price, in dollars, when x prints are produced. How many prints should be produced in order to maximize revenue?

C 17. Communication The average cost is defined as $\dfrac{C(x)}{x}$, where $C(x)$ is the cost function.

a) Prove that the average cost is smallest (if ever) only when the average cost equals the marginal cost.
b) Suppose that $C(x) = x^3 - 2x^2 + 4x$ is the cost function for a manufacturing operation, where x is measured in ten thousands of units. Is there a production level that has minimal average cost? If so, what is it?

Career Connection: *Economic Prediction*

Economics studies the way a society uses scarce resources, such as capital, land, labour, raw materials, and equipment, to provide goods and services. Further, economists analyse the results of their research to determine the costs and benefits of making, distributing, and using resources in a particular way. In seeking to optimize the use of these resources, economists employ many tools that are similar to those used in calculus optimization problems. The mathematical models of economics are critical in predicting the nature and length of business cycles, the effects of a specific rate of inflation on the economy, the effects of tax legislation on unemployment levels, or the likely movement of interest rates.

Technology Extension

Racing Strategy Using TI InterActive!™

Fran is riding in a mountain bike race starting at point A and finishing at point C. The end point C is 16 km east of the starting point A, and 7 km north of the major road. Fran can ride her mountain bike at 25 km/h on the road and at 15 km/h off road. She can choose any point at which to leave the road.

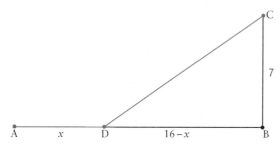

The problem is to find the point D where Fran should leave the road to minimize her time. Let x be the distance she travels on the road. Then, her total time is represented by the expression

$f(x)$ = time on road + time off road

$= \dfrac{\text{distance on road}}{\text{speed on road}} + \dfrac{\text{distance off road}}{\text{speed off road}}$

$= \dfrac{x}{25} + \dfrac{\sqrt{7^2 + (16 - x)^2}}{15}$

First, define a function of time in terms of variable x.

$$f(x) := \dfrac{x}{25} + \dfrac{\sqrt{7^2 + (16 - x)^2}}{15}$$

"Done"

Next, define a derivative function and call it $f1(x)$.

$$f1(x) := \dfrac{d}{dx}(f(x))$$

"Done"

The derivative function can be displayed.

$f1(x)$

$$\dfrac{x - 16}{15\sqrt{x^2 - 32 \cdot x + 305}} + \dfrac{1}{25}$$

To find the minimum time, set the first derivative equal to 0 and solve for x.

$\text{solve}(f1(x) = 0, x)$

$x = 10.75$

In order to use this value later for the second derivative test, store the value in variable k.

$ans \to k$

$x = 10.75$

In order to use the second derivative test, define the second derivative and name it $f2(x)$.

$$f2(x) := \dfrac{d^2}{dx^2}(f(x))$$

"Done"

Display the expression for the second derivative.

$f2(x)$

$$\dfrac{49}{15 \cdot (x^2 - 32 \cdot x + 305)^{3/2}}$$

Finally, evaluate the second derivative at the value of x found when the first derivative was set equal to 0.

$f2(k)$

$$\dfrac{49}{15 \cdot (x^2 - 32 \cdot x + 305)^{3/2}} = \dfrac{64}{13125}$$

Warning: Operation might introduce false solutions

Since the first derivative is equal to 0 when $x = 10.75$ and the second derivative is positive, there is a local minimum at $x = 10.75$.

Therefore, Fran should ride 10.75 km on the road.

Web Connection

A trial version of TI InterActive!™ is provided by the manufacturer. Go to **www.mcgrawhill.ca/links/CAF12** and follow the instructions there.

A second solution method is to use the spreadsheet in TI InterActive!™. To access the spreadsheet option, click on the ▦ icon on the toolbar. A spreadsheet screen will open. Enter the headings as shown in the screen. You will need to make the columns wide enough to accommodate the headings. Be sure to make column F wide enough to show several decimal places.

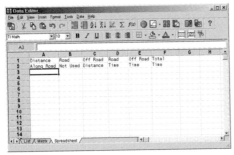

In the first column enter values for the distance that Fran travels along the road. This could vary from 0 km to 16 km. As a first step, use an increment of 1 km. The formula to accomplish this is shown in the entry line just above the column headers in the screen below. It has been copied down to cell A19. To do this, enter the formula in cell A4, grab the small square in the lower right corner of the cell and drag it down to cell A19.

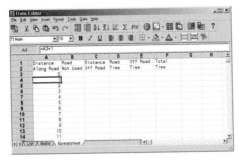

The "Road Not Used" column refers to the amount of road left after Fran turns off the road. This amount is calculated by finding the difference between 16 and the road distance in column A. The formula is shown in the entry line in the screen in the next column. Copy the formula down to cell B19.

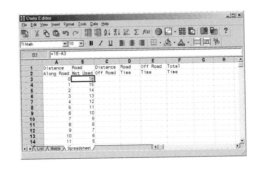

For the distance off road, use the Pythagorean relation with sides of length 7 and the value in column B. The formula is shown in the entry line in the screen below, and copied down the column. The values have all been formatted to show three digits after the decimal point.

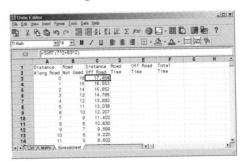

The "Road Time" in column D of this screen is found by dividing the distance in column A by the speed of 25 km/h. It is formatted to three decimal places and copied to row 19.

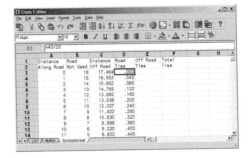

In the same way, the "Off Road Time" in column E is found by dividing the Distance Off Road in column C by the speed of 15 km/h and copying the formula down to row 19.

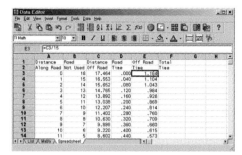

Column F shows the total of the on-road time in column D and the off-road time in column E. These values have been formatted to eight decimal places in order to compare later values.

In this screen, cell F14 has been highlighted to show that this cell has the smallest total time for this spreadsheet.

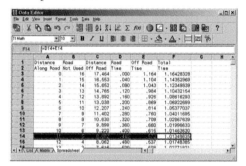

This value depends upon the value 11 found in cell A14. This is not necessarily the lowest value, but it does indicate that the lowest value could be found somewhere between 10 and 12, in cells A13 and A15, respectively. Using this information, we recalculate the spreadsheet for values of the on-road distance starting at 10 km and going up to 12 km using increments of 0.1 km. Each column must be copied down to row 23.

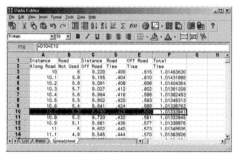

Again, the cell containing the least time has been highlighted. Using an argument similar to that in the previous spreadsheet, we can conclude that the best route for Fran to take would be somewhere between 10.7 km and 10.8 km. Based upon this information, here is one final spreadsheet going from 10.7 km to 10.8 km in steps of 0.01 km.

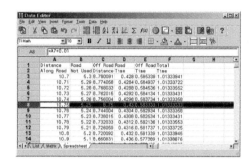

From this spreadsheet, we get the same result, $x = 10.75$, as we did using the computer algebra system in TI InterActive!™.

Practise

1. Fran's friend Roberta is not quite as fit as Fran, so she rides on the road at 20 km/h and off road at 10 km/h. At what point should Roberta leave the road to minimize her time?

2. Someone gave Fran the wrong information about the distance from A to B. It is actually only 14 km. How does this change the solutions to the original problem and Exercise 1 above?

3. Fran has decided that 12 km/h is the fastest that she can ride off road. Using a distance from S to T of 16 km, how fast should she ride on the road so that, with the optimal strategy, she goes exactly 10 km on the road? What if she wants to go 8 km on the road?

Investigate & Apply: Functions From Graphs

In this chapter, we have developed tools that allow us to sketch a function if we know its equation. Another common problem is to determine the equation of a function when we are given its graph. Using the regression features of a graphing calculator or graphing software can often solve this problem. However, we are limited to the types of regression that our technology provides. For example, regressions found on most calculators do not give the equations of rational functions.

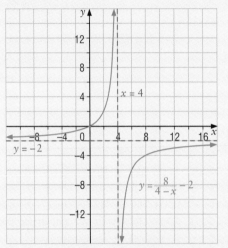

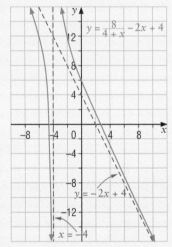

This investigation challenges you to find possible rational functions that have a variety of given asymptotes, and to develop some general methods of working with such problems.

1. Consider the lines $x = 4$, $x = -\dfrac{7}{2}$, $y = -2$, and $y = 3 - 2x$ as potential asymptotes of a rational function $y = f(x)$. Find possible expressions for $f(x)$ for the various cases when some or all of these asymptotes are present. Some cases may not be possible when you are restricted to rational functions. Provide a sketch or calculator screen for each successful case. Explain why the remaining cases are impossible for rational functions.

2. Summarize the methods you have used in step 1. Briefly explain how to proceed in the various cases that involve a combination of vertical, horizontal, and oblique asymptotes. Be sure to include an explanation for impossible cases. Try to generalize where possible. (Is the expression for $f(x)$ unique in each case? Can you determine the most general expression that will succeed?)

3. Based on your study in this investigation, pose an interesting problem involving determining the equation of a rational function given its asymptotes. Solve the problem yourself to make sure the solution is reasonable. Then, present the problem to your classmates for them to solve.

6.1 Increasing and Decreasing Functions

Refer to the Key Concepts on page 317.

1. Without graphing, determine intervals of increase and decrease for each function.
a) $f(x) = 20 + x - x^2$
b) $y = x^3$
c) $g(x) = x^3 - 4x + 3$
d) $h(x) = x^2 + x^4$
e) $y = x^3 + 6x^2 + 9x + 5$
f) $f(x) = x^4 - 4x^3 - 8x^2 - 1$

2. A ball is tossed into the air and its height, in metres, t seconds after it is tossed, is given by the formula $h = 1 + 20t - 5t^2$. Determine the time intervals during which the ball's height is increasing, and during which the ball's height is decreasing.

6.2 Maximum and Minimum Values

Refer to the Key Concepts on pages 326–327.

3. Find the absolute maximum and minimum values of each function. Sketch the graph in each case.
a) $f(x) = 3 + 2(x + 1)^2$ for $x \in [-3, 2]$
b) $f(x) = 2x^2 - x^4 - 16$ for $x \in [-3, 2]$
c) $f(x) = -2x^3 + 3x^2$ for $x \in [-2, 2]$
d) $f(x) = -(x^5 + 3x^3 + x)$ for $x \in [-1, 2]$

4. Given the graph of $y = f(x)$, estimate,
i) the absolute maximum and minimum values of the function
ii) the local maximum and minimum values of the function
a)

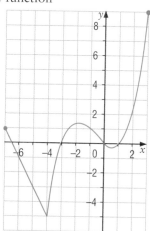

b)

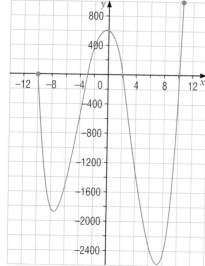

5. A company manufactures high-end speakers and estimates that its profit, in thousands of dollars, is $P(n) = -5n^2 + 500n + 5$, for n speakers, $n \in (0, 50]$. How many speakers should the company manufacture in order to maximize profit?

6.3 Concavity and the Second Derivative Test

Refer to the Key Concepts on page 337.

6. i) State the intervals on which f is concave upward or concave downward.
ii) State the coordinates of the points of inflection.
a)

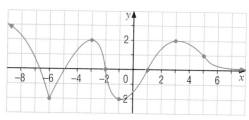

b)

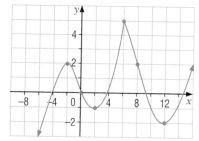

7. Find the intervals on which each curve is concave upward or downward, and state the points of inflection.

a) $f(x) = 3 + 4x - 2x^2$

b) $y = 5x^3 + 12x^2 - 3x + 2$

c) $y = 16 + 4x + x^2 - x^3$

d) $y = x^4 - x^3 - 3x^2 + 5x - 12$

e) $g(x) = x^4 - 2x^3 + x^2 - 2$

f) $y = \dfrac{x-2}{5-x}$ g) $y = \dfrac{x^2}{x^2+4}$

h) $y = \dfrac{x^2}{x^2-4}$ i) $h(x) = x + \dfrac{1}{x}$

8. Find the local maximum and minimum values of each function.

a) $f(x) = x^2 - x^3$ b) $y = 2x^2 - 8x + 3$

c) $k(x) = 3x^2 - 24x + 15$ d) $y = \dfrac{x^2}{x-1}$

e) $g(x) = x^2 + \dfrac{16}{x}$ f) $y = x^4 - 8x^2 + 5$

9. The population of a city is modelled by the equation $P(t) = \dfrac{5t+1}{3t+2}$, $t \in [0, 20]$, where t is the time, in years, after 1960. Use the second derivative test to determine whether the rate of change of the population is increasing or decreasing.

6.4 Vertical Asymptotes

Refer to the Key Concepts on pages 346–347.

10. Consider the graph of f.

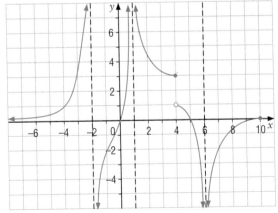

a) Determine the equations of the vertical asymptotes.

b) Find the following.

i) $\lim\limits_{x \to 6^-} f(x)$ ii) $\lim\limits_{x \to 6^+} f(x)$ iii) $\lim\limits_{x \to -2^-} f(x)$

iv) $\lim\limits_{x \to -2^+} f(x)$ v) $\lim\limits_{x \to -2} f(x)$ vi) $\lim\limits_{x \to 1^-} f(x)$

vii) $\lim\limits_{x \to 1^+} f(x)$ viii) $\lim\limits_{x \to 4^-} f(x)$ ix) $\lim\limits_{x \to 4^+} f(x)$

11. Find each limit.

a) $\lim\limits_{x \to 3^-} \dfrac{5}{3-x}$ b) $\lim\limits_{x \to 3^+} \dfrac{5}{3-x}$

c) $\lim\limits_{x \to -4^-} \dfrac{-3}{x+4}$ d) $\lim\limits_{x \to -4^+} \dfrac{-3}{x+4}$

e) $\lim\limits_{x \to 1} \dfrac{2}{(x-1)^2}$ f) $\lim\limits_{x \to -6^-} \dfrac{1}{(x+6)^2}$

g) $\lim\limits_{x \to -3^-} \dfrac{x}{(x+3)^2}$ h) $\lim\limits_{x \to -3^+} \dfrac{x}{(x+3)^2}$

i) $\lim\limits_{x \to -4^-} \dfrac{x+2}{x^2+5x+4}$

12. Find the vertical asymptotes for each function and sketch the graph near the asymptotes.

a) $y = \dfrac{1}{x+4}$ b) $y = \dfrac{x+1}{x^2+5x+6}$

6.5 Horizontal and Oblique Asymptotes

Refer to the Key Concepts on page 358.

13. State the equations of the horizontal and vertical asymptotes.

a)

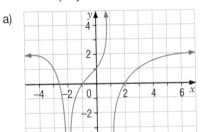

b)

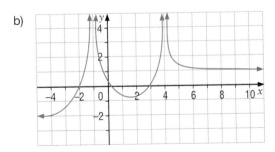

14. Find each limit.

a) $\displaystyle\lim_{x \to \infty} \frac{5}{x}$

b) $\displaystyle\lim_{x \to -\infty} \frac{5}{x}$

c) $\displaystyle\lim_{x \to \infty} \frac{3-2x}{x+4}$

d) $\displaystyle\lim_{x \to -\infty} \frac{3-2x}{x+4}$

e) $\displaystyle\lim_{x \to \infty} \frac{4-x^2}{2x^2-3}$

f) $\displaystyle\lim_{x \to \infty} \frac{3x^2-4x+2}{x^2-3x+5}$

g) $\displaystyle\lim_{x \to -\infty} \frac{5x^3-2x^2}{5-x^3}$

h) $\displaystyle\lim_{x \to \infty} (x^4-6x^2)$

i) $\displaystyle\lim_{x \to \infty} |x|$

15. Find the vertical and horizontal asymptotes.

a) $y = \dfrac{4x-3}{2-x}$

b) $y = \dfrac{x-5}{x+4}$

c) $y = \dfrac{3}{x^2-2x-15}$

d) $y = \dfrac{x}{3x^2-5x+2}$

e) $y = \dfrac{6x^2}{2x^2-5x-3}$

f) $y = \dfrac{x^3}{x^3-1}$

16. Find the equations of all oblique asymptotes.

a) $y = \dfrac{3x-2x^2+6}{x}$

b) $y = \dfrac{2x^3-5}{2x^2}$

c) $y = \dfrac{5x^2+3x-2}{x-1}$

d) $y = \dfrac{6x^2-5}{3x+1}$

e) $y = \dfrac{x^3+4x^2+5x+16}{x^2+4}$

f) $y = \dfrac{x+x^2-x^4}{x^3-1}$

17. Find the horizontal, vertical, and oblique asymptotes. Use them, together with the intercepts, to sketch the graph.

a) $y = \dfrac{x+2}{x-4}$

b) $y = \dfrac{x}{x-5}$

c) $y = \dfrac{x^2+2}{x}$

18. A company estimates that its cost per unit, in dollars, of manufacturing x pairs of sunglasses is modelled by the equation $C(x) = \dfrac{\sqrt{2x^2+20}}{x}$. What is the long-term cost per unit, accurate to the nearest cent?

6.6 Curve Sketching

Refer to the Key Concepts on page 369.

19. Sketch the following functions without using technology. For each curve, determine enough

information to make an accurate graph. Include intercepts, asymptotes, extrema, points of inflection, and any other significant details, justifying your results with analytic methods.

a) $y = x^3 - 3x^2$

b) $y = 3x^5 - 10x^3 + 45x$

c) $y = x^3 - x^4$

d) $y = \dfrac{4}{2+x}$

e) $y = \dfrac{1-x^2}{1+x^2}$

f) $y = \dfrac{1+x^2}{1-x^2}$

g) $y = \dfrac{x^3-1}{x^3+1}$

h) $y = \dfrac{1}{x^3-x}$

i) $y = \dfrac{1-x^2}{x^3}$

20. Using a graphing calculator or graphing software, produce a graph showing all the important aspects of each function.
Use the graphing calculator to estimate
i)   the intervals of increase and decrease
ii) extreme values
iii) intervals of concavity
iv) inflection points
Use calculus to find the above quantities exactly.

a) $y = 2x^3 - 3x^2 + 6$

b) $y = \dfrac{x^2+11x-20}{x^2}$

c) $y = x - \dfrac{1}{x^2-1}$

6.7 Introducing Optimization Problems

Refer to the Key Concepts on page 381.

21. The National Gallery in Ottawa has a large collection of modern abstract art.
An avant-garde painting is to have a rectangular central abstract theme covering 384 cm^2 of canvas with an orange 6-cm margin at the top and bottom and a black 4-cm margin on each side. Find the dimensions of the canvas that will cover the smallest area.

22. A rectangular bin, 1 m high, is going to be constructed in the corner of a garage to contain odds and ends. The walls of the garage will provide two walls of the bin. If the total length of the other two walls for the bin is to be 4 m, what dimensions of the bin will maximize the capacity?

23. A cedar chest (closed box) is to be built, but to reduce costs, the base and the back of the chest will be made of pine. The cost of the cedar is $8/m² and the cost of the pine is $4/m². The ends of the chest are to be square.
a) Find the dimensions of the least expensive chest that can be built if the capacity must be 2 m³.
b) Find the dimensions of the largest chest that can be built for $1200.

24. Half of the roofline of the attic of a house is given by the equation $3x + 4y = 12$. A rectangular storage area is to be constructed in the attic. The attic is 10 m deep from front to back. What dimensions will yield the maximum capacity for the storage area?

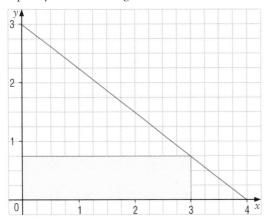

25. A rod with isosceles-triangular cross section is machined from a cylindrical steel rod of diameter 2 cm. The strength of the rod is directly proportional to the product of the base of the triangle and the square of the height of the triangle. What are the dimensions of such a rod that has maximum strength?

26. The percent concentration of a certain drug in the bloodstream t hours after the drug is administered is given by $P(t) = \dfrac{0.2t}{t^2 + 4}$, where $t \in [0, 5]$. Find
a) the percent concentration after 30 min
b) the maximum percent concentration and the time at which it occurs

27. Two factories, located 20 km apart, are emitting particulate matter. The first plant emits four times the particulate matter of the second. In either case, the concentration of particulate matter falling to earth is inversely proportional to the square of the distance from the plant. At what point on the line joining the two plants will the concentration of particulate matter be the least?

6.8 Optimization Problems in Business and Economics

Refer to the Key Concepts on page 391.

28. For the given cost and price functions, find the production level that will maximize profit.
a) $C(x) = 300\,000 + 10x + 0.5x^2$,
$p(x) = 25 - 0.01x$
b) $C(x) = 6000 + 0.1x + 0.01x^2$,
$p(x) = 2 - 0.001x$.

29. Leopard golf clubs usually sell for $1300. At this price, the retailer can sell, on average, 20 sets per week. For every $50 reduction in price, sales of the golf clubs increase by two sets per week. Similarly, for every $50 increase in price, sales decrease by two sets per week. Determine the optimum price to maximize revenue.

30. The cost of making x mechanical pencils is given by $C(x) = 2000 + 2.4x + 0.0008x^2$. Market research has found that when the price of each pencil is $3, the retailer sells 1000 pencils per month. For every 10¢ reduction in price, the number of pencils sold per month increases by 100, and similarly, for every 10¢ increase in price, the number of pencils sold per month decreases by 100. Determine the price that the retailer should charge for the pencils to maximize profits.

Chapter Test

Achievement Chart

Category	Knowledge/Understanding	Thinking/Inquiry/Problem Solving	Communication	Application
Questions	All	7, 10, 16	4, 9, 16	9, 10–16

1. Find each limit.

a) $\lim\limits_{x \to -3^-} \dfrac{x+2}{x^2-9}$

b) $\lim\limits_{x \to -3^+} \dfrac{x+2}{x^2-9}$

c) $\lim\limits_{x \to -\infty} \dfrac{4x^2-5x+2}{2x^2+3x-7}$

d) $\lim\limits_{x \to -\infty} \dfrac{2x^2-3x^3}{x^2-4}$

2. Find all the asymptotes of each curve.

a) $y = \dfrac{2-4x}{2x+7}$

b) $y = \dfrac{x^3-9}{x^2-4}$

3. a) Find the intervals on which the curve $y = \dfrac{x}{(x+1)^2}$ is concave upward and the intervals on which it is concave downward.

b) Find any points of inflection.

4. For the curve $y = 2 - 12x + 9x^2 - 2x^3$,

a) find the intervals of increase or decrease

b) find the local maximum and minimum values

c) find the intervals of concavity

d) find any points of inflection

e) sketch the curve

5. Determine the critical numbers and find the absolute maximum and minimum values of the function $f(x) = x^3 - 6x^2 + 9x + 2$ for $x \in [0.5, 4.5]$.

6. Find the critical numbers of the function $f(x) = \dfrac{x^2+1}{x}$, and determine whether they correspond to local maximum points or local minimum points.

7. Sketch the function $f(x) = \dfrac{x}{x^2-9}$ without using technology. Determine enough information to make an accurate graph. You should include intercepts, asymptotes, extrema, points of inflection, and any other significant details, justifying your results with analytic methods.

8. If 2400 cm^2 of material are available to construct an open-topped box that is to have a square base, find the dimensions that create the box of maximum volume.

9. Two cottages without electrical service are situated 20 m and 40 m from a buried electrical power line. Lines drawn from the cottages that meet the power line at right angles are 30 m apart.

a) Where should the junction box be located on the power line to minimize the length of connecting cable to the cottages?

b) Are there other ways to connect the cottages to the power line? Discuss the merits of these alternatives.

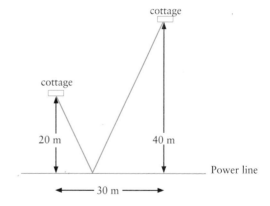

10. When Marion's Muffins sells muffins for $6 per dozen, sales are 100 dozen per day. For every 10¢ per dozen reduction in price, sales increase by 20 dozen per day, and similarly, for every 10¢ per dozen increase in price, sales decrease by 20 dozen per day.

a) Determine the price that maximizes revenue.

b) If the cost for baking x dozen muffins is $C(x) = 300 + x + 0.01x^2$, determine the production level that maximizes profit.

11. The strength of a piece of lumber is given by the formula $S = clw^2$, where c is a constant that depends on the properties of the wood, and l and w represent the length and width, respectively, of the cross section of the lumber. A tree has circular cross section with radius of 24 cm. Find the dimensions of the cross section of the lumber that provide the greatest strength.

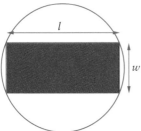

12. A cottage is to have floor space of 100 m², and is to be partitioned by a wall into two equal parts. Determine the dimensions of the cottage that will keep the total length of the walls to a minimum.

13. The concentration in mg/cm³ of a particular drug in a patient's bloodstream is given by the formula $C(t) = \dfrac{0.12t}{t^2 + 2t + 2}$, where t is the number of hours after the patient has taken the drug.

a)   After how many hours will the concentration of the drug be a maximum?
b)   What is the maximum concentration?

14. The demand function for a certain candy is $p(x) = \dfrac{32}{x^2 - 32x + 320}$, where x is the number of candies sold, in thousands, and p is the price, in dollars. Determine the number of candies sold in order to maximize revenue.

15. A town models its property tax revenue, in thousands of dollars, with the formula $y = 200\sqrt{x + 5} - x\sqrt{x}$, where x is the number of new houses built. With how many new houses will property tax revenue be maximized?

Achievement Check

Knowledge/Understanding

Thinking/Inquiry/Problem Solving

Communication

Application

16. A 1-km track is to be built with two straight sides and semicircles at the ends, as in the figure.
a)   Find the exact dimensions of the track that encloses the maximum rectangular area. Explain your solution.
b)   Find the dimensions that enclose the maximum total area. Why do you think tracks are not usually built in this shape? Explain.

Challenge Problems

1. A rectangle lies in the first quadrant with one vertex at the origin and two of the sides along the coordinate axes. The fourth vertex lies on the parabola $y = 27 - x^2$. Find the maximum area of the rectangle and explain why it is a maximum.

2. Show that when any positive number is decreased by its reciprocal and then increased by five times the square of its reciprocal, the result is never less than $\dfrac{11}{4}$.

3. If $f(x) = x^p(1 - x)^q$, where p and q are integers such that $p \geq 2$, $q \geq 2$, and $p \neq -q$, show that the critical numbers of f are $x = 0$, $x = \dfrac{p}{p+q}$, and $x = 1$.

4. Determine the absolute maximum of $y = x(r^2 + x^2)^{-\frac{2}{3}}$ on the interval $x \in [0, r]$, where r is a constant.

5. a) For which values of a and b does the function $f(x) = x^3 + ax^2 + bx + 2$ have a local minimum at $x = 1$ and a local maximum at $x = -1$?
b) Find a cubic function $f(x) = ax^3 + bx^2 + cx + d$ that has a local maximum at $(1, 1)$ and a local minimum at $(3, 0)$.

6. Prove that the function $f(x) = x^{13} + 26x^7 + 637x$ has neither a local maximum nor a local minimum value.

7. If $f(x)$ has a maximum value at $x = k$, show that the function $g(x) = -f(x)$ has a minimum value at $x = k$.

8. a) Find the dimensions of the largest rectangle that can be inscribed in a circle of radius k.
b) Find the dimensions of the largest rectangle that can be inscribed in an equilateral triangle with side length k if one side of the rectangle lies on one side of the triangle.
c) Find the dimensions of the largest right-circular cylinder that can be inscribed in a sphere of radius k.

9. A juice can in the shape of a right circular cylinder has a fixed capacity. If the material used for the sides of the can costs 0.5¢/cm^2 and the material for the top and the bottom costs 0.25¢/cm^2, find the ratio of height to radius that results in a minimum cost.

10. A warehouse with a rectangular floor is to be constructed with a partition parallel to the front dividing the warehouse into a shipping area of $20\,000$ m^2 and a repair area of 5000 m^2. The following information is gathered:
i) The outside walls at both sides and across the front will cost $300 per metre of length.
ii) The partition wall across the store will cost $150 per metre of length.
iii) The back wall (mainly loading bays) will cost $500 per metre of length.
Calculate the dimensions of the rectangular building that will give the required floor space at the lowest cost for the walls.

11. Describe how the graph of each function varies as c varies. Sketch the graphs of several members of each family, concentrating on showing the extrema and the changes in concavity.
a) $y = x^3 + cx$
b) $f(x) = x^3 + cx^2$
c) $f(t) = t^4 + ct^3$
d) $g(x) = x^2\sqrt{c^2 - x^2}$
e) $y = \dfrac{cx}{1 + c^2x^2}$
f) $h(x) = \dfrac{cx^2}{1 + c^2x^2}$

Problem Solving Strategy

Solving Fermi Problems

About how many recordings are played by all the radio stations in Ontario in a day?

Problems that involve estimation are called Fermi problems. They are named after Enrico Fermi (1901–1954), a leading research scientist who won the Nobel Prize for physics in 1938 and spent the last part of his career as a professor at the University of Chicago. He liked to show his students that they had the knowledge to answer seemingly impossible questions.

The importance of Fermi problems lies in the difference between *guessing* and *estimation*. Although guessing may produce a reasonable answer to a problem, you do not know how much confidence to place in the answer. When estimating the answers to Fermi problems, you will need to make some assumptions. If the estimated answer seems unreasonable, go back and check the assumptions you have made. Consider this Fermi problem: About how many peanuts in the shell are needed to fill a shower stall? Assume that there is an average of two peanuts per shell.

Understand the Problem

1. What information are you given?
2. What are you asked to find?
3. Do you need an exact or an approximate answer?

Think of a Plan

This is a volume problem in which you need to estimate how many small objects are needed to fill a large object.

The number of small objects, n, can be found using the formula

$$n = \frac{\text{large volume}}{\text{small volume}}$$

Carry Out the Plan

A shower stall approximates a square-based prism. You can use your research skills to determine that the side length of the base is about 0.9 m, and the height is about 1.9 m. Therefore, the volume of a shower stall, in cubic centimetres, is about (90)(90)(190), or about 1 540 000 cm³.

Assume that peanuts in a shell approximate a cylinder with a diameter of about 1.5 cm and a height of about 4 cm. The volume, V, in cubic centimetres, of a cylinder with radius r and height h, in centimetres, is given by

$$V = \pi r^2 h$$
$$= \pi (0.75)^2 (4)$$
$$\doteq 7$$

The volume of peanuts in the shell is about 7 cm³.
Thus,

$$n = \frac{1\,594\,000}{7}$$
$$\doteq 220\,000$$

But there is an average of two peanuts per shell. Thus, about 440 000 peanuts in the shell would be needed to fill a shower stall.

Look Back

Does the answer seem reasonable?

Is there a way to improve the estimate?

Fermi Problems
1. Locate the information you need.
2. Decide what assumption(s) to make.
3. Estimate the solution to the problem.
4. Check that your estimate is reasonable.

Practise

Use your research skills to locate any missing information. You could use such sources as the Internet, a reference book, or an expert on the topic. For some problems, you may need to use a survey or measurement. Then, solve each problem.

1. About how many $10 bills would it take to paper the walls of all the classrooms in your school?

2. About how many flat toothpicks would be needed to cover the floor of your school gym?

3. Estimate the number of bananas it would take to fill all the lockers in your school.

4. About how many table tennis balls would it take to fill a minivan?

5. Estimate the number of pianos in Ontario.

6. Estimate the number of pizzas that will be delivered in Ontario this year.

7. About how many minutes do all the students in your school spend on the phone in a month?

8. About how many recordings are played by the radio stations in Ontario in a day?

9. Estimate the number of drops of water in Lake Ontario.

10. About how many times does a grade 12 student laugh in a day?

11. Estimate the total number of times the students in your school press a calculator key in a school day.

1. a) Copy the grid.

1	2	3	4	5
6	7	8	9	10
11	12	13	14	15
16	17	18	19	20
21	22	23	24	25

b) Choose any number in the first row and circle it. Then, cross out all the numbers in the same column below the circled number.
c) Circle any one of the remaining numbers in the second row. Then cross out all the numbers in the same column above and below the circled number. Repeat this process for the third and fourth rows.
d) Circle the remaining number in the fifth row and cross out all the numbers in the same column above the circled number.
e) Add the five circled numbers and record the result.
f) Repeat steps 1 to 5 by circling a different number in the first row. How does the sum of the circled numbers compare with your result from part f)?
g) Repeat parts b) to f) on a 3-by-3 grid.

1	2	3
4	5	6
7	8	9

What is the sum of the circled numbers?
h) Repeat parts b) to f) on a 4-by-4 grid. What is the sum of the circled numbers?
i) Choose one of the grids you used and explain why the sum of the circled numbers is always the same number.

2. Prove that the sum of three consecutive integers is divisible by 3, the sum of five consecutive integers is divisible by 5, but the sum of four consecutive integers is not divisible by 4.

3. How can you use only a 5-min sand timer and a 9-min sand timer to time a food item that needs to cook for 13 min?

4. Each side of the square measures a units. The vertices of the square are the centres of the quarter-circles. The radii of the circles are the same. Find an expression for the area of the shaded region.

5. In chess, queens can attack horizontally, vertically, or diagonally. Place eight queens on a chessboard so that no queen is vulnerable to attack from another queen.

6. Express the length of the hypotenuse of a right triangle in terms of its area, A, and its perimeter, P.

7. The point P is anywhere inside the rectangle ABCD. Show that $a^2 + c^2 = b^2 + d^2$.

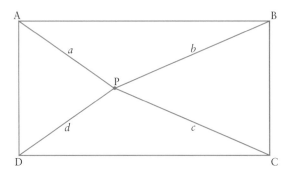

8. Periodically, surveys are mailed to households across the province to determine product use and buying patterns. In one survey, 1012 forms were returned, of which 937 forms were considered valid. One set of questions asked whether the respondents had purchased a VCR, a CD player, a computer, or a car in the past three years. 282 respondents answered yes to all four, 314 replied yes to at least three, 426 said yes to at least two, and all responded yes to at least one. How many had purchased exactly one, two, or three of these items in the last three years?

9. A right triangle has short sides that measure 6 cm and 8 cm. The triangle is to be rotated in space about one of its three sides. What is the maximum possible volume of the resulting solid?

10. If $n = 5^x + 5^x + 5^x + 5^x + 5^x$, find an expression for the value of n^5.

11. If $n(n - 1)(n - 2)(n - 3)(n - 4) = 95\,040$, what is the value of n?

12. Twelve toothpicks are used to make a figure with 6 congruent regions, as shown. If one more toothpick is added, how can the toothpicks be rearranged to make another figure with 6 congruent regions?

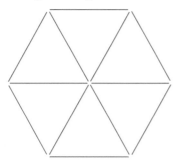

13. In how many ways can you write the number 81 as the sum of consecutive whole numbers?

14. About how many Canadians make a living writing fiction novels?

15. Estimate the number of donut shops in Canada.

16. About what percent of the land area in your city or town is covered by buildings?

17. Estimate the total number of hours that college and university students in your province spend at lectures and laboratories in a year.

18. About how many mailboxes are within 2 km of your school?

19. How many loonies would you need to build a tower to the moon?

20. How many whiskers are on all the cats in Ontario?

Chapter 7

Exponential and Logarithmic Functions

Specific Expectations	Section
Identify, through investigations, using graphing calculators or graphing software, the key properties of exponential functions of the form a^x ($a > 0$, $a \neq 1$) and their graphs.	7.1
Describe the graphical implications of changes in the parameters a, b, and c in the equation $y = ca^x + b$.	7.1
Determine the limit of an exponential function.	7.1
Determine, from the equation of an exponential function, the key features of the graph of the function, using the techniques of differential calculus, and sketch the graph by hand.	7.1
Define the logarithmic function $\log_a x$ ($a > 1$) as the inverse of the exponential function a^x, and compare the properties of the two functions.	7.2
Express logarithmic equations in exponential form, and vice versa.	7.2
Simplify and evaluate expressions containing logarithms.	7.2, 7.3
Solve exponential and logarithmic equations, using the laws of logarithms.	7.4
Solve simple problems involving logarithmic scales.	7.5
Pose and solve problems related to models of exponential functions drawn from a variety of applications, and communicate the solutions with clarity and justification.	7.5, 7.6, 7.7, 7.8
Identify e as $\lim_{n \to \infty} \left(1 + \dfrac{1}{n}\right)^n$ and approximate the limit, using informal methods.	7.6
Define $\ln x$ as the inverse function of e^x.	7.6
Determine the derivatives of combinations of the basic polynomial, rational, exponential, and logarithmic functions, using the rules for sums, differences, products, quotients, and compositions of functions.	7.6, 7.7
Determine the equation of the tangent to the graph of an exponential or a logarithmic function.	7.6, 7.7
Determine, from the equation of a simple combination of polynomial, rational, or exponential functions, the key features of the graph of the combination of functions, using the techniques of differential calculus, and sketch the graph by hand.	7.6
Determine the derivatives of the exponential functions a^x and e^x and the logarithmic functions $\log_a x$ and $\ln x$.	7.6, 7.7

MODELLING MATH

What is the source of power for satellites that orbit Earth? Will that power ever run out? Why do mountain climbers need oxygen at high altitudes? Why do airplane cabins need to be pressurized? How can we compare the strength of earthquakes, and relate it to how much damage is done? You will investigate these and other questions in this chapter. All of the phenomena mentioned here involve changes that can be modelled by exponential functions. You will see that exponential models predict increases that are more and more rapid, or decreases that approach certain values asymptotically. Such models are widely applicable to many situations in nature.

Review of Prerequisite Skills

1. Exponent laws
Simplify.

a) $(-5)^2$ b) 2^{-3} c) $(-27)^{\frac{1}{3}}$

d) $4^{-2} + \left(\dfrac{1}{4}\right)^0$ e) $125^{\frac{2}{3}}$ f) $16^{\frac{5}{2}}$

2. Writing numbers in exponential form
Write each number as a power with the indicated base.

a) 64, base 2   b) 1, base 12

c) $\sqrt{3}$, base 3   d) $\dfrac{1}{64}$, base 4

3. Exponent laws
Simplify, using the exponent laws.

a) $(27x^2y^3)\left(\dfrac{1}{3}x^6y\right)$

b) $\dfrac{(fg^2)^2 h^3}{fg^3 h}$

c) $\dfrac{x^{-1} + y^{-1}}{(x+y)^{-1}}$

d) $\dfrac{m^{-3}n^{-6}}{m^5 n^{-2}}$

e) $\dfrac{(9cd)^{\frac{3}{2}}}{(27s^3t^{-4})^{\frac{2}{3}}}$

f) $(3a^4b^2)^3(3a^2b)^{-2}$

4. Transformations
Describe the transformations performed on the graph of $y = f(x)$.

a) $y = 2f(x)$
b) $y = f(3x)$
c) $y = -f(x)$
d) $y = 4f(x) + 2$
e) $y = f(-4x) + 1$
f) $y = 0.5f(-x) - 7$
g) $y = f\left(\dfrac{1}{3}x\right) + \dfrac{1}{4}$
h) $y = -7f(x) + 3$

5. Transformations
Graph each function using transformations on the graph of $y = x^2$.
a) $y = x^2$

b) $y = (x - 3)^2$
c) $y = 4x^2$
d) $y = -3x^2 - 1$
e) $y = -2(x + 5)^2 + 7$

6. Compound interest
Use the formula for compound interest, $A = P(1 + i)^n$, to find the amount of interest earned and the final amount for each investment.
a) $300 invested at 5%, compounded annually, for 8 years
b) $7000 invested at 7.25%, compounded annually, for 1.5 years
c) $4000 invested at 3.25%, compounded semi-annually, for 12 years
d) $2900 invested at 7.5%, compounded semi-annually, for 5 years
e) $10 000 invested at 2%, compounded quarterly, for 4 years
f) $1600 invested at 4.75%, compounded monthly, for 7 years

7. Inverses
a) Find the inverse of each function.
i) $y = x^2$ ii) $y = 2x + 3$
iii) $y = x^3$
b) Decide whether each inverse in part a) is a function. Explain.

8. Limits (Sections 6.4, 6.5) Determine each limit.

a) $\lim\limits_{x \to 0^+} \dfrac{1}{x^2}$ b) $\lim\limits_{x \to 0^-} \dfrac{1}{x^2}$

c) $\lim\limits_{x \to 0} \dfrac{1}{x^2}$ d) $\lim\limits_{x \to \infty} \dfrac{3x + 2}{x + 1}$

e) $\lim\limits_{x \to -\infty} \dfrac{4x - 3}{3x + 2}$ f) $\lim\limits_{x \to -\infty} \dfrac{x^2 + 2x + 5}{2x - 3}$

9. Asymptotes (Sections 6.4, 6.5) Sketch a graph having the following properties.
a) vertical asymptote at $x = 0$, horizontal asymptote at $y = 0$, function is increasing for $x < 0$ and increasing for $x > 0$
b) vertical asymptote at $x = 2$, horizontal asymptote at $y = -1$, function is concave up
c) vertical asymptote at $x = -3$, oblique asymptote $y = x$, function is concave down
d) vertical asymptotes at $x = -4$ and $x = 4$, horizontal asymptotes at $y = 2$ and $y = -2$

10. Polynomial equations (Section 2.5) Solve for x.
a) $x^{10} - 1 = 0$
b) $x^6 - 7x^3 - 8 = 0$
c) $x^8 - 17x^4 + 16 = 0$
d) $x^6 - 4x^4 - x^2 + 4 = 0$

11. Exponential equations William has $100 to spend. He spends half of his money on the first day, half of the remaining amount on the second day, half of the remaining amount on the third day, and so on. (The amount he spends each day is rounded up to the nearest cent.) How long does his money last?

12. Exponential equations Gwen performs one push-up this week, two the next week, and doubles the amount every week thereafter. After how many weeks is she performing more than 1000 push-ups?

13. Exponential equations Dilip and Sara start with no money. Dilip receives $10 the first day, $20 the second day, $30 the third day, and so on, with the amounts increasing by $10 each day. Sara receives $1 the first day, $2 the second day, $4 the third day, and so on, with the amounts doubling each day.

a) Who receives at least $50 on a single day first?
b) Who receives at least $100 on a single day first?
c) Sketch a graph of the amount received on each day for both Dilip and Sara for the first 10 days.

14. Exponential equations You win a prize and are offered Option A, which is $1 000 000, or Option B, which is $0.01 on the first day, $0.02 on the second day, and the amount doubles each subsequent day.
a) Determine the accumulated amount for Option B after 2 days, 3 days, 4 days, and 5 days.
b) After how many days is the accumulated amount in Option B greater than the amount received in Option A?
c) Repeat part b) if Option A is to receive $1 000 000 000.
d) Repeat part b) if Option A is to receive $1 000 000 000 000.
e) Repeat part b) if Option A is to receive $1 000 000 000 000 000.
f) Repeat part b) if Option A is to receive $1 000 000 per day.

Historical Bite: What is a Mathematician?

The mathematician Paul Halmos (1916–) explains what a mathematician does: "The mathematician is interested in extreme cases—in this respect he is like the industrial experimenter who breaks lightbulbs, tears sheets, and bounces cars on ruts. How widely does reasoning apply, he wants to know, and what happens when it doesn't? What happens when you weaken one of the assumptions, or under what conditions can you strengthen one of the conclusions? It is this perpetual asking of such questions that makes for a broader understanding, better technique, and greater elasticity for future problems."

Exponential Functions

Exponential functions, such as $y = 3^x$ and $y = \left(\dfrac{1}{4}\right)^x$, are used to model a wide variety of natural phenomena. For example, a bacterial culture that doubles in size every hour might be modelled by the function $y = 2^t$, where t is in hours. The amount of a radioactive isotope with a half-life of 1000 years might be modelled by the function $y = \left(\dfrac{1}{2}\right)^{\frac{t}{1000}}$, where t is in years.

Exponential functions can be written in the form $f(x) = a^x$, where the base, a, is a positive constant not equal to 1, that is, $a \in (0, 1)$ or $a \in (1, \infty)$. The exponent, x, is a variable that can be any real number, unless there is some restriction on the domain. Exponential relationships are used to model compound interest, population growth, and resource consumption.

We can perform all the usual transformations—translations, reflections, and stretches—on the graphs of exponential functions. The following investigation explores the effect of these transformations on exponential functions.

Investigate & Inquire: Transforming Exponential Functions

1. Graph the function $y = 2^x$. Then, graph each function below and use the information from the graphs to copy and complete the table.

Equation	Transformation of graph of $y = 2^x$	Domain	Range	End Behaviour	Equation of asymptote(s)	Intercepts
$y = 2^x + 3$						
$y = 2^x - 5$						
$y = (3)2^x$						
$y = (-4)2^x$						
$y = (-4)2^x + 3$						

2. a) Describe the effect of c on the graph when transforming $y = a^x$ into $y = ca^x$. What happens to the graph if $c < 0$?
b) Describe the effect of b on the graph when transforming $y = a^x$ into $y = a^x + b$
i) if $b > 0$ **ii)** if $b < 0$

3. Without constructing a table of values,
a) describe how to graph $y = (2)3^x + 3$, given the graph of $y = 3^x$
b) describe how to graph $y = (-3)5^x - 7$, given the graph of $y = 5^x$
c) describe how to graph $y = ba^x + c$, given the graph of $y = a^x$

Next, we will explore changing the value of the base, a.

Investigate & Inquire: How the Base of an Exponential Function Influences Its Graph

1. Use graphing technology to investigate the graphs of exponential functions with different bases.

a) Graph $y = 2^x$, $y = 3^x$, $y = 5^x$, and $y = 11^x$.

b) Graph $y = \left(\dfrac{1}{2}\right)^x$, $y = \left(\dfrac{1}{3}\right)^x$, $y = \left(\dfrac{1}{5}\right)^x$, and $y = \left(\dfrac{1}{11}\right)^x$.

2. a) Describe the changes to the graphs of $y = a^x$ as a increases, for $a \in (1, \infty)$.

b) Describe the changes to the graphs of $y = a^x$ as a decreases, for $a \in (0, 1)$.

3. a) Compare the graphs in step 1, parts a) and b), in pairs. That is, compare the graphs of $y = 2^x$ and $y = \left(\dfrac{1}{2}\right)^x$, and then the graphs of $y = 3^x$ and $y = \left(\dfrac{1}{3}\right)^x$, and so on. How are the graphs in each pair alike? How are they different?

b) Without graphing, describe how the graphs of $y = 6^x$ and $y = \left(\dfrac{1}{6}\right)^x$ differ and what they have in common. Use graphing technology to confirm your answer.

4. What point do all exponential functions appear to have in common? Explain why this is so.

5. a) Graph the functions $y = 0^x$ and $y = 1^x$. Describe the graphs. Are these exponential functions? Explain.

b) What happens if you try to graph $y = (-2)^x$ on a graphing calculator or graphing software? Set up a table of values of $y = (-2)^x$ using the TABLE SETUP screen, with a **TblStart** value of −2 and a **ΔTbl** value of 0.1. Explain why we have the restriction $a \in (0, 1)$ or $a \in (1, \infty)$ for the exponential function $y = a^x$.

The graph of $f(x) = a^x$, where $a \in (1, \infty)$ and $x \in (-\infty, \infty)$, is continuous and always increasing. When $a \in (0, 1)$, the graph is continuous and always decreasing.

Look at the graphs of the exponential functions $f(x) = a^x$ for various values of the base a. Notice that, regardless of the base, all of these graphs pass through the same point, $(0, 1)$, because $a^0 = 1$ for $a \neq 0$. Also, note that the x-axis is a horizontal asymptote and that the graphs never touch or cross the x-axis, since $a^x > 0$ for all values of x. Thus, the exponential function $f(x) = a^x$ has domain $(-\infty, \infty)$ and range $(0, \infty)$ for $a > 0$.

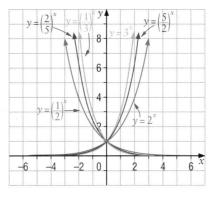

Now, we take a closer look at the function $y = a^x$, where $a \in (0, 1)$ or $a \in (1, \infty)$.

$a \in (1, \infty)$: As x approaches infinity, the graph of $y = a^x$ increases rapidly, and as x approaches negative infinity, the graph is asymptotic to the x-axis. Thus:

If $a \in (1, \infty)$, $\displaystyle\lim_{x \to -\infty} a^x = 0$ and $\displaystyle\lim_{x \to \infty} a^x = \infty$.

Furthermore, the larger the base a, the more rapidly the function increases as x approaches infinity. As x approaches negative infinity, the larger the base a, the more rapidly the graph of the function approaches its asymptote, the x-axis.

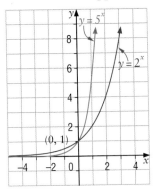
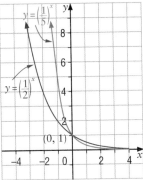

$a \in (0, 1)$: As x approaches infinity, the graph is asymptotic to the x-axis, and as x approaches negative infinity, the graph of $y = a^x$ increases rapidly. Thus:

If $a \in (0, 1)$, $\lim\limits_{x \to -\infty} a^x = \infty$ and $\lim\limits_{x \to \infty} a^x = 0$.

Furthermore, the smaller the base a, the more rapidly the graph of the function approaches its asymptote, the x-axis, as x approaches infinity. As x approaches negative infinity, the smaller the base a, the more rapidly the function increases.

Can a be less than 0 for $y = a^x$? That is, can $y = a^x$ have a negative base? The answer is yes, but the resulting function is so badly discontinuous that it has no practical use. In the Investigation above, $y = (-2)^x$ was graphed. Note from the table of values that, for many values of x, the function is not defined. For example, $(-2)^{\frac{1}{2}}$, or $\sqrt{-2}$, is not

defined in the real numbers. Neither are $(-2)^{\frac{1}{4}}$, $(-2)^{\frac{1}{6}}$, and so on. Since many expressions with negative bases cannot be evaluated, we restrict the definition of the exponential function to positive values of a. Since $1^x = 1$ for all values of x, $f(x) = 1^x$ is not considered an exponential function. Since

$$0^x = \begin{cases} 0, & x > 0 \\ \text{undefined}, & x \leq 0 \end{cases}$$

$f(x) = 0^x$ is not considered an exponential function either. Thus, we restrict a in the exponential function $y = a^x$ to positive real numbers not equal to 1, that is, $a \in (0, 1)$ or $a \in (1, \infty)$.

Example 1 Transformations of an Exponential Function

Use the graph of $y = 3^x$ to sketch the graph of each function. Use technology to confirm your results.
a) $y = 3^x + 4$
b) $y = -3^x$ (Note: this is not the same as $y = (-3)^x$, which is a discontinuous function.)

Solution

a) The graph of $y = 3^x + 4$ is obtained by starting with the graph of $y = 3^x$ and translating it four units upward. We see from the graph that the line $y = 4$ is a horizontal asymptote. The asymptote has moved up 4 units from the original asymptote, $y = 0$.

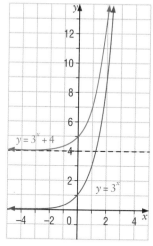

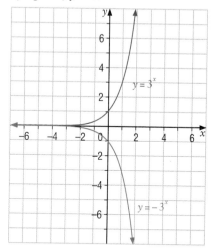

b) Again, we start with the graph of $y = 3^x$ and reflect it in the x-axis to get the graph of $y = -3^x$. The horizontal asymptote is $y = 0$.

Example 2 Transformations of an Exponential Function

a) Use the graph of $y = 2^x$ to sketch the graph of $y = 2^{x-2} - 3$.
b) State the asymptote, the domain, and the range of this function.

Solution

a) To graph $y = 2^{x-2}$ using the graph of $y = 2^x$, we translate the original graph 2 units to the right. Then, we graph $y = 2^{x-2} - 3$ by translating $y = 2^{x-2}$ downward 3 units. To summarize, we graph $y = 2^{x-2} - 3$ by translating the graph of $y = 2^x$ to the right 2 units and downward 3 units.

b) We see from the graph that the horizontal asymptote is $y = -3$. It has been translated downward 3 units along with the graph.
The domain is R and the range is $(-3, \infty)$.

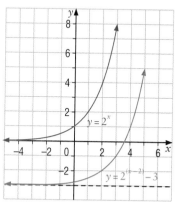

Example 3 An Exponential Model for Light Transmitted by Water

The equation $s = 0.8^d$ models the fraction of sunlight, s, that reaches a scuba diver under water, where d is the depth of the diver, in metres.
a) Use graphing technology to graph the sunlight, $s = 0.8^d$, that reaches a scuba diver, using a suitable domain and range.
b) Determine what percent of sunlight reaches a diver 3 m below the surface of the water.

Solution

a) The graph of $s = 0.8^d$ is shown. For Window variables, we use the domain [0, 20] because depth cannot be negative. We use trial and error to find a suitable upper limit of the domain. Since s is a proportion, we use the range [0, 1].

b) Use the $\boxed{\text{TRACE}}$ key to find the value of s when $d = 3$. Confirm the solution algebraically.

$s = d^3$

$\quad = 0.8^3$

$\quad = 0.512$

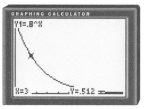

This means that only about 50% of the sunlight above the water will reach a diver 3 m below the surface of the water.

Example 4 Limit of an Exponential Function

Find $\displaystyle\lim_{x \to 2^-} 4^{\frac{1}{x-2}}$.

Solution 1 Graphing Calculator Method

Since the function $f(x) = 4^{\frac{1}{x-2}}$ is not continuous at $x = 2$, we cannot substitute $x = 2$ to find the limit. We will use a table of values to determine the limit. Enter the function in the Y= editor of a graphing calculator. Then, set up a table using the TABLE SETUP screen. Use Ask mode for the independent variable (x, in this case).

  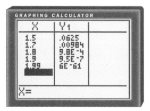

Enter x-values that approach 2 from the left. From the table, it appears that $4^{\frac{1}{x-2}}$ approaches zero very quickly as x approaches 2 from the left. Thus, it appears that

$\displaystyle\lim_{x \to 2^-} 4^{\frac{1}{x-2}} = 0$.

Solution 2 Paper and Pencil Method

As x approaches 2 from the left, $x - 2$ approaches zero, and is negative. Thus, $\dfrac{1}{x-2}$

approaches negative infinity. We can rewrite $\displaystyle\lim_{x \to 2^-} 4^{\frac{1}{x-2}}$ as $\displaystyle\lim_{z \to -\infty} 4^z$, where $z = \dfrac{1}{x-2}$. Recall

from earlier that, if $a \in (1, \infty)$, then $\displaystyle\lim_{x \to -\infty} a^x = 0$. Thus, $\displaystyle\lim_{z \to -\infty} 4^z = 0$, so $\displaystyle\lim_{x \to 2^-} 4^{\frac{1}{x-2}} = 0$.

Key Concepts

- If $a \in (1, \infty)$, then $\lim_{x \to -\infty} a^x = 0$ and $\lim_{x \to \infty} a^x = \infty$. The function $f(x) = a^x$ has domain $x \in (-\infty, \infty)$ and range $y \in (0, \infty)$.
- If $a \in (0, 1)$, then $\lim_{x \to -\infty} a^x = \infty$ and $\lim_{x \to \infty} a^x = 0$. The function $f(x) = a^x$ has domain $x \in (-\infty, \infty)$ and range $(0, \infty)$.
- The graph of $y = -a^x$ is a reflection of the graph of $y = a^x$ in the x-axis.
- The graph of $y = ca^{x-p} + b$ is obtained by graphing the original function $y = a^x$, and transforming it as follows:
  a) Stretch the graph vertically by a factor of c if $|c| > 1$; compress the graph vertically by a factor of c if $0 < |c| < 1$.
  b) If $c < 0$, reflect the graph in the x-axis.
  c) Translate the graph left p units if $p > 0$, and right p units if $p < 0$.
  d) Translate the graph up b units if $b > 0$, and down b units if $b < 0$.

Communicate Your Understanding

1. a) Is the domain of every exponential function the same? Explain.

b) Is the range of every exponential function the same? Explain.

2. a) Given the graph of $y = 3^x$, explain how to graph $y = \left(\dfrac{1}{3}\right)^x$ without using technology or a table of values.

b) Given the graph of $y = 6^x$, describe how to graph $y = (-4)6^x - 5$.

3. Explain why the function $y = a^x$ is not considered an exponential function

a) when $a = 1$ b) when $a = 0$ c) when $a < 0$

Practise

A **1.** a) Explain the similarities and differences among the graphs of $y = 2^x$, $y = 6^x$, and $y = 9^x$. In your explanation, pay attention to the y-intercepts and the limits as x approaches positive and negative infinity.

b) Repeat part a) for the graphs of $y = \left(\dfrac{1}{2}\right)^x$, $y = \left(\dfrac{1}{6}\right)^x$, and $y = \left(\dfrac{1}{9}\right)^x$.

2. Graph each pair of functions on the same set of axes. First, use a table of values to graph $f(x)$, and then, use your graph of $f(x)$ to graph $g(x)$. Check your work using graphing technology.

a) $f(x) = 3^x$ and $g(x) = \left(\dfrac{1}{3}\right)^x$

b) $f(x) = 5^x$ and $g(x) = \left(\dfrac{1}{5}\right)^x$

c) $f(x) = 6^x$ and $g(x) = \left(\dfrac{1}{6}\right)^x$

d) $f(x) = 10^x$ and $g(x) = \left(\dfrac{1}{10}\right)^x$

3. a) Use a table of values to graph $f(x) = 2^x$.

b) Describe how to graph $g(x) = \left(\dfrac{1}{3}\right)(2^x)$ and $h(x) = (3)2^x$ using the graph of $f(x) = 2^x$.

c) Graph $g(x) = \left(\dfrac{1}{3}\right)(2^x)$ and $h(x) = (3)2^x$ on the same set of axes as $f(x)$. Confirm your results with graphing technology.

d) State the domain and range of each function.

4. Use the given graphs to sketch a graph of each of the following functions without using a table of values or technology. State the y-intercept, domain, range, and equation of the asymptote of each function.

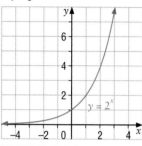

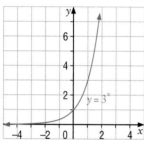

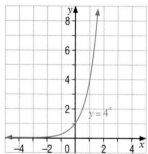

a) $f(x) = -2^x$
b) $g(x) = 3^{x+2}$
c) $h(x) = 2^x + 3$
d) $f(x) = (3)3^x - 5$
e) $y = -\left(\dfrac{1}{3}\right)^x$
f) $f(x) = \left(\dfrac{1}{2}\right)^x + 3$
g) $h(x) = (-2)\left(\dfrac{1}{3}\right)^{x+4} - 6$
h) $y = (3)\left(\dfrac{1}{4}\right)^{x+3} + 2$

5. For each function,
i) state the y-intercept
ii) state the domain and range
iii) state the equation of the asymptote
iv) draw a graph of the function

a) $f(x) = 3^x + 2$
b) $g(x) = -4^x$
c) $h(x) = (-2)7^x - 5$
d) $g(x) = \left(\dfrac{1}{3}\right)^x + 1$
e) $f(x) = -3\left(\dfrac{1}{4}\right)^x$
f) $h(x) = 2\left(\dfrac{1}{2}\right)^x - 7$

6. Evaluate.
a) $\lim\limits_{x \to -\infty} 3^x$
b) $\lim\limits_{x \to \infty} 8^{3x-1}$
c) $\lim\limits_{x \to \infty} 4^{-x}$
d) $\lim\limits_{x \to \infty} 2^x$
e) $\lim\limits_{x \to 0^-} 3^{\frac{1}{x}}$
f) $\lim\limits_{x \to 0^+} 3^{\frac{1}{x}}$
g) $\lim\limits_{x \to \infty} 6^{\frac{1}{x}}$
h) $\lim\limits_{x \to \infty} 5^{-x^2}$
i) $\lim\limits_{x \to -\infty} (2^x + 1)$
j) $\lim\limits_{x \to 4^-} 3^{\frac{1}{x-4}}$

Apply, Solve, Communicate

B **7.** Application In Example 3 on page 417, it would be almost completely dark underwater if only 0.1% of the sunlight above the water reached a diver. At what depth does this occur?

8. Inquiry/Problem Solving Randolf bought a computer system for $4000. The system depreciates at a rate of 20% each year.
a) Determine an exponential function to model the value of the system over time.
b) Graph the function you found in part a).
c) Use your graph to determine the value of Randolf's computer system 3 years from now.
d) Verify your result from part c) algebraically.

9. Inquiry/Problem Solving Roy bought an antique slide rule in 2001 for $25. The value of the collector's item is increasing and can be approximately determined by the expression $y = 25(1.03)^t$, where t is the number of years since 2001, and y is the value, in dollars.
a) Graph the value of the slide rule over time.

b) Find the approximate value of the slide rule in 2015.

c) Determine approximately when the slide rule will have a value of $50.

10. Collette bought a $1500 compound interest savings bond with a 5% annual interest rate.

a) Graph the growth of Collette's savings bond over time.

b) Use your graph to determine the value of her bond when it matures 15 years from now.

Web Connection

To find current and historical values for the Bank of Canada prime lending rate, go to **www.mcgrawhill.ca/links/CAF12** and follow the link.

11. Application If $f(x) = 4^x$, show that $\dfrac{f(x+h) - f(x)}{h} = 4^x \left(\dfrac{4^h - 1}{h} \right)$.

12. Communication A sample of radioactive iodine-131 atoms has a half-life of about 8 days. This means that after 8 days, half of the atoms will have transformed into some other type of atom. A formula that models the number of iodine-131 atoms that remain is $P = P_0(2^{-\frac{t}{8}})$, where P is the number of iodine-131 atoms that remain after time t, in days, and P_0 is the number of iodine-131 atoms that are initially present. Suppose that $1\,000\,000$ iodine-131 atoms are initially present.

a) How many iodine-131 atoms remain after 24 days?

b) How many iodine-131 atoms remain after 80 days?

c) How many iodine-131 atoms remain after 360 days?

d) Does the result in part c) make sense? Comment on the domain of validity of the model.

e) According to nuclear physics, the transformation of radioactive atoms is a discrete process, that is, every so often an individual atom transforms. There is always a whole number of untransformed atoms remaining. Thus, a graph of this process would not be continuous. Yet the exponential model is continuous. Comment on the validity of using a continuous model for a phenomenon that is essentially discrete. Explain why the model is nevertheless a good one. Over what domain is the model good?

13. Explain how you would graph the following functions given the graph of $y = 2^x$. Then, graph each function and state its domain and range.

a) $y = 2^{|x|}$
b) $y = 2^{-|x|}$

14. Evaluate each limit.

a) $\lim\limits_{x \to \infty} 5^{|x|}$
b) $\lim\limits_{x \to -\infty} 5^{|x|}$

c) $\lim\limits_{x \to \infty} 3^{-|x|}$
d) $\lim\limits_{x \to -\infty} 3^{-|x|}$

15. In this section, we stated that exponential functions with positive bases are continuous functions. In this exercise, you will explore the meaning of exponential expressions with irrational exponents.

a) Explain the meaning of $5^{\frac{3}{2}}$ in terms of powers and roots.

b) Explain the meaning of $5^{1.4}$ in terms of powers and roots.

c) Explain the meaning of $5^{1.41}$ in terms of powers and roots.

d) Explain the meaning of $5^{1.414}$ in terms of powers and roots.

e) Explain the meaning of $5^{1.4142}$ in terms of powers and roots.

f) Use the idea behind parts a) to e), and the idea of the limit, to explain the meaning of $5^{\sqrt{2}}$.

Logarithmic Functions

Suppose you have an investment and would like to determine how long it will take to double. If you start with \$500 invested at 6% per year, compounded annually, the value, A, in dollars, of your investment after t years is given by $A = 500(1.06)^t$. To find out how long the investment will take to double, you need to solve the equation $1000 = 500(1.06)^t$, or $2 = (1.06)^t$.

This equation can be solved by using trial and error on a scientific calculator, by using a graphical approximation, or by using logarithms. Logarithmic functions are related to exponential functions in a special way. In the following investigation, you will discover how they are related.

Investigate & Inquire: Inverse of an Exponential Function

1. a) The number of bacteria in a culture starts at 1, and doubles every hour. Let y represent the number of bacteria, and x represent the time, in hours. Make a table of values relating x and y.
b) What exponential function relates y to x?

2. To determine when there will be 15 bacteria in the culture, what equation would have to be solved?

3. a) Graph $y = 2^x$ and its inverse on the same set of axes. Recall that, to find the inverse function, interchange the x- and y-values.
b) Describe the graphical relationship between a function and its inverse, and their relationship to the line $y = x$.
c) Explain how the graph of the inverse can be used to approximate the solution to the equation determined in step 2.

4. Find an approximate solution for each equation by carefully graphing an appropriate function and its inverse.
a) $3^x = 12$ **b)** $6^x = 17$ **c)** $-2^x = -9$

5. Make a general statement explaining how to solve exponential equations graphically.

To find the inverse of the exponential function $y = a^x$, we exchange x and y to obtain $x = a^y$. The resulting inverse function is called a **logarithmic function**. If $x = a^y$, then the **logarithm** of x to base a, $y = \log_a x$, is defined as the exponent to which the base a must be raised to obtain x. For example, if we want to evaluate $\log_3 9$, the question is, "To what exponent must 3 be raised to give 9?" The answer is 2, so $\log_3 9 = 2$. In exponential form, $\log_3 9 = 2$ is written $3^2 = 9$.

$y = \log_a x$ is equivalent to $x = a^y$

exponent   base   base   exponent

Example 1 Evaluating Logarithms

Evaluate.

a) $\log_2 32$ b) $\log_3 81$ c) $\log_4 \dfrac{1}{16}$

Solution

a) We can evaluate $\log_2 32$ by determining to what exponent the base 2 must be raised to get the result 32. Since $2^5 = 32$, the exponent is 5. Thus, $\log_2 32 = 5$.

b) We can evaluate $\log_3 81$ by determining to what exponent the base 3 must be raised to get the result 81. Since $3^4 = 81$, the exponent is 4. Thus, $\log_3 81 = 4$.

c) We can evaluate $\log_4 \dfrac{1}{16}$ by determining to what exponent the base 4 must be raised to get the result $\dfrac{1}{16}$. Since $\dfrac{1}{16}$ is between zero and one, the exponent must be negative. We know that $4^{-2} = \dfrac{1}{16}$. Thus, $\log_4 \dfrac{1}{16} = -2$.

The results of Example 1 can be summarized in the following table.

Logarithmic Form	Exponential Form
$\log_2 32 = 5$	$2^5 = 32$
$\log_3 81 = 4$	$3^4 = 81$
$\log_4 \dfrac{1}{16} = -2$	$4^{-2} = \dfrac{1}{16}$

Since the functions $y = a^x$ and $y = \log_a x$ are inverses of each other, their graphs are reflections of each other in the line $y = x$. Note also the intercepts. For $y = a^x$, we see that $a^0 = 1$, so the y-intercept is 1. Since $a^0 = 1$ can also be written as $\log_a 1 = 0$, we see that the x-intercept of $y = \log_a x$ is 1.

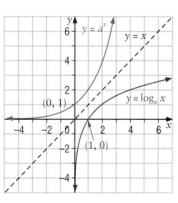

From Section 7.1, we know that the domain of $y = a^x$ is the set of all real numbers, or $x \in (-\infty, \infty)$, and the range is $y \in (0, \infty)$. In general, for inverses, the domain and range are reversed. That is, the domain of $f(x)$ is equal to the range of $f^{-1}(x)$, and the range of $f(x)$ is equal to the domain of $f^{-1}(x)$. So, the domain of $y = \log_a x$ is $x \in (0, \infty)$ and the range is $y \in (-\infty, \infty)$.

Look carefully at the domain of the function $y = \log_a x$ and note that $x > 0$. Another way of looking at this is by rewriting $y = \log_a x$ as $x = a^y$. Since a^y is always positive, $x > 0$.

Since $a \in (0, 1)$ or $a \in (1, \infty)$ for the function $y = a^x$, $a \in (0, 1)$ or $a \in (1, \infty)$ for its inverse $y = \log_a x$. In this section, we will be looking only at values of a in the interval $(1, \infty)$.

Since the graph of $y = a^x$ has a horizontal asymptote (the x-axis), its inverse, $y = \log_a x$, has a vertical asymptote (the y-axis). We can also see this by looking at the ranges of the two functions.

Observing the behaviour of the graphs, we note that $\lim\limits_{x \to 0^+} \log_a x = -\infty$. It is more difficult to tell the behaviour of $y = \log_a x$ as $x \to \infty$ from the graph. Is there a horizontal asymptote? If $y = \log_a x$ had a horizontal asymptote, then its inverse, $y = a^x$, would have a vertical asymptote. Since $y = a^x$ does not have a vertical asymptote, $y = \log_a x$ does not have a horizontal asymptote. Thus, $\lim\limits_{x \to \infty} \log_a x = \infty$, if $a > 1$.

Properties of Logarithms

If we rewrite the logarithmic function $y = \log_a x$ as $x = a^y$, we can discover other properties of logarithms.

Investigate & Inquire: Exploring Logarithms

1. Rewrite each logarithm as an exponential, and then determine y.
a) $y = \log_2 1$ b) $y = \log_5 1$ c) $y = \log_7 1$ d) $y = \log_{300} 1$

2. Make and test a conjecture about the value of $\log_a 1$, for any $a > 1$.

3. Repeat step 1 for the following logarithms.
a) $y = \log_3 3$ b) $y = \log_8 8$ c) $y = \log_{13} 13$ d) $y = \log_{302} 302$

4. Make and test a conjecture about the value of $\log_a a$, for any $a > 1$.

5. Repeat step 1 for the following logarithms.
a) $y = \log_4 (4^2)$ b) $y = \log_7 (7^3)$ c) $y = \log_{11} (11^{14})$ d) $y = \log_9 (9^2)$

6. Make and test a conjecture about the value of $\log_a a^x$, for any $a > 1$ and any $x \in R$.

7. The equation $y = 2^{\log_2 11}$ can be rewritten using logarithms. First, let $z = \log_2 11$. Then,

$$y = 2^z$$
$$z = \log_2 y$$
$$\log_2 11 = \log_2 y$$

Rewrite each power as a logarithm, and then determine y.
a) $y = 3^{\log_3 7}$ b) $y = 7^{\log_7 33}$ c) $y = 12^{\log_{12} 8}$ d) $y = 4^{\log_4 853}$

8. Make and test a conjecture about the value of $a^{\log_a x}$, if $a > 1$ and $x > 0$.

9. Make a list of your conjectures from steps 2, 4, 6, and 8. These are four very important properties of logarithms.

Example 2 Transformations of Logarithmic Functions

Graph each function and its inverse on the same set of axes.
a) $y = \log_2 x$　　　b) $y = -\log_2 x$　　　c) $y = \log_2 (-x)$

Solution

a) The inverse of $y = \log_2 x$ is $y = 2^x$.
Graph $y = \log_2 x$. Then, reflect the graph in
the line $y = x$ to obtain the graph of its inverse,
$y = 2^x$.

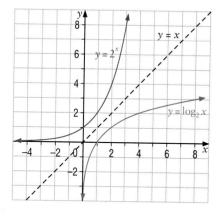

b) To graph $y = -\log_2 x$, we start with the graph
of $y = \log_2 x$ from part a), and reflect it in
the x-axis.

To find the inverse of $y = -\log_2 x$, switch the x- and
y-coordinates and solve for y.
$$x = -\log_2 y$$
$$-x = \log_2 y$$
$$y = 2^{-x}$$

To graph $y = 2^{-x}$, reflect the graph of $y = -\log_2 x$ in
the line $y = x$.

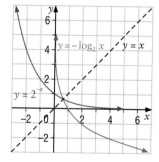

c) To graph $y = \log_2 (-x)$, we start with the graph
of $y = \log_2 x$ from part a), and then, reflect it in
the y-axis.

To find the inverse of $y = \log_2 (-x)$, reverse the x- and
y-coordinates.
$$x = \log_2 (-y)$$
$$-y = 2^x$$
$$y = -2^x$$

To graph $y = -2^x$, reflect the graph of $y = \log_2 (-x)$ in the
line $y = x$.

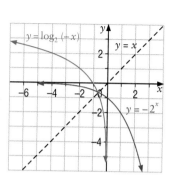

Example 3 Graphing Logarithmic Functions

Graph each function and state the domain, the range, and the equation of the vertical asymptote.
a) $y = \log_{10}(x - 1)$
b) $f(x) = 2 + \log_3 x$

Solution

a) We obtain the graph of $y = \log_{10}(x - 1)$ by translating the graph of $y = \log_{10} x$ to the right 1 unit. From the graph, we observe that the domain is $x \in (1, \infty)$, the range is $y \in (-\infty, \infty)$, and the vertical asymptote is the line $x = 1$.

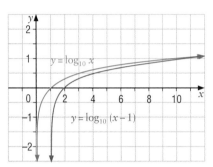 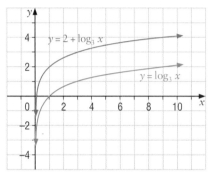

b) The graph of $f(x) = 2 + \log_3 x$ is obtained by translating the graph of $f(x) = \log_3 x$ upward 2 units. From the graph, we observe that the domain is $x \in (0, \infty)$, the range is $y \in (-\infty, \infty)$, and the vertical asymptote is the y-axis.

Example 4 Determining the Doubling Time for an Investment

Solve the equation $1000 = 500(1.06)^t$ to determine how long it will take to double $500 invested at 6%, compounded annually.

Solution

We use graphing technology to graph $y = 500(1.06)^x$.

We are trying to determine the x-value for which $y = 1000$. So, we graph $y = 1000$ on the same screen, and find the point of intersection.

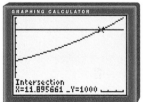

Window variables:
$x \in [0, 15]$,
$y \in [0, 1200]$

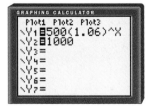  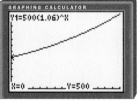

We use the Intersect operation to determine that $y = 1000$ when $x \doteq 11.90$. Therefore, the investment doubles in about 12 years.

In Example 4, we solved the equation $1000 = 500(1.06)^x$, by graphing. This equation can be rewritten as $2 = (1.06)^x$, or $x = \log_{1.06} 2$. Unfortunately, the $\boxed{\text{LOG}}$ key on a calculator determines the logarithm only to base 10, so we cannot use it (yet) to evaluate a logarithm to base 1.06. In Section 7.3, we will obtain a formula for changing the base of a logarithm. With the help of this formula and a calculator, logarithms to any base can be determined. For now, we will solve equations such as the one in Example 4 by graphing.

Example 5 Domain of a Logarithmic Function

Without graphing, find the domain of the function $f(x) = \log_3 (9 - x^2)$.

Solution

The function $f(x) = \log_a x$ is defined only when $x > 0$. This means that the function $f(x) = \log_3 (9 - x^2)$ is defined only when $(9 - x^2) > 0$.
$$(9 - x^2) > 0$$
$$(3 - x)(3 + x) > 0$$

Use an interval chart to determine when this inequality is true.

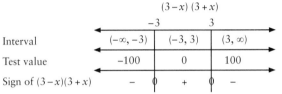

The product is positive when $x \in (-3, 3)$.

Thus, the domain of $f(x) = \log_3 (9 - x^2)$ is $x \in (-3, 3)$.

Key Concepts

- The inverse of $y = a^x$ is $y = \log_a x$.
- $y = \log_a x$ is equivalent to $a^y = x$.
- The function $y = \log_a x$ has domain $x \in (0, \infty)$ and range $y \in (-\infty, \infty)$.
- Four important properties of logarithms are
  $$\log_a 1 = 0$$
  $$\log_a a = 1$$
  $$\log_a (a^x) = x$$
  $$a^{\log_a x} = x$$
- The $\boxed{\text{LOG}}$ key on a calculator determines the logarithm to base 10.

Communicate Your Understanding

1. Compare and contrast the graphs of $y = 5^x$ and $y = \log_5 x$.
2. a) Explain how to obtain the graph of $y = \log_a x$ given the graph of $y = a^x$.
b) Explain the relationship between exponential functions and logarithmic functions.
3. Given $y = \log_a x$, explain what happens if the base is 1.
4. Compare and contrast the domain, range, intercepts, and asymptotes for exponential and logarithmic functions.

Practise

A **1.** Copy and complete the table.

Logarithmic Form	Exponential Form
	$10^2 = 100$
$\log_2 64 = 6$	
	$2^3 = 8$
$\log_3 9 = 2$	
$\log_5 \dfrac{1}{25} = -2$	
	$3^{-2} = \dfrac{1}{9}$
$\log_7 1 = 0$	
$\log_4 2 = \dfrac{1}{2}$	
	$4^{-\frac{3}{2}} = 0.125$
	$36^{\frac{1}{2}} = 6$

2. Evaluate.
a) $\log_3 3^3$
b) $\log_{11} 11$
c) $\log_9 1$
d) $\log_2 16$
e) $\log_3 \dfrac{1}{27}$
f) $\log_{64} \sqrt{4}$
g) $5^{\log_5 25}$
h) $2^{\log_2 \pi}$

3. Use graphing technology to graph each pair of functions on the same set of axes. State the domain and range of each function.
a) $y = 2^x$ and $y = \log_2 x$
b) $y = 4^x$ and $y = \log_4 x$
c) $f(x) = 8^x$ and $g(x) = \log_8 x$

4. Determine the equation of the inverse of each function. Graph each equation and its inverse.
a) $y = 3^x$
b) $y = \log_4 x$

5. Graph each function using transformations. State the domain, the range, and the equation of the vertical asymptote.
a) $f(x) = -\log_4 x$
b) $y = \log_3(-x)$
c) $f(x) = 2 + \log_{10} x$
d) $f(x) = \log_2(x - 1)$
e) $y = \log_5(x + 2)$
f) $y = \log_3(x + 1) - 2$

6. Without graphing, determine the domain of each function.
a) $f(x) = \log_3(25 - x^2)$
b) $y = \log_7(27 - x^3)$
c) $y = \log_3(x - 1)$
d) $y = \log_{10}(x - 4)$

Apply, Solve, Communicate

B **7.** How long will it take to triple an investment of $1000 at 7.5%, compounded annually?

8. Communication a) Write an equation to represent the accumulated amount of a $1500 mutual fund invested at 8%, compounded annually. Determine how long it will take for the investment to
i) increase to $2000
ii) double
b) If the interest rate is doubled, how is the doubling time of the investment affected? Explain.

9. Application Wyatt invested $1500 at 8.5%, compounded annually, when he was 18 years old. Use a graph to determine Wyatt's age when his original investment has doubled.

10. Communication a) The number of gophers living in a field in the summer can be modelled by the equation $y = 100(1.1)^n$, where n is the number of years from the present. Plot the graph of the gopher population to determine how long it will take for the gopher population to
i) increase to 150
ii) double
b) i) Using the equation in part a), determine the number of gophers after 1000 years. Is this realistic?
ii) What do you think is the domain of validity of the equation in part a)? Explain.
iii) What might affect the gopher population so that the equation in part a) is no longer valid?

11. Application The intensity of light in a particular river is reduced by 4% for each metre below the surface of the water. This relationship can be modelled by the equation $I(d) = I_0(0.96)^d$, where $I(d)$ is the intensity of light, in lumens, at depth d, in metres, and I_0 is the original intensity. Use a graph to determine how far

below the water's surface the light has to travel so that the intensity is
a) $0.8 I_0$ b) $0.5 I_0$ c) $0.2 I_0$

12. Inquiry/Problem Solving Pollution affects the clarity of water. The intensity of light below a particular polluted river's surface is reduced by 5% for each metre below the surface of the water. Write an exponential equation to model this relationship, using question 11 as a guide.
a) What percent of the original intensity of light penetrates to 4 m below the surface of the water?
b) At what depth does 40% of the original intensity of light remain?
c) What implications does the reduction of the sun's intensity have for plant life under water?

13. How long will it take, to the nearest month, for $2500 to grow to $4000, if it is invested at 7%, compounded monthly?

14. During the 1990s, the world's population was growing at a rate of 1.4% per year. In 1999, the world's population reached 6 billion.
a) Assuming the growth rate remains constant, write an equation relating the population to the time in years after 1999.
b) Sketch a graph of the relation in part a).
c) Use the graph to determine the world's population in 2015.
d) Use the graph to predict the year in which the world's population will have doubled since 1999.

15. Inquiry/Problem Solving The formula $K = [[\log_{10}(n)]] + 1$ is useful in computer programming. (The function $[[x]]$ truncates x by removing the decimal part; for example,

$[[3]] = 3$, $[[2.79]] = 2$.) Apply this formula with a few positive integers (both large and small) and state a hypothesis about what the formula determines.

16. There are initially 2000 bacteria in a culture. The number of bacteria doubles every hour, so the number of bacteria after t hours will be $N = 2000(2)^t$.
a) Plot a graph of this relation.
b) When does the formula cease to be valid?

17. The pH of a chemical solution is a measure of its acidity and is defined as $pH = -\log_{10}[H^+]$, where H^+ is the concentration of hydrogen ions in moles per litre.
a) Graph the relation.
b) What is the pH value of a solution with a hydrogen concentration of 0.000 38 mol/L?
c) Find the hydrogen concentration for a pH value of 7.

C **18. a)** Find the domain of the function $f(x) = \log_2(\log_{10} x)$.
b) Find $f^{-1}(x)$.

19. In this section, we have discussed only logarithms with positive integer bases, such as 2, 3, 4, and so on. Can logarithms have other bases? Graph each function and its inverse. Is the inverse a continuous function?

a) $f(x) = \left(\dfrac{1}{2}\right)^x$ b) $y = (0.25)^x$

c) $g(x) = \left(\dfrac{3}{2}\right)^x$

7.3 Laws of Logarithms

With the properties of logarithms learned in Section 7.2, we can work with only a limited number of logarithmic situations. There are other properties of logarithms that are useful for solving exponential and logarithmic equations. Such equations arise in a variety of contexts, such as investments and bacterial growth.

In the following investigation, you will explore three very important properties of logarithms, dealing with products, powers, and quotients.

Investigate & Inquire: Laws of Logarithms

1. a) Copy and complete the table.

$\log_a x$	$\log_a y$	$\log_a (xy)$
$\log_2 4 =$	$\log_2 8 =$	$\log_2 32 =$
$\log_3 9 =$	$\log_3 27 =$	$\log_3 243 =$
$\log_2 16 =$	$\log_2 32 =$	$\log_2 512 =$
$\log_4 64 =$	$\log_4 16 =$	$\log_4 1024 =$
$\log_5 25 =$	$\log_5 5 =$	$\log_5 125 =$

b) Examine the results of each row. Make a conjecture about the product law for logarithms.

c) Test your conjecture by evaluating $\log_6 (36 \times 216)$, and make any necessary adjustments to your original conjecture.

2. Make and test a conjecture about the power law of logarithms: $\log_a p^c = c \log_a p$.

3. a) Copy and complete the table.

$\log_a x$	$\log_a y$	$\log_a \dfrac{x}{y}$
$\log_2 32 =$	$\log_2 8 =$	$\log_2 \dfrac{32}{8} =$
$\log_3 27 =$	$\log_3 9 =$	$\log_3 \dfrac{27}{9} =$
$\log_2 32 =$	$\log_2 16 =$	$\log_2 \dfrac{32}{16} =$
$\log_4 64 =$	$\log_4 16 =$	$\log_4 \dfrac{64}{16} =$
$\log_5 25 =$	$\log_5 5 =$	$\log_5 \dfrac{25}{5} =$

b) Examine the results of each row. Make a conjecture about the quotient law for logarithms.

c) Test your conjecture by evaluating $\log_3 \dfrac{243}{27}$, and make any necessary adjustments to your original conjecture.

The patterns in the investigation show three laws of logarithms.

> Product law: $\log_a (pq) = \log_a p + \log_a q$
>
> Power law: $\log_a (p^c) = c \log_a p$
>
> Quotient law: $\log_a \dfrac{p}{q} = \log_a p - \log_a q$

Because logarithms can be written as exponents, the laws of exponents can be used to justify corresponding laws of logarithms. To show the product law, we let $\log_a p = X$ and $\log_a q = Y$. Then, rewriting in exponential form,

$\log_a p = X$ becomes $a^X = p$ and
$\log_a q = Y$ becomes $a^Y = q$
So,

$$
\begin{aligned}
\log_a (pq) &= \log_a (a^X a^Y) && \text{(substitution)} \\
&= \log_a (a^{X+Y}) && \text{(exponents law)} \\
&= X + Y && (\log_a a^x = x)
\end{aligned}
$$

Substituting for X and Y,
$\log_a (pq) = \log_a p + \log_a q$.

Web Connection

For a visual explanation of the product law of logarithms, go to
www.mcgrawhill.ca/links/CAF12
and follow the link.

In questions 13 and 14 on page 435, you will show how to derive the power law for logarithms and the quotient law for logarithms.

Since logarithms with base 10 are very common, $\log_{10} x$ is usually written as $\log x$. As we mentioned in Section 7.2, the ⬚LOG key on a calculator determines logarithms to base 10.

Example 1 The Laws of Logarithms

Evaluate each expression using the laws of logarithms.

a) $\log_6 4 + \log_6 9$
b) $2 \log_9 3$
c) $\log_3 324 - \log_3 4$
d) $\log 2 + \log 50$
e) $\log_2 112 - \log_2 7$
f) $\log_3 \sqrt[3]{9}$

Solution

a)
$$
\begin{aligned}
\log_6 4 + \log_6 9 &= \log_6 (4 \times 9) && \text{(product law)} \\
&= \log_6 36 \\
&= \log_6 (6^2) \\
&= 2
\end{aligned}
$$

b)
$$
\begin{aligned}
2 \log_9 3 &= \log_9 (3^2) && \text{(power law)} \\
&= \log_9 9 \\
&= 1
\end{aligned}
$$

This expression can be evaluated without using the power law.
$$
\begin{aligned}
2 \log_9 3 &= 2 \log_9 9^{\frac{1}{2}} \\
&= 2 \left(\frac{1}{2} \right) \\
&= 1
\end{aligned}
$$

c)
$$
\begin{aligned}
\log_3 324 - \log_3 4 &= \log_3 \frac{324}{4} \\
&= \log_3 81 \\
&= 4
\end{aligned}
$$

d) Remember, $\log x$ means $\log_{10} x$.
$$
\begin{aligned}
\log 2 + \log 50 &= \log (2)(50) && \text{(product law)} \\
&= \log 100 \\
&= \log 10^2 \\
&= 2
\end{aligned}
$$

e) $\log_2 112 - \log_2 7 = \log_2 \dfrac{112}{7}$ (quotient law)

$$= \log_2 16$$

$$= 4$$

f) $\log_3 \sqrt[3]{9} = \log_3 (9^{\frac{1}{3}})$

$$= \frac{1}{3} \log_3 9 \text{ (power law)}$$

$$= \frac{2}{3}$$

Example 2 Using the Laws of Logarithms

Express as a single logarithm.

a) $\log_7 30 - \log_7 10$ b) $\log 12 + \dfrac{1}{2} \log 7 - \log 2$ c) $\log_3 (x^2 - 1) - \log_3 (x + 1)$

Solution

a) $\log_7 30 - \log_7 10 = \log_7 \dfrac{30}{10}$ (quotient law)

$$= \log_7 3$$

b) Remember, $\log x$ means $\log_{10} x$.

$\log 12 + \dfrac{1}{2} \log 7 - \log 2 = \log 12 + \log 7^{\frac{1}{2}} - \log 2$ (power law)

$$= \log \frac{(12)(\sqrt{7})}{2} \qquad \text{(product and quotient laws)}$$

$$= \log 6\sqrt{7}$$

c) $\log_3 (x^2 - 1) - \log_3 (x + 1) = \log_3 \dfrac{(x^2 - 1)}{x + 1}$

$$= \log_3 \frac{(x + 1)(x - 1)}{x + 1}$$

$$= \log_3 (x - 1), \qquad x > 1$$

Example 3 Using the Laws of Logarithms

Expand.
a) $\log_6 (x^2 y^3)$ b) $\log_2 \dfrac{\sqrt[4]{a}}{bc}$

Solution

a) $\log_6 (x^2 y^3) = \log_6 x^2 + \log_6 y^3$

$$= 2 \log_6 x + 3 \log_6 y$$

b) $\log_2 \dfrac{\sqrt[4]{a}}{bc} = \log_2 \sqrt[4]{a} - \log_2 (bc)$

$$= \log_2 a^{\frac{1}{4}} - (\log_2 b + \log_2 c)$$

$$= \frac{1}{4} \log_2 a - \log_2 b - \log_2 c$$

Recall Example 4 in Section 7.2 (page 426), which we could solve only by graphing because the calculator LOG key determines logarithms only to base 10. With a simple formula, we can change the base of the logarithm, and use the calculator to evaluate it. For example, suppose we want to evaluate $\log_2 11$ on a calculator. To change the base to 10, we start with $y = \log_2 11$ and proceed as follows.

	$y = \log_2 11$
Write in exponential form.	$2^y = 11$
Take the logarithm to base 10 of each side of the equation.	$\log_{10}(2^y) = \log_{10} 11$
Use the power law.	$y \log_{10} 2 = \log_{10} 11$
Solve for y.	$y = \dfrac{\log_{10} 11}{\log_{10} 2}$

Thus, $\log_2 11 = \dfrac{\log_{10} 11}{\log_{10} 2}$.

We can now evaluate the logarithm on a calculator.

The general formula for converting a logarithm from one base to another, called the change of base formula, is $\log_b x = \dfrac{\log_a x}{\log_a b}$.

Example 4 Using the Change of Base Formula

Write each logarithm with base 10, and then evaluate it on a calculator. Round your results to four decimal places.
a) $\log_5 14$ b) $\log_{\frac{1}{3}} 7$

Solution

a) $\log_5 14 = \dfrac{\log_{10} 14}{\log_{10} 5}$

$\doteq 1.6397$

b) $\log_{\frac{1}{3}} 7 = \dfrac{\log_{10} 7}{\log_{10} \dfrac{1}{3}}$

$\doteq -1.7712$

Example 5 Doubling Time for an Investment

How long does it take for an investment of $500 to double at 7% interest, compounded annually?

Solution

The amount, A, in dollars, of an investment of $500 at 7% interest, compounded annually, for t years, is $A = 500(1.07)^t$. For the investment to double, $A = \$1000$. Thus,

$1000 = 500(1.07)^t$

$2 = (1.07)^t$

$t = \log_{1.07} 2$

Use the change of base formula to change to base 10.

$t = \dfrac{\log 2}{\log 1.07}$

$\doteq 10.2448$

It takes approximately 10 years and 3 months for an investment of $500 to double at 7% interest, compounded annually.

Practise

A **1.** Copy and complete the table.

Single Logarithm	Sum or Difference of Logarithms
$\log_2 (12 \times 5)$	
	$\log_4 2 + \log_4 11$
$\log_6 (kg)$	
	$\log_8 14 - \log_8 3$
$\log_{13} \dfrac{h^2}{f}$	
	$\log_3 \pi - \log_3 5$
	$\log_{10} 1 - \log_{10} 7$
	$2 \log_{11} x + 6 \log_{11} x$
	$\log_{12} \dfrac{5}{3} + \log_{12} 4$

2. Rewrite each expression using the power law.

a) $\dfrac{1}{2} \log_4 5$

b) $\log_6 9^3$

c) $\dfrac{1}{5} \log_8 18$

d) $\log_2 7^{-5}$

e) $\log_6 \sqrt{22}$

f) $\log_9 \dfrac{1}{\sqrt{13}}$

3. Express as a single logarithm.

a) $\log_3 5 + \log_3 8 + \log_3 15$

b) $\log_4 8 - \log_4 10 + \log_4 3$

c) $\log_2 19 + \log_2 4 - \log_2 31$

d) $\dfrac{1}{2} \log 17 - \log 5$

e) $\log (a + b) + \log (a^3)$

f) $\log (x + y) - \log (x - y)$

g) $4 \log x - 3 \log y$

h) $\log_3 ab + \log_3 bc$

4. Rewrite each expression with no logarithms of products, quotients, or powers.

a) $\log_7 (5x)$

b) $\log_2 (m^3 n^2)$

c) $\log_3 (abc)$

d) $\log_9 (\sqrt[3]{y^2} + y)$

e) $\log_8 \dfrac{\sqrt[4]{m}}{n}$

f) $\log_6 (xy)^5$

g) $\log_4 \dfrac{a^2 b}{\sqrt{c}}$

h) $\log_3 \dfrac{1}{\sqrt{jk}}$

5. Evaluate.

a) $\log_8 32 + \log_8 2$

b) $\log_2 72 - \log_2 9$

c) $\log_4 192 - \log_4 3$

d) $\log_{12} 9 + \log_{12} 16$

e) $\log_2 6 + \log_2 8 - \log_2 3$

f) $\log_3 108 - \log_3 4$

g) $\log_8 6 - \log_8 3 + \log_8 4$

h) $\log_2 80 - \log_2 5$

i) $\log 1.25 + \log 80$

j) $\log_2 8^{27}$

6. Evaluate to four decimal places using a calculator.
a) $\log_5 12$ b) $\log_2 13$ c) $\log_7 9$
d) $\log_6 15$ e) $\log_9 8$ f) $\log_3 6$
g) $\log_4 7$ h) $\log_8 4$

Apply, Solve, Communicate

B **7.** Application Driving in fog at night greatly reduces the intensity of light from an approaching car. The relationship between the distance, d, in metres, that your car is from the approaching car and the intensity of light, $I(d)$, in lumens (lm), at distance d, is given by
$$d \doteq -166.67 \log \frac{I(d)}{125}$$
a) Solve the equation for $I(d)$.
b) How far away from you is an approaching car if $I(d) = 40$ lm?

8. Inquiry/Problem Solving Energy is needed to transport a substance from outside a living cell to inside the cell. This energy is measured in kilocalories per gram molecule, and is given by the relationship $E = 1.4 \log \dfrac{C_1}{C_2}$, where C_1 represents the concentration of the substance outside the cell, and C_2 represents the concentration inside the cell.
a) Find the energy needed to transport the exterior substance into the cell if the concentration of the substance inside the cell is
i) double the concentration outside the cell
ii) triple the concentration outside the cell
b) What is the sign of E if $C_1 < C_2$? Explain what this means in terms of the cell.

9. Communication Which is greater, $\log_6 7$ or $\log_8 9$? Explain.

10. The formula for the gain in voltage of an electronic device is $A_v = 20(\log V_o - \log V_i)$, where V_o is the output voltage and V_i is the input voltage.
a) Rewrite the formula as a single logarithm.
b) Verify the gain in voltage for $V_o = 22.8$ and $V_i = 14$ using both versions of the formula.

11. When a rope is wrapped around a fixed circular object, the relationship between the

larger tension T_L and the smaller tension T_S is modelled by $0.434\mu\theta = \log \dfrac{T_L}{T_S}$, where μ is the friction coefficient and θ is the wrap angle in radians.

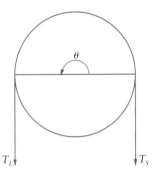

a) Rewrite the formula using the laws of logarithms.
b) If the wrap angle is π (in radians), and a 200 N force is balancing a 250 N force, what is the friction coefficient?
c) If the rope is wrapped around the object 2.5 times, what force is now needed to balance the 250 N force?

C **12.** Show that if $\log_b a = c$ and $\log_y b = c$, then $\log_a y = c^{-2}$.

13. Use the product law of logarithms to prove the quotient law of logarithms,
$$\log_a \frac{p}{q} = \log_a p - \log_a q$$
where $a \in (1, \infty)$, $p, q \in (0, \infty)$.

14. Use the product and quotient laws of logarithms to prove the power law of logarithms $\log_a (p^c) = c \log_a p$, where $a \in (1, \infty)$, p, $q \in (0, \infty)$, $c \in (-\infty, \infty)$.

15. Derive the change of base formula,
$$\log_a x = \frac{\log_b x}{\log_b a}.$$

16. Find the error in the following calculation.
$$\log_3 0.1 < 2 \log_3 0.1$$
$$= \log_3 (0.1)^2$$
$$= \log_3 0.01$$
$$\log_3 0.1 < \log_3 0.01$$
Thus, $0.1 < 0.01$.

Exponential and Logarithmic Equations

There are many applications of exponential and logarithmic equations, including problems involving atmospheric pressure, the intensity of light passing through glass or water, and the power source for satellites.

In order to solve exponential equations that model such applications, we need to solve for the variable in the exponent. We do this by rewriting the equation in terms of logarithms, usually to base 10 to make using a calculator easier. (Recall that $\log x$ means $\log_{10} x$.) Consider Example 1.

Example 1 An Exponential Equation

Solve the equation $3^x = 11$.

Solution 1 Paper and Pencil Method

$$3^x = 11$$
$$\log 3^x = \log 11 \text{ (base 10 logarithm of each side)}$$
$$x \log 3 = \log 11 \text{ (power law)}$$
$$x = \frac{\log 11}{\log 3}$$
$$\doteq 2.1827$$

We can check the solution by substituting $x = 2.1827$ into the original equation.

$$3^x = 3^{2.1827}$$
$$\doteq 11$$

Solution 2 Graphing Calculator Method

We can also find the solution to $3^x = 11$ graphically, as we did in Section 7.2. First, we input $y = 3^x$ and $y = 11$ in the Y= editor of a graphing calculator or graphing software.

Then, we use the Intersect operation to find the x-coordinate of the point of intersection of the two graphs.

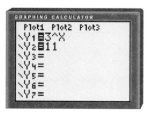

Window variables:
$x \in [-4.7, 4.7], y \in [-12.4, 12.4]$

The solution is $x = 2.1827$, to four decimal places.

Example 2 Solving Exponential Equations Using Logarithms

Solve   a) $5^{2x+3} = 30$ b) $3^{x+6} = 7$ c) $4(7^{x-2}) = 8$

Solution

a)
$$5^{2x+3} = 30$$
$$\log 5^{2x+3} = \log 30 \qquad \text{(base 10 logarithm of each side)}$$
$$(2x+3)\log 5 = \log 30 \qquad \text{(power law)}$$

$$2x + 3 = \frac{\log 30}{\log 5}$$

$$2x = \frac{\log 30}{\log 5} - 3$$

$$x = \frac{1}{2}\left(\frac{\log 30}{\log 5}\right) - \frac{3}{2}$$

$$\doteq -0.4434$$

b)
$$3^{x+6} = 7$$
$$\log 3^{x+6} = \log 7$$
$$(x+6)\log 3 = \log 7$$

$$x = \frac{\log 7}{\log 3} - 6$$

$$\doteq -4.2288$$

c)
$$4(7^{x-2}) = 8$$
$$7^{x-2} = 2$$
$$\log 7^{x-2} = \log 2$$
$$(x-2)\log 7 = \log 2$$

$$x = \frac{\log 2}{\log 7} + 2$$

$$\doteq 2.3562$$

Here are guidelines for solving exponential equations similar to those in Example 2.

1. Isolate the term containing the variable on one side of the equation.

2. Take the base 10 logarithm of each side of the equation.

3. Apply the power law of logarithms to rewrite the equation without exponents.

4. Solve for the variable and check the result.

We will use these steps to solve the problem in Example 3.

Example 3 Satellite Power Supply

The power source used by satellites is called a radioisotope. The power output of the radioisotope is given by the equation $P = 50(0.996^t)$, where P is the power, in watts, and t is the time, in years. If the equipment in the satellite needs at least 15 W of power to function, for how long can the satellite operate before needing recharging?

Solution

We need to determine the value of t when $P = 15$.

$$P = 50(0.996^t)$$
$$15 = 50(0.996^t)$$
$$\frac{15}{50} = 0.996^t$$
$$0.3 = 0.996^t$$
$$\log 0.3 = \log 0.996^t$$
$$\log 0.3 = t \log 0.996$$
$$t = \frac{\log 0.3}{\log 0.996}$$
$$\doteq 300.39$$

Thus, in theory, the satellite can operate for about 300 years.

We can also solve logarithmic equations using the laws of logarithms.

Example 4 A Logarithmic Equation

Solve the equation $\log_4(x + 3) = 2$.

Solution

We can solve this equation algebraically using the laws of logarithms.

Using the property $y = \log_a x \Leftrightarrow x = a^y$, we can rewrite the equation $\log_4(x + 3) = 2$ in exponential form, and then solve.

$$\log_4(x + 3) = 2$$
$$(x + 3) = 4^2$$
$$x + 3 = 16$$
$$x = 13$$

The solution is $x = 13$.

Example 5 Solving Logarithmic Equations

Solve and check.
a) $\log x = 5$ b) $\log_9(x - 5) + \log_9(x + 3) = 1$ c) $\log x = 3 \log 7$

Solution

a) $\log x = 5$
$$10^5 = x$$
$$x = 100\,000$$
Check $x = 100\,000$:
L.S. $= \log x$ **R.S.** $= 5$
$ = \log 100\,000$
$ = \log 10^5$
$ = 5$
 **L.S. = R.S.**
The solution is $x = 100\,000$.

b) $\log_9 (x - 5) + \log_9 (x + 3) = 1$
$\quad \log_9 [(x - 5)(x + 3)] = 1$
$\quad \log_9 (x^2 - 2x - 15) = 1$
$\quad\quad x^2 - 2x - 15 = 9^1$
$\quad\quad x^2 - 2x - 24 = 0$
$\quad\quad (x - 6)(x + 4) = 0$
$\quad\quad\quad x = 6 \text{ or } x = -4$

Check $x = 6$:
L.S. $= \log_9 (x - 5) + \log_9 (x + 3)$ R.S. $= 1$
$\quad = \log_9 (6 - 5) + \log_9 (6 + 3)$
$\quad = \log_9 1 + \log_9 9$
$\quad = 0 + 1$
$\quad = 1$

$\quad\quad\quad$ L.S. $=$ R.S.

Check $x = -4$:
L.S. $= \log_9 (x - 5) + \log_9 (x + 3)$ R.S. $= 1$
$\quad = \log_9 (-4 - 5) + \log_9 (-4 + 3)$
$\quad = \log_9 (-9) + \log_9 (-1)$

This cannot be evaluated, because the logarithm of a negative number is undefined. Thus, $x = -4$ is an extraneous solution.

The solution is $x = 6$.

c) $\log x = 3 \log 7$
$\quad \log x = \log 7^3$
$\quad\quad x = 7^3$
$\quad\quad = 343$

Check $x = 343$:
L.S. $= \log x$ R.S. $= 3 \log 7$
$\quad = \log 343$
$\quad = \log 7^3$
$\quad = 3 \log 7$
$\quad\quad$ L.S. $=$ R.S.
The root is $x = 343$.

Here are guidelines for solving logarithmic equations such as those in Examples 4 and 5.

1. Isolate the terms with variables to one side of the equation.

2. Use the laws of logarithms to express each side of the equation as a single logarithm.

3. Simplify each side of the equation.

4. Solve and check.

Example 6 The Relationship Between Altitude and Atmospheric Pressure

Atmospheric pressure, P, depends on the altitude above sea level, and is measured in kilopascals (kPa). For altitudes up to 10 km above sea level, the atmospheric pressure is approximately $P = 101.3(1.133)^{-x}$, where x is the altitude, in kilometres. A mountain climber is experiencing atmospheric pressure of 89 kPa. How high above sea level is the mountain climber, to the nearest 10 m?

Solution

$$P = 101.3(1.133)^{-x}$$
$$89 = 101.3(1.133)^{-x}$$
$$\frac{89}{101.3} = 1.133^{-x}$$
$$-x = \log_{1.133}\left(\frac{89}{101.3}\right)$$
$$x = -\log_{1.133}\left(\frac{89}{101.3}\right)$$
$$= -\frac{\log\left(\frac{89}{101.3}\right)}{\log 1.133}$$
$$\doteq 1.037$$

The mountain climber is 1040 m above sea level, to the nearest 10 m.

Next, we will solve a more complex exponential equation.

Example 7 Solving an Exponential Equation by Factoring

Solve $3^{2x} - 3^x - 12 = 0$, and illustrate your results graphically.

Solution

First, we factor to isolate the exponential term.
If we let $z = 3^x$, it becomes clearer that the equation is quadratic and can be factored.
$$z^2 - z - 12 = 0$$
$$(z - 4)(z + 3) = 0$$
Substituting $z = 3^x$ back into the equation, we get
$(3^x - 4)(3^x + 3) = 0$

$3^x - 4 = 0$ or $3^x + 3 = 0$

$3^x = 4$ $\qquad\qquad$ $3^x = -3$

$\log 3^x = \log 4$ $\qquad$ Since $3^x > 0$, there is no solution for $3^x = -3$.

$x \log 3 = \log 4$

$$x = \frac{\log 4}{\log 3}$$
$$\doteq 1.2619$$

The solution is $x \doteq 1.2619$.

We can also represent the solution graphically, using the Zero operation.

  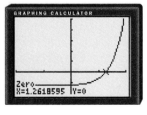

Window
variables:
$x \in [-2, 2]$,
$y \in [-20, 50]$

Key Concepts

- To solve exponential equations of the form found in Examples 1 and 2, first isolate the term containing the exponential variable on one side of the equation, then take the logarithm of each side of the equation, and apply the laws of logarithms to solve for the variable.
- To solve logarithmic equations of the form found in Examples 4 and 5, first isolate the terms with variables on one side of the equation, then use the laws of logarithms to express each side of the equation as a single logarithm, and simplify to solve for the variable.

Communicate Your Understanding

1. Describe two ways to verify the solution(s) to a logarithmic equation or an exponential equation.

2. Explain why logarithms are helpful in solving exponential equations.

3. Give an example of an exponential equation that cannot be solved exactly using the laws of logarithms. How would you solve the equation in this case?

Practise

Round your solutions to four decimal places, if necessary.

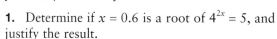 **1.** Determine if $x = 0.6$ is a root of $4^{2x} = 5$, and justify the result.

2. Solve for x and check your solution.
a) $\log x = 0$ b) $7^{4x-1} = 7$
c) $3^{x+3} = 9$ d) $\log_2 x = 8$
e) $\log_x 49 = 2$ f) $\log_{10} x = 3$
g) $\log_x 8 = \dfrac{3}{2}$ h) $\log_{10} 0.1 = x$

3. a) Solve each equation using the properties of logarithms.
b) Illustrate each solution graphically.
i) $\log_2 (x + 6) = 3$ ii) $\log_6 (x + 3) = 1$

4. Solve.
a) $5^x = 8$ b) $6^{3x} = 10$
c) $4^{\frac{x}{2}} = 7$ d) $3^{x+2} = 5$
e) $2^{6x-1} = 28$ f) $2^{4x} = 9^{x-1}$
g) $6(3)^{2x-3} = 18$ h) $2(7)^{4x-5} = 30$

5. Solve and check.
a) $4 \log_5 x = \log_5 625$
b) $-\log_3 1 = \log_3 7 - \log_3 x$

c) $\log_6 n = \dfrac{3}{4} \log_6 16$
d) $-\log_2 x - \log_2 3 = \log_2 12$
e) $\log 12 = \log 8 - \log x$
f) $\log 2^{3x} = \log 35$
g) $4 \log_6 x = \log_6 25$
h) $2 \log_7 x = \log_7 81$

6. Solve for x. Use a graphing calculator to verify your solution.
a) $\log x = -3$
b) $\log (x - 11) = 20$
c) $\log (4x - 1) = 39$
d) $\log_3 (5 - x) = 3$
e) $\log_2 (x + 6) + \log_2 3 = \log_2 30$
f) $\log_3 x + \log_3 (x - 1) = \log_3 (2x)$
g) $\log_6 (x + 3) + \log_6 (x - 2) = 1$
h) $\log_4 (x - 1) + \log_4 (x + 2) = 1$
i) $\log_2 (x + 1) - \log_2 (x - 1) = 1$
j) $1 - \log (x - 4) = \log (x + 5)$

7. Communication a) Show that $x = \log_5 4$ is a root of the equation $5^{2x} + 5^x - 20 = 0$.
b) Are there any other roots? Explain.

8. Solve for x and check your solution.
a) $2^{2x} - 2^x - 6 = 0$ b) $3^{2x} + 2(3^x) - 15 = 0$
c) $7^{2x} + 3(7)^x - 10 = 0$ d) $10^{2x} + 5(10)^x + 4 = 0$
e) $6^{2x} - 2(6)^x - 15 = 0$ f) $4^{2x} + 9(4)^x + 14 = 0$

Apply, Solve, Communicate

9. The function $A = P(1.06)^n$ represents the amount, A, in dollars, in an investment n years from now, where P is the original investment, or principal, in dollars. If Seth invests $1000 now, find how long it will take to accumulate to
a) $1226.23   b) $1664.08
c) double his original investment
d) $5000.00

10. Application The intensity of light, I, in lumens, passing through a certain type of glass is given by $I(t) = I_0(0.97)^x$, where I_0 is the initial intensity and x is the thickness of the glass, in centimetres.
a) What thickness of the glass will reduce the intensity of light to half its initial value?
b) What effect does doubling the thickness of the glass have on the intensity of light passing through it?

11. Application The average annual salary, S, in dollars, of employees at a particular job in a manufacturing company is modelled by the equation $S = 25\,000(1.05)^n$, where $25\,000 is the initial salary, which increases at 5% per year.
a) How long will it take the salary to increase by 50%?
b) If the starting salary is $35\,000, how long will it take the salary to increase by 50%? Explain your answer.

12. How long, to the nearest month, will it take for an investment of $600 at 5.5%, compounded annually, to
a) double?   b) triple?
c) accumulate to $900?

13. Inquiry/Problem Solving The speed, v, in kilometres per hour, of a water skier who drops the towrope, can be given by the formula $v = v_0(10)^{-0.23t}$, where v_0 is the skier's speed at the time she drops the rope, and t is the time, in seconds, after she drops the rope. If the skier drops the rope when travelling at a speed of 65 km/h, how long will it take her to slow to a speed of 13 km/h?

14. Inquiry/Problem Solving On average, the number of items, N, per day, on an assembly line, that a quality assurance trainee can inspect is $N = 40 - 24(0.74)^t$, where t is the number of days worked.
a) After how many days of training will the employee be able to inspect 32 items?
b) The company expects an experienced quality assurance employee to inspect 45 items per day. After the training period of 15 days is complete, how close will the trainee be to the experienced employee's quota?

15. The number of hours, $H(t)$, that cheese will remain safe to eat decreases exponentially as the temperature of the surrounding air, t, in degrees Celsius, increases. For a particular type of cheese, this relationship is represented by $H(t) = 140(10)^{-0.034t}$. To the nearest hour, how long will the cheese remain safe to eat if it is stored at
a) 0°C?   b) 16°C?   c) 25°C?

16. Use the formula from Example 6 (page 439) to determine the altitude of a rock climber, if the atmospheric pressure is approximately 95 kPa.

17. The designers of aircraft must know the external pressure in order to control the pressure inside the aircraft. What range of external pressure must be controlled for a small airplane with a maximum altitude of 10 km?

18. The intensity of the sunlight below the surface of a large body of water is reduced by 4.6% for every metre below the surface. Show that the depth at which the sunlight has intensity $I(d)$, in lumens, is given by

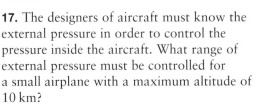

$$d \doteq -48.9 \log \frac{I(d)}{I_0}, \text{ where } I_0 \text{ is the initial}$$

intensity and d is the depth, in metres.

19. Solve for x and check your solution.
a) $\log_2 x + \log_4 x + \log_8 x + \log_{16} x = 25$
b) $2(5^{6x}) - 9(5^{4x}) + 13(5^{2x}) - 6 = 0$

Logarithmic Scales

Logarithmic scales are useful for measuring quantities that can have a very large range, because logarithms enable us to make large or small numbers more manageable to work with. Examples of logarithmic scales include the Richter scale, which measures earthquakes, the pH scale, which measures acidity, and the decibel scale, which measures sound.

The intensities of earthquakes vary over an extremely wide range. To make such a wide range more manageable, a compressed range, called the Richter scale, is used. To make the scale convenient, a "standard earthquake," with a certain intensity I_0, is given a magnitude of 0. Earthquakes with intensities weaker than this standard are so weak that they are hardly ever discussed. Only magnitudes greater than 0 are used in practice.

The magnitude, M, of an earthquake is given by the equation $M = \log \dfrac{I}{I_0}$, where I is the intensity of the earthquake, and I_0 is the intensity of a standard earthquake. Thus, a range of earthquake intensities from I_0 to about $800\,000\,000 I_0$ corresponds to a range in magnitudes on the Richter scale from 0 to about 8.9.

The equation $M = \log \dfrac{I}{I_0}$ can also be written $I = I_0 \times 10^M$. From this equation, you can see that, for every increase in the intensity of an earthquake by a factor of 10, the magnitude on the Richter scale increases by 1. For example, an earthquake of magnitude 4 is 10 times as intense as an earthquake of magnitude 3, and 100 times as intense as an earthquake of magnitude 2.

Example 1 The Richter Scale

a) On September 26, 2001, an earthquake in North Bay measured 5.0 on the Richter scale. What is the magnitude of an earthquake 3 times as intense as North Bay's earthquake?

b) On February 10, 2000, Welland experienced an earthquake of magnitude 2.3 on the Richter scale. On July 22, 2001, St. Catharines experienced an earthquake of magnitude 1.1. How many times more intense was the earthquake in Welland?

Solution

a) We use the formula $M = \log \dfrac{I}{I_0}$, and let I_1 be the intensity of North Bay's earthquake.

Thus, $\log \dfrac{I_1}{I_0} = 5.0$.

An earthquake three times as intense as North Bay's earthquake has an intensity of $3I_1$. So, the magnitude of an earthquake three times as intense as North Bay's earthquake is

$$M = \log \frac{I}{I_0}$$

$$= \log \frac{3I_1}{I_0}$$

$$= \log 3 + \log \frac{I_1}{I_0}$$

$$= \log 3 + 5.0 \qquad \text{Substitute the magnitude of North Bay's earthquake.}$$

$$\doteq 5.477$$

So, an earthquake of magnitude 5.5 is three times as intense as an earthquake of magnitude 5.0.

b) Let $M_1 = 2.3$, the magnitude of the earthquake in Welland, and let $M_2 = 1.1$, the magnitude of the earthquake in St. Catharines. We want to find $\dfrac{I_1}{I_2}$. We use the exponential form of the Richter scale equation, $I = I_0 \times 10^M$.

$$\frac{I_1}{I_2} = \frac{I_0 \times 10^{M_1}}{I_0 \times 10^{M_2}}$$

$$= 10^{M_1 - M_2}$$

$$= 10^{2.3 - 1.1}$$

$$\doteq 15.8489$$

Therefore, the earthquake in Welland was almost 16 times as intense as the earthquake in St. Catharines.

The pH scale, which measures the acidity of substances, is another logarithmic scale. The pH of a solution is a measure of relative acidity in moles per litre, mol/L, compared with neutral water, which has a pH of 7. If pH < 7, the solution is classified as acidic, and if pH > 7, the solution is basic or alkaline. The pH scale ranges from 0 to 14.

The pH scale is widely used by chemists, for example, who regularly test the pH level of drinking water to ensure that it is safe from contaminants. The pH of a solution can be represented by the equation $\text{pH} = \log \dfrac{1}{[H^+]}$, where $[H^+]$ is the number of moles of hydrogen ions per litre. This can be rewritten as follows to eliminate the fraction.

$$\text{pH} = \log \frac{1}{[H^+]}$$

$$= \log [H^+]^{-1}$$

$$= -\log [H^+] \quad \text{(power law)}$$

The pH scale makes very small numbers manageable. For example, if $[H^+] = 0.000\,001$ mol/L, pH = 6. The equation pH = $-\log[H^+]$ can be rewritten as $[H^+] = 10^{-pH}$. Thus, when the pH level increases by 1, $[H^+]$ is divided by 10. For example, a substance with pH = 4 has $\frac{1}{10}$ the H^+ concentration of a substance with pH = 3, and $\frac{1}{100}$ the H^+ concentration of a substance with pH = 2.

Example 2 Liquids and pH

a) The hydrogen concentration of a sample of water is 6.82×10^{-8} moles of H^+ per litre of water. What is the pH level of the water?

b) A sample of orange juice has a pH level of 3.5. Find its hydrogen ion concentration.

Solution

a) To solve for pH, we use the formula pH = $-\log[H^+]$ and substitute $[H^+] = 6.82 \times 10^{-8}$.

$$\begin{align} pH &= -\log[H^+] \\ &= -\log(6.82 \times 10^{-8}) \\ &\doteq 7.166 \end{align}$$

Therefore, the water has a pH level of approximately 7.2, which means it is slightly basic.

b) We use the formula pH = $-\log[H^+]$ and solve for $[H^+]$ to determine the hydrogen ion concentration of the juice.

$$\begin{align} pH &= -\log[H^+] \\ 3.5 &= -\log[H^+] \\ -3.5 &= \log[H^+] \\ [H^+] &= 10^{-3.5} \\ &\doteq 3.16 \times 10^{-4} \end{align}$$

Thus, the hydrogen ion concentration of the orange juice is about 3.2×10^{-4} mol/L.

The decibel scale, dB, also a logarithmic scale, measures sound levels. The human ear can detect a very wide range of sounds, ranging from a soft whisper to loud machinery. The threshold of pain is about 120 dB. Examples of other decibel measurements include normal conversation at about 50 dB, and a jet takeoff at about 140 dB.

The decibel is one tenth of a bel, which is named after the inventor Alexander Graham Bell. Bell is most famous for having invented the telephone, but he worked on many other projects throughout his life, including developing hydrofoils and teaching people with hearing disabilities to speak.

The minimum intensity detectable by the human ear is $I_0 = 10^{-12}$ W/m^2 (watts per square metre), and is used as the reference point. The sound level corresponding to an intensity I watts per square metre is $L = 10 \log \frac{I}{I_0}$.

Example 3 Sound Levels and Risk of Hearing Damage

Damage to the ear can occur with sound levels that are greater than or equal to 85 dB. Find the sound level of a rock concert with an intensity of 80 W/m^2 to determine if fans at the concert are at risk for hearing damage.

Solution

We use the decibel formula, and substitute $I = 80$ and $I_0 = 10^{-12}$.

$$L = 10 \log \frac{I}{I_0}$$

$$= 10 \log \frac{80}{10^{-12}}$$

$$\doteq 139.03$$

Therefore, the concert has a sound level of 139 dB, which means that people attending the concert may be at risk for hearing damage.

Key Concepts

- Logarithmic scales convert large ranges of numbers into smaller, more manageable ranges of numbers.
- Some applications of logarithmic scales are the Richter scale, which applies to earthquakes; the pH scale, which applies to acidity levels; and the decibel scale, which applies to sound levels.

Communicate Your Understanding

1. Can an earthquake have a negative magnitude on the Richter scale? If so, what kind of an earthquake would it be?

2. Explain how to determine how many times as intense an earthquake of magnitude 5 is as an earthquake of magnitude 4.

3. a) Describe what pH measures.
b) Which would you expect to have a higher pH level, baking soda or vinegar? Explain.

4. If the pain threshold for sound is 120 dB, and a jet engine has a sound intensity level of 140 dB, what does this imply for an air traffic controller? a maintenance worker on the ground?

Apply, Solve, Communicate

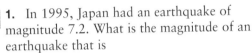

A 1. In 1995, Japan had an earthquake of magnitude 7.2. What is the magnitude of an earthquake that is
a) twice as intense?
b) 1.5 times as intense?
c) 3 times as intense?

2. Application Human blood must be maintained in a pH range of 7.35 to 7.45. Calculate the corresponding [H⁺] range.

3. a) Show that, if one sound is 10 decibels louder than a second sound, then the first sound is 10 times as intense as the second sound.
b) A hair dryer has a sound intensity level of 70 dB and an air conditioner has a sound intensity level of 50 dB. How many times as intense is the sound from the hair dryer as the sound from the air conditioner?

4. Inquiry/Problem Solving Earthquakes of magnitude 7.0 or greater can cause metal buildings to collapse. On December 23, 1985, in Mackenzie

Region, Northwest Territories, an earthquake of magnitude 6.9 occurred. On Vancouver Island, on June 23, 1946, an earthquake about 2.5 times as intense occurred. Was the Vancouver Island earthquake strong enough to cause metal buildings to collapse?

5. The absolute magnitude of a star, M, is related to its luminosity, L, by the formula $M = 4.72 - \log \dfrac{L}{L_0}$, where L_0 is the luminosity of the sun. The luminosity is the rate at which the star emits light, and is measured in watts.
a) Determine the absolute magnitude of the sun.
b) The absolute magnitude of Sirius, the star that, other than the sun, appears brightest from Earth, is 1.41. Is Sirius more or less luminous than the sun? By what factor?
c) Repeat part b) for Canopus, the star that appears second brightest from Earth, which has an absolute magnitude of -4.7.
d) A distant object called a quasar has a luminosity of about 10^{38} W. The sun's luminosity is about 4×10^{26} W. Determine the absolute magnitude of the quasar.

Web Connection
For more on solar eclipses, and some spectacular photos, go to
www.mcgrawhill.ca/links/CAF12
and follow the links.

6. Communication An airplane altimeter is a gauge that indicates the height of the plane

The height of aircraft is still usually measured in feet, not metres.

above ground. It works based on air pressure, according to the formula $h = 18\,400 \log \dfrac{P_0}{P}$, where h is the height of the airplane above the ground, in metres, P is the air pressure at height h, and P_0 is the air pressure at ground level. Air pressure is measured in kilopascals.

a) Air pressure at the ground is 102 kPa. If the air pressure outside the airplane is 32.5 kPa, what is the height of the airplane?
b) How high would the airplane have to be flying for the outside air pressure at that height to be half of the air pressure at ground level?
c) If the weather changes, then the air pressure at ground level may change. How do pilots take this into account?

7. Communication a) Estimate the typical air pressure at the peak of Mount Everest. Use the formula from question 6.
b) Do research to determine whether your estimate in part a) is reasonable.
c) Use the results of part a) to explain why climbers of tall mountains often use oxygen tanks to help them breathe.

8. Inquiry/Problem Solving Another logarithmic scale is used for welding glasses, which protect the eyes from bright light. The shade number of welding glasses is given by the equation

shade # $= \dfrac{7(-\log_{10} T)}{3} + 1$, where T is the fraction of visible light that the glass transmits.
a) When there is a solar eclipse, it is safe to look at it through #14 welding glasses. What fraction of visible light is transmitted by #14 welding glasses?
b) A furnace repair person should wear #2 welding glasses. What fraction of visible light is transmitted by #2 welding glasses?
c) How many times as much visible light is transmitted by #2 welding glasses as by #14 welding glasses?

9. For electric welding, a safe fraction of visible light is 5.1795×10^{-5}. What shade number of welding glasses, to the nearest unit, should an electric welder use?

10. Application Johannes Kepler (1571–1630) discovered a relationship between the average distance of a planet to the sun, in millions of kilometres, and the time, in days, it takes the

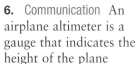

planet to orbit the sun. Data for some planets are recorded in the table.

Planet	d (10^6 km)	t (days)
Mercury	58	88
Venus	107	225
Earth	149	365
Mars	227	686
Jupiter	773	4329

a) Construct a scatter plot of the data on a graphing calculator or graphing software.
b) Copy and complete the following table by taking the logarithm to base 10 of the values in the table above.

Planet	$\log d$	$\log t$
Mercury		
Venus		
Earth		
Mars		
Jupiter		

c) Construct a scatter plot of the data in part b) on a graphing calculator or graphing software. What type of function is best for modelling these data?
d) Use regression to find the equation of best fit for your scatterplot in part c). Write the equation using $\log d$ and $\log t$ as the variables.
e) Rewrite your equation in part d) without using logarithms. This is the relationship between the time of orbit and the distance from the sun.
f) Use your equation from part e) to calculate the time it takes for Saturn, where $d = 1430$, to orbit the sun.

11. Inquiry/Problem Solving In the days before electronic calculators were widely available, students used tables of logarithms and antilogarithms to facilitate calculations. These methods originated about 400 years ago, at a time when certain mathematicians and scientists were searching for methods to simplify complicated calculations.
A logarithm table allows you to estimate $\log x$, where $x \in [1, 10]$. An antilogarithm table allows you to estimate 10^y, where $y \in [0, 1]$.
a) Use the properties of logarithms to explain a method for using tables of logarithms and antilogarithms to determine each quantity.
i) 2469×491
ii) $\sqrt[3]{181}$
iii) $4830 \div 21.73$
b) Verify the method you explained in part a) by testing it, using a calculator, on the problems in part a).
c) Estimate how much time would be saved, for someone doing calculations by hand, by using the method you outlined in part a).

12. Communication The Weber–Fechner law states that the amount of a perception is proportional to the logarithm of the stimulus.
a) Write a paragraph to explain why this feature of perception is helpful for humans or animals. Consider sight, smell, hearing, and taste.
b) The Weber–Fechner law seems to say that perception is inherently logarithmic. Does this mean that logarithmic scales for perceived quantities (such as sound and light) are more natural than others? Or are logarithmic scales for such quantities only helpful in certain circumstances? Write a paragraph to explain your thoughts on this issue.

Derivatives of Exponential Functions

When we use exponential functions to model realistic situations, we need to be able to determine their rates of change. Thus, in this section, we study the derivatives of exponential functions.

You will need a graphing calculator or graphing software for the two investigations that follow.

Investigate & Inquire: Derivatives of Exponential Functions

In this activity, you will explore the derivatives of exponential functions using a graphing calculator or graphing software.

1. a) Graph each exponential function and its derivative on the same set of axes. Use the nDeriv function on the graphing calculator or graphing software.
   i) $y = 2^x$ ii) $y = 3^x$ iii) $y = 4^x$ iv) $y = 5^x$
   b) What type of function does the derivative appear to be in each case?

2. a) Conjecture what the graph of the derivative of $y = 6^x$ looks like.
   b) Test your conjecture using graphing technology.
   c) Make a general statement about the derivatives of exponential functions.

3. Without graphing, describe the graph of the derivative of $y = 7^x$.

4. For each function in step 1, is the graph of the derivative above or below the graph of the function?

It seems that the derivative of an exponential function is also an exponential function. We can verify this by computing the derivative of the exponential function $f(x) = a^x$ using the definition of the derivative:

$$f'(x) = \lim_{h \to 0} \frac{f(x+h) - f(x)}{h}$$

$$= \lim_{h \to 0} \frac{a^{x+h} - a^x}{h}$$

$$= \lim_{h \to 0} \frac{a^x(a^h - 1)}{h}$$

$$= a^x \lim_{h \to 0} \frac{a^h - 1}{h}$$

We can factor a^x from the limit because it does not depend on h. Provided that the limit on the previous line exists, we have shown that the derivative of an exponential function is proportional to itself. How do we determine the proportionality constant, $\lim_{h \to 0} \frac{a^h - 1}{h}$?

We can get an idea of what the limit might be by using tables.

We start with the limits for $y = 2^x$ and $y = 3^x$. Input the functions

$y = \dfrac{2^h - 1}{h}$ and $y = \dfrac{3^h - 1}{h}$ in the Y= editor of a graphing

calculator or graphing software.

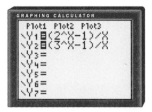

We set up a table on the TABLE SETUP screen to estimate the limits as h approaches 0 from both sides.

From the table, it appears that $\lim\limits_{h \to 0} \dfrac{2^h - 1}{h} \doteq 0.69$ and

$\lim\limits_{h \to 0} \dfrac{3^h - 1}{h} \doteq 1.1$.

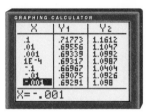

So, from $f'(x) = a^x \lim\limits_{h \to 0} \dfrac{a^h - 1}{h}$, it appears that $\dfrac{d}{dx}(2^x) \doteq (0.69)2^x$ and $\dfrac{d}{dx}(3^x) \doteq (1.1)3^x$.

In your work in the previous investigation, notice that the graph of $y = 2^x$ is above the graph of its derivative, and the graph of $y = 3^x$ is below the graph of its derivative. This is verified by the approximate derivatives of $y = 2^x$ and $y = 3^x$. You will investigate graphs of exponential functions with bases $a \in [2, 3]$ next.

Investigate & Inquire: A Special Exponential Function

1. Since the graph of $y = 2^x$ is above the graph of its derivative, and the graph of $y = 3^x$ is below the graph of its derivative, do you think there is a function whose graph coincides with the graph of its derivative? Explain.

2. a) Using a graphing calculator or graphing software, graph $y = 2.5^x$ and its derivative on the same set of axes.
b) Is the graph of the derivative above or below the graph of the function? If you cannot tell from your graph, zoom in until you can.

3. a) Continue to graph $y = a^x$ and its derivative for values of $a \in [2, 3]$ until you find the base, to two decimal places, for which the graphs of the function and the derivative coincide as nearly as possible.
b) In part a), how many values of a did you have to test? Compare your result with a classmate's. Do you think your method, or your classmate's method, was more efficient?
c) Write an expression for the derivative of $f(x) = a^x$, where a is the value you found in part a).

As seen above,

$$\dfrac{d}{dx} a^x = a^x \lim\limits_{h \to 0} \dfrac{a^h - 1}{h}$$

There is a special number, denoted e, for which the limit in the previous equation is 1.

$$\lim\limits_{h \to 0} \dfrac{e^h - 1}{h} = 1$$

The derivative formula for an exponential function with e as the base is simply

$$\frac{d}{dx}(e^x) = e^x$$

The graph of the function $y = e^x$ coincides with the graph of its derivative. The number e is irrational, and its value is approximately 2.718282. You can use a calculator to display more decimal places.

Thus, the exponential function $f(x) = e^x$ has the property that it is its own derivative. The slope of a tangent to the curve $y = e^x$ is equal to the y-coordinate of the point of tangency. In particular, if $f(x) = e^x$, then $f'(0) = e^0 = 1$. This means that, of all the possible exponential functions $y = a^x$, $y = e^x$ is only one that crosses the y-axis with a slope of 1.

Every function of the form $f(x) = ke^x$, where k is a constant, is equal to its own derivative. These are the only functions that have this property.

Graphically, the relationship between $y = e^x$, $y = 2^x$, and $y = 3^x$ is shown. Recall that, for the function $y = a^x$, where $a > 1$, the larger the base, the more rapidly the function increases as x increases.

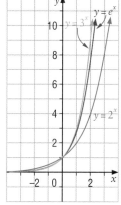

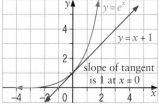

In Example 1, we will determine the limits at infinity of exponential functions with base e.

Example 1 Limits of Exponential Functions With Base e

Evaluate.
a) $\lim_{x \to \infty} e^x$ b) $\lim_{x \to \infty} e^{-x}$

Solution

Since $f(x) = e^x$ is an exponential function, we can use what we learned in Section 7.1 about infinite limits of exponential functions.

a) Since $e \in (1, \infty)$, $\lim_{x \to \infty} e^x = \infty$.

b) Since $e \in (1, \infty)$, $\lim_{x \to \infty} e^{-x} = 0$.

The two limits are also clear from the graphs of the functions.

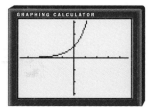

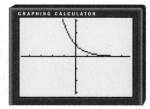

Window variables:
$x \in [-4.7, 4.7]$, $y \in [-3.1, 3.1]$

Example 2 Derivatives of Exponential Functions

Differentiate.

a) $y = x^3 e^x$ b) $y = e^{7x}$

Solution

a) Using the product rule, we have

$y = x^3 e^x$

$\dfrac{dy}{dx} = x^3 \dfrac{d}{dx}(e^x) + e^x \dfrac{d}{dx}(x^3)$

$\quad = x^3 e^x + 3x^2 e^x$

b) To use the chain rule, we let $u = 7x$. Then, we have $y = e^u$.

$y = e^u$

$\dfrac{dy}{dx} = \dfrac{dy}{du}\dfrac{du}{dx}$

$\quad = e^u \dfrac{d(7x)}{dx}$

$\quad = 7e^u$

$\quad = 7e^{7x}$

In general, using the chain rule, if $y = e^{g(x)}$,

$\dfrac{dy}{dx} = \dfrac{dy}{dg}\dfrac{dg}{dx}$

$\quad = e^{g(x)}g'(x)$

In order to solve exponential equations involving e, we need to know the inverse of the function $y = e^x$. We know that the inverse of $y = a^x$ is $y = \log_a x$. Since e is just a special case of an exponential function, the inverse of $y = e^x$ is just $y = \log_e x$. Because this function is frequently used in mathematics and the sciences, it has a special name and notation. It is called the **natural logarithm function**, and is written $y = \ln x$. Use the ⎣LN⎦ key on a calculator to evaluate the **natural logarithm** (the logarithm to base e).

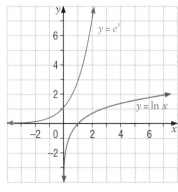

All the properties of logarithms also apply to the natural logarithm.

1. $\ln 1 = 0$ because we must raise e to the exponent 0 to get 1
2. $\ln e = 1$ because we must raise e to the exponent 1 to get e
3. $\ln e^x = x$ because we must raise e to the exponent x to get e^x
4. $e^{\ln x} = x$ because $\ln x$ is the exponent to which we must raise e to get x

The product, quotient, and power laws also apply to the natural logarithm.

$\ln xy = \ln x + \ln y$

$\ln \dfrac{x}{y} = \ln x - \ln y$

$\ln x^p = p \ln x$

A very common application of exponential functions is to model growth and decay. For example, a population of bacteria with plenty of food, water, and oxygen may grow exponentially. A collection of radioactive atoms typically transforms ("decays") into another type according to an exponential model. The rate at which exponential growth or decay occurs is proportional to the amount of the quantity that is growing or decaying.

If n represents the quantity at time t, then $\dfrac{dn}{dt}$ represents the instantaneous rate of change of n. So, for exponential growth or decay, $\dfrac{dn}{dt} = kn$, where k is the growth constant. If $k < 0$, then the quantity is decaying. If $k > 0$, then the quantity is growing. The solution of this equation is $n = n_0 e^{kt}$, where n_0 is the initial amount, that is $n(0) = n_0$. We can verify that $n = n_0 e^{kt}$ is a solution to this equation.

$$\text{L.S.} = \frac{dn}{dt} \qquad \text{R.S.} = kn$$

$$= \frac{d}{dt}(n_0 e^{kt})$$

$$= kn_0 e^{kt}$$

$$= kn$$

$$\text{L.S.} = \text{R.S.}$$

Thus, exponential growth and decay can be modelled by an equation of the form $n = n_0 e^{kt}$, where n_0 is the initial amount, and k is the growth constant, where $k > 0$ for growth and $k < 0$ for decay.

Example 3 Bacterial Growth

The bacteria in a tuna sandwich left out of the refrigerator grows exponentially. There are 600 bacteria initially, and time is measured in minutes. The growth constant is $k = 0.012$ in this situation.
a) Determine an exponential equation that models this situation.
b) When will there be 1800 bacteria in the sandwich?

Solution

a) Let P represent the number of bacteria in the sandwich. Then, $P = P_0 e^{kt}$, where P_0 is the initial number of bacteria, k is the growth constant, and t is time, in minutes.

We are given that $P_0 = 600$ and $k = 0.012$. Thus,
$P = 600e^{0.012t}$

b) **Solution 1** Paper and Pencil Method
$$P = 600e^{0.012t}$$
$$1800 = 600e^{0.012t}$$
$$3 = e^{0.012t}$$

We rewrite the equation in logarithmic form.
$\ln 3 = 0.012t$

$$t = \frac{\ln 3}{0.012}$$
$$\doteq 91.551$$

Solution 2 Graphing Calculator Method

$$P = 600e^{0.012t}$$
$$1800 = 600e^{0.012t}$$
$$3 = e^{0.012t}$$

Use the Intersect operation on a graphing calculator, or graphing software, to find the solution.

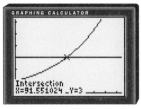 

Window variables:
$x \in [0, 186], y \in [0, 6.2]$

From the screen, in about 91.6 min, or 1 h 32 min, the population of bacteria will have tripled.

Example 4 Graphing Exponential Functions

Graph the function $y = xe^x$.

Solution

- Frame the curve

Since $y = x$ and $y = e^x$ are both defined for $x \in (-\infty, \infty)$, the domain of $y = xe^x$ is $x \in (-\infty, \infty)$.

Since the function is defined for all x, it does not have a vertical asymptote. As x approaches positive infinity, both x and e^x increase without bound, so there is no horizontal asymptote in that direction. As x approaches negative infinity, e^x approaches zero very quickly. So even though the magnitude of x is increasing without bound, it is overpowered by the behaviour of e^x. Thus, $\lim_{x \to -\infty} xe^x = 0$. The x-axis is a horizontal asymptote. We can verify this by setting up a table using the TABLE SETUP screen of a graphing calculator.

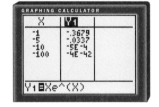

- Find important points
The y-intercept is 0. (Let $x = 0$.)
The x-intercepts occur when $y = 0$.
$y = xe^x$
$0 = xe^x$
$x = 0$ (since $e^x > 0$)
Thus, both the x- and y-intercepts occur at the origin.

Next, we determine the coordinates of any local extrema.

$$\frac{dy}{dx} = \frac{d}{dx}(xe^x)$$
$$= x \frac{d}{dx}(e^x) + e^x \frac{d}{dx}(x)$$
$$= xe^x + e^x$$

To find the critical numbers, we set $\dfrac{dy}{dx} = 0$.

$$xe^x + e^x = 0$$
$$x + 1 = 0 \qquad \text{(divide by } e^x)$$
$$x = -1$$

To determine whether a maximum or a minimum occurs at this critical number, we determine the second derivative.

$$\frac{d^2y}{dx^2} = \frac{d}{dx}(xe^x + e^x)$$
$$= \frac{d}{dx}(xe^x) + \frac{d}{dx}(e^x)$$
$$= xe^x + e^x + e^x$$
$$= xe^x + 2e^x$$

Then, we substitute the critical number.
$$(-1)e^{-1} + 2e^{-1} = e^{-1} > 0$$
Thus, a minimum occurs at $x = -1$. The y-value of the minimum point is $-e^{-1} \doteq -0.368$.
The final important points are the points of inflection. We must determine where the second derivative changes sign, so we let $\dfrac{d^2y}{dx^2} = 0$.

$$xe^x + 2e^x = 0$$
$$x + 2 = 0$$
$$x = -2$$

Since the second derivative is negative to the left of $x = -2$ and positive to the right, this is a point of inflection. The y-value of the point of inflection is $-2e^{-2}$, or approximately -0.271.

- Add details

Since there is a minimum at $x = -1$, the function is decreasing for $x \in (-\infty, -1)$ and increasing for $x \in (-1, \infty)$.
From above, the second derivative is negative to the left of $x = -2$ and positive to the right. Thus, the graph is concave downward for $x \in (-\infty, -2)$ and concave upward for $x \in (-2, \infty)$

Since $f(-x) \neq -f(x)$ and $f(-x) \neq f(x)$, the function is neither even nor odd.

- Sketch the curve

The completed sketch is shown.

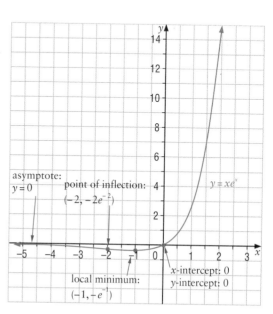

Example 5 Determining the Equation of a Tangent to an Exponential Function

Find an equation of the tangent to the graph of $y = e^{-2x}$ at the point where $x = 0.5$.

Solution

First, we find $\dfrac{dy}{dx}$.

$$\dfrac{dy}{dx} = e^{-2x} \dfrac{d}{dx}(-2x)$$

$$= -2e^{-2x}$$

When $x = 0.5$,

$$\dfrac{dy}{dx} = -2e^{-2(0.5)}$$

$$= -2e^{-1}$$

Since we are finding the equation of the tangent when $x = 0.5$, we need to know the value of $y = e^{-2x}$ when $x = 0.5$.

$$y = e^{-2x}$$

$$= e^{-1}$$

Therefore, the equation of the tangent at $(0.5, e^{-1})$ is

$$y - e^{-1} = -2e^{-1}(x - 0.5)$$

$$y = -2e^{-1}x + e^{-1} + e^{-1}$$

$$= -2e^{-1}(x - 1)$$

or $y \doteq -0.736x + 0.736$

 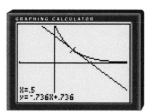

Window variables:
$x \in [-1, 2], y \in [-1, 1]$

Compound Interest and Exponential Functions

In the following investigation, you will explore the relation between compound interest and exponential functions with base e.

Investigate & Inquire: Compound Interest and e

1. Suppose P dollars is invested at $i\%$ per year, compounded annually. Write an equation to represent the amount of money, A, in dollars, in the investment after 1 year. In your equation, let r represent the interest rate, $i\%$, written as a decimal.

2. Repeat step 1 for compounding twice per year.

3. Repeat step 1 if the interest is compounded three times per year.

4. Repeat step 1 if the interest is compounded n times per year.

5. Suppose you invested \$1 at 10% interest, compounded n times per year. Copy and complete the table.

n	A	n	A
1	1.10	1000	
10		10 000	
100		100 000	

6. Evaluate $e^{0.1}$. What number do the values in the A column appear to be approaching?

7. Considering the results of steps 4 to 6, what do you think is the value of $\lim\limits_{n \to \infty}\left(1 + \dfrac{0.1}{n}\right)^n$?

8. Complete the table in step 5 for several other values of the interest rate, r. Compare your results to the value of e^r. Make a conjecture about the value of $\lim\limits_{n \to \infty}\left(1 + \dfrac{r}{n}\right)^n$.

From the investigation, note that e^x can be written as a limit: $e^x = \lim\limits_{n \to \infty}\left(1 + \dfrac{x}{n}\right)^n$.

By setting $x = 1$, it follows that e itself can be written as $e = \lim\limits_{n \to \infty}\left(1 + \dfrac{1}{n}\right)^n$.

The final amount, A, in dollars, of a 1-year investment is given by $A = P\left(1 + \dfrac{r}{n}\right)^n$, where P is the principal, or initial investment, r is the interest rate written as a decimal, and n is the number of compounding periods per year. The more compounding periods there are, the higher the return on the investment. In fact, with **continuous compounding**, the number of compounding periods approaches infinity, and we have

$$A = \lim\limits_{n \to \infty} P\left(1 + \dfrac{r}{n}\right)^n$$

$$= P \lim\limits_{n \to \infty}\left(1 + \dfrac{r}{n}\right)^n$$

$$= Pe^r$$

If the investment lasts for t years, then $A(t) = Pe^{rt}$.

Example 6 Comparing Compounding Frequency

Sari invests \$1000 for 10 years at a rate of 5%.
a) How much will her investment be worth after 10 years with each type of compounding?
i) yearly   ii) monthly   iii) daily   iv) continuous
b) Compare your results from part a).

Solution

a) i) For yearly compounding, we have

$$A = P\left(1 + \dfrac{r}{n}\right)^{nt}$$

$$= 1000\,(1 + 0.05)^{10}$$

$$\doteq 1628.89$$

Her investment will be worth \$1628.89 with yearly compounding.

ii) For monthly compounding, we have

$$A = P\left(1 + \frac{r}{n}\right)^{nt}$$

$$= 1000\left(1 + \frac{0.05}{12}\right)^{12 \times 10}$$

$$\doteq 1647.01$$

Her investment will be worth $1647.01 with monthly compounding.

iii) For daily compounding, we have

$$A = P\left(1 + \frac{r}{n}\right)^{nt}$$

$$= 1000\left(1 + \frac{0.05}{365}\right)^{365 \times 10}$$

$$\doteq 1648.66$$

Her investment will be worth $1648.66 with daily compounding.

iv) For continuous compounding, we have

$$A = Pe^{rt}$$

$$= 1000e^{0.05(10)}$$

$$\doteq 1648.72$$

Her investment will be worth $1648.72 with continuous compounding.

b) There is a significant difference between yearly compounding and monthly compounding. But after that, the differences become much smaller for the time periods discussed here. The difference between daily and continuous compounding is only 6 cents over 10 years!

In Example 6, continuous compounding represents a limiting value for the amount of interest an investment can earn. In general, financial institutions do not actually offer this type of compounding.

Key Concepts

- e is the number such that $\lim_{h \to 0} \dfrac{e^h - 1}{h} = 1$, and e has an infinite decimal expansion for which $e \doteq 2.718\,282$ is an approximation.

- If $f(x) = e^x$, then $f'(x) = e^x$, or $\dfrac{d}{dx}(e^x) = e^x$.

- $\dfrac{d}{dx}e^u = e^u \dfrac{du}{dx}$ or $\dfrac{d}{dx}e^{g(x)} = e^{g(x)}g'(x)$

- Exponential growth and decay can be modelled by an equation of the form $n = n_0 e^{kt}$, where n_0 is the initial amount, and k is the growth constant, where $k > 0$ for growth and $k < 0$ for decay.

- $e^x = \lim_{n \to \infty}\left(1 + \dfrac{x}{n}\right)^n$, which means that $e = \lim_{n \to \infty}\left(1 + \dfrac{1}{n}\right)^n$

Practise

1. Evaluate.

a) $\lim\limits_{x \to -\infty} e^x$

b) $\lim\limits_{x \to -\infty} e^{-x}$

c) $\lim\limits_{x \to \infty} e^{2x}$

d) $\lim\limits_{x \to \infty} e^{-3x}$

2. Differentiate.

a) $y = \dfrac{4}{e^x}$

b) $g(x) = x^6 e^x$

c) $f(x) = e^{\sqrt{x}}$

d) $y = x^2 e^{-x}$

e) $y = \dfrac{e^x}{x}$

f) $g(x) = \dfrac{e^{-x}}{1 - e^{-2x}}$

g) $y = (1 + 5e^{3x})^2$

h) $h(x) = \sqrt{x + e^{1-x^2}}$

3. a) Rewrite 2^x in the form e^{kx}.

b) Differentiate $y = 2^x$.

c) Differentiate $y = a^x$, where $a > 1$.

4. Find the equation of the tangent to the function at the given point.

a) $y = e^x$ at $(0, 1)$

b) $y = e^{-x}$ when $x = 2$

c) $f(x) = e^{-4x}$ when $x = 3$

d) $g(x) = e^{x^2}$ when $x = 4$

e) $y = e^{x^2 + 2x}$ when $x = 2$

f) $f(x) = e^x e^{-x}$ when $x = 5$

5. Find y' if $e^{xy} = x + y$.

6. Find the local extrema of each function.

a) $h(x) = e^x - x$

b) $f(x) = \dfrac{e^x}{x}$, $x > 0$

c) $h(x) = -xe^{-x}$

7. Find the intervals of increase and decrease for each function.

a) $g(x) = xe^{-4x}$

b) $h(x) = xe^{3x}$

8. Find the point(s) of inflection for each function.

a) $f(x) = xe^{2x}$

b) $f(x) = x^2 e^x$

9. For each function, identify the domain, range, intercepts, symmetry, asymptotes, intervals of increase or decrease, local extrema, concavity, and points of inflection. Then, sketch the curve.

a) $f(x) = (x^2 - 1)e^{-x}$

b) $g(x) = x^4 e^x$

c) $y = xe^{2x}$

d) $y = xe^{x^2}$

e) $h(x) = e^{\frac{1}{x^2}}$

f) $y = \dfrac{e^x}{x^2}$

g) $y = x^2 e^{-x^2}$

h) $y = \dfrac{e^x}{1 - e^x}$

10. a) Find the first, second, third, and fourth derivatives of $y = e^{2x}$.

b) State a formula for the nth derivative, $y^{(n)}$.

11. Determine each of the following limits.

a) $\lim\limits_{n \to \infty} \left(1 + \dfrac{k}{n}\right)^n$

b) $\lim\limits_{n \to \infty} \left(1 + \dfrac{2}{n}\right)^n$

c) $\lim\limits_{n \to \infty} \left(1 + \dfrac{6x}{n}\right)^n$

Apply, Solve, Communicate

B **12. Communication** How can you use transformations and the solution to Example 4 (page 454) to determine all the important information about the graph of $y = xe^{-x}$?

13. Inquiry/Problem Solving The equation $P = 250e^{0.04t}$ represents the number of bacteria present in a sink, where P is the population of bacteria and t is time, in hours.

a) How many bacteria are there at $t = 0$? Explain how you know.
b) Estimate how long it will take the population to
i) double
ii) triple
iii) grow to 20 000
c) At what rate is the bacteria population growing after 10 h? 20 h?
d) Why would you want to make sure you keep your sink clean? Explain.

14. Inquiry/Problem Solving The public works department of a town counted 400 rats one year. It is predicted that the rat population will grow exponentially for the next few years. If t is time, in years, then the growth constant for the rat population is estimated to be 0.018.
a) Write an equation to model the rat population in the town.
b) How long will it take the population to
i) double?   ii) triple?
c) Find the rate of change of the rat population after
i) 10 years   ii) 25 years
d) How important is it to control the rat population earlier rather than later? Explain.

15. Application Erika bought a computer system for $5000. The value of the system decreases exponentially with the decay constant $k = -0.11$ if time is measured in years.
a) Write an equation to model the value of the computer system over the years.
b) How long will it take for the value of the computer system to decrease to
i) $2500?   ii) 10% of its original value?

16. a) Heather invested $2000 at 7%, compounded annually. How long, to three decimal places, will it take her investment to
i) double?   ii) triple?
b) Heather used continuous compounding to estimate the doubling and tripling times in part a). How close were her estimates to the actual times?

17. Communication a) Repeat question 16 a) i) for each type of compounding.

i) semi-annual   ii) monthly   iii) daily
b) Compare the results of question 16 a) with the results of question 17 a). Does continuous compounding make a big difference in the doubling time of the investment in this case? Is there a situation for which continuous compounding is much better than any other type of compounding?

18. The position function of an object moving through a resisting medium has equation $y = 20t + 400e^{-0.05t}$, where y is in millimetres and t is in seconds.
a) Determine expressions for the velocity and acceleration.
b) What are the object's position, velocity, and acceleration after 5 s?

19. The value, in dollars, of a machine is modelled by the equation $V(t) = 50\,000e^{-0.4t}$, after t years, $t \in [0, 10]$.
a) What is the value of the machine after 5 years? 10 years?
b) What is the rate of change of the machine's value after 5 years? 10 years?

20. In a particular circuit, the current, in amperes, can be found using the formula $I = 0.6(1 - e^{-0.1t})$, after t seconds.
a) What value does the current approach, as t increases without bound?
b) Find the rate of change of the current after 40 s.
c) Find the rate of change of the current after 60 s.

C **21.** Telephone wires hang between two poles 20 m apart. The wires hang in a curve modelled by the equation $y = 30\left(e^{\frac{x}{40}} + e^{\frac{-x}{40}}\right) - 50$, where the x- and y-coordinates are measured in metres and the origin is on the ground below the lowest point on the curve.
a) Sketch a graph of this curve. What is the domain?
b) How much do the telephone wires sag between the two support poles?

22. Investors use something called the rule of 70 to decide how long it will take an investment to double. To find the approximate time needed for an investment to double, divide 70 by the interest rate (neglecting the percent symbol). So, an investment will double in approximately 7 years if it is invested at 10% interest.

a) Use the continuous compounding equation $A(t) = Pe^{rt}$ to derive the rule of 70.

b) Use the rule of 70 to determine how long it would take an investment to double at each interest rate.

i) 5%   ii) 14%   iii) 8%

c) Use the equation $A(t) = P\left(1 + \dfrac{r}{n}\right)^{nt}$, where P is the principal, r is the interest rate expressed as a decimal, n is the number of compounding periods per year, and t is time, in years, to determine how long it would take each investment in part b) to double with annual compounding. How accurate is the rule of 70?

Historical Bite: Euler and the symbol e

Leonhard Euler (1707–1783) introduced the symbol e for the base of the natural logarithm, at the end of 1727 or the beginning of 1728. Euler was also the first, in 1777, to use the letter i for $\sqrt{-1}$.

Technology Extension

Graphs of Exponentials and Logarithms Using TI InterActive!™

$f(x) := a^x$ "Done"

$f1(x) := \dfrac{d}{dx}(f(x))$ "Done"

Graph of $y = a^x$

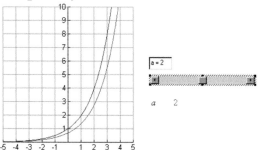

Create a graph with equation $y1(x) := f(x)$ and $y2(x) := f1(x)$. Format the graph with the following window settings: xMin = –5, xMax = 5, yMin = 0 and yMax = 10. Use a slider to control the variable a. Let the value of a vary from –1 to 5 in steps of 0.1. Add a math box near your slider to show the value of a.

1. Move the slider to the right. What is the effect of increasing the value of a?

2. What happens to the graph when the value of a is 1? Explain.

3. What happens to the graph when the value of a is between 0 and 1?

4. What happens to the graph when the value of a is 0? Explain.

5. What happens to the graph when the value of a is less than 0? Explain.

Web Connection

A trial version of TI InterActive!™ is provided by the manufacturer. Go to **www.mcgrawhill.ca/links/CAF12** and follow the instructions there.

6. Using the slider, find a value for a so that the two graphs are identical. If necessary, change the controls on the slider to get more accuracy.

Graph of $y = \log_a x$

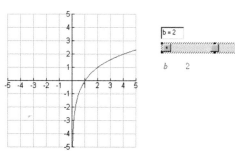

Create a graph with equation $y1(x) := \log(x, b)$. Format the graph with the following window settings: xMin = –5, xMax = 5, yMin = –5 and yMax = 5. Add a slider to control the variable b, the base of the logarithm. Let the value of b vary from –1 to 5 in steps of 0.1. Add a math box near your slider to show the value of b.

1. Using your graph, find each value.
a) $\log_2 4$ b) $\log_4 2$

2. Move the slider to the right. What is the effect of increasing the value of b?

3. What happens to the graph when the value of b is 1? Why does this happen?

4. What happens to the graph when the value of b is between 0 and 1?

5. What happens to the graph when the value of b is 0? Why does this happen?

6. What happens to the graph when the value of b is less than 0? Why does this happen?

7. Based on your findings, how would you change the window settings?

Derivatives of Logarithmic Functions

Earlier in this chapter, we worked with logarithmic functions. Now, we will find the derivatives of these functions.

We start with the simplest derivative, that of the function $y = \ln x$. First, we rewrite the equation $y = \ln x$ in the form $e^y = x$.

We take the derivative of each side of $e^y = x$ with respect to x.

$$\frac{d}{dx}(e^y) = \frac{d}{dx}(x)$$

$$e^y \frac{dy}{dx} = 1 \qquad \text{(implicit differentiation)}$$

$$\frac{dy}{dx} = \frac{1}{e^y}$$

But $e^y = x$, from above. Thus,

$$\frac{dy}{dx} = \frac{1}{x}$$

This derivative can be illustrated graphically.

 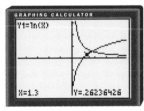

Window variables:
$x \in [-4.7, 4.7]$, $y \in [-3.1, 3.1]$
or use the ZDecimal instruction.

Note that the derivative is defined only for $x > 0$, since the function is defined only for $x > 0$.

We can use natural logarithms to find the derivative of an exponential function or a logarithmic function with any base. Example 1 shows this.

Example 1 Derivatives of Exponential and Logarithmic Functions

Differentiate each function.
a) $y = 2^x$ b) $y = \log_3 x$

Solution

a) $y = 2^x$
We take the natural logarithm of both sides.
$\ln y = \ln 2^x$
$ = x \ln 2$

Differentiating both sides with respect to x, we obtain

$$\frac{d}{dx}(\ln y) = \frac{d}{dx}(x \ln 2)$$

$$\frac{1}{y}\frac{dy}{dx} = \ln 2$$

$$\frac{dy}{dx} = y \ln 2$$

Substituting $y = 2^x$ gives us

$$\frac{dy}{dx} = 2^x \ln 2$$

b) $y = \log_3 x$

We rewrite in exponential form.

$$3^y = x$$

Taking the natural logarithm of both sides, we get

$$\ln 3^y = \ln x$$
$$y \ln 3 = \ln x$$

Differentiating both sides with respect to x gives us

$$\ln 3 \frac{dy}{dx} = \frac{1}{x}$$

$$\frac{dy}{dx} = \left(\frac{1}{\ln 3}\right)\frac{1}{x}$$

Here are guidelines for determining the derivative of an exponential function with base $a \neq e$.

1. Take the natural logarithm of both sides.

2. Rewrite the equation with no exponents.

3. Differentiate both sides with respect to x.

4. Solve for $\dfrac{dy}{dx}$.

To determine the derivative of a logarithmic function with base $a \neq e$, rewrite the function in exponential form and proceed as above.

Exponential, Logarithmic, and Power Functions

In the following investigation you will compare the rates of change of exponential functions and power functions.

Investigate & Inquire: Comparing Rates of Change

1. Consider the functions $f(x) = 2^x$ and $g(x) = x^{\frac{1}{2}}$.
a)   Sketch the derivative of each function on the same set of axes.
b)   Determine the value of x for which $f'(x) = g'(x)$.
c)   Determine the values of x for which $f'(x) > g'(x)$.
d)   Determine the values of x for which $f'(x) < g'(x)$.

2. Repeat step 1 for the same f and for the function $g(x) = 2x$.

3. Repeat step 1 for the same f and for the function $g(x) = x^2$.

4. Repeat step 1 for the same f and for the function $g(x) = x^3$.

5. Summarize the results of steps 1 to 4. Make some general comments comparing the rates of change of power functions and the exponential function $f(x) = 2^x$.

6. Do your conclusions in step 5 also apply to other power functions and other exponential functions? Explain. How would you confirm these more general conclusions?

7. There is a saying that eventually any exponential function beats any power function. Explain what this saying means. Do your conclusions in steps 5 and 6 support this saying? Explain.

Example 2 Differentiating Exponential and Logarithmic Functions

Differentiate with respect to x.
a) $y = x \ln x$ b) $y = \log(x^8 + 1)$ c) $3^y = x^2 + 1$

Solution

a) $y = x \ln x$

$$\frac{dy}{dx} = x \frac{d}{dx}(\ln x) + \ln x \frac{d}{dx}(x)$$

$$= x\left(\frac{1}{x}\right) + \ln x$$

$$= 1 + \ln x$$

b) $y = \log(x^8 + 1)$
We rewrite the function as an exponential equation.
$10^y = x^8 + 1$
Taking the natural logarithm of both sides, we get
$\ln 10^y = \ln(x^8 + 1)$
$y \ln 10 = \ln(x^8 + 1)$
Differentiating both sides with respect to x gives us

$$\ln 10 \frac{dy}{dx} = \frac{1}{x^8 + 1} \frac{d}{dx}(x^8 + 1)$$

Finally, we solve for $\dfrac{dy}{dx}$.

$$\frac{dy}{dx} = \frac{8x^7}{(x^8 + 1)\ln 10}$$

c) $3^y = x^2 + 1$
We take the natural logarithm of both sides.
$\ln 3^y = \ln(x^2 + 1)$
$y \ln 3 = \ln(x^2 + 1)$

Then, we differentiate both sides with respect to x.

$$\ln 3 \frac{dy}{dx} = \frac{1}{x^2 + 1} \frac{d}{dx}(x^2 + 1)$$

$$\frac{dy}{dx} = \frac{2x}{(x^2 + 1)\ln 3}$$

Example 3 Maximum and Minimum Values

Determine the maximum and minimum values of $y = x^2 \ln x$.

Solution

First, we find the derivative of $y = x^2 \ln x$.

$$\frac{dy}{dx} = x^2 \frac{d}{dx}(\ln x) + \ln x \frac{d}{dx}(x^2)$$

$$= \frac{x^2}{x} + 2x \ln x$$

$$= x + 2x \ln x$$

Now, we determine when $\frac{dy}{dx} = 0$.

$$\frac{dy}{dx} = 0$$

$$x + 2x \ln x = 0$$

$$x(1 + 2 \ln x) = 0$$

$$x = 0 \quad \text{or} \quad 1 + 2 \ln x = 0$$

Since $x = 0$ is not in the domain of the function, we reject it.

$$2 \ln x = -1$$

$$\ln x = -\frac{1}{2}$$

$$x = e^{-\frac{1}{2}}$$

Next, we determine $\frac{d^2y}{dx^2}$ at the critical number.

$$\frac{d^2y}{dx^2} = 1 + 2x\left(\frac{1}{x}\right) + 2 \ln x$$

$$= 3 + 2 \ln x$$

$$\left.\frac{d^2y}{dx^2}\right|_{x=e^{-\frac{1}{2}}} = 3 + 2 \ln e^{-\frac{1}{2}}$$

$$= 3 + 2\left(-\frac{1}{2}\right)$$

$$= 2$$

Since $\left.\dfrac{d^2y}{dx^2}\right|_{x=e^{-0.5}} > 0$, there is a local minimum at $x = e^{-\frac{1}{2}}$. The y-value at this point is given by

$$x^2 \ln x = \left(e^{-\frac{1}{2}}\right)^2 \ln e^{-\frac{1}{2}}$$

$$= e^{-1}\left(-\dfrac{1}{2}\right)$$

$$= -\dfrac{e^{-1}}{2}$$

Thus, there is a local minimum at the point $\left(e^{-\frac{1}{2}}, \ -\dfrac{e^{-1}}{2}\right)$, or approximately $(0.607, -0.184)$.

We illustrate the solution using a graphing calculator.

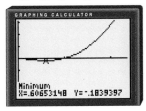

Window variables:
$x \in [0, 2.35], \ y \in [-3.1, 3.1]$

Example 4 Analysis of a Population of Algae

A population of algae in a swimming pool starts at 2500. After 15 min, the population is 5000. This population can be modelled by an equation of the form $P = P_0(a^t)$, where P is the population after t hours, and P_0 is the initial population.
a) Determine the values of P_0 and a.
b) Find the algae population after 10 min.
c) Find the rate of change of the algae population after
i) 1 h   ii) 3 h

Solution

a) The initial population of algae is 2500, so $P_0 = 2500$. After 15 min, the population is 5000. Thus,

$$P = 2500a^t$$
$$5000 = 2500a^{0.25} \qquad \text{15 min is 0.25 h.}$$
$$2 = a^{0.25}$$
$$2^4 = (a^{0.25})^4$$
$$a = 16$$

Thus, the population can be modelled by the equation $P = 2500(16)^t$, where t is time, in hours.

b) 10 min is equivalent to $\frac{1}{6}$ h.

$$P = 2500(16)^t$$
$$= 2500(16)^{\frac{1}{6}}$$
$$\doteq 3968.50$$

The population after 10 min is approximately 3969.

c) To find the rate of change of the algae population, we determine the derivative of P with respect to t.

$$P = 2500(16)^t$$
$$\ln P = \ln [2500(16)^t]$$
$$= \ln 2500 + t \ln 16$$

Differentiate both sides with respect to t.

$$\frac{1}{P} \frac{dP}{dt} = \ln 16$$
$$\frac{dP}{dt} = P \ln 16$$
$$= 2500(16)^t \ln 16$$

i) After 1 h, the rate of change is given by

$$\frac{dP}{dt} = 2500(16) \ln 16$$
$$\doteq 110\,903.5$$

The algae are increasing at a rate of about 110 000 per hour after 1 h.

ii) After 2 h, the rate of change is given by

$$\frac{dP}{dt} = 2500(16)^2 \ln 16$$
$$\doteq 1\,774\,456.8$$

The algae are increasing at a rate of almost 1.8 million per hour after 2 h.

Key Concepts

- $\frac{d}{dx} (\ln x) = \frac{1}{x}$

- Steps for determining the derivative of an exponential function with base $a \neq e$:
  a) Take the natural logarithm of both sides.
  b) Rewrite the equation with no exponents.
  c) Differentiate both sides with respect to x.
  d) Solve for $\frac{dy}{dx}$.

- To determine the derivative of a logarithmic function with base $a \neq e$, rewrite the function in exponential form and proceed as for an exponential function.

Communicate Your Understanding

1. Explain why $\frac{d}{dx}(\ln x) = \frac{1}{x}$ makes sense geometrically.

2. Is it possible to draw a tangent with slope $-\frac{1}{2}$ on the curve $y = \ln x$? Explain.

3. Explain what is wrong with the following reasoning:
$$y = 2^x$$
$$\frac{dy}{dx} = x(2^{x-1})$$

Practise

A 1. Differentiate.

a) $y = \ln(9x - 2)$

b) $y = \log_5(9x - 7)$

c) $y = 3^x$

d) $y = \log_4(x^2 + 3)$

e) $h(x) = \ln 2x^2$

f) $f(x) = -x \ln x$

g) $g(x) = x^2 5^x$

h) $h(x) = 4^x \ln x$

i) $y = 2^{x^2}$

2. Differentiate.

a) $f(x) = \dfrac{1}{1 + \ln x}$

b) $y = \ln(x + \ln x)$

c) $g(x) = \sqrt{\ln x}$

d) $y = \log_4 \sqrt{x}$

3. Find the local extrema of each function.

a) $f(x) = \dfrac{\ln x}{x}$

b) $y = x \ln x$

4. For the function $f(x) = x(\ln x)^2$, determine

a) the local extrema

b) the points of inflection

5. Sketch the graph of each function.

a) $y = \ln x^2$

b) $g(x) = \ln(2x + 3)$

c) $y = \dfrac{\ln x}{x}$

d) $y = x \ln x$

6. Find the equation of the tangent to the curve at the given point.

a) $y = x^2 \ln x$, $(1, 0)$

b) $y = \log x$, $(100, 2)$

c) $y = \ln(x^2 - 3)$, $(2, 0)$

7. a) Find the first, second, third, and fourth derivatives of $y = \ln x$.

b) Determine a formula for the nth derivative, $y^{(n)}$.

Apply, Solve, Communicate

B 8. Communication The population, P, of algae in a fish tank can be modelled by a function of the form $P = P_0 a^t$, where P_0 is the initial population and t is time, in hours. At $t = 0$, the algae population is measured to be 200. At $t = 3$, the population is 800.

a) Determine the values of P_0 and a.

b) How long will it take the population to double?

c) Determine the rate of change of the algae population after each time.

i) 1 h

ii) 6 h

d) Will this model hold true for all time?

9. Application The number of bacteria in a petri dish is initially 1000, but reaches 10 000 in 2 h.

a) If the number of bacteria grows exponentially, determine an equation to model the growth.

b) Find the rate of growth after 5 h.

10. The mass, m, in grams, that remains of a radioactive substance after t hours is given by the equation $m = 2(2)^{-\frac{t}{15}}$.

a) Determine the initial mass of the radioactive substance.

b) Determine the half-life of the substance.

c) Find the rate of decrease of the mass after 5 h.

11. Application Use graphing technology to show that the tangent to the curve $y = \ln x$ at the point $(e, 1)$ also passes through $(0, 0)$.

12. The population of foxes in a provincial park has been modelled using the equation $P(t) = \dfrac{50 \ln(t + 1)}{t + 1} + 40$, where t is the time in years.
a) Determine the maximum population of foxes.
b) What is the predicted long-term stable fox population?

13. An automatic door has been programmed so that the angle, in degrees, that the door is open has equation $a(t) = 180t(2)^{-t}$, where t is the time in seconds, $t \in [0, 8]$.
a) Determine an equation for the speed at which the angle is changing.
b) Use technology to determine the maximum door angle. When does this occur?
c) How quickly is the door closing after 5 s?

14. As lava from a volcano cools, it flows more slowly. The distance, in kilometres, from the crater to the leading edge of lava during a particular volcanic eruption is modelled with the equation $s(t) = 12(2 - 0.8^t)$, where t is in hours.
a) Determine the derivative $s'(t)$. What does it represent?
b) How fast is the lava travelling down the mountain after 1 h? 4 h?

c) Rewrite the given equation, solving for t.
d) Determine the derivative of t with respect to s. What does it represent?
e) Determine the value of $t'(s)$ when the lava is 5 km from the crater.

15. Inquiry/Problem Solving
a) Show that
$$\frac{d}{dx}(a^x) = a^x \ln a$$
b) Show that $\dfrac{d}{dx}(\ln x^n) = \dfrac{n}{x}$.
c) Show that $\dfrac{d}{dx}(\ln nx) = \dfrac{d}{dx}(\ln x)$.

C **16.** Find y' if $y = x^{\ln x}$.

17. Sketch the graph of $x^y = y^x$, where $x > 0$ and $y > 0$.

18. Consider the functions $f(x) = e^{kx}$ and $g(x) = x^m$, where k and m are positive constants.
a) Show that, for large enough values of x, $f(x) > g(x)$, no matter what the values of k and m are. (Hint: Using logarithms may be helpful.)
b) Show that, for large enough values of x, $f'(x) > g'(x)$, no matter what the values of k and m are.
c) There is a saying that eventually exponentials beat powers. Do your results in parts a) and b) support this saying? Explain.

Achievement Check

Knowledge/Understanding

Thinking/Inquiry/Problem Solving

Communication

Application

The value of a certain car purchased in 2001 can be approximated by the function $V(t) = 25(0.85)^t + 10$, where t is the time, in years, from the date of purchase, and V is the value, in thousands of dollars.
a) Evaluate and interpret $V(3)$.
b) Find an expression for $V'(t)$, including units.
c) Evaluate and interpret $V'(3)$.
d) Use $V(t)$, $V'(t)$, and any other considerations you think are relevant to write a paragraph in support of, or in opposition to, the following statement.

From a monetary point of view, it is best to keep this vehicle as long as possible.

Applications of Exponential and Logarithmic Functions

Since logarithms are inverses of exponential functions, they are helpful in solving exponential equations. In this section, we apply properties of logarithms to solve exponential growth and decay problems, such as bacterial growth, the growth of financial investments, and the cooling of hot objects.

Quantities growing exponentially increase at a rate proportional to their size. Quantities decaying exponentially decrease at a rate proportional to their size. In both cases, the rate of change of the quantity with respect to time is proportional to the value of the quantity at that time.

Exponential growth can be modelled by an equation of the form $P = P_0 e^{kt}$, $k > 0$, where P is the amount at time t, P_0 is the initial amount, and the constant k is the relative growth rate.

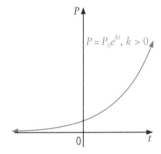

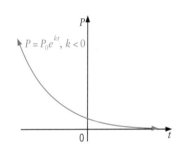

Exponential decay can be modelled by the same equation, the only difference being that $k < 0$.

An exponential model of bacterial growth is appropriate for a colony of bacteria that has plenty of resources (food, water, oxygen) and plenty of room to grow, without the presence of competing populations or predators.

Example 1 Growth of a Bacterial Population

A population of 800 *E. coli* bacteria doubles every 15 min.
a) Determine a formula for the number of bacteria at time t.
b) Interpret the value of k obtained in part a).
c) How long will it take for the population to reach 10 200 cells?

Web Connection

In 2000, Walkerton, Ontario suffered a fatal *E. coli* outbreak due to a polluted water supply. For more information on the disaster, and how the community of Walkerton has come to terms with it, go to **www.mcgrawhill.ca/links/CAF12** and follow the links.

Solution

a) We use the formula for exponential population growth, $P = P_0 e^{kt}$. From our given information, we substitute $P = 1600$, $P_0 = 800$, and $t = 15$ in the formula to solve for k.

$$P = P_0 e^{kt}$$
$$1600 = 800e^{15k}$$
$$2 = e^{15k}$$
$$\ln 2 = 15k$$
$$k = \frac{\ln 2}{15}$$
$$\doteq 0.046\,21$$

So, the number of *E. coli* bacteria at time t is represented by $P = 800e^{0.046\,21t}$.

b) We interpret k as the *relative* growth rate. This means that the bacteria population is growing at a relative rate of about 4.6% per minute. This is much like compound interest. Here the "interest rate" is 4.6% per minute, but the compounding is continuous.

c) We use the formula $P = 800e^{0.046\,21t}$, substitute $P = 10\,200$, and then solve for t.
$$P = 800e^{0.046\,21t}$$
$$10\,200 = 800e^{0.046\,21t}$$
$$12.75 = e^{0.046\,21t}$$
$$\ln 12.75 = 0.046\,21t$$
$$t = \frac{\ln 12.75}{0.046\,21}$$
$$\doteq 55.086$$

So, in about 55.1 min, the population of *E. coli* bacteria will have grown to 10 200.

The cooling of an object can be modelled by an exponential decay equation. According to Newton's law of cooling, the difference between the temperature of an object and the temperature of its surroundings decreases exponentially according to the formula $T - T_S = (T_0 - T_S)e^{kt}$, where T is the temperature of the object at time t, T_S is the temperature of the object's surroundings, T_0 is the initial temperature of the object, and the constant k is the relative rate of cooling of the object. In other words, Newton's law of cooling states that the temperature *difference* between an object and its surroundings changes at a rate proportional to the temperature difference at the current time. Note that, since the temperature difference is decreasing, k is negative.

Example 2 Forensic Medicine

The temperature of a recently deceased body is measured and found to be 28°C at 3:30 p.m., and 25°C at 4:30 p.m. The air temperature in the room is 20°C. Assuming that the body temperature was 37°C at the time of death, when did the individual die?

Solution

Assume that Newton's law of cooling applies:
$$T - T_S = (T_0 - T_S)e^{kt}$$
First, we use the given information to determine the value of k. We are given that $T_S = 20$ and $T_0 = 37$. Thus,
$$T - 20 = (37 - 20)e^{kt}$$
$$T = 20 + 17e^{kt}$$

Let t be measured in hours. Let $t = s$ represent 3:30 p.m., and let $t = s + 1$ represent 4:30 p.m. When $t = s$, $T = 28$, and when $t = s + 1$, $T = 25$. Substituting this information into the previous equation results in the two equations
$$28 = 20 + 17e^{ks}$$
$$25 = 20 + 17e^{k(s+1)}$$
which simplify to
$$8 = 17e^{ks}$$
$$5 = 17e^{k(s+1)}$$
Dividing the second equation by the first results in
$$\frac{5}{8} = e^{k(s+1-s)}$$
$$\frac{5}{8} = e^k$$
Thus,
$$k = \ln\left(\frac{5}{8}\right)$$
$$\doteq -0.47$$

The value of k means that the difference between the body temperature and room temperature is decreasing by about 47% every hour.

Finally, we find the value of t at 3:30 p.m. by substituting the value 28 for T in $T = 20 + 17e^{-0.47t}$.
$$28 = 20 + 17e^{-0.47t}$$
$$\frac{8}{17} = e^{-0.47t}$$
$$-0.47t = \ln\left(\frac{8}{17}\right)$$
$$t = \frac{\ln\left(\frac{8}{17}\right)}{-0.47}$$
$$\doteq 1.6$$

Thus, at 3:30 p.m., 1.6 hours (1 h and 36 min) have passed since death. Therefore, the individual died at about 2:00 p.m.

Radioactive decay is another phenomenon that can be accurately modelled with exponential functions.

Example 3 Carbon Dating

Carbon-14 is a radioactive substance with a half-life of 5730 years. It is used to determine the age of artifacts. An archaeologist discovers that the burial cloth on an Egyptian mummy has 45% of the carbon-14 that it contained originally. How long ago was the mummy buried?

Solution

We use the formula $P = P_0 e^{kt}$. First we determine the value of k using the half-life. When $t = 5730$, $P = 0.5P_0$. Thus,

$$P = P_0 e^{kt}$$
$$0.5P_0 = P_0 e^{5730k}$$
$$\ln 0.5 = 5730k$$
$$k = \frac{\ln 0.5}{5730}$$
$$\doteq -1.21 \times 10^{-4}$$

Having determined the value of k, we can now substitute the data for the present, $P = 0.45P_0$, and determine the value of t.

$$0.45P_0 = P_0 e^{kt}$$
$$\ln 0.45 = kt$$
$$t = \frac{\ln 0.45}{k}$$
$$= \frac{\ln 0.45}{-1.21 \times 10^{-4}}$$
$$\doteq 6600$$

Web Connection

Carbon dating is critical for archaeological research work of all kinds. For more information, go to **www.mcgrawhill.ca/links/CAF12** and follow the links.

Therefore, the mummy was buried about 6600 years ago.

Key Concepts

- Exponential growth and decay can be modelled by an equation of the form $P = P_0 e^{kt}$, where P is the amount at time t, P_0 is the initial amount, and the constant k is the relative growth rate. For growth, the constant k is positive, and for decay, the constant k is negative.
- For a quantity that grows or decays exponentially, the rate of change of the quantity with respect to time is proportional to the value of the quantity at that time.

Communicate Your Understanding

1. Explain the relationship between exponential growth and exponential decay. How are they similar? How do they differ?

2. Explain how the laws of logarithms can be used to help solve exponential growth and decay problems.

3. How do you know when an exponential model is appropriate? Discuss limitations of the model in your explanation.

Practise

1. Solve for the variable in each of the following.
a) $5000 = 4000(1 + 0.075)^n$
b) $2600 = 1900(1 + 0.0575)^n$
c) $8500 = 5800\left(1 + \dfrac{0.065}{2}\right)^{2n}$
d) $3000 = 1700\left(1 + \dfrac{0.0875}{4}\right)^{4n}$
e) $10\,000 = 2500e^{0.08t}$
f) $12\,000 = 9000e^{0.09t}$
g) $7000 = 1200e^{12k}$
h) $2400 = 400e^{10k}$

Apply, Solve, Communicate

2. A cup of hot chocolate, in a room temperature of 21°C, cools according to Newton's law of cooling. Determine the rate of cooling, k, of the hot chocolate if it cools from 86°C to 65°C in 15 min.

3. A population of termites is increasing according to the formula $P = P_0 e^{kt}$. Determine the length of time, t, that it takes this population to triple its initial population of 1800 if it doubles in 0.035 days.

 4. How long will it take $6500 to double if it is invested
a) at 9%, compounded annually?
b) at 8.75%, compounded quarterly?
c) at 6.5%, compounded semi-annually?
d) at 6%, compounded monthly?
e) at 8%, compounded continuously?
f) at 9.5%, compounded continuously?

5. A population of 1500 algae doubles every 8 h.
a) Determine a formula for the number of algae at time t.
b) How long will it take for the population to reach 25 000?

6. Inquiry/Problem Solving Helena would like to amass $11 000 to give to her nephew Fritz for a high school graduation present. Fritz will be graduating in 12 years, and Helena plans to invest $4000 now, compounded annually.
a) What interest rate is necessary for Helena to realize her plans?

b) If Helena would like to give the same gift to her niece Simone, who will be graduating in 15 years, what interest rate would be necessary for a similar investment of $4000?

7. Communication, Inquiry/Problem Solving A piece of steel will be forged into a turbine. The steel is held in a furnace at a temperature of 1250°C, and once it is taken from the furnace it can be worked until it reaches a temperature of 1100°C, after which time it will become too hard to forge successfully. Experiments have shown that the relative cooling rate for this grade of steel is about $k = 1.4\%$ per minute. Suppose that the temperature of the forge shop is 30°C.
a) Determine a formula for the temperature of the steel t minutes after it is taken out of the furnace.
b) How long can the workers forge the steel before it must be returned to the furnace for reheating?
c) Suppose that the room temperature in the forge shop were 15°C instead of 30°C. Determine if the result of part b) would change in this case, and if so, by how much.
d) According to the formula of part a), if the steel were left out of the furnace, how long would it take to reach the temperature of the forge shop? Is this realistic? Comment on the validity of the model.

8. A van's engine has overheated to 190°C, so the driver pulls over to the side of the road and shuts off the engine. The engine cools to 150°C in 5 min. The engine must cool to 80°C before the driver can start the van again. If the outside temperature is 28°C, how long will it be before the driver can restart the van?

9. A sample of 700 cells in a medical research lab triples every 30 min.
a) Determine a formula for the number of cells at time t.
b) How long will it take for the population to reach 18 000?

10. Thorium-234 has a half-life of 25 days.
a) How long would it take for 30 000 g of thorium-234 to decay to 500 g?
b) How long until there is no thorium-234 left? Explain.

11. Richard has $12 000 and wants it to grow to $30 000. Is it better for him to invest his money at 7%, compounded continuously, or at 7.25%, compounded quarterly? Justify your answer with full solutions.

12. The population of a city doubles every 25 years. At this rate, how long will it take for the population to triple?

13. Communication Suppose the rate of increase of a population is proportional to the current population.
a) The population of Mississauga increased from 33 310 to 315 056 from 1951 to 1981. Use this information to predict the population of Mississauga in 2021. How confident are you in your prediction?
b) The population of Caledon increased from 8767 to 26 645 in the same 30-year period. Predict the population of Caledon in 2031. Is your prediction realistic? Explain.

14. Application Hot bricks lose heat according to Newton's law of cooling.
a) If the bricks have an initial temperature of 350°C, the air temperature is 20°C, and the cooling constant is 0.2, determine the temperature of the bricks after 10 min.
b) How long it will take for the bricks to cool to 75°C?

15. The half life of radium is 1656 years. How long will it take for 50 g of radium to decay to 12 g?

16. Application The table represents the number of bacteria in a researcher's sample at various times.

Time (min)	Number of Bacteria
0	2 000
10	3 297
20	5 437
30	8 963
40	14 778
50	24 365

a) Use graphing technology to graph the data.
b) Use your graph to estimate the doubling time of these cells.
c) Use your graph to estimate the tripling time of these cells.
d) Use your graph to estimate the number of cells after 60 min.
e) Use graphing technology to find a function that models this data.
f) Determine an equation in the form $P = P_0 e^{kt}$ that represents this data. Use the data from the table or your graph to verify your equation.

Achievement Check

Knowledge/Understanding

Thinking/Inquiry/Problem Solving

Communication

Application

The electric charge of a capacitor in a circuit decays exponentially according to the formula $Q = Q_0 e^{\frac{-t}{RC}}$, where R and C are positive constants depending on the circuit, and Q_0 is the charge at time $t = 0$, where $Q_0 \neq 0$. Recall that half-life is the time it takes to reduce a quantity to half its initial amount. The time constant is the time to decay to $\frac{1}{e}$ times the original value. Show that the charge, Q, and the electrical current, $I = \frac{dQ}{dt}$, have the same time constant. Describe the time constant graphically.

Investigate & Apply: Local Linearization

Knowledge/Understanding

Thinking/Inquiry/Problem Solving

Communication

Application

The following exploration examines a technique for obtaining function values when the derivative is more readily available than the function values.

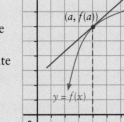

For a function that has a smooth graph, the tangent line to the graph at a point is a good approximation to the graph for nearby points. This means we can approximate values of the function at such points with values of the tangent.

1. The slope of the tangent to the graph of $y = f(x)$ at $x = a$ is $f'(a)$. Show that the equation of the tangent line is $y = f(a) + f'(a)(x - a)$.

2. For a fixed value of a, show from first principles that, for values of x close to a, $f(x) \doteq f(a) + f'(a)(x - a)$.

This expression is a linear function that approximates $f(x)$ near a quite well. It is called the **local linearization** of $f(x)$ near $x = a$. We looked at local linearity in Section 1.2. After zooming in a sufficient number of times, every smooth graph starts to look like a straight line.

3. Suppose we want to calculate the exact value of the limit $\displaystyle\lim_{x \to 0} \frac{e^{2x} - 1}{x}$. Direct substitution gives us $\dfrac{0}{0}$, which is undefined. By representing the numerator by $f(x)$ and the denominator by $g(x)$, use local linearity to find $\displaystyle\lim_{x \to 0} \frac{e^{2x} - 1}{x}$.

4. Confirm your result using a graphing calculator.

5. Create a new example to demonstrate your understanding of this technique.

Review of Key Concepts

7.1 Exponential Functions

Refer to the Key Concepts on page 419.

1. a) Explain the similarities and differences between the graphs of $y = 3^x$ and $y = 5^x$. In your explanation, pay attention to the y-intercepts and the limits as x approaches positive and negative infinity.

b) Repeat part a) for the graphs of $y = \left(\dfrac{1}{3}\right)^x$ and $y = \left(\dfrac{1}{5}\right)^x$.

2. a) Use a table of values to graph $f(x) = 4^x$.
b) Graph $g(x) = 4^{-x}$ and $h(x) = -4^x$ using the graph of $f(x) = 4^x$.
c) State the y-intercept, the domain and range, and an equation of the vertical asymptote of each function.

3. For each function,
i) draw a graph
ii) state the y-intercept
iii) state the domain and range
iv) state an equation of the horizontal asymptote
a) $h(x) = (3)4^x$
b) $y = 2^{-x} - 5$
c) $g(x) = 4\left(\dfrac{1}{3}\right)^x + 2$

4. Evaluate.
a) $\lim\limits_{x \to -\infty} 5^x$ **b)** $\lim\limits_{x \to 0^+} 7^{-\frac{1}{x}}$
c) $\lim\limits_{x \to \infty} 6^{\frac{1}{x}}$ **d)** $\lim\limits_{x \to -3^+} 4^{\frac{1}{x+3}}$

5. Louisa bought a rookie baseball card in 2001 for $2.50. The value of the card is expected to increase and can be approximated by the expression $y = 2.5(1.07)^t$, where t is the number of years since 2001, and y is the value, in dollars.
a) Graph the value of the card over time.
b) Find the approximate value of the card in 2007.
c) Determine approximately when the card will have a value of $70.

7.2 Logarithmic Functions

Refer to the Key Concepts on page 427.

6. Copy and complete the table.

Exponential Form	Logarithmic Form
$5^2 = 25$	
	$\log_3 81 = 4$
$3^x = 18$	
	$\log(x - 6) = 9$

7. Evaluate.
a) $\log_4 64$ **b)** $\log_8 1$

8. Use graphing technology to graph the functions $y = 5^x$ and $y = \log_5 x$ on the same set of axes. State the domain and range of each function.

9. Determine the equation of the inverse of each function. Graph each equation and its inverse.
a) $y = \log_7 x$ **b)** $f(x) = 3^{-x}$

10. Graph each function. State the domain, the range, and the equation of the asymptote.
a) $y = \log_2 (x + 3)$ **b)** $y = 3 \log x - 2$

11. Without graphing, determine the domain of each function.
a) $y = \log_3 x^2$
b) $f(x) = \log\left(\dfrac{1}{x}\right)$
c) $g(x) = \log_4 (1 - x^2)$

12. How long will it take to double an investment of $500 at 12%, compounded quarterly?

7.3 Laws of Logarithms

Refer to the Key Concepts on page 434.

13. Write as a sum or difference of logarithms.
a) $\log_3 (xy)$ **b)** $\log_7 (x - 1)(x + 5)$
c) $\log\left(\dfrac{x}{2y}\right)$ **d)** $\log_4 \dfrac{a^2}{3}$

14. Express as a single logarithm.
a) $\log_5 21 - \log_5 7 + \log_5 2$
b) $5 \log m + 6 \log n$

c) $\dfrac{1}{3}\log_2 27 - \log_2 9$

d) $\log_7(x-2) + 2\log_7(x+2)$

15. Evaluate.

a) $\log_4 32 - \log_4 2$ b) $\log_6 27 + \log_6 8$

c) $\log_3 \sqrt{3}$ d) $\log_8 4$

16. Evaluate to four decimal places using a calculator.

a) $\log_2 5$ b) $\log 7$ c) $\log_3 8$

17. Is $\log_2 5$ the same as $\log_5 2$? Explain.

18. Kepler's third law of planetary motion relates P, the period of a planet's orbit, to R, the planet's mean distance from the sun, through the equation $\log P = \dfrac{1}{2}(\log k + 3\log R)$, where k is a constant.

a) Rewrite the formula as a single logarithm.
b) Rewrite the formula in exponential form.
c) Rewrite the formula, solving for P.

7.4 Exponential and Logarithmic Equations

Refer to the Key Concepts on page 441.

19. Solve for x and check your solution.

a) $2\log_4 x = \log_4 64$
b) $7^{3x} = 8^{2x}$
c) $3(4)^{6x+5} = 25$
d) $\log(x+8) + \log(x-1) = 1$
e) $(5)^{2x} - (5)^x - 20 = 0$
f) $\log_7 x + \log_7 3 = \log_7 24$

20. Emilio invests $1000 at 7.5%, compounded semi-annually. How long, to the nearest month, will it take for the investment to

a) accumulate to $1500?
b) double?   c) triple?

21. Canada's population has been increasing at a rate of about 1.17% per year since 1971, when the population was 21 962 082.

a) Write an equation that models the population of Canada in year x.
b) Use the formula in part a) to determine the population in 2001.

c) Write an equation to calculate the time it takes for the population to reach P people.
d) In what year should Canada's population reach 50 000 000?

22. There are initially 5000 bacteria in a culture. The number of bacteria doubles every 2 h, so the number of bacteria after t hours will be

$$N = 5000\,(2)^{\frac{t}{2}}.$$

a) How many bacteria are present after 12 h?
b) How long will it take until there are 1 000 000 bacteria present?

23. The population of a city increases at a rate of $r\%$ per annum. The population at any time is $P(t)$ with initial population, P_0.

a) Write a formula for $P(t)$.
b) Solve the formula in part a) for t, using base 10 logarithms.

24. In a particular circuit, the current I, in amperes, can be found using the formula $I = 0.8(1 - 10^{-0.0434t})$, after t seconds.

a) What is the current in the circuit after 5 s?
b) Rewrite the equation for I, solving for t.
c) Use the equation in part b) to determine the time it takes for the current to reach 0.5 A.

7.5 Logarithmic Scales

Refer to the Key Concepts on page 446.

25. a) Determine the pH level of a cheese for which $[H^+] = 3.3 \times 10^{-4}$ mol/L.
b) Is the cheese acidic or basic?

26. A subway train has a sound level of 100 dB and normal conversation has a sound level of 50 dB. How many times as intense as the conversation at the subway station is the sound of the subway train?

27. Japan had an earthquake of magnitude 4.8 on the Richter scale in 1906, and an earthquake of magnitude 7.2 in 1995. How many times as intense as the earthquake in 1906 was the 1995 earthquake?

28. The A notes on a piano have frequencies according to the following table. Let f, in Hertz (Hz), represent the frequency of A note n, where $x = 1$ corresponds to the lowest A note on the piano.

x	f (Hz)
1	27.5
2	55
3	110
4	220
5	440
6	880
7	1760

a) Construct a scatter plot with x on the horizontal axis and $\log_2 f$ on the vertical axis.

b) What type of curve would fit the data on the scatter plot? Do a regression to determine an equation relating $\log_2 f$ to x.

c) Write the equation you determined in part b) in exponential form.

d) Determine the frequency of the 8th A note.

7.6 Derivatives of Exponential Functions

Refer to the Key Concepts on page 458.

29. Differentiate.

a) $y = e^x$

b) $y = x^3 e^{-x}$

c) $f(x) = x^2 e^x$

d) $y = \dfrac{e^x}{x}$

e) $h(x) = e^{2x}$

f) $g(x) = \dfrac{e^x}{1 + e^{-3x}}$

g) $y = \dfrac{2}{e^x}$

h) $f(x) = (1 - e^{2x})^2$

i) $k(x) = \dfrac{e^{\sqrt{x}}}{e^{-1}}$

j) $y = xe^{\sqrt{x}}$

30. Find an equation of the tangent to the curve $y = e^x$ at the point where $x = 1$.

31. The atmospheric pressure, p, in kilopascals, for distances up to 10 km above sea level, is given by the formula $p = 101.3e^{-0.125x}$, where x is the altitude, in kilometres, above sea level. At what altitude will the atmospheric pressure be approximately 70 kPa?

32. Determine the local extrema, inflection points, and all asymptotes of each function. Then, sketch a graph of each function.

a) $y = x - e^x$

b) $y = \dfrac{e^x}{x + 2}$

33. The power output, in watts, of a certain battery system decreases at a rate proportional to the power, and is defined by the equation $P(t) = 50e^{-0.004t}$, where t is the time in days.

a) Determine the equation representing the rate of change of the power output.

b) At what rate is the power output decreasing after 100 days?

34. The cost, in dollars, of producing x CDs is given by the equation $C(x) = 10x - 75x^2 e^{-x} + 1500$.

a) Determine an equation for the marginal cost.

b) Determine the marginal cost of producing 100 CDs.

c) Determine the marginal cost of producing 1000 CDs.

7.7 Derivatives of Logarithmic Functions

Refer to the Key Concepts on page 468.

35. Differentiate.

a) $g(x) = \ln x^7$

b) $y = 8^x$

c) $h(x) = \ln(5x + 1)$

d) $g(x) = \log(4x + 15)$

e) $y = 2^x \log_2 (x - 8)$

f) $y = \log_3(7x^2 + 2)$

g) $f(x) = \dfrac{4^x}{1 + x}$

h) $y = \dfrac{1}{x \ln x}$

36. Sketch the graph of $f(x) = \ln(x + 1)$.

37. Find the equation of the tangent to each curve at the given point.

a) $y = 5^x$, at the point where $x = 5$

b) $g(x) = 3^x$, $(3, 27)$

c) $f(x) = \left(\dfrac{1}{2}\right)^x$, $(-3, 8)$

d) $y = 7^x$, $(2, 49)$

38. The population, P, of a certain kind of bacteria, after t hours, is represented by an equation of the form $P = P_0 a^t$. There were 6400 bacteria after 90 min and 12 800 bacteria after 2 h. Find the rate of growth after 90 min.

39. Determine the local extrema, inflection points, and all asymptotes of the function $y = x^2 - \ln x$. Graph the function.

40. When a particular medication is swallowed by a patient, the concentration of the active ingredient, in parts per million, in the blood-stream is given by the equation $C(t) = 150t(0.5)^t$, after t hours.
a) Estimate the highest concentration of the medicine.
b) How fast is the concentration decreasing after 2 h?

7.8 Applications of Exponential and Logarithmic Functions

Refer to the Key Concepts on page 474.

41. How long will it take $7000 to triple if it is invested at
a) 8.5%, compounded semi-annually
b) 9%, compounded continuously

42. Over a span of 20 years, the population of Brampton increased from 51 003 to 149 030. The population of Brampton in 2000 was 310 792.
a) Assuming that the same population model applies for the entire relevant domain, when was the population 51 003?
b) Research population statistics for Brampton. When was its population 51 003?
c) Compare your results from parts a) and b). Explain any differences or similarities.

43. Stainless steel (300 grade) is water quenched so that it will be soft enough to be milled easily. In the water-quenching process, steel at a temperature of 1070°C is placed in a tank full of water. Fresh water is circulated into the tank to maintain the water temperature at about 27°C. After 1 min, the temperature of the steel has decreased to 850°C. When the steel has reached a temperature of 38°C, it is removed from the tank. Determine when the steel should be removed from the tank.

44. A population of mould doubles every 3 h. If the initial population was 600, how long will it take to reach a population of 40 000?

45. The rate of growth of the world's urban population varies at a rate proportional to the existing population. In 1989, the world's urban population was approximately 2.3 billion. In 1999, it had reached 3 billion.
a) Determine an equation representing the world's urban population between 1989 and 1999.
b) Assuming the same model applies for a further 20 years, what would the world's urban population be in 2019?

46. Atmospheric pressure varies exponentially up to an altitude of about 10 km above sea level. The pressure at sea level is 100 kPa and at an altitude of 2 km the pressure is 75.73 kPa.
a) Determine a formula for the atmospheric pressure at an altitude of x km.
b) What is the atmospheric pressure at an altitude of 5 km?
c) What is the atmospheric pressure at the altitude where the model ceases to be accurate?

47. The intensity of light passing through glass varies exponentially with the thickness of the glass. Light with intensity of 2 lumens is shone through a 5-mm-thick piece of glass and passes through with an intensity of 0.736 lumens.
a) Determine a formula for the intensity of light passing through a sample of this type of glass with thickness x mm.
b) Determine a formula for the intensity of light, with initial intensity of I_0 passing through this type of glass with thickness x mm.
c) What effect will doubling the thickness have?

Chapter Test

Achievement Chart

Category	Knowledge/Understanding	Thinking/Inquiry/Problem Solving	Communication	Application
Questions	All	10, 11, 16, 21	1, 12, 20, 21	2, 8, 14, 15, 17–19, 21

1. Graph the function $f(x) = 3^x$.
a) What is the relationship between
$f(x) = 3^x$ and $g(x) = \left(\dfrac{1}{3}\right)^x$?

b) Use your graph of $f(x)$ to graph $g(x)$.

2. Use the graph of $f(x) = 5^x$ to sketch a graph of each function.

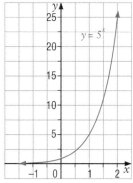

a) $g(x) = -3(5^x)$
b) $h(x) = 5^{x-4} - 6$
c) $k(x) = 2\left(\dfrac{1}{5}\right)^x + 7$

3. Evaluate.
a) $\lim\limits_{x \to \infty} 2^{3x}$
b) $\lim\limits_{x \to \infty} 4^{-x}$
c) $\log_2 32$
d) $\log_7 12$
e) $\log_6 9 + \log_6 4$
f) $\dfrac{1}{2} \log_5 25$

4. Solve for x and check your solution. Round your solution to four decimal places, if necessary.
a) $3^{x-2} = 27$
b) $\log_3(x + 7) = \log_3(x + 2) + 1$
c) $2^{2x} - 3(2^x) + 2 = 0$
d) $2\log_4(x + 1) + \log_4(x - 2) = 2$

5. Differentiate.
a) $f(x) = \dfrac{e^{-x}}{x}$
b) $y = xe^x$

c) $y = e^x x^{-5}$
d) $g(x) = \ln x^5$
e) $h(x) = \log(8x + 7)$
f) $y = \log_4(x - 2)$

6. Find an equation of the tangent at the given point.
a) $y = 4^x$, $(2, 16)$
b) $f(x) = e^x$, at the point where $x = 2$

7. The atmospheric pressure, p, in kilopascals, is given by $p = 101.3e^{-0.125x}$, where x is the altitude in kilometres above sea level. How high above sea level would you have to go to have an atmospheric pressure of 59 kPa?

8. a) Graph the function $y = \log_2(x + 3) + 4$.
b) State the domain, the range, and the equation of the vertical asymptote.

9. How long will it take $500 to double if it is invested
a) at 8%, compounded annually?
b) at 8%, compounded continuously?

10. Iodine-135 has a half-life of 8 days. How long would it take for 28 kg of iodine-135 to decay to 200 g?

11. In 1994, California had an earthquake with magnitude 6.8. What would the magnitude be of an earthquake that is 1.8 times as intense?

12. The power gain of an amplifier, in decibels, is the difference between the output and input sound levels. By what ratio does an amplifier increase the power of a sound signal if the power gain is 55 dB?

13. Sketch the graph of $y = x\ln(4x - 5)$, showing all the important information.

14. Determine the local extrema, inflection points, and all asymptotes of each function. Then, sketch a graph of the function.
a) $y = e^x - x^2$
b) $y = \dfrac{1}{\ln x}$

15. Strontium-87 is used in the study of bones. After one hour, 78.1 mg remains of a 100 mg sample. What is the half-life of strontium-87, to the nearest tenth?

16. The intensity of the sunlight below the surface of a river is reduced by 4.6% for every metre below the surface. Show that the intensity of the sunlight $I(d)$ is related to the depth d by $d = -48.9 \log \dfrac{I(d)}{I_0}$, where I_0 is the light intensity at the surface.

17. The total cost, in dollars, to produce x litres of insecticide is modelled by the equation $C(x) = 200.2\sqrt{\ln(10x+1)}$.
a) Determine the equation representing the marginal cost.
b) What are the total cost and marginal cost of producing 1000 L of the insecticide?

18. The mass, in kilograms, of salt in a brine solution as a solution of different concentration is being poured into the container, is $M = 20(1.5 + e^{-0.02t})$, where t is the time in minutes.
a) Determine an equation for the rate of change of the mass of salt in the brine solution.

b) After 5 min, what is the rate of change of the mass of the salt in the solution?

19. An object is taken from room temperature of 20°C to the refrigerator, where the temperature is 5°C. After one hour, the temperature of the object is 12°C.
a) What will the temperature be after one more hour?
b) What will the temperature be after two more hours?
c) When will the temperature reach 7°C?

20. A model for growth of a population that is appropriate in certain circumstances is known as the logistic model, which has equation $P(t) = \dfrac{M}{1 + \dfrac{1}{P_0}(M - P_0)e^{-kt}}$, where M is the maximum sustainable population, P_0 is the initial population, and k is a constant relative to the growth rate of the population being studied. A model for the world's population, in billions, is given as $P(t) = \dfrac{50}{1 + 7.2e^{-0.0038t}}$, where t is the number of years after 2000.
Use a graph to help explain why this model would be more appropriate than an exponential model.

Achievement Check

Knowledge/Understanding

Thinking/Inquiry/Problem Solving

Communication

Application

21. Coroners estimate the time of death from body temperature using the simple rule that a body cools about 1°C in the first hour after death and about $\dfrac{1}{2}$°C for each additional hour. The temperature is measured using a small probe inserted into the liver, which holds body heat well. Assuming an air temperature of 20°C and a living body temperature of 37°C, the temperature, $T(t)$, in degrees Celsius, is given by $T(t) = 20 + 17e^{-kt}$, where $t = 0$ is the instant that death occurred.
a) For what value of k will the body cool by 1°C in the first hour?
b) Using the value of k found in part a), after how many hours will the temperature of the body be decreasing at a rate of $\dfrac{1}{2}$°C per hour?
c) Using the value of k found in part a), show that, 24 h after death, the coroner's rule gives approximately the same temperature as the formula.

Challenge Problems

1. If the following expression continues indefinitely, find the value for the expression. Give the answer correct to two decimal places.

$$\sqrt[3]{1+\sqrt[3]{1+\sqrt[3]{1+\sqrt[3]{1+...}}}}$$

2. A quantity modelled by the equation $f(x) = 10^{-kx}$ decreases 40% in value as x changes from 3 to 7.5. Determine the value of k.

3. Graph each pair of functions on the same set of axes. State the domain and range of each function.
a) $y = 2^{|x|}$ and $y = 2^{-|x|}$
b) $y = e^{|x|}$ and $y = e^{-|x|}$

4. It is observed that the activity of a radioactive element decreases exponentially according to the formula $A = A_0(10)^{-kt}$, and decreases to 0.35 of its original quantity in 5 h. Find the half-life of the element.

5. If $a = \log_7 (11 - 6\sqrt{2})$ and $b = \log_7 (45 + 29\sqrt{2})$, find $3a + 2b$ in simplest form.

6. For what values of x is the graph of $y = e^{-x^2}$ concave downward?

7. Find the quadratic polynomial $f(x) = ax^2 + bx + c$ that best fits the function $g(x) = e^x$ near $x = 0$ in the sense that $f(0) = g(0)$, $f'(0) = g'(0)$, and $f''(0) = g''(0)$. Using a graphing calculator or graphing software, sketch the graphs of f and g on the same axes. What do you notice? Repeat the procedure to find the cubic that best fits the function. For the cubic, you will need the property that $f'''(0) = g'''(0)$.

8. a) Continue the method of problem 7 to find the polynomial $f_n(x)$ of degree n that best fits the function $g(x) = e^x$.

b) Let $S_n(x) = \sum_0^n x^n$ be a geometric series with common ratio x. Evaluate $S_n(x)$, and show that,

if $-1 < x < 1$, the limit $S(x) = \lim_{n \to \infty} S_n(x)$ exists. This function is sometimes written as $S(x) = \sum_0^\infty x^n$, an infinite series.

c) Suppose that $-k < x < k < r$. Show that $\left| \dfrac{x^r}{r!} \right| < \dfrac{|x|^k}{k!} \left(\dfrac{|x|}{k} \right)^{r-k}$.

d) Write the function $f_n(x)$ from part a) as a series (not necessarily geometric). Use the inequality in part c) to show that the series is bounded by an expression that includes a geometric series with common ratio $s \in (-1, 1)$.

e) Based on parts a) and d), write an expression for the function $g(x) = e^x$ as an infinite series.

9. Let $f_n(x) = \left(1 + \dfrac{x}{n} \right)^n$.

a) Find $f_n'(x)$.

b) Show that $\lim_{n \to \infty} f_n(x) = \lim_{n \to \infty} f_n'(x)$, if the limits exist.

c) Given that the limits in part b) do exist, explain why your conclusion in part b) is evidence for the fact that $\lim_{n \to \infty} \left(1 + \dfrac{x}{n} \right)^n = e^x$.

1. A backyard hockey rink is to be built in the shape shown. The quarter circles at the corners must have radius 3 m.

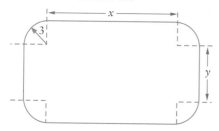

The boards for the rink have already been purchased, so the rink must have a perimeter of 75 m.
a) Determine the dimensions of the rink that maximize the ice surface. Is this a useful shape for the game of hockey? Explain.
b) Professional NHL rinks use dimensions 61 m by 26 m (200 ft by 85 ft), so the ratio of the length to the width of the rink is approximately 12:5. The radius of the quarter circles at the corners is 8.5 m (28 ft). Determine the surface area of a rink with a length to width ratio of 12:5 and a perimeter of 75 m. How much ice is lost by not choosing the optimum shape determined in part a), as a percent of the optimum?

2. A plastic candy container is in the shape of a square-based rectangular prism surmounted by a cylinder. The diameter of the cylinder is equal to the width of the prism's base, and the heights of the prism and cylinder are equal. The volume of the container is 300 mL. Determine the dimensions of the container that minimize the amount of plastic used.

3. The motion of a yo-yo can be described by the equation $s(t) = 90t^3 - 270t + 200$, where s is

the distance, in centimetres, that the yo-yo is above the floor t seconds after it is dropped.
a) From what height is the yo-yo dropped?
b) Determine the minimum height of the yo-yo.
c) At what time does the yo-yo return to the hand?
d) Determine the intervals of increase and decrease of $s(t)$. Explain what is happening with the yo-yo during each interval.

4. Determine equations of all of the asymptotes of each function.
a) $y = \dfrac{1}{x^2 + 6x + 9}$
b) $y = \dfrac{2x^2}{x^2 - 1}$
c) $y = \dfrac{6x - 1}{1 - 2x}$
d) $y = \dfrac{2x^2 - x + 1}{x + 1}$

5. Determine the local extrema and the points of inflection of each function.
a) $f(x) = x^4 - 8x^3$
b) $f(x) = \dfrac{x}{x^2 + 9}$

6. Use the following information to sketch a possible graph of $y = f(x)$.
• asymptotes: $x = 0$ and $y = x + 1$
• points: local minimum at $(1, 3)$, local maximum at $(-1, -1)$, no intercepts, no points of inflection.

7. A manufacturer of calculators estimates that the cost of making x units is $C(x) = 50\,000 + 35x$. Market research has found that monthly demand is 2000 calculators when the price is set at \$28. For every \$2 drop in price, the number of calculators sold per month increases by 500.
a) Determine the price function.
b) Determine the manufacturing level that maximizes profit.
c) Determine the manufacturing level that maximizes revenue. Explain why a company just starting might be more interested in maximizing revenue than maximizing profit.

8. Sketch a graph of $y = \dfrac{x}{(x - 1)^2}$. Include intercepts, asymptotes, extrema, points of inflection, and any other significant details.

9. Given the function $f(x) = \dfrac{x^2 - 3}{x^3}$,
a) find the intervals of increase or decrease
b) find the local extrema

c) find the intervals of concavity
d) find any points of inflection
e) sketch the curve

10. a) Graph the function $f(x) = 3^x$.
b) Use your graph of $f(x)$ to graph $g(x) = 2(3^x)$, $h(x) = 3^x - 1$, $k(x) = -(3^x)$, and $r(x) = \left(\dfrac{1}{3}\right)^x$.

11. Evaluate.
a) $\displaystyle\lim_{x \to \infty} \left(\dfrac{1}{4}\right)^x$ b) $\displaystyle\lim_{x \to \infty} 3^{x-1}$

12. Evaluate.
a) $\log_3 81$ b) $\log_{12} 16 + \log_{12} 9$
c) $\log_6 3 + \left(\dfrac{1}{2}\right) \log_6 5 - \log_6 2$

13. Solve for x.
a) $3 \log_2 x = \log_2 8$
b) $9^{x+1} = 729$
c) $\log (x - 5) + \log (x + 3) = 1$
d) $e^{2x} - e^x - 6 = 0$

14. Graph the function $y = \ln (x + 3) - 3$. State the domain, the range, and the equation of the asymptote.

15. How long, to the nearest month, will it take $5500 invested at 6%, compounded annually, to
a) accumulate to $8000?
b) double?

16. In 1964, Alaska experienced an earthquake of magnitude 8.6 on the Richter scale. What is the magnitude of an earthquake that is twice as intense as Alaska's earthquake?

17. The brightness, I, of a star is the amount of visible light received from it. The magnitude scale is designed so two stars whose magnitudes, m, differ by 5 have a brightness ratio of 100.
That is, $\dfrac{I_2}{I_1} = 100^{\frac{m_1 - m_2}{5}}$.

Notice that the exponent is $m_1 - m_2$ and not $m_2 - m_1$, so that if $m_1 > m_2$, star 1 is less bright than star 2.
a) Verify this formula for two stars whose magnitude differs by 5.
b) Star magnitudes can be negative. Sirius, the brightest star in the sky, has a magnitude of -1.42. The moon has a magnitude of -12.5. How much brighter is the moon than Sirius?
c) The brightness ratio between our sun and Sirius is about 1.2×10^{25}. What is the magnitude of the sun?

18. Differentiate.
a) $y = x^2 e^{-x}$ b) $y = 2xe^{\sqrt{x}}$
c) $y = \dfrac{e^{3x}}{x}$ d) $y = \dfrac{5}{e^{-x}}$
e) $y = \ln (x^2)$ f) $y = \log_3 (x + 1)$

19. Find the equation of the tangent to the graph of $y = 4^x$ at $(3, 64)$.

20. The equation $P = 300e^{0.01t}$ represents the number of bacteria present in a hamburger not stored in the refrigerator, where P is the population of bacteria, and t is time, in minutes.
a) Determine the original population of bacteria.
b) After how much time will there be approximately 11 000 bacteria in the hamburger?

21. The population of a certain city doubles every 15 years. At this rate, how long will it take the population to triple?

22. Metal loses heat according to the formula $T = T_0 e^{-0.2t}$, where T_0 is a the difference in temperature between the surrounding air and the initial temperature of the metal.
a) If the initial temperature of the metal was $300°C$ and the air temperature is $20°C$, find the temperature of the metal after 5 min.
b) How long will it take for the metal to cool to $100°C$?

Chapter 8

Extension: Trigonometric Functions and Their Derivatives

Many phenomena in nature are periodic, and so can be modelled using combinations of sine and cosine functions, which are the basic periodic functions. The rhythms of Earth, such as its daily rotation, the seasons, the tides, weather, and so on, can all be modelled using trigonometric functions. Many of our bodily rhythms can also be modelled using trigonometric functions. Examples are the rhythms of our heart beats, our breathing, the concentration of various substances in our bloodstreams, and the electrical and chemical rhythms in our brains. But trigonometric functions are used for many things other than modelling periodic phenomena. Wherever angles are essential in problems, such as when a baseball is hit and its initial path is inclined at a particular angle, trigonometric functions are helpful.

Review of Prerequisite Skills

1. Distance between two points Determine the distance between the points in each pair.
a) (1, 2) and (3, 5)
b) (−2, 4) and (1, −7)

2. Even functions (Section 1.1) a) State the definition of an even function.
b) Determine whether each function is even.
i) $f(x) = x^2$
ii) $f(x) = x^2 - x^3$
iii) $f(x) = x^2 - x^4$
iv) $f(x) = \cos x$

3. Odd functions (Section 1.1) a) State the definition of an odd function.
b) Determine whether each function is odd.
i) $f(x) = x^3$
ii) $f(x) = x^3 - x^2$
iii) $f(x) = x - x^3$
iv) $f(x) = \sin x$

4. Circle geometry A circular arc has length 3 cm, and the radius of the circle is 2 cm. Determine the measure of the angle subtended by the arc
a) in radians
b) in degrees

5. Circle geometry Assume that Earth moves around the sun at a constant speed in a circle of radius 150 000 000 km.
a) What angle does Earth's path subtend in one day?
b) How far does Earth travel in one day?
c) What is the Earth's speed of motion around the sun in kilometres per hour?

6. Circle geometry As Earth rotates on its axis, each point on Earth travels in a circle. The radius of the circle depends on the latitude of the point.
a) Look up the latitude of your location on Earth.
b) Assuming that Earth is a sphere of radius 6400 km, calculate the radius of your path.
c) Determine the circumference of your path.
d) Determine the speed at which your location moves around Earth (in kilometres per hour).

Web Connection

To review trigonometry interactively, go to
www.mcgrawhill.ca/links/CAF12
and follow the links.

7. Angle measures Write each angle in degrees.
a) π rad
b) $\dfrac{\pi}{2}$ rad
c) $\dfrac{\pi}{3}$ rad
d) $\dfrac{\pi}{4}$ rad
e) $\dfrac{\pi}{6}$ rad
f) 1 rad

8. Angle measures Write each angle in radians.
a) 15°
b) 75°
c) 105°
d) 120°
e) 150°
f) 700°

9. Trigonometric functions Determine the values of $\sin \theta$, $\cos \theta$, and $\tan \theta$.

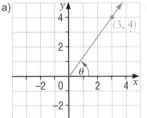
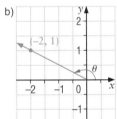

10. Trigonometric functions Use appropriate right-angled triangles to determine exact values for the following quantities.

θ	$\sin \theta$	$\cos \theta$	$\tan \theta$
30° or $\dfrac{\pi}{6}$			
45° or $\dfrac{\pi}{4}$			
60° or $\dfrac{\pi}{3}$			

11. Trigonometric functions Use a calculator to determine the sine, cosine, and tangent of the following angles, rounded to four decimal places.
a) 27.7°
b) 81.4°
c) 0.8 rad
d) $\dfrac{\pi}{7}$ rad

12. Trigonometric functions Use your calculator to determine an angle, in radians, rounded to two decimal places, for which
a) $\sin \theta = 0.34$
b) $\cos \theta = 0.6$
c) $\tan \theta = 4$

13. Trigonometric functions If $\sin \theta = 0.5$ and $\cos \theta = \dfrac{\sqrt{3}}{2}$, determine $\tan \theta$ without determining θ.

14. Trigonometric identities Draw a unit circle centred at the origin O. Label a point A on the circle in the first quadrant. Drop a perpendicular from A to intersect the x-axis at B. Label $\angle AOB$ as θ.
a) Consider the right-angled triangle OAB, and use the Pythagorean theorem to prove that $\sin^2 \theta + \cos^2 \theta = 1$.
b) Is there an angle θ for which $\sin \theta = 0.8$ and $\cos \theta = 0.2$? If so, determine the angle. If not, explain why not.

15. Determining angles Draw a unit circle centred at the origin.
a) Sketch an angle θ in the first quadrant, $\theta \in \left[0, \dfrac{\pi}{2}\right]$. Then, sketch the related angles $-\theta$, $\pi - \theta$, $2\pi - \theta$, and $\pi + \theta$.
b) Repeat part a) if the starting angle θ is in the second quadrant, $\theta \in \left[\dfrac{\pi}{2}, \pi\right]$.
c) Repeat part a) if the starting angle θ is in the third quadrant, $\theta \in \left[\pi, \dfrac{3\pi}{2}\right]$.
d) Repeat part a) if the starting angle θ is in the fourth quadrant, $\theta \in \left[\dfrac{3\pi}{2}, 2\pi\right]$.

16. Determining coordinates of points For each diagram, determine the coordinates of the point A.

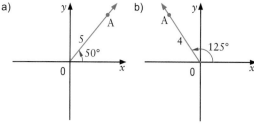

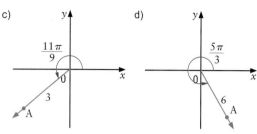

17. Determining angles For each diagram, determine the angle θ, in radians.

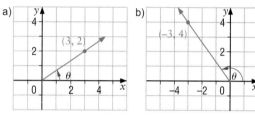

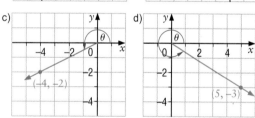

18. Graphing trigonometric functions Sketch a graph of two cycles of each function.
a) $y = \sin x$
b) $y = \cos x$
c) $y = \tan x$
d) $y = \sin \left(x - \dfrac{\pi}{3}\right)$
e) $y = 3 \cos (2x)$

19. Solving trigonometric equations Solve each equation for $\theta \in [0, 2\pi]$. Round your answers to the nearest hundredth, if necessary.
a) $3 \cos \theta = \cos \theta + 2$
b) $2 \sin^2 \theta + \sin \theta - 1 = 0$
c) $6 \sin^2 \theta - \sin \theta - 5 = 0$
d) $\sin^2 \theta + \sin \theta - 6 = 0$

20. Slopes of lines; Trigonometric functions
a) Sketch the line joining the origin with the point (3, 4).
b) Determine the slope of the line in part a).
c) Determine the tangent of the angle that the line in part a) makes with the x-axis.
d) Compare the results of parts b) and c). What conclusion can you draw?
e) Is the conclusion you made in part d) true for all lines through the origin? If so, provide a convincing argument. If not, find an example for which it is not true.

The Reciprocal Trigonometric Functions
The following reciprocal trigonometric functions are defined.

Cosecant: $\csc \theta = \dfrac{1}{\sin \theta}$

Secant: $\sec \theta = \dfrac{1}{\cos \theta}$

Cotangent: $\cot \theta = \dfrac{1}{\tan \theta}$

---

21. Trigonometric identities Rewrite each expression so that no denominators remain.
a) $\dfrac{1}{\sin x} + \dfrac{1}{\cos x}$
b) $\dfrac{1}{\sin^2 x} + \dfrac{1}{\cos^2 x}$
c) $\dfrac{1}{\tan x} - \dfrac{3}{\cos x}$
d) $\dfrac{1}{2 \cos x} - \dfrac{4}{3 \sin x}$

22. Trigonometric identities Simplify each expression so that no denominators remain.
a) $\dfrac{\tan x}{\sin x}$
b) $\dfrac{\sin x}{\tan x}$
c) $\dfrac{\sin x}{\sin^3 x}$

23. Trigonometric identities Write each expression in terms of sine and cosine only.
a) $\sec x \csc x$
b) $\tan x \sec x$
c) $\sec^2 x$
d) $\cot x \sec x$

24. Trigonometric identities Show that each identity is valid.
a) $\cot \theta = \dfrac{\cos \theta}{\sin \theta}$
b) $\cot \theta = \dfrac{\csc \theta}{\sec \theta}$
c) $\dfrac{\sec \theta}{\tan \theta} = \csc \theta$

25. Trigonometric functions Determine the exact value of each quantity.
a) $\csc \dfrac{\pi}{3}$
b) $\sec \dfrac{\pi}{4}$
c) $\cot \dfrac{\pi}{4}$
d) $\sec 0$
e) $\csc 0$
f) $\cot \pi$
g) $\csc 30°$
h) $\sec 90°$
i) $\cot 60°$

26. Trigonometric identities Consider the identity $\sin^2 \theta + \cos^2 \theta = 1$.
a) Divide each term of the identity by $\sin^2 \theta$ to obtain another relation. Express this relation using the reciprocal trigonometric functions. For which values of θ is the resulting relation valid?
b) Divide each term of the identity by $\cos^2 \theta$ to obtain another relation. Express this relation using the reciprocal trigonometric functions. For which values of θ is the resulting relation valid?

Addition and Subtraction Formulas

The main goal of this chapter is to determine the derivatives of the basic trigonometric functions. In order to use first principles to find the derivative of the function $f(x) = \sin x$, we need to determine the following limit.

$$f'(x) = \lim_{h \to 0} \frac{f(x+h) - f(x)}{h}$$
$$= \lim_{h \to 0} \frac{\sin(x+h) - \sin(x)}{h}$$

It may not be clear how to determine this limit, because we are unfamiliar with expanding expressions such as $\sin(x + h)$. This requires an addition formula for the sine function.

In this section, we develop addition and subtraction formulas for the sine, cosine, and tangent functions. Starting with the sine function, we want a formula that expresses $\sin(x + h)$ in terms of $\sin x$ and $\sin h$. In general, we want a formula for $\sin(a + b)$ in terms of $\sin a$ and $\sin b$. Consider the diagram.

The diagram has been constructed so that $\angle RQU$, $\angle RUT$, $\angle UPS$, and $\angle RST$ are all right angles. To simplify the calculations, we scale the diagram so that the measure of segment RT is 1 unit. The general strategy for developing the desired formulas is to express various segments in the diagram in terms of trigonometric functions of angles a, b, and $a + b$. Then, we use relations among the segments to determine relations among the trigonometric functions.

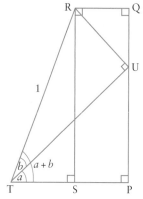

To carry out this strategy, we need to determine $\angle RUQ$.

First note that, in $\triangle TUP$, $\angle TUP = \dfrac{\pi}{2} - a$. Then, since $\angle TUP + \angle RUQ = \dfrac{\pi}{2}$, it follows that $\angle RUQ = a$.

Note that in $\triangle TRS$,
$$\sin(a + b) = \frac{RS}{RT}$$
$$= RS \qquad (\text{since } RT = 1)$$

Also,
$$RS = QP$$
$$= UP + QU$$

Thus,
$$\sin(a + b) = UP + QU$$

We can express UP and QU in terms of trigonometric functions of a and b. In $\triangle TRU$,

$$\sin b = \frac{RU}{RT} \qquad\qquad \cos b = \frac{TU}{TR}$$
$$= RU \quad (\text{since } RT = 1) \qquad = TU \quad (\text{since } TR = 1)$$

In △TUP,

$$\sin a = \frac{UP}{TU}$$

$$= \frac{UP}{\cos b}$$

or

UP = sin *a* cos *b*

In △RQU,

$$\cos a = \frac{QU}{RU}$$

$$= \frac{QU}{\sin b}$$

or

QU = cos *a* sin *b*

Since sin (*a* + *b*) = UP + QU, we have the addition formula for sine,

$$\sin (a + b) = \sin a \cos b + \cos a \sin b$$

By following a similar strategy using the fact that TS = TP – SP, the following addition formula for cosine can be determined.

$$\cos (a + b) = \cos a \cos b - \sin a \sin b$$

Once we have the basic identity sin(*a* + *b*) = sin *a* cos *b* + cos *a* sin *b*, we can obtain an identity for the sine of the difference of two angles simply by substituting –*b* for *b* in the formula and recalling that sin (–*b*) = –sin *b* and cos (–*b*) = cos *b*.

$$\sin (a - b) = \sin (a + [-b])$$
$$= \sin a \cos (-b) + \cos a \sin (-b)$$
$$= \sin a \cos b + \cos a (-\sin b)$$
$$= \sin a \cos b - \cos a \sin b$$

The formula for cos (*a* – *b*) can be obtained in the same way.

$$\cos (a - b) = \cos (a + [-b])$$
$$= \cos a \cos (-b) - \sin a \sin (-b)$$
$$= \cos a \cos b - \sin a (-\sin b)$$
$$= \cos a \cos b + \sin a \sin b$$

The subtraction formulas for sine and cosine are

$$\sin (a - b) = \sin a \cos b - \cos a \sin b$$
$$\cos (a - b) = \cos a \cos b + \sin a \sin b$$

Addition and subtraction formulas for tangent functions are obtained from the addition and subtraction formulas for sine and cosine. For instance,

$$\tan (a + b) = \frac{\sin (a + b)}{\cos (a + b)}$$

$$= \frac{\sin a \cos b + \cos a \sin b}{\cos a \cos b - \sin a \sin b}$$

We would prefer to express tan (*a* + *b*) in terms of tan *a* and tan *b*, so we divide the numerator and denominator by cos *a* cos *b*.

$$\tan (a + b) = \frac{\dfrac{\sin a \cos b}{\cos a \cos b} + \dfrac{\cos a \sin b}{\cos a \cos b}}{\dfrac{\cos a \cos b}{\cos a \cos b} - \dfrac{\sin a \sin b}{\cos a \cos b}}$$

$$= \frac{\dfrac{\sin a}{\cos a} + \dfrac{\sin b}{\cos b}}{1 - \dfrac{\sin a}{\cos a}\dfrac{\sin b}{\cos b}}$$

$$= \frac{\tan a + \tan b}{1 - \tan a \tan b}$$

Recalling that $\tan(-b) = -\tan b$, we can find the subtraction formula for tangent using this addition formula, as we did with sine and cosine.

$$\tan(a - b) = \tan[a + (-b)]$$

$$= \frac{\tan a + \tan(-b)}{1 - \tan a \tan(-b)}$$

$$= \frac{\tan a - \tan b}{1 + \tan a \tan b}$$

Thus, the addition and subtraction formulas for tangent are

$$\tan(a + b) = \frac{\tan a + \tan b}{1 - \tan a \tan b} \qquad (\tan a \tan b \neq 1)$$

$$\tan(a - b) = \frac{\tan a - \tan b}{1 + \tan a \tan b} \qquad (\tan a \tan b \neq -1)$$

In Example 1, some of the addition formulas are verified with specific values. Testing values does not prove that the identities we derived are valid (for proof, we need the derivations above), but it is a useful habit to develop, as it is a good way to discover errors.

Example 1 Testing Addition and Subtraction Formulas

a) Test the formula $\cos(a + b) = \cos a \cos b - \sin a \sin b$ for $a = \dfrac{\pi}{4}$, $b = \dfrac{\pi}{2}$.

b) Test the formula $\sin(a + b) = \sin a \cos b + \cos a \sin b$ for $a = \dfrac{\pi}{6}$, $b = \dfrac{\pi}{3}$.

c) Test the formula $\tan(a - b) = \dfrac{\tan a - \tan b}{1 + \tan a \tan b}$ for $a = 0$.

Solution

a) Consider the left side and the right side separately and verify that they are equal.

$$\text{L.S.} = \cos(a + b) \qquad\qquad \text{R.S.} = \cos a \cos b - \sin a \sin b$$

$$= \cos\left(\frac{\pi}{4} + \frac{\pi}{2}\right) \qquad = \cos\left(\frac{\pi}{4}\right)\cos\left(\frac{\pi}{2}\right) - \sin\left(\frac{\pi}{4}\right)\sin\left(\frac{\pi}{2}\right)$$

$$= \cos\left(\frac{3\pi}{4}\right) \qquad\qquad = \left(\frac{1}{\sqrt{2}}\right)(0) - \left(\frac{1}{\sqrt{2}}\right)(1)$$

$$= -\frac{1}{\sqrt{2}} \qquad\qquad\qquad = -\frac{1}{\sqrt{2}}$$

$$\text{L.S.} = \text{R.S.}$$

b) **L.S.** $= \sin\left(\dfrac{\pi}{6} + \dfrac{\pi}{3}\right)$ **R.S.** $= \sin a \cos b + \cos a \sin b$

$\qquad\quad = \sin\left(\dfrac{\pi}{2}\right)$ $\qquad\qquad = \sin\left(\dfrac{\pi}{6}\right)\cos\left(\dfrac{\pi}{3}\right) + \cos\left(\dfrac{\pi}{6}\right)\sin\left(\dfrac{\pi}{3}\right)$

$\qquad\quad = 1$ $\qquad\qquad\qquad = \left(\dfrac{1}{2}\right)\left(\dfrac{1}{2}\right) + \left(\dfrac{\sqrt{3}}{2}\right)\left(\dfrac{\sqrt{3}}{2}\right)$

$\qquad\qquad\qquad\qquad\qquad\quad = \dfrac{1}{4} + \dfrac{3}{4}$

$\qquad\qquad\qquad\qquad\qquad\quad = 1$

L.S. = R.S.

c) **L.S.** $= \tan(a - b)$ **R.S.** $= \dfrac{\tan a - \tan b}{1 + \tan a \tan b}$

$\qquad\quad = \tan(0 - b)$ $\qquad\qquad = \dfrac{\tan 0 - \tan b}{1 + \tan 0 \tan b}$

$\qquad\quad = \tan(-b)$ $\qquad\qquad = \dfrac{0 - \tan b}{1 + 0}$

$\qquad\quad = -\tan b$ $\qquad\qquad = -\tan b$

L.S. = R.S.

The addition and subtraction formulas can be useful tools for solving trigonometric equations.

Example 2 Using Addition and Subtraction Formulas to Solve Trigonometric Equations

Solve for x in the domain $[0, 2\pi]$.

a) $\sin x \cos \dfrac{\pi}{6} - \cos x \sin \dfrac{\pi}{6} = \dfrac{1}{2}$ b) $\cos \dfrac{\pi}{4} \cos x - \sin \dfrac{\pi}{4} \sin x = 1$

c) $\tan x - \tan 1 = 1 + \tan x \tan 1$ d) $\sin\left(x + \dfrac{\pi}{4}\right) = \sqrt{2}\,\cos x$

Solution

a) The left side of the equation, $\sin x \cos \dfrac{\pi}{6} - \cos x \sin \dfrac{\pi}{6}$, is in the pattern of the $\sin(a - b)$ formula with $a = x$ and $b = \dfrac{\pi}{6}$, so it can be simplified to a single trigonometric function.

$\sin x \cos \dfrac{\pi}{6} - \cos x \sin \dfrac{\pi}{6} = \dfrac{1}{2}$

$\qquad\qquad\quad \sin\left(x - \dfrac{\pi}{6}\right) = \dfrac{1}{2}$

We need to find x in the domain $[0, 2\pi]$. This means we need to find angles $\left(x - \dfrac{\pi}{6}\right)$, in the interval $\left[-\dfrac{\pi}{6}, \dfrac{11\pi}{6}\right]$, whose sine is $\dfrac{1}{2}$. The angles can be read from the graph of the sine function. Remember to choose **Radians** from the Mode settings.

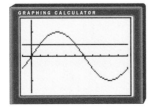

Window variables:

$x \in \left[-\dfrac{\pi}{6}, \dfrac{11\pi}{6}\right], \; y \in [-1.5, 1.5]$

$$x - \frac{\pi}{6} = \frac{\pi}{6} \quad \text{or} \quad x - \frac{\pi}{6} = \frac{5\pi}{6}$$
$$x = \frac{\pi}{3} \qquad\qquad x = \pi$$

The roots of the equation are $\frac{\pi}{3}$ and π.

b) The left side of the equation, $\cos\frac{\pi}{4}\cos x - \sin\frac{\pi}{4}\sin x$, is in the pattern of the $\cos(a + b)$ formula with $a = \frac{\pi}{4}$ and $b = x$.

$$\cos\frac{\pi}{4}\cos x - \sin\frac{\pi}{4}\sin x = 1$$
$$\cos\left(\frac{\pi}{4} + x\right) = 1$$

We need to find x in the domain $[0, 2\pi]$. This means we need to find angles $\left(\frac{\pi}{4} + x\right)$, in the interval $\left[\frac{\pi}{4}, \frac{9\pi}{4}\right]$, whose cosine is 1. The angles can be read from the graph of the cosine function.

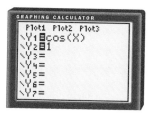 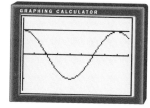

Window variables:
$$x \in \left[0, \frac{9\pi}{4}\right], \ y \in [-1.5, \ 1.5]$$

There is only one value of $\frac{\pi}{4} + x$ in the interval $\left[\frac{\pi}{4}, \frac{9\pi}{4}\right]$ whose sine is 1.

$$\frac{\pi}{4} + x = 2\pi$$
$$x = \frac{7\pi}{4}$$

The required root is $\frac{7\pi}{4}$.

c) $\tan x - \tan 1 = 1 + \tan x \tan 1$

Each side of the equation has a familiar pattern. The left side is the numerator of the $\tan(a - b)$ formula and the right side is the denominator. Divide both sides by $(1 + \tan x \tan 1)$.

$$\frac{\tan x - \tan 1}{1 + \tan x \tan 1} = 1 \qquad (\tan x \tan 1 \neq -1)$$
$$\tan(x - 1) = 1$$

We need to find x in the interval $[0, 2\pi]$. This means we need to find angles $(x - 1)$, in the interval $[-1, 2\pi - 1]$, that have a tangent of 1. The angles can be read from the graph of the tangent function.

Window variables:
$$x \in [-1, \ 2\pi - 1], \ y \in [-1.5, \ 1.5]$$

There are two values of $(x - 1)$ in the interval $[-1, 2\pi - 1]$ that have a tangent of 1.

$$x - 1 = \frac{\pi}{4} \quad \text{or} \quad x - 1 = \frac{5\pi}{4}$$

$$x = 1 + \frac{\pi}{4} \qquad x = 1 + \frac{5\pi}{4}$$

$$\doteq 1.7854 \qquad \doteq 4.9270$$

The roots of the equation are approximately 1.7854 and 4.9270.
If we test these roots, neither violates the restriction $\tan x \tan 1 \neq -1$.

d) $\sin\left(x + \frac{\pi}{4}\right) = \sqrt{2} \cos x$

Expand using the addition formula for sine. $\qquad \sin x \cos\left(\frac{\pi}{4}\right) + \cos x \sin\left(\frac{\pi}{4}\right) = \sqrt{2} \cos x$

$$\frac{1}{\sqrt{2}} \sin x + \frac{1}{\sqrt{2}} \cos x = \sqrt{2} \cos x$$

Multiply both sides by $\sqrt{2}$. $\qquad\qquad\qquad\qquad \sin x + \cos x = 2 \cos x$

$$\sin x = \cos x$$

Divide both sides by $\cos x$. $\qquad\qquad\qquad\qquad\qquad \tan x = 1$

In the interval $[0, 2\pi]$, $x = \frac{\pi}{4}$ or $x = \frac{5\pi}{4}$. The roots of the equation are $\frac{\pi}{4}$ and $\frac{5\pi}{4}$.

Key Concepts

- Addition and subtraction identities for sine, cosine, and tangent:

$$\sin(a + b) = \sin a \cos b + \cos a \sin b$$
$$\sin(a - b) = \sin a \cos b - \cos a \sin b$$
$$\cos(a + b) = \cos a \cos b - \sin a \sin b$$
$$\cos(a - b) = \cos a \cos b + \sin a \sin b$$
$$\tan(a + b) = \frac{\tan a + \tan b}{1 - \tan a \tan b}$$
$$\tan(a - b) = \frac{\tan a - \tan b}{1 + \tan a \tan b}$$

Communicate Your Understanding

1. Note that the sign on the right side of the identity for $\sin(a - b)$ must be $-$, since, if $a = b$, the left side of the equation is $\sin 0 = 0$, so the right side of the equation must be identically zero (i.e., zero no matter what values a and b have). Explain why the sign on the right side of the identity for $\sin(a + b)$ must be $+$.

2. Using arguments like those of question 1, explain why the signs on the right sides of the identities for the addition and subtraction formulas for cosine must be what they are.

3. Repeat question 2 for tangent.

Practise

1. Express as a single trigonometric function, then evaluate.

a) $\sin 45° \cos 15° - \cos 45° \sin 15°$

b) $\sin 45° \cos 15° + \cos 45° \sin 15°$

c) $\cos 45° \cos 15° - \sin 45° \sin 15°$

d) $\cos 45° \cos 15° + \sin 45° \sin 15°$

e) $\dfrac{\tan \dfrac{\pi}{12} + \tan \dfrac{\pi}{6}}{1 - \tan \dfrac{\pi}{12} \tan \dfrac{\pi}{6}}$

2. Express as a single trigonometric function.

a) $\sin A \cos B - \cos A \sin B$

b) $\sin M \cos N + \cos N \sin M$

c) $\cos A \cos 2A - \sin A \sin 2A$

d) $\sin A \sin B - \cos A \cos B$

e) $\sin x \sin y + \cos x \cos y$

f) $\dfrac{2 \tan x}{1 - \tan^2 x}$

g) $\cos^2 x - \sin^2 x$

h) $\cos^2 x + \sin^2 x$

3. Expand. Then, determine the exact value of each quantity.

a) $\sin\left(\dfrac{\pi}{3} + \dfrac{\pi}{4}\right)$

b) $\cos\left(\dfrac{\pi}{2} - \dfrac{\pi}{3}\right)$

c) $\tan\left(\dfrac{\pi}{4} + \dfrac{\pi}{6}\right)$

Apply, Solve, Communicate

4. Application Solve for x where $x \in [0, 2\pi]$.

a) $\sin x \cos 2 + \cos x \sin 2 = -0.5$

b) $\cos x \cos 1 - \sin x \sin 1 = 0.4$

c) $\cos 3x \cos x - \sin 3x \sin x = 0$

d) $\sin 2x \cos x - \cos 2x \sin x = 0$

e) $2 \cos (2 + x) - \sqrt{3} = 0$

f) $\sin 2x \cos 3x = -1 - \cos 2x \sin 3x$

g) $\cos 2x \cos x = \sin 2x \sin x$

h) $\dfrac{\tan x + \tan \dfrac{\pi}{3}}{1 - \tan x \tan \dfrac{\pi}{3}} = \sqrt{3}$

i) $\tan 3x - \tan x = 3 (1 + \tan 3x \tan x)$

j) $\cos 5x \cos x = \sin 5x \sin x - 0.5$

k) $4 \sin 2x \cos x = 4 \cos 2x \sin x + 2$

l) $\dfrac{3(\tan x + \tan 1)}{4(1 - \tan x \tan 1)} = 1$

m) $6 \sin 5x \cos 3x = 3 + 6 \cos 5x \sin 3x$

5. Inquiry/Problem Solving The two lines $y = 2x - 4$ and $y = 3x - 6$ have the same x-intercept. Let the angle between the first line and the x-axis be α, the angle between the second line and the x-axis be β, and the acute angle between the two lines be θ.

a) How are the slopes of the lines related to $\tan \alpha$ and $\tan \beta$?

b) Express $\tan \theta$ in terms of the slopes of the lines.

c) Determine the measures of the angles α, β, and θ.

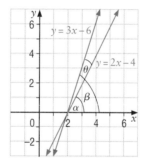

6. Application Develop the addition formula for cosine:

$\cos (a + b) = \cos a \cos b - \sin a \sin b$

Model your development of this identity on the one used for the addition formula for sine.

7. Communication Show that each statement is true.

a) $\cos (\pi + x) = -\cos x$

b) $\sin (\pi + x) = -\sin x$

c) $\cos (\pi - x) = -\cos x$

d) $\sin (\pi - x) = \sin x$

e) $\tan (\pi + x) = \tan x$

f) $\tan (\pi - x) = -\tan x$

g) $\sin\left(\dfrac{3\pi}{2} + x\right) = -\cos x$

h) $\cos\left(-\dfrac{\pi}{2} - x\right) = -\sin x$

8. Simplify.

a) $\dfrac{\sin(x-30^\circ)+\cos(60^\circ-x)}{\sin x}$

b) $\dfrac{\tan\left(\dfrac{\pi}{4}-x\right)-\tan\left(\dfrac{\pi}{4}+x\right)}{\tan x}$

9. Suppose that x and y are in the interval $\left[0,\dfrac{\pi}{2}\right]$, $\sin x = \dfrac{4}{5}$, and $\cos y = \dfrac{5}{13}$.

a) Determine the value of $\cos x$ and $\sin y$.
b) Find the following.
i) $\sin(x+y)$ ii) $\cos(x-y)$ iii) $\tan(x+y)$

10. If x is in the interval $\left[0,\dfrac{\pi}{2}\right]$, y is in the interval $\left[\dfrac{\pi}{2},\pi\right]$, $\sin x = \dfrac{3}{5}$, and $\tan y = -\dfrac{3}{4}$, determine each value.
a) $\sin(x-y)$ b) $\cos(x+y)$ c) $\tan(x-y)$

11. Inquiry/Problem Solving a) Write the following expression as a sum of two terms, where each term is a product in which x does not appear in one factor and h does not appear in the other factor.

$\dfrac{\cos(x+h)-\cos(x)}{h}$

b) Repeat part a) for the expression $\dfrac{\sin(x+h)-\sin(x)}{h}$.

C **12. a)** Derive the addition formula for secant.

$$\sec(a+b)=\frac{\sec a\ \sec b}{1-\tan a\ \tan b}$$

b) Derive a similar formula for $\sec(a-b)$.

13. a) Derive the addition formula for cosecant.

$$\csc(a+b)=\frac{\csc a\ \csc b}{\cot a+\tan b}$$

b) Derive a similar formula for $\csc(a-b)$.

14. a) Derive the addition formula for cotangent.

$$\cot(a+b)=\frac{\cot a\ \cot b-1}{\cot a+\cot b}$$

b) Derive a similar formula for $\cot(a-b)$.

15. Communication Determine the conditions on angles x and y so that each equation is satisfied.
a) $\sin(x+y)=\sin(x-y)$
b) $\cos(x+y)=\cos(x-y)$
c) $\sin x+\sin y=\cos x+\cos y$

16. a) Derive the following transformation formula for tangent.

$$\tan x+\tan y=\frac{\sin(x+y)}{\cos x\cos y}$$

b) Derive a transformation formula for $\tan x-\tan y$ similar to the one in part a).

Historical Bite: Early Trignometry

Trigonometry has its roots in early mathematical descriptions of the heavens. It was recognized that the apparent paths of stars and planets are often circles, or nearly circles. The earliest known table of values related to trigonometry was produced by the Greek mathematician Hipparchus (190–120 B.C.) in 150 BC. Ptolemy (85–165 A.D.) made use of identities that are equivalent to addition formula for sine, the sine law, and several others. Arabic mathematicians worked with sines and cosines, and by 980 A.D. made use of the double angle formula for sine. The Arab word *jaib*, meaning fold, was translated into Latin by European mathematicians as *sinus*, from which we get the modern word sine. In 1542 the Polish astronomer Copernicus (1473–1543) summarized all of the trigonometry relevant for astronomy.

Double-Angle Formulas

The double-angle formulas are formulas for sin $2a$, cos $2a$, and tan $2a$. In this section, we use the addition formulas for the sine, cosine, and tangent functions to obtain these formulas. The double-angle formulas are quite useful for solving trigonometric equations and arise frequently in applications of trigonometry.

Start with the addition formula for sine.
$$\sin (a + b) = \sin a \cos b + \cos a \sin b$$

Let $b = a$ to obtain
$$\sin 2a = \sin (a + a)$$
$$= \sin a \cos a + \cos a \sin a$$
which simplifies to the double-angle formula for sine:

$$\sin 2a = 2 \sin a \cos a$$

The double-angle formula for cosine is obtained in the same way as that for sine. Set $b = a$ in the addition formula for cosine:
$$\cos (a + b) = \cos a \cos b - \sin a \sin b$$
$$\cos 2a = \cos (a + a)$$
$$= \cos a \cos a - \sin a \sin a$$
$$= \cos^2 a - \sin^2 a$$

Using the Pythagorean identity $\sin^2 a + \cos^2 a = 1$, we can write the double-angle formula for cosine in two other forms. For instance, if we solve the Pythagorean identity for $\sin^2 a$,
$$\sin^2 a = 1 - \cos^2 a$$
and substitute the result into the double-angle formula, we get
$$\cos 2a = \cos^2 a - (1 - \cos^2 a)$$
$$= \cos^2 a - 1 + \cos^2 a$$
$$= 2\cos^2 a - 1$$

Alternatively, we could solve the Pythagorean identity for $\cos^2 a$,
$$\cos^2 a = 1 - \sin^2 a$$
and substitute the result into the original version of the double-angle formula to get
$$\cos 2a = \cos^2 a - \sin^2 a$$
$$= 1 - \sin^2 a - \sin^2 a$$
$$= 1 - 2\sin^2 a$$

Thus, we have three versions of the double-angle formula for cosine.

$$\cos 2a = \cos^2 a - \sin^2 a$$
$$\cos 2a = 2\cos^2 a - 1$$
$$\cos 2a = 1 - 2\sin^2 a$$

The three versions are equivalent, but, in particular situations, one form may be more convenient than the others.

Example 1 Simplifying a Trigonometric Expression

Simplify $\dfrac{\sin 2x}{1 - \cos 2x}$. State any restrictions on the variable in the domain $[0, 2\pi]$.

Solution

We use the double-angle formulas for sine and cosine.

$$\frac{\sin 2x}{1 - \cos 2x} = \frac{2 \sin x \cos x}{1 - (1 - 2 \sin^2 x)}$$

$$= \frac{2 \sin x \cos x}{2 \sin^2 x}$$

$$= \frac{\cos x}{\sin x}$$

$$= \cot x$$

The denominator cannot be equal to 0, so

$$1 - \cos 2x \neq 0$$

$$\cos 2x \neq 1$$

$$2x \neq \frac{\pi}{2}, \frac{3\pi}{2}, \frac{5\pi}{2}, \frac{7\pi}{2}$$

$$x \neq \frac{\pi}{4}, \frac{3\pi}{4}, \frac{5\pi}{4}, \frac{7\pi}{4}$$

Example 2 Solving Trigonometric Equations

Solve for x in the domain $[0, 2\pi]$.
a) $4 \sin x \cos x - 1 = 0$ b) $\cos 2x + \sin x = 0$

Solution

a) $4 \sin x \cos x - 1 = 0$
Rewrite $4 \sin x \cos x$ using the double-angle formula $\sin 2a = 2 \sin a \cos a$.
$$2(2\sin x \cos x) - 1 = 0$$
$$2(\sin 2x) - 1 = 0$$
$$\sin 2x = \frac{1}{2}$$

Since x is restricted to the domain $[0, 2\pi]$, $2x$ is restricted to the domain $[0, 4\pi]$. The solutions for $2x$ in this domain are

$$2x = \frac{\pi}{6} \text{ or } \frac{5\pi}{6} \text{ or } \frac{13\pi}{6} \text{ or } \frac{17\pi}{6}$$

Thus,

$$x = \frac{\pi}{12} \text{ or } \frac{5\pi}{12} \text{ or } \frac{13\pi}{12} \text{ or } \frac{17\pi}{12}$$

The roots of the equation are $\dfrac{\pi}{12}, \dfrac{5\pi}{12}, \dfrac{13\pi}{12}$, and $\dfrac{17\pi}{12}$.

b) $\cos 2x + \sin x = 0$
In trigonometric equations such as this one, where there are two different angles, it is usually a good strategy to make changes, if possible, so that only one angle appears. (This process is called matching arguments, since an angle is often called an argument of a trigonometric function.) Here we can use the double-angle formula to express $\cos 2x$ in terms of trigonometric functions of x. The double-angle formula of cosine has three versions from which to choose. We choose the one that matches the other term in the equation, $\sin x$.

$\cos 2x = 1 - 2\sin^2 x$

Thus,

$(1 - 2\sin^2 x) + \sin x = 0$

$2\sin^2 x - \sin x - 1 = 0$

Factoring gives us

$(\sin x - 1)(2\sin x + 1) = 0$

$\sin x = 1$ or $\sin x = -\dfrac{1}{2}$

$x = \dfrac{\pi}{2}$ or $x = \dfrac{7\pi}{6}$ or $x = \dfrac{11\pi}{6}$

The roots of the equation are $\dfrac{\pi}{2}$, $\dfrac{7\pi}{6}$, and $\dfrac{11\pi}{6}$.

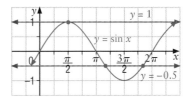

Having developed the double-angle formulas for sine and cosine, we now turn to the double-angle formula for tangent. It can be derived by starting with the addition formula for tangent and setting $b = a$.

$\tan 2a = \tan(a + a)$

$= \dfrac{\tan a + \tan a}{1 - \tan a \tan a}$

$= \dfrac{2\tan a}{1 - \tan^2 a}$

$$\tan 2a = \dfrac{2\tan a}{1 - \tan^2 a} \qquad (\tan a \neq \pm 1)$$

Example 3 Spotlight Position

A painting, 1 m tall, is to be hung 0.8 m down from the ceiling. A spotlight is to be mounted on the ceiling so that the angles marked θ in the diagram are equal. Determine the position on the ceiling where the spotlight must be mounted.

Solution

Using the two right triangles in the diagram and the tangent ratio $\dfrac{\text{opposite}}{\text{adjacent}}$, we have

$\tan \theta = \dfrac{0.8}{L}$

$\tan 2\theta = \dfrac{1.8}{L}$

$\dfrac{2\tan \theta}{1 - \tan^2 \theta} = \dfrac{1.8}{L}$ (double-angle formula for tangent)

We can now substitute for $\tan \theta$.

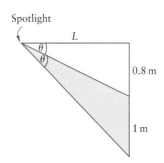

$$\frac{2\left(\dfrac{0.8}{L}\right)}{1-\left(\dfrac{0.8}{L}\right)^2} = \frac{1.8}{L}$$

$$\frac{\dfrac{1.6}{L}}{\dfrac{L^2-0.64}{L^2}} = \frac{1.8}{L}$$

$$\frac{1.6L}{L^2-0.64} = \frac{1.8}{L}$$

$$0.2L^2 = 1.152$$

$$L^2 = 5.76$$

$$L = 2.4$$

The distance from the wall to the spotlight is 2.4 m. Note that we did not have to solve for θ to find the solution to the problem. We needed only $\tan\theta$.

Key Concepts

- Double-angle formula for sine
  $\sin 2a = 2\sin a \cos a$
- Double-angle formulas for cosine
  $\cos 2a = \cos^2 a - \sin^2 a$
  $\cos 2a = 2\cos^2 a - 1$
  $\cos 2a = 1 - 2\sin^2 a$
- Double-angle formula for tangent
  $\tan 2a = \dfrac{2\tan a}{1-\tan^2 a}$ $(\tan a \neq \pm 1)$

Communicate Your Understanding

1. Explain how to derive a double-angle formula starting from an addition formula.
2. The strategy often used when solving trigonometric equations is to match arguments and express the equation in terms of one trigonometric function. Explain what this means and why the strategy is used.

Practise

A **1.** Express as a single sine or cosine function.
a) $10 \sin x \cos x$
b) $5 \sin(2x) \cos(2x)$
c) $\sin(6x) \cos(6x)$
d) $4 \sin \dfrac{x}{2} \cos \dfrac{x}{2}$
e) $\cos^2 \dfrac{\theta}{2} - \sin^2 \dfrac{\theta}{2}$
f) $2 \cos^2 5\theta - 1$
g) $1 - 2 \sin^2 \dfrac{2\theta}{3}$
h) $2 \cos^2(3\theta - 2) - 1$

2. Simplify each expression. State any restrictions on the variable in the domain $[0, 2\pi]$.
a) $\dfrac{\sin 2a}{\cos a}$
b) $2 \tan a \cos^2 a$
c) $2 \sin^2 a + \cos 2a$

Apply, Solve, Communicate

B **3.** Inquiry/Problem Solving Expand using a double-angle formula.
a) $3 \sin 4x$
b) $6 \cos 6x$
c) $1 - \cos 8x$
d) $\tan 4x$
e) $\cos 2x - \dfrac{\sin 2x}{\sin x}$

4. Communication a) If you know the values of $\sin \dfrac{x}{2}$ and $\cos \dfrac{x}{2}$, how can you determine the value of $\sin x$ without calculating x?
b) If you know the value of $\sin \dfrac{x}{2}$, is it possible to determine the value of $\cos x$ without calculating x? If so, explain how.

5. Solve for x in the domain $[0, 2\pi]$.
a) $\cos 2x + \cos x + 1 = 0$
b) $\cos 2x = \sin x$
c) $3 \tan x = \tan 2x$
d) $\sin x = 6 \sin 2x$
e) $\sin 2x \cos x + \sin^2 x = 1$
f) $\sin 2x + \sin x = 0$
g) $\sin 2x - \cos 2x = 0$
h) $3 \cos 2x + 2 + \cos x = 0$
i) $\sin 2x = \tan x$
j) $2 \sin x \cos x = \cos 2x$
k) $3 \sin 2x - \cos x = 0$
l) $3 \sin x + \cos 2x = 2$
m) $5 - 13 \sin x = 2 \cos 2x$

6. Two ropes (2 m and 3 m long) used to stabilize a pole for a volleyball net are anchored to the ground. The angle between the two ropes is equal to the angle between the ground and the lower rope. Determine the distance from the base of the pole to the point at which the ropes are anchored to the ground.

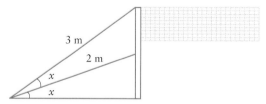

7. Application a) Express $\sec 2\theta$ in terms of $\sec \theta$ and $\tan \theta$.
b) Express $\csc 2\theta$ in terms of $\csc \theta$ and $\sec \theta$.

8. Application Determine formulas for
a) $\sin 3\theta$ in terms of $\sin \theta$
b) $\cos 3\theta$ in terms of $\cos \theta$
c) $\tan 3\theta$ in terms of $\tan \theta$

C **9.** Express $\sin 2\theta$ and $\cos 2\theta$ in terms of $\tan \theta$.

10. Determine $\sin 2\theta$ if $\sin \theta + \cos \theta = \dfrac{1}{2}$.

11. If $\cos 4\theta - \cos 2\theta = \dfrac{7}{8}$, determine the possible values of $\cos \theta$ in the domain $[0, 2\pi]$.

12. Inquiry/Problem Solving A right circular cone is inscribed in a sphere of radius 30 cm. The semi-vertical angle of the cone is x, as shown.

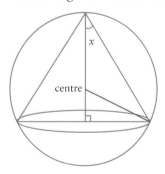

a) Determine an expression for the volume of the cone in terms of x.
b) When the volume of the cone is 9000π cm³, show that x satisfies the equation $8\cos^6 x - 8\cos^4 x + 1 = 0$.
c) Use graphing technology to solve the equation of part b). Explain what the solutions mean.

Limits of Trigonometric Functions

To determine the derivative of a trigonometric function using the definition of the derivative, we need to know certain basic limits of trigonometric functions. These limits are developed in this section.

The first limits we need are the limits of $\sin \theta$ and $\cos \theta$ as θ approaches 0. Since sine and cosine are continuous functions, these limits are just the values of the functions at $\theta = 0$.

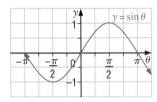

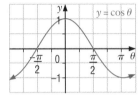

$$\lim_{\theta \to 0} \sin \theta = 0 \qquad\qquad \lim_{\theta \to 0} \cos \theta = 1$$

The next limit we need, one of the most important for trigonometric functions, is

$$\lim_{\theta \to 0} \frac{\sin \theta}{\theta}.$$

Substituting $\theta = 0$ into the expression results in $\frac{0}{0}$, which is undefined. In the following investigation, you will use a calculator to get a sense of whether this limit exists, and if so, what its value might be. It is not clear whether to use degrees or radians, so you will use both.

Investigate & Inquire: An Important Trigonometric Limit

1. Using angles in degrees, construct tables of values for $\dfrac{\sin \theta}{\theta}$ for values of θ approaching 0 from the left and from the right.

2. Examine the tables in step 1. Does it appear that $\lim\limits_{\theta \to 0} \dfrac{\sin \theta}{\theta}$ exists? If so, what appears to be the value of the limit when θ is in degrees?

3. Repeat step 1 using angles in radians.

4. Examine the tables in step 3. Does it appear that $\lim\limits_{\theta \to 0} \dfrac{\sin \theta}{\theta}$ exists? If so, what appears to be the value of the limit when θ is in radians?

5. In the diagram, AO = 1 and θ is a small angle, in radians. Find the lengths of AB and the arc AC of the circle centred at O. How is this evidence for the statement
$$\lim_{\theta \to 0} \frac{\sin \theta}{\theta} = 1?$$

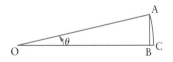

From the investigation, it seems that $\lim\limits_{\theta \to 0} \dfrac{\sin \theta}{\theta}$ exists, and is equal to about 0.017 if θ is in degrees, and equal to 1 if θ is in radians. The number 1 is a lot simpler to work with, and the resulting differentiation formulas are also much simpler, so when it comes to differentiating trigonometric functions, θ is always measured in radians. On a graphing calculator, the limit also appears to be 1 when θ is measured in radians. The screen shows the graph without the axes showing, so we can see the function at $x = 0$ better.

The number 0.017 may seem strange at first glance, but it arises naturally—see question 10 in Section 8.4.

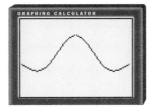

Window variables:
$x \in [-2\pi, 2\pi]$, $y \in [-1.5, 1.5]$
Use the Format settings to turn the axes off.

$$\lim_{\theta \to 0} \frac{\sin \theta}{\theta} = 1 \qquad \text{(valid when } \theta \text{ is measured in radians)}$$

Now that we know the three basic trigonometric limits, $\lim\limits_{\theta \to 0} \sin \theta = 0$, $\lim\limits_{\theta \to 0} \cos \theta = 1$, and $\lim\limits_{\theta \to 0} \dfrac{\sin \theta}{\theta} = 1$, we are able to determine many others.

Web Connection
For an animated demonstration of $\lim\limits_{x \to 0} \dfrac{\sin x}{x} = 1$, go to **www.mcgrawhill.ca/links/CAF12** and follow the links.

Example 1 Determining Another Important Trigonometric Limit
Determine $\lim\limits_{\theta \to 0} \dfrac{\cos \theta - 1}{\theta}$.

Solution
Substituting $\theta = 0$ into the expression fails, since the result, $\dfrac{0}{0}$, is undefined. Before determining the limit using algebra, we get a sense for what it might be by setting up tables of values using the TABLE SETUP screen. Remember that we are using radians for the angle measure, as we anticipate that this might lead to a simpler result than using degrees.

Approaching 0 from the right: Approaching 0 from the left:

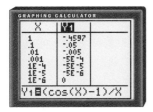
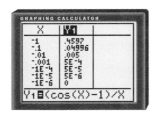

Remember that 1E-6 means 1×10^{-6} or 0.000 001.

It seems that the limit is 0. Let us verify this with a convincing algebraic argument.

$$\lim_{\theta \to 0} \frac{\cos \theta - 1}{\theta} = \lim_{\theta \to 0} \left[\frac{\cos \theta - 1}{\theta} \times \frac{\cos \theta + 1}{\cos \theta + 1} \right]$$

$$= \lim_{\theta \to 0} \frac{\cos^2 \theta - 1}{\theta(\cos \theta + 1)}$$

$$= \lim_{\theta \to 0} \frac{- \sin^2 \theta}{\theta(\cos \theta + 1)} \qquad \text{Since } \sin^2 \theta + \cos^2 \theta = 1, \text{ then } \cos^2 \theta - 1 = -\sin^2 \theta.$$

$$= \lim_{\theta \to 0} \left[\frac{\sin \theta}{\theta} \times \frac{- \sin \theta}{(\cos \theta + 1)} \right]$$

$$= 1 \times \frac{-0}{1+1} \qquad \text{We use the product law of limits.}$$

$$= 0$$

The limits $\lim\limits_{\theta \to 0} \dfrac{\sin \theta}{\theta} = 1$ and $\lim\limits_{\theta \to 0} \dfrac{\cos \theta - 1}{\theta} = 0$ are used in determining the derivative formulas for sine and cosine in Section 8.4. We continue to explore limits of trigonometric functions in this section.

Example 2 Determining More Trigonometric Limits

Determine each limit.

a) $\lim\limits_{x \to 0} \dfrac{\sin x}{2x}$ 　　b) $\lim\limits_{x \to 0} \dfrac{\sin 2x}{x}$ 　　c) $\lim\limits_{x \to 0} \dfrac{3 \tan x - \sin x}{x \cos x}$

a) **Solution 1** Paper and Pencil Method

The first method to try is to substitute $x = 0$ into the expression. This fails, since the numerator and denominator are both 0 when $x = 0$. Instead, look for the basic limit, $\lim\limits_{x \to 0} \dfrac{\sin x}{x}$.

$$\lim_{x \to 0} \frac{\sin x}{2x} = \lim_{x \to 0} \left(\frac{1}{2} \right) \left(\frac{\sin x}{x} \right)$$

$$= \left(\frac{1}{2} \right)(1)$$

$$= \frac{1}{2}$$

Solution 2 Graphing Calculator Method

We use the TABLE SETUP screen to set up tables of values for x approaching 0 from the right and from the left.

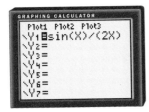

The result from the graphing calculator agrees with the result in Solution 1:
$$\lim_{x \to 0} \frac{\sin x}{2x} = \frac{1}{2}.$$

b) **Solution 1** Use the Double-Angle Formula

Using the double-angle formula for sine, we obtain

$$\lim_{x \to 0} \frac{\sin 2x}{x} = \lim_{x \to 0} \frac{2 \sin x \cos x}{x}$$

$$= \lim_{x \to 0} \left[\frac{\sin x}{x} \, 2 \cos x \right]$$

$$= 1 \times 2 \times 1$$

$$= 2$$

Solution 2 Use First Principles

Matching the pattern for the basic limit,

$$\lim_{x \to 0} \frac{\sin x}{x}, \text{ we get}$$

$$\lim_{x \to 0} \frac{\sin 2x}{x} = \lim_{x \to 0} \left[\frac{\sin 2x}{x} \times \frac{2}{2} \right]$$

$$= 2 \lim_{2x \to 0} \frac{\sin 2x}{2x} \quad \text{(Note that as } x \to 0, 2x \to 0)$$

$$= 2 \times 1$$

$$= 2$$

c) $\lim\limits_{x \to 0} \dfrac{3 \tan x - \sin x}{x \cos x}$

The strategy here is to express the function in terms of sine and cosine, simplify, and look for the basic limit $\lim\limits_{x \to 0} \dfrac{\sin x}{x}$.

$$\lim_{x \to 0} \frac{3 \tan x - \sin x}{x \cos x} = \lim_{x \to 0} \frac{3 \dfrac{\sin x}{\cos x} - \sin x}{x \cos x}$$

$$= \lim_{x \to 0} \left[\frac{3 \dfrac{\sin x}{\cos x} - \sin x}{x \cos x} \times \frac{\cos x}{\cos x} \right]$$

$$= \lim_{x \to 0} \frac{3 \sin x - \sin x \cos x}{x \cos^2 x}$$

$$= \lim_{x \to 0} \frac{\sin x (3 - \cos x)}{x \cos^2 x}$$

$$= \lim_{x \to 0} \left[\frac{\sin x}{x} \times \frac{3 - \cos x}{\cos^2 x} \right]$$

$$= 1 \times \frac{3 - 1}{1^2}$$

$$= 2$$

Example 3 Determining Another Trigonometric Limit

Determine $\lim\limits_{\theta \to 0} \dfrac{\cos \theta}{\theta}$.

Solution

Substituting $\theta = 0$ into the expression produces $\dfrac{1}{0}$, which is undefined. There are no algebraic simplifications, so we suspect that the limit does not exist.

As θ gets closer and closer to 0, the numerator gets closer and closer to 1, whereas the denominator gets closer and closer to 0, so that the entire expression gets larger and larger in magnitude. Thus, the limit does not exist.

As θ approaches 0 through positive values, the expression is positive, whereas when θ approaches 0 through negative values, the expression is negative. So, we can express more precisely that the limit does not exist as follows:

$$\lim_{\theta \to 0^+} \frac{\cos \theta}{\theta} = \infty \qquad \lim_{\theta \to 0^-} \frac{\cos \theta}{\theta} = -\infty$$

Examine the graph of the function $y = \dfrac{\cos \theta}{\theta}$ on a graphing calculator. The calculator screen is consistent with the conclusion that the limit does not exist. The function $y = \dfrac{\cos \theta}{\theta}$ has an infinite discontinuity at $\theta = 0$.

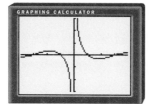

Window variables:
$x \in [-2\pi, 2\pi], \; y \in [-3, 3]$

Key Concepts

- Three fundamental limits of trigonometry are

$$\lim_{\theta \to 0} \sin \theta = 0 \qquad \lim_{\theta \to 0} \cos \theta = 1 \qquad \lim_{\theta \to 0} \frac{\sin \theta}{\theta} = 1$$

Communicate Your Understanding

1. Suggest two ways to use a graphing calculator to determine an approximate value for a limit.

2. In trying to determine a limit such as $\lim\limits_{\theta \to 0} \dfrac{\sin \theta}{\theta}$, why does substituting $\theta = 0$ not work?

3. Describe the strategies used to evaluate trigonometric limits.

Practise

B **1.** Determine the value of each limit, if it exists.

a) $\lim\limits_{x \to 0} \dfrac{\sin x}{x}$

b) $\lim\limits_{x \to 0} \dfrac{\sin(x-1)}{x}$

c) $\lim\limits_{x \to 1} \dfrac{\sin x}{x}$

d) $\lim\limits_{x \to 0} \dfrac{\sin x}{3}$

e) $\lim\limits_{x \to 0} \dfrac{\sin x}{3x}$

f) $\lim\limits_{x \to 0} \dfrac{\sin 3x}{x}$

g) $\lim\limits_{x \to 0} \dfrac{\sin 3x}{4x}$

h) $\lim\limits_{x \to 0} \dfrac{\sin 5x}{2x}$

2. Evaluate each limit, if it exists.

a) $\lim\limits_{x \to 0} \dfrac{\tan 5x}{2x}$

b) $\lim\limits_{x \to 0} \dfrac{\sin^2 3x}{4x}$

c) $\lim\limits_{x \to 0} \dfrac{\sin^2 3x}{4x^2}$

d) $\lim\limits_{x \to 0} \dfrac{\sin^2 3x}{4x^3}$

e) $\lim\limits_{x \to 0} \dfrac{\cos x - 1}{x}$

f) $\lim\limits_{x \to 0} \dfrac{\cos x - 1}{\sin x}$

g) $\lim\limits_{x \to 0} \dfrac{\cos^2 x - 1}{x^2}$

h) $\lim\limits_{x \to 0} \dfrac{5 \tan x - \sin x}{x \cos x}$

i) $\lim\limits_{x \to 0} \dfrac{1 - \cos x}{\tan x}$

Apply, Solve, Communicate

3. Communication **a)** Use a calculator to approximate the value of $\dfrac{\tan x - x}{x^3}$ for $x = 0.1$, $x = 0.01$, $x = 0.001$, and $x = 0.0001$.
b) Use the results of part a) to estimate the value of $\lim\limits_{x \to 0} \dfrac{\tan x - x}{x^3}$.
c) Use a calculator to approximate the value of $\dfrac{\tan x - x}{x^3}$ for $x = 0.000\,01$, $0.000\,001$, and $0.000\,000\,1$. Explain why this result is not consistent with the result of part b).

4. Communication **a)** Evaluate $\lim\limits_{x \to 0} \dfrac{\tan 6x}{2x}$.
b) Describe how you evaluated the limit in part a).

5. Application **a)** Evaluate $\lim\limits_{x \to 0} \dfrac{\cos 2x - 1}{x^2}$.
b) Describe how you evaluated the limit in part a).

6. Thinking/Inquiry/Problem Solving Evaluate $\lim\limits_{h \to 0} \dfrac{\sin(a + h) - \sin a}{h}$.

7. Thinking/Inquiry/Problem Solving Evaluate $\lim\limits_{h \to 0} \dfrac{\cos(a + h) - \cos a}{h}$.

8. Application Does $\lim\limits_{x \to 0} \dfrac{\sin x}{|x|}$ exist? If so, what is it? If not, why not?

9. Thinking/Inquiry/Problem Solving Evaluate $\lim\limits_{x \to 0} \dfrac{\sin(\cos x)}{\dfrac{1}{\cos x}}$.

C **10.** Determine the value of each limit, if it exists.

a) $\lim\limits_{x \to 0} \dfrac{\cos x - 1}{x^2}$

b) $\lim\limits_{x \to \infty} x \sin\left(\dfrac{1}{x}\right)$

c) $\lim\limits_{x \to 0} \dfrac{\sin(\tan x)}{\sin x}$

11. Determine each limit.

a) $\lim\limits_{x \to 0} \dfrac{\sin 5x}{\sin 2x}$

b) $\lim\limits_{x \to 0} \dfrac{\sin^2 5x}{\sin^2 2x}$

c) $\lim\limits_{x \to 0} \dfrac{\sin^2 3x}{\sin 4x}$

d) $\lim\limits_{x \to 0} \dfrac{\sin 3x}{\tan 4x}$

e) $\lim\limits_{x \to 0} \dfrac{\sin^2 3x}{\tan^2 4x}$

f) $\lim\limits_{x \to 0} \dfrac{\tan 3x}{\tan 4x}$

8.4 Derivatives of the Sine, Cosine, and Tangent Functions

In this section, we develop the derivatives of the sine, cosine, and tangent functions.

Investigate & Inquire: Path of the Shadow of a Ball Moving in a Circle

A small ball is attached to a string 1 m long. The ball is swung around counterclockwise in a vertical circle at a constant rate of one radian per second.

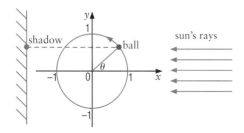

Sunlight from the right of the diagram shines on the ball and casts a shadow on a vertical screen that is several metres to the left of the y-axis. The shadow's motion on the screen is parallel to the y-axis and between $y = -1$ and $y = 1$. The sun's rays are parallel to the x-axis, so the position of the shadow has the same y-value as that of the ball at every time.

When the ball is at the point $(1, 0)$, a stopwatch starts timing the motion. Let t represent the time reading on the stopwatch and let (x, y) represent the position of the ball. Note that t is measured in seconds, and x and y are measured in metres.

1. Let θ be the angle between the string attaching the ball to the origin and the x-axis. Given that the rate at which the ball revolves is 1 rad/s, determine a relation between θ and t.

2. Use the diagram to express the x- and y-coordinates of the position of the ball in terms of θ.

3. Express the x- and y-coordinates of the position of the ball in terms of t.

4. In your notebook, sketch one cycle of the graph of the function $y(t)$ obtained in Step 3. Leave room on your page for one of the same size under it that you will sketch in Step 9. Although y represents the position of the ball, in this investigation focus your attention on the fact that y is also the position of the shadow. Thus, the graph of $y(t)$ is the position function of the shadow for the first 2π seconds of the motion. Conjecture a formula for $y(t)$.

5. From the discussions about rates of change in Chapter 3, we know that the rate of change of the position of an object is its velocity. We can estimate the velocity of the shadow by finding the limits of average rates of change. For example, to estimate the velocity $v\left(\frac{\pi}{6}\right)$ of the shadow at $t = \frac{\pi}{6}$, copy and complete the table.

t	Δt	$y(t)$	$y(t + \Delta t)$	$\Delta y = y(t + \Delta t) - y(t)$	$v = \dfrac{\Delta y}{\Delta t}$
$\dfrac{\pi}{6}$	0.2				
$\dfrac{\pi}{6}$	0.1				
$\dfrac{\pi}{6}$	0.05				
$\dfrac{\pi}{6}$	0.01				
$\dfrac{\pi}{6}$	0.001				
$\dfrac{\pi}{6}$	0.0001				

6. From the table in step 5, estimate the velocity of the shadow at $t = \dfrac{\pi}{6}$.

7. Using the same method as in steps 5 and 6, estimate the velocity of the shadow at the following values of t: $0, \dfrac{\pi}{4}, \dfrac{\pi}{3}, \dfrac{\pi}{2}, \pi, \dfrac{3\pi}{2}$, and 2π.

8. Some of the velocities estimated in step 7 are positive and some are negative. Explain what the sign of the velocity means.

9. Using the data generated in steps 7 and 8, plot a graph of velocity vs. time for the shadow. Place it directly beneath the graph drawn in step 4, so that the corresponding t-values for each graph are aligned. In this way, the position of the shadow at a particular time is given in the upper graph, and the velocity at the same time is given directly below it in the lower graph.

10. Conjecture a formula for the velocity function.

11. Is the velocity zero when the shadow is smallest, or when the shadow is largest? Explain.

12. Use the results of the investigation to conjecture a derivative formula for a trigonometric function.

Another way to discover the derivative function is with the aid of technology. Enter $y = \sin x$ on a graphing calculator as Y1. Now use the nDeriv function of the calculator as follows. Graph the two functions.

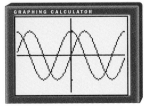

Window variables:
$x \in [-2\pi, 2\pi]$, $y \in [-1.5, 1.5]$

It appears that the derivative of the sine function is the cosine function.

Conjecture: $\dfrac{d}{dx}(\sin x) = \cos x$

The algebraic argument that follows verifies this conjecture, and makes use of the definition of the derivative, the addition formula for sine, and the basic trigonometric limits.

If $f(x) = \sin x$, then, by the definition of the derivative,

$$f'(x) = \lim_{h \to 0} \frac{f(x+h) - f(x)}{h}$$

$$= \lim_{h \to 0} \frac{\sin(x+h) - \sin x}{h}$$

Expand using the addition formula for sine: $f'(x) = \lim_{h \to 0} \dfrac{(\sin x \cos h + \cos x \sin h) - \sin x}{h}$

Rearrange and look for basic limits: $f'(x) = \lim_{h \to 0} \dfrac{(\sin x \cos h - \sin x) + \cos x \sin h}{h}$

$$= \lim_{h \to 0} \frac{\sin x(\cos h - 1) + \cos x \sin h}{h}$$

$$= \lim_{h \to 0} \left(\sin x \, \frac{\cos h - 1}{h} + \cos x \, \frac{\sin h}{h} \right)$$

$$= \sin x \lim_{h \to 0} \frac{\cos h - 1}{h} + \cos x \lim_{h \to 0} \frac{\sin h}{h}$$

Since h varies but x is fixed in the limiting process, $\sin x$ and $\cos x$ can be factored to the left of the limit signs.

Since $\lim\limits_{h \to 0} \dfrac{\cos h - 1}{h} = 0$ and $\lim\limits_{h \to 0} \dfrac{\sin h}{h} = 1$, as determined in Section 8.3,

$$f'(x) = \sin x \times 0 + \cos x \times (1)$$
$$= \cos x$$

Remember that, since the fundamental limit $\lim\limits_{h \to 0} \dfrac{\sin h}{h} = 1$ is valid only if the angle h is measured in radians, the derivative formula just derived is valid only if the angles are measured in radians.

$$\frac{d}{dx}(\sin x) = \cos x \text{ (for } x \text{ measured in radians)}$$

The derivative of the cosine function can be obtained using the Pythagorean trigonometric identity and differentiating implicitly.

$$\sin^2 x + \cos^2 x = 1$$

Differentiating implicitly with respect to x and using the chain rule, we get

$$2 \sin x \times \frac{d}{dx}(\sin x) + 2 \cos x \times \frac{d}{dx}(\cos x) = 0$$

$$2 \sin x \cos x + 2 \cos x \frac{d}{dx}(\cos x) = 0$$

$$\frac{d}{dx}(\cos x) = \frac{-2 \sin x \cos x}{2 \cos x}$$

$$= -\sin x$$

$$\frac{d}{dx}(\cos x) = -\sin x \text{ (for } x \text{ measured in radians)}$$

The derivative of the tangent function can be found by expressing $\tan x$ in terms of $\sin x$ and $\cos x$ and using the quotient rule to differentiate.

$$y = \tan x$$

$$= \frac{\sin x}{\cos x}$$

$$\frac{dy}{dx} = \frac{\cos x \, \frac{d}{dx}(\sin x) - \sin x \, \frac{d}{dx}(\cos x)}{\cos^2 x}$$

$$= \frac{\cos x(\cos x) - \sin x(-\sin x)}{\cos^2 x}$$

$$= \frac{\cos^2 x + \sin^2 x}{\cos^2 x}$$

$$= \frac{1}{\cos^2 x}$$

$$= \sec^2 x$$

$$\frac{d}{dx}(\tan x) = \sec^2 x$$

Web Connection

For an animated development of the trigonometric derivatives, go to
www.mcgrawhill.ca/links/CAF12
and follow the links.

Example 1 Derivatives of Trigonometric Functions

Differentiate.
a) $y = 2 \sin (3x + 4)$ b) $y = \cos^3 (4x^2 - 7)$ c) $y = 2 \sin x \cos x$

Solution

a) Using the chain rule, we have
$$\frac{dy}{dx} = 2 \cos(3x + 4) \, \frac{d}{dx}(3x + 4)$$
$$= 6 \cos(3x + 4)$$

b) Using the chain rule repeatedly, we get
$$\frac{dy}{dx} = 3 \cos^2(4x^2 - 7) \, \frac{d}{dx}[\cos(4x^2 - 7)]$$

$$= 3 \cos^2(4x^2 - 7)[-\sin(4x^2 - 7)] \, \frac{d}{dx}(4x^2 - 7)$$

$$= 3 \cos^2(4x^2 - 7)[-\sin(4x^2 - 7)](8x)$$

$$= -24x \cos^2(4x^2 - 7) \sin(4x^2 - 7)$$

c) **Solution 1** Use the Double-Angle Formula
Recognizing the pattern of the double-angle formula, we have
$$y = 2 \sin x \cos x$$
$$= \sin 2x$$

Using the chain rule, we get
$$y' = (\cos 2x)(2)$$
$$= 2 \cos 2x$$

Solution 2 Use the Product Rule

Using the product rule with $f(x) = 2 \sin x$ and $g(x) = \cos x$, we get
$$y = f(x) g(x)$$
$$y' = g(x) f'(x) + f(x) g'(x)$$
$$= \cos x\ (2 \cos x) + 2 \sin x\ (-\sin x)$$
$$= 2\ (\cos^2 x - \sin^2 x)$$
$$= 2 \cos 2x$$

Example 2 Derivatives of More Complicated Trigonometric Functions

a) Show that $\dfrac{d}{dx}(3 \ln(\tan x) - e^{\sin^2 x}) = \dfrac{3 \sec^2 x}{\tan x} - e^{\sin^2 x} \sin 2x.$

b) Show that if $y = \dfrac{x}{\tan x}$, then $y' = \cot x - x \csc^2 x.$

Solution

a) Use the chain rule on the composite functions.

Let $y = 3 \ln(\tan x) - e^{\sin^2 x}$.
$$\frac{dy}{dx} = \frac{3}{\tan x}\frac{d}{dx}(\tan x) - e^{\sin^2 x}\frac{d}{dx}(\sin^2 x)$$
$$= \frac{3}{\tan x}(\sec^2 x) - (e^{\sin^2 x})2 \sin x \frac{d}{dx}(\sin x)$$
$$= \frac{3 \sec^2 x}{\tan x} - (e^{\sin^2 x})2 \sin x \cos x$$
$$= \frac{3 \sec^2 x}{\tan x} - e^{\sin^2 x} \sin 2x$$

b) **Solution 1** Paper and Pencil Method

Using the quotient rule with $f(x) = x$ and $g(x) = \tan x$, we get
$$y = \frac{x}{\tan x}$$
$$y' = \frac{gf' - fg'}{g^2}$$
$$= \frac{\tan x(1) - x(\sec^2 x)}{\tan^2 x}$$
$$= \frac{\tan x - x \sec^2 x}{\tan^2 x}$$

Rewriting as two fractions, and expressing in terms of sine and cosine, we get
$$y' = \frac{\tan x}{\tan^2 x} - x\left(\frac{\sec^2 x}{\tan^2 x}\right)$$
$$= \frac{1}{\tan x} - x\left(\frac{\dfrac{1}{\cos^2 x}}{\dfrac{\sin^2 x}{\cos^2 x}}\right)$$
$$= \cot x - x\left(\frac{1}{\sin^2 x}\right)$$
$$= \cot x - x \csc^2 x$$

Solution 2 Computer Algebra Method

We use a computer algebra system to find the derivative.

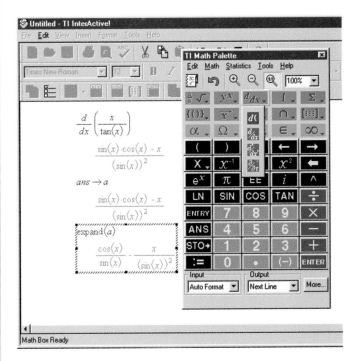

First we determine the derivative, and then store it in variable a. Since the solution is not yet in the format asked for, we expand it. We can see that the first term is equal to $\cot x$ and the second term is equal to $x \csc^2 x$. Thus,

$$y' = \cot x - x \csc^2 x$$

Example 3 Finding Tangents and Local Extrema

For the function $f(x) = 4x - \tan x$ in the interval $\left[-\dfrac{\pi}{2}, \dfrac{\pi}{2}\right]$, find

a) an equation of the tangent at the point where $x = \dfrac{\pi}{4}$

b) the local extrema

Solution

a) $f(x) = 4x - \tan x$
$f'(x) = 4 - \sec^2 x$

The slope of the tangent is $f'\left(\dfrac{\pi}{4}\right)$.

$$f'\left(\frac{\pi}{4}\right) = 4 - \sec^2\left(\frac{\pi}{4}\right)$$

$$= 4 - \frac{1}{\left(\cos\dfrac{\pi}{4}\right)^2}$$

$$= 4 - \frac{1}{\left(\dfrac{1}{\sqrt{2}}\right)^2}$$

$$= 2$$

The point of tangency is

$$\left(\frac{\pi}{4}, f\left(\frac{\pi}{4}\right)\right) = \left(\frac{\pi}{4}, 4\left(\frac{\pi}{4}\right) - \tan\frac{\pi}{4}\right)$$

$$= \left(\frac{\pi}{4}, \pi - 1\right)$$

The equation of the tangent, using the point-slope method, is

$$y - (\pi - 1) = 2\left(x - \frac{\pi}{4}\right)$$

$$y = 2x + \frac{\pi}{2} - 1$$

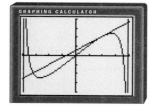

Window variables:

$$x \in \left[-\frac{\pi}{2}, \frac{\pi}{2}\right],$$

$$y \in [-4, 4]$$

b) Determine the x-values for which the derivative is zero or does not exist. The derivative is $f'(x) = 4 - \sec^2 x$.

The x-values for which $\sec^2 x$ does not exist are $-\dfrac{\pi}{2}$ and $\dfrac{\pi}{2}$, but these are asymptotes, not local extrema. Thus, we need determine only the x-values for which the derivative is zero. Setting the derivative equal to zero and solving for x, we get

$$4 - \sec^2 x = 0$$
$$\sec^2 x = 4$$
$$\cos^2 x = \frac{1}{4}$$
$$\cos x = \frac{1}{2} \quad \text{or} \quad \cos x = -\frac{1}{2}$$
$$x = \frac{\pi}{3} \quad \text{or} \quad -\frac{\pi}{3}$$

To test the critical numbers, we use the second derivative test.

$$f'(x) = 4 - \sec^2 x$$
$$= 4 - (\cos x)^{-2}$$

The second derivative is

$$f''(x) = 2(\cos x)^{-3}(-\sin x)$$

$$= \frac{-2\sin x}{\cos^3 x}$$

Substituting the critical numbers into the formula for the second derivative, we get

$$f''\left(\frac{\pi}{3}\right) = \frac{-2\sin\dfrac{\pi}{3}}{\cos^3\dfrac{\pi}{3}} \qquad\qquad f''\left(-\frac{\pi}{3}\right) = \frac{-2\sin\left(-\dfrac{\pi}{3}\right)}{\cos^3\left(-\dfrac{\pi}{3}\right)}$$

$$= \frac{-2\dfrac{\sqrt{3}}{2}}{\left(\dfrac{1}{2}\right)^3} \qquad\qquad\qquad = \frac{2\dfrac{\sqrt{3}}{2}}{\left(\dfrac{1}{2}\right)^3}$$

$$= -8\sqrt{3} < 0 \qquad\qquad\qquad = 8\sqrt{3} > 0$$

There is a local maximum at $x = \dfrac{\pi}{3}$. There is a local minimum at $x = -\dfrac{\pi}{3}$.

The y-coordinates of the local extrema are as follows:

$$f\left(\frac{\pi}{3}\right) = 4\left(\frac{\pi}{3}\right) - \tan\frac{\pi}{3} \qquad\qquad f\left(-\frac{\pi}{3}\right) = 4\left(-\frac{\pi}{3}\right) - \tan\frac{\pi}{3}$$

$$= \frac{4\pi}{3} - \sqrt{3} \qquad\qquad\qquad = -\frac{4\pi}{3} + \sqrt{3}$$

There is a local maximum at $\left(\dfrac{\pi}{3}, \dfrac{4\pi}{3} - \sqrt{3}\right)$ and a local minimum at $\left(-\dfrac{\pi}{3}, -\dfrac{4\pi}{3} + \sqrt{3}\right)$.

Key Concepts

- The trigonometric derivative formulas are valid only for *radian measure*.

$$\frac{d}{dx}\sin x = \cos x \qquad \frac{d}{dx}\cos x = -\sin x \qquad \frac{d}{dx}\tan x = \sec^2 x$$

Communicate Your Understanding

1. Why is radian measure used exclusively when dealing with the derivatives of trigonometric functions?

2. Which of the three functions $y = \sin^3 x$, $y = \sin x^3$ and $y = (\sin x)^3$ are identical? How would you differentiate each of these functions?

3. a) Sketch the graph of the cosine function in the domain $x \in [-\pi, \pi]$. Directly below it, sketch the graph of the sine function. Make sure to use the same scale for each graph and to align the y-axes of both graphs.
b) Sketch some tangents on the cosine graph. Measure the slopes of the tangents, and compare the slopes with the corresponding heights of the sine graph (directly below). What conclusion does this support?

4. Given the derivative of the sine function, how is the derivative of the cosine function developed? How is the derivative of the tangent function developed?

5. In Example 3 above, the function $f(x) = 4x - \tan x$ is odd. Explain how this fact can be used to provide a partial verification of the calculations.

Practise

B **1.** Determine the derivative of y with respect to x for each function.

a) $y = \sin(4x + 7)$ b) $y = \sin(x^2 + 3)$

c) $y = \cos(5x + 3)$ d) $y = 3\tan(2x + 3)$

e) $y = \cos(3x^2 - 1)$ f) $y = \tan(5x^2 + 1)$

g) $y = \sin(\cos^2 x)$ h) $y = \sin(\cos x)$

2. Differentiate.

a) $f(x) = \dfrac{\tan x}{x}$ b) $y = x\sin(3x - 2)$

c) $y = x^2 \sin(2x^2 + 5)$ d) $f(x) = \dfrac{\cos x}{x}$

e) $g(x) = x\cos(8x - 17)$

f) $y = x^2 \cos(0.4x^2 + 9)$

g) $y = 5x^2 \tan^3(3x^2 - 1)$

h) $h(x) = 4x^2 \sin^3(6x^2 - 2)$

3. Find the derivative.

a) $y = \sin^3(\cos^2 x)$ b) $f(x) = \cos^4(\sin x^3)$

c) $y = x\cos(\tan x)$ d) $y = \sin(e^x)$

e) $h(x) = \cos(\ln x)$ f) $g(x) = \ln(\sin(e^x))$

g) $y = \sin^2 x + \cos^2 x$ h) $f(x) = \dfrac{\sin x}{1 + \cos x}$

Apply, Solve, Communicate

4. Determine the equation of the tangent to the curve at the given point.

a) $y = x\sin 2x,\ \left(\dfrac{\pi}{4}, \dfrac{\pi}{4}\right)$

b) $y = \cos^2 x,\ \left(\dfrac{\pi}{3}, \dfrac{1}{4}\right)$

c) $y = \dfrac{1}{\tan^2 x},\ \left(\dfrac{\pi}{4}, 1\right)$

5. Determine any extrema.

a) $y = \cos x - \sin x,\ x \in [-\pi, \pi]$

b) $y = \sin^2 x - \sin x,\ x \in [-\pi, \pi]$

c) $y = 2\cos x - \cos 2x,\ x \in \left[\dfrac{\pi}{2}, \dfrac{3\pi}{2}\right]$

d) $y = \dfrac{1}{\cos x} + \tan x,\ x \in \left[-\dfrac{\pi}{2}, \dfrac{\pi}{2}\right]$

6. Determine the points of inflection.

a) $y = 2\cos x + \sin 2x,\ x \in [0, \pi]$

b) $y = 2\sin^2 x - 1,\ x \in [-\pi, \pi]$

c) $y = \sin x - \tan x,\ x \in \left[-\dfrac{\pi}{2}, \dfrac{3\pi}{2}\right]$

7. Communication/Inquiry/Problem Solving Begin with the function $f(x) = \sin x$.

a) Determine the derivative of f. Then, determine the second derivative of f. Continue to find the first eight derivatives of f. Report any pattern that you notice.

b) What is the 87th derivative of f? What is the 138th derivative of f?

c) Develop a formula for the nth derivative of the sine function.

d) Develop a formula for the nth derivative of the cosine function.

C **8.** Application The equation $y'' + k^2 y = 0$ is known as a differential equation, since it involves a function y and its derivatives. This equation is widely used in applications to model physical systems that oscillate. For example, y could represent the voltage in an electrical circuit, or the position of a vibrating airplane wing.

a) Show that the function $y = A\sin kx + B\cos kx$ satisfies the differential equation for all values of the constants A, B, and k.

b) Show that the function $y = C\sin(kx + D)$ satisfies the differential equation for all values of the constants C, D, and k.

9. A line passes through the point $\left(-\sqrt{3}, -\dfrac{\pi}{6}\right)$ and is tangent to the graph of $y = \sin x$ at a point for which $x \in \left[0, \dfrac{\pi}{2}\right]$. Determine the equation of the line.

10. Inquiry/Problem Solving This question explains where the number 0.017… comes from when we use degrees to determine $\lim\limits_{\theta \to 0^+} \dfrac{\sin \theta}{\theta}$. (See the investigation in Section 8.3.) Let the angle A be measured in degrees. Define θ to be the same angle as A, but measured in radians.

a) Express θ in terms of A. Determine $\dfrac{d\theta}{dA}$.

b) Let $y = \sin \theta$. Using the chain rule, and the result of part a), determine $\dfrac{dy}{dA}$. The result is the derivative formula for the sine function that is valid when the angle is measured in degrees.

c) Compare the formula obtained in part b) to the result obtained in Step 1 of the investigation in Section 8.3. Is the formula consistent with this result? What is the exact value of the number 0.017...?

d) Determine the derivative formula for the cosine function if the angle is measured in degrees.

11. a) Sketch the graph of the function $y = \sin |x|$. For which values of x is the function not differentiable?

b) Repeat part a) for the function $y = |\sin x|$.

12. Determine the values of x for which the derivative of the function $f(x) = \cos\left(x + \dfrac{1}{x}\right)$ is 0.

13. Determine $\displaystyle\lim_{h \to 0} \dfrac{\tan\left(\dfrac{\pi}{4} + h\right) - 1}{h}$.

14. a) Find a function whose derivative is $\tan^2 x$.

b) Find a function whose derivative is $\tan x$.

c) Find a function whose derivative is $\sec x$.

Achievement Check

Knowledge/Understanding

Thinking/Inquiry/Problem Solving

Communication

Application

A baseball hit at an angle θ to the horizontal, with initial velocity v_0, has horizontal range, R, in metres, given by $R = \dfrac{v_0^2}{g} \sin (2\theta)$.

The constant $g = 9.8 \text{ m/s}^2$ represents the acceleration due to gravity.

a) Sketch R for an appropriate value of v_0 for $\theta \in \left[0, \dfrac{\pi}{2}\right]$. Is this domain appropriate? Explain.

b) What angle gives the maximum range?

c) What is the maximum range?

Historical Bite: Geometry in Ancient Greece

The word trigonometry comes from the Greek words for triangle, *trigon*, and measurement, *metron*. Geometry was taken very seriously by the ancient Greeks, and Archimedes (287–212 B.C.) is said to have died as a result of concentrating so hard on a geometric problem that he failed to notice that his home city of Syracuse was under Roman attack. The soldier at whom Archimedes snapped, "Do not disturb my circles," lost his temper and killed the mathematician on the spot.

Technology Extension

Using the TI-92 for Trigonometry

A computer algebra system such as the TI-92 can help keep track of all the relationships used in trigonometry.

The double-angle formulas for sine and cosine are derived from the addition formulas. Examples are shown in this screen, using the tExpand function.

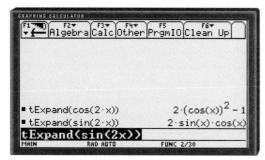

This screen demonstrates some basic relationships that can be derived from the addition and subtraction formulas for sine and cosine. The last is a numerical example of the relationship $\cos(2\pi - \theta)$, where $\theta = \dfrac{\pi}{6}$.

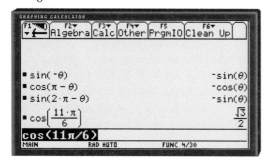

Trigonometric equations can be solved as well, but some care must be taken in interpreting solutions. In this example, a basic equation involving the cosine function is solved using the solve function on the Algebra menu. The result represents two sets of solutions.

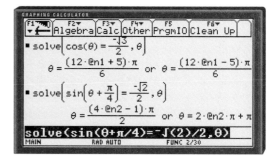

The first set of solutions should be interpreted as $\theta = \dfrac{(12n + 5)\pi}{6}$ and $\theta = \dfrac{(12n - 5)\pi}{6}$. The ampersand and the digit 1 on either side of the variable n indicate that these solutions should be interpreted as all possible solutions in the domain $\theta \in R$. All of the solutions can be obtained by substituting integer values for n. The digit 1 indicates that this is the first trigonometric equation that has been solved in this work session. Similarly, the digit 2 in the second set of solutions indicates that this is the second equation that has been solved. The second set of solutions should be interpreted as $\theta = \dfrac{(4n - 1)\pi}{2}$ and $\theta = 2n\pi + \pi$, or $\theta = (2n + 1)\pi$.

Trigonometric limits can be evaluated easily using a computer algebra system. The two basic limits for trigonometry are shown in the screen below, using the limit function on the Calculus menu.

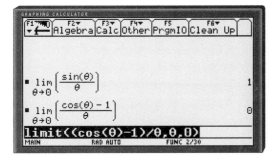

Finally, trigonometric derivatives are shown in this screen. Note how the chain rule has been used to evaluate the derivatives in the second and third expressions, using the differentiate function on the Calculus menu.

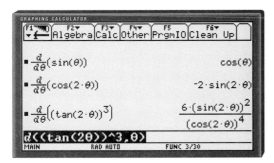

Practise

1. Use a computer algebra system to reduce each expression to a simpler form
   a) $\cos(-\theta)$ b) $\sin(\pi + \theta)$
   c) $\tan(\pi + \theta)$ d) $\sec(2\pi - \theta)$
   e) $\sin(\pi - \theta)$ f) $\csc(2\pi - \theta)$
   g) $\tan(\pi - \theta)$ h) $\cos\left(\dfrac{\pi}{2} - \theta\right)$

2. Determine whether each function is even or odd.
   a) $f(x) = \sin\theta$ b) $f(x) = \cos\theta$
   c) $y = \tan\theta$

3. Solve each equation.
   a) $4\sin^2\theta - 1 = 0$
   b) $2\sin 2\theta + 2\sin\theta = 2\sqrt{3}\cos\theta + \sqrt{3}$
   c) $\sqrt{3}\tan^2\theta + (\sqrt{3} - 1)\tan\theta = 1$
   d) $2\sin 2\theta(\cos\theta - \sin\theta) - 2\cos 2\theta$
      $= \sin\theta - \cos\theta$

4. Evaluate using a computer algebra system.
   a) $\lim_{h \to 0} \dfrac{\sin 2h}{h}$ b) $\lim_{x \to 0} \dfrac{\sin ax}{x}$

   c) $\lim_{x \to \infty} x\sin\dfrac{1}{x}$ d) $\lim_{x \to 1^+} \dfrac{\sin x}{x^2}$

   e) $\lim_{x \to 0} \dfrac{\tan 5x}{\sin 3x}$ f) $\lim_{h \to \infty} \dfrac{\sin h}{1 - \cos h}$

5. Differentiate.
   a) $\cos^2 x$ b) $\sin x^3$
   c) $x^3\tan 2x$ d) $\sin^2 e^x$
   e) $\cos 2x\sin 3x$ f) $\dfrac{\sin 2x}{\cos 3x}$

8.5 Modelling With Trigonometric Functions

The periodic behaviour of sine and cosine functions, which are collectively known as **sinusoidal functions**, makes them well suited for modelling many of the rhythmic phenomena of our world. The rotation of Earth, the motions of the planets around the sun, the seasons, the tides, even some of the rhythms of our bodies are sinusoidal, or nearly so. Trigonometric functions are also used extensively to model oscillating systems and the motion of all kinds of waves: everything from electric circuits to vibrating machinery, and including descriptions of light, sound, music, the distribution of electrons within an atom, and many other situations.

Tidal forces on Earth are due to the gravitational pull of the sun and the moon on Earth. In this investigation, you will determine a formula that models the tides, and then use that formula to calculate the time between successive peak tides. You will use a very simplified model. The actual situation is quite complicated, and depends on many factors, such as the shape of nearby coastlines, the shape of the ocean floor, and the size of the body of water. For example, in most places on Earth there are about two high tides per day, but there is only one high tide per day in the region of Tonkin in Vietnam. Also, the times at which the high tides occur vary from day to day almost everywhere on Earth, but not in Tahiti, an island in the Pacific Ocean, where the high tides occur at the same time every day!

Investigate & Inquire: Modelling the Tides

1. Consider the sun to be fixed. The sun causes the water on Earth to "bulge" in two places: toward the sun at the point on Earth facing the sun, and away from the sun at the point on Earth facing away from the sun. To simplify the calculations, assume that the bulges do not move, and that Earth just rotates through them.

Then, a specific point on Earth will encounter a water bulge every 12 h, as Earth rotates. Assuming that the ocean level is a sinusoidal function of time, write a function of the form $y = \sin kt$, where t is time, in hours, to model the ocean level experienced at a specific point on Earth. The period should be 12 h, since that is the time between peaks. Determine the value of k. (Note that we are assuming that the amplitude of the tides caused by the sun is 1 unit.)

2. Imagine that the moon is overhead right now. Since it orbits Earth, moving in the same direction that Earth rotates, it will take more than 24 h for the moon to be directly overhead again. (When 24 h have passed, the moon will have moved along its orbit a bit, so it will take a little more time before Earth catches up again so that the moon is overhead.)

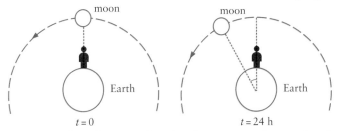

Determine how long it takes for the moon to be overhead again. (It takes 27.3 days for the moon to go around Earth once.)

3. Use the period you found in step 2 to write a sine function that models the tides due to the moon. The amplitude should be 2.2 times greater than the amplitude in the formula for the tides due to the sun. (This ratio will be worked out in Example 1.) Thus, the function should be of the form $y = 2.2 \sin mt$. Determine the value of m.

Web Connection

Go to

www.mcgrawhill.ca/links/CAF12

to obtain daily tide data.

4. Add the two functions found in steps 1 and 3 to obtain a model for the tides. Sketch a graph of the tide-model function over a period of several days.

5. Judging from the graph, is the time interval between high tides roughly constant? What is the period? Does this agree with the observation that there are roughly two high tides per day at most places on Earth?

6. The following data are from Burncoat Head, Nova Scotia, on the Bay of Fundy, which holds the world record for the highest tide. Compare these data with your model by plotting the data points on a scatterplot and superimposing your model on the plot.

Hour	00	01	02	03	04	05	06	07	08	09	10	11
Height (m)	11.6	10.4	8.1	5.5	3.0	1.4	0.8	1.5	3.4	6.2	8.9	11.0

Hour	12	13	14	15	16	17	18	19	20	21	22	23
Height (m)	11.8	11.1	9.2	6.5	3.9	1.8	0.8	0.9	2.3	4.9	7.8	10.3

7. Use **SinReg** on the STAT CALC menu of a graphing calculator to fit a trigonometric regression curve to the data of step 6. Compare the regression curve with the model from step 4. How accurate is the model?

  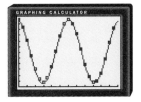

Window variables:
$x \in [0, 24]$,
$y \in [0, 12]$

In step 1 of the investigation, it was assumed that water bulges caused by the sun do not move. However, they will move, since Earth moves around the sun, completing one circuit of its orbit per year. You might like to explore how to modify your formula from the investigation to take this into account.

As mentioned previously, tidal forces on Earth are due to the gravitational pull of the sun and the moon on Earth. More precisely, tidal forces are due to the fact that gravitational forces decrease with distance. Because the sun's pull on the side of Earth facing it is greater than the sun's pull on the side of Earth facing away from it (since it is farther away), Earth tends to be stretched. The moon's pull has the same effect as the sun, and when the directions of the two stretches line up, as when there is a full moon or a new moon, then the tides are especially high.

As an approximation, we can imagine that the water bulges stay in roughly the same place as Earth rotates through them. Since there is a water bulge on each side of Earth, any particular place on Earth encounters a bulge (high tide) twice per day in this approximation. (In reality, high tides are about 12.5 h apart.)

Tidal forces act on the solid part of Earth as well as on the water. As municipal public works departments are well aware, there are more water-main breaks at full moon and new moon than at other times of the month!

Example 1 Comparison of the Tidal Forces Due to the Sun and the Moon

The tidal force is the rate of change of the gravitational force.
a) Determine the tidal forces on Earth due to the sun and the moon.
b) Compare the two forces.

We need the following data.
Mass of sun: 2.0×10^{30} kg
Mass of moon: 7.4×10^{22} kg
Mass of Earth: 5.98×10^{24} kg
Distance between sun and Earth: 1.5×10^{11} m
Distance between moon and Earth: 3.84×10^{8} m
$G = 6.67 \times 10^{-11}$ N m^2/kg^2

The unit of force used here is the newton, N.

Solution

a) The function that describes the gravitational force of the sun on Earth is

$$F(x) = G\frac{Mm}{x^2}$$

where F is the force, G is a constant that makes the units come out conveniently, M is the mass of the sun, m is the mass of Earth, and x is the distance between the sun and Earth.

To determine the tidal force acting on Earth, we differentiate F with respect to x:

$$F'(x) = -2G\frac{Mm}{x^3}$$

For the gravitational force of the moon on Earth, the same formula works provided that M is the mass of the moon, and x is the distance between Earth and the moon.

Hence, the tidal force acting on Earth due to the moon is

$$F'(x) = -2G\frac{M_{\text{moon}}m}{x_{\text{moon}}^3}$$

b) To compare the relative strengths of the tidal forces, we can ignore the minus sign, since it tells us only about the direction of the forces. Substituting the values for the sun and Earth gives

$$\text{Tidal force of the sun on Earth} = \frac{2(6.67 \times 10^{-11})(2.0 \times 10^{30})(5.98 \times 10^{24})}{(1.5 \times 10^{11})^3}$$

$$= 4.7 \times 10^{11}$$

Similarly, substituting the values for the moon and Earth gives

$$\text{Tidal force of the moon on Earth} = \frac{2(6.67 \times 10^{-11})(7.4 \times 10^{22})(5.98 \times 10^{24})}{(3.84 \times 10^8)^3}$$

$$= 1.0 \times 10^{12}$$

The ratio of the two expressions (without simplifying first) is about 2.2. Thus, the tidal force exerted by the moon is more than twice as big as the tidal force exerted by the sun.

Is the result of the preceding example surprising? The fact that the *tidal* force of the moon on Earth is greater than that of the sun on Earth is interesting, especially in light of the fact that the *gravitational* force of the moon on Earth is much smaller than the gravitational force of the sun on Earth. You can determine the ratio of the gravitational forces in question 1 on page 529.

If the sun, Earth, and the moon did not move relative to each other, and Earth did not rotate, then the tides would be constant. However, they do move, and so the tides go in and out.

An object hung from a car's rearview mirror starts to swing when the car picks up speed or slows down, but stays steady if the car has been going at a constant speed in the same direction for a while. This motion is the subject of the following example.

Example 2 Pendulum Swinging in a Moving Car

a) A car accelerates in a straight line at 1.4 m/s². Determine the angle θ that a pendulum hanging from the rearview mirror makes with respect to a vertical line.
b) If the acceleration of the car begins to increase at the rate of 0.2 m/s³, at what rate does the pendulum's angle increase?

Solution

a) Consider the forces acting on the pendulum bob. Gravity tries to pull the bob (marked B in the diagram) down with a force equal to the weight mg of the bob. (The mass, in kilograms, of the bob is m, and $g = 9.8$ m/s² is a constant that describes the strength of Earth's gravity.)

For simplicity, we assume that the only other force acting on the bob is the tension, T, in the rope. The tension can be broken up into two components. The vertical component,

$T \cos \theta$, must balance the weight exactly (since the pendulum does not rise or fall).

$T \cos \theta = mg$

The horizontal component, $T \sin \theta$, provides the acceleration that forces the pendulum to keep up with the car. According to Newton's second law of motion, the force $T \sin \theta$ is equal to the mass of the bob times its acceleration, a. Putting all this together, we get

$T \sin \theta = ma$

Dividing the second equation by the first results in

$\tan \theta = \dfrac{a}{g}$

Substituting the given data gives us

$\tan \theta = \dfrac{1.4}{9.8}$

$ = \dfrac{1}{7}$

From the diagram of the pendulum, we can see that $\theta \in \left[0, \dfrac{\pi}{2}\right]$.

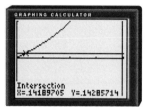

Window variables:

$x \in \left[0, \dfrac{\pi}{2}\right]$, $y \in [-1, 1]$

Thus, $\theta \doteq 0.1419$ rad (or approximately 8°).

b) We need to find $\dfrac{d\theta}{dt}$. Differentiating $\tan \theta = \dfrac{a}{g}$ implicitly with respect to time, we get

$\tan \theta = \dfrac{a}{g}$

$\sec^2 \theta \dfrac{d\theta}{dt} = \dfrac{1}{g} \dfrac{da}{dt}$ \qquad Note that g is a constant.

$\dfrac{d\theta}{dt} = \dfrac{1}{g \sec^2 \theta} \dfrac{da}{dt}$

Substituting $g = 9.8$, $\theta = 0.1419$, and $\dfrac{da}{dt} = 0.2$, we get

$\dfrac{d\theta}{dt} = \left(\dfrac{1}{9.8 \sec^2 0.1419} \right)(0.2)$

$\phantom{\dfrac{d\theta}{dt}} \doteq 0.02$

The angle changes at a rate of approximately 0.02 rad/s.
Converting to degrees, we obtain

$\dfrac{d\theta}{dt} = 0.02 \left(\dfrac{180}{\pi} \right)$

$\phantom{\dfrac{d\theta}{dt}} \doteq 1.15$

The angle changes at a rate of approximately 1.15°/s.

In reality, accelerations are rarely smooth. If you try this yourself (while someone else is driving!), the pendulum will probably start swinging wildly after a short time. Note that the results of the example do not depend on the length of the pendulum.

Example 3 Maximum Area of a Triangle Inscribed in a Quarter-Circle

In computer geometry programs, points may be animated along an arc of a circle. In the figures, the point A on a quarter-circle of radius $10\sqrt{2}$ can be dragged or animated along the arc. The inscribed right triangle changes as A moves along the arc. What is the maximum area of the right triangle?

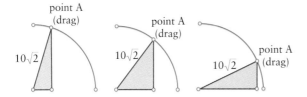

Solution 1 Use Calculus

We let θ represent one of the acute angles in the triangle. Then, the unknown sides of the triangle are $10\sqrt{2}\,\sin\theta$ and $10\sqrt{2}\,\cos\theta$. The area of the triangle is

$$A = \left(\frac{1}{2}\right)(10\sqrt{2}\,\sin\theta)(10\sqrt{2}\,\cos\theta)$$

$$= 100\sin\theta\cos\theta$$
$$= 50\sin 2\theta \qquad \text{(double-angle formula)}$$

The maximum area occurs when $\dfrac{dA}{d\theta} = 0$.

$$\frac{dA}{d\theta} = 100\cos 2\theta$$
$$0 = 100\cos 2\theta$$
$$0 = \cos 2\theta$$

Since θ is acute, $\theta \in \left[0, \dfrac{\pi}{2}\right]$. Thus, $2\theta \in [0, \pi]$.

$$2\theta = \frac{\pi}{2}$$

$$\theta = \frac{\pi}{4}$$

Substituting this value into the formula for A gives the maximum area.

$$A = 50\sin 2\theta$$
$$= 50\sin 2\left(\frac{\pi}{4}\right)$$
$$= 50$$

We verify that this is a maximum using the second derivative test.

$$A'' = -200 \sin 2\theta$$

$$A''\left(\frac{\pi}{4}\right) = -200 \sin \frac{\pi}{2}$$

$$= -200 < 0$$

Thus, $\theta = \frac{\pi}{4}$ gives the maximum area of 50.

Solution 2 Use Trigonometry

As in Solution 1, the area of the triangle is $A = 50 \sin 2\theta$.

The maximum value of any sine function is equal to its amplitude. Thus, the maximum value of the area of the triangle is 50.

Example 4 Teaching a Child to Catch

Grace is tossing a ball to her young nephew, who insists on standing 3 m away. At what angle should she throw the ball so that it arrives with minimum speed?

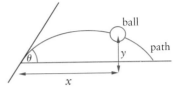

The path of the ball is given by

$$y = (\tan \theta)x - \left(\frac{g}{2v_0^2 \cos^2 \theta}\right)x^2$$

where θ is the angle from the horizontal that the ball is tossed, g is the acceleration due to gravity, v_0 is the initial speed with which the ball is thrown, x is the horizontal position of the ball, and y is the vertical position. Assume that the ball is caught at the same height from which it is thrown, and label this height $y = 0$. All distances are in metres.

Solution

We need an expression for the final speed, v, in terms of θ. The path of the ball, $y = f(x)$, is a quadratic function, with vertex halfway between Grace and her nephew. By symmetry, the final speed v equals the initial speed v_0, provided that there is no air resistance. Thus,

$$y = (\tan \theta)x - \left(\frac{g}{2v^2 \cos^2 \theta}\right)x^2$$

We know that at the arrival point (the nephew), $y = 0$ and $x = 3$, so we can substitute these values and solve for v.

$$0 = 3 \tan \theta - \frac{3^2 g}{2v^2 \cos^2 \theta}$$

$$\frac{9g}{2v^2 \cos^2 \theta} = 3 \tan \theta$$

$$v^2 = \frac{3g}{2 \sin \theta \cos \theta}$$

$$= \frac{3g}{\sin 2\theta}$$

We can find the minimum speed using calculus, as in Solution 1 of Example 3 on page 527, but it is often simpler in problems like this to use basic trigonometry.

$$v^2 = \frac{3g}{\sin 2\theta}$$

$$v = \sqrt{\frac{3g}{\sin 2\theta}}$$

The minimum speed occurs when $\sin 2\theta$ is a maximum. The maximum value for any sine function is equal to its amplitude. Thus, the minimum speed occurs when $\sin 2\theta = 1$.

$$\sin 2\theta = 1$$

$$2\theta = \frac{\pi}{2}$$

$$\theta = \frac{\pi}{4}$$

The minimum catching speed for her nephew occurs when Grace throws the ball at an angle of $\frac{\pi}{4}$ radians.

Key Concepts

- Sine and cosine functions are also called sinusoidal functions.
- Periodic behaviour can often be modelled by sinusoidal functions.

Communicate Your Understanding

1. What is a sinusoidal function? For what kinds of phenomena are sinusoidal functions useful models?
2. Most of the applications studied in this section have models based on sine or cosine functions. Why do you think the tangent function did not appear very much?
3. For a swinging pendulum, explain what angular speed means.

Apply, Solve, Communicate

B 1. Application The gravitational force between a body and Earth is given by

$$F(x) = G\frac{Mm}{x^2}$$

where F is the force, G is a constant, M is the mass of the body, m is the mass of Earth, and x is the distance between the body and Earth. The following data are relevant:
Mass of the sun: 2.0×10^{30} kg
Mass of the moon: 7.4×10^{22} kg

Mass of Earth: 5.98×10^{24} kg
Distance between sun and Earth: 1.5×10^{11} m
Distance between moon and Earth: 3.84×10^8 m
$G = 6.67 \times 10^{-11}$ N m^2/kg^2
a) Determine the gravitational force that the sun exerts on Earth.
b) Determine the gravitational force that the moon exerts on Earth.
c) Determine the ratio of the quantity in part a) to the quantity in part b).
d) Compare the result of part c) to the result of Example 1 (pages 524–525).

2. Inquiry/Problem Solving Consider the tidal forces acting on a futuristic spacecraft with mass 10^4 kg, at the surface of a star. Assume that the spacecraft has a shield that can withstand the intense heat at the surface of the star.
a) How great would the sun's tidal force on the spacecraft be if it were at the sun's surface? (The radius of the sun is about 7×10^8 m.)
b) Repeat part a) for a white dwarf star that has the same mass as the sun, but has a radius of only 10^6 m.
c) Repeat part a) for a neutron star that has the same mass as the sun, but has a radius of only 10^4 m.

3. Communication A right triangle has a hypotenuse of $10\sqrt{2}$ cm.
a) To determine the maximum area of such a triangle, let x represent the length of one of the unknown sides of the triangle. Use the Pythagorean theorem to determine a formula, in terms of x, for the length of the other unknown side of the triangle. Then, determine the expression for the area of the triangle and find its maximum value.
b) Compare this method of solution to the method of Example 3. Which do you prefer? Explain.

4. Application Two sides of a triangle have lengths 15 m and 20 m. The angle between them is increasing at a rate of $\dfrac{\pi}{90}$ rad/s. At what rate is the length of the third side changing when the angle between the other two sides is $\dfrac{\pi}{3}$?

5. The position, x, of the midpoint of a vibrating violin string is described by the formula $x = 0.05 \cos(880\,\pi t)$, where x is measured in centimetres and t is measured in seconds.
a) Determine formulas for the velocity and acceleration of the midpoint of the string.
b) Determine the maximum speed of vibration of the string, in centimetres per second.
c) Show that the acceleration and position satisfy the differential equation
$$\dfrac{d^2x}{dt^2} + (880\pi)^2\, x = 0.$$

6. A piston in a car engine moves up and down because its shaft is attached to a crank that moves in a circle at a constant rate, as shown in the diagram.

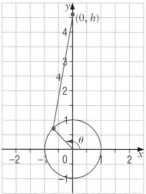

a) Determine a formula for h in terms of θ.
b) Determine a formula for the velocity of the piston in terms of the rotational velocity of the crank, $\dfrac{d\theta}{dt}$.
c) For which angles is the piston speed zero?
d) For which angles is the piston speed a maximum?

7. Inquiry/Problem Solving The electricity flowing through the wires in your home is alternating current (AC). The word "alternating" means that the electricity changes direction. A simplified model of the current is $V = 120 \cos 120\pi t$, where V is the voltage, in volts, and t is the time, in seconds.
a) How many cycles does the electricity make per second? (That is, what is the frequency of oscillation?)
b) How many times does the electricity change direction per second?
c) The force that pushes the electricity through the wires is called the electric force field, or electric field for short. The value of the electric field is the negative of the derivative of the voltage. Determine a formula for the electric field.
d) When is the electric field at a maximum? What is the value of the voltage at those times?
e) When is the electric field zero? What is the value of the voltage at those times?

8. Determine the maximum perimeter of a right triangle with hypotenuse $10\sqrt{2}$ cm.

9. Application A weather balloon rises straight up in the air, starting from the ground at point A. An observer located at point B, 1 km from A, is tracking the balloon with a telescope. The angle between the telescope's line of sight and the ground is θ. The balloon rises at a constant speed of 10 km/h.
a) Determine a formula for θ in terms of time t.
b) Determine the rate at which θ is changing when $\theta = \dfrac{\pi}{6}$.

10. An isosceles triangle is inscribed in a circle of radius r. Determine the angle θ for which the area of the triangle is a maximum.

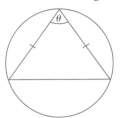

11. Inquiry/Problem Solving a) A projectile thrown over level ground, at an angle θ to the ground, has a range R given by $R = \left(\dfrac{v^2}{g}\right) \sin 2\theta$, where v is the initial speed, in metres per second, and $g = 9.8$ m/s². Determine the angle of projection θ for which the range is a maximum.

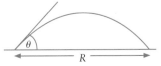

b) If the projectile is thrown over a slope, then the range is $R = \dfrac{2v^2}{g}\left(\dfrac{\sin(\theta - \phi)\cos\theta}{\cos^2\phi}\right)$, where ϕ is the angle that the slope makes with the horizontal.

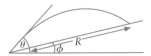

Determine an expression for the angle θ, in terms of the angle ϕ, for which the range is a maximum.

c) Test the result of part b) by substituting the appropriate value of ϕ for the special case of part a). Do you obtain the same result as in part a) in this way?

12. A pendulum is swinging back and forth. The angle θ that the pendulum's string makes with a vertical line can be modelled by the function $\theta = 0.15 \cos 6t$. Determine the maximum angular speed $\dfrac{d\theta}{dt}$ and the maximum angular acceleration $\dfrac{d^2\theta}{dt^2}$ of the pendulum.

B **13.** A rising weather balloon is being tracked with a telescope by an observer 1 km away from the point at which the balloon was launched. The balloon has a component of velocity of 10 km/h upward, and a light breeze causes the balloon to have a horizontal component of velocity of 5 km/h, directly away from the observer. The angle between the telescope's line of sight and the ground is θ.
a) Determine a formula for θ in terms of time t.
b) Determine the rate at which θ is changing when $\theta = \dfrac{\pi}{6}$.

14. Communication An isosceles triangle is circumscribed about a circle of radius r.
a) Determine the angle θ between the two equal sides of the triangle for which the area of the triangle is a minimum.
b) Determine the angle θ for which the perimeter of the triangle is a minimum.
c) Compare the results of parts a) and b). Did you expect them to be the same? Explain.

15. A hockey player is rushing down the ice on a path parallel to the boards and 2 m wide of the net. If the width of the net is 2 m, at what point should the player release the puck to maximize the shot angle to the net? (The shot angle is the angle formed by the puck and the two goalposts.)

Sunlight (and most light) has a mixture of colours in it. However, laser light is nearly monochromatic, that is, it contains only one colour. A certain beam of monochromatic light can be described by the function $E = A \cos(kx + wt)$, where E is the electric field in the light beam, A is the amplitude of the electric field, x is the position along the beam of light, t is time, and k and w are constants that characterize the light. Notice that E depends on two variables, x and t.

a) If we could take a "photograph" of the profile of a light beam, the profile would look sinusoidal. This amounts to substituting a particular time into the formula for E. For example, we could substitute $t = 0$ to get $E = A \cos(kx)$. The distance between peaks of this profile is known as the wavelength of the light. If the wavelength of this light is 6×10^{-7} m, determine the value of k.

b) Sketch a graph of the function of part a) for two periods of oscillation.

c) Instead of taking a "photograph" of the profile, we could focus on a particular location on the x-axis (such as $x = 0$), and measure E as the light wave passes by. Again we would get a sinusoidal variation in the value of the electric field $E = A \cos(wt)$. The distance between peaks of this graph is known as the period of the light, and the reciprocal of the period is known as the frequency of the light. If the frequency of this light beam is 5×10^{14} oscillations per second, determine the period. Also determine the value of w, which is known as the angular frequency.

d) Sketch the graph of the function of part c) for two periods of oscillation.

e) Do some research on light to find out what colour of light is being dealt with in this exercise. Report on and justify your findings.

f) Determine the product of the wavelength and the frequency of this light beam. What are the units of this quantity? What does this quantity have to do with the light beam?

g) Is the light beam travelling to the left or to the right along the x-axis?

In Leamington, Ontario, the number of daylight hours in a day, S, is about 15 h on the longest day of the year, and about 9 h on the shortest day of the year, where S represents the length of time between sunrise and sunset.

How well can this phenomenon be modelled using trigonometric functions? Use the following questions to guide your investigation, and create a summary report.

1. Construct a formula for S, assuming that it can be modelled by a sinusoidal function of time.

2. On which days of the year is the magnitude of the rate of change of S a maximum?

3. How does the fact that a year is a little longer than 365 days affect the validity of the model in the long run?

4. Use data for sunrise and sunset to test the model that you have constructed. How good is your model?

Web Connection

To find sunrise and sunset data, go to **www.mcgrawhill.ca/links/CAF12** and follow the links.

5. How is the amplitude of the modelling function affected by a change in latitude? (Note that, above the Arctic circle, the longest day of the year is 24 h long.) Modify your formula to take latitude into account. Test your formula using sunrise and sunset data for places with various latitudes. How good is your model?

6. Are there any other factors that would have an effect on the formula?

8.1 Addition and Subtraction Formulas

Refer to the Key Concepts on page 496.

1. Express as a single trigonometric function. Then, evaluate.
a) $\sin 64° \cos 4° - \cos 64° \sin 4°$
b) $\sin 32° \cos 13° + \cos 32° \sin 13°$
c) $\cos 45° \cos 15° - \sin 45° \sin 15°$
d) $\cos 45° \cos 15° + \sin 45° \sin 15°$
e) $\dfrac{\tan 35° + \tan 10°}{1 - \tan 35° \tan 10°}$

8.2 Double-Angle Formulas

Refer to the Key Concepts on page 502.

2. Express as a single sine or cosine function.
a) $50 \sin x \cos x$ b) $15 \sin 3x \cos 3x$
c) $2\cos^2(3\theta + 2) - 1$ d) $8 \sin \dfrac{x}{2} \cos \dfrac{x}{2}$
e) $\cos^2 2x - \sin^2 2x$ f) $2\cos^2 10\theta - 1$
g) $1 - 2\sin^2 \dfrac{2\theta}{5}$ h) $\sin 7x \cos 7x$

3. Solve for x where $x \in [0, 2\pi]$.
a) $\sin 3 \cos x + \cos 3 \sin x = 0.5$
b) $\cos x \cos \pi - \sin x \sin \pi = 0$
c) $\cos 2x \cos x - \sin 2x \sin x = 0$
d) $\sin 2x \cos x + \cos 2x \sin x = 1$
e) $\sin x \cos x = -1 - \cos x \sin x$
f) $\dfrac{\tan x - \tan \dfrac{\pi}{2}}{1 + \tan x \tan \dfrac{\pi}{2}} = 1$
g) $3 \sin 2x \cos x + 3 \sin^2 x = 0$
h) $\sin 2x - \sin x = 0$
i) $\sin x - \cos x = 0$
j) $3 \cos 2x + 2 = 0$
k) $\sin 2x - \tan x = 0$
l) $\sin 2x - \cos 2x = 0$
m) $2 \sin 2x = \cos x$
n) $3 \sin x = 2 - \cos 2x$

4. Suppose that $x \in \left(0, \dfrac{\pi}{2}\right)$, $y \in \left(\dfrac{\pi}{2}, \pi\right)$,

$\sin x = \dfrac{3}{5}$, and $\tan y = -\dfrac{3}{4}$. Determine the value of each of the following.
a) $\sin 2(x - y)$ b) $\cos 2(x + y)$
c) $\tan 2(x - y)$ d) $\sin 2x + \cos 2x$

5. Marion estimates that the angle of elevation to the edge of an 11 m cliff is half the angle of elevation to the top of the 13 m tree that is on the edge of the cliff. How far away from the base of the cliff is Marion standing?

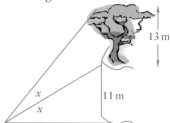

6. Determine the value of $\sin 2(x - y)$, if $\sin x = \dfrac{5}{13}$, $x \in \left[0, \dfrac{\pi}{2}\right]$, $\cos y = -\dfrac{4}{5}$, and $y \in \left[\dfrac{\pi}{2}, \pi\right]$.

8.3 Limits of Trigonometric Functions

Refer to the Key Concepts on page 508.

7. Determine each limit.
a) $\lim\limits_{x \to 0} \dfrac{\sin 3x}{4x}$ b) $\lim\limits_{x \to 0} \dfrac{\sin \dfrac{1}{2} x}{x}$
c) $\lim\limits_{x \to 0} \dfrac{\sin x \cos x}{x}$ d) $\lim\limits_{x \to 0} 2 \dfrac{\tan^2 x}{x^2}$
e) $\lim\limits_{x \to 0} \dfrac{\tan x - x}{x^2}$

8.4 Derivatives of the Sine, Cosine, and Tangent Functions

Refer to the Key Concepts on page 517.

8. Determine the derivative of y with respect to x for each function.
a) $y = \sin(3x^2 + 5)$ b) $y = 4x^3 \sin^2(6x^2 - 2)$
c) $y = x^2 \cos(4x^2 + 7)$ d) $y = \sin^2(\cos^3 x + \tan x)$
e) $y = \sin^3(\cos x^3)$ f) $y = \cos(e^x)$
g) $y = \cos(\ln(\tan x))$ h) $y = \ln(\sin(e^x))$
i) $y = \dfrac{(\sin x)}{x}$ j) $y = \sin^2 x + \cos^2 x$

9. Determine the points of inflection and the local maximum and minimum values of the function $y = 2 \sin x + \sin^2 x$ in the domain $[0, 2\pi]$.

10. Determine the equation of the line that is tangent to the graph of $y = 2 \sin x + \sin^2 x$ at the point $\left(\dfrac{\pi}{6}, \dfrac{5}{4}\right)$.

8.5 Modelling With Trigonometric Functions

Refer to the Key Concepts on page 529.

11. A pulsar, thought to be a rapidly spinning neutron star, emits pulses of "light," in somewhat the same way that a lighthouse emits light. (The "light" emitted could be some combination of light, radio waves, X-rays, etc.) One of the most famous pulsars is the power source for the Crab nebula. This pulsar has a rotational period of about 0.033 s.

a) Assuming that the rate of rotation of the Crab pulsar is constant, use a sinusoidal function to model the pulses. Assume two pulses per rotation.

b) The actual rate of rotation of the Crab pulsar is decreasing so that it will stop in about 2500 years. Modify the model in part a) to take this new information into account.

c) The Crab pulsar is about 6×10^{16} km from Earth. At what rate does the light from the pulsar "sweep" across the face of Earth?

Web Connection

To learn more about pulsars, go to
www.mcgrawhill.ca/links/CAF12
and follow the links.

12. A trough is made from a sheet of metal 3 m wide by bending up one third of the sheet on each side through an angle θ. What value of θ will maximize the capacity of the trough?

13. Two sides of a triangle have lengths 15 m and 20 m. The angle between them is increasing at a rate of $\dfrac{\pi}{90}$ rad/s. At what rate is the area changing when the angle between the two given sides is $\dfrac{\pi}{3}$?

14. The period of a pendulum is nearly independent of its amplitude and its mass, although it does depend on its length according to the formula $T = 2\pi\sqrt{\dfrac{L}{g}}$, where L is the length of the pendulum, in metres, and $g = 9.8$ m/s^2.

a) For a certain grandfather clock, the period of the pendulum is 1 s. Determine the length of a pendulum that has this period.

b) Is the length found in part a) typical of grandfather clocks? If there is a difference, what do you think is the reason for the difference?

c) Construct a sinusoidal function that models a pendulum that has the period specified in part a).

d) The maximum amplitude of the pendulum occurs when the angle between the pendulum and a vertical line is 30°. Use this information to determine one of the constants in the formula of part c).

e) Determine the maximum angular speed of the pendulum and when it occurs.

f) Determine the maximum angular acceleration of the pendulum and when it occurs.

15. The surface area of one cell of a bee's honeycomb is given by

$$S(\theta) = 6ab + \frac{3}{2}a^2 \left(\frac{\sqrt{3} - \cos\theta}{\sin\theta} \right)$$

where θ is the angle of inclination at the base of the cell, a is the length of a hexagonal side, and b is the average depth of the cell. For a given a and b, determine the angle θ that minimizes the surface area. Note that honey bees actually construct their cells at this angle.

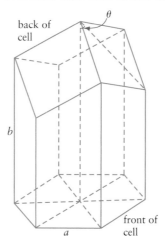

Chapter Test

Achievement Chart

Category	Knowledge/Understanding	Thinking/Inquiry/Problem Solving	Communication	Application
Questions	All	3, 4, 6, 7	3, 7	3, 5, 7

1. Determine each limit.

a) $\lim\limits_{x \to 0} \dfrac{\sin 2x}{\sin x}$ b) $\lim\limits_{x \to 0} \dfrac{\tan 20x}{x}$

2. Determine $\dfrac{dy}{dx}$ and $\dfrac{d^2y}{dx^2}$ in each case.

a) $y = 2 \sin 3x - 3 \cos 4x$ b) $y = \dfrac{\sin x}{1 + \tan x}$

3. The blood pressure of a person at rest is described by the formula $P = 100 + 20 \sin 6t$, where P is the pressure, in millimetres of mercury (mmHg), and t is the time, in seconds.
a) Determine the rate at which the heart beats, in beats per minute, assuming that one complete cycle of the pressure function corresponds to one heartbeat.
b) Determine the maximum and minimum values of the pressure. Are these healthy values for blood pressure?
c) How is the formula for blood pressure likely to change during times of physical exertion or while taking a math test?
d) How is the formula for blood pressure likely to change during times of relaxation or sleep?

4. Determine the values of n for which the nth derivative of the function $f(x) = \sin x + \cos x$ is equal to $f(x)$.

5. The cross section of a trough is an inverted isosceles triangle. Determine the vertex angle for which the capacity of the trough is a maximum if the equal side lengths of the triangle are constant.

6. A circle of radius 1 is centred at the origin O. Lines drawn from a point $(p, 0)$ are tangent to the circle at points A and B.

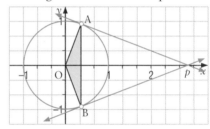

a) Determine the value of p for which the area of $\triangle$OAB is a maximum.
b) Determine the angle between OA and the x-axis for which the area of $\triangle$OAB is a maximum.
c) Determine the maximum area of $\triangle$OAB.

Achievement Check

Knowledge/Understanding

Thinking/Inquiry/Problem Solving

Communication

Application

7. The position function of a particle that moves along the x-axis is $x = 2\pi t + \sin 2\pi t$.
a) Determine a formula for the velocity of the particle.
b) Determine a formula for the acceleration of the particle.
c) When is the particle momentarily at rest?
d) When is the particle moving toward the left? toward the right?
e) When is the velocity of the particle increasing? decreasing?
f) When is the particle speeding up? slowing down?
g) Sketch the graphs of the position function, the velocity function, and the acceleration function for the particle.

Challenge Problems

1. a) Express $4 \sin x + 3 \cos x$ in the form $A \sin (x + \theta)$.
b) Show that it is always possible to write $a \sin x + b \cos x$ in the form $A \sin (x + \theta)$ by determining expressions for A and θ in terms of a and b.

2. a) Express $4 \sin x + 3 \cos x$ in the form $A \cos (x + \theta)$.
b) Show that it is always possible to write $a \sin x + b \cos x$ in the form $A \cos (x + \theta)$ by determining expressions for A and θ in terms of a and b.

3. Prove that $\dfrac{\sin x + \sin 2x + \sin 3x}{\cos x + \cos 2x + \cos 3x} = \tan 2x$ is an identity.

4. Find the acute angle of intersection between the lines $y = 2x - 1$ and $y = -4x + 5$.

5. Find the acute angle of intersection between the two curves $y = x^3$ and $y = x^2 + 4$.

6. If A, B, and C are angles in a triangle, by expanding $\tan (A + B + C)$, show that $\tan A \tan B \tan C = \tan A + \tan B + \tan C$.

7. Determine $\displaystyle\lim_{x \to 0} \dfrac{\sqrt{1 + \tan x} - \sqrt{1 + \sin x}}{x^3}$.

8. Determine $\displaystyle\lim_{x \to \infty} \dfrac{\sin \dfrac{2}{x}}{\sin \dfrac{1}{x}}$.

9. Show that the curves $y = e^{-x}$ and $y = e^{-x} \cos x$ are tangent to each other at each intersection point. Sketch the two curves.

10. The total electromotive force E in a circuit is related to the current I by $I \dfrac{dI}{dt} + rI = E$, where I and r are constants of the circuit. Given that $I = I_0 \cos(wt + b)$, and I_0, w, and b are constants, determine a formula for E.

Appendix A
Review of Prerequisite Skills

Angle measures

To convert the angle $\frac{2\pi}{3}$ from radian measure to degree measure, multiply the angle in radians by $\frac{180°}{\pi}$.

$$\frac{2\pi}{3} \text{ rad} = \frac{2\pi}{3} \times \frac{180°}{\pi}$$
$$= 120°$$

The angle measure in degrees is 120°.

To convert the angle 135° from degree measure to radian measure, multiply the angle in degrees by $\frac{\pi}{180°}$.

$$135° = 135° \times \frac{\pi}{180°}$$
$$= \frac{3\pi}{4} \text{ rad}$$
$$\doteq 2.36 \text{ rad}$$

The angle measure in radians in exact form is $\frac{3\pi}{4}$ rad. In approximate form, it is 2.36 rad.

1. Convert each angle from radians to degrees.
a) $\frac{3\pi}{2}$
b) $\frac{5\pi}{4}$
c) $\frac{7\pi}{6}$
d) $\frac{4\pi}{3}$
e) $\frac{5\pi}{6}$
f) 2π

2. Convert each angle from degrees to radians.
a) 30°
b) 45°
c) 60°
d) 180°
e) 360°
f) 540°

Circle geometry

An arc of a circle of radius 5 cm has length 15 cm. To determine the measure of the angle, in radians, that is subtended by the arc, use the formula $\theta = \frac{a}{r}$, where θ is the angle, in radians, a is the arc length, and r is the radius. Arc length and radius must be measured in the same unit.

$$\theta = \frac{a}{r}$$
$$= \frac{15}{5}$$
$$= 3$$

The angle measure in radians is 3 rad.

The measure of the angle in degrees can be determined by converting the measure from radians to degrees (see **Angle measures**).

1. Determine the measure, in radians, of the angle subtended by each arc.
a) arc length = 2 m, radius = 4 m
b) arc length = 35 m, radius = 7 m
c) arc length = 18 m, radius = 6 m

2. Determine the length, in metres, of the arc that subtends each angle.

a) angle = 5 rad, radius = 3 m   b) angle = 2 rad, radius = 8 m

c) angle = 7 rad, radius = 4 m

3. Determine the radius, in metres, of each circle, given the length of the arc and the angle it subtends.

a) arc length = 24 m, angle = 6 rad   b) arc length = 33 m, angle = 3 rad

Completing the square

To express $y = 4x^2 - 8x + 7$ in the form $y = a(x - p)^2 + q$, factor the coefficient of x^2 from the first two terms. Then, complete the square by adding the square of half the coefficient of x. The value that was added must also be subtracted to keep the function the same.

$$y = 4x^2 - 8x + 7$$
$$= 4(x^2 - 2x) + 7$$

Factor the coefficient of x^2 from the first two terms:

Add 1 to complete the square; subtract 1 to keep the function the same:

$$= 4(x^2 - 2x + 1 - 1) + 7$$

Write the perfect square trinomial as the square of a binomial:

$$= 4[(x - 1)^2 - 1] + 7$$

Expand and simplify:

$$= 4(x - 1)^2 - 4 + 7$$
$$= 4(x - 1)^2 + 3$$

The equation in the form $y = a(x - p)^2 + q$ is $y = 4(x - 1)^2 + 3$.

1. Write each function in the form $y = a(x - p)^2 + q$.

a) $y = x^2 + 6x + 4$ b) $y = x^2 - 10x + 5$ c) $y = x^2 - 2x - 11$ d) $y = 3x^2 + 6x - 6$

e) $y = x^2 - 2x - 8$ f) $y = 2x^2 - 12x + 3$ g) $y = -4x^2 + 16x - 9$ h) $y = 4x^2 + 24x - 5$

Complex numbers

To simplify $\sqrt{-360}$, first factor $\sqrt{-1}$ from the radical. Then, replace $\sqrt{-1}$ with i, and simplify the remaining radical.

$$\sqrt{-360} = \sqrt{-1} \times \sqrt{360}$$
$$= i \times \sqrt{360}$$
$$= i \times \sqrt{36} \times \sqrt{10}$$
$$= i \times 6 \times \sqrt{10}$$
$$= 6i\sqrt{10}$$

To simplify i^3, write it in the form $i^2 \times i$. Since $i^2 = -1$, $i^2 \times i = -i$. So, $i^3 = -i$.

To simplify $4 + \sqrt{-12}$, factor $\sqrt{-1}$ from the radical. Then, replace $\sqrt{-1}$ with i, and simplify the remaining radical.

$$4 + \sqrt{-12} = 4 + \sqrt{-1} \times \sqrt{12}$$
$$= 4 + i \times \sqrt{12}$$
$$= 4 + i \times \sqrt{4} \times \sqrt{3}$$
$$= 4 + i \times 2 \times \sqrt{3}$$
$$= 4 + 2i\sqrt{3}$$

To simplify $\dfrac{6+\sqrt{-27}}{3}$, first write the expression so that the radical is in simplest form. Then, simplify by dividing the numerator by the denominator.

$$\dfrac{6+\sqrt{-27}}{3} = \dfrac{6+\sqrt{-1}\times\sqrt{27}}{3}$$

$$= \dfrac{6+i\times\sqrt{27}}{3}$$

$$= \dfrac{6+i\times\sqrt{9}\times\sqrt{3}}{3}$$

$$= \dfrac{6+i\times3\times\sqrt{3}}{3}$$

$$= \dfrac{6+3i\sqrt{3}}{3}$$

$$= 2+i\sqrt{3}$$

1. Simplify.

a) $\sqrt{-25}$ b) $\sqrt{-16}$ c) $\sqrt{-7}$ d) $\sqrt{-56}$ e) $-\sqrt{-125}$

2. Simplify.

a) i^7 b) $4i\times 3i$ c) $-2i^3$ d) $(5i)(7i)$ e) $(-i\sqrt{5})(4i\sqrt{5})$

3. Simplify.

a) $5+\sqrt{-45}$ b) $8-\sqrt{-20}$ c) $\dfrac{12+\sqrt{-72}}{6}$ d) $\dfrac{15-\sqrt{-200}}{5}$ e) $\dfrac{-21+\sqrt{-18}}{3}$

Compound interest

To determine the final amount of a $500 investment, invested at 8%, compounded quarterly, for 10 years, use the compound interest formula, $A = P(1 + i)^n$.

A is the final amount, which is the value that is being calculated.

P is the principal, or the initial amount of the investment, which is $500.

i is the interest rate per compounding period, which is $0.08 \div 4$, or 0.02.

n is the number of compounding periods, which is 40, since interest is compounded 4 times a year for 10 years, and $4 \times 10 = 40$.

$$A = P(1 + i)^n$$
$$= 500(1 + 0.02)^{40}$$
$$= 500(1.02)^{40}$$
$$\doteq 1104.02$$

So, the final amount of the investment is $1104.02.

1. Determine the final amount of each investment using the compound interest formula.

a) $2000 invested at 8%, compounded annually, for 6 years

b) $4500 invested at 6.5%, compounded semi-annually, for 2 years

c) $6700 invested at 7.75%, compounded quarterly, for 20 years

d) $5000 invested at 6%, compounded monthly, for 5 years

Determining angles

To determine the angle θ in the following diagram, use the trigonometric ratio $\tan \theta = \dfrac{y}{x}$.

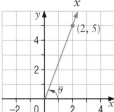

$$\tan \theta = \frac{y}{x}$$
$$= \frac{5}{2}$$
$$\theta \doteq 1.19 \text{ rad}$$

1. Determine the value of θ for each diagram.

a)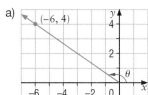

b)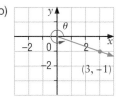

c)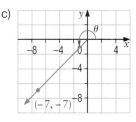

Determining coordinates of points

To determine the coordinates of P in the following diagram, multiply $\cos 30°$ and $\sin 30°$ by the length of the terminal arm, 2.

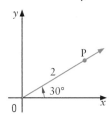

$$2 \cos 30° = 2\left(\frac{\sqrt{3}}{2}\right) \qquad 2 \sin 30° = 2\left(\frac{1}{2}\right)$$
$$= \sqrt{3} \qquad\qquad\qquad = 1$$

The coordinates are $(2 \cos 30°, 2 \sin 30°)$, or $(\sqrt{3}, 1)$.

1. Determine the coordinates of P for each diagram.

a)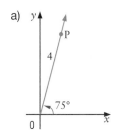

b)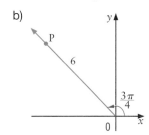

c)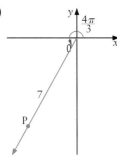

d)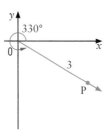

Distance between two points

To determine the distance between the points $(x_1, y_1) = (2, -5)$ and $(x_2, y_2) = (-4, 3)$, substitute the x- and y-values into the formula $d = \sqrt{(x_2 - x_1)^2 + (y_2 - y_1)^2}$.

$$
\begin{aligned}
d &= \sqrt{(x_2 - x_1)^2 + (y_2 - y_1)^2} \\
&= \sqrt{(-4 - 2)^2 + (3 - (-5))^2} \\
&= \sqrt{(-6)^2 + (8)^2} \\
&= \sqrt{36 + 64} \\
&= \sqrt{100} \\
&= 10
\end{aligned}
$$

The distance between the points is 10.

1. Determine the distance between each pair of points.
a) (2, 1) and (5, 4) b) (3, 6) and (4, −2) c) (1, −3) and (−4, 4)
d) (−7, −2) and (−1, −5) e) (9, −3) and (6, 3) f) (2, 4) and (3, −5)

Dividing a polynomial by a monomial

To simplify the expression $\dfrac{2x^3 - 6x^2 + 4x}{8x^2}$, divide all the terms by the greatest common factor, which is $2x$. State any restrictions on the variable.

$$
\begin{aligned}
\frac{2x^3 - 6x^2 + 4x}{8x^2} &= \frac{\dfrac{2x^3}{2x} - \dfrac{6x^2}{2x} + \dfrac{4x}{2x}}{\dfrac{8x^2}{2x}} \\
&= \frac{x^2 - 3x + 2}{4x}, \ x \neq 0
\end{aligned}
$$

1. Simplify.

a) $\dfrac{6y^2 + 15y}{3y}$ b) $\dfrac{8m + 16m^2 + 28m^3}{4m}$ c) $\dfrac{25x^2 + 5x}{10x}$ d) $\dfrac{8x^2y + 14xy^2 + 4x^3y^3}{16x^2y^2}$

Domain

To state the restrictions on the domain of $y = \dfrac{x+7}{x^2 + 2x - 15}$, determine the values of x for which the denominator is zero.

$x^2 + 2x - 15 = 0$

$(x + 5)(x - 3) = 0$

$x + 5 = 0$ or $x - 3 = 0$

$\quad x = -5 \qquad x = 3$

The restrictions are $x \neq -5$ and $x \neq 3$.

1. Determine the restrictions on the domain for each equation.

a) $f(x) = 11x^2 - 21x + 2$

b) $f(x) = \dfrac{3}{x + 4}$

c) $f(x) = \dfrac{x + 2}{x^2 - 2x + 24}$

d) $f(x) = \dfrac{x^2}{-3x^2 + 5x + 2}$

Equation of a horizontal or vertical line given a point on the line

To determine an equation of the vertical line passing through $(x_1, y_1) = (-3, 4)$, substitute the value of x_1 into the equation $x = x_1$.

$x = x_1$

$x = -3$

An equation of the line is $x = -3$.

To determine an equation of the horizontal line passing through $(x_1, y_1) = (-3, 4)$, substitute the value of y_1 into the equation $y = y_1$.

$y = y_1$

$y = 4$

An equation of the line is $y = 4$.

1. Determine an equation for each line.

a) passing through the point $(-2, 3)$ and horizontal

b) passing through the point $(1, 1)$ and vertical

Equation of a line given the slope and a point

To determine an equation of the line passing through the point $(4, -1)$ whose slope is 2, substitute the slope for m, substitute the x-coordinate for x_1, and substitute the y-coordinate for y_1 in the equation $y - y_1 = m(x - x_1)$. Then, simplify the equation.

$\quad y - y_1 = m(x - x_1)$

$y - (-1) = 2(x - 4)$

$\quad y + 1 = 2x - 8$

$\qquad y = 2x - 9$

An equation of the line is $y = 2x - 9$.

1. Determine an equation for each line.

a) slope of 3 and passing through the point (2, 5)

b) slope of –1 and passing through the point (3, –6)

2. Determine an equation for the line that is parallel to the line $y = 5x - 2$ and passes through the point (2, 4).

Equation of a line given the slope and *y*-intercept

To determine an equation of the line whose slope is 3 and whose *y*-intercept is 2, substitute the slope for *m* and substitute the *y*-intercept for *b* in the equation $y = mx + b$.

$y = mx + b$

$ = 3x + 2$

An equation of the line is $y = 3x + 2$.

1. Determine an equation for each line.

a) slope 2 and *y*-intercept 1   b) slope –4 and *y*-intercept 4

Equation of a line given two points

If the two points $(x_1, y_1) = (-2, 2)$ and $(x_2, y_2) = (1, 8)$ are known, the slope, *m*, of the line joining these points can be determined by substituting the *x*- and *y*-values into the formula

$$m = \frac{y_2 - y_1}{x_2 - x_1}.$$

$$m = \frac{y_2 - y_1}{x_2 - x_1}$$

$$ = \frac{8 - 2}{1 - (-2)}$$

$$ = \frac{6}{3}$$

$$ = 2$$

The slope of the line is 2. An equation of the line can be determined by substituting the slope *m* and the point $(x_1, y_1) = (-2, 2)$ into the formula $y - y_1 = m(x - x_1)$.

$y - y_1 = m(x - x_1)$

$y - 2 = 2(x - (-2))$

$ = 2(x + 2)$

$ = 2x + 4$

$y = 2x + 6$

An equation of the line is $y = 2x + 6$.

1. Determine an equation of each line.

a) passing through the points (1, 5) and (–1, –2)

b) passing through the points (4, 4) and (7, 1)

Equation of a line given the *x*- and *y*-intercepts

The line with an *x*-intercept of 4 and a *y*-intercept of –2 passes through the two points $(4, 0)$ and $(0, -2)$. The slope, *m*, of the line connecting these points can be determined by substituting the *x*- and *y*-values into the formula $m = \dfrac{y_2 - y_1}{x_2 - x_1}$.

$$m = \frac{y_2 - y_1}{x_2 - x_1}$$
$$= \frac{-2 - 0}{0 - 4}$$
$$= \frac{-2}{-4}$$
$$= \frac{1}{2}$$

The slope, *m*, of the line is $\dfrac{1}{2}$. The *y*-intercept, *b*, is –2. Substitute these values into the equation $y = mx + b$.

$$y = mx + b$$
$$y = \frac{1}{2}x - 2$$

An equation of the line is $y = \dfrac{1}{2}x - 2$.

1. Determine an equation for each line.

a) *x*-intercept 1 and *y*-intercept 4   b) *x*-intercept 3 and *y*-intercept –2

Evaluating functions

To evaluate the function $f(x) = x^3 - 2x^2 + 5x + 6$ for $f(3)$, substitute 3 for *x*. Then, simplify.

$$f(x) = x^3 - 2x^2 + 5x + 6$$
$$f(3) = 3^3 - 2(3)^2 + 5(3) + 6$$
$$= 27 - 18 + 15 + 6$$
$$= 30$$

To determine if $f(2) > f(-1)$ for $f(x) = -x + 3$, evaluate $f(2)$ and $f(-1)$ and compare them.

$$f(x) = -x + 3 \qquad\qquad f(x) = -x + 3$$
$$f(2) = -2 + 3 \qquad\qquad f(-1) = -(-1) + 3$$
$$= 1 \qquad\qquad\qquad\qquad = 1 + 3$$
$$\qquad\qquad\qquad\qquad\qquad = 4$$

Since $1 < 4$, then $f(2) < f(-1)$. The statement $f(2) > f(-1)$ is false.

1. If $f(x) = x^3 + 3x^2 - 4x - 7$, determine the value of

a) $f(0)$ b) $f(3)$ c) $f(-2)$ d) $f\left(-\dfrac{2}{3}\right)$

e) $f(3.1)$ f) $f(n)$ g) $f(-3x)$ h) $f(x^2)$

2. If $f(x) = x^2 - 5$, determine the value of

a) $f(2)$ b) $f(-5)$ c) $f(\sqrt{7})$ d) $f(x + 2)$

3. If $f(x) = \sqrt{x - 3}$, determine the value of

a) $f(3)$ b) $f(7)$ c) $f(4)$ d) $f(x^2)$

4. If $f(x) = |x - 6|$, determine the value of

a) $f(1)$ b) $f(8)$ c) $f(-4)$ d) $f(6)$

5. Determine whether each statement is true or false for $f(x) = (x + 2)^2$.

a) $f(1) > f(0)$ b) $f(2) < f(-1)$ c) $f(-7) \le f(3)$ d) $f(-2) > f(-3)$

Exponential equations

To solve $8^x = 16^{x-1}$, first rewrite the equation using a common base. When the bases are equal, the exponents are equal. Thus, the equation can be solved by equating the exponents.

$$8^x = 16^{x-1}$$

Rewrite using a common base: $(2^3)^x = (2^4)^{x-1}$

Simplify the exponents: $2^{3x} = 2^{4x-4}$

Equate the exponents: $3x = 4x - 4$

Solve for x: $4x - 3x = 4$

$$x = 4$$

The solution is $x = 4$.

To solve $2^{x+5} - 2^{x+3} = 192$, first remove a common factor and simplify the equation. Then, equate the exponents and solve for x.

$$2^{x+5} - 2^{x+3} = 192$$

Remove a common factor: $2^x(2^5 - 2^3) = 192$

Simplify the expression: $2^x(32 - 8) = 192$

$$2^x(24) = 192$$

$$2^x = 8$$

Rewrite using a common base: $2^x = 2^3$

Equate the exponents and solve for x: $x = 3$

The solution is $x = 3$.

1. Solve for x.

a) $3^x = 81$ b) $4^{x-2} = 16^x$ c) $6^x = 216^{x-3}$ d) $9^{x-5} = 27^{x+1}$

e) $5^{x+1} + 5^x = 750$ f) $7^{x+3} - 7^x = 342$ g) $2^{x-3} + 2^{x+2} = 33$ h) $4^{x-2} + 4^{x-5} = 65$

Exponent laws

To multiply powers with the same base, add the exponents.

$$x^2 \times x^3 = x^{2+3}$$
$$= x^5$$

To divide powers with the same base, subtract the exponents.

$$x^5 \div x^2 = x^{5-2}$$
$$= x^3$$

To raise a power to an exponent, multiply the exponents.

$$(x^2)^4 = x^{2 \times 4}$$
$$= x^8$$

a^n means a multiplied by itself n times, when n is a positive integer.

$$2^5 = 2 \times 2 \times 2 \times 2 \times 2$$
$$= 32$$

a^{-n} means $\dfrac{1}{a^n}$, where $n > 0$.

$$2^{-5} = \dfrac{1}{2^5}$$
$$= \dfrac{1}{32}$$

$a^0 = 1$, where $a \neq 0$.

$$10^0 = 1$$

$a^{\frac{1}{n}}$ means $\sqrt[n]{a}$, where n is a positive integer.

$$16^{\frac{1}{4}} = \sqrt[4]{16}$$
$$= 2$$

$a^{\frac{m}{n}}$ means $(\sqrt[n]{a})^m$, where n is a positive integer and m is an integer.

$$81^{\frac{3}{4}} = (\sqrt[4]{81})^3$$
$$= 3^3$$
$$= 27$$

$(ab)^n$ means $(a^n)(b^n)$.

$$(5x)^2 = (5^2)(x^2)$$
$$= 25x^2$$

$\left(\dfrac{a}{b}\right)^n$ means $\dfrac{a^n}{b^n}$, where $b \neq 0$

$$\left(\dfrac{3}{5}\right)^3 = \dfrac{3^3}{5^3}$$
$$= \dfrac{27}{125}$$

1. Rewrite each expression using positive exponents only.

a) $5x^{-3}$ b) $(3x)^{-4}$ c) $7 + x^{-6}$ d) $(5x^{-3})^{-2} - 6x^{-1} + 2x - x^3$

2. Expand and simplify each expression.

a) $x^{\frac{1}{2}}(3x^2 + 1)^2$ b) $(3x^4 - 5)(2x + 3)$ c) $4x(x^2 - 1)(x^3 + 2)$ d) $\sqrt{x^2 + 5}\sqrt{2x - 4}$

3. Evaluate.

a) $(-3)^4$ b) 4^{-5} c) 21^0 d) $36^{\frac{1}{2}}$ e) $625^{\frac{3}{4}}$

4. Simplify.

a) $(4x^3y^5)(5x^6y^2)$ b) $\dfrac{a^6b^7c^4}{(a^3b^2)^2c}$ c) $(m^2n^{-5})^2(m^{-3}n^4)^3$ d) $\dfrac{(x^2y^{-9})^{\frac{1}{3}}}{(x^{-2}y^6)^{\frac{1}{6}}}$

Factoring $a^2 - b^2$

To factor $16x^2 - 25$, use the equation $a^2 - b^2 = (a + b)(a - b)$. In this case, $a = 4x$ and $b = 5$.

$$a^2 - b^2 = (a + b)(a - b)$$
$$16x^2 - 25 = (4x)^2 - 5^2$$
$$= (4x + 5)(4x - 5)$$

1. Factor.

a) $x^2 - 4$ b) $y^2 - 100$ c) $4n^2 - 49$ d) $25m^2 - 81$ e) $1 - 36x^2$ f) $4y^2 - 9x^2$

Factoring $a^3 - b^3$ or $a^3 + b^3$

To factor $8x^3 - 27$, use the equation $a^3 - b^3 = (a - b)(a^2 + ab + b^2)$.
In this case, $a = 2x$ and $b = 3$.

$$a^3 - b^3 = (a - b)(a^2 + ab + b^2)$$
$$8x^3 - 27 = (2x)^3 - (3)^3$$
$$= (2x - 3)[(2x)^2 + (2x)(3) + 3^2]$$
$$= (2x - 3)(4x^2 + 6x + 9)$$

To factor $27z^3 + 64$, use the equation $a^3 + b^3 = (a + b)(a^2 - ab + b^2)$.
In this case, $a = 3z$ and $b = 4$.

$$a^3 + b^3 = (a + b)(a^2 - ab + b^2)$$
$$27z^3 + 64 = (3z)^3 + (4)^3$$
$$= (3z + 4)[(3z)^2 - (3z)(4) + 4^2]$$
$$= (3z + 4)(9z^2 - 12z + 16)$$

1. Factor.

a) $x^3 - 1$ b) $x^3 - y^3$ c) $27 - 64a^3$ d) $8a^3 - 1$ e) $\dfrac{x^3}{8} - 1$ f) $\dfrac{1}{a^3} - \dfrac{1}{27}$

2. Factor.

a) $x^3 + 8$ b) $8z^3 + 1$ c) $c^3 + 125d^3$ d) $1000x^3 + 729w^6$ e) $1 + \dfrac{8q^3}{27}$ f) $\dfrac{1}{125} + \dfrac{1}{27y^3}$

Factoring $ax^2 + bx + c$, $a = 1$

To factor $x^2 - 8x + 12$, where $a = 1$, $b = -8$, and $c = 12$, use a table to find two integers whose product is $c = 12$ and whose sum is $b = -8$. The only two integers with a product of 12 and a sum of -8 are -6 and -2.
Thus, $x^2 - 8x + 12 = (x - 6)(x - 2)$.

Product of 12		Sum
12	1	13
−12	−1	−13
6	2	8
−6	−2	−8
4	3	7
−4	−3	−7

1. Factor.

a) $x^2 - x - 20$

b) $y^2 + 3y - 10$

c) $n^2 - 5n - 36$

d) $m^2 + 9m + 18$

e) $x^2 - 11x + 30$

f) $c^2 - 2c - 24$

g) $16 + 15y - y^2$

h) $x^2 + 12xy + 32y^2$

i) $c^2 - 3cd - 28d^2$

Factoring $ax^2 + bx + c$, $a \neq 1$

To factor $3x^2 + 13x + 10$, where $a = 3$, $b = 13$, and $c = 10$, find two integers whose product is $a \times c = 30$, and whose sum is $b = 13$. The only two integers with a product of 30 and a sum of 13 are 10 and 3.

Product of 30		Sum
30	1	31
15	2	17
10	3	13
6	5	11

Break up the middle term: $\qquad$ $3x^2 + 13x + 10 = 3x^2 + 3x + 10x + 10$

Group terms: $\qquad\qquad\qquad\qquad\qquad$ $= (3x^2 + 3x) + (10x + 10)$

Remove common factors: $\qquad\qquad\qquad$ $= 3x(x + 1) + 10(x + 1)$

Remove a common binomial factor: $\qquad$ $= (3x + 10)(x + 1)$

Thus, $3x^2 + 13x + 10 = (3x + 10)(x + 1)$.

1. Factor.

a) $3x^2 - 2x - 8$

b) $2c^2 + 7c - 4$

c) $4m^2 - 11m + 6$

d) $5y^2 + 8y + 3$

e) $3n^2 + n - 2$

f) $6x^2 - 17x - 3$

g) $3x^2 - 5xy - 12y^2$

h) $5x^2 - 14x + 8$

i) $4x^2 + 23x + 15$

j) $2p^2 + pq - q^2$

Finite differences

Finite differences are calculated from tables of values in which the x-coordinates are evenly spaced. First differences are found by subtracting consecutive y-coordinates. Second differences are found by subtracting consecutive first differences, and so on.

If the first differences are constant, the relation is linear. If the second differences are constant, the relation is quadratic. Otherwise, the relation is neither linear nor quadratic.

This relation is linear.

x	y	1st Differences
1	3	
		$5 - 3 = 2$
2	5	
		$7 - 5 = 2$
3	7	
		$9 - 7 = 2$
4	9	
		$11 - 9 = 2$
5	11	

This relation is quadratic.

x	y	1st Differences	2nd Differences
1	50		
		$32 - 50 = -18$	
2	32		$-14 - (-18) = 4$
		$18 - 32 = -14$	
3	18		$-10 - (-14) = 4$
		$8 - 18 = -10$	
4	8		$-6 - (-10) = 4$
		$2 - 8 = -6$	
5	2		

This relation is neither linear nor quadratic.

x	y	1st Differences	2nd Differences
1	2		
		$4 - 2 = 2$	
2	4		$4 - 2 = 2$
		$8 - 4 = 4$	
3	8		$8 - 4 = 4$
		$16 - 8 = 8$	
4	16		$16 - 8 = 8$
		$32 - 16 = 16$	
5	32		

1. Use finite differences to determine whether each relation is linear, quadratic, or neither.

a)

x	y
1	5
2	8
3	11
4	14
5	17

b)

x	y
1	2
2	5
3	10
4	17
5	26

c)

x	y
1	9
2	7
3	5
4	3
5	1

d)

x	y
1	-33
2	-31
3	-27
4	-20
5	-9

e)

x	y
1	-3
2	-5
3	-3
4	3
5	13

f)

x	y
1	-1
2	1
3	-1
4	1
5	-1

Function notation

The point for which $f(5) = 3$ has x-coordinate 5 and y-coordinate 3. To graph this point, locate the coordinates $(5, 3)$.

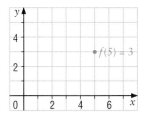

1. Graph the point that satisfies each condition.
   a) $f(1) = -3$ b) $f(-4) = 2$ c) $f(0) = 6$ d) $f(7) = 4$
   e) $f(-3) = 0$ f) $f(-2) = -1$

Functions and relations

For the graph of $y = x^2 - 5$, the domain is all real numbers, and the range is $y \geq -5$.

The curve is a parabola opening upward whose vertex is $(0, -5)$.

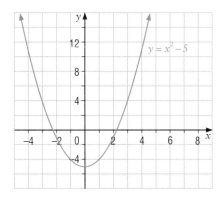

The relation is a function, since there is no vertical line that intersects the graph more than once. In other words, for every x-value, there is exactly one y-value.

1. State the domain and range of each relation, graph the relation, and then determine if it is a function.
   a) $y = 5x + 2$
   b) $3x - 4y - 8 = 0$
   c) $y = 2x^2 + 3$
   d) $y = 4(x - 2)^2 + 1$
   e) $x^2 + y^2 = 25$
   f) $x^2 + y^2 + 8x - 2y - 8 = 0$
   g) $y = -\dfrac{5}{x}$
   h) $x^2 + y^2 - 4x + 10y + 20 = 0$
   i) $y = \sqrt{3x + 2}$

Graphing quadratic functions

The graph of $y = 2(x + 3)^2 - 8$ has vertex at $(-3, -8)$, opens upward, and has been vertically stretched by a factor of 2 relative to the graph of $y = x^2$. The graph can be sketched using this information.

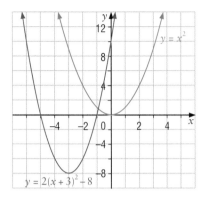

1. State the vertex, the direction of opening, and the vertical stretch factor relative to the graph of $y = x^2$ for each parabola. Then, sketch the graph.

a) $y = x^2 + 2$

b) $y = -x^2 - 1$

c) $y = 2x^2$

d) $y = 3(x + 4)^2$

e) $y = -2(x - 1)^2 + 4$

f) $y = 0.5(x + 2)^2 + 3$

g) $y = -(x + 1)^2 - 5$

h) $y = \dfrac{1}{4}(x - 3)^2 + 1$

Graphing trigonometric functions

To graph two cycles of $y = 4 \cos\left(x - \dfrac{\pi}{2}\right)$, graph two cycles of $y = \cos x$ translated to the

right by $\dfrac{\pi}{2}$, and stretched vertically by a factor of 4.

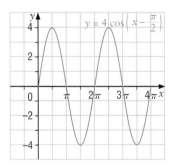

To graph two cycles of $y = \tan \dfrac{1}{2}x + 3$, graph two cycles of $y = \tan x$ translated upward by 3, and stretched horizontally by a factor of 2.

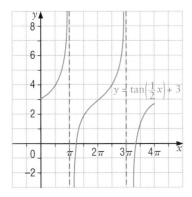

1. Graph two cycles of each function.

a) $y = 3\sin x$　　　b) $y = \tan 2x$　　　c) $y = \cos(x + \pi) - 1$

Graphs of functions using technology

When $y = \dfrac{2}{x}$ is graphed using the ZStandard instruction on a graphing calculator, it should appear as it does here. The domain is $x \neq 0$. The range is $y \neq 0$.

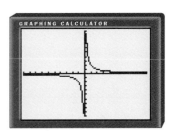

Window variables:
$x \in [-10, 10], y \in [-10, 10]$

When $y = \sqrt{x} + 2$ is graphed using the Window variables shown, it should appear as it does here. The domain is $x \in [0, \infty)$. The range is $y \in [2, \infty)$.

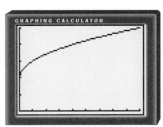

Window variables:
$x \in [0, 9], y \in [0, 5]$

1. Graph each function using a graphing calculator or graphing software. State the Window variables that you used. Then, state the domain and range of the function.

a) $y = \dfrac{4}{x}$　　　b) $y = -\dfrac{1}{x}$　　　c) $y = \dfrac{2}{x} + 5$　　　d) $y = \sqrt{x + 3}$

e) $y = \sqrt{4 - x}$　　f) $y = -\sqrt{x} + 5$

Interpreting graphs of functions

To evaluate $f(4)$ on a graph, find the value of $f(x)$ when $x = 4$.
When $x = 4$, $f(x) = -6$.

The domain of a function is the set of all values of x for which the function has a y-value. The range of a function is the set of all y-values for the function.

For the graph of $f(x) = \dfrac{-x^2 + 4}{2}$, the domain is the set of all real numbers. The range is $y \in (-\infty, 2]$.

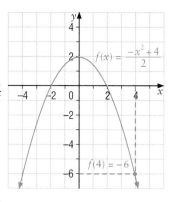

1. a) Determine the value of
i) $f(0)$ ii) $f(1)$ iii) $f(-1)$ iv) $f(-2)$

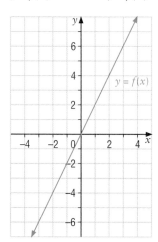

b) State the domain and the range.

2. a) Determine the value of
i) $f(0)$ ii) $f(-2)$ iii) $f(2)$ iv) $f(1)$

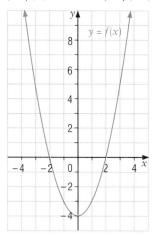

b) State the domain and the range.

Inverses

To find the inverse of $f(x) = 5x + 7$, first rewrite the function as $y = 5x + 7$.
Then, interchange x and y and solve for y.

$$x = 5y + 7$$
$$x - 7 = 5y$$
$$\frac{x - 7}{5} = y$$

The reason we can interchange x and y is that a function and its inverse are reflections of each other in the line $y = x$.

We use the notation $f^{-1}(x)$ to express the inverse of $f(x)$. So, the inverse
of $f(x) = 5x + 7$ is $f^{-1}(x) = \frac{x - 7}{5}$.

Since $f^{-1}(x)$ passes the vertical line test, that is, there is exactly one value of $f(x)$ for each
value of x, it is a function.

1. Find the inverse of each function, and determine whether the inverse is also a function.

a) $f(x) = 3x - 1$ 　　　　 b) $f(x) = 4x^2 + 2$ 　　　　 c) $f(x) = 3x^3 - 8$

d) $f(x) = \sqrt{2x + 3}$ 　　　　 e) $f(x) = \dfrac{3x + 4}{7x - 2}$

Operations with complex numbers

To simplify the expression $3(5 + 8i) - 4(3 + 7i)$, expand to remove the brackets, and, then,
collect like terms.

$$3(5 + 8i) - 4(3 + 7i) = 15 + 24i - 12 - 28i$$
$$= 3 - 4i$$

To simplify the expression $\dfrac{4 - 3i}{2i}$, rationalize the denominator. To do this, multiply the
numerator and the denominator by i. Then, use the property $i^2 = -1$.

$$\frac{4 - 3i}{2i} = \frac{(4 - 3i)(i)}{(2i)(i)}$$
$$= \frac{4i - 3i^2}{2i^2}$$
$$= \frac{4i - 3(-1)}{2(-1)}$$
$$= \frac{4i + 3}{-2}$$

To simplify the expression $\dfrac{3 + 2i}{4 - 5i}$, rationalize the denominator. To do this, multiply the
numerator and the denominator by the conjugate of the denominator. Then, use the
property $i^2 = -1$.

$$\frac{3+2i}{4-5i} = \frac{(3+2i)(4+5i)}{(4-5i)(4+5i)}$$

$$= \frac{12+23i+10i^2}{16-25i^2}$$

$$= \frac{12+23i+10(-1)}{16-25(-1)}$$

$$= \frac{12+23i-10}{16+25}$$

$$= \frac{2+23i}{41}$$

1. Simplify.

a) $(4 + 3i) + (2 - 7i)$ b) $(5 + 8i) - (3 + 4i)$

c) $(i - 9) - (3 + 2i)$ d) $2(3i - 1) - 3(2i - 5)$

2. Simplify.

a) $\dfrac{i-3}{i}$ b) $\dfrac{4-7i}{5i}$ c) $\dfrac{5i}{3+2i}$ d) $\dfrac{8+3i}{1-4i}$

Pythagorean theorem

To find the length of AC in $\triangle$ABC, use the Pythagorean theorem: $AC^2 = AB^2 + BC^2$.

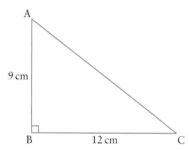

$(AC)^2 = 9^2 + 12^2$

$\qquad = 81 + 144$

$\qquad = 225$

$AC = \sqrt{225}$

$\qquad = 15$

1. Solve for x in each triangle.

a)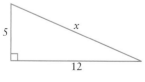

b)

c)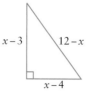

Rationalizing expressions

To rationalize the denominator of $\dfrac{x}{\sqrt{x+25}-5}$, first multiply the numerator and the denominator by the conjugate of the denominator, which is $\sqrt{x+25}+5$. Then, simplify the expression.

$$\frac{x}{\sqrt{x+25}-5} = \frac{x}{\sqrt{x+25}-5} \times \frac{\sqrt{x+25}+5}{\sqrt{x+25}+5}$$

$$= \frac{x(\sqrt{x+25}+5)}{x+25-25}$$

$$= \frac{x(\sqrt{x+25}+5)}{x}$$

$$= \sqrt{x+25}+5$$

1. Rationalize the denominator of each expression.

a) $\dfrac{24}{\sqrt{x+4}+\sqrt{x}}$

b) $\dfrac{7x}{\sqrt{x+7}-\sqrt{x}}$

c) $\dfrac{4x}{\sqrt{5x}-\sqrt{x}}$

d) $\dfrac{x+4}{\sqrt{x+5}-1}$

e) $\dfrac{x^2}{\sqrt{x^2+9}-3}$

f) $\dfrac{12x}{\sqrt{x+6}-\sqrt{x-6}}$

Similar triangles

Consider the following figure.

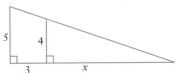

Since the larger triangle and the smaller triangle are similar, the ratios of the corresponding sides are equal. We can use this property to determine the value of x.

$$\frac{5}{4} = \frac{3+x}{x}$$

$$5x = 4(3+x)$$

$$5x = 12 + 4x$$

$$5x - 4x = 12$$

$$x = 12$$

1. Solve for x in each triangle.

a)

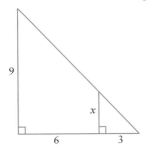

b)

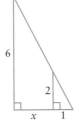

c)

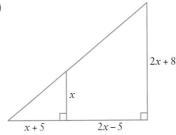

Simplifying compound rational expressions

To simplify the rational expression $\dfrac{\frac{1}{x+4} - \frac{1}{4}}{x}$, multiply the numerator and denominator by the common denominator of the numerator, that is, $4(x + 4)$. Then, simplify. To find the restrictions, determine which values of x result in a denominator of 0.

Multiply the numerator and the denominator by $4(x + 4)$:

$$\frac{\frac{1}{x+4} - \frac{1}{4}}{x} = \frac{\left(\frac{1}{x+4} - \frac{1}{4}\right) \times 4(x+4)}{x \times 4(x+4)}$$

Simplify:

$$= \frac{4 - (x+4)}{4x(x+4)}$$

$$= \frac{-x}{4x(x+4)}$$

Divide the numerator and the denominator by the common factor x and state the restrictions on the variable:

$$= \frac{-1}{4(x+4)}; \ x \neq -4, \ x \neq 0$$

1. Simplify. State the restrictions on the variable.

a) $\dfrac{\frac{1}{x+7} - \frac{1}{7}}{x}$

b) $\dfrac{\frac{4}{x-3} + \frac{4}{3}}{x}$

c) $\dfrac{\frac{1}{(x+6)^2} - \frac{1}{36}}{x}$

Simplifying expressions

To simplify the expression $3(x + 2)(x - 4) - 2(x^2 - 3)$, expand to remove the brackets, and, then, collect like terms.

$$3(x + 2)(x - 4) - 2(x^2 - 3) = 3(x^2 - 2x - 8) - 2(x^2 - 3)$$
$$= 3x^2 - 6x - 24 - 2x^2 + 6$$
$$= x^2 - 6x - 18$$

1. Simplify.
a) $2(x + 4) + 3(x + 4)$

b) $8(y - 3) - (y + 6)$

c) $6(x - 4) + 2(3 + x)$

d) $2(w + 7) - (w - 3) + 3(w - 2)$

e) $-5(y - 3) + 7(2 - y) + 6(y + 1)$

f) $4(x^2 + x - 5) + 3(x^2 - 2x + 8)$

g) $3(x - 3)(x + 4) + (x - 2)(x + 5)$

h) $4(a - 1)(a - 4) + (a + 2)^2$

i) $3(x + 2)(x - 7) + 2(x + 4)(x + 3)$

Simplifying rational expressions

To simplify the rational expression $\dfrac{x^2 + 2x - 8}{3x^2 + 11x - 4}$, factor the numerator and the denominator, if possible. To find the restrictions on the variable x, determine the values of x

that make the denominator equal to zero. Then, divide the numerator and the denominator by the common factor.

$$\frac{x^2 + 2x - 8}{3x^2 + 11x - 4} = \frac{(x-2)(x+4)}{(3x-1)(x+4)}$$

$$= \frac{x-2}{3x-1}, \ x \neq \frac{1}{3}, \ x \neq -4$$

The solution is $\frac{x-2}{3x-1}$. The restrictions on the variable are $x \neq \frac{1}{3}$ and $x \neq -4$.

1. Simplify each expression and state the restrictions on the variable.

a) $\dfrac{x^2 + 3x + 2}{x + 2}$

b) $\dfrac{x - 5}{x^2 - 2x - 15}$

c) $\dfrac{2x^2 + 3x - 5}{x - 1}$

d) $\dfrac{5x^2 + 11x + 2}{x^2 - x - 6}$

e) $\dfrac{2x^2 + 5x - 12}{4x^2 - 9}$

f) $\dfrac{6x^2 - 11x - 10}{8x^2 - 18x - 5}$

Slopes and *y*-intercepts

To determine the slope and the *y*-intercept of the equation $-3x + y + 4 = 0$, rewrite the equation in the form $y = mx + b$.

$$-3x + y + 4 = 0$$

$$y = 3x - 4$$

The slope is the value of *m*, and the *y*-intercept is the value of *b*. The slope is 3 and the *y*-intercept is -4.

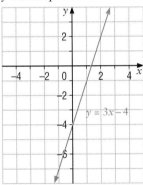

1. Determine the values of the slope and the *y*-intercept for each line. Then, graph the line.

a) $y = 4x + 1$

b) $y = x - 2$

c) $y = 3x + 5$

d) $y = -7x + 3$

e) $y = 3x$

f) $y = -8$

g) $y = 5x + 2$

h) $4x - y = 3$

i) $7x + 2y - 5 = 0$

j) $y = x$

k) $4(x + 3) - y = 8$

l) $\dfrac{y - 4}{3x} = 2$

Slopes of lines

To determine the slope, *m*, of a line given two points on the line, (x_1, y_1) and (x_2, y_2), use the formula $m = \dfrac{y_2 - y_1}{x_2 - x_1}$.

The slope of the line passing through $(1, 2)$ and $(3, 5)$ is

$$m = \frac{5-2}{3-1}$$

$$= \frac{3}{2}$$

1. Determine the slope of the line passing through each pair of points.

a) $(-1, 5), (3, 7)$ b) $(2, 8), (7, 5)$ c) $(-2, -6), (1, 5)$

d) $(-5, -6), (-1, -3)$ e) $\left(\frac{1}{2}, 2\right), (5, 1)$ f) $\left(-\frac{5}{3}, \frac{3}{2}\right), \left(\frac{2}{3}, 3\right)$

g) $(1.2, 3.1), (5.9, -6.1)$ h) $(-3.2, 4.7), (-1.7, 2.1)$

Solving first-degree inequalities

To solve the inequality $\frac{2x-1}{2} < \frac{5x+8}{4}$, isolate the variable in the same way that you would for a linear equation, except reverse the inequality symbol when you multiply or divide both sides by a negative number.

$$\frac{2x-1}{2} < \frac{5x+3}{4}$$
$$4(2x-1) < 2(5x+3)$$
$$8x-4 < 10x+6$$
$$-2x < 10$$

Reverse the inequality symbol since we are dividing both sides by -2:

$$\frac{-2x}{-2} > \frac{10}{-2}$$
$$x > -5$$

To graph this solution, use an open dot to show that -5 is not a part of the solution. (If the solution is $x \geq -5$, a closed dot is used.)

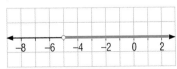

1. Solve each inequality and graph the solution.

a) $4x - 1 > 3x + 5$ b) $2(x - 5) \leq 6(x - 4)$ c) $-3(3x + 2) + 5 < 6(x - 2) + 1$

d) $\frac{x+3}{6} \geq \frac{x-5}{3}$ e) $\frac{x+2}{4} > \frac{x-9}{8} + 3$ f) $\frac{4+5x}{3} + 5 \leq x - \frac{7}{2}$

Solving quadratic equations by factoring

To solve $x^2 - 5x = 6$ by factoring, first write the equation in the form $ax^2 + bx + c = 0$.

$$x^2 - 5x = 6$$
$$x^2 - 5x - 6 = 0$$

Factor the left side:

$$(x - 6)(x + 1) = 0$$

Use the zero product property: $x - 6 = 0$ or $x + 1 = 0$

$x = 6$ or $x = -1$

The roots are 6 and -1.

To solve $2x^2 + 9x = -10$ by factoring, first write the equation in the form $ax^2 + bx + c = 0$.

$$2x^2 + 9x = -10$$
$$2x^2 + 9x + 10 = 0$$

Find two integers whose product is $a \times c$, or 20, and whose sum is b, or 9. The only two integers with a product of 20 and a sum of 9 are 4 and 5.

Break up the middle term: $2x^2 + 4x + 5x + 10 = 0$

Group terms: $(2x^2 + 4x) + (5x + 10) = 0$

Remove common factors: $2x(x + 2) + 5(x + 2) = 0$

Remove a common binomial factor: $(2x + 5)(x + 2) = 0$

Use the zero product property: $2x + 5 = 0$ or $x + 2 = 0$

$2x = -5$ or $x = -2$

$x = -\dfrac{5}{2}$ or $x = -2$

The roots are $-\dfrac{5}{2}$ and -2.

1. Solve by factoring.

a) $x^2 + 9x + 20 = 0$ b) $y^2 + 2 = 3y$ c) $b^2 + 7b = 30$ d) $a^2 + 8a + 15 = 0$

2. Solve by factoring.

a) $3x^2 + x = 2$ b) $4x^2 - 20x = -25$ c) $25y^2 - 9 = 0$ d) $9x^2 - 4x = 0$

Solving quadratic equations by graphing

To solve $x^2 + 3x = 4$ by graphing, first write the equation in the form $ax^2 + bx + c = 0$.

$$x^2 + 3x = 4$$
$$x^2 + 3x - 4 = 0$$

Next, graph the related quadratic function $y = x^2 + 3x - 4$ using paper and pencil, a graphing calculator, or graphing software.

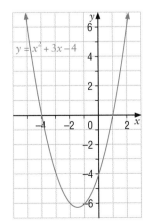

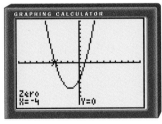

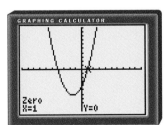

Window variables:
$x \in [0, 9]$, $y \in [0, 5]$

Use the Zero operation to find the solutions.

The graph intersects the x-axis at $(1, 0)$ and $(-4, 0)$. The solutions of $x^2 + 3x = 4$ are $x = 1$ and $x = -4$.

Another way of solving this is by graphing $f(x) = x^2 + 3x$ and $g(x) = 4$, and finding their point of intersection.

1. Solve by graphing.

a) $x^2 = 4x + 5$

b) $x^2 + 5x = -4$

c) $x^2 - 16 = 0$

d) $-x^2 + 8 = 7x$

e) $6x - 5 = x^2$

f) $x^2 + 8x = -12$

Solving radical equations

To solve the radical equation $\sqrt{x + 3} - \sqrt{2x - 1} = -1$, isolate one radical on the left side of the equation.

$$\sqrt{x + 3} - \sqrt{2x - 1} = -1$$

Isolate one radical to the left side of the equation:

$$\sqrt{x + 3} = -1 + \sqrt{2x - 1}$$

Square both sides:

$$x + 3 = 1 - 2\sqrt{2x - 1} + 2x - 1$$

Simplify:

$$-x + 3 = -2\sqrt{2x - 1}$$

Square both sides again:

$$x^2 - 6x + 9 = 4(2x - 1)$$

Simplify:

$$x^2 - 6x + 9 = 8x - 4$$

$$x^2 - 14x + 13 = 0$$

$$(x - 13)(x - 1) = 0$$

$$x = 13 \text{ or } x = 1$$

Check $x = 13$:

L.S. $= \sqrt{x + 3} - \sqrt{2x - 1}$ R.S. $= -1$

$= \sqrt{13 + 3} - \sqrt{2(13) - 1}$

$= \sqrt{16} - \sqrt{25}$

$= 4 - 5$

$= -1$

L.S. $=$ R.S.

Check $x = 1$:

L.S. $= \sqrt{x + 3} - \sqrt{2x - 1}$ R.S. $= -1$

$= \sqrt{1 + 3} - \sqrt{2(1) - 1}$

$= \sqrt{4} - \sqrt{1}$

$= 2 - 1$

$= 1$

L.S. $\ne$ R.S.

Thus, $x = 1$ is an extraneous root, introduced when both sides of the equation were squared. The only solution is $x = 13$.

1. Solve each equation.

a) $2\sqrt{x - 3} + 3 = 7$

b) $\sqrt{x - 5} = \sqrt{5 - x}$

c) $\sqrt{x - 4} = 10 - \sqrt{x + 16}$

d) $\sqrt{7 - 3x} = \sqrt{2x + 7} - 1$

Solving trigonometric equations

To solve the equation $2\cos^2 x - 3\cos x + 1 = 0$ for $x \in [0, 2\pi]$, factor the equation.

$$2\cos^2 x - 3\cos x + 1 = 0$$

$$(2\cos x - 1)(\cos x - 1) = 0$$

$2\cos x - 1 = 0$ or $\cos x - 1 = 0$

$\qquad 2\cos x = 1 \qquad\qquad \cos x = 1$

$\qquad \cos x = \dfrac{1}{2}$

By the CAST rule, the cosine of an angle is positive in the first and fourth quadrants.

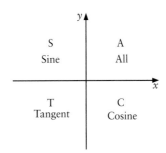

$\cos x = \dfrac{1}{2} \qquad\qquad \cos x = 1$

$x = \dfrac{\pi}{3}$ or $x = \dfrac{5\pi}{3} \qquad x = 0$ or 2π

The solutions are $0, \dfrac{\pi}{3}, \dfrac{5\pi}{3}$, and 2π.

1. Solve each equation for $x \in [0, 2\pi]$.

a) $5\sin x = 3\sin x + 1$

b) $\tan^2 x = 2\tan x - 1$

c) $\cos^2 x - 5\cos x + 6 = 0$

The quadratic formula

To solve $5x^2 + 4x = 1$, write the equation in the form $ax^2 + bx + c = 0$.

$5x^2 + 4x = 1$

$5x^2 + 4x - 1 = 0$

Then, substitute $a = 5$, $b = 4$, and $c = -1$ into the quadratic formula

$x = \dfrac{-b \pm \sqrt{b^2 - 4ac}}{2a}$ and simplify.

$$x = \dfrac{-b \pm \sqrt{b^2 - 4ac}}{2a}$$

$$= \dfrac{-4 \pm \sqrt{4^2 - 4(5)(-1)}}{2(5)}$$

$$= \dfrac{-4 \pm \sqrt{36}}{10}$$

$$= \dfrac{-4 \pm 6}{10}$$

So, $x = \dfrac{-4+6}{10}$ or $x = \dfrac{-4-6}{10}$

$\qquad = \dfrac{2}{10} \qquad\qquad\quad = \dfrac{-10}{10}$

$\qquad = \dfrac{1}{5} \qquad\qquad\quad\; = -1$

The roots are $\dfrac{1}{5}$ and -1.

To solve $x^2 - 3x - 1 = 0$, substitute $a = 1$, $b = -3$, and $c = -1$ into the quadratic formula. Then, simplify.

$$x = \frac{-b \pm \sqrt{b^2 - 4ac}}{2a}$$

$$= \frac{-(-3) \pm \sqrt{(-3)^2 - 4(1)(-1)}}{2(1)}$$

$$= \frac{3 \pm \sqrt{13}}{2}$$

The exact roots are $\dfrac{3 + \sqrt{13}}{2}$ and $\dfrac{3 - \sqrt{13}}{2}$. The approximate roots are 3.3 and -0.3.

To solve $2x^2 - 2x + 5 = 0$, substitute $a = 2$, $b = -2$, $c = 5$ into the quadratic formula. Then, simplify, substituting i for $\sqrt{-1}$.

$$x = \frac{-b \pm \sqrt{b^2 - 4ac}}{2a}$$

$$= \frac{-(-2) \pm \sqrt{(-2)^2 - 4(2)(5)}}{2(2)}$$

$$= \frac{2 \pm \sqrt{-36}}{4}$$

$$= \frac{2 \pm 6\sqrt{-1}}{4}$$

$$= \frac{2 \pm 6i}{4}$$

$$= \frac{1 \pm 3i}{2}$$

The exact roots are $\dfrac{1 + 3i}{2}$ and $\dfrac{1 - 3i}{2}$.

1. Solve using the quadratic formula.

a) $2x^2 - 3x + 1 = 0$ b) $10x^2 = 21x - 9$ c) $3x^2 + 2 = 5x$

2. Solve using the quadratic formula. Express solutions as exact roots and as approximate roots, to the nearest tenth.

a) $5x^2 + 2x - 2 = 0$ b) $3x^2 - 2x - 2 = 0$ c) $2x^2 + 7 = 8x$

d) $4x^2 + 4x = 14$ e) $10x^2 = 4x + 4$ f) $6x^2 + 5x = 3$

3. Solve using the quadratic formula. Express solutions as exact roots.

a) $3x^2 + 2x + 5 = 0$ b) $2x^2 + 4x = -7$ c) $3x^2 = 6x - 4$

d) $x^2 + 1 = x$ e) $4x^2 - 3x = -10$ f) $y^2 + 25 = 0$

Transformations

The graph of $f(x) + 5$ is a vertical translation of $f(x)$ by 5 units upward.

The graph of $f(x - 1)$ is a horizontal translation of $f(x)$ by 1 unit to the right.

The graph of $4f(x)$ is a vertical stretch (expansion) of $f(x)$ by a factor of 4.

The graph of $f(2x)$ is a horizontal stretch (compression) of $f(x)$ by a factor of $\dfrac{1}{2}$.

The graph of $-f(x)$ is a reflection of $f(x)$ in the x-axis.

The graph of $f(-x)$ is a reflection of $f(x)$ in the y-axis.

To graph $y = -2(x + 3)^2$, shift the graph of $y = x^2$ to the left by 3 units, then stretch it vertically by a factor of 2, and finally reflect it in the x-axis.

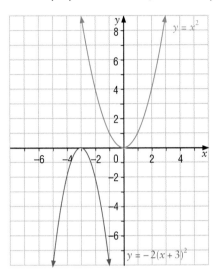

1. Determine whether the transformation of $f(x)$ is a vertical translation, a horizontal translation, a vertical stretch, a horizontal stretch, a vertical reflection, or a horizontal reflection.

a) $f(x) + 2$ b) $5f(x)$ c) $f(6x)$ d) $-f(x)$ e) $f(x - 4)$

f) $f(-x)$ g) $f(x + 7)$ h) $f\left(\dfrac{1}{4}x\right)$ i) $f(x) - 5$ j) $10f(x)$

2. Describe the transformations being applied to $f(x)$.

a) $3f(-x)$ b) $f(2x) - 3$ c) $-f(x + 2)$ d) $\dfrac{1}{3}f(-5x)$ e) $-4f\left(-\dfrac{3}{4}x - 1\right) + 7$

3. Graph each function by performing transformations on the graph of $y = x^2$.

a) $y = x^2 + 4$ b) $y = 3(x + 1)^2$ c) $y = (-2x - 5)^2 + 2$ d) $y = -4(3x + 2)^2 - 5$

Trigonometric functions

To determine the values of $\sin \theta$, $\cos \theta$, and $\tan \theta$ in the graph below, first determine the length of the terminal arm, r.

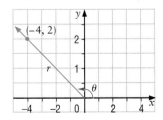

$$r = \sqrt{x^2 + y^2}$$
$$= \sqrt{(-4)^2 + 2^2}$$
$$= \sqrt{16 + 4}$$
$$= \sqrt{20}$$
$$= 2\sqrt{5}$$

Now the three trigonometric values can be determined.

$$\sin\theta = \frac{y}{r} \qquad \cos\theta = \frac{x}{r} \qquad \tan\theta = \frac{y}{x}$$
$$= \frac{2}{2\sqrt{5}} \qquad = \frac{-4}{2\sqrt{5}} \qquad = \frac{2}{-4}$$
$$= \frac{1}{\sqrt{5}} \qquad = -\frac{2}{\sqrt{5}} \qquad = -\frac{1}{2}$$

To determine the value of $\sin 38°$, make sure your calculator is set to degrees and use the [SIN] key.

$$\sin 38° \doteq 0.6157$$

To determine the value of $\cos 0.4$, make sure your calculator is set to radians and use the [COS] key.

$$\cos 0.4 \doteq 0.9211$$

To determine the value of θ, in degrees, if $\tan\theta = 1.15$, make sure your calculator is set to degrees and use TAN^{-1}.

$$\tan\theta = 1.15$$
$$\theta = \tan^{-1} 1.15$$
$$\doteq 48.99°$$

To determine the value of θ, in radians, if $\cos\theta = -0.94$, make sure your calculator is set to radians and use the COS^{-1}.

$$\cos\theta = -0.94$$
$$\theta = \cos^{-1}(-0.94)$$
$$\doteq 2.79 \text{ rad}$$

If $\sin\theta = 0$ and $\cos\theta = 1$, the value of $\tan\theta$ can be determined without calculating θ by using the trigonometric identity $\tan\theta = \dfrac{\sin\theta}{\cos\theta}$.

$$\tan\theta = \frac{\sin\theta}{\cos\theta}$$
$$= \frac{0}{1}$$
$$= 0$$

The value of $\tan\theta$ is 0.

1. Determine the values of $\sin\theta$, $\cos\theta$, and $\tan\theta$.

a)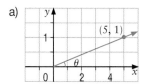

b)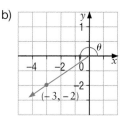

c)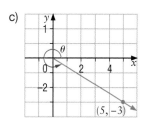

2. Determine the sine, cosine, and tangent ratios for each angle.

a) 77°   b) 148°   c) 33°   d) 0.7 rad   e) 4.3 rad   f) $\dfrac{8\pi}{5}$ rad

3. Determine the measure of each angle in both radians and degrees.

a) $\sin\theta = 0.84$ b) $\cos\theta = -0.91$ c) $\tan\theta = -0.14$

4. Determine each value without calculating θ.

a) $\tan\theta$ when $\sin\theta = \dfrac{1}{\sqrt{2}}$ and $\cos\theta = \dfrac{1}{\sqrt{2}}$

b) $\cos\theta$ when $\sin\theta = -\dfrac{\sqrt{3}}{2}$ and $\tan\theta = \sqrt{3}$

c) $\sin\theta$ when $\tan\theta = 0$ and $\cos\theta = -1$

Trigonometric identities

To prove the trigonometric identity $\sin x \tan x \cos x = 1 - \cos^2 x$, use the quotient identity, which is $\dfrac{\sin x}{\cos x} = \tan x$, and the Pythagorean identity, which is $\sin^2 x + \cos^2 x = 1$.

	L.S. $= \sin x \tan x \cos x$	R.S. $= 1 - \cos^2 x$

Use the quotient identity:
$$= \sin x\, \frac{\sin x}{\cos x}\, \cos x$$
$$= \sin^2 x$$

Use the Pythagorean identity:
$$= 1 - \cos^2 x$$

$$\text{L.S.} = \text{R.S.}$$

Thus, $\sin x \tan x \cos x = 1 - \cos^2 x$.

1. Prove each trigonometric identity.

a) $\dfrac{\cos x}{\sin x} = \dfrac{1}{\tan x}$

b) $\dfrac{\sin^2 x}{\tan^2 x} = 1 - \sin^2 x$

c) $\cos x = \dfrac{\sin^3 x}{\tan x} + \cos^3 x$

Word problems

Harlan has been given a 32-cm by 18-cm rectangular sheet of construction paper and wants to cut out square pieces from the corners, as shown, in order to fold the paper into a box. The base of the box must have an area of 176 cm^2. What are the dimensions of the squares Harlan must cut out of the corners to make this box?

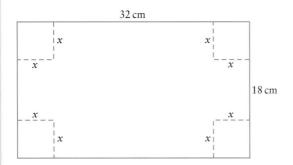

From the diagram, the length of each side of the corners Harlan is cutting out is x. So the dimensions of the base will be $32 - 2x$ by $18 - 2x$.

The area of the base can be modelled by the equation $176 = (32 - 2x)(18 - 2x)$. Expand and simplify the equation. Then, solve for x.

$176 = (32 - 2x)(18 - 2x)$

$176 = 576 - 64x - 36x + 4x^2$

$176 = 576 - 100x + 4x^2$

$0 = 400 - 100x + 4x^2$

$0 = 100 - 25x + x^2$

$0 = (20 - x)(5 - x)$

$20 - x = 0$ or $5 - x = 0$

$\qquad x = 20 \qquad\quad x = 5$

If x, the side length of the corners being cut, is 20 cm, then the dimensions of both sides of the base are negative, which is impossible.

Therefore, we can exclude the solution $x = 20$. Thus, $x = 5$ is the only solution.

The dimensions of the squares that Harlan must cut are 5 cm by 5 cm.

1. A garden is to be planted around the edges of a 15-m by 25-m tract of land such that the width of the garden is equal on all sides of the property, and the area of the garden is equal to the area of the property. Find the width of the garden, rounded to the nearest tenth of a metre if necessary.

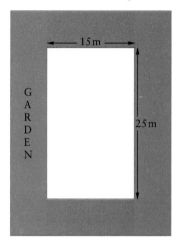

Writing numbers in exponential form

To write 8 in exponential form using base 2, determine how many times 2 must be multiplied by itself to equal 8.

2 must be multiplied by itself 3 times, so $8 = 2^3$.

Recall:

$x^0 = 1$, where x is a real number and $x \neq 0$

$x^{-1} = \dfrac{1}{x}$, where x is a real number and $x \neq 0$

$x^{\frac{1}{2}} = \sqrt{x}$, where x is a real number and $x \geq 0$

1. Write each number in exponential form, with the specified base.

a) 81, base 3   b) 1, base 7   c) $\sqrt{10}$, base 10   d) $\dfrac{1}{125}$, base 5

Appendix B

Graphing Calculator Keystrokes

TI-83 Plus/TI-83

Function or Instruction and Description	Keystroke(s), Menu, or Screen
abs function The abs function is used to find the absolute value of a real number, or to graph an absolute value function.	To select the abs function from the MATH NUM menu, press MATH ▶ 1. **Example:** To graph the function $y = |x|$, enter the Y= editor. Press MATH ▶ 1 X,T,Θ,n) to input the equation of the function in Y1.  Press ZOOM 6 to use the ZStandard instruction to graph the function in the standard viewing window. You will see 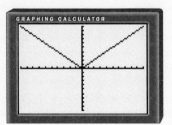
Ans function The Ans function is a reference to the most recent numerical value determined by your calculator.	To select the Ans function, press 2nd (-). **Example:** Here is a simple demonstration of how the Ans function is used. You will learn to apply it in more useful settings. Press 1 + 1 ENTER. The value stored in the Ans function is now 2. Press + 1 ENTER. (When the Ans function appears at the beginning of an expression, you do not have to press 2nd (-) to select it.)

Function or Instruction and Description	Keystroke(s), Menu, or Screen

You will see

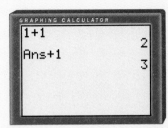

The value stored in the Ans function is now 3.

Ask mode

Ask mode gives you more freedom when setting up a table of values in the TABLE screen.

To select Ask mode, press $\boxed{\text{2nd}}$ $\boxed{\text{WINDOW}}$ to enter the TABLE SETUP screen. Using the arrow keys, highlight **Indpnt:Ask** and press $\boxed{\text{ENTER}}$. When **Indpnt:Ask** is selected, the values of **TblStart** and Δ**Tbl** have no bearing on the table. Make sure **Depend:Auto** is selected.

When **Indpnt:Ask** and **Depend:Auto** are selected, the dependent variable will be calculated automatically when you enter an independent variable manually.

Example:

To find $\lim\limits_{x \to 0^+} \dfrac{1}{x^2}$ using a numerical method, enter the Y= editor

and input the function $y = \dfrac{1}{x^2}$ in Y1.

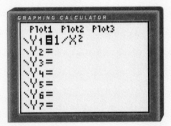

Press $\boxed{\text{2nd}}$ $\boxed{\text{WINDOW}}$ to enter the TABLE SETUP screen and select **Indpnt:Ask** and **Depend:Auto**.

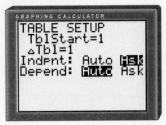

Function or Instruction and Description	Keystroke(s), Menu, or Screen
	Press [2nd] [GRAPH] to enter the TABLE screen. Suppose you want to determine the values of the function for the following values of x: 1, 0.1, 0.01, 0.001, 0.0001. Input the first value and press [ENTER]. The dependent variable is automatically calculated according to the equation stored in Y1, and displayed in the Y1 column. Enter the remaining x-values in the same way.

You will see

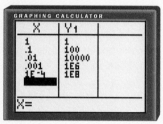

CATALOG menu

The CATALOG menu is used to select any function on the TI-83 or TI-83 Plus.

To display the CATALOG menu, press [2nd] 0.

Example:

Determine the value of the derivative of the function $y = x^3$ when $x = 2$ by selecting the nDeriv function from the CATALOG menu. (Note that the nDeriv function can also be found on the MATH menu.)

Press [2nd] 0 to access the CATALOG menu. Notice that the **ALPHA** command has automatically been selected for you. Press **N** to scroll down to those functions having first letter n. Using the [▼] key, scroll down to **nDeriv**.

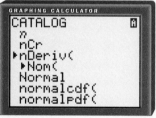

Press [ENTER] to select the nDeriv function, and then press [X,T,Θ,n] [^] 3 [,] [X,T,Θ,n] [,] 2 [)] [ENTER].

You will see

Function or Instruction and Description	Keystroke(s), Menu, or Screen

ClrAllLists instruction

The ClrAllLists instruction is used to clear the numbers in all lists.

To select the ClrAllLists instruction from the MEMORY menu, press [2nd] [+] 4.

Press [ENTER] to execute the instruction. The message **Done** will be displayed.

ClrDraw instruction

The ClrDraw instruction removes all drawn elements from the viewing window.

To select the ClrDraw instruction from the DRAW menu, press [2nd] [PRGM] 1.

If you select the ClrDraw instruction when a graph is displayed, the graph will be replotted with all drawn elements removed.

If you execute the ClrDraw instruction in the home screen, the calculator removes all drawn elements from the current graph and displays the message **Done**. When you return to the graphing window, all drawn elements will be cleared.

Connected mode

When the calculator is in Connected mode, points are plotted and joined by a smooth curve.

To select Connected mode, press [MODE] and then [▼] [▼] [▼] [▼] to highlight Connected. Press [ENTER].

Dot mode

When the calculator is in Dot mode, points are plotted but not joined by a smooth curve.

To select Dot mode, press [MODE] and then [▼] [▼] [▼] [▼] [▶] to highlight **Dot**. Press [ENTER].

Function or Instruction and Description	Keystroke(s), Menu, or Screen

Example:

A common use of Dot mode is for Graphing piecewise functions. Use the ZDecimal instruction to graph the piecewise curve

$$f(x) = \begin{cases} 1, & x \in (-\infty, 1) \\ x - 2, & x \in [1, \infty) \end{cases}$$

in Connected mode.

You will see

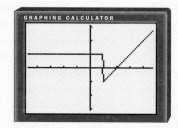

Notice how the graphing calculator connects the two pieces of the function. To avoid this, use Dot mode to graph the function.

You will see

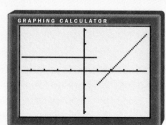

DrawInv instruction

The DrawInv instruction draws the inverse of a function.

To select the DrawInv instruction from the DRAW menu, press [2nd] [PRGM] 8.

Example:

Clear any previous drawings by pressing [2nd] [PRGM] 1 [ENTER].

To draw the function $y = x^2 + 3$ and its inverse, input the function as Y1 in the Y= editor. Input the function $y = x$ so that the mirror line appears on the graph. Use the ZSquare instruction to square the viewing window.

Press [2nd] [PRGM] 8 to select the DrawInv instruction.

Press [VARS] [▶] 1 1 to enter Y1 as the function to draw.

Function or Instruction and Description	Keystroke(s), Menu, or Screen

You will see

Press ENTER.

You will see

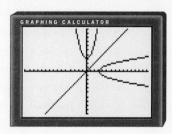

dy/dx operation
The dy/dx operation finds the value of the derivative at a point on a graph. The dy/dx operation is used in the graphing window.

To find the value of the derivative at a point on a graph, display the graph on the screen. The x-value of the point at which you want to find the derivative must appear on the x-axis of the screen to use the dy/dx operation.

Example:
To find the value of the derivative at the point $(2, 5)$ for the curve $y = x^3 - 2x + 1$, use the Y= editor to input and graph the function.

Press 2nd TRACE to display the CALCULATE menu. To select the dy/dx operation, press 6:dy/dx.

Press 2 ENTER to input the x-value of the point. Alternatively, you can use the arrow keys to move the cursor to the desired point.

You will see

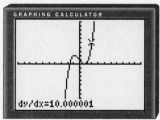

The solution appears in the bottom left corner of the screen. Since the calculator determines the derivative numerically, it displays an approximate solution. The exact solution is 10.

Function or Instruction and Description	**Keystroke(s), Menu, or Screen**

ENTRY function

The ENTRY function is used to recall the last expression entered in your calculator. This is especially useful if you make an error while inputting an expression.

When you key in an expression and execute it, that expression is stored in a buffer of the calculator. To recall the last expression, press [2nd] [ENTER]. The expression will be displayed in the home screen, where you can edit and execute it.

Example:
Input the expression $(2^2 + 3(4)/(3 + 4)$. Press [ENTER].

You will see

Note that the expression above has a missing closing bracket, at the end of the expression for the numerator, so the calculator does not find the correct solution. To correct the expression, press [2nd] [ENTER].

You will see

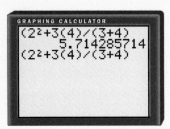

Use the arrow keys to move to the place where you want to insert the closing bracket. Press [2nd] [DEL] [)] to insert the bracket. Press [ENTER].

You will see

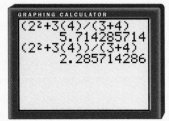

The correct solution is 2.285 714 286.

Function or Instruction and Description	**Keystroke(s), Menu, or Screen**

e^x function

The e^x function is used to raise the constant e to any exponent.

Example:

To find the value of e^1, press [2nd] [LN] to select the e^x function, and then press 1 [)] [ENTER].

You will see

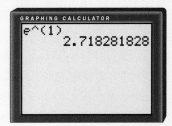

fMax function

The fMax function is used to find the point at which the maximum value of a function occurs, on a specified interval. The fMax function is used in the Home screen.

To select the fMax function from the MATH menu, press [MATH] and select 7:fMax.

Example:

To find the x-coordinate at which the maximum value of the function $y = x^3 - 2x^2 - 5x + 5$ occurs on the interval $(-2, 2)$, enter the Y= editor and input the function in Y1.

In the Home screen, press [MATH] 7 to select the fMax function. Press [VARS] [▶] 1 1 [,] [X,T,Θ,n] [,] [(-)] 2 [,] 2 [)] [ENTER]. The calculator will display the x-value at which the maximum occurs. Press [VARS] [▶] 1 1 [(] [2nd] [(-)] [)] [ENTER] to determine the maximum value of the function on the interval.

You will see

fMin function

The fMin function is used to find the point at which the minimum value of a function occurs, on a specified interval. The fMin function is used in the Home screen.

To select the fMin function from the MATH menu, press [MATH] and select 6:fMin. Follow the same steps as for the fMax function, substituting fMin for fMax.

Function or Instruction and Description	Keystroke(s), Menu, or Screen

Format settings

Format settings define the appearance of a graph on the display. Format settings apply to all graphing modes.

To display the Format settings, press [2nd] [ZOOM].

To change a Format setting, press [▼], [▶], [▲], and [◀], as necessary, to move the cursor to the setting you want to select, and press [ENTER] to select it.

Example:
The default setting **AxesOn** means that the x- and y-axes are displayed on a graph. If you do not wish to display the axes, press [▼], [▼], [▼], [▶], and [ENTER] to select **AxesOff**.

G–T mode

In G–T mode, the viewing window is split into two halves: the left part contains a graph, and the right part contains a table of values.

To enter G–T mode, press [MODE] and use the arrow keys to highlight **G–T**. Press [ENTER].

To work in the left half, press [GRAPH] or [TRACE], or use the CALCULATE or ZOOM menu. To work in the right half, press [2nd] [GRAPH].

In G–T mode, all other screens are full size.

Example:
Use the ZStandard instruction to graph the curve $y = x^2$ in G–T mode in the standard viewing window.

You will see

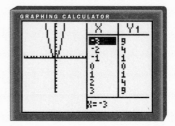

Note that the values shown in the table do not necessarily correspond to the values shown on the graph. To make them correspond, you must set up the viewing window and the TABLE SETUP screen appropriately.

Function or Instruction and Description	Keystroke(s), Menu, or Screen

Graph styles

Varying Graph styles allows you to differentiate functions that are graphed together.

To set the Graph style for a function, press ⃞Y= to display the Y= editor.

Use the ⃞◄ key to move the cursor to the left of the function to be graphed. Press the ⃞ENTER key repeatedly to choose an appropriate Graph style.

Graph styles available may vary depending on which graphing mode you are in.

In Func (function) graphing mode, the following styles are available.

Line   A smooth curve connects points. This is the default style in Connected mode.

Thick   A thick smooth curve connects points.

Above   Shading covers the area above the graph.

Below   Shading covers the area below the graph.

Path   A circular cursor traces the leading edge of the graph and draws a path.

Animate A circular cursor traces the leading edge of the graph without drawing a path.

Dot   A small dot represents each point. This is the default style in Dot mode.

Example:
To graph $y = x^3 - 2x^2 - 5x + 5$ and its first and second derivative functions on the same set of axes, enter the functions in the Y= editor as Y1 = X^3−2X^2 − 5X + 5, Y2 = nDeriv(Y1,X,X) and Y3 = nDeriv(Y2,X,X). The default Graph style is Line. Leave Y1 as Line style. Move the cursor to the left of Y2 using the arrow keys. Press ⃞ENTER to change the Graph style to Thick. Move the cursor to the left of Y3 using the arrow keys. Press ⃞ENTER six times to change the Graph style to Dot.

Function or Instruction and Description	Keystroke(s), Menu, or Screen
	Change the Window variables to values such as Xmin = −3, Xmax = 4, Ymin = −10, Ymax = 10, and Xres = 2. Press the GRAPH key to display the graphs.

You will see

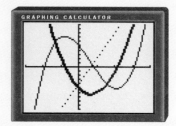

Graphing piecewise functions
You can use the Y= editor to graph piecewise functions.

Example:
To graph the piecewise function
$$y = \begin{cases} x^2, & x \le 0 \\ x, & x > 0 \end{cases}$$

press Y= to display the Y= editor, and in Y1, press (X,T,Θ,n x^2) (X,T,Θ,n 2nd MATH 6 0) to input the first piece of the function. Then, press + (X,T,Θ,n) (X,T,Θ,n 2nd MATH 3 0) to input the rest of the function.

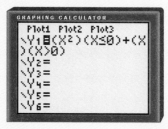

The two pieces can also be entered separately in Y1 and Y2 as follows:

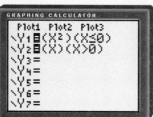

Function or Instruction and Description	Keystroke(s), Menu, or Screen
	Use the ZDecimal instruction to view the graph in the ZDecimal window. You will see 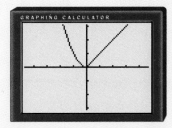 Note that if the piecewise function has jumps in it, you need to use Dot mode.
Intersect operation The Intersect operation finds the coordinates of a point of intersection of two functions.	To find a point of intersection, display the graphs on the screen. The x-coordinate of the point of intersection must appear on the display to use the Intersect operation. **Example:** To find the point of intersection of $y = 3x - 2$ and $y = -x + 6$, use the Y= editor to input both functions and graph them. Press 2nd TRACE to display the CALCULATE menu. To select the Intersect operation, press **5**. The equation stored in Y1 is displayed in the top left corner of the screen. Press ENTER to choose Y1 as the first function. Now, the equation stored in Y2 is displayed in the top left corner of the screen. Press ENTER to choose Y2 as the second function. Press ▶ or ◀ to move the cursor to the point that is your guess for the point of intersection, and then press ENTER. You will see 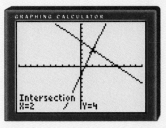 Notice that the cursor appears on the point of intersection, and the coordinates of the point of intersection are displayed.

Function or Instruction and Description	Keystroke(s), Menu, or Screen

ΔList function

The ΔList function is used to generate a list of the differences between consecutive elements in a specified list.

Example:
To determine the relationship between x and y in the table of values, enter the x-values in L1 and the y-values in L2.

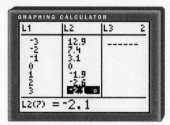

Use the ΔList function to determine the first differences of the y-values. Press the STAT key and select 1:Edit. Use the arrow keys to move the cursor to L3. Press 2nd STAT ▶ to access the LIST OPS menu, and select 7:ΔList. Press 2nd 1) to input L2 into the function.

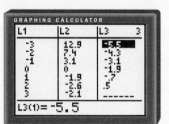

Press ENTER.
You will see

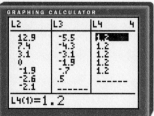

The first differences are not equal, so the relationship is not linear. Perform the ΔList function on L3 and store the second differences in L4.

The second differences are equal. Thus, the relationship between x and y is quadratic.

Function or Instruction and Description	Keystroke(s), Menu, or Screen

ln function

The ln function is used to find the natural logarithm of a positive number.

To select the ln function, press [LN].

Example:
To find the natural logarithm of 298, press [LN] 298 [)] [ENTER].

You will see

log function

The log function is used to find the logarithm to base 10 of a positive number.

To select the log function, press [LOG].

Example:
To find the logarithm of 37 to base 10, press [LOG] 37 [)] [ENTER].

You will see

Maximum operation

The Maximum operation finds the maximum of a function within a specified interval. The Maximum operation is used in the graphing window.

Example:
To find a local maximum of $y = x^3 - 2x^2 - 5x + 5$, input the function in the Y= editor. Press [2nd] [TRACE] to display the CALCULATE menu. Press 4 to select the Maximum operation.

You will see

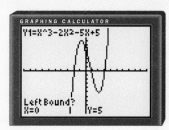

Function or Instruction and Description	Keystroke(s), Menu, or Screen

Press ▾ or ▴, if necessary, to move the cursor onto the function.

Press ▸ or ◂ to move the cursor to the left of the maximum (or enter a value). Select the *x*-value for the left bound of the interval by pressing ENTER.

Press ▸ to move the cursor to the right of the maximum (or enter a value). Select the *x*-value for the right bound of the interval by pressing ENTER.

Press ◂ (or enter a value) to select an *x*-value for a guess at the maximum, and then press ENTER.

You will see

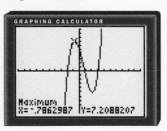

Minimum operation

The Minimum operation finds the minimum of a function within a specified interval. The Minimum operation is used in the graphing window.

To find a local minimum of a function, input it in the Y= editor. Press 2nd TRACE to display the CALCULATE menu. Press 3 to select the Minimum operation. Then, proceed as for the Maximum operation, substituting minimum for maximum as necessary.

Mode settings

Mode settings control the way the calculator displays and interprets numbers and graphs.

To display the Mode settings, press MODE. The default settings are shown here.

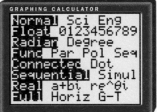

To change a mode setting, press ▾, ▸, ▴, and ◂, as necessary, to move the cursor to the setting you want to select, and press ENTER to select it.

Example:
The default setting **Radian** means that angles are measured in radians. If you wish angles to be measured in degrees, press ▾, ▾, ▸, and ENTER to select **Degree**.

Function or Instruction and Description	Keystroke(s), Menu, or Screen

nDeriv function

The nDeriv function is used to calculate an approximate value for the derivative of a function at a specified point or to graph the derivative of a function. The nDeriv function can be used in the Home screen or the Y= editor.

To select the nDeriv function, press MATH 8.

Example:

In the Home screen, to find the value of the derivative of the function $y = x^2 + 2x + 1$ at the point (3, 16), press MATH 8 to select the nDeriv function. Then, press X,T,Θ,n x^2 + 2 X,T,Θ,n + 1 , to input the function and press X,T,Θ,n , to input the variable with respect to which you want to find the derivative. Press 3) to input the x-value of the point at which you want to find the derivative, and press ENTER.

You will see

Example:

To graph the function $y = \ln x$ and its derivative on the same set of axes, enter the Y= editor and input Y1 = ln(X) and Y2 = nDeriv(Y1,X,X). Notice that the third parameter is X,T,Θ,n rather than a fixed numerical value. By using X,T,Θ,n rather than a fixed value, the function works for all values of x.

Change the Window variables to values such as Xmin = –1, Xmax = 4, Ymin = –5, and Ymax = 5. Press GRAPH to display the graphs.

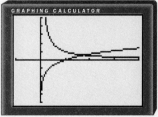

Function or Instruction and Description	Keystroke(s), Menu, or Screen

Sequence function

The Sequence function can be used to generate elements of a sequence.

Example:

To enter the integers between –3 and 3 inclusive into L1, press [STAT] to access the STAT EDIT menu and select 1:Edit.... Using the arrow keys, move the cursor to highlight L1. Press [2nd] [STAT] [▶] to access the LIST OPS menu, and select 5:seq(. Press [X,T,Θ,n] [,] [X,T,Θ,n] [,] to enter the expression and the variable. Press [(-)] 3 [,] 3 [,] 1 [)] to input the starting value for the variable, the ending value, and the increment value.

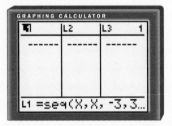

Press [ENTER].

You will see

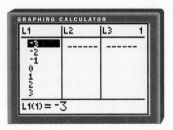

STAT CALC menu

The STAT CALC menu lists all the regression instructions you will need in this textbook. They are
LinReg (linear regression), QuadReg (quadratic regression), CubicReg (cubic regression), QuartReg (quartic regression), ExpReg (exponential regression), PwrReg (power regression), and SinReg (sinusoidal regression). A similar method is used for each regression instruction.

Example:

To use the cubic regression instruction on the following set of data, enter the data points in L1 and L2 for x and y, respectively.

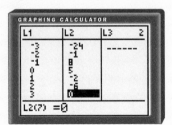

Function or Instruction and Description	Keystroke(s), Menu, or Screen

Graph L2 versus L1 on a scatter plot using the STAT PLOTS menu. Adjust the viewing window automatically using the ZoomStat instruction. Adjust Xscl and Yscl in the Window variables if necessary. In this case, Yscl was adjusted to 5.

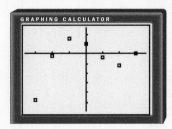

From the graph, the data appear to be cubic, and so a cubic regression can be performed. To select the cubic regression instruction, press STAT ▶ to access the STAT CALC menu. Select 6:CubicReg.

Specify the Xlist name, L1, by pressing 2nd 1 ,.

Specify the Ylist name, L2, by pressing 2nd 2 ,.

Press VARS ▶ 1 to list possible Y variables. To store the regression equation in Y1, select 1:Y1. Press ENTER.

You will see

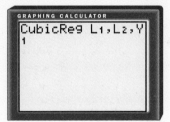

Press ENTER.
You will see

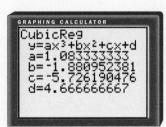

Function or Instruction and Description	Keystroke(s), Menu, or Screen

The regression equation is stored in the Y= editor. If you wish to view the curve of best fit on your scatter plot, press GRAPH.

You will see

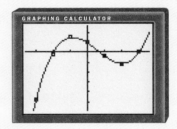

STAT EDIT menu
The STAT EDIT menu is used when you wish to store, edit, and view lists of data in the stat list editor.

To display the STAT EDIT menu, press STAT.

You will see

To display the stat list editor, press STAT 1:Edit.

You will see

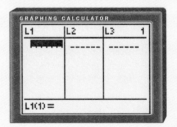

Lists of data can be stored in lists named L1 through L6. To clear data from a specific list, for example, L1, press STAT 4:ClrList 2nd 1 ENTER.

To clear data from all lists, use the ClrAllLists instruction.

Example:
Enter the table shown in lists L1 and L2.

L1	L2
2	0
3	12
4	24
5	35

Function or Instruction and Description	Keystroke(s), Menu, or Screen

Use the ClrAllLists instruction to clear all data from lists L1 to L6.

Press [STAT] 1:Edit to display the stat list editor. To enter the data in L1, press 2 [ENTER] 3 [ENTER] 4 [ENTER] 5 [ENTER]. To enter the data in L2, press [▶] 0 [ENTER] 12 [ENTER] 24 [ENTER] 36 [ENTER].

You will see

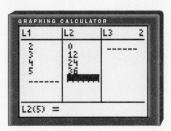

STAT PLOTS menu
The STAT PLOTS menu allows you to plot data in several different ways. In this textbook, you will use it to plot scatter plots.

To display the STAT PLOTS menu, press [2nd] [Y=].

Example:
Plot the data in a scatter plot.

L_1	L_2
2	0
3	12
4	24
5	36

Enter the data in lists L1 and L2 using the STAT EDIT menu.

Press [2nd] [Y=] to display the STAT PLOTS menu.

You will see

Press [ENTER] to select Plot1 or use the [▼] key to select Plot2 or Plot3 and press [ENTER]. To turn on a plot, press [ENTER].

Function or Instruction and Description	Keystroke(s), Menu, or Screen

You will see

To select a scatter plot, press ▼ [ENTER].

If the Xlist is not already L1, press ▼ [2nd] 1 [ENTER].

If the Ylist is not already L2, press ▼ [2nd] 2 [ENTER].

Choose the type of mark for the data points by pressing ▶ or ◀ to highlight the desired mark, and then press [ENTER].

To display the plot, press [ZOOM] 9 to select the ZoomStat instruction. Adjust Xscl and Yscl if necessary. In this case, Yscl has been set to 5.

You will see

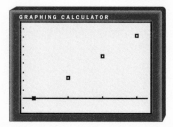

TABLE SETUP screen

A table of values can be calculated and displayed for any function that can be input in the Y= editor.

Example:

To display a table of values for the function $y = 2x^2 - 8$, enter the function into the Y= editor.

If you wish the table of values to be generated automatically, press [2nd] [WINDOW] to display the TABLE SETUP screen. To define the initial value for the independent variable, x, set TblStart to the initial value you want for your table of values, for example, −3.

Set ΔTbl to the value of the desired increment for the independent variable, for example, 1.

If you wish the values for both the independent variable, x, and the dependent variable, y, to be displayed automatically, select Indpnt:Auto and Depend:Auto.

Function or Instruction and Description	Keystroke(s), Menu, or Screen

For this example, you will see

Display the table of values by pressing 2nd GRAPH. For this example, you will see

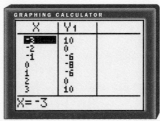

For instructions on how to choose the values for the independent variable, see the Ask mode entry.

Tangent operation

The Tangent operation is used to draw a tangent to a curve.

To draw the tangent to a point on a graph, display the graph on the screen. The x-value of the point at which you want to draw the tangent must appear on the x-axis of the screen.

Example:

To draw a tangent to the point $(2, 6)$ on the graph of the function $y = x^2 + 2$, enter the Y= editor and graph the function. When the graph is displayed, press 2nd PRGM 5 to select the Tangent operation.

Press 2 ENTER to input the x-coordinate of the point at which you want to graph the tangent. The tangent will be graphed on the screen.

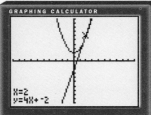

Notice that the equation of the tangent, $y = 4x - 2$, appears in the bottom left corner of the screen.

Function or Instruction and Description	Keystroke(s), Menu, or Screen

Value operation

The Value operation evaluates a function for a specified value of x.

Example:

To evaluate the function $y = x^2 + 3x - 4$ for $x = -3$, input the function in the Y= editor.

Press [2nd] [TRACE] to display the CALCULATE menu. Press [ENTER] to select the Value operation.

You will see

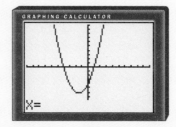

Enter the value -3 for x. Press [ENTER].

You will see

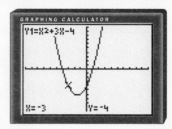

Note: The value for which you evaluate a function must lie between Xmin and Xmax of the viewing window used for the graph.

Vertical instruction

The Vertical instruction is used to graph vertical lines.

To select the Vertical instruction, press [ZOOM] 4 to enter the ZDecimal window and press [2nd] [PRGM] to access the DRAW menu. Then, select 4:Vertical.

Move the cursor to the x-coordinate through which the line will pass, and press [ENTER].

You will see, for example,

Function or Instruction and Description	Keystroke(s), Menu, or Screen
	You can also execute the Vertical instruction from the Home screen by pressing [2nd] [PRGM] to access the DRAW menu. Select 4:Vertical and input the *x*-value of the vertical line you wish to draw. Press [ENTER] and the line will be drawn.
Window variables The Window variables define the current viewing window.	To display the current Window variable values, press [WINDOW]. To change a Window variable, press ⏷ or ⏶ to move the cursor to the Window variable you want to change. Enter the new value and then press [ENTER].
Y= editor The Y= editor is used to define or edit a function.	Press [MODE] ⏷ ⏷ ⏷ [ENTER] to ensure that the calculator is in the Func graphing mode. To display the Y= editor, press [Y=]. To move the cursor to the next function, press [ENTER] or ⏷. To move the cursor from one function to another, press ⏷ or ⏶. To erase a function, highlight the function and press [CLEAR]. The independent variable is X. To input X, press [X,T,Θ,*n*] or [ALPHA] [STO▸]. When you input the first character of a function, the = is highlighted. This indicates that the function is selected. To deselect a function, move the cursor to the = symbol of the function and press [ENTER]. **Example:** To input $y = 4x + 5$ using the Y= editor, press the [Y=] key. You will see 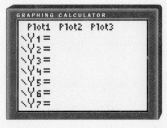 If any functions have already been input in the Y= editor, clear them using the [CLEAR] key. Press 4 [X,T,Θ,*n*] [+] 5 [ENTER].

Function or Instruction and Description	Keystroke(s), Menu, or Screen

You will see

ZBox instruction

The ZBox instruction adjusts the settings of the viewing window to display the contents of a rectangle constructed on the screen by the user.

Example:

To determine the number of x-intercepts of the function $y = 2x^2 - 5x + 3$, graph the function in the standard viewing window.

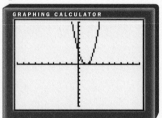

The number of x-intercepts is not clear from the graph.

Press [ZOOM] to display the ZOOM menu. Select **1:ZBox**. The coordinates of the cursor appear at the bottom of the screen.

Using the arrow keys, move the cursor to the desired location of the first corner of the rectangle. Press [ENTER].

You will see, for example,

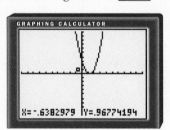

Move the cursor to the desired location of the diagonally opposite corner of the rectangle. You will see the rectangle on the screen.

Function or Instruction and Description	Keystroke(s), Menu, or Screen
	Press ENTER. The viewing window is adjusted and updated to contain the contents of the rectangle, and the selected function is replotted. 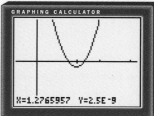 It is now clear that the function has two *x*-intercepts.
ZDecimal instruction The ZDecimal instruction replots all graphs and resets the Window variables to preset values, so that each pixel in the viewing window corresponds to one decimal place. This window is sometimes called the friendly window.	**Example:** Graph the function $y = \dfrac{1}{x - 2}$ in the standard viewing window. You will see 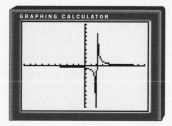 The calculator is in Connected mode, and so connects the points to the left and right of the vertical asymptote, $x = 2$. Press ZOOM to display the ZOOM menu. Select 4:ZDecimal. The viewing window is adjusted and updated and the graph is replotted. 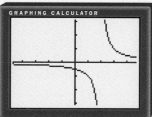 This time, the calculator detects an error when $x = 2$, and so does not connect the points to the left and right of the vertical asymptote.

Function or Instruction and Description	Keystroke(s), Menu, or Screen

Zero operation

The Zero operation finds the zeros or x-intercepts of functions. If a function has two or more x-intercepts, they must be found separately by repeated use of the Zero operation.

Example:

To find the x-intercepts of $y = x^2 + 2x - 8$, input the function in the Y= editor.

Press [2nd] [TRACE] to display the CALCULATE menu. Press 2 [ENTER] to select the zero operation.

You will see

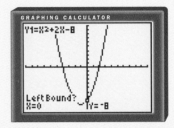

Press ▾ or ▴, if necessary, to move the cursor onto the function.

To find the left x-intercept, press ▸ or ◂ to move the cursor to the left of the left x-intercept (or enter a value). Select the x-value by pressing [ENTER].

Press ▸ to move the cursor to a location between the left x-intercept and the right x-intercept (or enter a value). Select the x-value by pressing [ENTER].

Press ◂ (or enter a value) to select an x-value for a guess at the left x-intercept, and then press [ENTER].

You will see

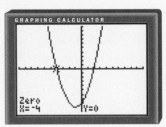

Repeat the instructions above, adjusting as necessary, to find the right x-intercept.

Function or Instruction and Description	Keystroke(s), Menu, or Screen

Zoom In instruction
The Zoom In instruction allows you to magnify the part of the graph that surrounds the cursor location.

Example:
To determine the number of x-intercepts of the function $y = 2x^2 - 5x + 3$, graph the function in the standard viewing window.

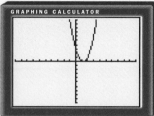

The number of x-intercepts is not clear from the graph.

Press ZOOM to display the ZOOM menu. Select 2:Zoom In. The zoom cursor (+) is displayed on the graph, at the origin.

Use the arrow keys to move the cursor to the point that is to be the centre of the new viewing window. Choose a point near where the graph appears to intersect the x-axis. Press ENTER.

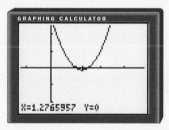

The viewing window is adjusted and updated and the selected function is replotted, centred on the cursor location. The number of x-intercepts is still not clear.

You can zoom in on the graph again by pressing ENTER to zoom out at the same point, or by moving the cursor to the point you want as the centre of the new viewing window, and then pressing ENTER.

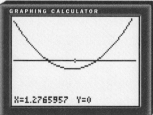

The function has two x-intercepts.

Function or Instruction and Description	Keystroke(s), Menu, or Screen

ZOOM menu

The ZOOM menu contains instructions that allow you to adjust the viewing window quickly.

To display the ZOOM menu, press $\boxed{\text{ZOOM}}$.

You will see

Zoom Out instruction

The Zoom Out instruction allows you to decrease the scale of the axes in the viewing window, centering the graph on the cursor location.

To use the Zoom Out instruction, follow the instructions for the Zoom In instruction, but select 3:Zoom Out instead of 2:Zoom In from the ZOOM menu.

ZoomStat instruction

The ZoomStat instruction redefines the Window variables to display all statistical data points on the screen.

Example:
To display a scatter plot of the following set of data, enter the x- and y-values in L1 and L2, respectively.

x	y	x	y
−3	−25	1	−1
−2	−1	2	−5
−1	7	3	−1
0	5		

In the STAT PLOT menu, set up Plot1 to display the data, and turn it on.

Press $\boxed{\text{ZOOM}}$ to display the ZOOM menu. Press 9 to display all your data using the ZoomStat instruction.

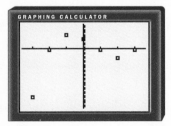

You may need to adjust Xscl or Yscl to be better able to interpret the graph.

Function or Instruction and Description	Keystroke(s), Menu, or Screen

ZSquare instruction
The ZSquare instruction allows you to adjust the viewing window so that graphs are plotted using equal-sized scales on both the x- and y-axes.

Press ZOOM to access the ZOOM menu. Press **5** to display a graph using the ZSquare instruction.

Example:
To graph $y = x^2 - 4$ using the ZSquare instruction, input the function using the Y= editor.

Press ZOOM **5** to display the graph using the ZSquare instruction.

You will see, for example,

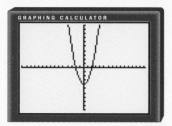

Note: The calculator will square the window based on the current Window variables. For this example, the ZStandard instruction had just been applied, so the window was squared based on the standard window.

ZStandard instruction
The ZStandard instruction adjusts the current settings of the Window variables to those of the standard viewing window.

Press ZOOM to access the ZOOM menu. Press **6** to display a graph in the standard viewing window using the ZStandard instruction.

If you press WINDOW after using the ZStandard instruction, you will see the settings of the standard viewing window:

Function or Instruction and Description	Keystroke(s), Menu, or Screen
$\sqrt{}$ operation	The $\sqrt{}$ operation is used to calculate the square root of a non-negative number. **Example:** To find the square root of 336.3, press 2nd x^2 336 . 3) ENTER. You will see 
$\sqrt[x]{}$ operation The $\sqrt[x]{}$ operation is used to calculate any root of a number.	**Example:** To find the fourth root of 81, press 4 MATH 5 to select the $\sqrt[x]{}$ operation. Then, press 81 ENTER. You will see 

TI-92 Plus/TI-92

Function or Instruction and Description	Keystroke(s), Menu, or Screen

abs function

The abs function is used to graph the absolute value function.

Go to the Y= editor. To select the abs function, press $\boxed{\text{2nd}}$ 5 to access the MATH menu. Select 1:Number and then 2:abs.

Press X $\boxed{)}$ $\boxed{\blacklozenge}$ R to display the graph of the function $y = |x|$.

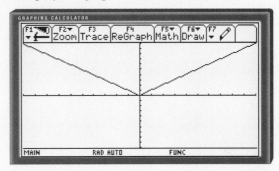

Algebra menu

The Algebra menu is used to perform algebraic operations on expressions.

To display the Algebra menu from the Home screen, press $\boxed{\text{F2}}$. You will see

Calculus menu

The Calculus menu is used to perform operations on functions that require the methods of calculus.

To display the Calculus menu from the Home screen, press $\boxed{\text{F3}}$. You will see

Function or Instruction and Description	Keystroke(s), Menu, or Screen

Define operation

The Define operation allows you to define your own functions, and use them as you use functions already built into the graphing calculator.

To select the Define operation from the Other menu, press [F4] and select 1:Define.

Example:
To define a function $f(x) = x^2$, select the Define operation from the Other menu and press F [(] X [)] [=] X [^] 2 [ENTER].

To determine, for example, the value of $f(10)$, press F [(] 10 [)] [ENTER].

You will see

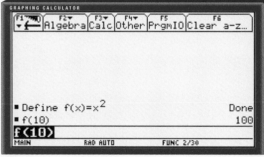

differentiate function

The differentiate function is used to find derivatives of any order of a function.

To select the differentiate function from the Calculus menu, press [F3] 1.

Example:
To find the derivative of the function $y = (x^3 - x + 1)^2$, select the differentiate function. Press [(] X [^] 3 [-] X [+] 1 [)] [^] 2 [,] to input the function, and press X [)] to indicate the variable with respect to which you are differentiating.
Press [ENTER].0

You will see

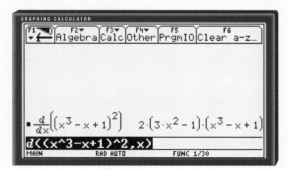

Example:
To define functions $f1(x)$ and $f2(x)$ as the first and second derivatives of the function $f(x) = x^3 - 2x^2 - 5x + 5$, select the

Function or Instruction and Description	Keystroke(s), Menu, or Screen

Define operation from the Other menu and press F $\boxed{(}$ X $\boxed{)}$ $\boxed{=}$ X $\boxed{\wedge}$ 3 $\boxed{-}$ 2 X $\boxed{\wedge}$ 2 $\boxed{-}$ 5 X $\boxed{+}$ 5 $\boxed{\text{ENTER}}$.

Select the Define operation again and press F 1 $\boxed{(}$ X $\boxed{)}$ $\boxed{=}$. Then, press $\boxed{\text{F3}}$ to access the Calculus menu and select 1:*d*(differentiate. Press F $\boxed{(}$ X $\boxed{)}$ $\boxed{,}$ to input $f(x)$ as the function to be differentiated, and press X $\boxed{)}$ to tell the calculator to differentiate with respect to x. Press $\boxed{\text{ENTER}}$.

Select the Define operation again and press F 2 $\boxed{(}$ X $\boxed{)}$ $\boxed{=}$. Then, press $\boxed{\text{F3}}$ to access the Calculus menu and select 1:*d*(differentiate. Press F $\boxed{(}$ X $\boxed{)}$ $\boxed{,}$ to input $f(x)$ as the function to be differentiated, and press X $\boxed{,}$ to tell the calculator to differentiate with respect to x. When finding derivatives of order two or above, you must enter a third parameter to indicate the order. Press 2 $\boxed{)}$ to tell the calculator to take the second derivative. Press $\boxed{\text{ENTER}}$.

You will see

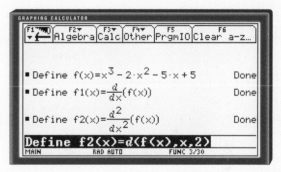

expand function
The expand function expands and simplifies a product of polynomials.

To select the expand function from the Algebra menu, press $\boxed{\text{F2}}$ 3.

Example:
To expand $(4x + 3y)(x - y)$, press
$\boxed{\text{F2}}$ 3 $\boxed{(}$ 4 X $\boxed{+}$ 3 Y $\boxed{)}$ $\boxed{(}$ X $-$ Y $\boxed{)}$ $\boxed{)}$ $\boxed{\text{ENTER}}$.

You will see

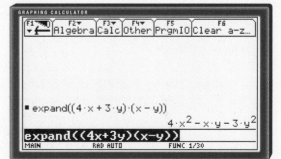

Function or Instruction and Description	Keystroke(s), Menu, or Screen

factor function

The factor function factors a polynomial.

To select the factor function from the Algebra menu, press F2 2.

Example:
To factor $3x^2 - 5x + 2$, press F2 2 3 X ^ 2 – 5 X + 2)
ENTER.

You will see

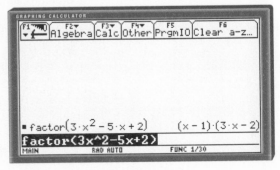

Graph instruction

The Graph instruction is used in the Home screen to display the graph of a function in the viewing window.

To select the Graph instruction from the Other menu, press F4 2.

Example:
To graph the function $y = x^3$, select the Graph function from the Other menu. Press X ^ 3 ENTER.

You will see

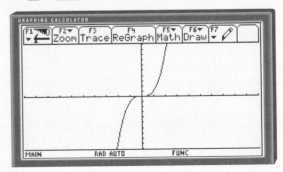

GRAPH screen

The GRAPH screen displays the graphs of functions and plots entered in the Y= editor.

To display the GRAPH screen, press ♦ R. Any functions and plots that you have entered in the Y= editor will be displayed in the viewing window. You can change the appearance of the viewing window by adjusting the window variables in the WINDOW screen, or by using the features in the ZOOM menu.

Example:
To graph the function $y = x^3 - 2x^2 - 5x + 5$, press ♦ W to enter the Y= editor. Using the arrow keys, move the cursor to y1 and press X ^ 3 – 2 X ^ 2 – 5 X + 5 ENTER.

Function or Instruction and Description	Keystroke(s), Menu, or Screen
	You will see 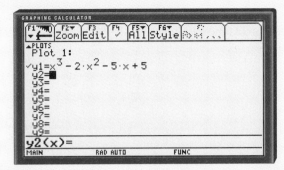
	Press ◆ R to graph the function: 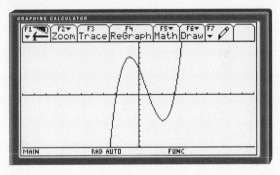
integrate function The integrate function is used to find the antiderivative of a function.	To select the integrate function from the Calculus menu, press F3 2. **Example:** To find the antiderivative of the function $y = 3x^2 + 4x + 5$, select the integrate function from the Calculus menu. Press 3 X ^ 2 + 4 X + 5 , to input the expression to be integrated, and press X) to tell the calculator to integrate with respect to x. Press ENTER. You will see 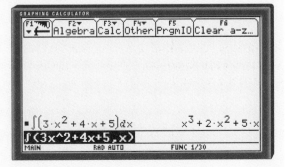

Function or Instruction and Description	Keystroke(s), Menu, or Screen

limit function

The limit function is used to approximate the limit of an expression.

To select the limit function, press F3 to access the Calculus menu from the Home screen, and select 3:limit.

Example:

To find $\lim_{x \to \infty} \dfrac{4x^2 + 5x + 6}{3x^2 - 2x - 4}$, press F3 3 to select the limit function.
Press (4 X ^ 2 + 5 X + 6) ÷ (3 X ^ 2 − 2 X − 4)) ,
to input the expression and X , to input the variable. Input the x-value of the limit by pressing 2nd J). Press ENTER.

You will see

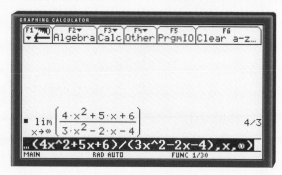

Example:

To find $\lim_{x \to 2} \dfrac{x^2 - 4}{x - 2}$, press F3 3 to select the limit function. Press
(X ^ 2 − 4) ÷ (X − 2)) , to input the expression and
X , to input the variable. Input the x-value of the limit by pressing 2). Press ENTER.

You will see

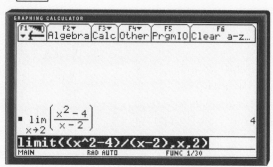

Example:

To find $\lim_{x \to 0^+} \dfrac{1}{x}$, press F3 3 to select the limit function.
Press 1 ÷ X , to input the expression and X , to input the variable. Input the x-value of the limit by pressing 0 , . Then, press 1) to tell the calculator you want to find the limit as

Function or Instruction and Description	**Keystroke(s), Menu, or Screen**

x approaches 0 from the positive side (any positive number will do here; 1 was chosen arbitrarily). Notice that the syntax is slightly different for one-sided limits. Press ENTER.

You will see

If you enter −1 instead of 1 as the last parameter of the function, you will see

The limit is evaluated from the left instead of the right. Again, any negative number will do here.

Other menu
The Other menu is used to perform a variety of miscellaneous functions, operations, and instructions.

To display the Other menu from the Home screen, press F4.

You will see

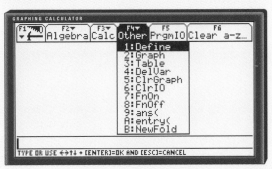

Function or Instruction and Description	Keystroke(s), Menu, or Screen

polyEval function

The polyEval function is used to determine the value of a polynomial expression for specified values of the variable.

To select the polyEval function, press 2nd 5 3 to access the MATH List menu, and select **C:polyEval**.

Example:

To find the value of the polynomial function $y = 3x^4 - 2x^2 + 5x + 1$ at $x = 3$, select the polyEval function from the MATH List menu. You must enter the polynomial expression as a list of coefficients in descending order. For this example, press 2nd (3 , 0 , (-) 2 , 5 , 1 2nd) , . Then, input the x-value and execute the function by pressing 3) ENTER.

You will see

Example:

To find the values of the polynomial function $y = x^3 - 2x^2 - 5x + 5$ at $x = 0$, 1, and 2, select the polyEval function from the MATH List menu. Enter the polynomial expression as a list of coefficients in descending order by pressing 2nd (1 , (-) 2 , (-) 5 , 5 2nd) , . Then, input the x-values as a list by pressing 2nd (0 , 1 , 2 2nd)) ENTER.

You will see

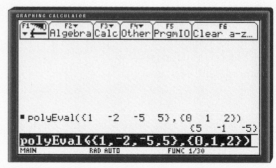

Function or Instruction and Description	Keystroke(s), Menu, or Screen

propFrac function

The propFrac function is used to find the proper fraction form of rational numbers and rational expressions.

To select the propFrac function, press F2 to access the Algebra menu. Select 7:propFrac. This function is useful for finding oblique asymptotes of functions.

Example:
To find the proper fraction form of $\frac{18}{11}$, press F2 7 to select the propFrac function. Press 18 ÷ 11) to input the number and press ENTER.

You will see

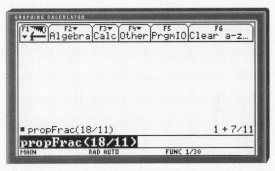

Example:
To find the proper fraction form of $\frac{x^3 - 2x^2 - x + 1}{x - 2}$, press F2 7 to select the propFrac function. Press (X ^ 3 − 2 X ^ 2 − X + 1) / (X − 2))) to input the expression and press ENTER.

You will see

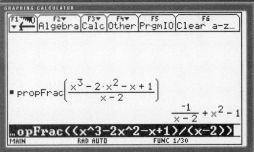

solve function

The solve function solves an algebraic equation for a variable.

To select the solve function from the Algebra menu, press F2 1.

Example:
To use the solve function to find the critical numbers of the function $f(x) = x^3 - 2x^2 - 5x + 5$, use the Define operation to define $f(x)$. Then, use the Define operation and the differentiate function to define $f1(x)$ as the derivative of $f(x)$.

Function or Instruction and Description	Keystroke(s), Menu, or Screen

Select the solve function by pressing ⌊F2⌋ 1. Press F 1 ⌊(⌋ X ⌊)⌋ ⌊=⌋ 0 ⌊,⌋ to enter the equation to be solved, and press X ⌊)⌋ to tell the calculator to solve for *x*. Press ⌊ENTER⌋.

You will see

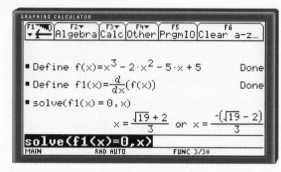

tExpand function

The tExpand function is used to expand trigonometric expressions involving integer multiples of angles, sums of angles, and differences of angles into trigonometric expressions involving single angles.

To select the tExpand function from the Algebra Trig menu, press ⌊F2⌋ 9 1.

Example:

To expand the expression cos 2θ, select the tExpand function from the Algebra Trig menu. Press ⌊COS⌋ 2 ⌊θ⌋ ⌊)⌋ ⌊)⌋ ⌊ENTER⌋.

You will see

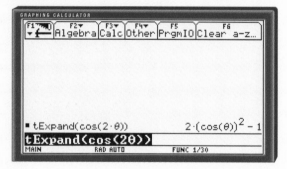

Example:

To expand the expression sin (*a* + *b*), select the tExpand function from the Algebra Trig menu. Press ⌊SIN⌋ A ⌊+⌋ B ⌊)⌋ ⌊)⌋ ⌊ENTER⌋.

Function or Instruction and Description	Keystroke(s), Menu, or Screen

You will see

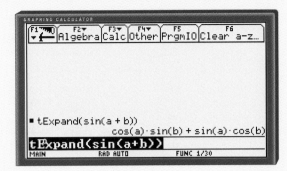

when function

The when function can be used to define and graph piecewise functions.

To select the when function from the CATALOG menu, press [2nd] 2 to access the CATALOG menu and press W to move the cursor to functions beginning with the letter w. Then, use the arrow keys to move the cursor to the when function and press [ENTER].

Example:

To define and graph the piecewise function

$$y = \begin{cases} x^2, x \in (-\infty, 0] \\ x, \ \ x \in (0, \infty) \end{cases}$$

select the Define operation from the Other menu.
Press F [(] X [)] [=]. Then, select the when function from the CATALOG menu and enter X. Press [2nd] 5 8 4 to select the less than or equal to symbol from the MATH Test menu, and press 0 [,].

Next, input the part of the function that is graphed when x is less than or equal to 0 by pressing X [^] 2 [,]. Then, input the part of the function that is graphed when x is greater than 0 by pressing X [)] [ENTER].

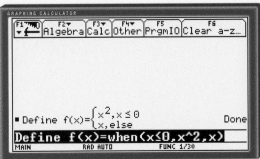

Function or Instruction and Description	Keystroke(s), Menu, or Screen

It is important to note that the second parameter entered, x^2, is graphed when the first parameter, $x \leq 0$, is true. Likewise, the third parameter entered, x, is graphed when the condition $x \leq 0$ is *not* true.

Enter the Y= editor. Place the cursor at y1 and press F ⃞ X ⃞. Press ⬥ R to display the graph of the function.

You will see

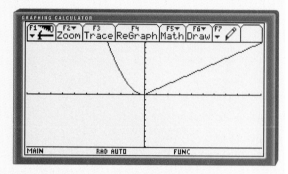

You can also find limits for piecewise functions defined using the when function. To find $\lim_{x \to 0} f(x)$, press F3 3 from the Home screen to select the limit function. Press F ⃞ X ⃞ ⃞ X ⃞ 0 ⃞ ENTER.

You will see

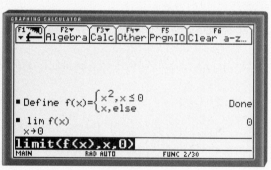

Answers

Chapter 1

For answers containing diagrams or graphs, refer to the Student e-book.

Review of Prerequisite Skills, pp. 4–5

1. a) 3 **b)** 3 **c)** $\frac{19}{8}$ **d)** 5 **e)** 2.811 **f)** $a^3 + a^2 - 2a + 3$

g) $8x^3 + 4x^2 - 4x + 3$ **h)** $-x^3 + x^2 + 2x + 3$ **2. a)** 1 **b)** 0

c) 0 **d)** -1 **e)** $\frac{1}{2}$ **f)** $2a - a^2$ **g)** $1 - 4x^2$ **h)** $1 - x^2$ **3. a)** 3 **b)** 2

c) 4 **d)** 6 **4. a)** 2 **b)** 0 **c)** 4 **d)** 3 **5. a) i)** -2 **ii)** -2 **iii)** 0

iv) 3; domain: $-4 \leq x \leq 4$, range: $-2 \leq y \leq 3$ **b) i)** -1 **ii)** 1 **iii)** 1

iv) 3; domain: R, range: R **6. a)** slope: 2; y-intercept: -4

b) slope: 3; y-intercept: 8 **c)** slope: $\frac{1}{2}$; y-intercept: -3

d) slope: 2; y-intercept: -9 **7. a)** $y = x + 2$ **b)** $y = 5x - 5$

c) $y = -2x + 4$ **8. a)** $y = 3x - 1$ **b)** $y = -x + 6$ **c)** $y = 2x + 9$

9. a) $y = -\frac{3}{2}x + 3$ **b)** $y = \frac{7}{5}x - 7$ **c)** $y = 2x + 4$

10. a) $y = -4x + 6$ **b)** $y = \frac{1}{4}x + \frac{7}{4}$

11. a) $x = 2$ **b)** $y = -1$

12. a) vertex: $(5, 6)$; direction of opening: up; vertical stretch of factor 2 **b)** vertex: $(1, -2)$; direction of opening: down; no vertical stretch or compression **c)** vertex: $(-4, 1)$; direction of opening: up; vertical compression of factor $\frac{1}{2}$ **d)** vertex: $(-1, -9)$; direction of opening: down; vertical compression of factor 0.4

13. a) $y = (x + 3)^2 - 4$ **b)** $y = 2(x + 2)^2 - 5$

c) $y = 3(x - 1)^2 - 10$ **d)** $y = 5\left(x + \frac{9}{10}\right)^2 - \frac{1}{20}$

14. a) domain: $\{x \mid x \in R, x \neq 0\}$; range: $\{y \mid y \in R, \ y \neq 0\}$

b) domain: $\{x \mid x \in R, x \neq 0\}$; range: $\{y \mid y \in R, \ y \neq 0\}$

c) domain: $\{x \mid x \in R, x \neq 0\}$; range: $\{y \mid y \in R, \ y \neq 0\}$

d) domain: $\{x \mid x \in R, x \geq 0\}$; range: $\{y \mid y \in R, \ y \geq 0\}$

e) domain: $\{x \mid x \in R, x \leq 1\}$; range: $\{y \mid y \in R, \ y \geq 0\}$

f) domain: $\{x \mid x \in R, x \geq -5\}$; range: $\{y \mid y \in R, \ y \leq 0\}$

15. a) vertical stretch of factor 2 **b)** reflection in the x-axis **c)** vertical translation 4 units down **d)** horizontal compression of factor 3 **e)** vertical translation 1 unit up **f)** horizontal translation 5 units to the right **16. a)** vertical compression of factor $\frac{1}{2}$, horizontal translation 5 units to the right **b)** vertical stretch of factor 3, reflection in the x-axis, vertical translation 1 unit up **c)** horizontal compression of factor 2, vertical translation 9 units down **d)** vertical compression of factor $\frac{1}{3}$, reflection in the x-axis, vertical translation 3 units down, horizontal compression of factor 4, horizontal translation 1 unit left **17. a)** $x \leq \frac{9}{4}$ **b)** $x \in R$ **c)** $x \neq 1$ **d)** $x \in R$

e) $|x| \geq 4$ **f)** $x > 1$ **g)** $x \in R$ **h)** $x \neq -3$ **18.** 1–c, 2–b, 3–e,

4–a, 5–d, 6–f **19. a)** domain: $-4 \leq x \leq 1$; range: $0 \leq y \leq 2$ **b)** domain: $-2 \leq x \leq 3$; range: $-4 \leq y \leq 0$ **c)** domain: $-2 \leq x \leq 3$; range: $-4 \leq y \leq 0$ **d)** domain: $-5 \leq x \leq 0$; range: $-2 \leq y \leq 0$ **e)** domain: $-4 \leq x \leq 6$; range: $0 \leq y \leq 4$

f) domain: $-6 \leq x \leq 4$; range: $0 \leq y \leq 2$ **20. a)** domain: $0 \leq x \leq 4$; range: $-2 \leq y \leq 2$ **b)** domain: $-2 \leq x \leq 2$; range: $-4 \leq y \leq 4$ **c)** domain: $-2 \leq x \leq 2$; range: $-4 \leq y \leq 4$ **d)** domain: $-4 \leq x \leq 4$; range: $-4 \leq y \leq 4$ **e)** domain: $-2 \leq x \leq 2$; range: $-4 \leq y \leq 4$

f) domain: $-1 \leq x \leq 1$; range: $-4 \leq y \leq 4$ **21. a) i)** $x \in R$

b) i) $x \in R$ **c) i)** $x \geq -5$ **d) i)** $x \geq 3$ **1 e) i)** $x \in R$

22. a) $x = 6$ **b)** $x = 2$ **c)** $x = 5$ **d)** $x = -\frac{13}{2}$ **e)** $x = 2$

Section 1.1, pp. 18–22

Practise

1. a) $[-2, 2]$ **b)** $[4, 13]$ **c)** $(-4, -1)$ **d)** $(0, 4)$ **e)** $(-\infty, 2)$

f) $(-1, \infty)$ **g)** $(-\infty, -1]$ **h)** $[0, \infty)$ **2. a)** $|x| \leq 2$

b) $|x - 8.5| \leq 4.5$ **c)** $|x + 1.5| \leq 2.5$ **d)** $|x - 2| \leq 2$

e)–h) not possible **3. a)** odd **b)** neither **c)** even

4. a) even **b)** even **c)** even **5. a)** even **b)** even **c)** even

6. a) i) -1 **ii)** 3 **iii)** $\frac{1}{2}$ **iv)** $\frac{2}{3}$ **v)** $1 - k$ **vi)** k **b) i)** 4 **ii)** 4

iii) $\frac{1}{4}$ **iv)** $\frac{1}{9}$ **v)** k^2 **vi)** $(1 - k)^2$ **7. a) i)** $\frac{1}{9}$ **ii)** $\frac{1}{9}$ **iii)** 9 **iv)** 16

v) k^2 **vi)** $\left(\frac{1+k}{k}\right)^2$ **b) i)** $-\frac{3}{2}$ **ii)** $-\frac{3}{4}$ **iii)** $\frac{1}{2}$ **iv)** $\frac{1}{3}$ **v)** $\frac{1}{k-1}$ **vi)** k

8. Verbally: To calculate the stopping distance in metres, square the speed in kilometres per hour and then multiply by 0.006.

Numerically:

s	D	s	D
0	0	80	38.4
10	0.6	90	48.6
20	2.4	100	60
30	5.4	110	72.6
40	9.6	120	86.4
50	15	130	101.4
60	21.6	140	117.6
70	29.4	150	135

9. Verbally: Answers will vary. Algebraically: Answers will vary, depending on the assumptions made. If one assumes the relationship is linear, then $P = 10\,301.8 + 135.0(t - 1990)$, where t is the year.

10. a) i) odd **ii)** $(-\infty, \infty)$ **b) i)** even **ii)** $(-\infty, \infty)$ **c) i)** even **ii)** $(-\infty, \infty)$ **d) i)** neither **ii)** $(-\infty, \infty)$ **e) i)** even **ii)** $(-\infty, 0)$ or $(0, \infty)$ **f) i)** even **ii)** $(-\infty, \infty)$ **g) i)** neither **ii)** $(-\infty, \infty)$ **h) i)** neither **ii)** $(-\infty, 2)$ or $(2, \infty)$ **11. a)** $y = -0.76x + 11.47$ **b)** 2.35 **c)** 15.09 **12. a)** $y = -0.27x^2 + 3.74x - 2.05$ **b)** 9.53 **c)** $x = 0.57, 13.51$

Apply, Solve, Communicate

13. Let f and g be odd functions, and define
$F(x) = f(x)g(x)$. Then $F(-x) = f(-x)g(-x) = (-f(x))(-g(x))$
$= f(x)g(x) = F(x)$. Thus, $F(-x) = F(x)$ and F is even.
14. Let f and g be even functions, and define
$F(x) = \dfrac{f(x)}{g(x)}$. Then $F(-x) = \dfrac{f(-x)}{g(-x)} = \dfrac{f(x)}{g(x)} = F(x)$.
Thus, $F(-x) = F(x)$ and F is even. **15.** odd
16. a) $y = f(x)$ is odd, so that $f(-x) = -f(x)$ for all x in the
domain of f. Since 0 is in the domain of f, we have
$f(-0) = -f(0) \Rightarrow f(0) = -f(0) \Rightarrow 2f(0) = 0 \Rightarrow f(0) = 0$.
17. a) $V = 18\,000 - 2250t$ **b)** \$4500 **c)** $t \in [0, 8]$
d) annual depreciation **f)** Since the function is given to be
linear, its slope does not change. **18. b)** $P = 0.72(t - 1995)$
$+ 135.14$, where t is the year and P is thousands of
people **c)** 145 940 **d)** 1807; no **e)** 3196; no **f)** no
19. b) $P = 5.11(t - 1995) + 272.22$, where t is the year
and P is thousands of people **c)** 348 870 **d)** 1941
e) 2137; no **f)** no **20. b)** $E = 0.009I - 40.15$, where I is
income, in dollars, and E is pet expenses, in dollars
c) \$319.85 **d)** \$48 905.56 **e)** \$62 959.85; no **f)** –\$40.15;
no **g)** no **21. b)** $d = 0.008s^2 + 0.002s + 0.059$ **c)** The slope
increases as speed increases. **d)** This curve is steeper, and
the slope increases more quickly. **22. b)** $V = 954.19(1.12)^t$
c) The slope increases with time. **d)** \$2964 **23.** All
constant functions are even. $f(x) = 0$ is also odd.
24. The sum of an odd function and an even function can
be neither odd nor even, unless one of the functions is
$f(x) = 0$. **25.** Yes; only the function $f(0) = 0$. **26. b)** 25%:
\$14 400; 50%: \$25 000; 75%: \$43 300; 99%: \$248 700
c) 80% **d)** No; the cost would be infinite

Technology Extension, p. 24

Practise

3. a) $f(x) = \begin{cases} -2x & x < 1 \\ 2x - 4 & x \geq 1 \end{cases}$ **b)** $f(x) = 2|x - 1| - 2$

Section 1.2, p. 28

Apply, Solve, Communicate

1. a) vertical asymptotes: $x = -3$, $x = 2$; x-intercepts:
none; y-intercept: $-\dfrac{1}{6}$ **b)** vertical asymptotes: $x = -4$,
$x = 2$; x-intercepts: none; y-intercept: $-\dfrac{1}{8}$ **c)** vertical
asymptotes: $x = -\dfrac{5}{2}$, $x = \dfrac{2}{3}$; x-intercept: –1; y-intercept:
$-\dfrac{1}{10}$ **d)** vertical asymptotes: $x = 6$, $x = -5$; x-intercepts:
5, –4; y-intercept: $\dfrac{2}{3}$ **2. a)** none **b)** 0.731, 1.149 **c)** –3.578

d) 3.5822 **3. a)** (1, 2) **b)** none **c)** (–2, –2), (5.1401,
77.541), (–2.1401, –2.5406) **d)** none
4. a) domain: $x \neq 2$; range: $y \neq 0$ **b)** domain: $x \neq -1$;
range: $y > 0$ **c)** domain: $x \neq -2$, $x \neq 3$; range: $y < 0$
or $y \geq \dfrac{12}{25}$ **d)** domain: $-\sqrt{3} < x < \sqrt{3}$; range: $y \geq \dfrac{5}{3}$
5. c) It will not work in any window. In the window given
in part a), it will work for $y = \cos(2x)$ and $y = \cos(96x)$.
6. Answers will vary. **7.** Answers will vary. **8.** Answers
will vary. One possible set of window variables is given.
a) Xmin = –8.131, Xmax = 8.131, Ymin = –5, Ymax = 5
b) Xmin = –12.6148, Xmax = 12.6148, Ymin = –3,
Ymax = 3 **9.** domain: $-\sqrt{2.68} < x < \sqrt{2.68}$;
range: $y \geq \dfrac{1}{\sqrt{2.68}}$

Review of Key Concepts, pp. 30–31

1. a)

x	y
–2	0
–1	0.5
1	3
3	1.5

b) $[-4, \infty)$

2. a)

x	y
–6	8
–5	7
–4	6
–3	5
–2	6
–1	7
0	8

c) Take the sum of 5 and the distance between x and –3
on a number line.
3. a) $(-\infty, 0]$ **b)** $(-4, \infty)$ **c)** $[-5, 5]$ **4.** f is neither, g is odd,
h is even **5. a)** neither **b)** even **c)** odd **d)** even **e)** odd **f)** odd
7. a) $d = -1.14t + 26.57$ **b)** 10.61 **c)** 0.35
8. $y = 0.09x^2 + 0.08x + 0.03$ **9. a)** $P = 1231.40(t - 1990)$
$+ 32\,499.80$, where t is the year and P is the number of
passengers (in thousands). **b)** 38 656 800; higher
c) 2004; no **10. b)** At 60 km/h, fuel consumption is
10.1 L/100 km **c)** $F = 0.001\,56s^2 - 0.192\,68s + $
$16.043\,16$, where s is the speed in km/h and F is the fuel
consumption in L/100 km. **d)** The curve would be
higher, and the slope would be steeper. The lowest
point might change **e)** lower curve **11. a)** $x \neq -1$
b) $x \neq 3$ **c)** $x \geq -1$ **d)** $x < 3$ **e)** $|x| \geq 1$ **f)** $x \in R$
g) $x \neq 1$ **h)** $x \neq 2$, –3 **12.** Answers will vary.
13. Answers will vary.

Chapter Test, pp. 32–33

1. a) i) 1 **ii)** 1 **iii)** 4 **iv)** $\frac{1}{4}$ **b) i)** 0 **ii)** 2 **iii)** -7 **iv)** $\frac{7}{8}$

2. a) $(-4, 10)$ **b)** $(-\infty, 5]$ **c)** $[0, \infty)$ **3. a)** odd **b)** neither
c) even **4.** f is neither, g is even, h is odd **5. b)** The slope
has large positive values, reduces to 0 at $x = 0$, and then
increases to large positive values. **c)** odd **d)** $y = x^5$ has a
sharper turn on $(-1, 1)$, and is steeper outside this
interval. **6. a)** $V = 0.67r + 2.90$ **b)** 7.59 **c)** 12.28
7. b) $P = 0.193L^{0.507}$ **c)** 0.48 s **d)** 25 cm **e)** Shortening the
pendulum reduces the period; the clock takes less
time for each "tick". **8. a)** $x \ne \pm 1$ **b)** $x > -3$ **c)** $x \ne 3, -1$
d) $x \in \mathbb{R}$ **9. a)** even **b)** neither **c)** odd **d)** neither **e)** even
10. a) Answers may vary. The graph must show the vertical
asymptote at $x = 0$, the local minimum at $(7.94, 0.19)$,
and the x-intercept at -10. Graphs may also show that
the graph resembles the graph of $y = 0.001x^2$ for large
negative and positive values of x. **b)** Answers may vary.
The graph must show that $1000x$ dominates the function
at all values of x, so appears as a straight line through
the origin with slope 1000.

Challenge Problems, p. 34

1. 0.377 **2.** If the smallest number is x, the other numbers
are $x + 1$, $x + 2$, $x + 7$, $x + 8$, $x + 9$, $x + 14$, $x + 15$, and
$x + 16$. Thus, the total is $9x + 72$, or $9(x + 8)$. **3.** $-40°$
4. a) $2\sqrt{7}$ cm **b)** $2\sqrt{5}$ cm **c)** $2\sqrt{3}$ cm **5.** Double the first
number, triple the second number, and add the two
resulting numbers together. **6.** $\sqrt{a+x} + \sqrt{a-x} < 2\sqrt{a}$
for all x such that $0 < x \le a$ **9.** Answers may vary. The
graph must show the holes at $x = 1.21$ and $x = -1.32$,
and the x- and y-intercepts at $x = -1$ and $y = -1.5972$
respectively.

Problem Solving Strategy: Principles of Problem Solving, pp. 35–36

Apply, Solve, Communicate

1. 78.75 km/h **2.** one (from the box labelled 15¢)
3. a) Melissa **b)** Paolo

Problem Solving: Using the Strategies, p. 37

1. 12 **2.** Fill 5-L, pour into 9-L; fill 5-L, pour 4 L to fill
9-L; dump 9-L, pour remaining 1 L from 5-L into 9-L;
fill 5-L, pour into 9-L **3.** Juan and Sue cross; either one
returns; Alicia and Larry cross; other of Juan/Sue
returns; Juan and Sue cross. Total time: 15 min
4. pentagon and hexagon **5. a)** Cut so that each piece has
one face of the cube as its base, and the centre of the
cube as its other vertex. Note that you do not cut right
through the cube. **b)** Base: 20 cm square, height: 10 cm
6. Yes. **7.** $\frac{3\sqrt{3}}{2}$

Chapter 2

Review of Prerequisite Skills, pp. 40–41

1. a) $14x - 13$ **b)** $-8y - 25$ **c)** $3x^2 - 5x - 16$ **d)** $-18w + 38$

2. a) $2x + 3$ **b)** $2x^2 - 4x - 6$ **c)** $\frac{2m^2}{n} + 4n$ **d)** $3x^2 - 2x + 1 - \frac{4}{x}$

3. a) $t(t + 9)$ **b)** $(w + 14)(w - 14)$ **c)** $(x + 3)(x + 5)$
d) $(y - 6)(y + 3)$ **e)** $(x + 7)(x + 8)$ **f)** $(w - 19)^2$
g) $(t + 1)(t - 99)$ **h)** $(s + 1)(s + 89)$ **4. a)** $(2x - 1)(x - 3)$
b) $(3y + 1)(y - 4)$ **c)** $(4w + 1)(w + 2)$ **d)** $(5a - 3)(2a + 1)$
e) $(3t + 2)(2t + 1)$ **f)** $(5x + 3)(5x - 3)$ **5. a)** $x + 2, x \ne 1$
b) $\frac{x+3}{x-3}, x \ne 3$ **c)** $\frac{t-3}{t-4}, t \ne -2, 4$ **d)** $\frac{a-4}{a+6}, a \ne 5, -6$

6. a) $y = -1, \frac{3}{2}$ **b)** no solutions **c)** $m = 0, \frac{5}{2}$ **d)** $w = -\frac{1}{2}, \frac{4}{3}$

7. a) 0, 8 **b)** $-2, -5$ **c)** does not factor **d)** 4, 5 **8. a)** $2, \frac{1}{2}$

b) $-\frac{1}{2}, -3$ **c)** $1, -\frac{2}{3}$ **d)** $-\frac{5}{2}, \frac{1}{3}$ **9. a)** $\frac{1 \pm \sqrt{21}}{2}$; 2.8, -1.8

b) $\frac{-3 \pm \sqrt{5}}{2}$; $-2.6, -0.4$ **c)** $\frac{-1 \pm \sqrt{33}}{4}$; -1.7, 1.2

d) $\frac{-1 \pm \sqrt{5}}{4}$; -0.8, 0.3 **10. a)** $2i$ **b)** $10i$ **c)** $i\sqrt{13}$ **d)** $2i\sqrt{6}$

e) $3i\sqrt{3}$ **f)** $-4i\sqrt{2}$ **g)** i **h)** -30 **i)** -6 **j)** -3 **k)** 6 **l)** 12
11. a) $5 + 5i\sqrt{2}$ **b)** $-3 - 3i\sqrt{10}$ **c)** $-6 + 2i\sqrt{2}$ **d)** $2 + i\sqrt{2}$
12. a) $10 - i$ **b)** $9 - 10i$ **c)** $-14 - 7i$ **d)** $22 - 2i$ **13. a)** $1 - 2i$

b) $-\frac{2}{3} - \frac{5}{3}i$ **c)** $\frac{5}{2} + \frac{5}{2}i$ **d)** $\frac{3}{5} - \frac{14}{5}i$ **14. a)** $1 \pm i\sqrt{2}$ **b)** $\pm 3i$

c) $\frac{1 \pm i\sqrt{11}}{2}$ **d)** $\frac{-3 \pm i\sqrt{15}}{4}$ **15. a)** 10 **b)** -53 **c)** -0.5 **d)** -14.5

e) 1396 **f)** -1054 **16. a)** $\frac{13}{2}$ **b)** $-\frac{1}{2}$ **c)** 0 **d)** $-\frac{13}{2}$ **e)** -2

f) -0.49 **17. a)** -5 **b)** 10 **c)** -5 **d)** -3.44 **e)** -3.75 **f)** 10 195
18. a) $x > -2$ **b)** $x \le -18$ **c)** $x \ge -9$ **d)** $x > 0$ **e)** $x < 2$ **f)** $x \ge -1$

g) $x \ge -\frac{34}{15}$ **h)** $x > -2$ **19. a)** linear **b)** quadratic **c)** neither
d) quadratic **e)** linear **f)** neither **g)** quadratic **h)** linear

Section 2.2, pp. 51–53

Practise

1. a) $x + 5; x \ne -3$ **b)** $a - 2; a \ne 5$ **c)** $y + 3; y \ne 4$ **d)** $t - 2$;
$t \ne -2$ **2. a)** $x^2 + x + 2; x \ne -1$ **b)** $t^2 - t - 1; t \ne -4$
c) $a^2 - 1; a \ne 3$ **d)** $x^2 + 5x - 8; x \ne 1$ **e)** $m^2 + m - 2; m \ne -2$
f) $y^2 - 2; y \ne 4$ **3. a)** $x + 3; x \ne -\frac{5}{2}$ **b)** $y + 3; y \ne \frac{1}{3}$

c) $r - 6; r \ne \frac{1}{5}$ **d)** $2t - 3; t \ne -\frac{1}{2}$ **e)** $2r - 7; r \ne \frac{2}{3}$ **f)** $2x + 3$;

$x \ne -\frac{3}{5}$ **g)** $2x + 5$, remainder 30; $x \ne \frac{3}{4}$ **4. a)** $x + 2; x \ne \pm 1$

b) $x - 3$ **c)** $y + 5$ **d)** $a - 1; a \ne \pm 2$ **5. a)** $2x^2 + 3; x \ne 1$

b) $3z^2 + 5$; $z \neq -2$ **c)** $2m^2 - 3$; $m \neq -\dfrac{1}{2}$ **d)** $3n^2 - 4$; $n \neq \dfrac{3}{2}$

e) $2d + 3$ **f)** $4x - 3$ **g)** $4s + 1$; $s \neq \pm\sqrt{\dfrac{5}{3}}$ **h)** $3t - 4$; $t \neq \pm\sqrt{\dfrac{2}{7}}$

6. a) dividend: 125; divisor: 12; quotient: 10; remainder: 5
b) dividend: 350; divisor: 9; quotient: 38; remainder: 8
c) dividend: $a^2 - 5a + 6$; divisor: $a - 3$; quotient: $a - 2$;
remainder: 0 **d)** dividend: $2x^2 + 5x - 2$; divisor: $2x - 1$;
quotient: $x + 3$; remainder: 1 **e)** $t^3 + t^2 + t - 3$;
divisor: $t^2 + 1$; quotient: $t + 1$; remainder: 4
f) dividend: $6x^3 + 3x^2 - x$; divisor: $3x^2 - 2$;
quotient: $2x + 1$; remainder: $3x + 2$ **7.** In this form, the
quotient and divisor are interchangeable.
a) dividend: 255; divisor (or quotient): 11; quotient (or
divisor): 23; remainder: 2 **b)** dividend: $8y^3 + 6y^2 - 4y - 5$;
divisor (or quotient): $4y + 3$; quotient (or divisor):
$2y^2 - 1$; remainder: -2 **c)** dividend: $x^2 + x + 3$; divisor
(or quotient): x; quotient (or divisor): $x + 1$; remainder: 3

8. a) $\dfrac{x^2 + 4x + 2}{x + 4} = x + \dfrac{2}{x + 4}$; $x^2 + 4x + 2 = (x + 4)x + 2$

b) $\dfrac{x^2 - 3x - 8}{x - 3} = x + \dfrac{-8}{x - 3}$; $x^2 - 3x - 8 = (x - 3)x - 8$

c) $\dfrac{x^2 - 7x + 10}{x - 4} = x - 3 + \dfrac{-2}{x - 4}$; $x^2 - 7x + 10$

$= (x - 4)(x - 3) - 2$ **d)** $\dfrac{2x^2 + x - 3}{x + 2} = 2x - 3 + \dfrac{3}{x + 2}$;

$2x^2 + x - 3 = (x + 2)(2x - 3) + 3$

e) $\dfrac{4x^2 - 7x - 7}{x - 2} = 4x + 1 + \dfrac{-5}{x - 2}$; $4x^2 - 7x - 7$

$= (x - 2)(4x + 1) - 5$

f) $\dfrac{x^2 - 8}{x - 3} = x + 3 + \dfrac{1}{x - 3}$; $x^2 - 8 = (x - 3)(x + 3) + 1$

g) $\dfrac{5x^2 + 14x + 11}{x + 4} = 5x - 6 + \dfrac{35}{x + 4}$;

$5x^2 + 14x + 11 = (x + 4)(5x - 6) + 35$

h) $\dfrac{6x^2 - 5x - 5}{x - 4} = 6x + 19 + \dfrac{71}{x - 4}$; $6x^2 - 5x - 5$

$= (x - 4)(6x + 19) + 71$

Apply, Solve, Communicate

9. a) i) $x^2 + x + 1$, $x \neq 1$ **ii)** $x^2 + 2x + 4$, $x \neq 2$ **iii)** $x^2 + 3x + 9$,
$x \neq 3$ **b)** Descriptions will vary. The coefficients form
a geometric sequence. **c)** $x^2 + 4x + 16$, $x \neq 4$; $x^2 + 5x + 25$,
$x \neq 5$ **10. a)** $x^4 + x^3 + x^2 + x + 1$, $x \neq 1$
b) $x^4 + 2x^3 + 4x^2 + 8x + 16$, $x \neq 2$ **11. a)** $3x + 2$,
remainder $x + 1$ **b)** $y - 3$, remainder $-y$ **c)** $t + 2$,
remainder -11; $t \neq \pm\sqrt{2}$ **d)** $3d^2 - 2$, remainder $d - 2$;

$d \neq \pm\sqrt{\dfrac{3}{2}}$ **12.** Yes, in parts a), b), and d). No, in part c).

13. a) 12 **b)** 2 **c)** -10 **d)** 4 **14.** $4x + 2$ **15.** $3y - 2$

16. The fraction is not defined for $x = -3$. **17. a)** \$552.31
b) \$641.22 **c)** \$1650.19 **18. a)** 22 months; she has \$211.37
remaining after taking out \$500 at the end of the 22nd
month. **c)** The x-intercept should be between 22.4 and
22.5. That is when she has no money. **19. a) i)** $x + 1$,
$x \neq 1$ **ii)** $x^2 + x + 1$, $x \neq 1$ **iii)** $x^3 + x^2 + x + 1$, $x \neq 1$
iv) $x^4 + x^3 + x^2 + x + 1$, $x \neq 1$

b) $\dfrac{x^n - 1}{x - 1} = x^{n-1} + x^{n-2} + \cdots + 1$, $x \neq 1$ **20. a)** yes, x **b)** $\dfrac{x^{k+1} - 1}{x - 1}$

c) i) 1 **ii)** $1 + (1 + i)$ **iii)** $1 + (1 + i) + (1 + i)^2 = \dfrac{(1 + i)^3 - 1}{(1 + i) - 1}$

iv) $1 + (1 + i) + (1 + i)^2 + \cdots + (1 + i)^{k-1} = \dfrac{(1 + i)^k - 1}{i}$

d) \$230.04 **e)** \$230 038.69 **21. a)** no; no **b)** no; yes
c) The remainder must be of a lower degree than the
divisor. **22. a)** \$450.90 **b)** \$15 112.18

Section 2.3, pp. 59–61

Practise

1. a) -3 **b)** -2 **c)** 0 **d)** 12 **2. a)** -23 **b)** 85 **c)** 5 **d)** $\dfrac{9}{2}$ **3. a)** -9

b) 0 **c)** 1 **d)** 4 **e)** 0 **f)** 2 **4. a)** -7 **b)** -3 **c)** 0 **d)** -55 **5. a)** 12
b) 10 **c)** 1 **d)** 11 **e)** -10 **f)** -16 **g)** -45 **h)** 0 **i)** 22 **j)** 70 **k)** 136

l) 0 **m)** 11 **n)** -3 **6. a)** 19 **b)** 0 **c)** $-\dfrac{3}{8}$ **d)** 6 **e)** $\dfrac{8}{3}$ **f)** -1 **7. a)** 2

b) 4 **c)** -1 **d)** 3 **8.** $m = 2$, $n = -3$ **9.** $p = 1$, $q = 2$ **10.** $v = 6$,
$w = -11$

Apply, Solve, Communicate

11. 7 **12.** -20 **13. a)** 14 **14. a)** 12 **15. a)** 77 **b)** 77 **d)** At 500 m
either side of the centre point, the cable is 77 m above
the roadway. **16. a)** $-0.017d + 0.45$, remainder 25
b) At 50 m away horizontally, the hammer is 25 m high.
c) $-0.017d - 0.06$, remainder -2.3 **d)** The hammer landed
at a distance of less than 80 m. **17. a)** $0.5t + 3$, $R = 6$.
R is the number of tickets issued in the first 2 hours.
$Q(t)$ is the average number tickets issued between 2
hours and time t. **b)** Answers will vary. **c)** The formula is
impossible. It would require issuing a negative number of
tickets in each of the last 3 hours. **18. a)** Answers will
vary. **b)** $0.1t + 10.5$, $R = 77.5$. R is the number of trees
sold by December 5. $Q(t)$ represents the average number
of trees sold from December 5 to day t. **c)** no **19.** $k = 3$

20. $k = 1$ or 4 **21. a)** $ba^2 + ca + d = 0$ **b)** $a = \dfrac{-c \pm \sqrt{c^2 - 4bd}}{2b}$

22. a) quotient: $-Q(x)$; remainder: R **b)** Examples will vary.
c) $P(x) = Q(x)(x - b) + R \Rightarrow P(x) = -Q(x)(b - x) + R$.
23. Answers will vary. **24. a)** $x^2 - 1$ **b)** $x + 2$, remainder
$4x - 1$ **c)** $x^6 + x^4 + x^2 + 1$; $x \neq \pm 1$ **d)** $2x - 3$, remainder
$3x - 7$; $x \neq 0$, 1 **25.** The remainder upon division of $P(x)$

by $x^2 + a$ can be found by replacing x^2 with $-a$ wherever it occurs in $P(x)$. The remainder upon division of $P(x)$ by $x^2 + bx$ can be found by repeatedly replacing x^2 with $-bx$ wherever it occurs in $P(x)$. The conjectures can be justified using the division statements $P(x) = Q(x)$ $(x^2 + a) + R(x)$ and $P(x) = Q(x)(x^2 + bx) + R(x)$.

Section 2.4, pp. 68–70

Practise

1. a) yes **b)** no **c)** no **d)** yes **2. a)** no **b)** yes **c)** yes **d)** no **4. a)** yes **b)** no **c)** yes **d)** yes **e)** no **f)** yes **6. a)** $(x-1)(x-2)(x-3)$ **b)** $(x+1)(x+3)(x+4)$ **c)** $(x-3)(x+3)(x-2)$ **d)** $(x+3)(x^2+x-1)$ **e)** $(z+2)(z+4)(z-5)$ **f)** $(x+1)(x-4)(x+4)$ **g)** $(x-4)(x^2+2x+2)$ **h)** $(k+4)(k-3)(k+5)$ **i)** $(x-5)(x^2+5x-2)$ **j)** $(x-3)(x+1)(x+6)$ **7. a)** $(2x-1)(x-1)(x-3)$ **b)** $(y+1)(2y+1)(2y-3)$ **c)** $(x+2)(3x-1)(x-3)$ **d)** $(x-2)(3x-2)(x+2)$ **e)** $(x+1)(2x+3)(x+4)$ **f)** $(x-2)(2x^2+x+5)$ **g)** $(2x-1)(x-3)(3x+5)$ **h)** $(y+2)(2y-1)(2y+1)$ **i)** $(4x+3)(x-1)(x+1)$ **j)** $(3w-1)(2w^2+6w-5)$

Apply, Solve, Communicate

8. a) 16 **b)** 69 **c)** 23 **d)** average area cut, per year, from 2002 to $2000 + t$ **9. a) i)** $(x-3)(x+3)$ **ii)** $x+3, x \neq 3$ **b) i)** $(x+4)(x-2)$ **ii)** $x+4, x \neq 2$ **c) i)** $(x+1)(2x^2+2x-7)$ **ii)** $2x^2+2x-7, x \neq -1$ **10. a)** $\dfrac{f(x)}{x-b} = Q(x) + \dfrac{R(x)}{x-b}$

b) $f(b)$ **c)** $Q(x) = \dfrac{f(x)-f(b)}{x-b}$

d) Yes; reasons will vary. The numerator, $f(x) - f(b)$, is always divisible by the denominator, $x - b$. **e)** the slope of the secant from the point $(b, f(b))$ to the point $(x, f(x))$ **11. a)** 392 **b)** 1491 **c)** 497 **d)** average sulphur dioxide emitted per year from 2001 to $2000 + t$ **12. a)** $(x+1)(x+2)(x-3)(x+4)$ **b)** $(x-1)(x+1)(x-2)(x+2)(x+3)$ **c)** $(2x+1)^2(2x-1)$ **d)** $(2x-3)(2x-1)(2x+1)$ **13.** They are consecutive integers, with x the smallest. **14. a)** -72 **b)** 3 **15. a)** $(x-2), (x+4), (3x+1)$ **b)** No; a polynomial of degree 3 has at most 3 factors. **16.** $m = 3, n = -8$ **18. a) i)** $(x-1)(x^2+x+1)$ **ii)** $(x+1)(x^2-x+1)$ **iii)** $(x-3)(x^2+3x+9)$ **iv)** $(x+4)(x^2-4x+16)$ **v)** $(2x-1)(4x^2+2x+1)$ **vi)** $(4x+1)(16x^2-4x+1)$ **b)** $x+y; x^2-xy+y^2$ **c)** $x-y; x^2+xy+y^2$ **d)** $(2x+5)(4x^2-10x+25); (3x-4)(9x^2+12x+16)$ **e)** $(x^2+y^2)(x^4-x^2y^2+y^4)$ **f)** $x-y$ is not a factor of $x^{3n}+y^{3n}$; $x+y$ is a factor of $x^{3n}+y^{3n}$ if and only if n is odd. **g)** $x-y$ is a factor of $x^{3n}-y^{3n}$; $x+y$ is a factor of $x^{3n}-y^{3n}$ if and only if n is even. **19. a)** yes; yes **b)** yes; no **c)** no **d)** no **20.** $r + 3$ **21. a) i)** neither **ii)** both **iii)** $x + y$

iv) $x - y$ **v)** neither **vi)** both **vii)** $x + y$ **viii)** $x - y$ **b)** $x - y$ is not a factor of $x^n + y^n$; $x + y$ is a factor of $x^n + y^n$ if and only if n is odd; $x - y$ is a factor of $x^n - y^n$; $x + y$ is a factor of $x^n - y^n$ if and only if n is even. **c)** $x + y, x - y$ **d)** $x + y$
22. $a = 1$ or -1 **23. a)** 0 **b) i)** yes **ii)** no **iii)** yes
25. a) $\dfrac{1}{x^2}(x + 1)(x - 1)(3x^2 + 2)$ **b)** $(2x - 3y)(x + y)$

c) $\dfrac{1}{x^3}(x + 1)(x - 1)(x^2 - 2)(x^2 - 3)$

d) $\dfrac{1}{y^3}(y - x)(3y - x)(5y - x)$

Section 2.5, pp. 79–82

Practise

1. a) $-1, 4, -5$ **b)** $2, 7, -6$ **c)** $0, -3, 8$ **d)** $-6, 3$ **2. a)** $0, 2, -3$ **b)** $0, -3, -4$ **c)** $0, 3, -3$ **d)** $0, 2$ **3. a)** $-3, 1, -1$ **b)** $3, 2, -2$ **c)** $-4, 1$ **d)** $3, 4, -4$ **e)** $-1, 2, 3$ **f)** $3, -2$ **4. a)** $1, 7$ **b)** $2, 6, -3$ **c)** $-2, -3, 5$ **d)** $3, -4, 5$ **e)** $-1, 2, 4$ **f)** $1, 3$ **5. a)** $0, 2, -\dfrac{1}{2}$

b) $0, 3, \dfrac{1}{3}$ **c)** $0, \dfrac{2}{3}, -\dfrac{2}{3}$ **d)** $0, -\dfrac{1}{4}$ **6. a)** $-1, -\dfrac{1}{2}, -3$ **b)** $1, \dfrac{2}{3}$

c) $-1, \dfrac{2}{5}, 2$ **d)** $-1, \dfrac{7}{2}$ **e)** $3, -\dfrac{1}{2}$ **f)** $-2, \dfrac{2}{3}, -\dfrac{2}{3}$ **g)** $1, \dfrac{4}{3}, \dfrac{3}{2}$

h) $\dfrac{1}{2}, \pm 1$ **7. a) i)** $0, \pm 2\sqrt{2}$ **ii)** $0, \pm 2.83$ **b) i)** $3, \dfrac{-3 \pm \sqrt{13}}{2}$

ii) $3, 0.30, -3.30$ **c) i)** $4, 1 \pm \sqrt{3}$ **ii)** $4, 2.73, -0.73$

d) i) $-5, 1 \pm \sqrt{6}$ **ii)** $-5, 3.45, -1.45$ **e) i)** $-3, -1 \pm \sqrt{7}$

ii) $-3, 1.65, -3.65$ **f) i)** $-2, \dfrac{-3 \pm \sqrt{17}}{2}$ **ii)** $-2, 0.56, -3.56$

8. a) $-1, \dfrac{-3 \pm i\sqrt{3}}{3}$ **b)** $0, \pm i\sqrt{\dfrac{3}{5}}$ **c)** $4, \pm i\sqrt{\dfrac{5}{2}}$ **d)** $1, \dfrac{2 \pm i\sqrt{2}}{3}$

e) $-2, \dfrac{-3 \pm i\sqrt{31}}{4}$ **f)** $3, \dfrac{-3 \pm i\sqrt{23}}{8}$ **9. a)** $-1, 0.81, -4.31$

b) $-4, 1.19, -1.69$ **c)** -1 **d)** $-1.09, 1.57, 3.51$

e) $1.32, -1.32$ **f)** $-0.75, 1.16, 4.59$

g) $-1, 1.38, 0.27, -2.65$ **h)** $0.88, -0.79, -3.58$

10. a) $k(x^3 - 6x^2 + 3x + 10)$ **b)** $k(x^3 + 3x^2 - 10x - 24)$

c) $k(x^3 - 3x^2 + x + 1)$ **d)** $k(x^3 - 2x - 4)$

Apply, Solve, Communicate

11. 10 **12. a)** $V = \dfrac{1}{3}\pi(x+2)(4-x^2)$ **b)** $-2 \leq x \leq 2$

c) $\dfrac{1}{3}\pi(x+2)^2(2-x)$; when $x = 2$ or -2, the volume is 0.

13. a) $\dfrac{1}{3}\pi(10+x)(100-x^2)$ **b)** 6.49; radius: 7.61 m; height: 16.49 m **c)** The side lengths of the square base should be 13.79 m and the height should be 15.79 m.
14. 3 years **15.** Yes, in 1.1723 decades or about 12 years.

16. a) $\dfrac{1}{2}$ **b)** $-\dfrac{1}{2}, \dfrac{1}{5}, -\dfrac{1}{3}$ **c)** $\dfrac{1}{3}, \dfrac{3}{2}, -\dfrac{3}{2}$ **d)** $-\dfrac{3}{2}, \dfrac{3 \pm 3i\sqrt{3}}{4}$

e) $0, \pm\sqrt{\dfrac{2}{3}}$

f) 2, $-\frac{3}{4}$ **g)** 1, i, $-i$ **h)** 0, $\frac{3 \pm \sqrt{5}}{2}$ **17. a)** $k = 3$; the other

roots are 3 and –4. **b)** $k = -5$; the other roots are 1, $-\frac{1}{3}$.

18. a) 0, 4 **b)** 0, 4; 0, 2 **19.** –7, –8, –9 **20. a)** 0, –1, 2, 3
b) 1, 2, –2, –3 **c)** –2, 3 **d)** ± 1, $\pm \sqrt{3}$ **e)** –3, 2, $1 \pm \sqrt{3}$

f) ± 1, $\pm i$ **g)** –1, $\frac{1}{2}$ **h)** 1, 2, $-\frac{1}{2}$ **21.** 7 cm × 2 cm × 3 cm

22. 15 cm × 3 cm × 3 cm **23.** 25 cm × 20 cm × 5 cm
24. 12 cm × 12 cm × 7 cm **25.** 300 m × 300 m × 100 m
26. \$7 with no bottom, \$31 with a bottom. **27.** –3, ± 1, ± 2
28. Answers will vary. The simplest equation is
$x^3 - 7x^2 + x - 7 = 0$. **29. a)** Answers will vary. The graph
has x-intercepts 5, 2, and –3. **b)** Answers will vary.
For example; the coefficient of x^3 may be specified; the
y-intercept may be specified. **30.** Yes. It has three real
roots; some may have multiplicity greater than one.
31. a) $y = x^3 + x^2 - 5x - 5$ **b)** $2x^3 + 2x^2 - 10x - 10$
32. a) never **b)** always, counting complex roots and
multiplicity **c)** sometimes **d)** sometimes
e) sometimes **f)** never **33. a)** No, if the polynomial
is to have real coefficients. **b)** No, if the polynomial is to
have real coefficients. **c)** A polynomial must have an even
number of complex roots. **34. a)** n is odd, assuming a
double root is counted as two roots, and so on. **b)** n is
even, assuming a double root is counted as two roots,
and so on. **35. a)** no **b)** $1 - i$ **c)** $1 - i$, $3 - 2i$

Section 2.6, pp. 92–95

Practise

1. Estimates to the nearest tenth may vary for
local maximum and minimum values. **a)** domain: $x \in R$;
range: $y \in R$; local maximum: (1.4, 0.4); local minimum:
(2.6, –0.4); y-intercept: –6 **b)** domain: $x \in R$; range: $y \in R$;
local maximum: (2, 6); local minimum: (0, 2); y-intercept:
2 **c)** domain: $x \in R$; range: $y \geq -9$; local maximum:
(–0.5, 1.8); local minimums: (–2.3, –9) and (1.2, –9);
y-intercept: 0 **d)** domain: $x \in R$; range: $y \leq 9.9$; local
maximums: (–0.3, 6) and (3.9, 9.9); local minimum:
(1.8, –9.9); y-intercept: 5 **2.** Estimates to the nearest
tenth may vary. **a)** zeros: –3, –1, 2; $f(x) \geq 0$: $-3 \leq x \leq -1$,
$x \geq 2$; $f(x) < 0$: $-1 < x < 2$, $x < -3$ **b)** zeros: –2, –1, 2, 3;
$f(x) \geq 0$: $-2 \leq x \leq -1$, $2 \leq x \leq 3$; $f(x) < 0$: $x < -2$,
$-1 < x < 2$, $x > 3$ **c)** zeros: –2, –0.3; $f(x) \geq 0$: $x \leq -2$,
$x \geq -0.3$; $f(x) < 0$: $-2 < x < -0.3$ **d)** zeros: –3, –2, 1, 2;
$f(x) \geq 0$: $x \leq -3$, $-2 \leq x \leq 1$, $x \geq 2$; $f(x) < 0$: $-3 < x < -2$,
$1 < x < 2$ **3. a) i)** –2, 0, 2 **ii)** domain: $x \in R$; range: $y \geq -4$
iii) 0 **iv)** local maximum: (0, 0); local minimums:
$(-\sqrt{2}, -4)$ and $(\sqrt{2}, -4)$ **v)** even **vi)** The left-most y-values
are positive. The right-most y-values are positive.
b) i) 0 **ii)** domain: $x \in R$; range: $y \geq 0$ **iii)** 0 **iv)** no local

maximum; local minimum: (0, 0) **v)** even **vi)** The left-most
y-values are positive. The right-most y-values are
positive. **c) i)** –0.6, 0, 3.6 **ii)** domain: $x \in R$; range: $y \in R$
iii) 0 **iv)** local maximum: (–0.3, 0.3); local minimum:
(2.3, –8.3) **v)** none **vi)** The left-most y-values are negative.
The right-most y-values are positive. **d) i)** –1 **ii)** domain:
$x \in R$; range: $y \in R$ **iii)** 4 **iv)** no local maximum; no local
minimum **v)** none **vi)** The left-most y-values are negative.
The right-most y-values are positive. **e) i)** –1.6, 1.6
ii) domain: $x \in R$; range: $y \leq 6$ **iii)** 6 **iv)** local maximum:
(0, 6); no local minimum **v)** even **vi)** The left-most y-values
are negative. The right-most y-values are negative.
f) i) 0, 1.6 **ii)** domain: $x \in R$; range: $y \in R$ **iii)** 0 **iv)** local
maximum: (1.2, 3.3); local minimum: (0, 0) **v)** none
vi) The left-most y-values are positive. The right-most
y-values are negative. **g) i)** –1, 4 **ii)** domain: $x \in R$; range:
$y \in R$ **iii)** –4 **iv)** local maximum: (–1, 0); local minimum:
(2.3, –18.5) **v)** none **vi)** The left-most y-values are
negative. The right-most y-values are positive. **h) i)** 2, 4, 6
ii) domain: $x \in R$; range: $y \in R$ **iii)** 48 **iv)** local maximum:
(5.2, 3.1); local minimum: (2.8, –3.1) **v)** none
vi) The left-most y-values are negative. The right-most
y-values are positive. **i) i)** –2, 0, 1, 3 **ii)** domain: $x \in R$;
range: $y \geq -9$ **iii)** 0 **iv)** local maximum: (0.5, 1.6); local
minimums: (2.3, –9) and (–1.3, –9) **v)** none
vi) The left-most y-values are positive. The right-most
y-values are positive. **j) i)** –3, 0, 1 **ii)** domain: $x \in R$; range:
$y \leq 3$ **iii)** 0 **iv)** local maximums: (–3, 0) and (0.6, 3); local
minimum: (–1.3, –8.6) **v)** none **vi)** The left-most y-values
are negative. The right-most y-values are negative.

5. a) $-2 < x < 3$ **b)** $-\frac{3}{2} \leq x \leq \frac{1}{2}$ **c)** $-2 \leq x \leq 5$

d) $x \leq \frac{1}{2}$ or $x \geq 3$ **e)** $x \geq 0$ **f)** $x \leq -1$ or $\frac{1}{2} \leq x \leq 2$

g) $x \leq -5$ or $-1 \leq x \leq 0$ or $x \geq 2$ **h)** $-1 \leq x \leq 1$ or $x \geq 2$

i) $-\frac{3}{2} < x < 0$ or $x > 2$ **7. a)** $x > 2.24$ or $x < -2.24$

b) $x \leq -0.78$ or $x \geq 1.28$ **c)** $x < -2.37$ or $x > -0.63$
d) $x > 1.59$ **e)** $x \leq 0.59$ or $2 \leq x \leq 3.41$ **f)** $x < -2.70$ or
$-0.48 < x < 0.51$ **g)** $-2.41 \leq x \leq -1.73$ or $0.41 \leq x \leq 1.73$

Apply, Solve, Communicate

8. a) $x \leq -2.3$ or $x \geq 1.3$ **b)** $x < -1.1$ or $1.1 < x < 3.9$
c) $-1 \leq x \leq 0.5$ **d)** $-2 < x < -0.6$ or $x > 0.5$ **9. b)** 17.4 m
10. a) $V = 2\pi r^3$ **c)** domain: $r \geq 0$; range: $V \geq 0$

11. a) $A(x) = 14x^2$; $V(x) = 3x^3$ **b)** $x = \frac{14}{3}$ **c)** $0 < x < \frac{14}{3}$; $x > \frac{14}{3}$

12. a) Answers will vary; for example, $0 \leq T \leq 40$.

c) 110 lm **d)** 27°C **13. a)** $V(x) = \frac{\sqrt{3}}{4}x^3$ **b)** $x > 0$ **d)** 54.1 cm³

e) 3.6 cm **14. a)** $-3 < x < -1$ or $x > 1$ **b)** $x > 1$
15. Answers may vary. The simplest inequalities are given.

a) $x^2 - x - 2 \le 0$ **b)** $2x^2 - 7x - 4 > 0$ **16.** Answers will vary. **17.** $-7 \le x < -5$ **18.** $x < -6.43$

19. a) $r = \dfrac{3 - 2h}{3\pi}$, $S = 2h - \dfrac{4}{3}h^2 + \dfrac{18 - 24h + 8h^2}{9\pi}$,

$V = \dfrac{9h - 12h^2 + 4h^3}{9\pi}$ **b)** $h \le 1.5 - 0.15\pi$

Review of Key Concepts, pp. 107–110

1. a) i) 0, 2, –3 **ii)** At all x-intercepts, the curve crosses the x-axis. **iii)** There is one local maximum point and one local minimum point. **iv)** The left-most y-values are negative. The right-most y-values are positive.
v) no symmetry **b) i)** –1, 1, 3 **ii)** At all x-intercepts, the curve crosses the x-axis. **iii)** There is one local maximum point and one local minimum point. **iv)** The left-most y-values are positive. The right-most y-values are negative. **v)** no symmetry **c) i)** –4, –2, 0, 2 **ii)** At all x-intercepts, the curve crosses the x-axis. **iii)** There are two local minimum points and one local maximum point. **iv)** The left-most y-values are positive. The right-most y-values are positive. **v)** no symmetry
d) i) –5, 0, 4 **ii)** At all x-intercepts, the curve crosses the x-axis. **iii)** There is one local maximum point and one local minimum point. **iv)** The left-most y-values are negative. The right-most y-values are positive. **v)** no symmetry **e) i)** 2, –2 **ii)** At all x-intercepts, the curve crosses the x-axis. **iii)** There are two local maximum points and one local minimum point. **iv)** The left-most y-values are negative. The right-most y-values are negative.

v) even **2. a)** $V = \dfrac{10\pi(x^2 + 10x)^2}{x^2 + 10x - 25}$ **b)** $x > 5(\sqrt{2} - 1)$

c) The function has no zeros. **3. a)** $x + 8$; $x \ne -2$
b) $y^2 + 2y + 2$; $y \ne 1$ **c)** $2m - 1$, remainder 2; $m \ne -\dfrac{3}{2}$
d) $x^2 - 2x + 3$, remainder –18; $x \ne -3$ **e)** $3y - 2$, remainder $6y - 5$ **4. a)** $4x - 1$ **b)** 89 mm × 51 mm

5. a) $x^2 - x - 1$; $x \ne -3$ **b)** $x^2 - 3x - 5$; $x \ne \dfrac{1}{2}$

c) $x^3 - 3x + 1$; $x \ne \dfrac{4}{3}$ **6. a)** 6 **b)** 7 **c)** –2 **d)** 14 **e)** 11

7. a) 4 **b)** 7 **8. b)** $Q(t) = 0.5t + 25$, $R = 300$; $Q(t)$ is the averages sales between the 10th day after release and the tth day after release. R is the total sales 10 days after release. **c)** Answers will vary. **d)** No; after 82 days.

9. a) –18 **b)** $\dfrac{3}{2}$ **c)** 15 **11. a)** $(x + 1)^2(x - 3)$

b) $(x + 4)(x^2 + x - 1)$ **c)** $(x - 1)(x + 1)(2x - 1)$

d) $(x - 1)(x + 4)(3x + 4)$ **12.** one possibility is $x + 2$, $x - 4$

and $2x + 3$ **13. a)** 0, 3, –3 **b)** –1, 2 **c)** $\dfrac{1}{2}$, 3, –2

d) 1, $\dfrac{-5 \pm \sqrt{65}}{10}$ **14. a)** 1, $1 \pm \sqrt{2}$ **b)** –2, $\dfrac{2 \pm \sqrt{7}}{2}$ **c)** –1, $\pm 4i$

d) 3, $-1 \pm i\sqrt{3}$ **15.** 25 cm × 20 cm × 5 cm

16. a) Answers will vary. **b)** No; an exponential function has no zeros. **c) i)** No; an exponential function has no zeros. **17. a) i)** domain: $x \in$ R; range: $y \in$ R
ii) 0 **iii)** 0, –4, 4 **iv)** $f(x) > 0$: $-4 < x < 0$, $x > 4$; $f(x) \le 0$: $x \le -4$, $0 \le x \le 4$ **v)** odd
vi) The left-most y-values are negative. The right-most y-values are positive. **b) i)** domain: $x \in$ R; range: $y \ge -1$
ii) 0 **iii)** 0, 1, –1, 2 **iv)** $f(x) > 0$: $x < -1$, $0 < x < 1$, $x > 2$; $f(x) \le 0$: $-1 \le x \le 0$, $1 \le x \le 2$ **v)** none
vi) The left-most y-values are positive.

The right-most y-values are positive. **c) i)** domain: $x \in$ R; range: $y \in$ R **ii)** –16 **iii)** 2, –2, –4
iv) $f(x) > 0$: $-4 < x < -2$, $x > 2$; $f(x) \le 0$: $-2 \le x \le 2$, $x \le -4$ **v)** none **vi)** The left-most y-values are negative. The right-most y-values are positive. **d) i)** domain: $x \in$ R; range: $y \in$ R **ii)** –30 **iii)** –2, 3, 5 **iv)** $f(x) > 0$: $x < -2$, $3 < x < 5$; $f(x) \le 0$: $-2 \le x \le 3$, $x \ge 5$ **v)** none
vi) The left-most y-values are positive.

The right-most y-values are negative. **e) i)** domain: $x \in$ R; range: $y \le 36$ **ii)** 0 **iii)** 0, 3, –1, –4 **iv)** $f(x) > 0$: $-4 < x < -1$, $0 < x < 3$; $f(x) \le 0$: $x \le -4$, $-1 \le x \le 0$, $x \ge 3$ **v)** none
vi) The left-most y-values are negative. The right-most y-values are negative. **18. a) i)** domain: $x \in$ R; range: $y \ge -20.3$ **ii)** 0 **iii)** 0, 3, –3 **iv)** local maximum: $(0, 0)$; local minimums: $(-2.1, -20.3)$, $(2.1, -20.3)$
v) even **vi)** The left-most y-values are positive. The right-most y-values are positive.
b) i) domain: $x \in$ R; range: $y \in$ R **ii)** 0 **iii)** 0, 5
iv) local maximum: $(0, 0)$; local minimum: $(-3.3, -18.5)$
v) none **vi)** The left-most y-values are negative. The right-most y-values are positive. **c) i)** domain: $x \in$ R; range: $y \in$ R **ii)** 0 **iii)** 0, 2, –2 **iv)** local maximum: $(1.2, 3.1)$; local minimum: $(-1.2, -3.1)$ **v)** odd
vi) The left-most y-values are negative. The right-most y-values are positive. **d) i)** domain: $x \in$ R; range: $y \ge -16$ **ii)** 9 **iii)** 1, –1, 3, –3 **iv)** local maximum: $(0, 9)$; local minimums: $(-2.2, -16)$ and $(2.2, -16)$ **v)** even
vi) The left-most y-values are positive. The right-most y-values are positive. **e) i)** domain: $x \in$ R; range: $y \ge -2$ **ii)** –2 **iii)** 1.2, –1.2 **iv)** no local maximum; local minimum: $(0, -2)$ **v)** even **vi)** The left-most y-values are positive. The right-most y-values are positive. **f) i)** domain: $x \in$ R; range: $y \in$ R **ii)** 0 **iii)** 0, –3 **iv)** local maximum: $(0, 0)$; local minimum: $(-2, -4)$ **v)** none **vi)** The left-most y-values are positive. The right-most y-values are negative.
g) i) domain: $x \in$ R; range: $y \in$ R **ii)** 0 **iii)** 0, 2.6, 0.4 **iv)** local maximum: $(1.8, 2.1)$; local minimum: $(0.2, -0.1)$
v) none **vi)** The left-most y-values are positive. The right-most y-values are negative. **h) i)** domain: $x \in$ R; range: $y \in$ R **ii)** –3 **iii)** 2.4 **iv)** local maximum: $(-0.5, -2.4)$;

local minimum: $(1.2, -5.1)$ **v)** none **vi)** The left-most y-values are negative. The right-most y-values are positive. **19. a)** $x < -3$ or $x > 0$ **b)** $-4 < x < 1$
c) $x = -3$ **d)** $-4 \le x \le -2$ or $x \ge 2$ **e)** $x > 3.76$
20. a) $x < -2.56$ or $x > 1.56$ **b)** x is any real number
c) $-0.53 \le x \le 0.65$ or $x \ge 2.88$ **d)** $-1.41 < x < 1.41$
21. $0.82 < t < 1.96$, $6.93 < t \le 8$

22. a)

x	y	1st	2nd	3rd
-3	40			
		-16		
-1	24		-8	
		-24		48
1	0		40	
		16		48
3	16		88	
		104		48
5	120		136	
		240		48
7	360		184	
		424		
9	784			

b) 3 **c)** 1, 2, -13, 10 **d)** $y = x^3 + 2x^2 - 13x + 10$
23. a) $y = 2x^2 - 3x + 2$ **b)** $y = x^3 - 7x - 3$ **d)** $7 - x^2 + x^3 - x^4$
e) $y = 5x^2 + 2$ **f)** $y = -2x^3 + 9x^2$ **g)** $y = 3x^3 - 4x^2 - 6x + 7$
h) $y = -3x^2 + 4x - 5$ **24. a)** $y = a(x^3 - 2x^2 - 9x + 18)$
b) $y = b(x^3 + 4x^2 + x - 6)$ **c)** $y = c(x^4 - 5x^3 + 2x^2 + 8x)$
25. a) $y = x^3 - x^2 + x - 1$ **b)** $y = x^4 - 2x^3 + 3$
26. $y = \dfrac{1}{4}(x + 5)(x + 1)(x - 2)(x - 4)$
27. a) $y = x^3 - 6x^2 + 12x - 8$ **b)** $y = x^4 + 2$

Chapter Test, pp. 111–112

1. a) i) domain: $x \in R$; range: $y \in R$ **ii)** 0, 2, -3 **iii)** At all the x-intercepts, the curve crosses the x-axis. **iv)** turning points: maximum, minimum **v)** The left-most y-values are negative. The right-most y-values are positive. **vi)** none
b) i) domain: $x \in R$; range: $y \in R$ **ii)** -1, 1, 3 **iii)** At all the x-intercepts, the curve crosses the x-axis. **iv)** turning points: minimum, maximum **v)** The left-most y-values are positive. The right-most y-values are negative. **vi)** none
c) i) domain: $x \in R$; range: $y \ge -16$ **ii)** -4, -2, 0, 2 **iii)** At all the x-intercepts, the curve crosses the x-axis. **iv)** turning points: minimum, maximum, minimum **v)** The left-most y-values are positive. The right-most y-values are positive. **vi)** none **d) i)** domain: $x \in R$; range: $y \in R$
ii) 0, -5, 4 **iii)** At all the x-intercepts, the curve crosses the x-axis. **iv)** turning points: maximum, minimum **v)** The left-most y-values are negative. The right-most y-values

are positive. **vi)** none **e) i)** domain: $x \in R$; range: $y \le \dfrac{25}{4}$
ii) 2, -2 **iii)** At all the x-intercepts, the curve crosses the x-axis. **iv)** turning points: maximum, minimum, maximum **v)** The left-most y-values are negative. The right-most y-values are negative. **vi)** even **2. a)** $x^2 + 3x + 1$, remainder 4; $x \ne 2$ **b)** $y - 1$, remainder 1 **c)** $3x^2 - 5x + 2$, remainder 4; $x \ne -\dfrac{3}{2}$ **3.** $2x - 3$ **4. a)** -10 **b)** -2
5. $m = -4$, $n = -9$ **7. a)** $(x - 1)(x - 3)(x + 6)$
b) $(x + 1)(3x - 1)(x - 4)$ **8.** $x \pm 1$, $x \pm 5$, $2x \pm 1$, $2x \pm 5$, $3x \pm 1$, $3x \pm 5$, $6x \pm 1$, $6x \pm 5$ **9. a)** 3, 2, -2
b) -1, $3 \pm 2\sqrt{2}$ **c)** -2, $-1 \pm 2i$ **d)** 1, $\dfrac{1}{3}$, 8 **10.** 3.5 cm
11. a) $x \le -2$ or $x \ge 3$ **b)** $-4 < x < 1$ or $x > 3$
12. a) $-2.19 \le x \le 3.19$ **b)** $x > -4.14$
13. a) $y = a(x^3 - 6x^2 + 8x)$ **b)** $y = b(x^4 + 5x^3 + 2x^2 - 8x)$
14. $y = x^3 - 3x^2 - 2x + 5$ **15.** $y = 1 - 3x - 3x^2 - x^3$
16. a) when $t = 4.6$ **b)** when $t = 7.5$

Challenge Problems, p. 113

1. $4\left(\dfrac{3}{2}\right)^n + 1$ **2.** $-\dfrac{1}{3}$ **3.** 9:40 **4.** $(-2, 3)$; -13 **5.** 36
6. b) The square root is about $\pm(2.327 + 0.645i)$.
7. $V = (1 + 2x)(2 + 2x)(4 + 2x) - 8 = 8x^3 + 28x^2 + 28x$;
10 cm **8.** $\sqrt[3]{9} - \sqrt[3]{3}$, $\sqrt[3]{9}\left(\dfrac{-1 + i\sqrt{3}}{2}\right) - \sqrt[3]{3}\left(\dfrac{-1 - i\sqrt{3}}{2}\right)$,
$\sqrt[3]{9}\left(\dfrac{-1 - i\sqrt{3}}{2}\right) - \sqrt[3]{3}\left(\dfrac{-1 + i\sqrt{3}}{2}\right)$
9. 5.96 m **10.** $y = \dfrac{1}{200}x^2 + \dfrac{1}{5}x - \dfrac{1}{2}$

Cumulative Review: Chapters 1 and 2, pp. 114–115

1. a) neither **b)** even **2.** Yes. **3. a)** $(-\infty, \infty)$ **b)** $(-\infty, 1)$ or $(1, \infty)$ **c)** $[-3, 3]$ **4. b)–d)** Answers will vary. **5. b)–d)** Answers will vary. **6. a)** $(-\infty, \infty)$ **b)** **7.** Yes. **8. b)** $(-\infty, -5)$ or $(-5, 1)$ or $(1, \infty)$ **d)** x- and y-intercepts 0 **9. a)** \$1030.38 **b)** \$1127.16 **10. a) i)** 0 **ii)** 0, -2, 3 **iii)** minimum: $(-1.12, -4.06)$, maximum: $(1.79, 8.21)$ **iv)** graph crosses the x-axis **v)** increasing to the left, decreasing to the right **vi)** none **b) i)** 2 **ii)** -1, 1, 2 **iii)** maximum: $(-0.22, 2.11)$, minimum: $(1.55, -0.63)$ **iv)** graph crosses the x-axis **v)** decreasing to the left, increasing to the right **vi)** none
c) i) 0 **ii)** -4, -3, 0, 4 **iii)** maximums: $(-3.55, 6.63)$, $(2.60, 134.53)$; minimum: $(-1.30, -31.63)$ **iv)** graph crosses the x-axis **v)** decreasing to the left and the right **vi)** none
d) i) 0 **ii)** -3, 0, 4 **iii)** maximum: $(-1.69, 12.60)$, minimum: $(2.36, -20.75)$ **iv)** graph crosses the x-axis **v)** decreasing to

the left, increasing to the right **vi)** none **e) i)** 0 **ii)** 0 (double),
$-1, -2$ **iii)** minimums: $(-1.64, -0.62), (0, 0)$; maximum:
$(-0.61, 0.20)$ **iv)** graph crosses the x-axis except at the
minimum point $(0, 0)$ **v)** increasing to the left and the
right **vi)** none **11. a)** $m - 11$, R 72; $m \neq -6$

b) $2y + 5$; $y \neq \dfrac{4}{5}$ **c)** $x + 4$ **12. a)** 0 **b)** 0 **13.** no solution

14. a) $(x + 1)(x - 4)(x - 5)$ **b)** $(x + 1)(4x - 3)(x - 3)$

15. a) $0, \pm 5$ **b)** $\pm 1, \dfrac{1}{2}$ **c)** $3, -2, -4$ **d)** $2, 7, -4$ **e)** $1, \dfrac{1}{4}, 1 \pm \sqrt{7}$

f) $-3, 4 \pm I$ **16.** $y = k(x + 3)(x - 2)(x - 6); k \in R$

17. a) domain and range: $(-\infty, \infty)$ **b)** zeros: $-2, 1, 3$;
y-intercept: **c)** maximum: $(-0.79, 8.21)$, minimum:
$(2.12, -4.06)$ **d)** $f(x) > 0$ on $(-2, 1)$ or $(3, \infty)$, $f(x) < 0$
on $(-\infty, -2)$ or $(1, 3)$ **e)** neither even nor odd
f) decreasing to the left, increasing to the right

18. a) $x \in (-\infty, 0)$ or $(3, \infty)$ **b)** $x \in [-3, 2]$

c) $x \in [-5, -2]$ or $[3, \infty]$ **19. a)** $x \in (-2.19, 3.19)$

b) $x \in (-\infty, -5.81]$ or $[-1.71, 2.52]$ **20. a)** $y = 2x^2 - 2x - 3$

b) $y = x^4 + 2x^3 - x^2 - 2x$ **c)** $y = x^3 = x^2 - 4x + 4$

Chapter 3

Review of Prerequisite Skills, pp. 118–119

1. a) i) $4, 2$ **b) i)** $2, 3$ **c) i)** $1, 5$ **d) i)** $0, -2$ **e) i)** $-0.5, -1$
f) i) $-1, -4$ **g) i)** $-2, 1$ **h) i)** $-4, -5$

2. a) $y = 3x + 2$ **b)** $y = -\dfrac{19}{5}x + \dfrac{111}{5}$ **c)** $y = -\dfrac{11}{6}x - \dfrac{26}{3}$

d) $y = 2x + 7$ **e)** $y = 3$ **f)** $y = -2x$

3. a) $(x + 2)(x + 3)$ **b)** $(x - 3)(x - 4)$ **c)** $(x - 6)(x + 3)$

d) $(x + 7)(x - 2)$ **e)** $x(x - 7)(x - 2)$ **f)** $2x(x + 1)^2$

4. a) $(3x - 4)(x - 2)$ **b)** $(4x + 1)(x + 6)$ **c)** $(5x - 2)(3x + 1)$

d) $-2x(4x + 3)(2x - 3)$ **e)** $3(3x + 1)^2$ **f)** $2x(2x - 5)(x + 6)$

5. a) $(x + 5)(x - 5)$ **b)** $(3x + 4)(3x - 4)$ **c)** $4(4 + 3y)(4 - 3y)$

d) $y(y + 7)(y - 7)$ **6. a)** $(x - 3)(x^2 + 3x + 9)$

b) $(m + 4)(m^2 - 4m + 16)$ **c)** $(x^2 - 2)(x^4 + 2x^2 + 4)$

d) $8(2y + 3x)(4y^2 - 6xy + 9x^2)$

e) $(2x - 5y)(4x^2 + 10xy + 25y^2)$ **f)** $(x^2 + 2)(x^4 - 2x^2 + 4)$

g) $y(y - 7)(y^2 + 7y + 49)$ **h)** $4x(x + 1)(x^2 - x + 1)$

i) $2y(y - 2)(y^2 + 2y + 4)$ **j)** $x^2(3x + 4)(9x^2 - 12x + 16)$

k) $x^2(2x - 3)(4x^2 + 6x + 9)$ **l)** $3x^2(y + 3)(y^2 - 3y + 9)$

7. a) $(x - 1)(x + 2)(x + 4)$ **b)** $(x + 1)(x + 2)(x - 3)$

c) $(x + 1)(x - 3)(2x - 1)$ **d)** $(x + 2)(x + 3)(x - 4)$

e) $(x + 1)(x - 3)(x + 4)$ **f)** $(x - 2)(x + 3)(x + 4)$

g) $(x - 1)(x + 1)(x - 2)(x + 5)$ **h)** $(x + 2)^2(2x - 1)(2x + 3)$

i) $(x - 1)(x - 2)(x - 3)(x + 3)$ **8. a)** $x + 3, x \neq -2$

b) $x - 9, x \neq -1$ **c)** $2x + 1, x \neq 5$

d) $\dfrac{3x + 4}{x + 5}; x \neq 3, -5$ **e)** $\dfrac{x - 7}{2x - 1}; x \neq \dfrac{1}{2}, -\dfrac{1}{2}$

f) $\dfrac{3x + 2}{3x - 2}; x \neq \dfrac{1}{2}, \dfrac{2}{3}$ **9. a)** $-\dfrac{1}{2(x + 2)}; x \neq 0, -2$ **b)** $\dfrac{-2}{3(x + 3)};$

$x \neq 0, -3$ **c)** $-\dfrac{x + 10}{25(x + 5)^2}; x \neq 0, -5$ **10. a)** $\sqrt{x + 1} + 1; x > 0$

b) $3(\sqrt{x + 3} - \sqrt{x}), x \geq 0$ **c)** $x(\sqrt{x + 4} + \sqrt{x}), x \geq 0$

d) $\sqrt{x + 3} + 2, x \geq -3, x \neq 1$ **e)** $\sqrt{x^2 + 4} + 2, x \neq 0$

f) $\dfrac{x}{2}(\sqrt{x + 1} + \sqrt{x - 1}), x \geq 1$

11. a) translate 2 units up **b)** translate 3 units to the right
c) translate 1 unit down **d)** translate 2 units to the left
e) compress horizontally by a factor of 2 **12. a)** 20
b) $h^2 + 5h + 6$ **c)** 10 **d)** $h + 9, h \neq 0$ **13. a) i)** 6 **ii)** 5 **iii)** $h + 4$,
$h \neq 0$ **b) i)** 9 **ii)** 8 **iii)** $h + 7$, **c) i)** $-\dfrac{1}{8}$ **ii)** $-\dfrac{1}{6}$ **iii)** $-\dfrac{1}{2(h + 2)}, h \neq 0, -2$

d) i) 28 **ii)** 19 **iii)** $h^2 + 6h + 12, h \neq 0$ **14. a)** $y = 3x - 2$

b) $y = x^2 - 4$ **15.** 5.6 h **16.** 34.7 L/min **17.** 1.5 trucks/min

Section 3.1, pp. 127–129

Practise

1. a) i) 4.75 **ii)** 3.8125 **iii)** 3.1525 **iv)** 3.015 025
v) 3.001 500 25 **vi)** 1.75 **vii)** 2.3125 **viii)** 2.8525
ix) 2.985 025 **x)** 2.998 500 25 **b)** approaching 2 from
above, then from below **c)** 3 **d)** $y = 3x - 4$

2. a)–e) i) Answers will vary. **a) ii)** 4 **iii)** $y = 4x - 1$
b) ii) 4 **iii)** $y = 4x$ **c) ii)** 2 **iii)** $y = 2x - 3$ **d) ii)** -1 **iii)** $y = -x + 2$

e) ii) $\dfrac{1}{4}$ **iii)** $y = \dfrac{1}{4}x + 1$

Apply, Solve, Communicate

3. a) The slope represents the rate (in L/min) at which
water is draining out.

b) slope at P: -72; slope at R: -36 **c)** -72 **d)** -36

e) $V = 1.2t^2 - 120t + 3000$; slope at P: -72; slope at R: -36

f) 96 L/min **4. a)** Estimates will vary; sample estimates are
given. **i)** 77 **ii)** 79 **iii)** 74 **b) i)** 77.5 **ii)** 79 **iii)** 74.5 **c)** no; no

d) Answers will vary. **5.** Actual slope is $-\dfrac{2}{5}$.

6. 1250 people/year **7.** Answers will vary. **8. a) i)** 1.732
ii) -2.5 **iii)** 2.246 **iv)** 1.710 **v)** -9.966 **vi)** 0 **vii)** 2.165
viii) 2.723 **ix)** -1.409 **x)** -9.972 **b)** No limit. **d)** Answers
may vary. **e)** Answers may vary. The slope is -5π.

Section 3.2, pp. 137–139

Practise

1. a) $\dfrac{f(x) - f(2)}{x - 2}$ **b)** $m = \lim\limits_{x \to 2} \dfrac{f(x) - f(2)}{x - 2}$ **2. a)** $\dfrac{f(2 + h) - f(2)}{h}$

b) $m = \lim\limits_{h \to 0} \dfrac{f(2 + h) - f(2)}{h}$ **3. a)** 0 **b)** $y = 1$

4. a) 3 **b)** $y = 3x - 2$ **5. a)** 4 **b)** -4 **c)** $\dfrac{1}{4}$ **d)** $-\dfrac{1}{4}$

e) -1 **f)** -2 **g)** 1 **h)** $-\dfrac{1}{2}$

6. a) $y = -3x + 2$ **b)** $y = 4x + 8$ **c)** $y = -x - 5$
d) $x + 4y - 7 = 0$ **e)** $y = -3x + 11$ **f)** $x + 2y - 4 = 0$
7. a) i) -8 **ii)** -4 **iii)** 0 **iv)** 4

Apply, Solve, Communicate

8. a) i) $y = x$ **ii)** The definition is inadequate since
the tangent to a line is a coincident line. **b) i)** $y = 0$
ii) The definition is inadequate since the tangent crosses
the curve. **9. a) i)** 6 **ii)** $y = 6x - 18$
b) i) 0 **ii)** $y = -5$ **c) i)** -4 **ii)** $y = -4x + 8$ **d) i)** 12
ii) $y = 12x - 18$ **e) i)** -12 **ii)** $y = -12x + 24$ **f) i)** 1
ii) $y = x - 3$ **g) i)** $\frac{1}{4}$ **ii)** $y = \frac{1}{4}x + \frac{3}{2}$ **h) i)** 4 **ii)** $y = 4x - 3$
10. a) $y = x$ **b)** $y = 0$ **c)** $y = -2x + 7$ **d)** $y = \frac{1}{4}x - 1$
e) $y = \frac{4}{5}x + \frac{9}{5}$ **f)** $y = -\frac{1}{16}x + \frac{3}{4}$ **11. a) i)** $2a$
ii) $-4, -2, 0, 2, 4$ **b) i)** $3a^2$ **ii)** 12, 3, 0, 3, 12
c) i) $2a + 2$ **ii)** $-2, 0, 2, 4, 6$ **d) i)** $-\dfrac{6}{(a-3)^2}$
ii) $-\dfrac{6}{25}, -\dfrac{3}{8}, -\dfrac{2}{3}, -\dfrac{3}{2}, -6$ **e) i)** $\dfrac{a}{\sqrt{a^2+1}}$
ii) $-\dfrac{2}{\sqrt{5}}, -\dfrac{1}{\sqrt{2}}, 0, \dfrac{1}{\sqrt{2}}, \dfrac{2}{\sqrt{5}}$ **f) i)** $-\dfrac{2a}{(a^2+1)^2}$
ii) $\dfrac{4}{25}, \dfrac{1}{2}, 0, -\dfrac{1}{2}, -\dfrac{4}{25}$ **a)–f) iii)** Answers may vary.
12. a) 1.17×10^6 N **b)** 1.24×10^6 N **c)** 1.27×10^6 N
d) 1.32×10^6 N **13.** 9.79 m/s² **14. b)** yes **c)** 0 **d)** $t = 2$; the
slope is 0. **e)** 0 **f)** It is not useful, since you do not
discover what is happening until after it has happened.
15. a) $4a + 3$ **b)** $\left(\dfrac{11}{4}, \dfrac{187}{8} \right)$

16. a)

x	$f(x)$
10	$1.001\,000\,45 \times 10^{10}$
1	$1.010\,045\,12$
0.1	$1.104\,622\,13 \times 10^{-10}$
0.01	$2.593\,742\,46 \times 10^{-20}$
0.001	1.024×10^{-27}

b) 0

c)

x	$f(x)$
0.0001	$2.593\,742\,46 \times 10^{-30}$
0.000\,01	$1.104\,622\,13 \times 10^{-30}$
0.000\,001	$1.010\,045\,12 \times 10^{-30}$
0.000\,000\,1	$1.001\,000\,45 \times 10^{-30}$

d) yes

17. a) $y = 4x + 8$ **b)** $y = 12x + 16$, $y = 12x - 16$ **18.** At
$x = -1$, $y = 2x + 2$; at $x = 0$, $y = -x$; at $x = 1$, $y = 2x - 2$.
19. $\left(1, \dfrac{1}{2}\right), \left(-1, \dfrac{1}{2}\right)$ **20. a)** 1092 N **b)** Not possible

Section 3.3, pp. 153–156

Practise

1. a) 3 **b)** 4 **c)** 0 **d)** does not exist; infinite discontinuity
e) $\dfrac{1}{2}$ **2. a)** 4 **b)** 1 **c)** 1 **d)** 1 **e)** $\dfrac{1}{2}$ **f)** $\dfrac{1}{2}$ **g)** $\dfrac{1}{2}$ **h)** 2 **i)** 4
j) does not exist; jump discontinuity **k)** 3 **l)** 5 **m)** does not
exist; jump discontinuity **n)** 3 **3. a)** 12 **b)** 1 **c)** -3
d) undefined **e)** -3 **f)** -3 **g)** 6 **h)** 6 **i)** 12 **j)** does not exist; jump
discontinuity **4.** Question 1: removable discontinuity at
$x = -1$; infinite discontinuity at $x = 4$. Question 2:
removable discontinuity at $x = 1$; jump discontinuity at
$x = 4$; jump discontinuity at $x = 6$. Question 3: removable
discontinuity at $x = 2$; jump discontinuity at $x = 5$.
5. a) -2 **b)** -2 **c)** -2 **6. a)** 4 **b)** -1 **c)** does not exist; one-sided
limits are different (jump discontinuity) **7. a)** 2 **b)** -2
c) does not exist; one-sided limits are different (jump
discontinuity) **8. a)** -1 **b)** -1 **c)** -1 **9. a)** 0 **b)** does not exist
c) 0 **d)** 0 **e)** 0 **f)** -1 **g)** 1 **h)** does not exist **10. a)** 4 **b)** π **c)** 5
d) 16 **e)** 2 **f)** 17 **g)** 0 **h)** -2 **i)** 3 **j)** 8 **11. a)** 6 **b)** $\dfrac{1}{4}$ **c)** 2 **d)** $-\dfrac{1}{7}$
e) $\dfrac{5}{6}$ **f)** 5 **g)** -7 **h)** 3 **i)** $\dfrac{1}{27}$ **j)** 12 **k)** 4 **l)** $-\dfrac{1}{9}$

Apply, Solve, Communicate

12. a) 2 **b)** -3 **c)** $\sqrt{3}$ **d)** -1 **e)** $\dfrac{1}{2}$ **f)** 2 **g)** does not exist; jump
discontinuity **h)** does not exist **i)** 3 **j)** 0 **13. a)** $x = 2$ **b)** $x = 3$
c) $x = -1$ **d)** $x = 1$ **14. b) i)** 800 **ii)** 900 **iii)** does not exist
iv) 900 **v)** 1000 **vi)** does not exist **15. b) i)** 0.94 **ii)** 1.55
iii) does not exist **iv)** 1.55 **v)** 2.05 **vi)** does not exist
16. b) any whole number values of a **17.** At 0.25 km,
0.35 km, 0.45 km, ... **18. b)** $t = 0, 1, 2, 3$
19. a) $I(R) = \dfrac{2(5 + R)}{R}(1 - H(2 - R))$; $R \geq 0$ **c) i)** 0 **ii)** 7
iii) 0 **iv)** does not exist **20. a)** 0 **b)** 0 **21. a)** -6 **b)** 12 **c)** $-\dfrac{1}{2}$
22. Answers will vary. For example, $f(x) = \dfrac{1}{x}$, $g(x) = -\dfrac{1}{x}$.
23. $\dfrac{3}{2}$ **24.** $f(x)$ is not discontinuous anywhere.
25. $c = 0, \dfrac{1}{2},$ or $\dfrac{3}{2}$

Technology Extension, pp. 157–158

1. a) does not exist **b)** 0 **c)** 5 **d)** -2 **2. a)** 1 **b)** 3 **3. a)** 12 **b)** -6
4. a) $\sqrt{2}$ **b)** 0 **5. a)** 1 **b)** $2x$ **c)** $2x + 2$ **d)** $-\dfrac{1}{x^2}$ **e)** $-\dfrac{6}{x^3}$ **f)** $\dfrac{1}{2\sqrt{x}}$

Section 3.4, pp. 168–171

Apply, Solve, Communicate

1. a) $18 + 3h$ **b)** 18 **2. a)** $\dfrac{f(a + h) - f(a)}{h}$

b) $\lim_{h \to 0} \dfrac{f(a+h)-f(a)}{h}$ **3. a) i)** -3 m/s **ii)** -2 m/s **iii)** -1.2 m/s
iv) -1.1 m/s **v)** -1.02 m/s **b)** -1 m/s **4. a) i)** 15.5 m/s
ii) 17.95 m/s **iii)** 19.91 m/s **iv)** 20.155 m/s **v)** 20.351 m/s
b) 20.4 m/s **5. a) i)** 0 m/s **ii)** 1 m/s **iii)** 1.5 m/s **iv)** 1.9 m/s
b) 2 m/s **6. a) i)** 8 m/s **ii)** 7 m/s **iii)** 6.5 m/s **iv)** 6.1 m/s
b) 6 m/s **7.** $0.8a + 5$; 5.8 m/s, 6.6 m/s, 7.4 m/s
8. a) i) $-0.06°$C/min **ii)** $-0.08°$C/min **iii)** $-0.275°$C/min
iv) $-0.18°$C/min **b)** about $-0.12°$C/min **9. a) i)** $1.0°$C/h
ii) $0.75°$C/h **iii)** $1.15°$C/h **b)** about $0.95°$C/h **c) i)** $-1.25°$C/h
ii) $-1.2°$C/h **iii)** $-1.15°$C/h **d)** about $-1.2°$C/h
10. b) i) 43 **ii)** 167 **iii)** 50 **iv)** 100 **c)** Using an exponential
regression: $N = 87.68(1.16)^{t-1978}$ **d)** 82.8 **11. a) i)** 3650
ii) 3700 **iii)** 6200 **iv)** 6000 **b)** Estimates will vary.
c) $P = 66.43(t-1991)^3 - 755.19(t-1991)^2 + 7123.95$
$(t-1991) + 399\,722.24$; 4554.60 **d)** Answers may vary.
12. a) $-\dfrac{2}{3}$; **b)** $-\dfrac{4}{9}$ **13. a) i)** 61 **ii)** 49.21 **iii)** 48.1201 **b)** 48
14. $-\dfrac{250}{9}$ L/min **15. a) i)** 41 **ii)** 40.5 **iii)** 40.1 **b)** 40
16. a) i) 35.85 **ii)** 36.265 **iii)** 36.597 **iv)** 36.6385 **v)** 36.6717
b) 36.68 **c)** $40 - 1.66a$ **d)** after $\dfrac{4000}{83}$ s **e)** 40 m/s (down)
f) 481.928 m **17 b)** $v = 8 - 2a$ **18. a)** $-\dfrac{90}{x_0^2}$ **b) i)** -22.5 N
ii) -0.9 N **iii)** -0.009 N **c)** $-225\,000$ N
d) Both become very small. **19.** No

Review of Key Concepts, pp. 173–176

1. a)–c) i) Answers will vary. **a) ii)** 3 **iii)** $y = 3x - 1$ **b) ii)** 10
iii) $y = 10x - 16$ **c) ii)** $\dfrac{1}{4}$ **iii)** $y = \dfrac{1}{4}x + \dfrac{5}{4}$ **2. a)** 3.54; 3.37
b) 3.455 **c)** 2.315 **d)** Answers may vary. 3.5, 2.3
e) Answers may vary depending on method used. 2.98
3. a) Rate at which the body is eliminating the medicine
b) $\dfrac{10}{3}$ mg/h **4. a)** Answers will vary. **b)** Answers will vary.
-0.017 s/year, -0.049 s/year. **5. a)** $y = 4x - 3$ **b)** $y = 6x + 3$
c) $y = \dfrac{1}{6}x + 2$ **d)** $y = 1$ **e)** $y = -x + 4$ **f)** $y = -\dfrac{1}{2}x + \dfrac{3}{2}$
6. a) $y = 2x + 4$ **b)** $y = 2x - 3$ **c)** $y = \dfrac{1}{2}x + \dfrac{3}{2}$
d) $y = -\dfrac{1}{16}x + \dfrac{1}{2}$ **e)** $y = \dfrac{1}{8}x + \dfrac{3}{8}$ **f)** $y = -\dfrac{4}{3}x + \dfrac{11}{3}$
7. a) i) -8 **ii)** $y = -8x + 8$ **b) i)** 12 **ii)** $y = 12x - 16$
c) i) $\dfrac{1}{6}$ **ii)** $y = \dfrac{1}{6}x + \dfrac{7}{6}$ **d) i)** -4 **ii)** $y = -4x$
8. a) $2a - 3$ **b)** $-5, -3, -1, 1, 3$ **c)** $\left(\dfrac{3}{2}, -\dfrac{49}{4}\right)$
9. a) $y = 2x - 0.5$ **b)** Yes **10. a)** 2 **b)** -3 **c)** -3

d) does not exist; $\lim_{x \to -4^-} f(x) \neq \lim_{x \to -4^+} f(x)$
e) 3 **f)** 3 **g)** 0 **h)** 3 **i)** -3 **j)** -3 **k)** -3 **l)** -3 **11. a) i)** jump
discontinuity **ii)** removable discontinuity **iii)** continuous
b) No, unless the type of discontinuity is known. **12. a)** 3
b) 2 **c)** 3 **d)** does not exist; $\lim_{x \to -3^-} g(x) \neq \lim_{x \to -3^+} g(x)$
e) 4 **f)** 4 **g)** 4 **h)** 4 **i)** 3 **j)** 3 **k)** 4 **l)** 3 **m)** does not exist; $g(x)$
not defined. **n)** does not exist; $g(x)$ not defined
13. a) i) jump discontinuity **ii)** continuous **iii)** removable
discontinuity **iv)** discontinuous; end point
b) i) The value of $g(a)$ has no effect. **ii)** The value of $g(a)$
must equal $\lim_{x \to a} g(x)$ for $g(x)$ to be continuous at a.
14. a) 3 **b)** 3 **c)** 3 **15. a)** 1 **b)** 1 **c)** 1 **16. a)** 1 **b)** 1 **c)** 1 **17. a)** 0
b) 0 **c)** 0 **d)** 0 **e)** 0 **f)** -1 **g)** 1 **h)** does not exist **18. a)** 7 **b)** 12
c) -6 **d)** 5 **e)** $\dfrac{1}{10}$ **f)** 6 **g)** 0 **h)** $\dfrac{1}{2\sqrt{3}}$ **i)** 12
19. a) does not exist **b)** -1 **c)** $-\dfrac{1}{2}$ **d)** 0 **e)** does not exist
f) does not exist **g)** -7 **h)** does not exist **i)** does not exist
20. a) i) -24.5 m/s **ii)** -20.09 m/s **iii)** -19.649 m/s
b) -19.6 m/s **21.** 9.3 bacteria/s **22. b) i)** 0.07 **ii)** 0.005 **iii)** 0.01
c) Using a quadratic regression:
$P = (9.19 \times 10^{-4})(t - 1921)^2 + 0.003(t - 1921) + 13.19$
d) $0.039\,741\,11$

Chapter Test, p. 177

1. a) 7 **b)** 6 **c)** $y = 6x - 7$ **2. a) i)** 4 **ii)** 5 **iii)** does not exist
c) jump discontinuity at $x = 2$ **3. a)** $\dfrac{2}{5}$ **b)** $\dfrac{3}{2}$ **c)** 1 **d)** $-\dfrac{1}{4}$
e) $\dfrac{27}{20}$ **f)** $-\dfrac{1}{2}$ **4. a)** 11 **b)** 12 **c)** $\dfrac{3}{4}$ **d)** $\dfrac{5}{4}$ **5. a)** -5 m/s **b)** -7 m/s
6. 40π cm²/cm

Challenge Problems, p. 178

1. For the point $P\left(a, \dfrac{4}{a}\right)$, the slope of the tangent is
$-\dfrac{4}{a^2}$ and the equation of the tangent is $y = -\dfrac{4}{a^2}x + \dfrac{8}{a}$.
Thus, the x-intercept is $A(2a, 0)$ and the y-intercept is
$B\left(0, \dfrac{8}{a}\right)$. Then $\triangle$AOB $= \dfrac{1}{2}(2a)\left(\dfrac{8}{a}\right) = 8$. Therefore the
area of the triangle is 8, regardless of the value of a.
2. Answers will vary. **3. a)** $\dfrac{\sqrt{3}}{4}$ **b)** small triangle: $\dfrac{\sqrt{3}}{36}$;
second island: $\dfrac{\sqrt{3}}{3}$ **c)** $\dfrac{10\sqrt{3}}{27}$
d) $\dfrac{\sqrt{3}}{4}\left(1 + 3\left(\dfrac{1}{9}\right) + 12\left(\dfrac{1}{9}\right)^2 + 48\left(\dfrac{1}{9}\right)^3 + \cdots + 3 \cdot 4^{n-2}\left(\dfrac{1}{9}\right)^{n-1}\right)$
e) Yes; all but the first term in the series form a
geometric series with $a = \dfrac{1}{3}$ and $r = \dfrac{4}{9}$.

The area approaches $\dfrac{\sqrt{3}}{4}\left(1+\dfrac{\frac{1}{3}}{1-\frac{4}{9}}\right) = \dfrac{2\sqrt{3}}{5}$. **4.** $\dfrac{a}{3}$

5. $100 - 50\sqrt{2}$ m east of the origin and $150 - 100\sqrt{2}$ m north **6. a)** Ayida should turn the jetpack on after 2.51 s; she will land after 8.11 s. **b)** Ayida should turn the jetpack on after 3.56 s; she will land after 11.48 s. **c)** 378.78 m

Problem Solving Strategy: Solve a Simpler Problem, pp. 179–180

Apply, Solve, Communicate

1. $\dfrac{91}{30}$ **2.** 39 km **3.** 25 005 000 **4.** 0 **5.** 1027 **6.** $\dfrac{400}{31}$ m

7. 202 **8.** 728 **9. a)** 632 cm **b)** $75\,030\sqrt{3}$ cm^3 **10.** 3

Problem Solving: Using the Strategies, p. 181

1. 15.9 cm **2.** 16 **3.** 192.5 cm^3 **4.** 16π cm^2 **5.** 3 **6.** 9, 2, 2 **7. a)** (at most) $5n + 1$ **b)** 751 **c)** 23 **8.** Carys and Dianne

Chapter 4

Review of Prerequisite Skills, pp. 184–185

1. a) 7 **b)** -1 **c)** 2 **d)** $4x - 3$ **e)** $\dfrac{1}{6}$ **f)** $-\dfrac{1}{4}$ **2. a)** $y = 4x - 5$

b) $y = 4x + 4$ **c)** $y = 4x + 15$ **3. a)** $x \in \text{R}$ **b)** $x \in \text{R}$ **c)** $x \geq 0$

d) $x \in \text{R}$ **e)** $x \in \text{R}$ **f)** $x \neq 0$ **4. ii) a)** minimum: $(-1, 0)$

ii) b) minimum: $\left(\dfrac{1}{6}, \dfrac{23}{12}\right)$ **ii) c)** maximum: $(1, 1)$ **5. i) a)** $x \neq 0$

i) b) $x \geq -4$ **i) c)** $x \geq 0$ **6. b)** $t \in (0, 1)$ and $t \in (3, 4)$ **c)** $t \in (1, 3)$ **d)** Buy at $t = 0$ and sell at $t = 1$, or buy at $t = 3$ and sell

at t = 4. **7. a)** $\dfrac{1}{2x^3}$ **b)** $x^{\frac{1}{2}} - \dfrac{6}{x^{\frac{1}{3}}}$ **c)** $a + \dfrac{b}{x} - \dfrac{c}{x^2}$ **d)** $\dfrac{25}{x^6} - x^{\frac{3}{2}}$

8. a) $4x^{\frac{7}{2}} - 20x^{\frac{3}{2}} + 25x^{-\frac{1}{2}}$ **b)** $12x^4 + 27x^3 - 20x^2 - 45x$

c) $10m^4 - 22m^3 - 11m^2 + 18m - 3$ **d)** $3y^7 - 192y$

e) $\sqrt{k^3 + 6k^2 + 2k + 12}$ **f)** $2\sqrt{2}x + 1 - 2\sqrt{2} - \dfrac{1}{x}$ **9. a) i)** 6 **ii)** 4

iii) $3 + h$ **iv)** 3 **b) i)** 7 **ii)** 5 **iii)** $4 + h$ **iv)** 4 **c) i)** 22 **ii)** 8

iii) $4 + 3h + h^2$ **iv)** 4 **10. c)** $-4, -2, 0, 2, 4$ **11. b) i)** 0 **ii)** 0 **iii)** 0

12. b) i) 1 **ii)** -1 **iii)** does not exist **13. a)** does not exist **b)** does not exist **c)** does not exist **d)** 0 **e)** does not exist **f)** does not exist **14. a)** 8 m/s **b)** 24 m/s **15. a)** increasing **b)** decreasing **c)** 0 **d)** decreasing, constant, increasing **16.** 70 km/h **17. a)** 3.06 m^2/min, 4.58 m^2/min **b)** 1.2 h

18. a)

t	s	First differences	Second differences
1	5		
		15	
2	20		10
		25	
3	45		10
		35	
4	80		10
		45	
5	125		

b) m/s; velocities **c)** m/s^2; accelerations **d)** $s(t) = 5t^2$

Section 4.1, pp. 194–196
Practise

1. a) i) -4 **ii)** -2 **iii)** 0 **iv)** 2 **v)** 4 **b) i)** 12 **ii)** 3 **iii)** 0 **iv)** 3 **v)** 12 **c) i)** 9 **ii)** 0 **iii)** -3 **iv)** 0 **v)** 9 **2. a)** iv), **b)** ii), **c)** i), **d)** iii) **3. b) i)** 1 **ii)** 2 **4. a)** $-2, -1, 1$ **b)** $-2, 4$ **5. a)** 2 **b)** $2x$ **c)** $2t + 3$ **d)** $3b^2 - 2b$ **e)** $4x^3$ **f)** $6x - 2$ **g)** $1 - 3n^2$ **h)** 4

i) -2 **j)** $2 - 2x$ **6. a)** $-\dfrac{1}{(x+2)^2}$; same domain **b)** $\dfrac{1}{2\sqrt{x-3}}$;

function: $x \geq 3$, derivative: $x > 3$ **c)** $\dfrac{1}{2\sqrt{x}} - 1$; function:

$x \geq 0$, derivative: $x > 0$ **d)** $-\dfrac{2}{(x-4)^2}$; same domain

e) $\dfrac{3}{(x+1)^2}$; same domain **f)** $-\dfrac{2}{m^3}$; same domain

g) $1 - \dfrac{1}{x^2}$; same domain **h)** $-\dfrac{1}{2(q-1)^{\frac{3}{2}}}$; same domain

7. $\dfrac{1}{2\sqrt{x+1}}$; domain of f: $x \geq -1$; domain of f': $x > -1$

8. a) x^2; 1 **b)** x^2; 2 **c)** x^3; 3 **d)** $\sqrt{x}$; 9

Apply, Solve, Communicate

10. a) $-9.8t + 5$ **b)** 1.43 s **c)** 0.51 s **11. b)** increases

13. a) $\displaystyle\lim_{h \to 0^+} \dfrac{k(3+h) - k(3)}{h} \neq \lim_{h \to 0^-} \dfrac{k(3+h) - k(3)}{h}$

c) $k'(x) = \begin{cases} -1 & x < 3 \\ 1 & x > 3 \end{cases}$

14. b) $\displaystyle\lim_{h \to 0} \dfrac{M(h) - M(0)}{h}$ does not exist **15. a)** $\displaystyle\lim_{h \to 0} \dfrac{f(h) - f(0)}{h}$

does not exist. **16. b)** $x \in \text{R}$ **c)** $f'(x) = 2|x|$ **d)** $f'(0) = 0$ **17. b)** x any integer

Section 4.2, pp. 204–207
Practise

1. a) 0 **b)** $5x^4$ **c)** $9x^8$ **d)** $14x^{13}$ **e)** 0 **f)** 1 **g)** $54t^{53}$ **h)** 0 **i)** $-2x^{-3}$

j) $\frac{1}{3}x^{-\frac{2}{3}}$ k) $-\frac{1}{2}x^{-\frac{3}{2}}$ l) nx^{n-1} **2. a)** $12x^2$ b) $-15x^4$ c) $5x^{\frac{1}{4}}$

d) $15t^{\frac{2}{3}}$ e) $-\frac{2}{x^3}$ f) $-\frac{12}{x^5}$ g) $24x^2$ h) $\frac{x^3}{4}$ i) $\frac{1}{3}x^{-\frac{2}{3}}$ j) $-\frac{1}{2x\sqrt{x}}$

k) $8x^7$ l) $2x^{\sqrt{2}-1}$ **3. a)** -6 b) 12 c) -3 d) 2 e) -2 f) 3

4. a) $y = 4x - 6$ b) $y = -\frac{2}{3}x + 3$ **7. a)** $2x + 3$ b) $8x - 3$

c) $15x^2 - 12x + 2$ d) $70x^4 + 69x^2 - 65$ e) $-\frac{1}{x^2} - 9x^2$

f) $2x - 1$ g) $2x - 2$ h) $12 + 12x + 3x^2$ i) $-\frac{b}{x^2} - \frac{2c}{x^3}$

8. a) $4x^3 - 6x + 5$; domain of function and derivative: R

b) $x^2 - \frac{1}{2\sqrt{x}}$; The domains are different.

c) $4 + 10x^{-6}$; domain of function and derivative: $x \neq 0$
d) $3x^2 - 6x + 3$; domain of function and derivative: R
9. a) $y = 10x + 8$ b) $y = 7x - 20$ c) $y = 7x - 18$ d) $y = x - 6$
e) $y = -8x - 15$ f) $y = 4x$

Apply, Solve, Communicate
10. $(3, 36)$ **11.** $\left(2, \frac{3}{2}\right)$, $\left(-2, \frac{5}{2}\right)$

12. a) $(0, -4)$ b) $(\sqrt{5}, 5)$, $(-\sqrt{5}, 5)$ **13. a)** $\$17\,425.27$/year
b) The best time to buy is at the beginning.

14. $20.2, 0.6, -19$ **15. a)** $\frac{1}{2}kt^{-\frac{1}{2}}$ b) 0.005 cm/year

d) Answers will vary. **16.** 9 m/s, 11 m/s, 15 m/s
17. a) after 3 s b) 24.5 m/s c) 17.25 m d) no
18. $(-3, 121), (2, -4)$ **20.** $y = 4x, y = -4x$
21. $-1 + \sqrt{2}, -1 - \sqrt{2}$ **22. a)** $0.1 + 0.02x, 2.12$ **b)** 2.11
c) the rate at which cost is increasing as the xth copy
is made **23. a)** $\frac{1}{4}\pi d^2$ b) $\frac{160000}{\pi}$ m² **24. a)** $\frac{5}{3}x^{-\frac{2}{3}}$; the
rate at which cost is increasing as the xth unit is
completed **25. b)** $Q(x) = x^{n-1} + ax^{n-2} + a^2x^{n-3} + a^3x^{n-4}$
$+ \ldots + a^{n-1}$ **26. a)** $2\pi rh$ b) πr^2 **27. d)** Examples will vary.
29. b) everywhere c) $f'(x) = -2$ if $x \in (-\infty, -1)$, $f'(x) = 2x$
if $x \in [-1, 1]$, $f'(x) = 2$ if $x \in (1, \infty)$ **30. b)** $x = 3$ or -3
c) $f'(x) = \begin{cases} 2x & \text{if } x \in (-\infty, -3) \\ -2x & \text{if } x \in (-3, 3) \\ 2x & \text{if } x \in (3, \infty) \end{cases}$ **31. a)** $0.04t - 5$
b) $0.04t + 5$

Section 4.3, pp. 212–213

Practise
1. a) $4x^3 - 6x^2$ b) $9x^2 + 4x$ c) $5x^4 - 4x^3 - 6x^2 + 6x - 1$
d) $12x^2 + 2x - 12$ e) $\frac{9}{2}x^{\frac{7}{2}} - \frac{7}{2}x^{\frac{5}{2}}$ f) $9x^2 - 10x + 3$
g) $-60t^{-3} - 24t^{-5} - 25t^4 - 3t^2$ h) $4m^3 + 1 + 3m^{-4}$
i) $\frac{9}{2}y^{\frac{1}{2}} - 4 - y^{-\frac{3}{2}}$ j) $2y - \frac{3}{2}y^{\frac{1}{2}} + \frac{1}{2}y^{-\frac{1}{2}}$ k) $4x^{\frac{1}{3}} - \frac{65}{3}x^{\frac{10}{3}}$

l) $3 - 2k$ m) $4x^3$ n) $\frac{3}{2}x^{\frac{1}{2}} - \frac{35}{2}x^{\frac{5}{2}}$ o) $9x^{\frac{7}{2}} - 20x^3 - 21x^{\frac{1}{2}} + 35$

p) $15t^{\frac{3}{2}} + 3t^{-\frac{3}{2}} - 6t^{-4}$ q) $2abu + 3a^2u^2 - 4b^2u^3 - 5abu^4$

r) $2v + \frac{3}{2}v^{\frac{1}{2}} + \frac{1}{2}v^{-\frac{3}{2}}$ **2. a)** 0 b) -7 c) 21 d) 0 e) 1 f) 8

g) -14 h) $-\frac{1175}{3}$ **3. a)** 12 b) -16 c) -346 d) $1 - \frac{13\sqrt{2}}{8}$

4. a) $y = 3x - 3$ b) $y = \frac{11}{2}x - 26$ c) $y = \frac{45}{2}x - \frac{37}{2}$

d) $y = -\frac{3}{2}x + \frac{5}{2}$

Apply, Solve, Communicate
5. a) 5 b) -5 c) 5 **6. a)** $f(x) + xf'(x)$ b) $\frac{1}{2\sqrt{x}}f(x) + \sqrt{x}f'(x)$

c) $2tf(t) + t^2f'(t)$ d) $cm^{c-1}f(m) + m^cf'(m)$

e) $\frac{1}{x}f'(x) - \frac{1}{x^2}f(x)$ f) $2(x+2)f(x) + (x+2)^2f'(x)$

7. a) 24 000; 53 664 b) $12(6t^2 + 80t + 100)$; the rate of
increase, in people per year **d)** Answers will vary.
e) Answers will vary. **8. a)** $0.5335 - 0.3t - 0.0033t^2$

b) 0.5335 V/s c) -0.3962 V/s **9.** $\frac{-3 \pm \sqrt{39}}{3}$

10. a) i) $R'(x) = \frac{375}{\sqrt{x}} - 5$ **ii)** $\frac{75}{2\sqrt{10}} - 5$ **iii)** -1.25 **b)** The
manufacturer takes in less money by selling more
calculators, because the price is lower.
11. b) $7x^{\frac{5}{2}} + \frac{25}{2}x^{\frac{3}{2}} - \frac{21}{2}x^{\frac{1}{2}} + x^{-\frac{1}{2}}$
12. b) i) $2(x^2 + 3x + 1)(2x + 3)$ **ii)** $-6x^2(2 - x^3)$
iii) $2(1 - x)(x^3 + x)(-4x^3 + 3x^2 - 2x + 1)$
13. b) i) $3(x - 1)^2$ **ii)** $3(2x + 3)(x^2 + 3x - 1)^2$
iii) $3\left(\frac{1}{2\sqrt{x}} - 2x\right)(\sqrt{x} - x^2)^2$

Section 4.4, pp. 218–220

Practise
1. a) $\frac{1}{x^2}$; $\frac{1}{4}$ b) $\frac{2x^2 + 2x}{(2x+1)^2}$; $\frac{12}{25}$ c) $\frac{3x^2 - 4x + 3}{(x^2 - 1)^2}$; $\frac{7}{9}$

d) $\frac{-2x^2 - 4}{(x^2 + 3x - 2)^2}$; $-\frac{3}{16}$ e) $\frac{4 + 6x - 2x^2}{(3 - 2x)^2}$; 0

f) $\frac{x^3 + 3x^2 + 2}{(x+1)^3}$; $\frac{22}{27}$ g) $\frac{-1-x}{2\sqrt{x}(1-x)^2}$; $-\frac{3\sqrt{2}}{4}$

h) $\frac{3x^2 + 4x\sqrt{x} - 1}{2\sqrt{x}(\sqrt{x} - x^2)^2}$; $\frac{163\sqrt{2} + 232}{392}$ i) $\frac{7x^2 - 2x - 11}{(x^2 + 4x + 1)^2}$; $\frac{1}{13}$

j) $\frac{-2}{(x+2)^3}$; $-\frac{1}{32}$ k) $\frac{ad - bc}{(cx + d)^2}$; $\frac{ad - bc}{(2c + d)^2}$

l) $-\dfrac{1}{x^2}$, $x \neq -1$; $-\dfrac{1}{4}$ m) $\dfrac{5}{(1-2x)^2}$; $\dfrac{5}{9}$ n) $\dfrac{-1-x^2}{(x^2-1)^2}$; $-\dfrac{5}{9}$

o) $\dfrac{1-3x^2}{2\sqrt{x}(x^2+1)^2}$; $-\dfrac{11\sqrt{2}}{100}$ p) $\dfrac{2}{(x+1)^2}$, $x \neq 0$; $\dfrac{2}{9}$

q) $\dfrac{2x^5-36x^3}{(x^2-9)^2}$; $-\dfrac{224}{25}$ r) $\dfrac{-2x^5+9x^4-32x+48}{(x^4-16)^2}$; $f'(2)$

is not defined **2. a)** $y = -2x + 8$ **b)** $y = 8x - 11$

c) $y = -\dfrac{4}{9}x + \dfrac{11}{9}$ **d)** $y = 2x - 2$ **e)** $y = -\dfrac{1}{6}x + \dfrac{7}{6}$

f) $y = -\dfrac{1}{18}x + \dfrac{5}{2}$

Apply, Solve, Communicate

3. a) Since $y' = \dfrac{2}{(4x+3)^2}$, the slope is always positive.

b) Since $y' = \dfrac{-1}{(x-1)^2}$, the slope is always negative.

4. $(0, 0)$, $(-1, -1)$ **5.** $(0, 0)$, $(-2, 2)$

6. a) $-\dfrac{f'(x)}{(f(x))^2}$ **b)** $\dfrac{xf'(x)-f(x)}{x^2}$ **c)** $\dfrac{f(x)-xf'(x)}{(f(x))^2}$

7. a) $\dfrac{np'(n)-p(n)}{n^2}$ **b)** and **c)** Answers will vary.

d) $p(n) = nA(n)$, so that $p'(n) = A(n) + nA'(n)$. Thus, $p'(n) > A(n) \Rightarrow A(n) + nA'(n) > A(n) \Rightarrow nA'(n) > 0$ $\Rightarrow A'(n) > 0$. **e)** and **f)** Answers will vary. **8. a)** after 8 s

b) $\dfrac{-72}{(4+t)^2}$; velocity in metres per second **c)** -0.5 m/s

d) -4.5 m/s **e)** Answers will vary. **9. a)** $\dfrac{-40.8}{b^{0.6}(1+3.8b^{0.4})^2}$

c) Answers will vary. **10.** 0.2315 g/s

11. $y' = \dfrac{3x^2+6x-1}{(x+1)^2}$ **13. a)** $R = 0.6\ \Omega$ **b)** The maximum power is produced when $R = 0.6\ \Omega$.

Section 4.5, pp. 225–226

Practise

1. a) $3x^2 - 2$; $6x$ **b)** $x^3 + 6x^2 - 10x + 1$; $3x^2 + 12x - 10$

c) $-\dfrac{1}{x^2}$; $\dfrac{2}{x^3}$ **d)** $-\dfrac{1}{(t+2)^2} - 5$; $\dfrac{2}{(t+2)^3}$

e) $3x^2 - 4x + 1$; $6x - 4$ **f)** $-\dfrac{2}{(x-2)^2}$; $\dfrac{4}{(x-2)^3}$

g) $6 + 2u - 6u^2$; $2 - 12u$ **h)** $\dfrac{2x^2-2x+2}{(2x-x^2)^2}$;

$\dfrac{4x^3-6x^2+12x-8}{(2x-x^2)^3}$ **i)** $-3u^{-\frac{3}{2}}$; $\dfrac{9}{2}u^{-\frac{5}{2}}$ **j)** $3x^2 - \dfrac{2}{x^3}$; $6x + \dfrac{6}{x^4}$

2. a) 26 **b)** 2 **c)** $\dfrac{1}{2\sqrt{2}}$ **d)** $-\dfrac{3}{16}$ **3. a)** 108; 108 **b)** -25; -16

c) $-\dfrac{1}{16}$; $\dfrac{1}{32}$ **d)** $\dfrac{1}{3\sqrt{3}}$; $-\dfrac{1}{6\sqrt{3}}$ **e)** 13; 4 **f)** $-\dfrac{1}{27}$; $\dfrac{4}{81}$

Apply, Solve, Communicate

5. $f(x) = 4x^2 - 2x + 3$ **6. a)** t; 1 **b)** $A''(t)$ is the rate of increase in growth rate, which is therefore steadily increasing. **d)** Answers will vary. **7. a)** $\dfrac{144}{(6t^2+1)^2}$;

$-\dfrac{1728}{(6t^3+1)^3}$ **b)** It is slowing. **8. a)** $h'(t) = \dfrac{24t^2}{(8+t^3)^2}$

b) $h''(t) = \dfrac{48t(8-2t^3)}{(8+t^3)^3}$; the rate of change of growth rate

c) when $t = \sqrt[3]{4}$, $h' = \dfrac{\sqrt[3]{2}}{3}$ **d)** Answers will vary.

9. a) $4x^3 - 3x^2 + 10x + 2$; $12x^2 - 6x + 10$; $24x - 6$; 24; 0; 0 **b)** 0 **10. a)** $5x^4 + 4x^3 + 3x^2 + 2x + 1$; $20x^3 + 12x^2 + 6x + 2$; $60x^2 + 24x + 6$; $120x + 24$; 120; 0 **11.** -3 **12. a)** $f'' = g''h + 2g'h' + gh''$ **b)** $f''' = g'''h + 3g''h' + 3g'h'' + gh'''$

13. a) $f'(x) = \begin{cases} 2x & |x| > 1 \\ -2x & |x| < 1 \end{cases}$; domain: $x \neq \pm 1$,

$f''(x) = \begin{cases} 2 & |x| > 1 \\ -2 & |x| < 1 \end{cases}$; domain: $x \neq \pm 1$

c) The domain of f is $x \in \mathbb{R}$, while the domains of f' and f'' are $x \in \mathbb{R}$ such that $x \neq \pm 1$. **14. a)** $n(n-1)x^{n-2}$; $n(n-1)(n-2)x^{n-3}$ **b)** $n(n-1)(n-2) \dots 3 \times 2 \times 1 = n!$ **15. a)** one more than the degree of the polynomial **b)** 0

Section 4.6, pp. 237–239

Apply, Solve, Communicate

1. a) 0 **b)** A **c)** neither at A, stopped at B, neither at C **d)** the car is stopped **e)** the car returns to its starting point, stops, then goes back where it came from **2. a)** positive **b)** negative **c)** positive **d)** zero **e)** negative **3. a)** decreasing; negative **b) i)** negative **ii)** positive **iii)** zero **iv)** negative **4.** position function: b; velocity function: a; acceleration function: c **5.** speeding up for $t \in [0, 3]$ **6. a)** $v = 4$, $a = 0$ **b)** $v = 6t + 2$, $a = 6$ **c)** $v = 3t^2 - 8t + 5$, $a = 6t - 8$ **d)** $v = \dfrac{2t^3 + 3t^2}{(t+1)^2}$, $a = \dfrac{2t(t^2 + 3t + 3)}{(t+1)^3}$

e) $v = 6t^2 - 10t^{\frac{3}{2}} - 2t + \dfrac{9}{2}t^{\frac{1}{2}} - 2$, $a = 12t - 15t^{\frac{1}{2}} - 2 + \dfrac{9}{4}t^{-\frac{1}{2}}$

f) $v = \dfrac{3(2+\sqrt{t})}{(1+\sqrt{t})^2}$, $a = \dfrac{-3(\sqrt{t}+3)}{2\sqrt{t}(1+\sqrt{t})^3}$

7. a) $v = 3$, $a = 0$; 3 m/s, 0 m/s² **b)** $v = 8t - 7$, $a = 8$; 25 m/s, 8 m/s² **c)** $v = 3t^2 - 12t + 12$, $a = 6t - 12$; 12 m/s, 12 m/s² **d)** $v = \dfrac{3}{(1+t)^2}$, $a = \dfrac{-6}{(1+t)^3}$; $\dfrac{3}{25}$ m/s, $-\dfrac{6}{125}$ m/s²

e) $v = \dfrac{5}{2}t^{\frac{3}{2}} - 3t^{\frac{1}{2}}$, $a = \dfrac{15}{4}t^{\frac{1}{2}} - \dfrac{3}{2}t^{-\frac{1}{2}}$; 14 m/s, $\dfrac{27}{4}$ m/s²

f) $v = \dfrac{3t^2 + 24t - 2}{(t+4)^2}$, $a = \dfrac{100}{(t+4)^3}$; $\dfrac{71}{32}$ m/s, $\dfrac{25}{128}$ m/s²

8. −19.8 m/s and −29.6 m/s **9. a)** 19.6 m/s, 9.8 m/s, −9.8 m/s, −19.6 m/s **b)** 3 s **c)** 44.1 m **d)** 6 s **e)** −29.4 m/s **10. a) i)** 0 s **ii)** 10 s **b)** 1 m/s^2 **11. a)** −4 m/s, 4 m/s **b)** 4 s **c)** $t > 4$ **12. a) i)** 60 m/s **ii)** 2 s, 5 s **iii)** $0 \le t < 2$ and $5 < t \le 6$ **c)** 90 m **d)** 30 m/s^2 **e)** Answers will vary. **13. a)** $\frac{10}{49}$ s

b) $\frac{2 + \sqrt{454.8}}{9.8}$ s **c)** −21.326 m/s **14. a)** s_0 **b)** v_0 **c)** g

15. 10 m/s^2 **16. a)** positive for $0 \le t < 10$, negative for $t > 10$ **b)** 20 s **c)** $\frac{2000}{3}$ m **d)** −150 m/s

e) speeding up for $0 < t < 10$, $t > 20$; slowing for $10 < t < 20$ **17. a)** $v = 3t^2 − 12t + 9$; $a = 6t − 12$ **b)** toward: $1 < t < 3$; away: $0 < t < 1$, $t > 3$ **c)** speeding up: $1 < t < 2$, $t > 3$; slowing down: $0 < t < 1$, $2 < t < 3$ **18.** 12.544 m **19. a)** $s_h = 5.55t$, $v_h = 5.55$, $a_h = 0$ **b)** $s_v = 30 − 4.9t^2$, $v_v = −9.8t$, $a_v = −9.8$ **c)** after 0.567 s **d)** $v = \sqrt{30.9 + (9.8t)^2}$ **e)** 9.8 m/s^2, down **f)** 9.8 m/s^2, down

Extension: Antiderivatives, pp. 242–243

Practise

1. a) $5t + 10$ **b)** $2.3 − 9.8t$ **c)** $2.5t^2 + 3$ **2. a)** $3t^2 + 5$ **b)** $t^2 + t + 25$ **c)** $t^3 − 4t^2 + 10$ **3. a)** $x^2 + 3x + C$

b) $x^3 − 4x + C$ **c)** $3x^4 − 2x^3 + 2x^2 + C$ **d)** $\frac{x^5}{25} − \frac{x^4}{12} + C$

e) $−\frac{1}{x} + C$ **f)** $\frac{2}{3}x^{\frac{3}{2}} + C$ **g)** $\frac{3}{4}x^{\frac{4}{3}} + C$ **h)** $\frac{8}{3}x^{\frac{3}{2}} − \frac{1}{4x^2} + C$

i) $−\frac{1}{4x^4} − \frac{1}{3x^3} + C$ **4. a)** $y = 2x^2 − 5x$ **b)** $y = 2x^2 − 5x − 2$

c) $y = 2x^2 − 5x + 6$ **d)** $y = 2x^2 − 5x − 12$ **5. a)** $x^2 − x + 3$

b) $x^3 − 4x^2 + 6$ **c)** $9 − \frac{6}{x^2}$ **d)** $\frac{3}{5}x^5 − \frac{1}{x} + \frac{17}{5}$ **e)** $2x^{\frac{3}{2}} + 1$

f) $x^3 − 2x^2 + 2x + 2$ **6. a)** $y = \frac{x^4}{4}$ **b)** $y = \frac{3}{5}x^5 − 2x$

c) $y = \frac{1}{2}x^2 − \frac{4}{3}x^3$ **7. a)** $y = \frac{1}{2}x^2 + \frac{1}{2}$ **b)** $y = \frac{1}{4}x^4 + \frac{3}{4}$

c) $y = −\frac{1}{6}x^6 − \frac{5}{6}$ **d)** $y = −x$

Apply, Solve, Communicate

8. a) 2 m **b)** 4 m **c)** 8 m **9.** No. **10.** 3 s **11.** 8 **12. a)** 12 m/s^2 **b)** 192 m/s **c)** 1728 m **13. a)** 288 m **14. a)** 18.55 m/s **b)** 400 m

c) 13.636 s **15. a)** $F(x) = \frac{1}{3}(2 − x^3)$

16. $\frac{v_0 + \sqrt{v_0^2 + 19.6h_0}}{9.8}$ seconds

Technology Extension, p. 244

1. a) $−5x^{−6}$ **b)** $12x^3$ **c)** $12x^5 − 4x^3 + 18x^2 + 48x − 3$

d) $\frac{5}{2}x^{\frac{3}{2}} − \frac{1}{2}x^{−\frac{1}{2}}$ **e)** $\frac{−14x}{(x^2 − 5)^2}$ **f)** $\frac{3x^2 − 8x\sqrt{x} + 3}{2\sqrt{x}(3 − x^2)^2}$

2. a) $\frac{1}{3}x^3$ **b)** $\frac{3}{2}x^2 + x$ **c)** $\frac{1}{1 − x^2} − 1$ **d)** $\frac{2}{3}x^{\frac{3}{2}} + 2x^{\frac{1}{2}}$

Section 4.7, pp. 249–252

Apply, Solve, Communicate

1. a) $2500 − 2.1x$ **b)** the rate at which costs are increasing (per item) as the xth unit is completed **c)** $1870; The cost is $1870/item at the instant the 300th item is finished. **d)** $1868.95 **e)** Answers may vary. **2. a)** $950 − 0.006x$ **b)** $917 **c)** $917.997 **d)** Answers may vary. **3. a)** $5000 − 0.16n$ **b)** the rate of change of the revenue with respect to the number of cars sold **c)** $4864 **d)** $4863.92 **4. a)** $8x + 2x^2$ **b)** $8 + 4x$ **c)** $2808 **d)** $2810 **5. b)** entries: 600 000, 500 000, 400 000, 300 000, 200 000, 100 000, 0 **c)** $\frac{600\,000x − x^2}{200\,000}$ **d)** $\frac{300\,000 − x}{100\,000}$

e) $1 **f)** $2.05x − 0.000\,005x^2 − 110\,000$ **g)** $2.05 − 0.000\,01x$ **h)** −$0.95 **6. a)** $N'(y) = 0.8y^3 − 34.5y^2 + 391.7y − 964.325$ **b)** −472.125 **c)** The actual change, from 1994 to 1995, of the number of births per year was −502.575. **7. a)** $−0.8745x^4 + 21.0728x^3 − 160.1289x^2 + 407.358x − 233.2$ **c)** January: 522.2 kg; October: 451.6 kg **d)** January: 34.2 kg/month; October: 155.3 kg/month **e)** Answers will vary. **8. b)** entries: 60 000, 50 000, 40 000, 25 000, 20 000, 5000, 0 **c)** $6x − 0.0001x^2$ **d)** $6 − 0.0002x$ **e)** $5 **f)** $4.8x − 0.0001x^2 − 8000$ **g)** $4.8 − 0.0002x$ **h)** $0.80 **9. a)** $5000 − 5.6x$ **b)** $80 − 0.036x$ **c)** −4920 + 5.564x **d)** −$4502.70 **10. a)** $2200 + 0.18x^2$ **b)** $10\,000 − 0.15x^2$ **c)** $7800 − 0.33x^2$ **d)** $2223 **e)** 153.74 **11.** $0.044\,72/unit **12. a) i)** 3000 bacteria/hour **ii)** 192 000 bacteria/hour **iii)** 1 728 000 bacteria/hour **b)** increasing **13.** −220 **14. a)** $0.000\,26t^4 − 0.002t^3 − 0.0459t^2 + 0.1t + 4.404$ **b)** 4.404; 1.989 **15. a)** 420 − 10d **b)** 2 km: 400; 20 km: 220 **16.** 0.2255 years; $102.58 million/year **17.** 23 kg wheat/kg seed **18. a) i)** 0 **ii)** 14.16 **iii)** 6.40 **19.** $(a − d)x^3 + (b − e)x^2 + (c − f)x − g$; $3(a − d)x^2 + 2(b − e)x + c − f$ **20.** $C(x) = C_0 + 0.000\,25x + \frac{10}{x}$

Review of Key Concepts, pp. 254–257

1. a) x^2, 3 **b)** $x^3 + 4$, 1 **c)** $\sqrt{x}$, 4 **d)** x^2, 1 **e)** $\sqrt{x}$, 4 **f)** $x^3 + 20$, −3 **2. a)** 8 **b)** 19 **c)** $\frac{5}{4}$ **3.** $2a + 1$; −3, −1, 1, 3, 5

4. a) −16 **b)** −12 **c)** $\frac{1}{2}$ **d)** 12 **e)** $−\frac{3}{16}$ **f)** $−\frac{1}{4\sqrt{2}}$

5. $\frac{t}{2} + 10$; 11 m/s, 12 m/s, 13 m/s

7. a) $9x^8$ **b)** $16x^{\frac{1}{3}}$ **c)** $\frac{12}{x^5}$ **d)** $\frac{2}{\sqrt[4]{x}}$ **e)** $\frac{1}{2}x^{−6}$ **f)** $3(n + 1)x^n$

8. a) $2x + 4$ **b)** $15x^2 − 8x^3$ **c)** $5x^4 − 28x^3 + 9x^2$ **d)** $2x^3 + \frac{1}{x^2}$

e) $8x - 12$ f) $-\frac{1}{3}x^{-4} + \frac{1}{3}x^{-3}$ g) $\frac{1}{6\sqrt{x}} + \frac{1}{x\sqrt{x}}$

h) $\frac{3}{2}x^{-\frac{3}{4}} - x^{-\frac{2}{3}} - 2x^{-\frac{6}{5}}$ i) $6x^5 - 30x^4 + 48x^3 - 24x^2$

9. a) $y = -3x$ b) $y = -4x + 4$ c) $y = 4$ d) $y = 9ax - 8a$

10. a) $V'(t) = \frac{1}{\sqrt{t}}$; the rate of increase in value (dollars/month) b) Answers will vary. c) Answers will vary. 11. -9.8 m/s; -19.6 m/s; -49 m/s 12. $\left(\frac{1}{3}, 2\right)$

13. $y = 11x - 25$, $y = -x - 1$ 14. a) $3x^2 + 6x + 2$

b) $\frac{15}{2}x^{\frac{3}{2}} - 28x^{\frac{5}{2}}$ c) $-3t^{-2} - 8t^{-5}$ d) $5k^4 - 32k^3 + 57k^2 - 24k$

e) $12 + \frac{5}{\sqrt{x}}$ f) $3a^2x^2 - b^2$ 15. a) $y = 8x - 8$ b) $y = 33x + 60$

c) $y = \frac{13}{3}x - 9$ d) $y = -\frac{5}{16}x + \frac{9}{4}$ 16. a) -6 b) 45 c) -210

17. a) $2xg(x) + (x^2 + 2)g'(x)$ b) $-3x^{-4}g(x) + x^{-3}g'(x)$

c) $2axg(x) + ax^2g'(x)$ 18. a) $\frac{2 - 2x^2}{(x^2+1)^2}$ b) $\frac{2x^3 - 6x^2}{(x-2)^2}$

c) $\frac{1}{\sqrt{x}} - \frac{1}{2x\sqrt{x}}$ d) $-\frac{1}{(1-x)^2}$ e) $\frac{2 - 4t + t^2}{(2-t)^2}$ f) $-\frac{3}{2x\sqrt{x}}$

19. a) $y = 2x - 6$ b) $y = \frac{3}{2}x - 4$ c) $y = 2$

20. a) $\frac{2xg'(x) - g(x)}{2x\sqrt{x}}$ b) $\frac{xg'(x) - g(x)}{x^2}$

c) $\frac{g(x) + x(x+1)g'(x)}{(x+1)^2}$ 21. a) $\frac{500(2t - t^4)}{(1+t^3)^2}$; the rate of change of population in 100s of people/year b) $t = \sqrt[3]{2}$; the population reaches a maximum.

d) Answers will vary. 22. a) 2 b) $24x + \frac{1}{2x\sqrt{x}}$

c) $\frac{15}{4}\sqrt{x} - \frac{1}{4x\sqrt{x}}$ d) $6x + 2$ e) $-\frac{4}{(x+1)^3}$ f) $\frac{8}{(x+2)^3}$

23. 8 24. a) $s(t) = M - \frac{MC}{C+t}$; $\lim_{t \to \infty} s(t) = M$, but a mass of M is never reached. b) $\frac{M}{C}$ g/week c) $-\frac{2MC}{(C+t)^3}$

d) C weeks; $s''(C) = -\frac{M}{4C^2}$ 25. a) $v = 6t^2 + 8t - 1$;

$a = 12t + 8$ b) 127 m/s; 56 m/s²; 26. a) 3 s, 5 s

b) positive: $0 \le t < 3$, $t > 5$; negative: $3 < t < 5$

c) positive: $t > 4$; negative $0 \le t < 4$ d) -3 m/s

f) 112 m 27. a) 4.84 m/s b) -1.66 m/s² c) after 7.83 s

d) -6.5 m/s e) longer time on moon, same velocity

28. a) $15 + 0.14x$ \$50/unit c) \$50.07 d) Answers will vary.

29. a) i) -26 ii) 10 iii) 190 b) decreases for about 4.7 years, then increases 30. a) $P(x) = 1.1x - 0.0002x^2 - 480$

b) $P'(x) = 1.1 - 0.0004x$ c) i) $-$168; \$0.98 ii) \$20; \$0.90

iii) \$192; \$0.82 31. a) $8 + 0.018x$ b) $90 - 0.06x$

c) $82 - 0.078x$ d) \$66.40 32. a) $\frac{29.3}{\sqrt{d}}$ b) i) 4.14 ii) 2.93

33. a) $x^3 + C$ b) $x^5 + 2x^4 + C$ c) $4x^3 - \frac{3}{2}x^4 + \frac{1}{15}x^5 + C$

34. a) $-\frac{1}{2x} + C$ b) $8\sqrt{x} + C$ c) $-3x^{-2} + 4x^{-3} - 5x^{-1} + C$

35. $F(x) = \frac{2}{3}x^3 - \frac{3}{2}x^2 + \frac{37}{6}$ 36. a) 559.2 m b) 63.4 m/s

c) 18.953 s 37. a) 4 s b) 80 m c) $v(t) = \begin{cases} 40 - 10t & t \le 4 \\ -9.6(t-4) & t > 4 \end{cases}$

d) -38.4 m/s e) $s(t) = \begin{cases} -5t^2 + 40t & t \le 4 \\ -4.8(t-4)^2 + 40 & t > 4 \end{cases}$

Chapter Test, pp. 258–259

1. i) $f'(x) = \lim_{h \to 0} \frac{f(x+h) - f(x)}{h}$ or $f'(x) = \lim_{a \to x} \frac{f(a) - f(x)}{a - x}$

ii) a) $2x - 3$ b) $-\frac{1}{(x+2)^2}$ 2. a) $3x^2 - 4x + 4x^{-2}$ b) $\frac{3}{4}x^{-\frac{1}{4}}$

c) $6t^2 - 10t - 3$ d) $9x^{\frac{7}{2}} - 1$ e) $\frac{x^2 - 8x}{(x-4)^2}$ f) $\frac{x^2 - 6x - 2}{(x^2+2)^2}$

3. a) $y = 2x + 1$ b) $y = -\frac{7}{12}x - \frac{13}{4}$ c) $y = -\frac{9}{4}x - 2$

4. a) 62 b) $\frac{31\sqrt{2}}{8}$ c) 6 5. a) $\left(\frac{1}{2}, \frac{5}{4}\right)$ b) $y = -3x + \frac{11}{4}$

6. a) 1 b) $-\frac{29}{49}$ c) 70 d) $\frac{2}{9}$ 7. a) $0.02(5 - 0.01t)(10 - 0.12t)$

b) 0.8624 W/s 8. a) 9 m/s b) 12 m/s² c) 1 s, 3 s

d) $0 \le t < 1$, $t > 3$ e) -3 m/s f) 12 m 9. a) i) 124.5

ii) 252 iii) 712 b) Answers will vary.

10. b) entries: 40 000, 30 000, 20 000, 5000, 0

c) $4x - 0.0001x^2$ d) $4 - 0.0002x$ e) \$2/unit

f) $3.96x - 0.0001x^2 - 2500$ g) $3.96 - 0.0002x$

h) $-$2.04/unit 11. 0.1155 kg/m 12. a) $\frac{40}{7}$ s b) 340 m

c) $v(t) = \begin{cases} -9.8t & 0 \le t \le \frac{40}{7} \\ -56 & t > \frac{40}{7} \end{cases}$

e) The graph would curve to approach $v = -56$ as an asymptote. It would take longer to reach an adequate approximation of -56, and would result in a longer fall. 13. It would require the person to throw the ball at 103.83 m/s.

Challenge Problems, p. 260

1. $c = 1$, $d = 4$ 2. $y = 4x - 4$, $y = -4x - 4$ 6. $(0, 0)$ and $\left(\frac{5}{8}, \frac{125}{128}\right)$ 7. $4x^2 - 28x - 37 = 0$

9. a) empty b) -1.7819 cups/min c) -1.8187 cups/min

11. $y = -\frac{1}{2}x + \frac{3}{2}$, $x = 0$, $y = \frac{1}{2}x + \frac{3}{2}$

Problem Solving Strategy: Work Backward, pp. 261–262

Apply, Solve, Communicate

1. \$39, \$21, \$12 **2.** 606 **3.** $\dfrac{3700}{98}$ **4.** 2401 **5.** $\dfrac{17}{450}$

Problem Solving: Using the Strategies, p. 263

1. closed **3.** 9 **4.** 1L: Fill 9-L, pour 4L into smaller, dump 4-L, repeat step 2, then have 1L in 9-L container. 2L: Fill 9-L, pour 4L into smaller and dump, twice; 1L into 4-L; fill 9-L, 3L into 4-L container, dump, 4L into smaller, then have 2L left in 9-L container. 3L: Fill 4-L, pour into 9-L, twice; fill 4-L, pour 1L into 9-L, then have 3L left in 4-L container. 4L: Fill 4-L container. 5L: Fill 9-L container, pour 4L into 4-L container, then have 5L left in 9-L container. 6L: Same as 2L but omit last step, then have 6L in 9-L container. 7L: As 3L, then pour 3L into empty 9-L, fill 4-L and pour into 9-L, then have 7L in 9-L container. 8L: Fill 4L, pour into 9-L, twice. 9L: Fill 9-L. 10L: As 1L, then pour into empty 4L and fill 9-L, then have 1L in small, 9L in large. 11L: As 2L, then pour into empty 4-L, fill 9-L, then have 2L in small and 9L in large. 12L: Fill 4-L and pour into 9-L twice, fill 4-L, then have 4L in small, 8L in large. 13L: Fill both. **5.** W = 1, H = 9, L = 0 if: A = 6, O = 2, F = 4, E = 8; A = 7, O = 4, F = 3, E = 6; A = 8, O = 6, F = 2, E = 4 **6. b)** Yes. **c)** Pairs are in opposite positions relative to the centre. **7.** 62 **8.** Answers will vary. FLOUR, FLOOR, FLOOD, BLOOD, BROOD, BROAD, BREAD

Chapter 5

Review of Prerequisite Skills, pp. 266–267

1. A relation is a set of ordered pairs. Examples will vary. **2.** A function is a relation (set of ordered pairs) in which each element of the domain corresponds to exactly one element of the range; that is, no two ordered pairs have the same first element. Examples will vary. **3.** Mohammed is correct. Example: $\{(x, y) \mid x^2 + y^2 = 25; x, y \in \text{R}\}$ is a relation that is not a function. **4. a)** domain: R, range: R; a function; **b)** domain: R, range: R; a function; **c)** domain: R, range: $y \geq 8$; a function; **d)** domain: R, range: $y \geq -5$; a function; **e)** domain: $-8 \leq x \leq 8$, range: $-8 \leq y \leq 8$; not a function; **f)** domain: $-1 \leq x \leq 7$, range: $-6 \leq y \leq 2$; not a function; **g)** domain: $x \neq 0$, range: $y \neq 0$; a function; **h)** domain: $x \geq 3$, range: $y \geq 0$; a function.

5. a) 5 **b)** 24 **c)** 245 **6. a)** $\sqrt{3a - 5}$ **b)** $\sqrt{3x - 2}$ **c)** $\sqrt{3x^2 - 8}$ **7. a)** $5x + y - 48 = 0$ **b)** $6x + 14y - 41 = 0$ **c)** $x + 2y - 8 = 0$ **8. a)** $y = -3x + 25$ **b)** $y = \dfrac{9}{4}x - \dfrac{25}{4}$ **c)** $y = \dfrac{5}{9}x - \dfrac{55}{9}$

d) $y = x - 10.7$ **9. a)** $\sqrt{53}$ **b)** 5 **c)** $\dfrac{3\sqrt{65}}{2}$ **d)** $\dfrac{\sqrt{29}}{5}$

10. a) $2\sqrt{149}$ **b)** 24 **c)** $x = 10$ **11. a)** 3 **b)** $\dfrac{28}{3}$

c) 1.6 m **12.** 9.6 m **13. a)** $7x^6$ **b)** $-10x^{-\frac{5}{3}}$ **c)** $2x + 8$ **d)** $4x^3 + 18x^2 - 12$ **e)** $3x^2 - 2x - 6$ **f)** $36x^3 + 4$ **g)** $5x^4 + 8x^3 - 99x^2 + 28x$ **h)** $\dfrac{3x^4 + 12x^3}{(x + 3)^2}$ **i)** $\dfrac{6}{(5 - x)^2}$

j) $\dfrac{3}{\sqrt{x^3}}$ **14. a)** domain: $x \neq 0$; range $y \neq 0$; function **b)** domain $-5 \leq x \leq 5$; range: $-5 \leq y \leq 5$; not a function **c)** domain $x \in \text{R}$; range: $y \in \text{R}$; function **d)** domain: $-3 \leq x \leq 3$; range: $0 \leq y \leq 3$; function

15. a) $\dfrac{x - 2}{3}$ **b)** $\pm\sqrt{x - 5}$ **c)** $\sqrt[3]{x}$ **d)** $\dfrac{x^2 + 7}{3}, x \geq 0$, **e)** $\dfrac{1}{x}$ **f)** $\dfrac{2x + 3}{5x - 2}$ **16.** The inverse for part b) is not a function, since for $x > 5$ there are two values of y. All the others are functions.

Section 5.1, pp. 274–276

Practise

1. a) 3 **b)** 6 **c)** 8 **d)** Not defined; $f(6) = 12$ which is not in the domain of g. **e)** 5 **f)** Not defined; $g(0) = 7$ which is not in the domain of f. **2. a)** The domain of f is $-6 \leq x \leq 6$; the range is $0 \leq y \leq 6$. The domain of g is $-1 \leq x \leq 4$; the range is $-4 \leq y \leq 6$. **b) i)** 0 **ii)** 0 **iii)** 2 **iv)** -2 **v)** 2 **vi)** Undefined because 5 is not in the domain of g **3. a)** 145 **b)** 6 **c)** $64r^2 - 96r + 37$ **d)** $x^2 - 6x + 10$ **e)** $x - 6$ **f)** 26 **g)** $x^4 - 2$ **h)** 2 **i)** $9x^2 - 12x + 2$ **4. a)** -25 **b)** $\dfrac{3}{2}$ **c)** $-\dfrac{7}{25}$ **d)** $\dfrac{1}{3}$ **e)** $\dfrac{1}{x + 3} - 5$ **f)** -15 **g)** x **h)** $\dfrac{1}{2x - 5}$ **i)** $\dfrac{2}{x} - 5$ **j)** Undefined because 0 is not in the domain of f.

5. a) $(f \circ g)(x) = \dfrac{1}{4x + 3}, x \neq -\dfrac{3}{4}$; $(g \circ f)(x) = \dfrac{4}{x} + 3, x \neq 0$ **b)** $(f \circ g)(x) = 2x + 9, x \in \text{R}$; $(g \circ f)(x) = 2x + 3, x \in \text{R}$ **c)** $(f \circ g)(x) = \sqrt{x - 5}, x \geq 5$; $(g \circ f)(x) = \sqrt{x} - 5, x \geq 0$ **d)** $(f \circ g)(x) = \sqrt{4x + 9}, x \geq -\dfrac{9}{4}$; $(g \circ f)(x) = 4\sqrt{x + 8} + 1, x \geq -8$ **e)** $(f \circ g)(x) = x^2 + 4x + 4, x \in \text{R}$; $(g \circ f)(x) = x^2 + 2, x \in \text{R}$ **f)** $(f \circ g)(x) = 8x^3 + 60x^2 + 150x + 125, x \in \text{R}$; $(g \circ f)(x) = 2x^3 + 5, x \in \text{R}$ **g)** $(f \circ g)(x) = x^6 - x^2, x \in \text{R}$; $(g \circ f)(x) = x^6 - 2x^4 + x^2, x \in \text{R}$ **h)** $(f \circ g)(x) = \sqrt{x^8 + 49}, x \in \text{R}$; $(g \circ f)(x) = x^4 + 98x^2 + 2401 x \in \text{R}$ **6. a)** $x; x \in \text{R}$ **b)** $x; x \in \text{R}$ **c)** $x; x \geq 0$ **d)** $x; x \geq 0$

Apply, Solve, Communicate

7. a) $\sqrt{x+4}$ **b)** $x \geq -4$ **c)** $y \geq 0$ **d)** $\sqrt{x}+4$ **e)** $x \geq 0$ **f)** $y \geq 4$

8. a) $K = \frac{5}{9}(F - 32) + 273.15$ **b)** 269.26 K **9. a)** $A = 500t$

b) $r = \sqrt{\frac{A}{\pi}}$ **c)** $r = \sqrt{\frac{500t}{\pi}}$; radius (m) as a function of

time (min) **d)** 97.72 m **10. a)** $r = \sqrt[3]{\frac{75t}{2\pi}}$; r is in centimetres

b) 8.74 **11. a)** Delivery persons: one per 45 subscribers plus one replacement; Supervisors: one per 12 delivery persons **b)** $s = \frac{x+45}{540}$ **c)** 10 (you need more than 9)

12. a) $a(s) = 5s$ **b)** $w(a) = 0.05a + 200$
c) $w(s) = 0.25s + 200$ **d)** $825 **e)** $315

13. a) $r = 3000t + 1\,000\,000$
b) $V = \frac{4}{3}\pi(3000t + 1\,000\,000)^3$ represents volume
(in cubic kilometres) as a function of time (in seconds).
c) 4.780×10^{18} km^3 **14.** 221.7 km^2

15. a) $p = \sqrt{c^2 + 225}$ **b)** $c = \frac{25}{6}t$ **c)** $p = \sqrt{\left(\frac{25}{6}t\right)^2 + 225}$

represents distance (in metres) between the cyclist and lock as a function of time (in seconds). **d)** 44.28 m
16. Answers will vary. One possible answer is given in each. **a)** $f(x) = 32x + 3$; $g(x) = x^2$
b) $f(x) = \sqrt{x}$; $g(x) = 6x^2 + 7$ **c)** $f(x) = \sqrt{x}$; $g(x) = \frac{1}{x}$
d) $f(x) = x^{-5}$; $g(x) = 3x^2 - 5x^3$
17. $g(x) = x^2 - \frac{9}{2}$ **18.** $f(x) = \frac{1}{x+3}$

Section 5.2, pp. 282–283

Practise

2. a) $8x^3(x^4 - 5)$ **b)** $2(x^2 - 7x + 4)(2x - 7)$ **c)** $\frac{3x^2}{2\sqrt{x^3 - 9}}$

d) $\frac{1}{2(\sqrt[4]{2x+1})^3}$ **e)** $\frac{-5(2x+6)}{(x^2 + 6x - 3)^6}$ **f)** $\frac{-6x}{(3x^2 + 8)^2}$

3. a) $\frac{1}{\sqrt{2x+7}}$ **b)** $6x(x^2 + 6)^2$ **c)** $(3x - 1)^{-\frac{2}{3}}$ **d)** $8(x - 1)$

e) $\frac{x}{\sqrt{x^2 + 6}}$ **f)** $-\frac{2x+3}{(x^2 + 3x - 8)^2}$ **4. a)** -4 **b)** does not exist

c) 2 **d)** does not exist; $g(0)$ is negative, and negative numbers are not in the domain of f or f'.

Apply, Solve, Communicate

5. a) $\frac{dV}{dt} = 15$ (L/min); $\frac{dh}{dV} = 0.2$ (cm/L)

b) $\frac{dh}{dt} = 3$ (cm/min) **6. a)** 0.032π or 0.101 km^2/s

b) 0.016π or 0.050 km^2/s **c)** 0.0004π or 0.001 km^2/s

7. a) $\frac{39(x - 9)^2}{(x + 4)^4}$ **b)** $\frac{6}{\sqrt{x}} + 4$ **c)** $\frac{8x + 1}{2\sqrt{4x^2 + x}}$

d) $(4x - 1)^4(48x + 18)$ **e)** $(x^2 - 4)^2(20 + 18x - 35x^2)$

8. $18\,000\pi$ cm^3/min **9.** 420π m^2/day **10.** $\frac{8}{49\pi}$ m/min

11. 432 **12. a)** $\frac{2}{3}x(x^2 - 4)^{-\frac{2}{3}}$ **b)** $-15x^2(x^3 + 1)^{-6}$

c) $\frac{8(x^2 + 2x - 1)(x^2 + 1)^7}{(x + 1)^9}$ **d)** $\frac{1}{2}(3x + 2)^{-\frac{3}{2}}(3x + 4)$

e) $(3x - 2)^2(2x^2 + 5)^3(66x^2 - 32x + 45)$

f) $\frac{6(1 + x - x^2)(2x - 1)^2}{(x^2 + 1)^4}$ **g)** $\frac{3x^2}{2(x^3 - 1)^{\frac{3}{4}}(x^3 + 1)^{\frac{5}{4}}}$

1.

$F(x) = f(g(x))$	$f(x)$	$g(x)$	$g'(x)$	$f'(g(x))$	$F'(x) = f'(g(x))g'(x)$
$(x^7 + 3)^5$	x^5	$x^7 + 3$	$7x^6$	$5(x^7 + 3)^4$	$5(x^7 + 3)^4(7x^6)$
$(x^3 - 2x^2)^{-4}$	x^{-4}	$x^3 - 2x^2$	$3x^2 - 4x$	$-4(x^3 - 2x^2)^{-5}$	$-4(x^3 - 2x^2)^{-5}(3x^2 - 4x)$
$(x^4 + 5)^{\frac{1}{2}}$	$x^{\frac{1}{2}}$	$x^4 + 5$	$4x^3$	$\frac{1}{2}(x^4 + 5)^{-\frac{1}{2}}$	$\frac{1}{2}(x^4 + 5)^{-\frac{1}{2}}(4x^3)$
$\frac{1}{x^2 + 2x}$	$\frac{1}{x}$	$x^2 + 2x$	$2x + 2$	$-\frac{1}{(x^2 + 2x)^2}$	$-\frac{2x + 2}{(x^2 + 2x)^2}$
$\sqrt{2x - 1}$	$\sqrt{x}$	$2x - 1$	2	$\frac{1}{2}(2x - 1)^{-\frac{1}{2}}$	$\frac{1}{2}(2x - 1)^{-\frac{1}{2}}(2)$
$(x^2 + 5x - 8)^4$	x^4	$x^2 + 5x - 8$	$2x + 5$	$4(x^2 + 5x - 8)^3$	$4(x^2 + 5x - 8)^3(2x + 5)$

h) $\frac{1}{6}(x-2)^{-\frac{1}{2}}(x+2)^{-\frac{4}{3}}(x+10)$

i) $g'(x) = -x(x^2-3)^{-\frac{3}{2}}$

13. a) $h'(g(f(x)))g'(f(x))f'(x)$ **b)** $2g(h(x))g'(h(x))h'(x)$

c) $6g'([h(3x-2)]^2)h(3x-2)h'(3x-2)$

d) $g'\left(f\left(\frac{1}{\sqrt{x+1}}\right)\right) \cdot f'\left(\frac{1}{\sqrt{x+1}}\right) \cdot \left(-\frac{1}{2}\right)(x+1)^{-\frac{3}{2}}$

e) $f'\left(\frac{1}{x+g(x)}\right)(-1)\frac{1+g'(x)}{(x+g(x))^2}$

Technology Extension, p. 284

1. a) $f(x) = x^3;\ g(x) = x^2 - 5x + 6$ **b)** $f(x) = \sqrt{x}\ ;$
$g(x) = x^2 - 4$ **2.** 1st function: **a)** $(x^2 - 5x + 6)^3$
b) $x^6 - 5x^3 + 6$ **c)** 8000 **d)** 110 **e)** $3x^2$ **f)** $2x - 5$
g) $3(2x-5)(x^2-5x+6)^2$; 2nd function: **a)** $\sqrt{x^2-4}$
b) $x - 4;\ x \geq 0$ **c)** 0 **d)** not defined;
-2 is not in the domain of f **e)** $\frac{1}{2\sqrt{x}}$ **f)** $2x$ **g)** $x(x^2-4)^{-\frac{1}{2}}$

3. a) $r = \frac{3}{2}h$ **b)** $V = \frac{3\pi}{4}h^3$ **c)** 8.49 m **d)** 1 h 38 min 11 s

Section 5.3, pp. 289–290

Practise

1. a) Parts **i)** and **ii)** give $\frac{12}{5}$. **b)** Answers may vary.

2. a) $-\frac{x}{y}$ **b)** $-\frac{3x^2 + 2xy}{x^2 + 8y}$ **c)** $-\frac{x^2}{y^2}$ **d)** $\frac{4x}{y}$

e) $\frac{3}{3y^2+1}$ **f)** $-\frac{y}{x}$ **g)** $\frac{4x^3y - 2xy^3}{5y^4 + 3x^2y^2 - x^4}$ **h)** $-\sqrt{\frac{y}{x}}$

3. a) $x + 18y - 37 = 0$ **b)** $4x + 9y - 72 = 0$
c) $2x - 3y + 12 = 0$ **d)** $x + 4y - 6 = 0$

Apply, Solve, Communicate

4. a) i) 0 **ii)** $y = -5$ **b) i)** $\frac{1}{6}$ **ii)** $x - 6y - 11 = 0$ **c) i)** undefined

ii) $x = 12$ **d) i)** $\frac{3}{4}$ **ii)** $3x - 4y + 7 = 0$ **5. a)** $3x + 4y - 30 = 0$

7. $(-5, 0)$ if the satellite is moving clockwise; $(3, 8)$
if the satellite is moving counterclockwise.

8. a) $P + V\frac{dP}{dV} = k\frac{dT}{dV}$ **b)** Positive; all the variables in the

equation are positive. **c)** $P\frac{dV}{dT} + V\frac{dP}{dT} = k;\ k$ is positive

since $\frac{dV}{dT}$ is almost 0 and $\frac{dP}{dT}$ is positive.

9. a) $\frac{x(25 - 4(x^2 + y^2))}{y(25 + 4(x^2 + y^2))}$ **b)** $9x - 13y + 40 = 0$

c) $\left(\frac{5\sqrt{3}}{4}, \frac{5}{4}\right), \left(\frac{5\sqrt{3}}{4}, -\frac{5}{4}\right), \left(-\frac{5\sqrt{3}}{4}, \frac{5}{4}\right), \left(-\frac{5\sqrt{3}}{4}, -\frac{5}{4}\right)$

10. a) $-\sqrt[3]{\frac{y}{x}}$ **b)** $2\sqrt{3}x + 2y - \sqrt{3} = 0$

c) $\left(\frac{1}{2\sqrt{2}}, -\frac{1}{2\sqrt{2}}\right), \left(-\frac{1}{2\sqrt{2}}, \frac{1}{2\sqrt{2}}\right)$

11. $(1, 1), (-1, -1)$

13. The curve crosses itself at slopes of -1 and $+1$, so
there is no unique tangent.

Section 5.4, pp. 298–299

Practise

1. 140 **2. a)** $\frac{5}{256\pi}$ **b)** $-\frac{1}{5\pi}$ **3.** $-\frac{5}{12\pi}$

Apply, Solve, Communicate

4. 24 m²/min **5.** 4.42 rev/s **6.** $-\frac{1}{4\sqrt{3}}$ or -0.144 m/s

7. a) About 260 million years. **b)** 2.5×10^9 km³/year

c) 1.39×10^{12} kg/m³ **d)** -2421 kg/m³/year **8. a)** $\frac{25}{9\pi}$ m/min

b) $\frac{50}{147\pi}$ m/min **9.** 32.8 m/min **10.** 72π cm²/s

11. a) 75 km/h **b)** 75 km/h **c)** 75 km/h **d)** The results are equal.
e) Answers will vary. **f)** $x = x_0 - 45t$ and $y = y_0 - 60t$, where
$(x_0, 0)$ and $(0, y_0)$ are the initial positions of A and B,
respectively. t is in hours and distances are in kilometres.
12. a) 0.1587 mm³/s **b)** \$0.87/s **13.** 1.0 m/s **14.** 0.086 m/s
15. a) 13 158 m³/s **b)** 21.0 m/s

Review of Key Concepts, pp. 301–302

1. a) 3 **b)** 9 **c)** -5 **d)** $\frac{1}{5}$ **e)** $\frac{2x+7}{2x+3}$ **f)** $\frac{5x+8}{x}$ **g)** $\frac{5x+4}{x+4}$ **h)** -35
2. $g(-4) = -3$, and -3 is not in the domain of $f(x)$.
3. Answers will vary. One answer is $g(x) = x + 12$,

$f(x) = \sqrt[3]{x}$. **4.** $f(x) = \frac{1}{x}$ **5. a)** $r = 0.2t$ **b)** $V = \frac{4}{3}\pi r^3$

c) $V = \frac{4}{375}\pi t^3$ gives volume, in cubic millimetres, as a

function of time in minutes. **d)** 7238 mm³ **6. a) i)–iv)** x
b) The composition of a function with its inverse results
in x. **7. a)** $6x^5 - 75x^4 + 300x^3 - 375x^2$ **b)** $3(2x-5)(x^2-5x)^2$
c) The answer in part b) expands to the answer
in part a). Explanations will vary.

8. a) $4(2x+8)$ **b)** $\frac{2x+7}{2\sqrt{x^2+7x}}$ **c)** $\frac{-3(4x^3+5)}{(x^4+5x)^4}$

d) $\frac{1}{3}(16x^7)(2x^8-2)^{-\frac{2}{3}}$ **e)** $(3x+1)(6x^2+4x)^{-\frac{3}{4}}$

9. a) $2(4x^3 - 6x^2)(x^4 - 2x^3)$ **b)** $\frac{x+4}{\sqrt{x^2+8x-6}}$

c) $5(3x^2 + 9)(x^3 + 9x)^4$ **d)** $3(2x + 1)(x^2 + x - 10)^2$

e) $\frac{2}{5}x(x^2 + 12)^{-\frac{4}{5}}$ **f)** $\frac{4 - 3x^2}{(x^3 - 4x)^2}$ **g)** $-\frac{5}{2}(5x - 2)^{-\frac{3}{2}}$

h) $(x^2 + 2)(x^3 + 6x)^{-\frac{2}{3}}$ **10. a)** 0.754 m²/min

b) 2.93 mm/min **11. a) i)** $y = \pm\sqrt{36 - 9x^2}$; $\frac{dy}{dx} = \frac{-9x}{\pm\sqrt{36 - 9x^2}}$

ii) $\frac{dy}{dx} = -\frac{9x}{y}$ **b)** relations whose equations cannot be solved for y explicitly in terms of x

12. a) $-\frac{x}{y}$ **b)** $-\frac{3xy^2 + 8y}{2x^2y + 4x}$ **c)** $-\frac{2xy^3 + 2y}{3x^2y^2 + 2x}$ **d)** $\frac{-xy}{3y + x^2}$

e) $\frac{2(2 - x)}{3(y + 7)^2}$ **f)** $\frac{6 - 2x - y^3}{3xy^2 + 8}$ **13. a) i)** -1.5 **ii)** $3x + 2y - 2 = 0$

b) i) $-\frac{2}{9}$ **ii)** $2x + 9y - 24 = 0$ **c) i)** $-\frac{12}{47}$

ii) $12x + 47y + 176 = 0$ **d) i)** $-\frac{11}{102}$ **ii)** $11x + 102y + 168 = 0$

14. $\frac{1}{9\pi}$ **15.** $0.281\,25$ m/s **16.** -41.05 m/min **17.** 13.42 cm/s

18. a) 1.885 mm³/s **b)** 9.425 mm³/s **19.** 45 cm³/min

Chapter Test, p. 303

1. a) 6 **b)** 286 **c)** $36x^2 - 60x + 22$ **d)** $-6x^2 - 24x - 1$
e) $23 - 6x^2$ **f)** -133 **2.** No. Examples will vary. **3.** $7x - 2$
4. a) $\frac{1}{2x - 3}$ **b)** $\frac{2}{x} - 3$ **c)** No. $g(1.5) = 0$ and $f(0)$ is not
defined. **d)** f: domain: $x \neq 0$, range: $y \neq 0$; g: domain: R,
range: R **e)** $f \circ g$: domain: $x \neq 1.5$, range: $y \neq 0$; $g \circ f$:
domain: $x \neq 0$, range: $y \neq -3$ **5. a)** $\frac{x + 7}{3}$ **b)** x **c)** Yes.

6. a) $3(x^2 + 2x^4)^2(2x + 8x^3)$ **b)** $-\frac{2x + 1}{(x^2 + x - 3)^2}$

c) $\frac{4x^3 + 3}{2\sqrt{x^4 + 3x}}$ **d)** $-\frac{1}{2}(3x^2 + 6)(x^3 + 6x)^{-\frac{3}{2}}$

e) $\frac{1}{4}(3x^2 + 4x)(x^3 + 2x^2 - 5)^{-\frac{3}{4}}$

f) $4(x^5 + 6x^3 - x)^3(5x^4 + 18x^2 - 1)$ **g)** $\frac{-8x}{(x^2 - 2)^2}$

h) $\frac{x(x^3 - 3x + 4)}{2(x^2 - 1)^{\frac{1}{2}}(x^3 - 2)^{\frac{1}{2}}}$ **7.** $-\frac{1}{192\pi}$ m/min **8. a)** $y = x + 3$

b) $7x - 9y - 16 = 0$ **c)** $x + y - 2 = 0$
d) $x + 4y + 11 = 0$ **9.** $0.001\,99$ m/min **10.** 0.109 m/min

Challenge Problems, p. 304

1. $g(x) = x^2 - \frac{9}{2}$ **2.** $f(x) = \frac{1}{x + 3}$ **3. a)** 48 **b)** $g'(f(1))$

4. b) No; $f'(2) = 1$, while $g'(2) = -\frac{1}{4}$. No.

5. -1.6 cm/min **6.** -75 cm/s/cm **7.** $\left(1, \frac{1}{2}\right)$; yes,
approximately $(0.306, 0.914)$. **8.** 1

9. $\left(\frac{1}{2}, \frac{\sqrt{3}}{4}\right)$, $\left(-\frac{1}{2}, -\frac{\sqrt{3}}{4}\right)$, $\left(\sqrt{\frac{2}{3}}, -\frac{\sqrt{2}}{3}\right)$, $\left(-\sqrt{\frac{2}{3}}, \frac{\sqrt{2}}{3}\right)$

Cumulative Review: Chapters 3, 4, and 5, pp. 305–307

1. a) Answers will vary. **b)** -10 **c)** $y = -10x + 12$
2. a) 2.3; 0.7 **b)** Estimates will vary; 1.6 to 2.1 and
0.6 to 0.9 are reasonable. **c)** same as estimates in
b) but with units °C/s **d)** No. **3. a)** $g'(x) = 2x$

b) $y' = \frac{1}{2\sqrt{x - 1}}$ **c)** $m'(w) = -\frac{2}{w^3}$ **4.** $a = 2$; $f(x) = x^3$

5. a) 6 **b)** 51 **c)** 41 **d)** $4x^2 - 44x + 126$ **e)** 15 **f)** n

6. a) $\frac{1}{4x + 1}$ **b)** domain: $x \neq -\frac{1}{4}$, range: $y \neq 0$ **c)** $\frac{4}{x} + 1$

d) domain: $x \neq 0$ $y \neq 1$ **7.** Answers will vary. For
example, $f(x) = \sqrt[4]{x}$, $g(x) = x + 6$ **8. a) i)** -4 **ii)** $y = -4x - 4$

b) i) 4 **ii)** $y = 4x - 11$ **c) i)** $\frac{1}{6}$ **ii)** $y = \frac{1}{6}x + \frac{3}{2}$ **d) i)** $-\frac{1}{2}$

ii) $y = -\frac{1}{2}x + \frac{3}{2}$ **9. a)** 0.5 **b)** 0.5 **c)** 0.5 **d)** 0 **e)** 3.5 **f)** 3.5 **g)** 2

h) does not exist; left and right limits not equal **i)** 1 **j)** 1
k) 1 **l)** 1 **10. a)** $g'(x) = 35x^4 + 9x^2 - 5$

b) $y' = -15x^{-6} + \frac{1}{2\sqrt{x}}$ **c)** $s'(t) = \frac{1}{2\sqrt{t}} - \frac{1}{4\sqrt[4]{t^3}}$

d) $h'(x) = 2x - 12$ **11. a)** $r = \sqrt[3]{\frac{3t}{\pi}}$

b) 3.423 cm **12. a)** $4x(x^2 + 3)$ **b)** $\frac{7}{3}(7x - 4)^{-\frac{2}{3}}$

c) $-\frac{8x + 3}{(4x^2 + 3x - 2)^2}$ **d)** $\frac{4x + 1}{2\sqrt{2x^2 + x}}$ **13.** $y = 5x$ **14. a)** 2 **b)** $\frac{1}{5}$

c) does not exist **d)** 0 **e)** does not exist **f)** $\frac{1}{6}$ **g)** -6

h) does not exist **15. a)** $y = -5x - 3$ **b)** $y = \frac{53}{2}x - 55$

c) $y = \frac{79}{784}x - \frac{121}{196}$ **d)** $y = -11x + 2$ **16. a)** 8

b) not defined **c)** $\frac{17}{12\sqrt{3}}$ **d)** $\frac{7}{32}$ **17. a)** $-\frac{x}{y}$ **b)** $-\frac{3x^2 + 2xy}{x^2 + 10y}$

c) $-\frac{y}{x}$ **d)** $-\frac{y}{y^2 + x}$ **18. a)** $y = -\frac{1}{4}x + \frac{9}{4}$

b) $y = -\frac{5}{2}x + \frac{25}{2}$ **19. a)** 30.2 m/s **b)** 10.6 m/s **c)** 83 m

20. a) $V'(t) = \frac{7.6}{\sqrt{t}} + 1.43$ **b)** 5.23; 3.83

21. a) 1000; 6125 **b)** $75t^2 + 400$

22. a) $0.003\,75$; $-0.000\,468\,75$ **b)** After 4 years, the
thickness is increasing at a rate of $0.003\,75$ cm/year

and the thickening rate is decreasing at
$-0.000\,468\,75$ cm/year/year. **23. a)** $v = 10t + 3$; $a = 10$

b) $v = \dfrac{t + 12\sqrt{t} + 1}{2\sqrt{t}\,(1-t)^2}$; $a = \dfrac{1}{4}\,t^{-\frac{3}{2}}\,(1-t)^{-3}(3t^2 + 48t\sqrt{t} + 6t - 1)$

24. a) Since $t \geq 0$ by convention, the particle is always speeding up. **b)** Velocity is always positive, except for $t = 1$. The particle is speeding up for $t > 1$ and for $0 < t < k$, and slowing down for $k < t < 1$. $k = 0.057$, the solution on $(0, 1)$ of $3t^2 + 48t\sqrt{t} + 6t = 1$

25. $s = 3$ m and $v = -2$ m/s, when $t = 0$ **26. a)** $\dfrac{100}{\sqrt{x}}$

b) $10\,000 - 0.03x$ **c)** $10\,000 - 0.03x - \dfrac{100}{\sqrt{x}}$ **d)** \$9983.80/lens

27. -0.128 Ω/s **28.** 0.683 cm^3/min **29.** Yes, by 15 km/h.

Chapter 6

Review of Prerequisite Skills, pp. 310–311

1. a) 25 **b)** 4 **c)** 4 **d)** 0 **e)** 26 **f)** -1 **g)** no solution **h)** $\dfrac{13}{4}$ **i)** 21
j) 3 **k)** 1 **l)** $1, 5$ **2. a)** $-2, -3.732, -0.268$ **b)** $-1.526, 5.469$
c) $-1, 1$ **d)** no real solution **e)** 5.654 **f)** $-1, -1.182, 0.205$
g) $6.329, -4.563, -1.766$ **h)** $-1.056, 1.230, 7.483$
i) $-1.999, 2.001, 2999.999$ **j)** $-17.366, -1.956, 17.390$
3. a) 26 **b)** 2 **c)** 70 **d)** 2 **5. a)** True **b)** False **c)** False **d)** False
6. a) $[2, 5]$ **b)** $(-3, 11)$ **c)** $[0, 2]$ **d)** $(-4, 4]$

7. a) $2.01 < x < 2.99$ **b)** $2 < x \leq 22$ **c)** $0 \leq x \leq 1$

d) $-\pi < x < \pi$ **8. a)** $x \leq -\dfrac{1}{3}$ **b)** $x \in R$ **c)** $-\dfrac{1}{3} < x < \dfrac{1}{2}$

d) $-4 < x < 1$ **9.** 5 cm **10.** 5 cm **11. a)** none **b)** $x \neq 3$
c) $x \neq -4$ **d)** $x \neq 2$ or -3 **e)** $x \neq -3$ or 8 **f)** $x \neq 0$ or 5
g) $x \geq 0$ **h)** $x \geq 4$ or $x \leq -4$ **12. a)** x-intercepts: ± 1;
y-intercept: -1 **b)** x-intercepts: $4, -2$; y-intercept: -8
c) x-intercepts: $-3, -4$; g-intercept: 12 **d)** t-intercepts:

none; s-intercept: 5 **e)** r-intercepts: $-2, -\dfrac{3}{2}$;

V-intercept: 6 **f)** x-intercepts: $-5, 0$; y-intercept: 0
g) x-intercepts: $-1, -2, -3$; y-intercept: 6
h) x-intercepts: none; f-intercept: 7
13. x-intercepts: $0, \pm\sqrt{3}$; y-intercept: 0
14. a) odd **b)** even **c)** neither **d)** odd **15. a)** even **b)** odd
c) neither **d)** even **e)** neither **f)** odd **g)** neither **h)** even
16. a) $3x + 4$, R -3 **b)** $3x + 7$, R 4 **c)** $x - 3$, R 5
d) $x + 7$, R $34x + 98$

Section 6.1, pp. 317–318

Practise

1. a) $(-\infty, 2), (2, \infty)$ **b)** $(-\infty, -3), (-3, \infty)$
c) $(-\infty, -3), (-3, 3), (3, \infty)$ **d)** $(-\infty, -1), (-1, \infty)$

e) $(-\infty, -3), (-3, -2), (-2, 0), (0, \infty)$
f) $(-\infty, 0), (0, 1), (1, 2), (2, \infty)$ **g)** $(-\infty, -3), (-3, -1),$
$(-1, \infty)$ **h)** $(-\infty, -1), (-1, 0), (0, 4), (4, \infty)$
i) $(-\infty, -2), (-2, 0), (0, \infty)$ **j)** $(-\infty, -1), (-1, 0), (0, 2), (2, \infty)$
2. a) increase: $(-2, \infty)$; decrease: $(-\infty, -2)$
b) increase: $(-1, \infty)$; decrease: $(-\infty, -1)$
c) increase: $(-1, 0), (1, \infty)$; decrease: $(-\infty, -1), (0, 1)$
d) increase: $(-\infty, -1), (1, \infty)$; decrease: $(-1, 1)$
e) never increases; decrease: $(-\infty, \infty)$ **f)** increase: $(5, \infty)$;
decrease: $(-\infty, 5)$ **g)** increase: $(-\infty, -5), (5, \infty)$;
decrease: $(-5, 5)$ **h)** increase: $(-4, 4)$; decrease: $(-\infty, -4),$
$(4, \infty)$ **i)** increase: $(-2, \infty)$; decrease: $(-\infty, -2)$
j) increase: $(-\infty, 0), (2, \infty)$; decrease: $(0, 2)$
k) increase: $(-\infty, 0)$; decrease: $(0, \infty)$

l) increase: $\left(-\infty, -\sqrt{\dfrac{6}{5}}\right), \left(\sqrt{\dfrac{6}{5}}, \infty\right)$;

decrease: $\left(-\sqrt{\dfrac{6}{5}}, 0\right), \left(0, \sqrt{\dfrac{6}{5}}\right)$ **m)** increase: $(-\infty, 0),$

$(0, \infty)$; never decreases **n)** never increases; decrease:
$(-\infty, 0), (0, \infty)$

Apply, Solve, Communicate

3. $(2, 4)$ **4.** Answers will vary. **5. a)** $(0, \infty)$ **b)** No. **c)** No.

d) Answers will vary. **6. a)** $\left(0, \dfrac{40}{49}\right)$ **b)** 2.462 s **c)** 1.645 s

7. a) increase: $(1, \infty)$; decrease: $(-\infty, 1)$

b) increase: $\left(\dfrac{3}{2}, \infty\right)$; decrease: $\left(-\infty, \dfrac{3}{2}\right)$

c) increase: $\left(-\infty, \dfrac{2 - \sqrt{7}}{3}\right), \left(\dfrac{2 + \sqrt{7}}{3}, \infty\right)$;

decrease: $\left(\dfrac{2 - \sqrt{7}}{3}, \dfrac{2 + \sqrt{7}}{3}\right)$ **d)** increase: $(-\infty, -1 - \sqrt{6}),$

$(-1 + \sqrt{6}, \infty)$; decrease: $(-1 - \sqrt{6}, -1), (-1, -1 + \sqrt{6})$

8. a) $(0, 6)$ **b)** $(6, 12]$ **9. a)** $\left[0, \dfrac{25}{3}\right), \left(\dfrac{25}{3}, 15\right]$

b) Diving for the first 8.3 s and then climbing for 6.7 s.

10. a) $[0, 0.5)$ **b)** $(0.5, \infty)$ **11.** $k \leq \dfrac{1}{9}$ **12.** Answers will vary.

13. $f(n) \leq \lim_{x \to n^-} f(x)$ and $f(n) \leq \lim_{x \to n^+} f(x)$ must both be

satisfied. **14. a)** increase: $(0, \infty)$ decrease $(-1, 0)$
b) Answer will vary.

Section 6.2, pp. 327–329

Practise

1. a) absolute maximum: 12; absolute minimum: -6
b) absolute maximum: 3; no absolute minimum
2. a) absolute maximum: 5; absolute minimum: -1

b) absolute maximum: 4; absolute minimum: −2
c) absolute maximum: 9; absolute minimum: 5
d) absolute maximum: 22; absolute minimum: −3
e) absolute maximum: 1; absolute minimum: −53
f) absolute maximum: 1; absolute minimum: −224
g) absolute maximum: 21; absolute minimum: 3
h) absolute maximum: 18; absolute minimum: −14
i) absolute maximum: 70; absolute minimum: 6
j) absolute maximum: 65; absolute minimum: −161
k) absolute maximum: 4; absolute minimum: 1
l) absolute maximum: 17; absolute minimum: 1

3. a) critical numbers: $\frac{1}{2}$; local maxima: $\frac{1}{4}$

at $x = \frac{1}{2}$; local minima: none **b)** critical numbers: 2;
local maxima: none; local minima: 0 at $x = 2$ **c)** critical
numbers: 0, $\pm\sqrt{2}$; local maxima: 4 at $x = 0$; local
minima: 0 at $x = \pm\sqrt{2}$ **d)** critical numbers: ± 1; local
maxima: 5 at $x = -1$; local minima: −3 at $x = 1$
e) critical numbers: 0, $\frac{1}{4}$; local maxima: none; local

minima: $-\frac{1}{4}$ at $x = \frac{1}{4}$ **f)** critical numbers: $\frac{4}{3}$; local

maxima: none; local minima: $-\frac{4}{3}$ at $x = \frac{4}{3}$ **g)** critical

numbers: 0; local maxima: none; local minima: none
h) critical numbers: 0, ± 2; local maxima: 12 at $x = 0$;
local minima: −20 at $x = \pm 2$ **i)** critical numbers: 0, $\pm\sqrt{3}$;
local maxima: $6\sqrt{3}$ at $x = -\sqrt{3}$; local minima: $-6\sqrt{3}$ at
$x = \sqrt{3}$ **j)** critical numbers: −2; local maxima: none;

local minima: 0 at $x = -2$ **k)** critical numbers: 0, $\frac{1}{4}$, 1;

local maxima: $\frac{9}{32\sqrt[3]{2}}$ at $x = \frac{1}{4}$; local minima: 0 at $x = 0$

and $x = 1$ **l)** critical numbers: 0, 2; local maxima: none;
local minima: −4 at $x = 2$. **4. a)** min (2, 3) **b)** max (−1, 5)
c) min (1, −2); max (−1, 2) **d)** max (0, 0); min (1, −1),
(−1, −1) **e)** min (0, 0); max (0.74, 0.33) **f)** max (2, 10);
min (3, 9) **g)** min (0.40, −0.47) **h)** max (9, 9)

Apply, Solve, Communicate

5. $\frac{5}{3}$ m **6. a)** 2 m **b)** $\frac{4938}{49}$ m **c)** 9 s **7.** 23.57 m/s

8. a) 1.108F cm/s **9.** Answers will vary. **10. a)** $h = 0.0068t^4$
$- 0.3240t^3 + 5.2790t^2 - 33.4397t + 71.9825$ **b)** increasing
between 5:37 a.m. and 12:01 p.m., 6:19 p.m. and
7:00 p.m.; decreasing between 4:00 a.m. and 5:37 a.m.,
12:01 p.m. and 6:19 p.m.; neither increasing nor
decreasing at 5:37 a.m., 12:01 p.m. and 6:19 p.m.
c) 12:01 p.m.; 5:37 a.m. **11. a)** (20, 30]; [0, 20) **b)** After

20 years, the population is at a minimum of 4 million.
12. absolute maximum: 11 at $x = 2$;

absolute minimum: $-\frac{5}{4}$ at $x = -\frac{3}{2}$

13. absolute maximum: 16; absolute minimum: 0

14. $\frac{2}{3\sqrt{3}r^2}$ **15. a)** Yes. For example, $y = \frac{x}{1+x^2}$ has

absolute maximum at $\left(1, \frac{1}{2}\right)$ and absolute minimum at

$\left(-1, -\frac{1}{2}\right)$ **b)** Yes. **16. a)** Yes. **b)** No. For example,

$y = \frac{3}{4(2x-3)^2}$ has an infinite discontinuity at $x = \frac{3}{2}$.

Section 6.3, pp. 338–341

Practise

1. a) concave upward: (−6, −3), (1, 4), (12, 14); concave
downward: (−10, −6), (−3, 1), (4, 7), (7, 12)
b) (−6, −1), (−3, 0), (1, 4) (4, 0.8), (12, 2.5) **2.** concave
upward: (1, 7); concave downward: (−∞, 1), (7, ∞);
points of inflection at $x = 1$, $x = 7$
3. a) increasing: (−∞, 0), (2, 4), (6, ∞); decreasing: (0, 2),
(4, 6) **b)** concave upward: (1, 3), (5, 7), (8, ∞);
concave downward: (−∞, 1), (3, 5), (7, 8) **c)** 0, 2, 4, 6
d) 1, 3, 5, 7, 8 **4. a)** $x = -1$ gives a minimum; $x = 4$ gives a
maximum. **b)** $x = 0$ gives neither a maximum nor a
minimum; $x = 6$ gives a minimum. **c)** $x \doteq -0.07$ gives
neither a maximum nor a minimum. **5. a)** concave upward:
(−∞, ∞); never concave downward; points of inflection:
none **b)** never concave upward; concave downward:
(−∞, ∞); points of inflection: none **c)** concave upward:

$\left(\frac{1}{2}, \infty\right)$; concave downward: $\left(-\infty, \frac{1}{2}\right)$; points of

inflection: $\left(\frac{1}{2}, -\frac{1}{2}\right)$ **d)** concave upward: $\left(-\frac{2}{3}, \infty\right)$;

concave downward: $\left(-\infty, -\frac{2}{3}\right)$; points of inflection:

$\left(-\frac{2}{3}, \frac{169}{27}\right)$ **e)** concave upward: $\left(-\frac{7}{12}, \infty\right)$;

concave downward: $\left(-\infty, -\frac{7}{12}\right)$; points of inflection:

$\left(-\frac{7}{12}, \frac{8011}{432}\right)$ **f)** concave upward: $\left(-\infty, -\frac{1}{3}\right)$, (1, ∞);

concave downward: $\left(-\frac{1}{3}, 1\right)$; points of inflection:

$\left(-\frac{1}{3}, \frac{41}{27}\right)$, (1, −5) **g)** never concave upward; concave downward $(-\infty, \infty)$; points of inflection: none

h) concave upward: $\left(-\dfrac{1}{\sqrt{2}}, 0\right), \left(\dfrac{1}{\sqrt{2}}, \infty\right)$; concave

downward: $\left(-\infty, -\dfrac{1}{\sqrt{2}}\right), \left(0, \dfrac{1}{\sqrt{2}}\right)$; points of inflection:

$\left(-\dfrac{1}{\sqrt{2}}, 2+\dfrac{7}{4\sqrt{2}}\right), (0, 2), \left(\dfrac{1}{\sqrt{2}}, 2-\dfrac{7}{4\sqrt{2}}\right)$

i) concave upward: $(-\infty, 3)$; concave downward: $(3, \infty)$; points of inflection: none **j)** concave upward:

$\left(-\infty, -\dfrac{1}{\sqrt{3}}\right), \left(\dfrac{1}{\sqrt{3}}, \infty\right)$; concave downward: $\left(-\dfrac{1}{\sqrt{3}}, \dfrac{1}{\sqrt{3}}\right)$;

points of inflection: $\left(-\dfrac{1}{\sqrt{3}}, \dfrac{3}{4}\right), \left(\dfrac{1}{\sqrt{3}}, \dfrac{3}{4}\right)$ **k)** concave

upward: $(0, \infty)$; concave downward: $(-\infty, 0)$; points of inflection: none **6. a)** maximum 21 at $x = 4$ **b)** maximum 42 at $x = -2$; minimum -22 at $x = 2$ **c)** maximum 260 at $x = 8$; minimum 4 at $x = 0$ **d)** maximum 20 at $x = 2$; minimum 16 at $x = 4$ **e)** minimum -23 at $x = -3$ **f)** maximum 9 at $x = 1$; minimum 1 at $x = -1$ **g)** maximum 256 at $x = \pm 2$; minimum 0 at $x = 0$, $\pm 2\sqrt{2}$ **h)** minimum 3 at $x = -1$ **7. a)** maximum 10 at $x = 0$; minimum 1 at $x = \pm\sqrt{3}$ **b)** minimum $-\dfrac{1}{4}$ at $x = -1$

c) maximum -3 at $x = -3$; minimum 0 at $x = 0$

d) maximum $-\dfrac{27\sqrt[3]{2}}{2\sqrt[3]{9}}$ at $x = -\sqrt[3]{\dfrac{9}{2}}$ **8.** See student e-book.

Apply, Solve, Communicate

9. a) $f(x) > 0$ on $(0, \infty)$; $f(x) < 0$ on $(-\infty, 0)$; $f(x) = 0$ at $x = 0$; $f'(x) > 0$ on $(-3, 0), (0, \infty)$; $f'(x) < 0$ on $(-\infty, -3)$; $f'(x) = 0$ at $x = -3, 0$; $f''(x) > 0$ on $(-5, -1.5)$, $(0, \infty)$; $f''(x) < 0$ on $(-\infty, -5), (-1.5, 0)$; $f''(x) = 0$ at $x = 0, -1.5, -5$ **b)** Yes; $\left(-\dfrac{3}{2}, 0\right)$,

10. a) $C(0)$ equals fixed costs. **b)** Marginal cost is maximized. **11. a)** concave upward: $(100, \infty)$; concave downward: $(0, 100)$ **b)** $(100, 200)$ **12. a)** minimum 12; maximum 10 012 **b)** Answers will vary.

14. a) increases: $(-\infty, -2), \left(-\dfrac{2}{3}, \infty\right)$; decreases:

$\left(-2, -\dfrac{2}{3}\right)$ **b)** maximum 0 at $x = -2$; minimum $-\dfrac{2}{3}\sqrt[3]{4}$ at

$x = -\dfrac{2}{3}$ **c)** concave upward: $(-\infty, -2), (-2, 0)$; concave downward: $(0, \infty)$ **d)** $(0, 0)$ **15. a)** Answers will vary. **b)** Not possible. **c)–f)** Answers will vary.
16. a) ii) no extrema **iii)** $(0, 0)$ **b) ii)** maximum: $(-1, 0)$; minima: $(-0.539, -0.00025), (2.634, 321.764), (16.905, 41.861)$ **iii)** $(-0.8, -0.00011), (-0.287, -0.00013), (0, 0)$ **17.** No. **18.** $c = -12$, $d = 127$ **19.** Graphs will vary.

a) If $c > 0$, there is one maximum and two minima; if $c \le 0$, there is only one maximum. **20.** Graphs will vary.
21. Graphs will vary.
22. a) maxima at $(0, 0)$, $\left(\dfrac{1}{2}, 0\right)$; minima at

$(0.2298, -0.0119), (0.8702, -0.0539)$; points of inflection: $(0.0913, -0.00506), (0.3712, -0.00575), (0.7375, -0.0322)$ **b)** No. **c)** Answers will vary. For example, $x \in [-0.1, 1.1], y \in [-0.1, 0.1]$

Section 6.4, pp. 347–349

Practise

1. a) $x = -8, x = -5, x = -1, x = 4, x = 9$ **b) i)** ∞ **ii)** ∞ **iii)** $-\infty$
iv) $-\infty$ **v)** ∞ **vi)** ∞ **vii)** $-\infty$ **viii)** $-\infty$ **c) i)** ∞ **ii)** $-\infty$ **iii)** ∞ **iv)** $-\infty$

2. Answers will vary. For example, **a)** $f(x) = \dfrac{1}{x+3}$

b) $f(x) = \dfrac{1}{(x+2)(x-3)}$ **c)** $f(x) = \dfrac{1}{|x^2 - 25|}$ **3. a)** ∞ **b)** $-\infty$

c) $-\infty$ **d)** $-\infty$ **e)** ∞ **f)** $-\infty$ **4. a)** $-\infty$ **b)** ∞ **c)** ∞ **d)** $-\infty$ **e)** ∞ **f)** $-\infty$
g) Not possible; different on the two sides.
h) Not possible; different on the two sides.
i) Not possible; different on the two sides.
5. a) $x = 2$ **b)** $x = -2$ **c)** $x = 3$ **d)** $x = -4$ **e)** $x = 1, x = -1$
f) $x = 1, x = -1$ **g)** $x = -2, x = -4$ **h)** $x = 0, x = -2$
i) $x = 0, x = 3$ **j)** $x = 0, x = 2, x = -2$ **6.** Graphs will vary.

Apply, Solve, Communicate

7. a) \$1000; \$5000 **b)** ∞ **c)** No. **d)** No. **8.** ∞; $-\infty$
9. a) ∞ **b)** Answers will vary. **c)** Answers will vary.
10. $|x| < 0.01$ **11.** $-\infty$ **12. a)** It increases without bound.
b) If the particle reaches a speed equal to or greater than the speed of light, the mass of the particle will be undefined. **13. a)** $\lim\limits_{x \to a^-} f(x) = \infty$ if n is even and

$p(a) > 0$ or n is odd and $p(a) < 0$; $\lim\limits_{x \to a^-} f(x) = -\infty$ if n is

odd and $p(a) > 0$ or n is even and $p(a) < 0$
b) $\lim\limits_{x \to a^+} f(x) = \infty$ if $p(a) > 0$; $\lim\limits_{x \to a^+} f(x) = -\infty$ if $p(a) < 0$

14. a) No numerical value; operation has no meaning.
b) Answers will vary.

Section 6.5, pp. 359–361

Practise

1. a) horizontal asymptotes: $y = 2$ on the left, $y = -1$ on the right; vertical asymptotes: $x = -1, x = 4$ **b)** horizontal asymptotes: $y = 2$ on the left, $y = -2$ on the right; vertical asymptotes: $x = -4, x = 4$ **2. a)** No **b)** Yes; $y = 3 - x$
c) Yes; $y = 3x - 2$ **d)** No **e)** Yes; $y = x - 2$ **f)** No

3. a) 0 **b)** 0 **c)** 0 **d)** 0 **e)** 0 **f)** 3 **g)** 3 **h)** $-\dfrac{1}{2}$ **i)** 0 **4. a)** 1 **b)** 1

c) $\dfrac{1}{2}$ **d)** 5 **e)** 0 **f)** 0

Apply, Solve, Communicate

5. a) $y = -2$ **b)** $y = 0$ **c)** $y = -4$ **d)** $y = 1$ **e)** $y = 1$ **f)** $y = -2$

6. a) $y = 3x - 4$ **b)** $y = x$ **c)** $y = 2x + 2$ **d)** $y = 2x + \dfrac{4}{3}$

e) $y = x + 5$ **f)** $y = -x$

7. a) vertical asymptote: $x = 1$; horizontal asymptote: $g = 0$
b) vertical asymptote: $x = -2$; horizontal asymptote: $y = 3$
c) vertical asymptote: $x = -1$; horizontal asymptote: $y = 1$
d) vertical asymptote: $r = \dfrac{7}{2}$; horizontal asymptote: $v = 3$
e) vertical asymptote: $x = 1$; horizontal asymptote: $y = -3$
f) vertical asymptote: $t = \dfrac{1}{3}$; horizontal asymptote: $g = -3$

8. a) $y = 2x + 3$ **b)** $g = -2x$ **c)** $y = x$ **d)** $y = x + 4$ **e)** $s = 2 - t$
f) $y = x + 6$ **9. a) i)** \$4777.78 **ii)** \$3875 **iii)** \$3530.61
iv) \$3065.04 **b)** maximum at $t = 0$ **c)** \$3000 **d)** No. **e)** No.

10. a) ∞ **b)** 0 (after about 20 years) **11. a)** $c(x) = \dfrac{600}{x}$, $x \le 40$;
$c(x) = \dfrac{20x - 200}{x}$, $x > 40$ **b)** 20 **d)** No.

12. a) $A(x) = \dfrac{100 + 1200x}{x}$ **b)** New formula **c)** 1200 **d)** $-\infty$; no

e) yes **13.** $y = 2$ on the right, $y = -2$ on the left **14. a)** 1 **b)** $\dfrac{3}{2}$

15. a) $y = x^2$ **c) i)** $5x^2 - 5$ **ii)** $3x^2 - 5x + 5$ **d)** $k \ge 0$
16. a) 0.05 **b)** 0.0498

Section 6.6, pp. 370–374

Practise

1. a) vi **b)** viii **c)** iii **d)** ix **e)** v **f)** xi **g)** iv **h)** i **i)** x **j)** ii **k)** vii **l)** xii

Apply, Solve, Communicate

3. a) no extrema; point of inflection: $(0, 0)$
b) maximum: $(-6, 324)$; minimum: $(1, -19)$;
point of inflection: $\left(-\dfrac{5}{2}, \dfrac{305}{2}\right)$ **c)** no maximum;
minimum: $(0, -64)$; points of inflection: $(-2, 0)$, $(2, 0)$,
$\left(-\dfrac{2}{\sqrt{5}}, -\dfrac{4096}{125}\right)$, $\left(\dfrac{2}{\sqrt{5}}, -\dfrac{4096}{125}\right)$ **d)** maximum: $(-1, 2)$;
minimum: $(1, -2)$; points of inflection: $\left(-\dfrac{1}{\sqrt{2}}, \dfrac{7}{4\sqrt{2}}\right)$,
$(0, 0)$, $\left(\dfrac{1}{\sqrt{2}}, -\dfrac{7}{4\sqrt{2}}\right)$ **e)** maximum: $(0, 2)$;
minima: $(-1, -3)$, $(2, -30)$; points of inflection:
$\left(\dfrac{1 + \sqrt{7}}{3}, \dfrac{-230 - 80\sqrt{7}}{27}\right)$, $\left(\dfrac{1 - \sqrt{7}}{3}, \dfrac{-230 + 80\sqrt{7}}{27}\right)$
f) maximum: $(5, 27)$; minimum: $(1, -5)$; point of
inflection: $(3, 11)$ **4. a)** x-intercept: 2; y-intercept: -1,
no extrema; no points of inflection; asymptotes: $x = -2$,
$y = 1$ **b)** no x-intercept; y-intercept: 2; maximum: $(0, 2)$;

points of inflection: $\left(2, \dfrac{3}{2}\right)$, $\left(-2, \dfrac{3}{2}\right)$; asymptote $y = 0$;
even **c)** x-intercepts: ± 1; y-intercept: -1; minimum:
$(0, -1)$; points of inflection: $\left(\pm \dfrac{1}{\sqrt{3}}, -\dfrac{1}{2}\right)$; asymptote:
$y = 1$; even **d)** x-intercept: 0; y-intercept: 0; no extrema;
point of inflection $(0, 0)$; asymptotes: $x = \pm 2$, $y = 0$; odd

e) x-intercept: 0; y-intercept: 0; maximum: $\left(1, \dfrac{3}{2}\right)$;
minimum: $\left(-1, -\dfrac{3}{2}\right)$; points of inflections: $(0, 0)$,
$\left(\sqrt{3}, \dfrac{3\sqrt{3}}{4}\right)$, $\left(-\sqrt{3}, -\dfrac{3\sqrt{3}}{4}\right)$; asymptote: $y = 0$; odd
f) x-intercept: 0; y-intercept: 0; maximum: $(0, 0)$; no
points of inflection; asymptotes: $x = \pm 1$, $y = 2$; even
g) x-intercept: 0; y-intercept: 0; minimum: $(-1, -1)$;
point of inflection: $\left(-2, -\dfrac{8}{9}\right)$; asymptotes: $x = 1$, $y = 0$

h) no intercepts; maximum: $\left(-\dfrac{1}{\sqrt{3}}, -\dfrac{9\sqrt{3}}{2}\right)$; minimum:
$\left(\dfrac{1}{\sqrt{3}}, \dfrac{9\sqrt{3}}{2}\right)$; no points of inflection; asymptotes: $x = 0$,
$x = \pm 1$, $y = 0$; odd **i)** x-intercepts: ± 1; no y-intercept;
maximum $\left(\sqrt{3}, \dfrac{2}{3\sqrt{3}}\right)$; minimum: $\left(-\sqrt{3}, -\dfrac{2}{3\sqrt{3}}\right)$; points
of inflection: $\left(\sqrt{6}, \dfrac{5}{6\sqrt{6}}\right)$, $\left(-\sqrt{6}, -\dfrac{5}{6\sqrt{6}}\right)$; asymptotes:
$x = 0$, $y = 0$; odd **5. a)** asymptotes: $x = 0$, $y = x$;
no extrema **b)** asymptotes: $x = 1$, $y = 2x + 2$;
maximum: $\left(1 - \dfrac{1}{\sqrt{2}}, 4 - 2\sqrt{2}\right)$; minimum:
$\left(1 + \dfrac{1}{\sqrt{2}}, 4 + 2\sqrt{2}\right)$ **c)** asymptotes: $x = \pm 1$, $y = 2x + 1$;
maxima: $\left(-\dfrac{\sqrt{5 + \sqrt{17}}}{2}, -3.2\right)$, $\left(\dfrac{\sqrt{5 - \sqrt{17}}}{2}, 1.3\right)$;
minima: $\left(-\dfrac{\sqrt{5 - \sqrt{17}}}{2}, 0.7\right)$, $\left(\dfrac{\sqrt{5 + \sqrt{17}}}{2}, 6.2\right)$
d) asymptotes: $x = 0$, $y = x$; maximum: $(-2, -4)$;
minimum: $(2, 4)$ **e)** asymptotes: $x = 0$, $y = x - 2$;
no extrema **f)** asymptotes $t = \pm 1$, $h = t$; maximum:
$\left(-\sqrt{3}, -\dfrac{3}{2}\sqrt{3}\right)$; minimum: $\left(\sqrt{3}, \dfrac{3}{2}\sqrt{3}\right)$
g) asymptotes: $x = 0$, $y = -2x + 6$; minimum: $(-2, 13.5)$
h) asymptotes: $x = -2$, $y = x - 2$; maximum: $(-4, 8)$;
minimum: $(0, 0)$ **8. b)** $x = 0$, $x = 4$ **c)** $x = 2$ **10. a)** concave
downward: $(-\infty, -1.846)$, $(0.256, 1.590)$; concave
upward: $(-1.846, 0.256)$, $(1.590, \infty)$; points of inflection:
$(-1.846, 268.0)$, $(0.256, 1.296)$, $(1.590, -44.30)$

b) concave downward: $(-1.673, 0.203)$, $(1.470, \infty)$; concave upward: $(-\infty, -1.673)$, $(0.203, 1.470)$; points of inflection: $(-1.673, -303.756)$, $(0.203, 21.959)$, $(1.470, 188.047)$ **11. a)** minima: $(0, 0)$, $(6, 144)$ **b)** minimum: $(-0.79, 14.24)$; maximum: $(0.91, 0.28)$ **13. a)** asymptotes: $x = 0$, $y = x$; x-intercept $= 1$ (double)

b) $y = x + \dfrac{(k-3)x^2 + (2-2k)x + k}{x^3}$ **c)** $k \geq -1$ **d)** $k = 1, -3$

14. a) $x = 0$ **b)** g is concave upward for all x.

15. $f(x) = \dfrac{6}{125}x^3 + \dfrac{9}{125}x^2 - \dfrac{108}{125}x + \dfrac{132}{125}$

17. a) i) $p > \dfrac{2\sqrt{6}}{3}$ or $p < -\dfrac{2\sqrt{6}}{3}$ **ii)** $p = \dfrac{2\sqrt{6}}{3}$ or $-\dfrac{2\sqrt{6}}{3}$

iii) $-\dfrac{2\sqrt{6}}{3} < p < \dfrac{2\sqrt{6}}{3}$ **b)** Sketches will vary.

18. b) $\left(-\dfrac{b}{3a},\ d + \dfrac{2b^3}{27a^2} - \dfrac{bc}{3a} \right)$

c) $X = x + \dfrac{b}{3a}$; $Y = y - \left(d + \dfrac{2b^3}{27a^2} - \dfrac{bc}{3a} \right)$

d) $F(X) = aX^3 + \left(c - \dfrac{b^2}{3a} \right)X$ **e)** $y = F(X)$ is an odd function.

f) All cubic functions have odd symmetry with respect to their point of inflection. **19.** Every quadratic function has even symmetry with respect to its vertex. **20.** Answers will vary.

Section 6.7, pp. 382–387

Practise

1. $10\sqrt{10}$ **2.** 750 **3.** 15

Apply, Solve, Communicate

4. $4 \text{ m} \times 4 \text{ m}$ **5.** $20 \text{ m} \times 10 \text{ m}$

6. $4\sqrt{2} \text{ m} \times 4\sqrt{2} \text{ m}$ **7. a)** $\dfrac{25}{8} \text{ m} \times \dfrac{10}{3} \text{ m}$ **b)** $\dfrac{25}{9} \text{ m} \times \dfrac{25}{7} \text{ m}$

c) Area of each pen is greater in a). **8. a)** 1 m from each edge **b)** Answers will vary. **9. a)** $\sqrt{1365} \text{ cm} \times \sqrt{\dfrac{780}{7}} \text{ cm}$

b) no **10. a)** $2\sqrt{3} \text{ m} \times 2\sqrt{3} \text{ m}$ **b)** equilateral triangle with base $4\sqrt[4]{3} \text{ m}$ **c)** base: $4\sqrt{\dfrac{6}{4+\pi}}$; height of straight sides:

$\sqrt{\dfrac{3(4+\pi)}{2}} - \dfrac{\pi}{2}\sqrt{\dfrac{6}{4+\pi}}$ **d)** base: $4\sqrt{\dfrac{3}{6-\sqrt{3}}}$; height of

straight sides: $\sqrt{3(6-\sqrt{3})} - \dfrac{3}{\sqrt{6-\sqrt{3}}}$

11. a) $10 \text{ cm} \times 10 \text{ cm} \times 10 \text{ cm}$ **b)** Answers will vary.

12. $V \doteq 0.132 \text{ m}^3$; $\left(\dfrac{4+\sqrt{7}}{6} \right) \text{m} \times \left(\dfrac{1+\sqrt{7}}{6} \right) \text{m} \times \left(\dfrac{5-\sqrt{7}}{12} \right) \text{m}$

13. $\left(\dfrac{4+\sqrt{7}}{6} \right) \text{m} \times \left(\dfrac{1+\sqrt{7}}{3} \right) \text{m} \times \left(\dfrac{5-\sqrt{7}}{6} \right) \text{m}$

14. $1 \text{ m} \times \dfrac{1}{2} \text{ m} \times \dfrac{1}{2} \text{ m}$ **15.** cylindrical can

16. triangle sides: $4\sqrt[3]{25} \text{ cm}$; length: $\dfrac{4\sqrt[3]{25}}{\sqrt{3}} \text{ cm}$ **17.** four

pieces of length $\dfrac{1}{3} \text{ m}$; two pieces of length $\dfrac{4}{3} \text{ m}$

18. radius: $\dfrac{10}{\sqrt[3]{\pi}} \text{ cm}$; height: $\dfrac{10}{\sqrt[3]{\pi}} \text{ cm}$; no **19.** $30\sqrt{2} \text{ cm}$

20. $\sqrt{2} \text{ m} \times \dfrac{1}{\sqrt{2}} \text{ m}$ **21.** $10\sqrt{2} \text{ m}$ (North–South) $\times 3\sqrt{2} \text{ m}$

(East–West) **22. a)** $\dfrac{2187}{512}$ **b)** $\dfrac{27c^4}{256k^3}$ **23.** $\left(-\dfrac{6}{5}, \dfrac{3}{5} \right)$ **24.** 576,

after 24 h **25.** 99 **26.** 9.2 km from B **27.** $\sqrt[4]{30}$ m/s

28. $\dfrac{100}{1+\sqrt[3]{3}}$ m from the quieter band **29.** 0.077 m

30. 41.42% of the distance between planets, from the smaller planet **31.** $2k$

32. a) $I(x) = S\left(\dfrac{1}{x^2 + k^2} + \dfrac{1}{(20-x)^2 + k^2} \right)$

d) $10\sqrt{3}$ **33.** 7.27 m **34.** If $k \leq 2$, closest points are

$\left(\pm\dfrac{1}{\sqrt{2}}, \dfrac{1}{2} \right)$; if $k > 2$, closest point is right end point;

if $k < 1$, most distant point is right endpoint; if $k > 1$, most distant is $(0, 0)$; if $k = 1$, endpoints are both 1

unit away. **35. a)** height: $\dfrac{2k}{\sqrt{3}}$; radius: $\sqrt{\dfrac{2}{3}}k$ **b)** height: $\dfrac{1}{3}k$;

radius: $\dfrac{2}{3}k$ **36.** $\dfrac{2\pi r^3}{9\sqrt{3}}$ **37. a)** $Q(c) > 0$ (any type) or

$Q(c) = 0$ (minimum). **b)** Critical numbers of $P(x)$, if any, are y coordinates of critical numbers of $Q(x)$ or else are not in the range of $Q(x)$. **c)** $P'(Q(x)) > 0$ in any open interval containing a critical number of $Q(x)$

38. a) Yes; if the kick is straight, by 0.6 m **b)** 0.5846 m **39. a)** Answers will vary.

Section 6.8, pp. 392–394

Practise

1. a) 46 **b)** 250 **c)** 208 **d)** 15 **e)** 2

Apply, Solve, Communicate

2. a) x-value with longest vertical line segment from $R(x)$ down to $C(x)$ **d)** More production will earn more profit **3. a)** $C(x) = 0.0168x^2 + 302x + 70\,900$ **b)** \$1\,130\,000

c) \$2\,910\,000 **d)** 50\,000 **e)** 13\,000 **4.** 80 m **5. a)** $1090 - 2x$

b) \$545 **c)** 35.9% **6.** \$52.50 **7.** 37 or 38 **8. a)** \$1.85

b) \$2.21 **9.** 57.4 km/h **10.** \$200.50 **11.** 40th day; 100 t

12. a) 159.6 m from B **b)** Answers will vary.

13. Worst: 7 months; Best: 24 months **14.** 183

15. $20\sqrt{15} \text{ m} \times \dfrac{50\sqrt{15}}{3} \text{ m}$ **16.** 63 **17. b)** 10\,000 units

1. After 11.96 km. **2.** Road distance is 2 km less.
3. 18.44 km/h; 15.95 km/h

Review of Key Concepts, pp. 399–402

1. a) increase: $\left(-\infty, \frac{1}{2}\right)$; decrease: $\left(\frac{1}{2}, \infty\right)$

b) increase: $(-\infty, \infty)$ **c)** increase: $\left(-\infty, -\frac{2}{\sqrt{3}}\right), \left(\frac{2}{\sqrt{3}}, \infty\right)$;

decrease: $\left(-\frac{2}{\sqrt{3}}, \frac{2}{\sqrt{3}}\right)$ **d)** increase: $(0, \infty)$;
decrease: $(-\infty, 0)$ **e)** increase $(-\infty, -3), (-1, \infty)$;
decrease $(-3, -1)$ **f)** increase: $(-1, 0), (4, \infty)$;
decrease: $(-\infty, -1), (0, 4)$ **2.** increase: $(0, 2)$;
decrease: $(2, 4.05)$ **3. a)** absolute maximum: 21;
absolute minimum: 3 **b)** absolute maximum: −15;
absolute minimum: −79 **c)** absolute maximum: 28;
absolute minimum: −4 **d)** absolute maximum: 5; absolute
minimum: −58 **4. a) i)** absolute maximum: 9; absolute
minimum: −5 **ii)** local maximum: 1.5; local minima: −5,
−0.2 **b) i)** absolute maximum: 1000; absolute minimum:
−2550 **ii)** local maximum: about 600; local minima: −1850,
−2550 **5.** 50 **6. a) i)** concave upward: $(-2, 1), (5, \infty)$;
concave downward: $(-\infty, -6), (-6, -2), (1, 5)$ **ii)** $(-2, 0)$,
$(1, 0), (5, 1)$ **b) i)** concave upward: $(0, 6), (8, \infty)$; concave
downward: $(-\infty, 0), (6, 8)$ **ii)** $(0, 0), (6, 5), (8, 2)$
7. a) concave upward: none; concave downward: $(-\infty, \infty)$;
points of inflection: none **b)** concave upward: $\left(-\frac{4}{5}, \infty\right)$;

concave downward: $\left(-\infty, -\frac{4}{5}\right)$; points of inflection:

$\left(-\frac{4}{5}, \frac{238}{25}\right)$ **c)** concave upward: $\left(-\infty, \frac{1}{3}\right)$; concave

downward: $\left(\frac{1}{3}, \infty\right)$; points of inflection: $\left(\frac{1}{3}, \frac{470}{27}\right)$

d) concave upward: $\left(-\infty, -\frac{1}{2}\right), (1, \infty)$; concave downward:

$\left(-\frac{1}{2}, 1\right)$; points of inflection: $\left(-\frac{1}{2}, -\frac{241}{16}\right), (1, -10)$

e) concave upward: $\left(-\infty, \frac{3-\sqrt{3}}{6}\right), \left(\frac{3+\sqrt{3}}{6}, \infty\right)$;

concave downward: $\left(\frac{3-\sqrt{3}}{6}, \frac{3+\sqrt{3}}{6}\right)$; points of

inflection: $\left(\frac{3-\sqrt{3}}{6}, -\frac{71}{36}\right), \left(\frac{3+\sqrt{3}}{6}, -\frac{71}{36}\right)$

f) concave upward: $(-\infty, 5)$; concave downward: $(5, \infty)$;
points of inflection: none **g)** concave upward:

$\left(-\frac{2}{\sqrt{3}}, \frac{2}{\sqrt{3}}\right)$; concave downward: $\left(-\infty, -\frac{2}{\sqrt{3}}\right)$,

$\left(\frac{2}{\sqrt{3}}, \infty\right)$; points of inflection: $\left(\pm\frac{2}{\sqrt{3}}, \frac{1}{4}\right)$

h) concave upward: $(-\infty, -2), (2, \infty)$; concave downward:
$(-2, 2)$; points of inflection: none **i)** concave upward:
$(0, \infty)$; concave downward: $(-\infty, 0)$; points of inflection:
none **8. a)** local maximum: $\frac{4}{27}$; local minimum: 0
b) local maximum: none; local minimum: −5
c) local maximum: none; local minimum: −33
d) local maximum: 0; local minimum: 4
e) local maximum: none; local minimum: 12
f) local maximum: 5; local minimum: −11 (twice)
9. decreasing **10. a)** $x = -2, x = 1, x = 6$ **b) i)** $-\infty$ **ii)** $-\infty$ **iii)** ∞
iv) $-\infty$ **v)** does not exist **vi)** ∞ **vii)** ∞ **viii)** 3 **ix)** 1 **11. a)** ∞ **b)** $-\infty$
c) ∞ **d)** $-\infty$ **e)** ∞ **f)** ∞ **g)** $-\infty$ **h)** $-\infty$ **i)** $-\infty$ **12. a)** $x = -4$,
b) $x = -2, x = -3$ **13. a)** $x = -2, x = 1; y = 2$
b) $x = -1, x = 4; y = 1$ (right), $y = -2$ (left)
14. a) 0 **b)** 0 **c)** −2 **d)** −2 **e)** $-\frac{1}{2}$ **f)** 3 **g)** −5 **h)** ∞
i) ∞ **15. a)** vertical asymptote: $x = 2$; horizontal
asymptote: $y = -4$ **b)** vertical asymptote: $x = -4$;
horizontal asymptote: $y = 1$ **c)** vertical asymptote: $x = 5$,
$x = -3$; horizontal asymptote: $y = 0$

d) vertical asymptote: $x = 1$, $x = \frac{2}{3}$;

horizontal asymptote: $y = 0$ **e)** vertical asymptote:

$x = 3$, $x = -\frac{1}{2}$; horizontal asymptote: $y = 3$

f) vertical asymptote: $x = 1$; horizontal asymptote: $y = 1$
16. a) $y = 3 - 2x$ **b)** $y = x$ **c)** $y = 5x + 8$ **d)** $y = 2x - \frac{2}{3}$
e) $y = x + 4$ **f)** $y = -x$ **17. a)** V.A. $x = 4$, H.A. $y = 1$
b) V.A. $x = 5$, H.A. $y = 1$ **c)** V.A. $x = 0$, O.A. $y = x$
18. \$1.41 **19. a)** x-intercepts: 0, 3; y-intercept: 0;
asymptotes: none; maxima: $(0, 0)$; minima: $(2, -4)$;
points of inflection: $(1, -2)$ **b)** x-intercepts: 0; y-intercept:
0; asymptotes: none; maxima: none; minima: none;
points of inflection: $(-1, -38), (0, 0), (1, 38)$; odd
c) x-intercepts: 0, 1; y-intercept: 0; asymptotes: none;

maxima: $\left(\frac{3}{4}, \frac{27}{256}\right)$; minima: none; points of inflection:

$(0, 0), \left(\frac{1}{2}, \frac{1}{16}\right)$ **d)** x-intercepts: none; y-intercept: 2;
asymptotes: $x = -2, y = 0$; maximum: none; minimum:
none; points of inflection: none **e)** x-intercepts: ±1;
y-intercept: 1; asymptotes: $y = -1$; maximum: $(0, 1)$;

minimum: none; points of inflection: $\left(\pm\frac{1}{\sqrt{3}}, \frac{1}{2}\right)$; even

f) x-intercepts: none; y-intercept: 1; asymptotes: $x = 1$,
$x = -1, y = -1$; maximum: none; minimum: $(0, 1)$; points
of inflection: none; even **g)** x-intercept: 1; y-intercept: −1;
asymptotes: $x = -1, y = 1$; maximum: none; minimum:

none; points of inflection: $\left(0, -1\right), \left(\frac{1}{\sqrt[3]{2}}, -\frac{1}{3}\right)$

h) x-intercepts: none; y-intercept: none; asymptotes:

$x = -1$, $x = 0$, $x = 1$, $y = 0$; maximum: $\left(\dfrac{1}{\sqrt{3}}, -\dfrac{3\sqrt{3}}{2} \right)$;

minimum: $\left(-\dfrac{1}{\sqrt{3}}, \dfrac{3\sqrt{3}}{2} \right)$; points of inflection: none; odd

i) x-intercepts: ± 1; y-intercept: none; asymptotes: $x = 0$,

$y = 0$; maximum: $\left(-\sqrt{3}, \dfrac{2}{3\sqrt{3}} \right)$; minimum: $\left(\sqrt{3}, -\dfrac{2}{3\sqrt{3}} \right)$;

points of inflection: $\left(-\sqrt{6}, \dfrac{5}{6\sqrt{6}} \right)$, $\left(\sqrt{6}, -\dfrac{5}{6\sqrt{6}} \right)$; odd

20. a) increase: $(-\infty, 0)$, $(1, \infty)$; decrease: $(0, 1)$; maximum: $(0, 6)$; minimum: $(1, 5)$; concave upward:

$\left(\dfrac{1}{2}, \infty \right)$; concave downward: $\left(-\infty, \dfrac{1}{2} \right)$; point of

inflection: $\left(\dfrac{1}{2}, \dfrac{11}{2} \right)$ **b)** increase: $\left(0, \dfrac{40}{11} \right)$; decrease:

$(-\infty, 0)$, $\left(\dfrac{40}{11}, \infty \right)$; maximum: $\left(\dfrac{40}{11}, \dfrac{201}{80} \right)$;

minimum: none; concave upward: $\left(\dfrac{60}{11}, \infty \right)$; concave

downward: $(-\infty, 0)$, $\left(0, \dfrac{60}{11} \right)$, point of inflection:

$\left(\dfrac{60}{11}, \dfrac{211}{90} \right)$ **c)** increase: $(-\infty, -1.684)$, $(-0.372, 1)$,

$(1, \infty)$; decrease: $(-1.684, -1)$, $(-1, -0.372)$; maximum: $(-1.684, -2.229)$; minimum: $(-0.372, 0.789)$; concave upward: $(-1, 1)$; concave downward: $(-\infty, -1)$, $(1, \infty)$; points of inflection: none **21.** width: 24 cm; height: 36 cm

22. 2 m × 2 m **23. a)** $2\sqrt[3]{\dfrac{4}{9}}$ m × $\sqrt[3]{\dfrac{3}{2}}$ m × $\sqrt[3]{\dfrac{3}{2}}$ m

b) $\dfrac{20}{3}$ m × 5 m × 5 m **24.** width: 2 m; height: 1.5 m

25. height: $\dfrac{5}{3}$ cm; width of base: $\dfrac{2\sqrt{5}}{3}$ cm **26. a)** 0.0235%

b) 0.05% after 2 h **27.** 12.27 km from the factory emitting the larger amount **28. a)** 14.7 **b)** 86.4 **29.** \$900 **30.** \$3.56

Chapter Test, pp. 403–404

1. a) $-\infty$ **b)** ∞ **c)** 2 **d)** ∞ **2. a)** $x = -3.5$, $y = -2$ **b)** $x = 2$, $x = -2$, $y = x$ **3. a)** concave upward: $(2, \infty)$; concave

downward: $(-\infty, -1)$, $(-1, 2)$ **b)** $\left(2, \dfrac{2}{9} \right)$ **4. a)** increase:

$(1, 2)$; decrease: $(-\infty, 1)$, $(2, \infty)$ **b)** maximum: -2;

minimum: -3 **c)** concave upward: $\left(-\infty, \dfrac{3}{2} \right)$; concave

downward: $\left(\dfrac{3}{2}, \infty \right)$ **d)** $\left(\dfrac{3}{2}, -\dfrac{5}{2} \right)$ **5.** critical numbers: 1, 3; absolute maximum: 12.125; absolute minimum: 2 **6.** critical numbers: 1 gives minimum at $(1, 2)$, -1 gives

maximum at $(-1, -2)$ **7.** x-intercept: 0; y-intercept 0; asymptotes: $x = 3$, $x = -3$, $y = 0$; no extrema; point of inflection: $(0, 0)$; odd function

8. $20\sqrt{2}$ cm × $20\sqrt{2}$ cm × $10\sqrt{2}$ cm **9. a)** 10 m from the point opposite the nearer cottage

10. a) \$3.25 **b)** $183\dfrac{1}{3}$ dozen **11.** $l = 16\sqrt{3}$ cm, $w = 16\sqrt{6}$ cm

12. $5\sqrt{6}$ m by $\dfrac{10\sqrt{6}}{3}$ m **13. a)** 1.41 h **b)** 0.0249 mg/cm³

14. 18 000 **15.** 64

Challenge Problems, p. 405

1. 54 **4.** $\dfrac{1}{\sqrt[3]{4r}}$ **5. a)** $a = 0$, $b = -3$

b) $f(x) = \dfrac{1}{4}x^3 - \dfrac{3}{2}x^2 + \dfrac{9}{4}x$ **8. a)** $k\sqrt{2} \times k\sqrt{2}$

b) $\dfrac{k}{2}$ (along the side of the triangle) × $\dfrac{k\sqrt{3}}{4}$

c) $h = \dfrac{2k}{\sqrt{3}}$; $r = \dfrac{\sqrt{2}k}{\sqrt{3}}$ **9.** 1:1 **10.** Front: $100\sqrt{\dfrac{30}{19}}$ m;

side: $50\sqrt{\dfrac{95}{6}}$ m **11. a)** For $c = 0$, stationary point of inflection at $(0, 0)$. For $c > 0$, only intercept at $(0, 0)$; as c increases, slope at origin increases. For $c < 0$, x-intercepts at $-\sqrt{-c}$, 0, $\sqrt{-c}$; spreads and gets larger at maximum, smaller at minimum as $|c|$ increases **b)** x-intercepts: $-c$, 0; for $c > 0$, minimum at $(0, 0)$ and maximum at

$\left(-\dfrac{2}{3}c, \dfrac{4}{27}c^3 \right)$; for $c < 0$, minimum at $\left(-\dfrac{2}{3}c, \dfrac{4}{27}c^3 \right)$

and maximum at $(0, 0)$ **c)** x-intercepts: $-c$, 0; for $c = 0$, minimum at $(0, 0)$; for $c \neq 0$, stationary point of inflection at $(0, 0)$, other point of inflection at

$\left(-\dfrac{1}{2}c, -\dfrac{1}{16}c^4 \right)$; minimum at $\left(-\dfrac{3}{4}c, -\dfrac{27}{256}c^4 \right)$

d) x-intercepts: 0, $\pm c$; domain: $-c \leq x \leq c$; minimum at

$(0, 0)$; maximum at $\left(\pm\sqrt{\dfrac{2}{3}}c, \dfrac{2c^3}{3\sqrt{3}} \right)$ **e)** x-intercept: 0;

asymptote: $y = 0$; for $c > 0$, minimum at $\left(-\dfrac{1}{c}, -\dfrac{1}{2} \right)$ and

maximum at $\left(\dfrac{1}{c}, \dfrac{1}{2} \right)$; for $c < 0$, minimum at $\left(\dfrac{1}{c}, \dfrac{1}{2} \right)$

and maximum at $\left(-\dfrac{1}{c}, -\dfrac{1}{2} \right)$; points of inflection: $(0, 0)$,

$\left(\dfrac{\sqrt{3}}{c}, \dfrac{\sqrt{3}}{4} \right)$, $\left(-\dfrac{\sqrt{3}}{c}, -\dfrac{\sqrt{3}}{4} \right)$ **f)** x-intercept: 0; asymptote:

$y = \dfrac{1}{c}$; minimum at $(0, 0)$ if $c > 0$; maximum at $(0, 0)$ if

$c < 0$; points of inflection at $\left(\pm\dfrac{1}{\sqrt{3c}}, \dfrac{1}{4c} \right)$

Problem Solving Strategy: Solving Fermi Problems, pp. 406–407

Practise

1.–11. Answers will vary.

Problem Solving: Using the Strategies, pp. 408–409

1. e) 65 **g)** 15 **h)** 34 **3.** Start both timers. When 5-min timer is done, start cooking; use 4 min left in 9-min timer, and then restart 9-min timer. When it is done, you are done. **4.** $\left(1 - \dfrac{\pi}{4}\right)a^2$ **5.** Using standard notation: place queens at a2, b4, c6, d8, e3, f1, g7, h5. Other solutions are possible, including reflections and rotations. **6.** $h = \dfrac{P}{2} - \dfrac{2A}{P}$ **8.** one: 511, two: 112, three: 32 **9.** 128π cm^3 **10.** 5^{5x+5} **11.** 12 **13.** Four ways.

14.–20. Answers will vary.

Chapter 7

Review of Prerequisite Skills, pp. 412–413

1. a) 25 **b)** 0.125 **c)** -3 **d)** $\dfrac{17}{16}$ **e)** 25 **f)** 1024 **2. a)** 2^6 **b)** 12^0

c) $3^{0.5}$ **d)** 4^{-3} **3. a)** $9x^8y^4$ **b)** fgh^2 **c)** $\dfrac{(x+y)^2}{xy}$ **d)** $m^{-8}n^{-4}$

e) $\dfrac{3c^{\frac{3}{2}}d^{\frac{3}{2}}t^{\frac{8}{3}}}{s^2}$ **f)** $3a^8b^4$ **4. a)** vertical stretch of factor 2

b) horizontal compression of factor $\dfrac{1}{3}$ **c)** reflection in the x-axis **d)** vertical stretch of factor 4, vertical translation 2 units up **e)** horizontal compression of factor $\dfrac{1}{4}$, reflection in the y-axis, vertical translation 1 unit up **f)** vertical compression of factor 0.5, vertical translation 7 units down, reflection in the y-axis **g)** horizontal stretch of factor 3, vertical translation 0.25 units up **h)** vertical stretch of factor 7, reflection in the x-axis, vertical translation 3 units up **6. a)** interest: $143.24; amount: $443.24 **b)** interest: $774.89; amount: 7774.89 **c)** interest: $1889.43; amount: $5889.43 **d)** interest: $1290.63; amount: $4190.63 **e)** interest: $830.71; amount: $10 830.71 **f)** interest: $629.66; amount: $2229.66

7. a) i) $y = \pm\sqrt{x}$ **ii)** $y = \dfrac{x - 3}{2}$ **iii)** $y = \sqrt[3]{x}$ **b)** The inverse in part **i)** is not a function; for $x > 0$, there are two values of y for each value of x. The relations in parts **ii)** and **iii)** are functions. **8. a)** ∞ **b)** ∞ **c)** ∞ **d)** 3 **e)** $\dfrac{4}{3}$ **f)** $-\infty$

10. a) ± 1 **b)** -1, 2 **c)** ± 1, ± 2 **d)** ± 1, ± 2 **11.** 14 days **12.** 10 **13. a)** Dilip **b)** Sara **14. a)** $0.03, $0.07, $0.15, $0.31 **b)** 27 **c)** 37 **d)** 47 **e)** 57 **f)** 32

Section 7.1, pp. 419–421

Practise

1. a) All pass through $(0, 1)$ and have the x-axis as an asymptote on the left. $y = 9^x$ gets close to the x-axis on the left more quickly than $y = 2^x$, and goes up more sharply on the right. $y = 6^x$ is between the two.
b) All pass through $(0, 1)$ and have the x-axis as an asymptote on the right. $y = \left(\dfrac{1}{9}\right)^x$ gets close to the x-axis on the right more quickly than $y = \left(\dfrac{1}{2}\right)^x$, and goes up more sharply on the left. $y = \left(\dfrac{1}{6}\right)^x$ is between the two.

3. b) $g(x)$: vertical compression, factor $\dfrac{1}{3}$, of $f(x)$; $h(x)$: vertical stretch, factor 3, of $f(x)$
d) domain: $x \in$ R; range: $y > 0$ **4. a)** y-intercept: -1; domain: $x \in$ R; range: $y < 0$; asymptote: $y = 0$
b) y-intercept: 9; domain: $x \in$ R; range: $y > 0$; asymptote: $y = 0$ **c)** y-intercept: 4; domain: $x \in$ R; range: $y > 3$; asymptote: $y = 3$ **d)** y-intercept: -2; domain: $x \in$ R; range: $y > -5$; asymptote: $y = -5$ **e)** y-intercept: -1; domain: $x \in$ R; range: $y < 0$; asymptote: $y = 0$ **f)** y-intercept: 4; domain: $x \in$ R; range: $y > 3$; asymptote: $y = 3$

g) y-intercept: $-\dfrac{488}{81}$; domain: $x \in$ R; range: $y < -6$; asymptote: $y = -6$ **h)** y-intercept: $\dfrac{131}{64}$; domain: $x \in$ R; range: $y > 2$; asymptote: $y = 2$ **5. a) i)** 3 **ii)** domain: $x \in$ R; range: $y > 2$ **iii)** $y = 2$ **b) i)** -1 **ii)** domain: $x \in$ R; range: $y < 0$ **iii)** $y = 0$ **c) i)** -7 **ii)** domain: $x \in$ R; range: $y < -5$ **iii)** $y = -5$ **d) i)** 2 **ii)** domain: $x \in$ R; range: $y > 1$ **iii)** $y = 1$ **e) i)** -3 **ii)** domain: $x \in$ R; range: $y < 0$ **iii)** $y = 0$ **f) i)** -5 **ii)** domain: $x \in$ R; range: $y > -7$ **iii)** $y = -7$ **6. a)** 0 **b)** ∞ **c)** 0 **d)** ∞ **e)** 0 **f)** ∞ **g)** 1 **h)** 0 **i)** 1 **j)** 0

Apply, Solve, Communicate

7. 31 m **8. a)** $V = 4000(0.8)^t$; V is the value in dollars, t is the time in years **c)** estimate should be just over $2000 **d)** exact value is $2048 **9. b)** about $38 **c)** between 2024 and 2025 **10. b)** about $3100 **12. a)** 125 000 **b)** 977 **c)** none **d)** Answers will vary. **e)** Answers will vary.
13. a) Graph $y = 2^x$ for $x \geq 0$, then add its reflection in the y-axis. **b)** Graph $y = 2^x$ for $x \leq 0$, then add its reflection in the y-axis. **14. a)** ∞ **b)** ∞ **c)** 0 **d)** 0 **15. a)** $(\sqrt{5})^3$ **b)** $(\sqrt[10]{5})^{14}$

c) $(\sqrt[100]{5})^{141}$ **d)** $(\sqrt[1000]{5})^{1414}$ **e)** $(\sqrt[10\,000]{5})^{14\,142}$ **f)** $5^{\sqrt{2}} = \lim_{x \to \sqrt{2}} 5^x$

Section 7.2, pp. 428–429

Practise

1. The missing entries are: $\log_{10} 100 = 2$; $2^6 = 64$; $\log_2 8 = 3$; $3^2 = 9$; $5^{-2} = \dfrac{1}{25}$; $\log_3 \dfrac{1}{9} = -2$; $7^0 = 1$; $4^{\frac{1}{2}} = 2$;

$\log_4 0.125 = -\dfrac{3}{2}$; $\log_{36} 6 = \dfrac{1}{2}$ **2. a)** 3 **b)** 1 **c)** 0 **d)** 4 **e)** −3

f) $\dfrac{1}{6}$ **g)** 25 **h)** π **3. a)** $y = 2^x$: domain: $x \in \mathrm{R}$, range: $y > 0$;
$y = \log_2 x$: domain: $x > 0$, range: $y \in \mathrm{R}$ **b)** $y = 4^x$:
domain: $x \in \mathrm{R}$, range: $y > 0$; $y = \log_4 x$: domain: $x > 0$,
range: $y \in \mathrm{R}$ **c)** $f(x) = 8^x$: domain: $x \in \mathrm{R}$, range: $y > 0$;
$g(x) = \log_8 x$: domain: $x > 0$, range: $y \in \mathrm{R}$

4. a) $y = \log_3 x$ **b)** $y = 4^x$

5. a) domain: $x > 0$; range: $y \in \mathrm{R}$; asymptote: $x = 0$
b) domain: $x < 0$; range: $y \in \mathrm{R}$; asymptote: $x = 0$
c) domain: $x > 0$; range: $y \in \mathrm{R}$; asymptote: $x = 0$
d) domain: $x > 1$; range: $y \in \mathrm{R}$; asymptote: $x = 1$
e) domain: $x > -2$; range: $y \in \mathrm{R}$; asymptote: $x = -2$
f) domain: $x > -1$; range: $y \in \mathrm{R}$; asymptote: $x = -1$
6. a) $-5 < x < 5$ **b)** $x < 3$ **c)** $x > 1$ **d)** $x > 4$

Apply, Solve, Communicate

7. 15.2 years **8. a)** $A = 1500(1.08)^t$ **i)** 3.74 years
ii) 9.01 years **b)** decreases; about 4.67 years **9.** 26.5 years
old **10. a) i)** about 4.25 years **ii)** about 7.27 years
b) i) 2.47×10^{43}; not realistic **ii)** and **iii)** Answers will vary.
11. a) 5.47 m **b)** 17.0 m **c)** 39.4 m **12.** $I(d) = I_0(0.95)^d$
a) 81.45% **b)** 17.86 m **c)** Answers will vary. **13.** 81 months
14. a) $y = 6 (1.014)^x$ **c)** 7.49 billion **d)** 2049 (50 years)
15. The number of digits in the number.
16. b) When the population has no room to grow.
17. b) 3.4202 **c)** 10^{-7} **18. a)** $x > 1$ **b)** $f^{-1}(x) = 10^{2^x}$
19. a), b), c) inverses are continuous

Section 7.3, pp. 434–435

Practise

1. The missing entries are: $\log_2 12 + \log_2 5$; $\log_4 22$;
$\log_6 k + \log_6 g$; $\log_8 \dfrac{14}{3}$; $2\log_{13} h - \log_{13} f$; $\log_3 \dfrac{\pi}{5}$; $\log_{10} \dfrac{1}{7}$;
$\log_{11} x^8$; $\log_{12} \dfrac{20}{3}$ **2. a)** $\log_4 \sqrt{5}$ **b)** $3\log_6 9$ **c)** $\log_8 \sqrt[5]{18}$

d) $-5\log_2 7$ **e)** $\dfrac{1}{2}\log_6 22$ **f)** $-\dfrac{1}{2}\log_9 13$ **3. a)** $\log_3 600$

b) $\log_4 \dfrac{12}{5}$ **c)** $\log_2 \dfrac{76}{31}$ **d)** $\log \dfrac{\sqrt{17}}{5}$ **e)** $\log [a^3(a + b)]$

f) $\log \dfrac{x + y}{x - y}$ **g)** $\log \dfrac{x^4}{y^3}$ **h)** $\log_3 ab^2c$ **4. a)** $\log_7 5 + \log_7 x$

b) $3\log_2 m + 2\log_2 n$ **c)** $\log_3 a + \log_3 b + \log_3 c$

d) $\dfrac{1}{3} (\log_9 y + \log_9 (y + 1))$ **e)** $\dfrac{1}{4} \log_8 m - \log_8 n$

f) $5(\log_6 x + \log_6 y)$ **g)** $2\log_4 a + \log_4 b - \dfrac{1}{2}\log_4 c$

h) $-\dfrac{1}{2} (\log_3 j + \log_3 k)$ **5. a)** 2 **b)** 3 **c)** 3

d) 2 **e)** 4 **f)** 3 **g)** 1 **h)** 4 **i)** 2 **j)** 81 **6. a)** 1.5440 **b)** 3.7004
c) 1.1292 **d)** 1.5114 **e)** 0.9464 **f)** 1.6309 **g)** 1.4037 **h)** 0.6667

Apply, Solve, Communicate

7. a) $I(d) = 125 \left(10^{-\frac{d}{166.67}}\right)$ **b)** 82.5 m **8. a) i)** −0.421
ii) −0.668 **b)** negative; the cell gains energy.

9. $\log_6 7$ is greater. **10. a)** $A_V = \log_{10} \left(\dfrac{V_o}{V_i}\right)^{20}$ **b)** 4.24 V

11. a) 0.434 **$\mu\theta = \log T_L - \log T_S$** **b)** 0.071 **c)** 82.0 N
16. Since $\log_3 0.1$ is negative, $\log_3 0.1 > 2\log_3 0.1$

Section 7.4, pp. 441–442

Practise

1. No **2. a)** 1 **b)** 0.5 **c)** −1 **d)** 256 **e)** 7 **f)** 1000 **g)** 4 **h)** −1
3. a) i) $x = 2$ **ii)** $x = 3$ **4. a)** 1.2920 **b)** 0.4284 **c)** 2.8074
d) −0.5350 **e)** 0.9679 **f)** −3.8188 **g)** 2 **h)** 1.5979 **5. a)** 5

b) 7 **c)** 8 **d)** $\dfrac{1}{36}$ **e)** $\dfrac{2}{3}$ **f)** 1.7098 **g)** $\sqrt{5}$ **h)** 9 **6. a)** $\dfrac{1}{1000}$

b) $10^{20} + 11$ **c)** $\dfrac{10^{39} + 1}{4}$ **d)** −22 **e)** 4 **f)** 3 **g)** 3 **h)** 2

i) 3 **j)** 5 **7. b)** No. The equation gives $5^x = 4 \Rightarrow x = \log_5 4$,
or $5^x = -5$, which is impossible. **8. a)** $\log_2 3$ **b)** 1
c) $\log_7 2$ **d)** no solution **e)** $\log_6 5$ **f)** no solution

Apply, Solve, Communicate

9. a) 3.5 years **b)** 8.74 years **c)** 11.90 years **d)** 27.62 years
10. a) 22.8 cm **b)** reduces it by the same factor again
11. a) 8.31 years **b)** the same time **12. a)** 12 years 11 months
b) 20 years 6 months **c)** 7 years 7 months **13.** 3.04 s
14. a) 3.65 days **b)** 5.26 items below **15. a)** 140 h **b)** 40 h
c) 20 h **16.** 0.514 km above sea level **17.** From 29.06 kPa
to 101.3 kPa **19. a)** 4096 **b)** 0, 0.1260, 0.2153

Section 7.5, pp. 446–448

Apply, Solve, Communicate

1. a) 7.5 **b)** 7.4 **c)** 7.7 **2.** 3.548×10^{-8} to 4.467×10^{-8}
3. b) 100 **4.** Yes; magnitude 7.3 **5. a)** 4.72 **b)** yes, by a
factor of 2042 **c)** yes, by a factor of 2.63×10^9 **d)** −6.68
6. a) 9140 m **b)** 5539 m **c)** Answers will vary. **7. a)** 33.7 kPa
8. a) 2.68×10^{-6} **b)** 0.373 **c)** 139 000 times **9.** #11
10. b)

$\log d$	$\log t$
1.7634	1.9445
2.0294	2.3522
2.1732	2.5623
2.3560	2.8363
2.8882	3.6364

c) linear **d)** $\log t = 1.5019 \log d - 0.7010$ **e)** $t = 0.1991d^{1.5019}$
f) 10 916 days **11. a)** $(x, y, z,$ and a are numbers in $[0, 1])$
i) $\log(\text{answer}) = 3 + \log 2.469 + 2 + \log 4.91 = 5 + (1 + x)$.

Answer $= 10^6 \times$ antilog(x). **ii)** log (answer) $= \frac{1}{3}$ $(2 +$ log 1.81) $= \frac{1}{3}(2 + y) = z$. Answer $=$ antilog(z). **iii)** log(answer) $= 3 + \log 4.83 - (1 + \log 2.173) = 2 + a$. Answer $= 10^2 \times$ antilog(a).

Practise

1. a) 0 **b)** ∞ **c)** ∞ **d)** 0 **2. a)** $-\dfrac{4}{e^x}$ **b)** $x^5 e^x(6 + x)$ **c)** $\dfrac{e^{\sqrt{x}}}{2\sqrt{x}}$

d) $xe^{-x}(2 - x)$ **e)** $\dfrac{e^x}{x^2}(x - 1)$ **f)** $-\dfrac{e^{-x}(1 + e^{-2x})}{(1 - e^{-2x})^2}$

g) $30e^{3x}(1 + 5e^{3x})$ **h)** $\dfrac{1 - 2xe^{1-x^2}}{2\sqrt{x + e^{1-x^2}}}$ **3. a)** $e^{x \ln 2}$ **b)** $\ln 2 \ (2^x)$

c) $\ln a \ (a^x)$ **4. a)** $y = x + 1$ **b)** $y = -\dfrac{1}{e^2} x + \dfrac{3}{e^2}$

c) $y = -\dfrac{4}{e^{12}} x + \dfrac{13}{e^{12}}$ **d)** $y = 8e^{16}x - 31e^{16}$

e) $y = 6e^8 x - 11e^8$ **f)** $y = 1$ **5.** $\dfrac{1 - ye^{xy}}{xe^{xy} - 1}$ **6. a)** $(0, 0)$, minimum

b) $(1, e)$, minimum **c)** $\left(1, -\dfrac{1}{e}\right)$, minimum **7. a)** increasing

for $x < 0.25$, decreasing for $x > 0.25$ **b)** increasing for

$x > -\dfrac{1}{3}$, decreasing for $x < -\dfrac{1}{3}$ **8. a)** $\left(-1, -\dfrac{1}{e^2}\right)$

b) $(-2 + \sqrt{2}, (6 - 4\sqrt{2})e^{-2+\sqrt{2}}), (-2 - \sqrt{2}, (6 + 4\sqrt{2})e^{-2-\sqrt{2}})$

9. a) domain: $x \in$ R; range: $y \geq (2 - 2\sqrt{2}) \ e^{-1+\sqrt{2}}$; x-intercept: ± 1; y-intercept: -1; no symmetry; asymptote: $y = 0$; increases for $1 - \sqrt{2} < x < 1 + \sqrt{2}$; decreases for $x < 1 - \sqrt{2}, x > 1 + \sqrt{2}$; maximum: $(1 + \sqrt{2}, (2 + 2\sqrt{2})e^{-1-\sqrt{2}})$; minimum: $(1 - \sqrt{2}, (2 - 2\sqrt{2})e^{-1+\sqrt{2}})$; concave up for $x < 2 - \sqrt{3}, x > 2 + \sqrt{3}$; concave down for $2 - \sqrt{3} < x < 2 + \sqrt{3}$; points of inflection: $(2 - \sqrt{3}, (6 - 4\sqrt{3})e^{-2+\sqrt{3}}), (2 + \sqrt{3}, (6 + 4\sqrt{3})e^{-2-\sqrt{3}})$

b) domain: $x \in$ R; range: $y \geq 0$; only intercept at $(0, 0)$; no symmetry; asymptote: $y = 0$; increases for $x < -4, x > 0$; decreases for $-4 < x < 0$; maximum: $\left(-4, \dfrac{256}{e^4}\right)$; minimum: $(0, 0)$; concave up for $x < -6, x > -2$; concave down for $-6 < x < -2$; point of inflection: $\left(-6, \dfrac{1296}{e^6}\right), \left(-2, \dfrac{16}{e^2}\right)$

c) domain: $x \in$ R; range: $y \geq -\dfrac{1}{2e}$; only intercept at $(0, 0)$; no symmetry; asymptote: $y = 0$; increases for $x > -\dfrac{1}{2}$; decreases for $x < -\dfrac{1}{2}$; minimum: $\left(-\dfrac{1}{2}, -\dfrac{1}{2e}\right)$;

concave up for $x > -1$; concave down for $x < -1$; point of inflection: $\left(-1, -\dfrac{1}{e^2}\right)$

d) domain: $x \in$ R; range: $y \in$ R; x-intercept: 0; y-intercept: 0; odd function; no asymptotes; increases for all x; no maximum or minimum values; concave down for $x < 0$; concave up for $x > 0$; point of inflection: $(0, 0)$ **e)** domain: $x \neq 0$; range: $y > 1$; no intercepts; even function; asymptotes: $y = 1, x = 0$; increases for $x < 0$; decreases for $x > 0$; no maximum or minimum values; concave up for all x in the domain; no points of inflection **f)** domain: $x \neq 0$; range: $y > 0$; no intercepts; no symmetry; asymptotes: $x = 0, y = 0$; increases for $x < 0$, $x > 2$; decreases for $0 < x < 2$; minimum: $\left(2, \dfrac{e^2}{4}\right)$; concave up for all x in the domain; no points of inflection **g)** domain: $x \in$ R; range: $0 \leq y \leq \dfrac{1}{e}$; only intercept at $(0, 0)$; even function; asymptote: $y = 0$; increases for $x < -1, 0 < x < 1$; decreases for $-1 < x < 0$, $x > 1$; minimum: $(0, 0)$; maximum: $\left(\pm 1, \dfrac{1}{e}\right)$; concave up for $x < -\dfrac{\sqrt{5 + \sqrt{17}}}{2}, -\dfrac{\sqrt{5 - \sqrt{17}}}{2} < x < \dfrac{\sqrt{5 - \sqrt{17}}}{2},$ $x > \dfrac{\sqrt{5 + \sqrt{17}}}{2}$; concave down for $-\dfrac{\sqrt{5 + \sqrt{17}}}{2} < x < -\dfrac{\sqrt{5 - \sqrt{17}}}{2}, \dfrac{\sqrt{5 - \sqrt{17}}}{2} < x < \dfrac{\sqrt{5 + \sqrt{17}}}{2}$; points of inflection: $\left(-\dfrac{\sqrt{5 + \sqrt{17}}}{2}, \dfrac{5 + \sqrt{17}}{4e^{\frac{5+\sqrt{17}}{4}}}\right), \left(-\dfrac{\sqrt{5 - \sqrt{17}}}{2}, \dfrac{5 - \sqrt{17}}{4e^{\frac{5-\sqrt{17}}{4}}}\right),$ $\left(\dfrac{\sqrt{5 - \sqrt{17}}}{2}, \dfrac{5 - \sqrt{17}}{4e^{\frac{5-\sqrt{17}}{4}}}\right), \left(\dfrac{\sqrt{5 + \sqrt{17}}}{2}, \dfrac{5 + \sqrt{17}}{4e^{\frac{5+\sqrt{17}}{4}}}\right)$

h) domain: $x \neq 0$; range: $y < -1$ or $y > 0$; no intercepts; no symmetry; asymptote: $x = 0, y = 0, y = -1$; increases for all x in the domain; no maximum or minimum points; concave up for $x < 0$; concave down for $x > 0$; no points of inflection **10. a)** $y' = 2e^{2x}, y'' = 4e^{2x},$ $y''' = 8e^{2x}, y^{(iv)} = 16e^{2x}$ **b)** $y^{(n)} = 2^n e^{2x}$ **11. a)** e^k **b)** e^2 **c)** e^{6x}

Apply, Solve, Communicate

12. $y = xe^{-x}$ can be obtained by reflecting $y = xe^x$ in both the x- and y-axes. **13. a)** 250 **b) i)** 17.33 hours **ii)** 27.47 hours **iii)** 109.55 hours **c)** 14.92; 22.26 (bacteria/hour) **14. a)** $P = 400e^{0.018t}$ **b)** 38.51 years; 61.03 years **c)** 8.62; 11.29 (rats/year) **15. a)** $V = 5000e^{-0.11t}$ **b)** 6.3 years; 20.9 years **16. a) i)** 10.245 years **ii)** 16.238 years **b) i)** Her estimate was 0.343 years sooner. **ii)** Her estimate was 0.544 years sooner. **17. a) i)** 10.074 years **ii)** 9.931 years **iii)** 9.903 years

18. a) $v = 20 - 20e^{-0.05t}$, $a = e^{-0.05t}$
b) 411.5 mm, 4.43 mm/s, 0.78 mm/s² **19. a)** $6766.76, $915.78 **b)** –$2706.71/year, –$366.31/year **20. a)** 0.6 A
b) 0.001 A/s **c)** 0.0001 A/s **21. a)** domain: $-10 \le x \le 10$
b) 1.885 m **22. b) i)** 14 years **ii)** 5 years **iii)** 8.75 years
c) i) 14.2 years **ii)** 5.29 years **iii)** 9.01 years

Section 7.7, pp. 469–470

Practise

1. a) $\dfrac{9}{9x-2}$ **b)** $\dfrac{9}{(9x-7)\ln 5}$ **c)** $3^x \ln 3$ **d)** $\dfrac{2x}{(x^2+3)\ln 4}$ **e)** $\dfrac{2}{x}$

f) $-\ln x - 1$ **g)** $x5^x(2 + x \ln 5)$ **h)** $4^x\left(\dfrac{1}{x} + (\ln 4)(\ln x)\right)$

i) $x2^{x^2+1}\ln 2$ **2. a)** $\dfrac{-1}{x(1+\ln x)^2}$ **b)** $\dfrac{x+1}{x(x+\ln x)}$

c) $\dfrac{1}{2x\sqrt{\ln x}}$ **d)** $\dfrac{1}{2x \ln 4}$ **3. a)** $\dfrac{1}{e}$, maximum (when $x = e$)

b) $-\dfrac{1}{e}$, minimum (when $x = \dfrac{1}{e}$) **4. a)** 0, minimum

(when $x = 1$); $\dfrac{4}{e^2}$, maximum (when $x = \dfrac{1}{e^2}$) **b)** $\left(\dfrac{1}{e}, \dfrac{1}{e}\right)$

6. a) $y = x - 1$ **b)** $y = \dfrac{1}{100 \ln 10}x + 2 - \dfrac{1}{\ln 10}$ **c)** $y = 4x - 8$

7. a) $\dfrac{1}{x}, -\dfrac{1}{x^2}, \dfrac{2}{x^3}, -\dfrac{6}{x^4}$ **b)** $y^{(n)} = (-1)^{n-1}\dfrac{(n-1)(n-2)\cdots 1}{x^n}$

Apply, Solve, Communicate

8. a) $P_0 = 200$, $a = \sqrt[3]{4}$ **b)** 1.5 h
c) i) 146.7 bacteria/hour **ii)** 1478.7 bacteria/h
d) No. **9. a)** $P = 1000\,(10^{\frac{t}{2}})$ **b)** 364 071 bacteria/h
10. a) 2 g **b)** 15 h **c)** 0.0734 g/h **12. a)** 58 **b)** 40
13. a) $a'(t) = -180\,(2)^{-t}\,(t \ln 2 - 1)$ **b)** 95.5°, 1.4 s **c)** 13.9°/s
14. a) $s'(t) = -12 \ln 0.8(0.8)^t$; Velocity of the leading edge

of the lava. **b)** 2.1 km/h, 1.1 km/h **c)** $t = \dfrac{\ln\left(2 - \dfrac{s(t)}{12}\right)}{\ln 0.8}$

d) $\dfrac{dt}{ds} = -\dfrac{1}{(24-s)\ln 0.8}$. Rate of change of the time with

respect to distance. **e)** 0.24 h/km **16.** $2 \ln x\,(x^{\ln x - 1})$

Section 7.8, pp. 475–476

Practise

1. a) 3.0855 **b)** 5.6103 **c)** 5.9752 **d)** 6.5620 **e)** 17.3287
f) 3.1965 **g)** 0.1470 **h)** 0.1792

Apply, Solve, Communicate

2. –0.0260 (if t is in minutes) **3.** 0.0555 days
4. a) 8.043 years **b)** 8.008 years **c)** 10.836 years
d) 11.581 years **e)** 8.664 years **f)** 7.296 years

5. a) $N = 1500\left(2^{\frac{t}{8}}\right)$ **b)** 32.471 h **6. a)** 8.795 53%
b) 6.976 61% **7. a)** $T = 1220e^{-0.014t} + 30$ **b)** 9.37 min
c) it would be 0.12 min less **d)** infinitely long; not realistic
8. 20 minutes **9. a)** $N = 700(3^{2t})$, with t in hours
b) 1.4778 h or 88.67 min **10. a)** 147.67 days **b)** There will
never be none left, using this model. **11.** 7.25%, quarterly
is better; the quarterly plan takes only 12.75 years to
accumulate the desired amount, while the continuous
plan requires 13.09 years. **12.** 39.624 years
13. a) 6 301 906; this is not likely **b)** 169 912; possible,
since there is more space in Caledon **14. a)** 64.66°C
b) 8.96 min **15.** 3410 years **16. b)** 14 min **c)** 22 min
d) 40 000 **e)** $y = 1999.93(1.0513^x)$ **f)** $P = 2000e^{0.05t}$

Review of Key Concepts, pp. 478–481

1. a) $y = 5^x$ is steeper on the right and approaches $y = 0$
on the left more quickly. **b)** The graphs are the same as in
part a), but reflected in the y-axis.
2. c) $f(x)$: y-intercept: 1; domain: $x \in R$; range: $y > 0$;
asymptote: $y = 0$; $g(x)$: y-intercept: 1; domain: $x \in R$;
range: $y > 0$; asymptote: $y = 0$; $h(x)$: y-intercept: –1;
domain: $x \in R$; range: $y < 0$; asymptote: $y = 0$
3. a) ii) 3 **iii)** domain: $x \in R$; range: $y > 0$ **iv)** $y = 0$
b) ii) –4 **iii)** domain: $x \in R$; range: $y > -5$ **iv)** $y = -5$
c) ii) 6 **iii)** domain: $x \in R$; range: $y > 2$ **iv)** $y = 2$ **4. a)** 0 **b)** 0
c) 1 **d)** ∞ **5. b)** $3.75 **c)** 2050 (in 49.25 years)
6. The missing entries are: $\log_5 25 = 2$; $3^4 = 81$;
$\log_3 18 = x$; $10^9 = x - 6$ **7. a)** 3 **b)** 0 **8.** $y = 5^x$: domain:
$x \in R$; range: $y > 0$; $y = \log_5 x$: domain: $x > 0$; range:
$y \in R$ **9. a)** $y = 7^x$ **b)** $y = -\log_3 x$ **10. a)** domain: $x > -3$;
range: $y \in R$; asymptote: $x = -3$ **b)** domain: $x > 0$; range:
$y \in R$; asymptote: $x = 0$ **11. a)** $x \ne 0$ **b)** $x > 0$ **c)** $-1 < x < 1$
12. 5.862 years **13. a)** $\log_3 x + \log_3 y$; $x, y > 0$
b) $\log_7 (x - 1) + \log_7 (x + 5)$; $x > 1$ **c)** $\log x - \log 2 - \log y$;
$x, y > 0$ **d)** $2 \log_4 |a| - \log_4 3$; $a \ne 0$ **14. a)** $\log_5 6$
b) $\log (m^5 n^6)$ **c)** $-\log_2 3$ **d)** $\log_7 [(x - 2)(x + 2)^2]$ **15. a)** 2 **b)** 3
c) $\dfrac{1}{2}$ **d)** $\dfrac{2}{3}$ **16. a)** 2.3219 **b)** 0.8451 **c)** 1.8928 **17.** No;

$\log_2 5 > 2$ and $\log_5 2 < 0.5$ **18. a)** $\log\left(\dfrac{k^{\frac{1}{2}} \cdot R^{\frac{3}{2}}}{P}\right) = 0$

b) $\dfrac{k^{\frac{1}{2}} \cdot R^{\frac{3}{2}}}{P} = 10^0$ **c)** $P = k^{\frac{1}{2}} \cdot R^{\frac{3}{2}}$ **19. a)** 8 **b)** 0 **c)** –0.5784
d) 2 **e)** 1 **f)** 8 **20. a)** 5 years, 6 months **b)** 9 years,
5 months **c)** 14 years, 11 months
21. a) $P(x) = 21\,962\,082\,(1.0117)^{x-1971}$

b) 31 133 361 **c)** $x = \dfrac{\log \dfrac{P(x)}{21\,962\,082}}{\log 1.0117} + 1971$

d) 2041 **22. a)** 320 000 **b)** 15.3 h

23. a) $P(t) = P_0\left(1 + \dfrac{r}{100}\right)^t$ **b)** $t = \dfrac{\log\left(\dfrac{P(t)}{P_0}\right)}{\log\left(1 + \dfrac{r}{100}\right)}$

24. a) 0.31 A **b)** $t = -\dfrac{\log\left(1 - \dfrac{I}{0.8}\right)}{0.0434}$ **c)** 9.81 s

25. a) 3.5 **b)** acidic **26.** 100 000 **27.** 251 **28. b)** linear: $\log_2 f = x + \log_2 13.75$ **c)** $f = 13.75(2^x)$ **d)** 3520 Hz

29. a) e^x **b)** $x^2 e^{-x}(3 - x)$ **c)** $xe^x(2 + x)$ **d)** $\dfrac{e^x(x - 1)}{x^2}$ **e)** $2e^{2x}$

f) $\dfrac{e^x(1 + 4e^{-3x})}{(1 + e^{-3x})^2}$ **g)** $-\dfrac{2}{e^x}$ **h)** $-4e^{2x}(1 - e^{2x})$ **i)** $\dfrac{e^{\sqrt{x}+1}}{2\sqrt{x}}$

j) $e^{\sqrt{x}}\left(1 + \dfrac{\sqrt{x}}{2}\right)$ **30.** $y = ex$ **31.** 2.957 km

32. a) maximum: $(0, -1)$; asymptote: $y = x$ **b)** minimum: $(-1, e^{-1})$; asymptotes: $x = -2$, $y = 0$ **33. a)** $P'(t) = -0.2e^{-0.004t}$ **b)** 0.13 W/day **34. a)** $C'(x) = 10 + 75xe^{-x}(x - 2)$ **b)** \$10

c) \$10 **35. a)** $\dfrac{7}{x}$ **b)** $8^x \ln 8$ **c)** $\dfrac{5}{5x + 1}$ **d)** $\dfrac{4}{(4x + 15)\ln 10}$

e) $\dfrac{2^x}{(x - 8)\ln 2} + 2^x \ln(x - 8)$ **f)** $\dfrac{14x}{(7x^2 + 2)\ln 3}$

g) $\dfrac{4^x(x \ln 4 + \ln 4 - 1)}{(1 + x)^2}$ **h)** $-\dfrac{\ln x + 1}{(x \ln x)^2}$

37. a) $y = (5^5 \ln 5)x + 5^5 - 5^6 \ln 5$
b) $y = (27 \ln 3)x + 27 - 81 \ln 3$
c) $y = (-8 \ln 2)x + 8 - 24 \ln 2$
d) $y = (49 \ln 7)x + 49 - 98 \ln 7$
38. 6400 ln 4 bacteria/hour **39.** minimum:

$\left(\dfrac{1}{\sqrt{2}}, \dfrac{1}{2}(1 + \ln 2)\right)$; asymptote: $x = 0$

40. a) 79.6 ppm **b)** 14.5 ppm/h **41. a)** 13.198 years
b) 12.207 years **42. a)** 1966 (33.71 years before 2000)
43. after 19.2 min **44.** 18.177 h **45. a)** $P = 2.3e^{0.026\,57t}$
b) 5.1 billion **46. a)** $P(x) = 100e^{-0.139x}$ **b)** 49.9 kPa
c) 24.9 kPa **47. a)** $I = 2e^{-0.1999x}$ **b)** $I = I_0 e^{-0.1999x}$
c) 36.8% of the light compared to 5 mm.

Chapter Test, pp. 482–483

1. a) They are mirror images in the y-axis.
3. a) ∞ **b)** 0 **c)** 5 **d)** 1.2770 **e)** 2 **f)** 1 **4. a)** 5

b) $\dfrac{1}{2}$ **c)** 0, 1 **d)** 3 **5. a)** $\dfrac{-e^{-x}(x + 1)}{x^2}$

b) $e^x(1 + x)$ **c)** $e^x x^{-6}(x - 5)$ **d)** $\dfrac{5}{x}$ **e)** $\dfrac{8}{(8x + 7)\ln 10}$

f) $\dfrac{1}{(x - 2)\ln 4}$ **6. a)** $y = (16 \ln 4)x + 16 - 32 \ln 4$

b) $y = e^2 x - e^2$ **7.** 4.324 km
8. b) domain: $x > -3$; range: $y \in$ R; asymptote: $x = -3$
9. a) 9.01 years **b)** 8.66 years **10.** 57.03 days **11.** 7.1

12. by a factor of 316 228 **13.** The only significant point is $(2.5, 2.5 \ln 5)$, a point of inflection. **14. a)** point of inflection: $(\ln 2, 2 - (\ln 2)^2)$ **b)** asymptotes: $y = 0$ and $x = 1$;

point of inflection: $\left(e^{-2}, -\dfrac{1}{2}\right)$

15. 2.8 h **17. a)** $C'(x) = \dfrac{1001}{(10x + 1)\sqrt{\ln(10x + 1)}}$

b) \$607.58; \$0.033/L **18. a)** $\dfrac{dM}{dt} = -0.4e^{-0.02t}$

b) −0.362 kg/min **19. a)** 8.3°C **b)** 6.5°C **c)** 2.6 h
20. The asymptote indicates a maximum sustainable population of 50 billion, rather than continued exponential growth.

Challenge Problems, p. 484

1. 1.32 **2.** 0.0493 **3. a)** $y = 2^{|x|}$: domain: $x \in$ R; range: $y \geq 1$; $y = 2^{-|x|}$: domain: $x \in$ R; range: $0 < y \leq 1$
b) $y = e^{|x|}$: domain: $x \in$ R; range: $y \geq 1$; $y = e^{-|x|}$: domain: $x \in$ R; range: $0 < y \leq 1$ **4.** 3.3 h **5.** 6

6. $-\dfrac{1}{\sqrt{2}} < x < \dfrac{1}{\sqrt{2}}$ **7.** quadratic: $f(x) = 1 + x + \dfrac{1}{2}x^2$; cubic:

$f(x) = 1 + x + \dfrac{1}{2}x^2 + \dfrac{1}{6}x^3$ **8. a)** $f_n(x) = 1 + x + \dfrac{1}{2}x^2 + \ldots + \dfrac{1}{n!}x^n$

9. a) $f'_n(x) = \left(1 + \dfrac{x}{n}\right)^{n-1}$

Cumulative Review: Chapters 6 and 7, pp. 485–486

1. a) 20.0 m square including corners **b)** 325.8 m²; 17.3%
2. base: 6.6943 cm²; height of each part: 3.7495 cm **3. a)** 2 m
b) 20 cm **c)** after $\sqrt{3}$ s; $t \in [0, \sqrt{3}]$ **d)** decrease: $[0, 1)$, increase: $(1, \sqrt{3}]$; the yo-yo is falling when the function is decreasing, rising when the function is increasing.
4. a) $x = -3$, $y = 0$ **b)** $x = \pm 1$, $y = 2$ **c)** $x = \dfrac{1}{2}$, $y = -3$

d) $x = -1$, $y = 2x - 3$ **5. a)** minimum: $(6, -432)$; points of inflection: $(0, 0)$, $(4, -256)$ **b)** maximum: $\left(3, \dfrac{1}{6}\right)$;

minimum: $\left(-3, -\dfrac{1}{6}\right)$; points of inflection: $(0, 0)$,

$\left(3\sqrt{3}, \dfrac{\sqrt{3}}{12}\right)$, $\left(-3\sqrt{3}, -\dfrac{\sqrt{3}}{12}\right)$ **7. a)** $p(x) = 36 - 0.004x$

b) 125 **c)** 4500 **9. a)** increase: $(-3, 0)$ or $(0, 3)$; decrease: $(-\infty, -3)$ or $(3, \infty)$ **b)** minimum: $\left(-3, -\dfrac{2}{9}\right)$; maximum:

$\left(3, \dfrac{2}{9}\right)$ **c)** concave up: $(-3\sqrt{2}, 0)$ or $(3\sqrt{2}, \infty)$;

concave down: $(-\infty, -3\sqrt{2})$ or $(0, 3\sqrt{2})$

d) $\left(-3\sqrt{2}, -\dfrac{5\sqrt{2}}{36}\right)$, $\left(3\sqrt{2}, \dfrac{5\sqrt{2}}{36}\right)$ **11. a)** 0 **b)** ∞ **12. a)** 4 **b)** 2

c) 0.6754 **13. a)** 2 **b)** 2 **c)** 6.099 **d)** 1.0986

14. domain: $x > -3$; range: $y \in \mathbb{R}$; asymptote: $x = -3$
15. a) 6 years, 5 months **b)** 11 years, 11 months
16. 8.9 **17. b)** 27 000 times **c)** -64.1 **18. a)** $xe^{-x}(2-x)$
b) $e^{\sqrt{x}}(2+\sqrt{x})$ **c)** $\dfrac{e^{3x}}{x^2}(3x-1)$ **d)** $5e^x$ **e)** $\dfrac{2}{x}$ **f)** $\dfrac{1}{(x+1)\ln 3}$
19. $y = (64\ln 4)x + 64 - 192\ln 4$ **20. a)** 300 **b)** 6 h
21. 23.77 years **22. a)** 123°C **b)** 6.264 min

Chapter 8

Review of Prerequisite Skills, pp. 488–490

1. a) $\sqrt{13}$ **b)** $\sqrt{130}$ **2. a)** An even function is a function f satisfying $f(-x) = f(x)$ for all x in the domain. **b)** i), iii), and iv) are even. **3. a)** An odd function is a function f satisfying $f(-x) = -f(x)$ for all x in the domain. **b)** i), iii), and iv) are odd. **4. a)** 1.5 **b)** 85.944° **5. a)** 0.9863°
b) 2 582 131 km **c)** 107 589 km/h **6.** Answers will vary.
For latitude 45°: **b)** 4525.5 km **c)** 28 434 km
d) 1185 km/h **7. a)** 180° **b)** 90° **c)** 60° **d)** 45° **e)** 30°
f) 57.296° **8. a)** $\dfrac{\pi}{12}$ **b)** $\dfrac{5\pi}{12}$ **c)** $\dfrac{7\pi}{12}$ **d)** $\dfrac{2\pi}{3}$ **e)** $\dfrac{5\pi}{6}$ **f)** $\dfrac{35\pi}{9}$
9. a) $\dfrac{4}{5}, \dfrac{3}{5}, \dfrac{4}{3}$ **b)** $\dfrac{1}{\sqrt{5}}, -\dfrac{2}{\sqrt{5}}, -\dfrac{1}{2}$ **10.** $\sin\theta : \dfrac{1}{2}, \dfrac{1}{\sqrt{2}}, \dfrac{\sqrt{3}}{2}$;
$\cos\theta : \dfrac{\sqrt{3}}{2}, \dfrac{1}{\sqrt{2}}, \dfrac{1}{2}$; $\tan\theta : \dfrac{1}{\sqrt{3}}, 1, \sqrt{3}$ **11. a)** 0.4648,
0.8854, 0.5250 **b)** 0.9888, 0.1495, 6.6122 **c)** 0.7174,
0.6967, 1.0296 **d)** 0.4339, 0.9010, 0.4816
12. a) 0.35 **b)** 0.93 **c)** 1.33 **13.** $\dfrac{1}{\sqrt{3}}$ **14. a)** Hint: $AB = \sin\theta$,
$OB = \cos\theta$ **b)** No. $(0.8)^2 + (0.2)^2 \neq 1$ **16. a)** (3.2139,
3.8302) **b)** $(-2.2943, 3.2766)$ **c)** $(-2.2981, -1.9284)$
d) $(3, -3\sqrt{3})$ **17. a)** 0.588 rad **b)** 2.2143 rad **c)** 3.6052 rad
d) 5.7428 rad **19. a)** $0, 2\pi$ **b)** $\dfrac{\pi}{6}, \dfrac{5\pi}{6}, \dfrac{3\pi}{2}$ **c)** 1.57, 4.13, 5.30
d) no solution **20. b)** $\dfrac{4}{3}$ **c)** $\dfrac{4}{3}$ **d)** The slope of a line equals
the tangent of the angle it makes with the x-axis.
e) The statement in part d) is true if the angle is
measured counterclockwise from the x-axis. The slope of
a line and the tangent of the angle it makes with the
x-axis are both undefined when the line is vertical.
21. a) $\csc x + \sec x$ **b)** $\csc^2 x + \sec^2 x$ **c)** $\cot x - 3\sec x$
d) $\dfrac{1}{2}\sec x - \dfrac{4}{3}\csc x$ **22.** In all cases, $\sin x$ cannot equal 0.
a) $\sec x$ **b)** $\cos x$ **c)** $\csc^2 x$ **23. a)** $\dfrac{1}{\sin x \cos x}$ **b)** $\dfrac{\sin x}{\cos^2 x}$
c) $\dfrac{1}{\cos^2 x}$ **d)** $\dfrac{1}{\sin x}$ **25. a)** $\dfrac{2}{\sqrt{3}}$ **b)** $\sqrt{2}$ **c)** 1 **d)** 1 **e)** undefined
f) undefined **g)** 2 **h)** undefined **i)** $\dfrac{1}{\sqrt{3}}$
26. a) $1 + \cot^2\theta = \csc^2\theta$; $\theta \neq k\pi$, k any integer
b) $\tan^2\theta + 1 = \sec^2\theta$; $\theta \neq \dfrac{\pi}{2} + k\pi$, k any integer

Section 8.1, pp. 497–498

Practise

1. a) $\sin 30° = \dfrac{1}{2}$ **b)** $\sin 60° = \dfrac{\sqrt{3}}{2}$ **c)** $\cos 60° = \dfrac{1}{2}$
d) $\cos 30° = \dfrac{\sqrt{3}}{2}$ **e)** $\tan\dfrac{\pi}{4} = 1$ **2. a)** $\sin(A - B)$
b) $2\sin M \cos N$ **c)** $\cos 3A$ **d)** $-\cos(A + B)$ **e)** $\cos(x - y)$
f) $\tan 2x$ **g)** $\cos 2x$ **h)** 1
3. a) $\sin\dfrac{\pi}{3}\cos\dfrac{\pi}{4} + \cos\dfrac{\pi}{3}\sin\dfrac{\pi}{4} = \dfrac{\sqrt{6} + \sqrt{2}}{4}$
b) $\cos\dfrac{\pi}{2}\cos\dfrac{\pi}{3} + \sin\dfrac{\pi}{2}\sin\dfrac{\pi}{3} = \dfrac{\sqrt{3}}{2}$
c) $\dfrac{\tan\dfrac{\pi}{4} + \tan\dfrac{\pi}{6}}{1 - \tan\dfrac{\pi}{4}\tan\dfrac{\pi}{6}} = \dfrac{1 + \dfrac{1}{\sqrt{3}}}{1 - \dfrac{1}{\sqrt{3}}} = 2 + \sqrt{3}$

Apply, Solve, Communicate

4. a) $\dfrac{7\pi}{6} - 2, \dfrac{11\pi}{6} - 2$ **b)** 0.1593, 4.1239 **c)** $\dfrac{\pi}{8}, \dfrac{3\pi}{8}, \dfrac{5\pi}{8}, \dfrac{7\pi}{8},$
$\dfrac{9\pi}{8}, \dfrac{11\pi}{8}, \dfrac{13\pi}{8}, \dfrac{15\pi}{8}$ **d)** $0, \pi, 2\pi$ **e)** $\dfrac{11\pi}{6} - 2, \dfrac{13\pi}{6} - 2$
f) $\dfrac{3\pi}{10}, \dfrac{7\pi}{10}, \dfrac{11\pi}{10}, \dfrac{3\pi}{2}, \dfrac{19\pi}{10}$ **g)** $\dfrac{\pi}{6}, \dfrac{\pi}{2}, \dfrac{5\pi}{6}, \dfrac{7\pi}{6}, \dfrac{3\pi}{2}, \dfrac{11\pi}{6}$
h) $0, \pi, 2\pi$ **i)** 0.6245, 2.1953, 3.7661, 5.3369
j) $\dfrac{\pi}{9}, \dfrac{2\pi}{9}, \dfrac{4\pi}{9}, \dfrac{5\pi}{9}, \dfrac{7\pi}{9}, \dfrac{8\pi}{9}, \dfrac{10\pi}{9}, \dfrac{11\pi}{9}, \dfrac{13\pi}{9}, \dfrac{14\pi}{9}, \dfrac{16\pi}{9}, \dfrac{17\pi}{9}$
k) $\dfrac{\pi}{6}, \dfrac{5\pi}{6}$ **l)** 3.0689, 6.2105 **m)** $\dfrac{\pi}{12}, \dfrac{5\pi}{12}, \dfrac{13\pi}{12}, \dfrac{17\pi}{12}$
5. a) equal ($\tan\alpha = 2$, $\tan\beta = 3$) **b)** $\tan\theta = \dfrac{3 - 2}{1 + (3)(2)}$
c) $\alpha = 1.1071$, $\beta = 1.2490$, $\theta = 0.1419$ **8. a)** $\sqrt{3}$ ($\sin x \neq 0$)
b) $\dfrac{-4}{1 - \tan^2 x}$ **9. a)** $\cos x = \dfrac{3}{5}$, $\sin y = \dfrac{12}{13}$ **b) i)** $\dfrac{56}{65}$ **ii)** $\dfrac{63}{65}$
iii) $-\dfrac{56}{33}$ **10. a)** $-\dfrac{24}{25}$ **b)** -1 **c)** $\dfrac{24}{7}$
11. a) $\cos x\left(\dfrac{\cos h - 1}{h}\right) - \sin x\left(\dfrac{\sin h}{h}\right)$
b) $\sin x\left(\dfrac{\cos h - 1}{h}\right) + \cos x\left(\dfrac{\sin h}{h}\right)$
15. a) $\cos x = 0$ or $\sin y = 0$ **b)** $\sin x = 0$ or $\sin y = 0$
c) $x + y = \dfrac{\pi}{2} + 2k\pi$, k any integer or $x - y = (2k + 1)\pi$,
k any integer

Section 8.2, p. 503

Practise

1. a) $5\sin 2x$ **b)** $\dfrac{5}{2}\sin 4x$ **c)** $\dfrac{1}{2}\sin 12x$ **d)** $2\sin x$ **e)** $\cos\theta$
f) $\cos 10\theta$ **g)** $\cos\dfrac{4}{3}\theta$ **h)** $\cos(6\theta - 4)$ **2. a)** $2\sin a$; $a \neq \dfrac{\pi}{2}, \dfrac{3\pi}{2}$
b) $2\sin 2a$; $a \neq \dfrac{\pi}{2}, \dfrac{3\pi}{2}$ **c)** 1

Apply, Solve, Communicate

3. a) $6\sin 2x \cos 2x$ **b)** $12\cos^2 3x - 6$ or $6 - 12\sin^2 3x$ or $6\cos^2 3x - 6\sin^2 3x$ **c)** $2\sin^4 4x$ **d)** $\dfrac{2\tan 2x}{1 - \tan^2 2x}$

e) $2\cos^2 x - 1 - 2\cos x$ **4. a)** Use $\sin x = 2\sin\dfrac{x}{2}\cos\dfrac{x}{2}$.

b) Use $\cos x = 1 - 2\sin^2\dfrac{x}{2}$ **5. a)** $\dfrac{\pi}{2}, \dfrac{2\pi}{3}, \dfrac{4\pi}{3}, \dfrac{3\pi}{2}$

b) $\dfrac{\pi}{6}, \dfrac{5\pi}{6}, \dfrac{3\pi}{2}$ **c)** $0, \dfrac{\pi}{6}, \dfrac{5\pi}{6}, \pi, \dfrac{7\pi}{6}, \dfrac{11\pi}{6}, 2\pi$

d) $0, 1.4874, \pi, 4.7958, 2\pi$ **e)** $\dfrac{\pi}{6}, \dfrac{\pi}{2}, \dfrac{5\pi}{6}, \dfrac{3\pi}{2}$

f) $0, \dfrac{2\pi}{3}, \pi, \dfrac{4\pi}{3}, 2\pi$ **g)** $\dfrac{\pi}{8}, \dfrac{5\pi}{8}, \dfrac{9\pi}{8}, \dfrac{13\pi}{8}$

h) $1.2310, \dfrac{2\pi}{3}, \dfrac{4\pi}{3}, 5.0522$ **i)** $0, \dfrac{\pi}{4}, \dfrac{3\pi}{4}, \pi, \dfrac{5\pi}{4}, \dfrac{7\pi}{4}, 2\pi$

j) $\dfrac{\pi}{8}, \dfrac{5\pi}{8}, \dfrac{9\pi}{8}, \dfrac{13\pi}{8}$ **k)** $0.1674, \dfrac{\pi}{2}, 2.9741, \dfrac{3\pi}{2}$ **l)** $\dfrac{\pi}{6}, \dfrac{\pi}{2}, \dfrac{5\pi}{6}$

m) $0.2527, 2.8889$ **6.** 1.79 m

7. a) $\sec 2\theta = \dfrac{\sec^2\theta}{1 - \tan^2\theta} = \dfrac{\sec^2\theta}{2 - \sec^2\theta}$ **b)** $\dfrac{1}{2}\csc\theta\sec\theta$

8. a) $3\sin\theta - 4\sin^3\theta$ **b)** $4\cos^3\theta - 3\cos\theta$ **c)** $\dfrac{3\tan\theta - \tan^3\theta}{1 - 3\tan^2\theta}$

9. $\sin 2\theta = \dfrac{2\tan\theta}{1 + \tan^2\theta}; \cos 2\theta = \dfrac{1 - \tan^2\theta}{1 + \tan^2\theta}$ **10.** $-\dfrac{3}{4}$

11. $\theta: 1.2094, 1.9322, 4.3510, 5.0738; \cos\theta: \pm 0.3536$

12. a) $V = 18\,000\pi\sin^2 2x \cos^2 x$ **c)** $x = \dfrac{\pi}{4}$ or $x = 0.4523$

Section 8.3, pp. 508–509

Practise

1. a) 1 **b)** does not exist **c)** $\sin 1$ **d)** 0 **e)** $\dfrac{1}{3}$ **f)** 3 **g)** $\dfrac{3}{4}$ **h)** $\dfrac{5}{2}$

2. a) $\dfrac{5}{2}$ **b)** 0 **c)** $\dfrac{9}{4}$ **d)** does not exist **e)** 0 **f)** 0 **g)** -1 **h)** 4 **i)** 0

Apply, Solve, Communicate

3. a) $0.334\,67, 0.333\,35, 0.333\,33, 0.333\,33$ **b)** $\dfrac{1}{3}$

c) $0.333, 0, 0$ **4. a)** 3 **5. a)** -2 **6.** $\cos a$ **7.** $-\sin a$ **8.** Limit does not exist. Left hand limit $= -1$ and right hand limit $= 1$

9. $\sin 1$ **10. a)** $-\dfrac{1}{2}$ **b)** 1 **c)** 1 **11. a)** $\dfrac{5}{2}$ **b)** $\dfrac{25}{4}$ **c)** 0 **d)** $\dfrac{3}{4}$ **e)** $\dfrac{9}{16}$ **f)** $\dfrac{3}{4}$

Section 8.4, pp. 518–519

Practise

1. a) $4\cos(4x + 7)$ **b)** $2x\cos(x^2 + 3)$ **c)** $-5\sin(5x + 3)$
d) $6\sec^2(2x + 3)$ **e)** $-6x\sin(3x^2 - 1)$ **f)** $10x\sec^2(5x^2 + 1)$
g) $-2\cos x \sin x \cos(\cos^2 x)$ **h)** $-\sin x \cos(\cos x)$

2. a) $\dfrac{x\sec^2 x - \tan x}{x^2}$ **b)** $\sin(3x - 2) + 3x\cos(3x - 2)$

c) $2x\sin(2x^2 + 5) + 4x^3\cos(2x^2 + 5)$ **d)** $-\dfrac{x\sin x + \cos x}{x^2}$

e) $\cos(8x - 17) - 8x\sin(8x - 17)$
f) $2x\cos(0.4x^2 + 9) - 0.8x^3\sin(0.4x^2 + 9)$
g) $10x\tan^3(3x^2 - 1) + 90x^3\tan^2(3x^2 - 1)\sec^2(3x^2 - 1)$
h) $8x\sin^3(6x^2 - 2) + 144x^3\sin^2(6x^2 - 2)\cos(6x^2 - 2)$
3. a) $-6\cos x \sin x \sin^2(\cos^2 x)\cos(\cos^2 x)$
b) $-12x^2\cos x^3 \cos^3(\sin x^3)\sin(\sin x^3)$
c) $\cos(\tan x) - x\sin(\tan x)\sec^2 x$ **d)** $e^x\cos e^x$ **e)** $-\dfrac{\sin(\ln x)}{x}$
f) $\dfrac{e^x \cos e^x}{\sin e^x}$ **g)** 0 **h)** $\dfrac{1}{1 + \cos x}$

Apply, Solve, Communicate

4. a) $y = x$ **b)** $y = -\dfrac{\sqrt{3}}{2}x + \dfrac{\pi\sqrt{3}}{6} + \dfrac{1}{4}$ **c)** $y = -4x + \pi + 1$

5. a) minimum $-\sqrt{2}$ when $x = \dfrac{3\pi}{4}$, maximum $\sqrt{2}$ when $x = -\dfrac{\pi}{4}$ **b)** maxima: 0 when $x = \dfrac{\pi}{2}$, 2 when $x = -\dfrac{\pi}{2}$; minima: $-\dfrac{1}{4}$ when $x = \dfrac{\pi}{6}$ or $\dfrac{5\pi}{6}$ **c)** minimum -3 when $x = \pi$ **d)** none **6. a)** $\left(\dfrac{\pi}{2}, 0\right)$ **b)** $\left(-\dfrac{3\pi}{4}, 0\right), \left(-\dfrac{\pi}{4}, 0\right),$ $\left(\dfrac{\pi}{4}, 0\right), \left(\dfrac{3\pi}{4}, 0\right)$ **c)** $(0, 0), (\pi, 0)$ **7. a)** Every fourth one is the same. **b)** $-\cos x$; $-\sin x$ **c)** $\left(\dfrac{d}{dx}\right)^n \sin x = (-1)^{\frac{n}{2}} \sin x$, n even; $\left(\dfrac{d}{dx}\right)^n \sin x = (-1)^{\frac{n-1}{2}} \cos x$, n odd

d) $\left(\dfrac{d}{dx}\right)^n \cos x = (-1)^{\frac{n}{2}} \cos x$, n even;

$\left(\dfrac{d}{dx}\right)^n \cos x = (-1)^{\frac{n+1}{2}} \sin x$, n odd

9. $y = \dfrac{1}{2}x - \dfrac{\pi}{6} + \dfrac{\sqrt{3}}{2}$ **10. a)** $\dfrac{d\theta}{dA} = \dfrac{\pi}{180}$

b) $\dfrac{dy}{dA} = \dfrac{\pi}{180}\cos\theta$ **c)** $\dfrac{\pi}{180}$ **d)** $\dfrac{d}{dA}\cos A = -\dfrac{\pi}{180}\sin A$

11. a) not differentiable when $x = 0$ **b)** not differentiable when $x = k\pi$, k any integer **12.** $x = 1, x = -1,$

$x = \dfrac{k\pi \pm \sqrt{k^2\pi^2 - 4}}{2}$ (k any integer) **13.** 2 **14. a)** $\tan x - x$

b) $\ln(\sec x)$ **c)** $\ln(\sec x + \tan x)$

Technology Extension, p. 521

1. a) $\cos\theta$ **b)** $-\sin\theta$ **c)** $\tan\theta$ **d)** $\sec\theta$ **e)** $\sin\theta$ **f)** $-\csc\theta$
g) $-\tan\theta$ **h)** $\sin\theta$ **2. a)** odd **b)** even **c)** odd
3. (n is any integer) **a)** $\dfrac{\pi}{6} + 2n\pi, \dfrac{5\pi}{6} + 2n\pi, 2n\pi - \dfrac{\pi}{6}$

b) $\dfrac{\pi}{3} + 2n\pi, \dfrac{2\pi}{3} + 2n\pi, \dfrac{4\pi}{3} + 2n\pi$ **c)** $\dfrac{\pi}{6} + n\pi, \dfrac{3\pi}{4} + n\pi$
d) $\dfrac{\pi}{4} + n\pi, \dfrac{\pi}{6} + 2n\pi, \dfrac{5\pi}{6} + 2n\pi, \dfrac{\pi}{3} + 2n\pi, -\dfrac{\pi}{3} + 2n\pi$
4. a) 2 **b)** a **c)** 1 **d)** $\sin 1$ **e)** $\dfrac{5}{3}$ **f)** does not exist

5. a) $-2\sin x \cos x$ **b)** $3x^2\cos x^3$ **c)** $3x^2\tan 2x + 2x^3\sec^2 2x$
d) $2e^x\sin e^x \cos e^x$ **e)** $3\cos 3x \cos 2x - 2\sin 3x \sin 2x$
f) $\dfrac{2 \cos 3x \cos 2x + 3 \sin 3x \sin 2x}{\cos^2 3x}$

Section 8.5, pp. 529–531

Apply, Solve, Communicate

1. a) 3.5455×10^{22} N **b)** 2.0017×10^{20} N **c)** 177.12
2. a) -7.7784×10^{-3} N **b)** -2.668×10^{6} N **c)** -2.668×10^{12} N

3. a) other side: $\sqrt{200-x^2}$; $A = \dfrac{x}{2}\sqrt{200-x^2}$;

maximum A: 50 cm^2 **4.** 0.503 m/s
5. a) $v = -44\pi\sin(880\pi t)$; $a = -38\,720\pi^2\cos(880\pi t)$
b) 44π cm/s **6. a)** $h = \sin\theta + \sqrt{16-\cos^2\theta}$

b) $v = \left[\cos\theta + \dfrac{\sin 2\theta}{2\sqrt{16-\cos^2\theta}}\right]\dfrac{d\theta}{dt}$ **c)** $\theta = \dfrac{\pi}{2} + k\pi$,

where k is an integer **d)** $\theta = 0.2318 + 2k\pi$,
$\theta = 2.9098 + 2k\pi$, where k is an integer **7. a)** 60 **b)** 120
c) $14\,400\pi\sin 120\pi t$

d) $t = \dfrac{1}{240}, \dfrac{5}{240}, \dfrac{9}{240}, \dots; 0$

e) $t = 0, \dfrac{1}{120}, \dfrac{2}{120}, \dfrac{3}{120}, \dots; \pm 120$

8. $20 + 10\sqrt{2}$ cm **9. a)** $\theta = \tan^{-1} 10t$ **b)** 7.5 rad/h

10. $\dfrac{\pi}{3}$ **11. a)** $\dfrac{\pi}{4}$ **b)** $\dfrac{\pi}{4} + \dfrac{\phi}{2}$ **12.** 0.9 rad/s; 5.4 rad/s

13. a) $\theta = \tan^{-1}\left(\dfrac{10t}{1+5t}\right)$ **b)** $\dfrac{5}{8}(13 - 4\sqrt{3})$ rad/h

14. a) $\dfrac{\pi}{3}$ **b)** $\dfrac{\pi}{3}$ **15.** $2\sqrt{2}$ m from the goal line

Review of Key Concepts, pp. 534–535

1. a) $\sin 60° = \dfrac{\sqrt{3}}{2}$ **b)** $\sin 45° = \dfrac{1}{\sqrt{2}}$ **c)** $\cos 60° = \dfrac{1}{2}$

d) $\cos 30° = \dfrac{\sqrt{3}}{2}$ **e)** $\tan 45° = 1$ **2. a)** $25\sin 2x$ **b)** $\dfrac{15}{2}\sin 6x$

c) $\cos(6\theta + 4)$ **d)** $4\sin x$ **e)** $\cos 4x$ **f)** $\cos 20\theta$ **g)** $\cos\dfrac{4\theta}{5}$

h) $\dfrac{1}{2}\sin 14x$ **3. a)** $\dfrac{13\pi}{6} - 3, \dfrac{17\pi}{6} - 3$ **b)** $\dfrac{\pi}{2}, \dfrac{3\pi}{2}$

c) $\dfrac{\pi}{6}, \dfrac{\pi}{2}, \dfrac{5\pi}{6}, \dfrac{7\pi}{6}, \dfrac{3\pi}{2}, \dfrac{11\pi}{6}$ **d)** $\dfrac{\pi}{6}, \dfrac{5\pi}{6}, \dfrac{3\pi}{2}$ **e)** $\dfrac{3\pi}{4}, \dfrac{7\pi}{4}$

f) no solution; $\tan\dfrac{\pi}{2}$ is undefined **g)** $0, \pi, 2\pi, 4.0375,$

5.3873 **h)** $0, \pi, 2\pi, \dfrac{\pi}{3}, \dfrac{5\pi}{3}$ **i)** $\dfrac{\pi}{4}, \dfrac{5\pi}{4}$ **j)** $1.1503, 1.9913,$

$4.2919, 5.1329$ **k)** $0, \pi, 2\pi, \dfrac{\pi}{4}, \dfrac{3\pi}{4}, \dfrac{5\pi}{4}, \dfrac{7\pi}{4}$

l) $\dfrac{\pi}{8}, \dfrac{5\pi}{8}, \dfrac{9\pi}{8}, \dfrac{13\pi}{8}$ **m)** $\dfrac{\pi}{2}, \dfrac{3\pi}{2}, 0.2527, 2.8889$

n) $\dfrac{\pi}{6}, \dfrac{\pi}{2}, \dfrac{5\pi}{6}$ **4. a)** $\dfrac{336}{625}$ **b)** 1 **c)** $-\dfrac{336}{527}$ **d)** $\dfrac{31}{25}$ **5.** 38.1 m

6. $\dfrac{3696}{4225}$ **7. a)** $\dfrac{3}{4}$ **b)** $\dfrac{1}{2}$ **c)** 1 **d)** 2 **e)** 0 **8. a)** $6x\cos(3x^2 + 5)$

b) $12x^2\sin^2(6x^2 - 2) + 96x^4\sin (6x^2 - 2) \cos(6x^2 - 2)$
c) $2x\cos(4x^2 + 7) - 8x^3\sin (4x^2 + 7)$
d) $2\sin(\cos^3 x + \tan x)\cos(\cos^3 x + \tan x)$
$(\sec^2 x - 3\cos^2 x \sin x)$
e) $-9x^2\sin^2(\cos x^3) \cos(\cos x^3) \sin x^3$ **f)** $-e^x\sin e^x$

g) $-\sec^2 x \cot x \sin(\ln(\tan x))$ **h)** $\dfrac{e^x \cos e^x}{\sin e^x}$

i) $\dfrac{x \cos x - \sin x}{x^2}$ **j)** 0 **9.** points of inflection:

$\left(\dfrac{\pi}{6}, \dfrac{5}{4}\right), \left(\dfrac{5\pi}{6}, \dfrac{5}{4}\right)$; maximum 3 when $x = \dfrac{\pi}{2}$;

minimum -1 when $x = \dfrac{3\pi}{2}$ **10.** $y = \dfrac{3\sqrt{3}}{2}x - \dfrac{\pi\sqrt{3}}{4} + \dfrac{5}{4}$

11. Answers may vary. **a)** $y = \dfrac{A}{2}\left(\sin\left(\dfrac{4\pi t}{0.033}\right) + 1\right)$

b) $y = \dfrac{A}{2}\left(\sin\left(\dfrac{4\pi t}{0.033\left(2500 - \dfrac{t}{k}\right)}\right) + 1\right)$, where

$k = 3.154 \times 10^7$ s, the number of seconds in a year.
c) 1.1424×10^{19} km/s **12.** $60°$ or $\dfrac{\pi}{3}$ **13.** 2.62 m^2/s

14. a) 24.824 cm **c)** $x = a\sin(2\pi t + k)$

d) $a = \dfrac{L}{2} = 12.412$ cm **e)** 77.99 rad/s when $t = \dfrac{n}{2} - \dfrac{k}{2\pi}$,

n any integer **f)** 490 rad/s^2 when $t = \dfrac{n}{2} + \dfrac{1}{4} - \dfrac{k}{2\pi}$,

n any integer **15.** $54.74°$

Chapter Test, p. 536

1. a) 2 **b)** 20
2. a) $6\cos 3x + 12\sin 4x$; $-18\sin 3x + 48\cos 4x$

b) $\dfrac{\cos x + \sin x - \sec^2 x \sin x}{(1 + \tan x)^2}$;

The form of the answer will vary.

$\dfrac{-\sec x - 2 \sec^3 x - \sec^2 x \sin x - \sec x \sin^2 x + \cos x}{(1 + \tan x)^3}$

3. a) 57 **b)** $120, 80$; yes **c)** all constants increase

d) all constants decrease **4.** $4, 8, 12, \dots$ **5.** $90°$ **6. a)** $\pm\sqrt{2}$

b) $\dfrac{\pi}{4}$ **c)** $\dfrac{1}{2}$ **7. a)** $2\pi + 2\pi\cos(2\pi t)$ **b)** $-4\pi^2\sin(2\pi t)$

c) $t = \dfrac{1}{2}, \dfrac{3}{2}, \dfrac{5}{2}, \dots$ **d)** left: never; right: always except the

instants when it is stopped **e)** increasing when $\dfrac{1}{2} < t < 1$,

$\dfrac{3}{2} < t < 2, \dots$; decreasing when $0 < t < \dfrac{1}{2}, 1 < t < \dfrac{3}{2}, \dots$
f) Since $v \geq 0$, it is speeding up whenever velocity is
increasing, and slowing down whenever velocity is
decreasing.

Challenge Problems, p. 537

1. a) $5\sin(x + \theta)$, where $\sin\theta = \dfrac{3}{5}$, $\cos\theta = \dfrac{4}{5}$ ($\theta \doteq 36.87°$)

or $-5\sin(x + \theta)$, where $\sin\theta = -\dfrac{3}{5}$, $\cos\theta = -\dfrac{4}{5}$ ($\theta \doteq 216.87°$)

b) Take $A = \pm\sqrt{a^2 + b^2}$. Then θ is the angle such that $\sin\theta = \pm\dfrac{b}{\sqrt{a^2 + b^2}}$ and $\cos\theta = \pm\dfrac{a}{\sqrt{a^2 + b^2}}$. **2. a)** $5\cos(x + \theta)$,

where $\sin\theta = -\dfrac{4}{5}$, $\cos\theta = \dfrac{3}{5}$ ($\theta \doteq -53.13°$) or $-5\cos(x + \theta)$,

where $\sin\theta = \dfrac{4}{5}$, $\cos\theta = -\dfrac{3}{5}$ ($\theta \doteq 126.87°$)

b) Take $A = \pm\sqrt{a^2 + b^2}$. Then θ is the angle such that $\sin\theta = \mp\dfrac{a}{\sqrt{a^2 + b^2}}$ and $\cos\theta = \pm\dfrac{b}{\sqrt{a^2 + b^2}}$. **4.** $40.60°$

5. $9.27°$ **7.** $\dfrac{1}{4}$ **8.** 2 **10.** $E = I_0\cos(wt + b)(r - I_0w\sin(wt + b))$

Appendix A

Angle measures, p. 538

1. a) $270°$ **b)** $225°$ **c)** $210°$ **d)** $240°$ **e)** $150°$ **f)** $360°$

2. a) $\dfrac{\pi}{6}$; 0.52 rad **b)** $\dfrac{\pi}{4}$; 0.79 rad **c)** $\dfrac{\pi}{3}$; 1.05 rad

d) π; 3.14 rad **e)** 2π; 6.28 rad **f)** 3π; 9.42 rad

Circle geometry, p. 538

1. a) 0.5 **b)** 5 **c)** 3 **2. a)** 15 m **b)** 16 m **c)** 28 m **3. a)** 4 m
b) 11 m

Completing the square, p. 539

1. a) $y = (x + 3)^2 - 5$ **b)** $y = (x - 5)^2 - 20$
c) $y = (x - 1)^2 - 12$ **d)** $y = 3(x + 1)^2 - 9$ **e)** $y = (x - 1)^2 - 9$
f) $y = 2(x - 3)^2 - 15$ **g)** $y = -4(x - 2)^2 + 7$
h) $y = 4(x + 3)^2 - 41$

Complex numbers, p. 539

1. a) $5i$ **b)** $4i$ **c)** $i\sqrt{7}$ **d)** $2i\sqrt{14}$ **e)** $-5i\sqrt{5}$ **2. a)** $-i$ **b)** -12
c) $2i$ **d)** -35 **e)** 20 **3. a)** $5 + 3i\sqrt{5}$ **b)** $8 - 2i\sqrt{5}$ **c)** $2 + i\sqrt{2}$
d) $3 - 2i\sqrt{2}$ **e)** $-7 + i\sqrt{2}$

Compound interest, p. 540

1. a) $\$3173.75$ **b)** $\$5114.14$ **c)** $\$31\,102.34$ **d)** $\$6744.25$

Determining angles, p. 541

1. a) 2.55 rad **b)** 5.96 rad **c)** 3.93 rad

Determining coordinates of points, p. 541

1. a) $(1.04, 3.86)$ **b)** $(-3\sqrt{2}, 3\sqrt{2})$ **c)** $\left(-\dfrac{7}{2}, -\dfrac{7\sqrt{3}}{2}\right)$

d) $\left(\dfrac{3\sqrt{3}}{2}, -\dfrac{3}{2}\right)$

Distance between two points p. 542

1. a) $3\sqrt{2}$ **b)** $\sqrt{65}$ **c)** $\sqrt{74}$ **d)** $3\sqrt{5}$ **e)** $3\sqrt{5}$ **f)** $\sqrt{82}$

Dividing a polynomial by a monomial, p. 542

1. a) $2y + 5$, $y \neq 0$ **b)** $2 + 4m + 7m^2$, $m \neq 0$ **c)** $\dfrac{5x+1}{2}$, $x \neq 0$

d) $\dfrac{4x + 7y + 2x^2y^2}{8xy}$, $xy \neq 0$

Domain, p. 543

1. a) no restrictions **b)** $x \neq -4$ **c)** no restrictions
d) $x \neq 2$, $x \neq -\dfrac{1}{3}$

Equation of a horizontal or vertical line given a point on the line, p. 543

1. a) $y = 3$ **b)** $x = 1$

Equation of a line given the slope and a point, p. 543

1. a) $y = 3x - 1$ **b)** $y = -x - 3$ **2.** $y = 5x - 6$

Equation of a line given the slope and y-intercept, p. 544

1. a) $y = 2x + 1$ **b)** $y = -4x + 4$

Equation of a line given two points, p. 544

1. a) $y = \dfrac{7}{2}x + \dfrac{3}{2}$ **b)** $y = -x + 8$

Equation of a line given the x- and y-intercepts, p. 545

1. a) $y = -4x + 4$ **b)** $y = \dfrac{2}{3}x - 2$

Evaluating functions, p. 545

1. a) -7 **b)** 35 **c)** 5 **d)** $-\dfrac{89}{27}$ **e)** 39.221 **f)** $n^3 + 3n^2 - 4n - 7$
g) $-27x^3 + 27x^2 + 12x - 7$ **h)** $x^6 + 3x^4 - 4x^2 - 7$
2. a) -1 **b)** 20 **c)** 2 **d)** $x^2 + 4x - 1$ **3. a)** 0 **b)** 2 **c)** 1 **d)** $\sqrt{x^2 - 3}$
4. a) 5 **b)** 2 **c)** 10 **d)** 0 **5. a)** True **b)** False **c)** True **d)** False

Exponential equations, p. 546

1. a) 4 **b)** -2 **c)** 4.5 **d)** -13 **e)** 3 **f)** 0 **g)** 3 **h)** 5

Exponent laws, p. 546

1. a) $\dfrac{5}{x^3}$ **b)** $\dfrac{1}{81x^4}$ **c)** $7 + \dfrac{1}{x^6}$ **d)** $\dfrac{1}{25}x^6 - \dfrac{6}{x} + 2x - x^3$

2. a) $9x^{\frac{9}{2}} + 6x^{\frac{5}{2}} + x^{\frac{1}{2}}$ **b)** $6x^5 + 9x^4 - 10x - 15$
c) $4x^6 - 4x^4 + 8x^3 - 8x$ **d)** $\sqrt{2x^3 - 4x^2 + 10x - 20}$
3. a) 81 **b)** $\dfrac{1}{1024}$ **c)** 1 **d)** 6 **e)** 125 **4. a)** $20x^9y^7$
b) b^3c^3, $abc \neq 0$ **c)** $m^{-5}n^2$, $mn \neq 0$ **d)** xy^{-4}, $xy \neq 0$

Factoring $a^2 - b^2$, p. 548

1. a) $(x - 2)(x + 2)$ **b)** $(y - 10)(y + 10)$ **c)** $(2n - 7)(2n + 7)$
d) $(5m - 9)(5m + 9)$ **e)** $(1 - 6x)(1 + 6x)$
f) $(2y - 3x)(2y + 3x)$

Factoring $a^3 - b^3$ or $a^3 + b^3$, p. 548

1. a) $(x - 1)(x^2 + x + 1)$ **b)** $(x - y)(x^2 + xy + y^2)$
c) $(3 - 4a)(9 + 12a + 16a^2)$ **d)** $(2a - 1)(4a^2 + 2a + 1)$
e) $\left(\dfrac{x}{2} - 1\right)\left(\dfrac{x^2}{4} + \dfrac{x}{2} + 1\right)$ **f)** $\left(\dfrac{1}{a} - \dfrac{1}{3}\right)\left(\dfrac{1}{a^2} + \dfrac{1}{3a} + \dfrac{1}{9}\right)$
2. a) $(x + 2)(x^2 - 2x + 4)$ **b)** $(2z + 1)(4z^2 - 2z + 1)$
c) $(c + 5d)(c^2 - 5cd + 25d^2)$
d) $(10x + 9w^2)(100x^2 - 90xw^2 + 81w^4)$
e) $\left(1 + \dfrac{2q}{3}\right)\left(1 - \dfrac{2q}{3} + \dfrac{4q^2}{9}\right)$
f) $\left(\dfrac{1}{5} + \dfrac{1}{3y}\right)\left(\dfrac{1}{25} - \dfrac{1}{15y} + \dfrac{1}{9y^2}\right)$

Factoring $a^2 + bx + c$, $a = 1$, p. 549

1. a) $(x - 5)(x + 4)$ **b)** $(y + 5)(y - 2)$ **c)** $(n - 9)(n + 4)$
d) $(m + 6)(m + 3)$ **e)** $(x - 6)(x - 5)$ **f)** $(c - 6)(c + 4)$
g) $(16 - y)(1 + y)$ **h)** $(x + 8y)(x + 4y)$ **i)** $(c - 7d)(c + 4d)$

Factoring $a^2 + bx + c$, $a \neq 1$, p. 549

1. a) $(x - 2)(3x + 4)$ **b)** $(2c - 1)(c + 4)$ **c)** $(4m - 3)(m - 2)$
d) $(y + 1)(5y + 3)$ **e)** $(n + 1)(3n - 2)$ **f)** $(6x + 1)(x - 3)$
g) $(3x + 4y)(x - 3y)$ **h)** $(5x - 4)(x - 2)$ **i)** $(4x + 3)(x + 5)$
j) $(p + q)(2p - q)$

Finite differences, p. 549

1. a) linear **b)** quadratic **c)** linear **d)** neither **e)** quadratic
f) neither

Functions and relations, p. 551

1. a) domain: real numbers; range: real number; function
b) domain: real numbers; range: real numbers; function
c) domain: real numbers; range: $y \geq 3$; function
d) domain: real numbers; range: $y \geq 1$; function
e) domain: $-5 \leq x \leq 5$; range: $-5 \leq y \leq 5$; not a function
f) domain: $-9 \leq x \leq 1$; range: $-4 \leq y \leq 6$; not a function
g) domain: $x \neq 0$; range: $y \neq 0$; function
h) domain: $-1 \leq x \leq 5$; range: $-8 \leq y \leq -2$; not a function
i) domain: $x \geq -\dfrac{2}{3}$; range: $y \geq 0$; function

Graphing quadratic functions, p. 552

1. a) vertex: $(0, 2)$; opening: upward; vertical stretch
factor: 1 **b)** vertex: $(0, -1)$; opening: downward; vertical
stretch factor: 1 **c)** vertex: $(0, 0)$; opening: upward;
vertical stretch factor: 2 **d)** vertex: $(-4, 0)$; opening:
upward; vertical stretch factor: 3 **e)** vertex: $(1, 4)$;

opening: downward; vertical stretch factor: 2
f) vertex: $(-2, 3)$; opening: upward; vertical stretch
factor: 0.5 **g)** vertex: $(-1, -5)$; opening: downward;
vertical stretch factor: 1 **h)** vertex: $(3, 1)$; opening:
upward; vertical stretch factor: $\dfrac{1}{4}$

Graphs of functions using technology, p. 553

1. a) domain: $x \neq 0$; range: $y \neq 0$ **b)** domain: $x \neq 0$; range:
$y \neq 0$ **c)** domain: $x \neq 0$; range: $y \leq 5$ **d)** domain: $x \geq -3$;
range: $y \geq 0$ **e)** domain: $x \leq 4$; range: $y \geq 0$
f) domain: $x \geq 0$; range: $y \leq 5$

Interpreting graphs of functions, p. 554

1. a) i) 0 **ii)** 2 **iii)** -2 **iv)** -4 **b)** domain: real numbers; range:
real numbers **2. a) i)** -4 **ii)** 0 **iii)** 0 **iv)** -3 **b)** domain: real
numbers; range: $y \geq -4$

Inverses, p. 555

1. a) $f^{-1}(x) = \dfrac{x + 1}{3}$; function **b)** $f^{-1}(x) = \pm\dfrac{1}{2}\sqrt{x - 2}$; not a
function **c)** $f^{-1}(x) = \sqrt[3]{\dfrac{x + 8}{3}}$; function **d)** $f^{-1}(x) = \dfrac{x^2 - 3}{2}$,
$x \geq 0$; function **e)** $f^{-1}(x) = \dfrac{2x + 4}{7x - 3}$, $x \neq \dfrac{3}{7}$; function

Operations with complex numbers, p. 555

1. a) $6 - 4i$ **b)** $2 + 4i$ **c)** $-12 - i$ **d)** 13
2. a) $1 + 3i$ **b)** $-\dfrac{7}{5} - \dfrac{4}{5}i$ **c)** $\dfrac{10}{13} + \dfrac{15}{13}i$ **d)** $-\dfrac{4}{17} + \dfrac{35}{17}i$

Pythagorean theorem, p. 556

1. a) 13 **b)** 8 **c)** 7

Rationalizing expressions, p. 557

1. a) $6\left(\sqrt{x + 4} - \sqrt{x}\right)$ **b)** $x\left(\sqrt{x + 7} + \sqrt{x}\right)$ **c)** $\sqrt{5x} + \sqrt{x}$
d) $\sqrt{x + 5} + 1$ **e)** $\sqrt{x^2 + 9} + 3$ **f)** $x\left(\sqrt{x + 6} + \sqrt{x - 6}\right)$

Similar triangles, p. 557

1. a) 3 **b)** 2 **c)** 20

Simplifying compound rational expressions, p. 558

1. a) $-\dfrac{1}{7(x + 7)}$; $x \neq 0, -7$ **b)** $\dfrac{4}{3(x - 3)}$; $x \neq 0, 3$
c) $\dfrac{-(x + 12)}{36(x + 6)^2}$; $x \neq 0, -6$

Simplifying expressions, p. 558

1. a) $5x + 20$ **b)** $7y - 30$ **c)** $8x - 18$ **d)** $4w + 11$ **e)** $35 - 6y$
f) $7x^2 - 2x + 4$ **g)** $4x^2 + 6x - 46$ **h)** $5a^2 - 16a + 20$
i) $5x^2 - x - 18$

Simplifying rational expressions, p. 558

1. a) $x + 1$; $x \neq -2$ **b)** $\dfrac{1}{x+3}$; $x \neq 5, -3$ **c)** $2x + 5$; $x \neq 1$

d) $\dfrac{5x+1}{x-3}$; $x \neq -2, 3$ **e)** $\dfrac{x+4}{2x+3}$; $x \neq \pm\dfrac{3}{2}$

f) $\dfrac{3x+2}{4x+1}$; $x \neq \dfrac{5}{2}, -\dfrac{1}{4}$

Slopes and y-intercepts, p. 559

1. a) slope: 4; y-intercept: 1 **b)** slope: 1; y-intercept: −2
c) slope: 3; y-intercept: 5 **d)** slope: −7; y-intercept: 3
e) slope: 3; y-intercept: 0 **f)** slope: 0; y-intercept: −8
g) slope: 5; y-intercept: 2 **h)** slope: 4; y-intercept: −3
i) slope: −3.5; y-intercept: 2.5 **j)** slope: 1; y-intercept: 0
k) slope: 4; y-intercept: 4 **l)** slope: 6; y-intercept: 4

Slopes of lines, p. 559

1. a) $\dfrac{1}{2}$ **b)** $-\dfrac{3}{5}$ **c)** $\dfrac{11}{3}$ **d)** $\dfrac{3}{4}$ **e)** $-\dfrac{2}{9}$ **f)** $\dfrac{9}{14}$ **g)** $-\dfrac{9.2}{4.7}$ **h)** $-\dfrac{2.6}{1.5}$

Solving first-degree inequalities, p. 560

1. a) $x > 6$ **b)** $x \geq \dfrac{7}{2}$ **c)** $x > \dfrac{2}{3}$ **d)** $x \leq 13$ **e)** $x > 11$ **f)** $x \leq -\dfrac{59}{4}$

Solving quadratic equations by factoring, p. 560

1. a) $-4, -5$ **b)** $1, 2$ **c)** $3, -10$ **d)** $-3, -5$ **2. a** $-1, \dfrac{2}{3}$ **b)** $\dfrac{5}{2}$

c) $\pm\dfrac{3}{5}$ **d)** $0, \dfrac{4}{9}$

Solving quadratic equations by graphing, p. 561

1. a) $-1, 5$ **b)** $-1, -4$ **c)** ± 4 **d)** $-8, 1$ **e)** $1, 5$ **f)** $-2, -6$

Solving radical equations, pp. 562

1. a) $x = 7$ **b)** $x = 5$ **c)** $x = 20$ **d)** $x = 1$

Solving trigonometric equations, p. 562

1. a) $\dfrac{\pi}{6}, \dfrac{5\pi}{6}$ **b)** $\dfrac{\pi}{4}, \dfrac{5\pi}{4}$ **c)** no solution

The quadratic formula, p. 563

1. a) $1, \dfrac{1}{2}$ **b)** $\dfrac{3}{2}, \dfrac{3}{5}$ **c)** $1, \dfrac{2}{3}$ **2. a)** $\dfrac{-1\pm\sqrt{11}}{5}$; 0.5 or −0.9

b) $\dfrac{1\pm\sqrt{7}}{3}$; 1.2 or −0.5 **c)** $\dfrac{4\pm\sqrt{2}}{2}$; 2.7 or 1.3

d) $\dfrac{-1\pm\sqrt{15}}{2}$; 1.4 or −2.4 **e)** $\dfrac{1\pm\sqrt{11}}{5}$; 0.9 or −0.5

f) $\dfrac{-5\pm\sqrt{97}}{12}$; 0.4 or −1.2 **3. a)** $\dfrac{-1\pm i\sqrt{14}}{3}$ **b)** $\dfrac{-2\pm i\sqrt{10}}{2}$

c) $\dfrac{3\pm i\sqrt{3}}{3}$ **d)** $\dfrac{1\pm i\sqrt{3}}{2}$ **e)** $\dfrac{3\pm i\sqrt{151}}{8}$ **f)** $\pm 5i$

Transformations, p. 564

1. a) vertical translation **b)** vertical stretch **c)** horizontal compression **d)** vertical reflection **e)** horizontal translation **f)** horizontal reflection **g)** horizontal translation **h)** horizontal stretch **i)** vertical translation **j)** vertical stretch **2. a)** Vertical stretch by a factor of 3 and a horizontal reflection in the y-axis.

b) Vertical translation downward by 3 units and a horizontal compression by a factor of $\dfrac{1}{2}$.

c) Horizontal translation left by 2 units and a vertical reflection in the x-axis. **d)** Vertical compression by a fctor of $\dfrac{1}{3}$, a horizontal compression by a factor of $\dfrac{1}{5}$ and a horizontal reflection in the x-axis. **e)** Vertical stretch by a factor of 4, a vertical reflection in the x-axis, a horizontal stretch by a factor of $\dfrac{4}{3}$, a horizontal reflection in the y-axis, then a horizontal translation to the left by $\dfrac{4}{3}$ units and a vertical translation upward by 7 units.

Trigonometric functions, p. 565

1. a) $\dfrac{1}{\sqrt{26}}$; $\dfrac{5}{\sqrt{26}}$; $\dfrac{1}{5}$ **b)** $-\dfrac{2}{\sqrt{13}}$; $-\dfrac{3}{\sqrt{13}}$; $\dfrac{2}{3}$

c) $-\dfrac{3}{\sqrt{34}}$; $\dfrac{5}{\sqrt{34}}$; $-\dfrac{3}{5}$ **2. a)** 0.9744; 0.2250; 4.3315

b) 0.5299; −0.8480; −0.6249 **c)** 0.5446; 0.8387; 0.6494
d) 0.6442; 0.7648; 0.8423 **e)** −0.9162; −0.4008; 2.2858
f) −0.9511; 0.3090; −3.0777
3. a) 1.00 or 2.14; 57.1° or 122.9°
b) 2.71 or 3.57; 155.5° or 204.5° **c)** 3.00 or 6.14; 172.0° or 352.0° **4. a)** 1 **b)** $-\dfrac{1}{2}$ **c)** 0

Trigonometric identities, p. 567

1. Answers will vary.

Word problems, p. 568

1. 3.9 m

Writing numbers in exponential form, p. 569

1. a) 3^4 **b)** 7^0 **c)** $10^{\frac{1}{2}}$ **d)** 5^{-3}

Glossary

A

absolute extrema   Absolute maximum and absolute minimum values of a function.

absolute maximum value   A function f has an absolute maximum (or global maximum) value $f(c)$ at $x = c$ if $f(c) > f(x)$ for all x in the domain of f.

absolute minimum value   A function f has an absolute minimum (or global minimum) value $f(c)$ at $x = c$ if $f(c) < f(x)$ for all x in the domain of f.

absolute value   The distance of a number from zero on a real number line.

acceleration   The acceleration of an object is the rate of change of its velocity with respect to time.

acceleration function   The acceleration function $a(t)$ at time t is the derivative of the velocity function, and the second derivative of the position function,
$$a(t) = \frac{dv}{dt} = \frac{d^2 s}{dt^2}.$$

antiderivatives   The family of functions $f(x) + C$, where C is a constant, with common derivative $f'(x)$.

antidifferentiation   The process of going from a derivative function to a function that has that derivative.

arrow diagram   A diagram used to represent a function. The letter f denotes the function itself, whereas x and the associated value $f(x)$ are elements of the domain and range, respectively.

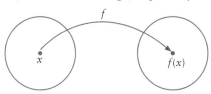

asymptote   A line that a curve approaches more and more closely. See horizontal asymptote, vertical asymptote, and linear oblique asymptote for precise definitions.

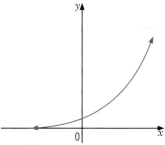

The x-axis is an asymptote.

asymptotic   Two curves are asymptotic if the vertical distance between them approaches zero in some limit.

average rate of change of y with respect to x   For a function $y = f(x)$, the average rate of change of y with respect to x over the interval $x \in [a, b]$ is
$$\frac{\Delta y}{\Delta x} = \frac{f(b) - f(a)}{b - a}.$$

average speed   The distance travelled by an object divided by the elapsed time.

average velocity   For an object that can move back and forth along a straight line, and has position function $s(t)$, the average velocity over the time interval from $t = a$ to $t = b$ is the change in position divided by the elapsed time, $\frac{\Delta s}{\Delta t} = \frac{s(b) - s(a)}{b - a}$.

C

chain rule   The chain rule can be used to differentiate composite functions. If two functions f and g are both differentiable and $F(x) = f(g(x))$, then the derivative of F is given by the product
$$F'(x) = f'(g(x))g'(x).$$
That is, differentiate the outer function, f, evaluate at the inner function, $g(x)$, and then multiply by the derivative of the inner function, g.

coefficient   The factor by which a variable is multiplied. For example, in the term $8y$, the coefficient is 8; in the term ax, the coefficient is a.

composite function   A function made up of (composed of) other functions. The composition of f and g is defined by $(f \circ g)(x) = f(g(x))$ and read as "f of g at x," or "f following g at x." In the composition $(f \circ g)(x)$, we first apply the function g to x, and then we apply the function f to the result.

concave downward   The graph of a function f is said to be concave downward on an interval (a, b) if it lies below all of its tangents on (a, b).

concave upward   The graph of a function f is said to be concave upward on an interval (a, b) if it lies above all of its tangents on (a, b).

constant coefficient   The number a_0 in a polynomial function $f(x) = a_n x^n + a_{n-1} x^{n-1} + \cdots + a_1 x + a_0$ is called a constant coefficient.

constant multiple rule   The derivative of a constant multiple of a function is the constant multiple times the derivative of the function. That is,
$$\frac{d}{dx}(cf(x)) = c\frac{df}{dx}.$$

constant rule   The derivative of a constant function is the zero function. That is, $\frac{d}{dx} c = 0$.

continuous compounding   When an investment P is compounded continuously at interest rate r, the value of the investment at time t is given by $A(t) = Pe^{rt}$.

continuous at a number   A function f is continuous at $x = a$ if $\lim_{x \to a} f(x) = f(a)$.

continuous function   A function f is said to be continuous if it is continuous at every number in its domain.

cost function   In business, the cost to produce x units of a commodity or service is called the cost function, $C(x)$.

critical number   A number c in the domain of f is a critical number of f if either $f'(c) = 0$ or $f'(c)$ does not exist.

critical point   If a number c in the domain of f is a critical number of f, then the point $(c, f(c))$ is called a critical point.

cubic function   A third-degree polynomial function.

cusp   A cusp is a point on the graph of a function at which the function is not differentiable and a tangent does not exist. For example, the function $y = |x|$ has a cusp at $(0, 0)$, since it is not differentiable at $x = 0$ and its graph does not have a tangent at $(0, 0)$.

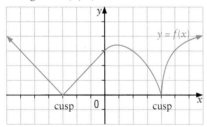

D

decreasing function   A function f is decreasing on an interval (a, b) if $f(x_2) < f(x_1)$ whenever $x_2 > x_1$ in the interval (a, b).

degree (of angle measure)   An angle measure equal to $\frac{1}{360}$ of one complete revolution.

degree (of a polynomial)   The degree of a polynomial $P(x) = a_n x^n + \cdots + a_2 x^2 + a_1 x + a_0$ (where $a_n \neq 0$), is the largest exponent of x, that is, n.

demand function   The price per unit, $p(x)$, that the marketplace is willing to pay for a given product or service at a production level of x units is known as the demand function (also called the price function).

dependent variable   In a relation, the variable whose value depends on the value of the independent variable. On a coordinate grid, the values of the dependent variable are plotted on the vertical axis.

derivative   The derivative of a function $y = f(x)$ is a function defined as
$$f'(x) = \lim_{h \to 0} \frac{f(x + h) - f(x)}{h}, \text{ or alternatively, as}$$
$$f'(a) = \lim_{x \to a} \frac{f(x) - f(a)}{x - a}.$$

difference   See method of finite differences.

difference rule   The derivative of a difference of functions is the difference of the derivatives. That is,
$$\frac{d}{dx} (f(x) - g(x)) = \frac{d}{dx} f(x) - \frac{d}{dx} g(x).$$

differentiable   A function f is said to be differentiable at a if $f'(a)$ exists.

differentiable on an interval   A function f is said to be differentiable on an interval if it is differentiable at every number in the interval.

differentiate   To differentiate a function means to determine its derivative.

discontinuity   A function has a discontinuity at $x = a$ if it is not continuous at $x = a$. For example, $f(x) = \frac{1}{x}$ has a discontinuity at $x = 0$.

discontinuous   A function is discontinuous at $x = a$ if it has a discontinuity at $x = a$.

dividend   The polynomial that is being divided in long division.

divisor   The polynomial that the dividend is divided by in long division.

domain   For a function that specifies one element of a set B for each element in a set A, the domain of a function is the set A. For a function $y = f(x)$, the domain is the set of all acceptable x-values.

E

even function   An even function satisfies the property $f(-x) = f(x)$ for all x in its domain. An even function is symmetric about the y-axis.

explicitly defined function   For a function $y = f(x)$, if a specific formula is given, where y is isolated on one side of the equation, then y is defined explicitly as a function of x. For example, the function $y = 3x^2 + 5x - 4$ is defined explicitly in terms of x.

exponential function   An exponential function has the form $y = ab^x$, where $a \neq 0$, $b > 0$, and $b \neq 1$.

extrapolate   Estimate values lying outside the range of given data. To extrapolate from a graph means to estimate coordinates of points beyond those that are plotted.

factor theorem   A polynomial $P(x)$ has $x - b$ as a factor if and only if $P(b) = 0$. More generally, a polynomial $P(x)$ has $ax - b$ as a factor if and only if $P\left(\dfrac{b}{a}\right) = 0$.

family of functions   A set of functions that can be written in the same form. For example, the functions $f(x) = x + 2$, $f(x) = 2x + 4$, $f(x) = 3x + 6$ belong to a family of functions, since they can all be written in the form $f(x) = k(x + 2)$.

Fermat's theorem   If a function f has a local maximum value or local minimum value at $x = c$, then either $f'(c) = 0$ or $f'(c)$ does not exist.

finite differences   See method of finite differences.

first derivative   The first derivative of a function $y = f(x)$ is $y = f'(x)$. The first derivative is identical to the derivative.

first derivative test   Let c be a critical number of a continuous function f.
If $f'(x)$ changes from positive to negative at c, then f has a local maximum at c.
If $f'(x)$ changes from negative to positive at c, then f has a local minimum at c.
If $f'(x)$ does not change sign at c, then f has neither a local maximum nor a local minimum at c.

first differences   See method of finite differences.

first principles   See method of first principles.

function   A function is a rule that specifies one and only one element of a set B for each element in a set A.

geometric series   A series of numbers in which each number after the first one is a constant multiple of the number preceding it.

horizontal asymptote   The line $y = L$ is called a horizontal asymptote of the curve $y = f(x)$ if either $\lim\limits_{x \to \infty} f(x) = L$ or $\lim\limits_{x \to -\infty} f(x) = L$, or both.

I

implicit differentiation   A method of differentiating a function that is defined implicitly, without needing to solve the original equation for y in terms of x.

implicitly defined function   A function y is defined implicitly in terms of x if y is not isolated on one side of the equation. For example, the equation $x^2 + xy - 4y^3 = 3x + 5y$ defines y implicitly as a function of x.

increasing function   A function f is increasing on an interval (a, b) if $f(x_2) > f(x_1)$ whenever $x_2 > x_1$ in the interval (a, b).

independent variable   In a relation, the variable whose value determines that of the dependent variable. On a coordinate grid, the values of the independent variable are on the horizontal axis.

infinite discontinuity   An infinite discontinuity occurs where a graph has a vertical asymptote.

infinite limit   If $\lim\limits_{x \to a} f(x) = \pm\infty$, then f has an infinite limit at $x = a$.

infinite limits at infinity   The function f has an infinite limit at infinity in any of the following four circumstances:
$\lim\limits_{x \to \pm\infty} f(x) = \pm\infty$.

inflection point   See point of inflection.

input variable   An element of the domain of a function.

instantaneous rate of change of y with respect to x   For a function $y = f(x)$, the instantaneous rate of change of y with respect to x over the interval $x \in [a, b]$ is
$$\lim_{\Delta x \to 0} \frac{\Delta y}{\Delta x} = \lim_{b \to a} \frac{f(b) - f(a)}{b - a}.$$
The instantaneous rate of change is identical to the rate of change.

instantaneous velocity   For an object that can move back and forth along a straight line, and has position function $s(t)$, the instantaneous velocity over the time interval from $t = a$ to $t = b$ is
$$\lim_{\Delta t \to 0} \frac{\Delta s}{\Delta t} = \lim_{b \to a} \frac{s(b) - s(a)}{b - a}.$$
The instantaneous velocity is identical to the velocity.

integral sign   The symbol, $\int$, used to represent antidifferentiation.

integral zero theorem   If $x = b$ is an integral zero of a polynomial with integral coefficients, then b is a factor of the constant term of the polynomial.

interpolate   To estimate values lying within the domain of given data. To interpolate from a graph means to estimate coordinates of points between those that are plotted.

interpolating polynomial   The interpolating polynomial for a set of n points $(x_0, y_0), (x_1, y_1), \ldots, (x_{n-1}, y_{n-1})$ is given by $P(x) = a_0 + a_1(x - x_0) + a_2(x - x_0)(x - x_1) + \cdots + a_n(x - x_0)(x - x_1)(x - x_2) \cdots (x - x_{n-1})$. An interpolating polynomial can be used to find the equation of a function, given sufficiently many points on its graph.

interval   A set of real numbers having one of these forms: $x > a$, $x \geq a$, $x < a$, $x \leq a$, $a < x < b$, $a < x \leq b$, $a \leq x < b$, or $a \leq x \leq b$.

inverse function   The inverse f^{-1} of a function f, if it exists, is defined by $f^{-1}(f(x)) = f(f^{-1}(x)) = x$.

J

jump discontinuity   A function f has a jump discontinuity at $x = a$ if $\lim\limits_{x \to a^-} f(x) = L$, $\lim\limits_{x \to a^+} f(x) = M$, and $L \neq M$.

L

leading coefficient   The number a_n, the coefficient of the highest power, in a polynomial function, $f(x) = a_n x^n + a_{n-1} x^{n-1} + \cdots + a_1 x + a_0$, of degree n.

left-hand limit   A limit written $\lim\limits_{x \to a^-} f(x)$, which is read "the limit of $f(x)$ as x approaches a from the left," used to determine the behaviour of a function, $f(x)$, to the left of $x = a$.

limit   A function f has a limit L as x approaches a, written $\lim\limits_{x \to a} f(x) = L$, provided that the values of $f(x)$ get closer and closer to L as x gets closer and closer to a, on both sides of a.

limit at infinity   A number L is a limit at infinity for a function f if the values of $f(x)$ get closer and closer to L as the absolute values of x get larger and larger, with either positive or negative values of x. We write either $\lim\limits_{x \to \infty} f(x) = L$ or $\lim\limits_{x \to -\infty} f(x) = L$, whichever is appropriate.

limit laws   Suppose that the limits $\lim\limits_{x \to a} f(x)$ and $\lim\limits_{x \to a} g(x)$ both exist and c is a constant. Then

$\lim\limits_{x \to a} [f(x) + g(x)] = \lim\limits_{x \to a} f(x) + \lim\limits_{x \to a} g(x)$	The limit of a sum is the sum of the limits.
$\lim\limits_{x \to a} [f(x) - g(x)] = \lim\limits_{x \to a} f(x) - \lim\limits_{x \to a} g(x)$	The limit of a difference is the difference of the limits.
$\lim\limits_{x \to a} [cf(x)] = c \lim\limits_{x \to a} f(x)$	The limit of a constant times a function is the constant times the limit of the function.
$\lim\limits_{x \to a} [f(x)g(x)] = \lim\limits_{x \to a} f(x) \lim\limits_{x \to a} g(x)$	The limit of a product is the product of the limits.
$\lim\limits_{x \to a} \dfrac{f(x)}{g(x)} = \dfrac{\lim\limits_{x \to a} f(x)}{\lim\limits_{x \to a} g(x)}$ if $\lim\limits_{x \to a} g(x) \neq 0$	The limit of a quotient is the quotient of the limits, if the limit of the denominator is not 0.
$\lim\limits_{x \to a} [f(x)]^n = [\lim\limits_{x \to a} f(x)]^n$	The limit of a power is the power of the limit.

linear function   A linear function is one of the form $y = mx + b$, for which the graph is a line.

linear model   A linear model is one for which the modelling function is linear.

linear oblique asymptote   The line $y = mx + b$ is a linear oblique asymptote for a curve $y = f(x)$ if the vertical distance between the curve and the line approaches 0 as the absolute value of x gets large for either positive or negative values of x. This is written as either $\lim\limits_{x \to \infty} [f(x) - (mx + b)] = 0$ or $\lim\limits_{x \to -\infty} [f(x) - (mx + b)] = 0$, or both.

linear regression   Regression to a linear function. See regression.

ln x   The natural logarithm function, with base e. See natural logarithm function.

local extrema   Local maximum and local minimum values of a function are often called local extreme values, or local extrema.

local linearity   A feature of all smooth curves. Any smooth curve will appear to be linear if you focus on a small enough (local) domain, and zoom in on it enough times using a graphing calculator.

local linearization   A linear function that best approximates a function, $f(x)$, near a fixed value of a. The linear function is called the local linearization of f near $x = a$.

local maximum point   A point on a graph for which all nearby points have a smaller y-coordinate.

local maximum value   A function f has a local maximum (or relative maximum) value $f(c)$ at $x = c$ if $f(c) > f(x)$ when x is close to c (on both sides of c).

local minimum point   A point on a graph for which all nearby points have a greater y-coordinate.

local minimum value   A function f has a local minimum (or relative minimum) value $f(c)$ at $x = c$ if $f(c) < f(x)$ when x is close to c (on both sides of c).

logarithm   The logarithm of a number is the value of the exponent to which a given base must be raised to produce the given number. For example, $\log_3 81 = 4$, because $3^4 = 81$.

logarithmic function   The inverse of the exponential function $y = a^x$ is the logarithmic function $x = a^y$. The function $x = a^y$ can be written as $y = \log_a x$, which is read as "y is equal to the logarithm of x, to the base a."

M

marginal cost function   The instantaneous rate of change of cost with respect to the number of items produced is the marginal cost. The marginal cost function, $C'(x)$, is the derivative of the cost function.

marginal profit function   The instantaneous rate of change of profit with respect to the number of items sold is the marginal profit function. The marginal profit function, $P'(x)$, is the derivative of the profit function.

marginal revenue function   The instantaneous rate of change of revenue with respect to the number of units sold is the marginal revenue function. The marginal revenue function, $R'(x)$, is the derivative of the revenue function.

marginal supply function   The instantaneous rate of change of supply with respect to the number of units sold. The marginal supply function, $p'(x)$, is the derivative of the supply function.

mathematical model   A mathematical description of a real situation. The description may include a diagram, a graph, a table of values, an equation, a formula, a physical model, or a computer model.

mathematical modelling   The process of describing a real situation in mathematical form.

method of finite differences   This method is used to determine the equation of a polynomial function given a table of values. From a table of values, differences in successive y-values, called the first differences, are calculated. If necessary, differences in successive first differences, called second differences, are calculated. The process is repeated as far as necessary.

method of first principles   The method by which the derivative of a function is determined using the definition of a derivative.

N

natural logarithm   Logarithm to base e.

natural logarithm function   The inverse of the exponential function $y = e^x$ is the logarithmic function $x = e^y$. The function $x = e^y$ can be written as $y = \log_e x$, or more frequently, $y = \ln x$.

non-linear relation   A relationship between two variables whose graph is not straight.

normal   The normal to a curve at a point is the line perpendicular to, and intersecting, the curve's tangent at that point.

O

oblique asymptote   See linear oblique asymptote.

odd function   An odd function satisfies the property $f(x) = -f(x)$ for all x in the domain of f. An odd function is rotationally symmetric about the origin.

one-sided infinite limits   One-sided infinite limits can be expressed as $\lim_{x \to a^+} f(x) = \infty$, $\lim_{x \to a^+} f(x) = -\infty$, $\lim_{x \to a^-} f(x) = \infty$, or $\lim_{x \to a^-} f(x) = -\infty$, whichever is appropriate.

one-sided limits   Limits that are used to determine the behaviour of a function, $f(x)$, to the left or to the right of $x = a$.

orthogonal Two curves are orthogonal if their tangents are perpendicular at their point of intersection.

orthogonal trajectories Two families of curves are orthogonal trajectories of each other if each curve in one family is orthogonal to every curve in the other family. For example, the two families of curves $x^2 - y^2 = A$ and $xy = B$ are orthogonal trajectories of each other for any values of A and B.

output variable An element of the range of a function.

P

periodic function A function is periodic with period p if $f(x + p) = f(x)$ for all x.

piecewise A function is defined piecewise if different formulas are used to define it on different parts of its domain. For example,
$$|x| = \begin{cases} x & \text{if } x \geq 0 \\ -x & \text{if } x < 0 \end{cases}$$

point of inflection A point P on a curve is said to be a point of inflection if the curve changes from concave upward to concave downward or from concave downward to concave upward (that is, it changes concavity) at P.

polynomial function A polynomial function is of the form $P(x) = a_n x^n + \cdots + a_2 x^2 + a_1 x + a_0$, where n is a positive integer.

position function The position function $s(t)$ of an object specifies its location as a function of time, t.

power function A power function has the form $y = x^n$.

power rule The derivative of a power function x^n is given by
$$\frac{d}{dx}(x^n) = nx^{n-1}.$$

price function See demand function.

product rule The derivative of a product $(fg)(x)$ of two functions $f(x)$ and $g(x)$ is given by $(fg)'(x) = f'(x)g(x) + f(x)g'(x)$.

profit function If x units of a product are sold, the profit function, $P(x)$, is obtained by subtracting the cost function from the revenue function, $P(x) = R(x) - C(x)$.

Q

quadratic function A second-degree polynomial function.

quadratic regression Regression to a quadratic function. See regression.

quartic function A fourth-degree polynomial function.

quintic function A fifth-degree polynomial function.

quotient rule The derivative of a quotient $\left(\dfrac{f}{g}\right)(x)$ of two functions $f(x)$ and $g(x)$ is given by
$$\left(\frac{f}{g}\right)'(x) = \frac{f'(x)g(x) - f(x)g'(x)}{[g(x)]^2}, \text{ provided } g(x) \neq 0.$$

R

radian The measure of the angle subtended at the centre of a circle by an arc equal in length to the radius of the circle. There are 2π radians in one complete revolution (360°).

range For a function that specifies one element of a set B for each element in a set A, the range of a function is the set of all elements of B for which there is a corresponding element of A. For a function $y = f(x)$, the range is the set of all acceptable y-values.

rate of change See instantaneous rate of change of y with respect to x.

rational function A rational function is a ratio of polynomial functions.

rational zero theorem If $x = \dfrac{b}{a}$ is a rational zero of a polynomial with integral coefficients, then b is a factor of the constant term of the polynomial, and a is a factor of the leading coefficient of the polynomial.

regression The process of regression fits the best curve of a given type (for example, linear, quadratic, or cubic) to a set of data.

remainder theorem If a polynomial, $P(x)$, of degree at least 1, is divided by $(x - b)$, the remainder is a constant, R. Furthermore, $R = P(b)$.

removable discontinuity A function f has a removable discontinuity at $x = a$ if $\lim\limits_{x \to a} f(x) = L$, and either $f(a) \neq L$ or $f(a)$ does not exist.

revenue function If x units of a product are sold and the price per unit is $p(x)$, then the revenue function is $R(x) = xp(x)$.

right-hand limit A limit written $\lim\limits_{x \to a^+} f(x)$, which is read "the limit of $f(x)$ as x approaches a from the right," used to determine the behaviour of a function, $f(x)$, to the right of $x = a$.

root   A solution of an equation.

rule of four   This refers to four ways of describing a function: verbally, numerically, algebraically and visually.

S

secant   A line passing through at least two different points on a curve.

second derivative   The function $f''(x)$ obtained by differentiating the first derivative of a function.

second derivative test
If $f'(c) = 0$ and $f''(c) > 0$, then f has a local minimum at c.
If $f'(c) = 0$ and $f''(c) < 0$, then f has a local maximum at c.
Note: The second derivative test does not apply when $f''(c) = 0$ and when $f''(c)$ does not exist.

second differences   See method of finite differences.

sinusoidal function   A sine or cosine function.

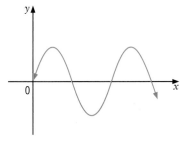

sinusoid   See sinusoidal function.

slant asymptote   See linear oblique asymptote.

slope   A measure of the steepness of a line. The slope m of a line containing the points $P(x_1, y_1)$ and $Q(x_2, y_2)$ is
$$m = \frac{\Delta y}{\Delta x} = \frac{y_2 - y_1}{x_2 - x_1}, \; x_2 \neq x_1.$$

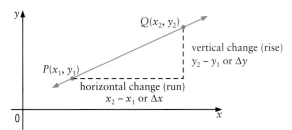

sum rule   The derivative of a sum of functions is the sum of the derivatives. That is,
$$\frac{d}{dx}(f(x) + g(x)) = \frac{d}{dx}f(x) + \frac{d}{dx}g(x).$$

supply function   The price per unit, $p(x)$, at which a manufacturer is willing to sell x units of a given product or service.

T

tangent   Suppose that a function $y = f(x)$ is differentiable at $x = a$. A line is tangent to the graph of f at $(a, f(a))$ provided that the line passes through $(a, f(a))$ and the slope of the line is $f'(a)$.

test for concavity   If $f''(x) > 0$ for all $x \in (a, b)$, then the graph of f is concave upward on (a, b). If $f''(x) < 0$ for all $x \in (a, b)$, then the graph of f is concave downward on (a, b).

test for intervals of increase/decrease   Suppose that f is differentiable on the interval (a, b). If $f'(x) > 0$ for all $x \in (a, b)$, then f is increasing on (a, b). If $f'(x) < 0$ for all $x \in (a, b)$, then f is decreasing on (a, b).

test intervals   Intervals that are determined by the real zeros of a polynomial function and used to determine the signs of the function.

turning points   Local maximum points and local minimum points on the graph of a function.

V

velocity function   The velocity function of an object is the rate of change of its position function, $s(t)$, with respect to time. The velocity function $v(t)$ at time t is the derivative of the position function, $v(t) = \dfrac{ds}{dt}$.

vertical asymptote   The line $x = a$ is called a vertical asymptote of the curve $y = f(x)$ if at least one of the following is true:
$$\lim_{x \to a} f(x) = \infty, \; \lim_{x \to a^+} f(x) = \infty,$$
$$\lim_{x \to a^-} f(x) = \infty, \; \lim_{x \to a} f(x) = -\infty,$$
$$\lim_{x \to a^+} f(x) = -\infty, \; \text{or} \; \lim_{x \to a^-} f(x) = -\infty.$$

Z

zero (of a function)   Any value of x for which the value of the function $f(x)$ is 0.

Technology Index

Index

Photo Credits

Cover Credit, back cover: Ron Watts/First Light; 3 top left, Eyewire Collection, top right Terry Donnelly/Weststock/ImageState, bottom © David Toase/PhotoDisc; 6 Mark Burnett/Photo Researchers; 22 Eyewire Collection; 29 © David Toase/ PhotoDisc; 33 Terry Donnelly/Weststock/ImageState; 39 top Peter J. Thompson/Thompson Sport Images, bottom Wayne Lynch/Parks Canada 10-101-07-04(10); 57 Peter J. Thompson/ Thompson Sport Images; 117 left Fernado Augusto/Associated Press/Canadian Press Picture Archives; right both Al Harvey; 121 Fernado Augusto/Associated Press/Canadian Press Archives; 130 Photo © NASA; 145 © Ryan McVay/PhotoDisc; 159 Ian Crysler; 161 Eric Sanford/First Light; 172 Al Harvey; 183 left Digital Vision/CORBIS RF #Act 20070, top right Corel Corporation #479075, bottom right Comstock Images #16959; 197 Digital Vision/CORBIS RF #Act 20070; 214 Comstock Images #16959; 221 Corel Corporation #479075; 228 © PhotoDisc *Volume 44* Image #44016; 233 © Vedros & Associates, Inc./ Picturesque/PictureQuest; 265 left © Russell Illiq/PhotoDisc, top right Photo Courtesy NOAO, from Digital Stock *Space and Spaceflight* #052, bottom right Corel Corporation # 836009; 268 © Malcolm Fife/PhotoDisc; 277 Dick Hemingway; 291© Russell Illiq/PhotoDisc; 292 Eyewire Photography; 293 right Photo Courtesy NOAO, from Digital Stock *Space and Spaceflight* #052;

296 Corel Corporation # 836009; 300 Jacques Descloitres, MODIS Land Rapid Response Team, NASA/GSFC; 309 top J. T Leonard/ Associated Press/Canadian Press Picture Archives, bottom left Science VU/Visuals Unlimited; bottom right Gilles Daigle/Ivy Images; 312 Lee Cohen/CORBIS/Magma; 319 Thomas J. Peterson/Stone/Getty Images; 330 Kevin Fleming/CORBIS/Magma; 342 Science VU/Visuals Unlimited; 411 top Saurabh Das/Associated Press/Canadian Press Picture Archive bottom left Anik F-1 Satellite Courtesy Telesat Canada, bottom right Pat Morrow/First Light; 438 Anik F-1 Satellite Courtesy Telesat Canada; 439 Pat Morrow/First Light; 443 Saurabh Das/Associated Press/Canadian Press Picture Archive, 446 Aaron Harris/Canadian Press Picture Archive; 487 left Mark E. Gibson/Visuals Unlimited, top right Eyewire Collection, bottom right Ottmer Beirwagen/Ivy Images; 518 © PhotoLink/PhotoDisc; 519 Mark E. Gibson/Visuals Unlimited; 522 Ottmer Beirwagen/Ivy Images; 533 Eyewire Collection.

Text Permissions

Chapter Expectations 2, 38, 116, 182, 264, 308, 410, © Queen's Printer for Ontario, 2002. Reproduced with permission; 104, 157, 244, 395–397, 517, 522–523, 570–612 Courtesy of Texas Instruments. Calculator templates: Texas Instruments.

ALGEBRA

Factoring Special Polynomials

$x^2 \pm 2xy + y^2 = (x \pm y)^2$

$x^2 - y^2 = (x - y)(x + y)$

$x^3 \pm y^3 = (x \pm y)(x^2 \mp xy + y^2)$

Rules for Exponents

Product	Quotient	Power
$(x^a)(x^b) = x^{a+b}$	$\dfrac{x^a}{x^b} = x^{a-b}$	$(x^a)^b = x^{ab}$
Power of a Product	**Rational Exponent**	**Negative Exponent**
$(xy)^a = x^a y^a$	$x^{\frac{1}{a}} = \sqrt[a]{x}$	$x^{-a} = \dfrac{1}{x^a}$

Logarithms

$y = \log_a x \Leftrightarrow a^y = x$

$\log_{10} x$ is usually written as $\log x$. $\log_e x$ is written as $\ln x$.

$\log_a a = 1$ $\log_e e = 1$

$\log_a a^x = x$ $\ln e^x = x$

$a^{\log_a x} = x$ $e^{\ln x} = x$

$\log_a (xy) = \log_a x + \log_a y$ $\log_b x = \dfrac{\log_a x}{\log_a b}$

$\log_a \left(\dfrac{x}{y} \right) = \log_a x - \log_a y$

$\log_a x^n = n \log_a x$

ANALYTIC GEOMETRY

Distance Between Two Points

The distance between two points, $P_1(x_1, y_1)$ and

$P_2(x_2, y_2)$, is $P_1P_2 = \sqrt{(x_2 - x_1)^2 + (y_2 - y_1)^2}$.

Quadratic Formula

If $ax^2 + bx + c = 0$, then $x = \dfrac{-b \pm \sqrt{b^2 - 4ac}}{2a}$.

Line

For a line through the points $P_1(x_1, y_1)$ and $P_2(x_2, y_2)$,

Slope: $m = \dfrac{y_2 - y_1}{x_2 - x_1}$

Forms of an equation of a line

Point-slope: $y - y_1 = m(x - x_1)$

Slope, y-intercept: $y = mx + b$, where b is the y-intercept

Equation of a Parabola

$y = a(x - p)^2 + q$ with vertex (p, q)

Equation of a Circle

$(x - h)^2 + (y - k)^2 = r^2$ with centre (h, k) and radius r

GEOMETRY

In the following, A represents area, P, perimeter, C, circumference, V, volume, and S, surface area.

Triangle

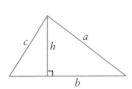

$A = \dfrac{1}{2} bh$

$A = \sqrt{s(s - a)(s - b)(s - c)}$,

where $s = \dfrac{1}{2}(a + b + c)$

$P = a + b + c$

Trapezoid

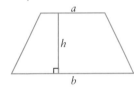

$A = \dfrac{1}{2}(a + b)h$

Circle

$A = \pi r^2$

$C = 2\pi r$

Cylinder

$V = \pi r^2 h$

$S = 2\pi rh + 2\pi r^2$

Sphere

$V = \dfrac{4}{3} \pi r^3$

$S = 4\pi r^2$

Cone

$V = \dfrac{1}{3} \pi r^2 h$

$S = \pi r^2 + \pi rs$

TRIGONOMETRY

Arc Length
$x = r\theta$

Angle Measure
$1° = \dfrac{\pi}{180}$ rad

$1 \text{ rad} = \dfrac{180°}{\pi}$

Pythagorean Theorem

$c^2 = a^2 + b^2$

Right Triangle Trigonometry

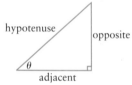

$\sin\theta = \dfrac{\text{opposite}}{\text{hypotenuse}}$

$\cos\theta = \dfrac{\text{adjacent}}{\text{hypotenuse}}$

$\tan\theta = \dfrac{\text{opposite}}{\text{adjacent}}$

$\sin\theta = \dfrac{y}{r} \quad \cos\theta = \dfrac{x}{r} \quad \tan\theta = \dfrac{y}{x}$

Fundamental Identities
$\sin^2\theta + \cos^2\theta = 1 \quad \tan\theta = \dfrac{\sin\theta}{\cos\theta} \quad \csc\theta = \dfrac{1}{\sin\theta}$

$\sec\theta = \dfrac{1}{\cos\theta} \quad \cot\theta = \dfrac{1}{\tan\theta}$

Cosine Law

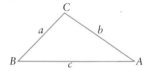

$a^2 = b^2 + c^2 - 2bc \cos A$
$b^2 = a^2 + c^2 - 2ac \cos B$
$c^2 = a^2 + b^2 - 2ab \cos C$

Sine Law
$\dfrac{\sin A}{a} = \dfrac{\sin B}{b} = \dfrac{\sin C}{c} \qquad \dfrac{a}{\sin A} = \dfrac{b}{\sin B} = \dfrac{c}{\sin C}$

Addition and Subtraction Formulas
$\sin(A \pm B) = \sin A \cos B \pm \cos A \sin B$
$\cos(A \pm B) = \cos A \cos B \mp \sin A \sin B$
$\tan(A \pm B) = \dfrac{\tan A \pm \tan B}{1 \mp \tan A \tan B}$

Double-Angle Formulas
$\sin 2A = 2 \sin A \cos A$
$\cos 2A = \cos^2 A - \sin^2 A$
$\qquad = 2\cos^2 A - 1$
$\qquad = 1 - 2\sin^2 A$
$\tan 2A = \dfrac{2\tan A}{1 - \tan^2 A}$

DERIVATIVES

First Principles
$f'(x) = \lim_{h \to 0} \dfrac{f(x+h) - f(x)}{h} \qquad f'(a) = \lim_{x \to a} \dfrac{f(x) - f(a)}{x - a}$

Power Rule
$\dfrac{d}{dx}(x^n) = nx^{n-1}$

Constant Multiple Rule
$\dfrac{d}{dx}[cf(x)] = c\dfrac{d}{dx}[f(x)]$

Sum and Difference Rules
$\dfrac{d}{dx}[f(x) \pm g(x)] = \dfrac{d}{dx}[f(x)] \pm \dfrac{d}{dx}[g(x)]$

Product Rule
$\dfrac{d}{dx}[f(x)g(x)] = g(x)\dfrac{d}{dx}[f(x)] + f(x)\dfrac{d}{dx}[g(x)]$

Quotient Rule
$\dfrac{d}{dx}\left(\dfrac{f(x)}{g(x)}\right) = \dfrac{g(x)\dfrac{d}{dx}[f(x)] - f(x)\dfrac{d}{dx}[g(x)]}{[g(x)]^2}$

Chain Rule
If $y = f(u)$ and $u = g(x)$, then $\dfrac{dy}{dx} = \dfrac{dy}{du}\dfrac{du}{dx}$.
If $F(x) = f(g(x))$, then $F'(x) = f'(g(x))g'(x)$.

Specific Functions
$\dfrac{d}{dx}(e^x) = e^x \qquad \dfrac{d}{dx}(\ln x) = \dfrac{1}{x}$

$\dfrac{d}{dx}(\sin x) = \cos x \qquad \dfrac{d}{dx}(\cos x) = -\sin x$

$\dfrac{d}{dx}(\tan x) = \dfrac{1}{\cos^2 x}$

$\qquad\qquad = \sec^2 x$